Teacher Wraparound Edition

Teen Health
Course 3

Mary H. Bronson, Ph.D.

Michael J. Cleary, Ed.D.

Betty M. Hubbard, Ed.D., C.H.E.S.

Contributing Author
Dinah Zike, M.Ed.

New York, New York   Columbus, Ohio   Chicago, Illinois   Peoria, Illinois   Woodland Hills, California

Glencoe

The *McGraw·Hill* Companies

Send all inquiries to:
Glencoe/McGraw-Hill
21600 Oxnard Street
Suite 500
Woodland Hills, California 91367

ISBN: 0-07-861099-0 (Student Edition)
ISBN: 0-07-861100-8 (Teacher Wraparound Edition)

Printed in the United States of America.

1 2 3 4 5 6 7 8 9   071/043   09 08 07 06 05 04

Contributors/Consultants

Michael Rulon
State of Wyoming SCASS Trainer
Health Educator
Johnson Junior High
Adjunct Faculty
Laramie County Community College
Cheyenne, Wyoming

Kristin Danielson Fink
Executive Director
Community of Caring
Washington, DC

Margo Harris
School and Community Health
  Specialist
Western Washington University
Antioch University, Seattle
Seattle, Washington

Inclusion Specialist
**Patricia Sullivan, M.S., Special
Education**
Chair, Department of Language Arts
Meade Middle School
Fort Meade, Maryland

Reading Specialist
Christine A. Hayashi, M.A.Ed., J.D.
Attorney at Law, Special Education
  Law
Adjunct Faculty, Educational
  Leadership and Policy Studies
  Development
California State University, Northridge
Northridge, California

Teacher Reviewers

Kim S. Bradford
Health Educator
Brawley Middle School
Mooresville, North Carolina

Julie Campbell-Fouch
Health Educator, Department Chair
Stanford Middle School
Long Beach, California

Pamela R. Connolly
Subject Area Coordinator for Health
  and Physical Education,
Diocese of Pittsburgh
Curriculum Coordinator for Health
  and Physical Education, North
  Catholic High School
Pittsburgh, Pennsylvania

Jill English, Ph.D., C.H.E.S.
Assistant Professor
California State University, Fullerton
Fullerton, California

Debra C. Harris, Ph.D.
Department Chair,
Health and Physical Education
  Instructor
West Linn High School
West Linn, Oregon

Joanne B. McLendon
Health Educator
Little Rock Central High School
Little Rock, Arkansas

Cheryl Miller Page, C.H.E.S.
Health Educator
Judson Middle School
Salem, Oregon

Renee Rainey
Physical Education Educator
Cowan Elementary School
Austin, Texas

Joan Stear
Health and Physical Education
  Educator
Andover Central Middle School
Andover, Kansas

Jeanne Title
Coordinator of Prevention Education
Napa County Office of Education and
  Napa Valley Unified School
  District
Napa, California

Lynn Westberg
Health Educator
Kearns High School
Kearns, Utah

Contents

Glencoe/McGraw-Hill's Health and Fitness Program TM6

Student Edition TM8

Teacher Wraparound Edition TM12

Teacher Classroom Resources TM16

ACTIVITIES TM16
- Building Health Skills Activities
- Concept-Mapping Activities
- Cross-Curriculum Activities
- Decision-Making Activities
- Enrichment Activities
- Health Labs
- Guide to Using the Internet
- Reading Tutor
- Reteaching Activities
- Student Activities Workbook

ASSESSMENT TM17
- Testing Program (Lesson Quizzes and Chapter Tests)
- Performance Assessment Activities

TEACHING RESOURCES TM17
- Inclusion Strategies
- Reproducible Lesson Plans
- Teaching Transparencies
- Parent Letters and Activities
- Summaries, Quizzes, and Activities

Student Modules TM18

- *Violence Prevention*
- *HIV/AIDS*
- *Healthy Relationships and Sexuality*

Spanish Resources TM19

- Student Edition
- Video and DVD Series
- Summaries, Quizzes, and Activities
- Vocabulary PuzzleMaker
- Parent Letters and Activities

Media and Technology Resources TM20

- *Teen Health* MindJogger Videoquiz
- *Teen Health* Video and DVD Series
- *Nutrition and Physical Activity: On Your Own Explorations*
- Vocabulary PuzzleMaker
- *Teen Health* at health.glencoe.com
- Interactive Online Student Edition
- TeacherWorks™
- Exam*View*® Pro Testmaker
- Audio Summaries (English, Spanish)
- Teaching Transparencies Binder

Skills at a Glance TM21

Reading and Writing Activities TM22

Inclusion Strategies TM24

National Health Education Standards TM26

Scope and Sequence TM28

Glencoe Professional Health Series TM36

Glencoe/McGraw-Hill's

Glencoe/McGraw-Hill's health and fitness program provides a comprehensive health curriculum for students in grades 6 through 12. *Teen Health*, the three-volume series for students in grades 6 through 8, combines scientifically accurate, age-appropriate health content with extensive instruction, practice, and application of the skills necessary to achieve optimal health and wellness. This solid foundation is built upon in *Glencoe Health*, the trusted high-school program. In addition to accurate health content and health-skill practice, high-school students are given additional opportunities to apply their knowledge and skills to real-world situations. *Foundations of Personal Fitness* expands upon the physical activity and fitness content presented in the health program. It contains up-to-date information on developing and assessing every aspect of fitness, and includes detailed instruction on eating for peak performance and maintaining a healthy body weight.

Teen Health

Middle School

Chapter	Course 1 (6th grade)	Course 2 (7th grade)	Course 3 (8th grade)
1	Living a Healthy Life	Learning About Your Health	Understanding Your Health
2	Mental and Emotional Health	Taking Responsibility for Your Health	Health Skills: The Foundation
3	Social Health	Physical Activity and Fitness	Being a Health Consumer
4	Personal Health	Food and Nutrition	Mental and Emotional Health
5	Nutrition and Physical Activity	Personal Health and Consumer Choices	Promoting Social Health
6	Growth and Development	Growth and Development	Relationships: The Teen Years
7	Preventing Diseases	Mental and Emotional Health	Conflict Resolution
8	Tobacco	Social Health: Family and Friends	Nutrition for Health
9	Alcohol and Other Drugs	Resolving Conflicts and Preventing Violence	Physical Activity and Fitness
10	Safety and the Environment	Tobacco	Your Body Image
11		Drugs and Alcohol	Medicines and Drugs
12		Understanding Communicable Diseases	Tobacco
13		Noncommunicable Diseases	Alcohol
14		Personal Safety and Injury Prevention	Personal Care
15		The Environment and Your Health	Your Body Systems
16			Growth and Development
17			Communicable Diseases
18			Noncommunicable Diseases
19			Safety and Emergencies
20			Environmental Health

Health and Fitness Program

Glencoe Health and Foundations of Personal Fitness

High School

Chapter	Glencoe Health	Foundations of Personal Fitness
1	Living a Healthy Life	Physical Activity and Personal Fitness
2	Building Health Skills and Character	Safety and Injury Prevention
3	Being a Health-Literate Consumer	Designing a Personal Fitness Program
4	Physical Activity for Life	Nutrition and Your Personal Fitness
5	Nutrition and Your Health	Your Body Composition
6	Managing Weight and Body Composition	Maintaining a Healthy Body Weight
7	Achieving Good Mental Health	Basics of Cardiorespiratory Endurance
8	Managing Stress and Anxiety	Developing Cardiorespiratory Endurance
9	Mental and Emotional Problems	Basics of Resistance Training
10	Skills for Healthy Relationships	Developing Muscular Fitness
11	Family Relationships	Basics of Flexibility
12	Peer Relationships	Personal Fitness Throughout Life
13	Violence Prevention	
14	Personal Care and Healthy Behaviors	
15	Skeletal, Muscular, and Nervous Systems	
16	Cardiovascular and Respiratory Systems	
17	Digestive and Urinary Systems	
18	Endocrine and Reproductive Systems	
19	Prenatal Development and Birth	
20	Adolescence and the Life Cycle	
21	Tobacco	
22	Alcohol	
23	Medicines and Drugs	
24	Communicable Diseases	
25	Sexually Transmitted Infections and HIV/AIDS	
26	Noncommunicable Diseases and Disabilities	
27	Injury Prevention and Safe Behaviors	
28	First Aid and Emergencies	
29	Environmental Health	

The Student Edition at a Glance

The *Teen Health* Student Edition is organized around 20 chapters, each containing independent lessons. The content introduces students to a comprehensive, skills-based health program with an emphasis on abstinence from high-risk behaviors. By laying the foundation for building lifelong health skills, the Student Edition helps students make positive health choices.

Chapter Opener

Each chapter opens with two introductory, motivational activities.

The **Health Online** feature incorporates technology and invites students to take an online health inventory to evaluate their current health knowledge and behaviors.

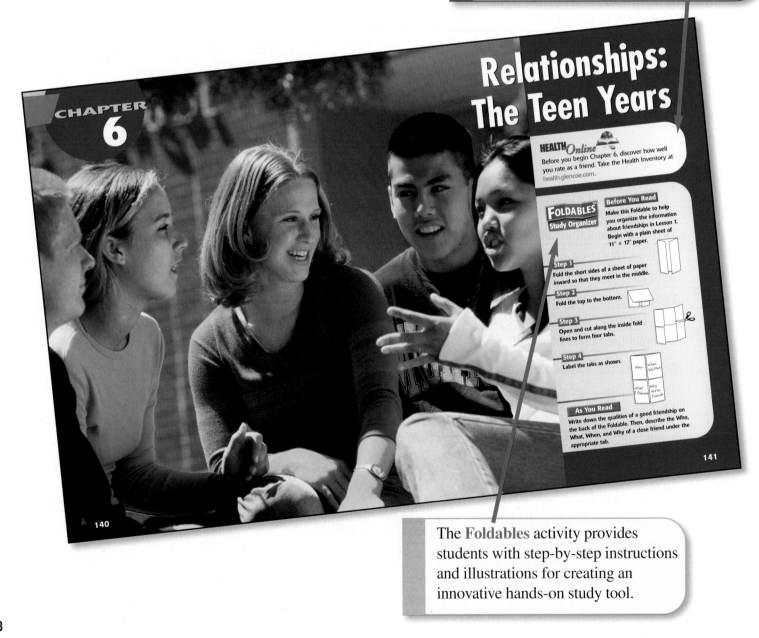

The **Foldables** activity provides students with step-by-step instructions and illustrations for creating an innovative hands-on study tool.

Teaching Health Skills

With the increasing attention given to skill development, students learn and practice ways to make healthy choices. Each chapter includes opportunities for students to apply, practice, and assess the skills they need to enhance their own and others' health.

Health Skills Activities help students learn to choose the behaviors that protect, promote, and maintain health and to avoid high-risk behaviors. Each activity provides students with an opportunity to practice skill development.

Caring

People with serious noncommunicable diseases often have special health needs. In small groups, identify some of these needs and discuss ways to acknowledge and support them. How can you demonstrate care and concern for someone at school or in the community who has a serious noncommunicable disease? Give two examples.

Lifestyle Behaviors and Disease

In general, it is difficult to predict who will develop a particular disease. For some diseases, however, researchers have identified certain risk factors. These are *characteristics that increase a person's chances of developing a disease.* Heredity, age, gender, and ethnic group are risk factors over which people have no control.

Fortunately, people do have control over a major group of risk factors—lifestyle behaviors. Examples include your eating habits, the amount of physical activity you get each day, and the amount of sleep you receive each night. Many diseases are the direct or indirect result of harmful lifestyle behaviors, such as using tobacco or eating too many fatty foods. Healthful lifestyle behaviors, on the other hand, can help prevent, control, or reduce the risk of certain diseases. Lifestyle behaviors may be influenced by cultural factors. For example, cultural traditions may include eating high-fat foods or a variety of fresh fruits and vegetables. Cultural influences can increase or decrease a person's risk for disease.

Although healthful lifestyle behaviors do not guarantee against noncommunicable diseases, they do help. By eating foods low in salt, for example, a person with a family history of high blood pressure can minimize his or her risk.

HEALTH SKILLS ACTIVITY

ADVOCACY

Promoting a Healthful Lifestyle
Be a role model by practicing healthful lifestyle behaviors. Here are some tips.

- **EAT HEALTHFUL FOODS.** Eat plenty of whole grains, fruits, and vegetables. Go easy on foods high in fat, sugar, or salt.
- **STAY PHYSICALLY ACTIVE.** Regular physical activity strengthens all body systems and helps the heart and lungs function better.
- **MAINTAIN A HEALTHY WEIGHT.** Keep your weight within the recommended range for your gender, height, age, and body frame.
- **GET ENOUGH REST.** Teens need at least nine hours of sleep a night.

- **MANAGE STRESS.** Use appropriate time management and stress reduction techniques.
- **AVOID TOBACCO AND SECONDHAND SMOKE.** Tobacco causes respiratory and heart diseases and cancer.
- **AVOID ALCOHOL AND OTHER DRUGS.** These substances harm the body and impair judgment.

WITH A GROUP
Working in small groups, select a noncommunicable disease. Prepare an article for the school newspaper emphasizing the role of healthful lifestyle behaviors in preventing that disease.

Expressing Emotions

People express emotions in different ways. We often learn how to express them from watching others who are close to us, such as family members. Learning to understand emotions and to express them in healthy ways is an important part of good mental and emotional health.

Expressing Anxiety and Fear

Have you ever felt anxious before giving a report or taking a test? When you are anxious or fearful, you take shorter breaths, your heart beats faster, and your muscles tense. Anxiety can help you accomplish more by releasing energy. However, too much anxiety and fear can cause you to lose sleep or even to panic. *Panic, a feeling of sudden, intense fear,* may be accompanied by physical symptoms such as dizziness and a pounding heart.

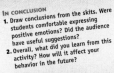

COMMUNICATING EMOTIONS

This activity will give you practice in communicating positive feelings.

WHAT YOU WILL NEED
- paper
- pen or pencil

WHAT YOU WILL DO
1. In a small group, develop a list of situations that could produce positive feelings for teens. An example might be receiving recognition from a coach after winning a track event.
2. Choose one of the situations on your list and write a skit in which someone expresses positive feelings to a friend.
3. Perform your skit for your classmates.
4. Have classmates evaluate your skit and, if necessary, describe a more effective method of communicating the positive emotions.

IN CONCLUSION
1. Draw conclusions from the skits. Were students comfortable expressing positive emotions? Did the audience have useful suggestions?
2. Overall, what did you learn from this activity? How will it affect your behavior in the future?

Hands-On Health are science-based health activities and hands-on experiments that require little or no scientific equipment. These activities give students a chance to learn through action while personalizing the concepts presented in the chapters.

TIME Health

TIME Health features are fun, educational articles developed for a middle-school audience by *TIME* magazine. Appearing at the end of each chapter, these colorful two-page spread features will engage student interest and increase familiarity with a journalistic writing style. Each feature is tailored to fit the content of a particular chapter and contains an activity to help students apply what they have learned. Many contain infographics and diagrams, giving students the opportunity to practice reading charts and graphs.

Diagrams, charts, and graphs
Present key health information in a high-interest format to enhance recall of facts and give students practice in evaluating information that is presented visually.

Article text
Contains up-to-date information on a specific health topic, written in a way that will appeal to teens and help them hone their media literacy and critical-thinking skills.

Time to Think...
Helps students develop reading comprehension skills by giving them the opportunity to apply what they have learned to a relevant activity.

Building Health Skills

At the end of every chapter, there is a Building Health Skills activity feature that addresses a skill identified in the National Health Education Standards. Created with teens in mind, they include colorful, lively designs intended to grab students' attention. These two-page features reinforce chapter content. A performance task is included at the end of each feature. The task measures the extent to which individual skills have been achieved. Building Health Skills can also be taught independently as hands-on skills lessons.

Practice
Students are given opportunities to practice the skill.

Model
Students are presented with positive role-modeling of the featured skill.

Apply/Assess
Finally, students perform the skill on their own and evaluate their performance.

Developing Good Character
Highlights core character traits to promote the integration of values into the health curriculum.

Developing Good Character

Fairness

When you show fairness, you treat others in the way you would want them to treat you. When you played with a sibling or a friend, you may have shared your toys or taken turns on a swing. As you got older and started participating in sports, you learned to play by the rules and be a team player. *How have you shown fairness in the past week?*

MEDIA WATCH

TRUTH IN ADVERTISING?

Think about the tobacco ads you've seen in stores or in magazines and newspapers. *Use your critical-thinking skills to analyze and interpret the media messages in these ads:* How do the ads portray tobacco use? How do the messages compare with the facts about tobacco?

Media Watch
Raises students' awareness about the media's impact on their lives and health.

CONNECT TO
Science

ULTRASOUND IMAGES
Ultrasound equipment, which uses sound waves to make pictures, allows doctors to see images of a fetus in the uterus. Such images enable them to check the size and position of the fetus and the amount of fluid surrounding the fetus. Ultrasounds taken at intervals in a pregnancy help monitor the progress of the fetus.

Connect to...
Provides cross-curriculum activities to help students see how health is related to other curriculum areas such as science, mathematics, language arts, and social studies.

Support for the Health Teacher

The Teacher Wraparound Edition provides complete lesson plans, teaching suggestions, supplemental information, cross-references, lesson and chapter review answers, and more—all conveniently "wrapped" around every page of the reduced Student Edition. Teachers will discover that the consistent, easy-to-follow lesson plan format gives a variety of teaching strategies to motivate students; to introduce, teach, and reinforce concepts; and to provide alternative teaching strategies for adapting the program to meet the individual needs of students.

Chapter Opener includes the following:
- Chapter at a Glance
- Health Skills
- Chapter Introduction
- Health Online
- Glencoe Technology
- TIME Health
- Foldables

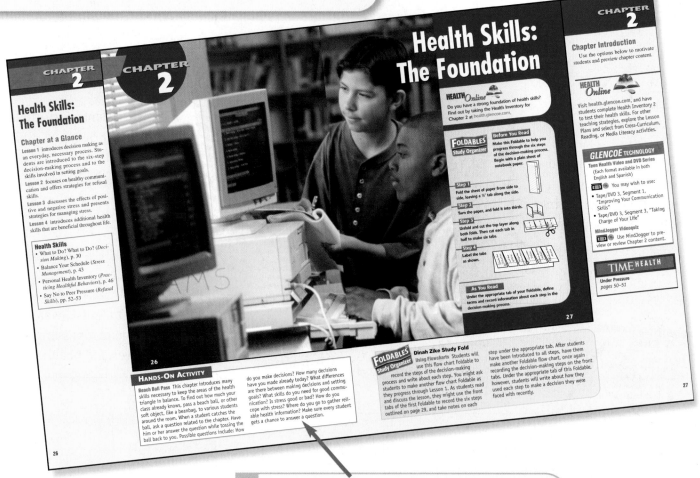

Hands-On Activity Every chapter jump-starts with a motivational hands-on activity intended to make students active participants in their health education.

Organized with the Teacher in Mind

Lesson Plans

The teaching material follows a consistent, easy-to-use pattern. The complete lesson cycle—1. FOCUS, 2. TEACH, 3. ASSESS, and 4. CLOSE— make it easy for you to plan a lesson. Included in the lesson plan you will find:

① FOCUS

- A list of student objectives
- Motivator activities—select from a Quick Write, which corresponds to the Student Edition, or a Bellringer activity
- A Vocabulary activity to help students build vocabulary skills

② TEACH

Various activities related to the lesson's content have been identified by one of four codes (**L1 L2 L3 INCL**) to give you an idea of their suitability for students of varying learning styles and abilities.

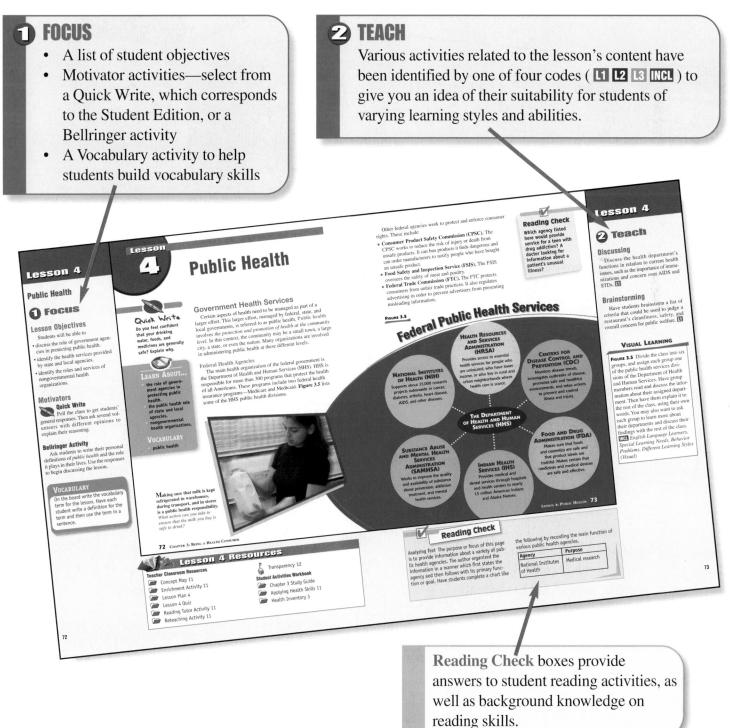

Reading Check boxes provide answers to student reading activities, as well as background knowledge on reading skills.

Teacher Wraparound Edition

③ ASSESS

- Assessment techniques including strategies for reteaching students who have difficulty mastering the important lesson concepts
- Enrichment activities designed for students who are able to explore the content further

What Teens Want to Know are Q & A features that explore teen-oriented issues. Use these features to respond to student questions and concerns with reliable answers.

④ CLOSE

An activity that brings closure to the lesson and recaps important concepts from the lesson.

Developing Good Character

These features offer teachers character education support and activity ideas.

Developing Good Character

Citizenship

Introduce the idea that being a good citizen means doing one's share to improve the community. Ask students to break into groups of four to brainstorm a variety of ways they could improve their school or community. Have them list their ideas on large chart paper, and make brief presentations to the class.

Health Online

Each Health Online box offers ways for teachers to access and make use of Glencoe's Health Web site. Students are encouraged to explore Web Links to complete a hands-on activity specifically related to the health content of a lesson.

HEALTH Online

Encourage students to explore the Web Links for this chapter and then complete the activity.

Health Skills Activity

These boxes provide step-by-step reinforcement for student skills-based activities.

HEALTH SKILLS ACTIVITY

REFUSAL SKILLS

Guide students in applying strategies for avoiding drugs. Have students read the activity introduction and discuss Megan's situation. Also, help students review and discuss the S.T.O.P. refusal skills.

Divide the class into groups. Have partners within each group role-play their scenario for the other group members.

Note: This skill is introduced in Chapter 6 on pages 149–150.

Bottom Column Annotations

Boxes at the bottom of the page give you additional information related to the content of the Student Edition. This information supplements the core lesson plan by focusing on various areas of interest. The categories include:

- Inclusion Strategies
- Cultural Perspectives
- Hands-On Activity
- Reading Check
- What Teens Want to Know
- More About. . .
- Health Literacy
- Beyond the Classroom
- Cooperative Learning Activity
- Dealing with Sensitive Issues
- Promoting Coordinated School Health
- Answers to Lesson Review

MORE ABOUT...

Scoliosis Scoliosis is a sideways curving of the spine. It is usually noticed between the ages of 10 and 14. The cause of 80 percent of cases is unknown. A scoliosis screening involves checking whether the patient's higher than the other. X-rays are sometimes performed. Many children have mild curves and need only periodic checkups to make sure the curve is not worsening. Of every 1,000 children screened, 6 require treat- e used to treat about 90 ren who require treatment, y require surgery.

HANDS-ON ACTIVITY

The Top Ten As a class, have students create a top ten list of healthy relationships. Ask students to brainstorm qualities a person needs in order to have a successful relationship. Examples may include honesty, respect, and caring. Select the ten most important write them Hav term on a separate slip of paper and rank them in order of 1–10 (most important to least important.) Collect all of the papers making sure that they are labeled and numbered. Ask two volunteers to count the votes. Have them calculate which quality

INCLUSION STRATEGIES

Special Learning Needs, Behavior Problems, English Language Learners, At-Risk, Different Learning Styles (Visual) To make the health triangle more meaningful, make a model of it using three strips of paper of the same length but of different colors. Label one strip *Physical Health,* another *Mental/Emotional Health,* and the third *Social Health.* Arrange the strips in a triangle shape. Tell students that the inside area of the triangle represents total health. By folding or cutting one of the strips, show them how the area of the triangle decreases if any side is shortened. Ask for volunteers to explain what the change in one side means in terms of total health.

Activities

Building Health Skills Activities further reinforce skill development with Reproducible Masters and Transparency Masters that correspond to the activities at the end of every chapter and the Web site. Guide students in applying health skills with step-by-step teaching suggestions.

Concept-Mapping Activities provide a developmental approach for students to practice concept mapping. They can be used to preview or review a lesson's content by visually reinforcing main ideas and clarifying relationships.

Cross-Curriculum Activities give students an opportunity to relate health information to the content of other subject areas including math, social studies, language arts, science, and the arts.

Decision-Making Activities give students an opportunity to practice the decision-making process as they consider a variety of hypothetical situations.

Enrichment Activities allow students the opportunity to explore lesson concepts further. Answers for the teacher are provided at the back of the booklet.

Health Labs give students experience with making observations and hypotheses, collecting and recording data, and forming conclusions based on analysis and interpretations of experimental results. Teacher pages provide help and answers to questions.

Guide to Using the Internet provides strategies for integrating Internet activities in the health classroom.

Reading Tutor helps students develop their reading skills. It outlines the essential information in each lesson of *Teen Health* and contains all vocabulary terms and definitions. The accompanying study guides can be used to review chapter content.

The Student Activities Workbook contains a Study Guide and Health Inventory for each chapter and an Applying Health Skills activity for each lesson. A Teacher Annotated Edition is available.

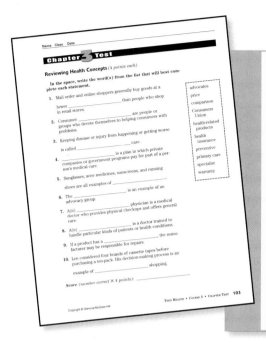

Assessment

Lesson Quizzes provide a one-page quiz for each lesson in *Teen Health*. Answers for the teacher are provided at the back of the booklet.

Chapter Tests provide two forms of tests, A and B. Either or both forms may be used as alternative or makeup tests. Answers for the teacher are provided at the back of the booklet.

Performance Assessment Activities assess learning in ways that require a student to manipulate information in flexible and creative ways.

Teaching Resources

Inclusion Strategies present detailed instructions for addressing the needs of students with different learning styles and ability levels. Specific strategies for each chapter of *Teen Health* are provided.

Reproducible Lesson Plans are provided for each lesson in *Teen Health*. The lesson plans include references to all resources available with *Teen Health*.

The Teaching Transparencies Binder includes 84 transparencies plus an activity booklet complete with teaching strategies for use with the transparencies.

Parent Letters and Activities include introductory teacher material about how to use these letters and how to inform parents or guardians of the instructional program and assessment techniques to be employed. This material appears in English and Spanish.

Summaries, Quizzes, and Activities include brief summaries of each of the 20 chapters of *Teen Health*. The summaries are followed by quizzes and activities that help students grasp the chapter content and assess their knowledge. Answers for the teacher are provided at the back of the booklet. Both English and Spanish versions are available. (Accompanied by audio summaries)

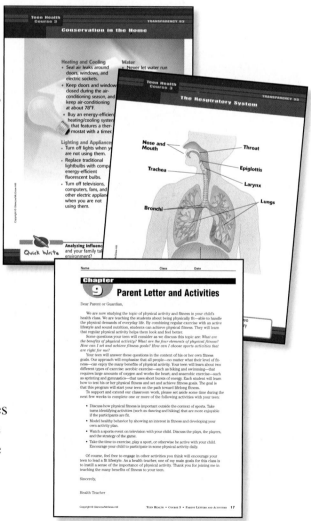

Student Modules

Violence Prevention

This module provides an in-depth look at the problem of violence and presents effective strategies for resolving conflicts and defusing potentially violent situations.

HIV/AIDS

By presenting clear, accurate, up-to-date information on HIV/AIDS, this full-color text is designed to help students recognize and abstain from risk behaviors associated with the spread of the disease.

Healthy Relationships and Sexuality

In this module relevant and appropriate information on relationships and sexuality is discussed, emphasizing the importance of abstinence from sexual activity before marriage.

Student Edition

La Salud de los Jóvenes is a complete Spanish translation of the English student edition. It will provide your Spanish-speaking students with the comprehensive health information and instruction in skill development they need for maximum wellness. The attractive photo and illustration program, engaging infographics, and fun hands-on activities will appeal to and motivate your Spanish-speaking students.

Video and DVD Series

Complete translations of each English segment in the three-volume series provide valuable information for today's teens. The content is presented in the following formats to maintain student interest: dramatizations and panel discussions, informative teen talk shows, and informal peer-group discussions.

Summaries, Quizzes, and Activities

Summaries, quizzes, and activities give Spanish-speaking students additional practice in comprehending and applying the main points of each chapter. Answer keys are provided at the back of the booklet. (Accompanied by audio summaries)

Vocabulary PuzzleMaker

Create custom crossword and word-search puzzles completely in Spanish to help your Spanish-speaking students learn important health vocabulary terms.

Parent Letters and Activities

These letters and activities allow you to keep Spanish-speaking parents informed about course content and encourage them to participate in their child's health education.

Media and Technology Resources

Teen Health MindJogger Videoquiz

***Teen Health* MindJogger Videoquiz** presents chapter quizzes in a fun, video-gameshow format. Available on both videocassettes and DVDs, the videoquizzes may be used for self-assessment or as an opportunity to preview or review chapter content.

Teen Health Video and DVD Series

Enliven classroom discussions with this three-volume series. Dramatizations and panel discussions, informative teen talk shows, and peer-group discussions are featured on a variety of topics relevant in the lives of today's teens. Both English and Spanish versions are available.

Nutrition and Physical Activity: On Your Own Explorations

Take students on an interactive journey through a typical Friday and Saturday in a teen's life with this multimedia CD-ROM program. Students will make critical decisions about food intake and physical activity and evaluate these choices to make sure that they are the most healthful ones.

Vocabulary PuzzleMaker

Build vocabulary skills with custom-designed puzzles. Create word searches and crossword puzzles using vocabulary words from each lesson in the text. Both English and Spanish versions are included on one CD-ROM.

Teen Health at health.glencoe.com

The *Teen Health* homepage at health.glencoe.com provides up-to-date resources and activities to complement Glencoe's comprehensive health program. The site includes fun and interactive online games and study tools for students, as well as links to informative health Web sites. Teachers can access a wealth of additional activities to enhance the student text, along with correlations to standards and professional articles.

Interactive Online Student Edition

Now students and teachers can access the entire text of *Teen Health* Course 3 from our Web site at

health.glencoe.com—every chapter and lesson, including all Health Inventories, activities, and Web links! Navigate from the table of contents directly to the lesson you need. Find every Lesson Review and Chapter Assessment for homework, review, and study convenience.

TeacherWorks™

Custom design your lesson plan with this easy-to-use CD-ROM. The electronic format allows teachers to select a pre-set plan or to create their own—either way, it offers access to electronic files of all reproducible resources at the click of a button.

Exam*View*® Pro Testmaker

This computer software test bank for Macintosh and IBM-compatible computers provides questions in various formats and the capability to add your own questions.

Audio Summaries (English, Spanish)

The audio CDs contain summaries of chapter content for review, for reteaching, or for use when you do not have time to teach a particular chapter. Each summary is accompanied by a chapter activity and test based on the content of the audio CD. Spanish summaries are also provided.

Teaching Transparencies Binder

This convenient three-ring binder contains 84 full-color transparencies and a *Teaching Strategies and Activities Instructor Guide*.

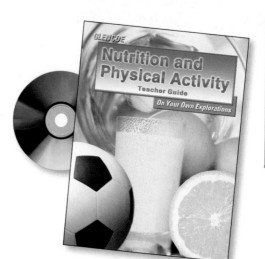

GLENCOE TECHNOLOGY

Teen Health Video and DVD Series
(Each format available in both English and Spanish)

You may wish to use:
- Tape/DVD 1, Segment 2, "Dealing with Your Emotions"
- Tape/DVD 3, Segment 2, "Building Confidence"

MindJogger Videoquiz

Use MindJogger to preview or review Chapter 4 content.

Skills at a Glance

Teen Health integrates skills throughout the core content. Below is a chart that identifies the skills presented in two skills-related features—Health Skills Activities (found within the lessons of each chapter) and Building Health Skills (found at the end of each chapter).

SKILL	TITLE	PAGES	TITLE	PAGES
Accessing Information	Health Care in the Community	66	Finding Facts About Your Body	408–409
	Finding Reliable Sources	78–79	Can I Catch What's in the News?	456
	Reading a Food Label	206	Locating Support Groups	496
	Scoliosis Screening	370	Local Weather Emerencies	522
Practicing Healthful Behaviors	Making Health a Habit	18	Protect Yourself from the Sun	346
	Personal Health Inventory	46	Protecting Yourself and Others	470–471
	Improving Your Self-Esteem	89	Preparing a Fire Safety Plan	512
	Activities for Fitness	231	Environment-Friendly Shopping	556
	Warm Up! Work Out! Cool Down!	244–245	Make the Most of It	560–561
	Medicine Safety in the Home	274		
Stress Management	Balance Your Schedule	43	Protecting Your Body	398
	Put Stress in Its Place	112–113	Coping with Mood Swings	430
	Relaxation Exercises	222	Managing Teen Stress	500–501
Analyzing Influences	Looking at Health Influences	22–23	Be Prepared	309
	Identifying Role Models	131	Seeing Beyond the Perfect Look	362–363
	Sharpen Your Body Image	262–263		
Communication Skills	A Friend in Need	11	Helping a Victim of Abuse	180
	Writing a Sympathy Note	107	Helping a Friend Stay Safe	324
	Sending the Right Message	136–137	Helping a Friend Choose Abstinence	460
Conflict Resolution	Working Through Conflicts	184–185	Resolving Conflicts with Parents	438–439
Refusal Skills	Say No to Peer Pressure	52–53	Choose to Refuse Tobacco	300
	Abstaining from Drugs	240	Saying No to a Drink	332
	Refusing Drugs	284	Avoiding Unsafe Behaviors	540–541
Decision Making	What to Do? What to Do?	30	Choosing Healthful Snacks	210
	If a Friend Seems Depressed	99	Helping a Friend	258
	A Matter of Character	121	Helping Someone Get Help	336–337
	When to Suggest a Mediator	171	Managing Chronic Conditions	483
Goal Setting	Know Your Limits	158–159	Steer Clear of Tobacco	314–315
Advocacy	Know Your Rights	61	Saying No to Drugs	292–293
	Public Health	74	Reducing Noise Levels	359
	Supporting Abstinence	153	Encouraging Healthy Eating	394
	Help Prevent School Violence	174	Get the Message Out	466
	Eating for Your Health	214–215	Promoting a Healthful Lifestyle	478

Reading and Writing Activities

Reading

The reading activities in *Teen Health* are designed to improve students' reading comprehension and understanding of health concepts. Reading Checks throughout the lessons prompt students to use comprehension, vocabulary, and study skills strategies during and after reading.

During Reading

The Reading Checks in the lessons are focused on comprehension, text analysis, vocabulary, and critical thinking strategies for nonfiction.

In the Student Edition:

Reading Check

Understand text organization. Look at the table and the bulleted list on these two pages. What are their similarities and differences?

In the Teacher Wraparound Edition:

With this material, the teacher can create a mini-lesson on text analysis for better comprehension.

Reading Check

Analyzing Text Thinking about how the author chose to organize information in nonfiction text helps students retain facts and understand difficult concepts. Point out to students that the purpose of these pages is to provide information about the stages of human development before birth and after birth. The chart titled "The Developing Baby" organizes information by time period and category. The bulleted list titled "The Life Cycle" organizes information more simply by time period. Ask students to identify and compare the time periods used in the chart and the list and to discuss the different types of information the chart and list provide.

After Reading

Other reading activities in the lessons challenge students to employ critical thinking after reading.

In the Student Edition:

Reading Check

Make your own judgments. Use information from the text to tell how well you think your family or community manages waste.

In the Teacher Wraparound Edition:

Teaching strategies provide examples of how to integrate reading skills into the health curriculum.

Reading Check

Evaluation and Analysis Making their own evaluations and analyses can aid students' comprehension of their part in waste management. Model making judgment statements based on how well the class does with waste management.

For example, point out the strategy of reducing garbage, and describe how the class does or does not do this already. Ask students to suggest ways to reduce garbage in the classroom. Write down your opinions and student suggestions in paragraph form for the students to use as a guide. Then have students think about ways their families or communities handle waste management. You may wish to have recycling brochures, local newspapers, or copies of town policies for students to use as research.

Reading Check Strategies

Vocabulary:	Study Skills:	Comprehension:
• Affixes and Roots	• Anticipation Guide	• Analyzing Text
• Analogies	• Skimming and Scanning	• Cause-and-Effect Relationships
• Antonyms	• Individual Response	• Distinguishing Subjective and Objective
• Compound Words	• K-W-L	• Evaluation and Analysis
• List/Group/Label	• Taking Notes	• If…, Then… Statements
• Synonyms		• Inferential Thinking
• Word Relationships		• Main Idea
• Word Sort		• Recognizing Patterns
• Word Study		• Supporting Details
		• Text Organization

Reading Tutor

This brand-new teaching resource is designed to help students improve their reading abilities. It features the essential information in each lesson of the student edition—including all vocabulary terms and definitions—in a condensed format. Each lesson summary is followed by activities that allow students to apply their knowledge of the material. Study guides for each lesson provide an additional review of chapter content. *Reading Tutor* is especially useful for learning disabled students and English language learners.

Writing

Teen Health writing activities help students improve their retention and understanding of health concepts while reinforcing important writing skills.

Quick Writes at the opening of each lesson give students the opportunity to use spontaneous writing to discover what they already know about health topics. In addition to promoting writing skills, Quick Writes also provide real-life application of the health content.

These writing tasks prompt students to create lists or compose short paragraphs that connect the content with their daily lives.

Journal Writing strategies in the Teacher Wraparound Edition allow students to compose private responses to questions that require critical thinking; to practice creative writing skills; or to deal confidentially with sensitive issues.

Inclusion Strategies

How Does *Teen Health* Make Health Accessible for All Students?

The Inclusion Strategies teacher resource booklet offers a variety of activities for every learning style and ability level. In addition, the *Teen Health* program incorporates a wealth of resources specifically designed to help students of every learning style and ability level succeed in achieving health literacy.

ADDRESSING STUDENT NEEDS	STUDENT EDITION	TEACHER WRAPAROUND EDITION (TWE)	TEACHER CLASSROOM RESOURCES (TCR)
Different Learning Styles	**Illustration program** is rich in variety and diversity. **Charts and tables** visually present materials for quick assimilation. **Vocabulary terms** are highlighted in blue. **Clearly marked heads**, subheads, and bulleted lists outline content. **Health Skills Activities** encourage alternative demonstration of health concepts. **Hands-On Health Activities** actively engage students of all learning styles.	**Inclusion Strategies** are specifically written and labeled for different learning styles, including bodily-kinesthetic and visual learners. **Teaching Strategies are coded Level 1, Level 2, and Level 3** for students of all ability levels. **Quick Demos** capture students' attention with teacher demonstrations. **Assessment Options** include a variety of formats.	**Concept-Mapping Activities** **Cross-Curriculum Activities** **Decision-Making Activities** **Enrichment Activities** **Health Labs** **Reteaching Activities** **Audio Summaries** **Full-Color Transparencies** **Performance Assessment** **MindJogger Videoquiz**
Physically, Visually, Hearing Impaired	**Quick Write** gets students thinking about the health topics before they begin. **Illustrations** focus on important content.	**Inclusion Strategies** are specifically written and labeled for students with various physical and mental impairments. **Teaching Strategies coded Level 1** provide options for teacher-directed activities. **Visual Learning** strategies present important concepts in an easily accessible visual format.	**Reteaching Activities** **Concept-Mapping Activities** **Decision-Making Activities** **Audio Summaries** **MindJogger Videoquiz** **Reading Tutor** **Vocabulary PuzzleMaker**
Gifted Students	**Enrichment Activities** give students an opportunity to extend their knowledge. **Applying Health Skills** activities encourage alternative demonstration of health concepts.	**Inclusion Strategies** are specifically written and labeled for gifted students. **Teaching Strategies coded L3** are appropriate for independent learners. **Critical Thinking** strategies challenge students with additional questions and situations. **Researching** activities provide further learning opportunities. **Health Literacy** provides expanded ideas and activities for the self-directed learner.	**Enrichment Activities** **Cross-Curriculum Activities** **Health Labs** **Student Activity Workbook** for independent study **Performance Assessment**

English Language Learners	**Vocabulary terms** are highlighted in blue. **Vocabulary review** is presented for each lesson. **Spanish Glosario** helps students learn each vocabulary term. *La Salud de los Jóvenes* motivates students and helps them become immersed in the health content.	**Inclusion Strategies** are specifically written and labeled for English Language Learners.	**Spanish Audio Summaries** **Spanish Summaries, Quizzes, and Activities** **Reading Tutor** **Spanish Vocabulary PuzzleMaker** **Parent Letters and Activities** (Spanish)
Learning Disabled	**Quick Write** captures student interest and engages them in reading and writing. **Charts and tables** visually present concepts for quick assimilation. **Vocabulary terms** are highlighted in blue. **Clearly marked heads**, subheads, and bulleted lists outline content.	**Vocabulary strategies** are presented for each lesson. **Reteaching strategies** reinforce lesson content before moving on.	**Cross-Curriculum Activities** **Reteaching Activities** **Concept-Mapping Activities** **Reading Tutor** **Health Labs** **Audio Summaries** **Vocabulary PuzzleMaker** **MindJogger Videoquiz**
Behavioral Disorders	**Short, focused lessons** hold students' attention. **Clearly marked heads**, subheads, and bulleted lists outline content. **Charts and tables** visually present concepts for quick assimilation. **Illustrations** focus on important content. **Health Skills Activities** and **Building Health Skills** develop important skills that can be practiced and applied to real-life situations. **Hands-On Health** activities actively engage students in health skills practice.	**Inclusion Strategies** are specifically written and labeled for students with behavioral disorders. **Cooperative Learning Activities** foster teamwork and assign specific roles to students who need focus. **Quick Demos** allow teachers to present hands-on demonstrations. **What Teens Want to Know** brings relevance to specific health topics.	**Reteaching Activities** **Concept-Mapping Activities** **Decision-Making Activities** **Full-Color Transparencies** **Audio Summaries** **MindJogger Videoquiz** **Vocabulary PuzzleMaker** *Professional Series:* **Planning a Coordinated School Health Program** **Dealing with Sensitive Issues**
At-Risk Students	**Short, focused lessons** hold students' attention. **Charts and tables** visually present concepts for quick assimilation. **Applying Health Skills** encourage alternative demonstration of health knowledge. **Health Skills Activities** and **Building Health Skills** develop important skills that can be practiced and applied to real-life situations.	**Inclusion Strategies** are specifically written and labeled for at-risk students. **Dealing with Sensitive Issues** provides strategies for at-risk students.	**Decision-Making Activities** **Parent Letters and Activities** **Reteaching Activities** **Audio Summaries** **MindJogger Videoquiz** **Vocabulary PuzzleMaker**

Teen Health Meets the National Health Education Standards

The National Health Education Standards were created with the goal of improving educational achievement for students and improving health in the United States through the promotion of health literacy. The seven Health Standards are each divided into several performance indicators.

Health Education Standard 1:

Students will comprehend concepts related to health promotion and disease prevention.

Performance Indicators:

As a result of health instruction in Grades 5-8, students will:

1.1 Explain the relationship between positive health behaviors and the prevention of injury, illness, disease and premature death.

1.2 Describe the interrelationship of mental, emotional, social and physical health during adolescence.

1.3 Explain how health is influenced by the interaction of body systems.

1.4 Describe how family and peers influence the health of adolescents.

1.5 Analyze how environment and personal health are interrelated.

1.6 Describe ways to reduce risks related to adolescent health problems.

1.7 Explain how appropriate health care can prevent premature death and disability.

1.8 Describe how lifestyle, pathogens, family history, and other risk factors are related to the cause or prevention of disease and other health problems.

Health Education Standard 2:

Students will demonstrate the ability to access valid health information and health-promoting products and services.

Performance Indicators:

As a result of health instruction in Grades 5-8, students will:

2.1 Analyze the validity of health information, products, and services.

2.2 Demonstrate the ability to utilize resources from home, school, and community that provide valid health information.

2.3 Analyze how media influences the selection of health information and products.

2.4 Demonstrate the ability to locate health products and services.

2.5 Compare the costs and validity of health products.

2.6 Describe situations requiring professional health services.

Health Education Standard 3:

Students will demonstrate the ability to practice health-enhancing behaviors and reduce health risks.

Performance Indicators:

As a result of health instruction in Grades 5-8, students will:

3.1 Explain the importance of assuming responsibility for personal health behaviors.

3.2 Analyze a personal health assessment to determine health strengths and risks.

3.3 Distinguish between safe and risky or harmful behaviors in relationships.

3.4 Demonstrate strategies to improve or maintain personal and family health.

3.5 Develop injury prevention and management strategies for personal and family health.

3.6 Demonstrate ways to avoid and reduce threatening situations.

3.7 Demonstrate strategies to manage stress.

Health Education Standard 4:

Students will analyze the influence of culture, media, technology, and other factors on health.

Performance Indicators:

As a result of health instruction in Grades 5-8, students will:

4.1 Describe the influence of cultural beliefs on health behaviors and the use of health services.

4.2 Analyze how messages from media and other sources influence health behaviors.

4.3 Analyze the influence of technology on personal and family health.

4.4 Analyze how information from peers influences health.

Health Education Standard 5:

Students will demonstrate the ability to use interpersonal communication skills to enhance health.

Performance Indicators:

As a result of health instruction in Grades 5-8, students will:

5.1 Demonstrate effective verbal and non-verbal communication skills to enhance health.

5.2 Describe how the behavior of family and peers affects interpersonal communication.

5.3 Demonstrate healthy ways to express needs, wants, and feelings.

5.4 Demonstrate ways to communicate care, consideration, and respect of self and others.

5.5 Demonstrate communication skills to build and maintain healthy relationships.

5.6 Demonstrate refusal and negotiation skills to enhance health.

5.7 Analyze the possible causes of conflict among youth in schools and communities.

5.8 Demonstrate strategies to manage conflict in healthy ways.

Health Education Standard 6:

Students will demonstrate the ability to use goal setting and decision-making skills to enhance health.

Performance Indicators:

As a result of health instruction in Grades 5-8, students will:

6.1 Demonstrate the ability to apply a decision-making process to health issues and problems individually and collaboratively.

6.2 Analyze how health-related decisions are influenced by individuals, family, and community values.

6.3 Predict how decisions regarding health behaviors have consequences for self and others.

6.4 Apply strategies and skills needed to attain personal health goals.

6.5 Describe how personal health goals are influenced by changing information, abilities, priorities, and responsibilities.

6.6 Develop a plan that addresses personal strengths, needs, and health risks.

Health Education Standard 7:

Students will demonstrate the ability to advocate for personal, family, and community health.

Performance Indicators:

As a result of health instruction in Grades 5-8, students will:

7.1 Analyze various communication methods to accurately express health information and ideas.

7.2 Express information and opinions about health issues.

7.3 Identify barriers to effective communication of information, ideas, feelings, and opinions about health issues.

7.4 Demonstrate the ability to influence and support others in making positive health choices.

7.5 Demonstrate the ability to work cooperatively when advocating for healthy individuals, families, and schools.

Correlation of National Health Education Standards

The Chapter Planning Guides in the Teacher Wraparound Edition include a lesson-by-lesson correlation of the *Teen Health* Student Edition to the National Health Education Standards. The health standards addressed are indicated by their specific performance indicator numbers.

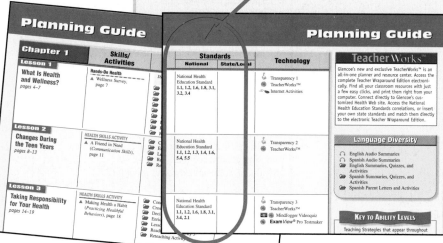

Content Strands	Chapter 1 Understanding Your Health	Chapter 2 Health Skills: The Foundation
Personal Health	• Recognizing health and wellness (1) • Balancing the health triangle (1) (2) • Managing stress in positive ways (1) (2) • Decision-making skills for wellness (1) • How health choices affect total health (1) (3) • Identifying risk behaviors (3) • Effect of risk behaviors on health (3) • How abstinence protects health (3) • Personal responsibility for health (3) • Analyzing influences on personal health (BHS) • Choosing healthful behaviors (BHS)	• Decision-making skills and health (1) • Strategies for decision making (1) • Goal-setting skills and health (1) • Strategies for setting goals (1) • Practicing refusal skills (2) (BHS) • Distinguishing types of stress (3) • Identifying stressors (3) • Practicing stress management skills (3) (4) • Practicing time management skills (3) (4) • Practicing healthful behaviors (4) • Analyzing internal and external influences on personal behavior (4) • Developing a plan to achieve a goal (BHS)
Consumer and Community Health	• Having regular medical and dental checkups (1) • Practicing good citizenship (2) • Recognizing the importance of health education (3)	• Accessing and evaluating health information (4) • Reliable sources of health information (4) • School personnel, health care providers, and religious leaders as support system (4) • Influence of culture, media, technology, and role models on personal behavior (4)
Injury Prevention and Safety	• Riding a bike without a helmet as a risk behavior (3)	• Decision-making skills and injury prevention (1) • Setting goals to prevent injury (1) • Importance of wearing safety belts (4)
Tobacco, Alcohol, and Other Drugs	• Avoiding tobacco, alcohol, and other drugs (2) (3)	
Nutrition and Physical Activity	• Eating balanced meals and snacks (1) (2) (3) • Being physically active (1) (2) (3)	• Setting fitness goals (1) • Being physically active to manage stress (3)
Environmental Health		• Influence of environment on personal behavior (4)
Family Living	• Maintaining healthy relationships with family and friends for social health (1) • Expressing emotions in healthy ways (1) (2) • Seeking input from parents and other trusted adults (2) • Supporting needs of family and friends (2) • Changes in family relationships during adolescence (2)	• Decision-making skills and family relationships (1) • Setting goals to improve relationships (1) • Body language in interpersonal communication (2) • Practicing speaking and listening skills (2) • Families as support systems (4) • Influence of family and friends on personal behavior (4)
Growth and Development	• Getting enough rest and sleep (1) (2) • Problem solving and weighing consequences for mental/emotional health (2) • Physical, mental/emotional, and social changes during adolescence (2) • Influence of peers on social growth (2)	• Physiological and psychological responses to stress (3)
Communicable and Noncommunicable Disease	• Avoiding disease to protect physical health (1) • Sexual activity as a risk behavior (3)	• Setting goals to avoid infection (1)

KEY: (BHS)=Building Health Skills; (1)=Lesson 1; (2)=Lesson 2; (3)=Lesson 3, etc.

Chapter 3 Being a Health Consumer	Chapter 4 Mental and Emotional Health	Chapter 5 Promoting Social Health
• Analyzing influences on personal buying decisions (1) (BHS) • Comparison-shopping skills for buying personal products (1)	• Signs of good mental and emotional health (1) • Interrelationships of personality, self-concept, and self-esteem to health (1) • Practicing skills to improve self-esteem (1) • Identifying and expressing emotions (2) • Practicing anger management skills (2) • Meeting emotional needs in healthy ways (2) • Recognizing signs of depression (3) • Practicing coping strategies in the death of a loved one (5) • Managing emotions in healthy ways (BHS) • Managing stress in healthy ways (BHS)	• Types of relationships (1) • Identifying personal values that form the basis of character (1) • Relationship of character to physical, mental/emotional, and social health (1) • Recognizing traits of good character (1)
• Analyzing advertising appeals (1) (3) • Health care providers and facilities (2) • Insurance and trends in health care (2) • Identifying health fraud (3) • Strategies for handling complaints (3) • Consumer groups for fraud protection (3) • The roles of federal, state, and local agencies, and nongovernmental organizations in consumer health (4) • Advocacy skills to promote public health (4) • Accessing and evaluating health information (BHS)	• Seeking help for clinical depression (3) (4) • Recognizing when to seek help from a mental health professional (4) • Counseling methods and drug treatments (4) • Sources of professional help for mental health problems (4)	• Citizenship as trait of good character (1) • Showing good character at school and in the community (1) • Financial consequences of teen parenthood (3) • Accessing reliable health information to help family (BHS)
• Role of federal Consumer Product Safety Commission in injury prevention (4)	• Depression and self-inflicted injury (3) • Recognizing signs of suicide (3) • Supporting others to prevent suicidal behaviors (3)	• Physical abuse and death caused by families (2)
• Role of federal Substance Abuse and Mental Health Services Administration in drug prevention and treatment services (4)	• Depression and use of alcohol or drugs (3) • Avoiding alcohol and other drugs when depressed (3)	• Effect of substance abuse on family (2)
	• Eating healthful meals when depressed (3) • Getting physical activity when depressed (3)	
• Role of agencies in natural disasters (4)		
• Advocacy skills for wise consumerism to protect health and safety of family and friends (1)	• Seeking help from parents if depressed (3) • Seeking help from family members for mental health problems (4) • Communication skills to comfort a friend (5)	• Character traits that contribute to family health (1) • Role and functions of families (2) • Coping skills when family changes occur (2) • Improving communication with family (2) • Ways to strengthen relationships (2) • Reasons to marry and factors affecting it (3) • Problems in marriages (3) • Communication skills to strengthen relationships (BHS)
• Getting checkups for preventive care (2)	• Distinguishing "normal" teen depression from clinical depression (3) • Getting enough sleep when depressed (3) • Stages in how people experience dying (5) • Stages in the grief process (5)	• Responsibilities of parenthood (3) • Analyzing influences on good parenting (3) • Physical health risks in teen pregnancy (3) • Consequences of teen parenthood (3)
• Roles of federal Food Safety and Inspection Service, Food and Drug Administration, and Centers for Disease Control and Prevention in disease prevention (4) • Role of National Institutes of Health in research (4)	• Anxiety disorders, personality disorders, and mood disorders (3) • Therapy and treatment for mental health problems (4)	• Effect of illness on family (2)

Scope and Sequence

Content Strands	Chapter 6 Relationships: The Teen Years	Chapter 7 Conflict Resolution
Personal Health	• Influence of cliques on personal behavior (1) • Differentiating positive and negative peer pressure (2) • Effects of peer pressure on decision making (2) • Practicing effective refusal skills (2) • Recognizing peer pressure (2) • Importance of practicing abstinence (3) • Emotional benefits of abstinence from sex (3) • Setting goals to practice abstinence (BHS)	• Practicing anger management skills (1) • Practicing conflict resolution skills (2) • Decision-making skills in choosing mediation (2) • Effective strategies for self-protection (3) • Protecting oneself from rape (3) • Practicing strategies to avoid abuse (4) • Communication skills to help a victim of abuse (4) • Developing a conflict resolution plan (BHS) • Practicing listening skills in peer mediation (BHS)
Consumer and Community Health	• Advocacy skills for supporting others to practice abstinence (3)	• Influence of the media on violence (3) • Advocacy skills for avoiding violence (3) • Community strategies for violence prevention (3) • Resources for the abused and abuser (4)
Injury Prevention and Safety	• Negative peer pressure and dangerous behaviors (2) • Negative peer pressure and abuse (2) • Choosing abstinence from driving recklessly (3) • Choosing abstinence from belonging to a gang (3)	• Reasons for conflicts (1) • Roles of anger, bullying, and group pressure on escalating conflicts (1) • Nonviolent strategies to conflict resolution (2) • Mediation as a strategy to avoid violence (2) • Requirements for a peer mediator (2) • Causes of violence (3) • Roles of gangs and weapons in violence (3) • Violence in schools (3) • Forms of abuse and long-term effects (4)
Tobacco, Alcohol, and Other Drugs	• Negative peer pressure and use of alcohol or other drugs (2) • Choosing abstinence from taking drugs (3)	• Role of alcohol and other drugs in violent crimes (1) (3)
Nutrition and Physical Activity		
Environmental Health		
Family Living	• Appraising the importance of social groups (1) • Identifying qualities of a good friendship (1) • Skills for making new friends (1) • Qualities of responsible dating (1) • Negative peer pressure and bad character (2) • Ways to show affection without sex (3)	• Influence of family on violence (3) • Choosing friends wisely to avoid violence (3) • Role of family and friends in abuse (4)
Growth and Development	• Choosing abstinence as the most effective way to avoid pregnancy (3)	• Protecting one's self from violence (3)
Communicable and Noncommunicable Disease	• Choosing abstinence as the most effective way to avoid HIV and other STDs (3)	

KEY: (BHS)=Building Health Skills; (1)=Lesson 1; (2)=Lesson 2; (3)=Lesson 3, etc.

Scope and Sequence

Chapter 8 Nutrition for Health	Chapter 9 Physical Activity and Fitness	Chapter 10 Your Body Image
• Internal influences on food choices (1) • Choosing foods low in fat, cholesterol, sugar, and sodium (2) (3) • Limiting intake of caffeine (2) • Maintaining a healthy weight (3) • Being physically active (3) • Eating a variety of fruits, vegetables, and grains (3) • Choosing healthy meals and snacks (4) • Choosing healthful food alternatives (BHS)	• Managing stress through relaxation exercises (1) • Staying active as a lifestyle choice (1) • The four elements of fitness (2) • Determining target pulse rate (2) • Goal-setting skills for achieving fitness (2) • Developing a physical activity plan (3) • Monitoring progress toward a fitness goal (3) • Refusal skills for avoiding drugs (4) • Developing a personal workout plan (BHS)	• Calculating personal Body Mass Index (1) • Balancing caloric intake and physical activity to achieve best weight (1) • Decision-making skills for helping a friend with an eating disorder (2) • Analyzing internal and external influences on personal body image (2) (BHS)
• Influence of the media on dietary behavior (1) • Identifying social, cultural, and financial influences on dietary behavior (1) • Analyzing food labels (3) • Promoting healthful food choices (BHS)	• Accessing help from experts on fitness goals (2) (3) • Advocacy skills for influencing others to engage in physical activity (BHS)	• Dangers of fad diets (1) • Influence of the media on dietary behavior (2) • Accessing services and support groups to help with eating disorders (2) • Researching weight management strategies (BHS)
• Food safety practices (3)	• Preventing injury during physical activity (4) • Using safe and proper equipment (4) • Knowing personal limits (4) • Treatment of sprains (4)	
	• Choosing to avoid drugs, including anabolic steroids (4) • Risks of illegal steroid use (4)	
• Reasons for needing nutritious food (1) • Role of the six types of nutrients (2) • Sources of nutrients (2) • Importance of fiber (2) • Principles of the Dietary Guidelines (3) • Using the Food Guide Pyramid (3) • Importance of a nutritious breakfast (4)	• Benefits of physical activity and fitness (1) • Distinguishing aerobic and anaerobic exercise (1) • The four elements of physical fitness (2) • Heart and lung endurance (2) • Muscle strength and muscle endurance (2) • The three phases of a workout (3) • Individual and team sports (4) • Importance of sports conditioning (4) • Role of good nutrition in sports (4)	• Defining body image (1) • Causes of overweight and underweight (1) • Calories as measure of energy (1) • Factors in maintaining a healthy weight (1) • Identifying types of eating disorders (2) • Causes, signs, and treatment of eating disorders (2)
	• Following weather-related safety guidelines when playing sports (4)	
• Influence of families on dietary behavior (1)	• Engaging in physical activity with family members (4)	• Family and friends as support for persons with eating disorders (2)
• Role of nutrients on growth and health (2)	• Choosing healthful foods for optimal growth and development needed for sports performance (4)	• Relationship of normal adolescent growth to underweight (1) • Fasting as cause of stunted growth (1) • Malnutrition caused by an eating disorder (2)
• Vitamins and minerals for disease prevention (2) • Reducing fat, cholesterol, and sodium to heart disease (2) • Relating fiber to lowering risk of cancer and heart disease (2) • Reducing the risk of a foodborne illness (3)		• Relationship of excess weight to chronic diseases (1) • Health problems related to underweight (1) • Risks of unhealthy weight control practices (1) (2) • Health problems caused by eating disorders (2)

Scope and Sequence

Content Strands	Chapter 11 Medicines and Drugs	Chapter 12 Tobacco
Personal Health	• Using medicines safely (1) • Refusal skills to resist peer pressure to use drugs (3) • Choosing alternatives to drug use (4)	• Resisting peer pressure to use tobacco (1) (3) • How tobacco use affects personal appearance (1) • Analyzing personal influences, and then choosing alternatives to smoking (3) • Avoiding situations where tobacco is used (3) • Avoiding tobacco use to achieve personal goals (BHS)
Consumer and Community Health	• Role of FDA in ensuring drug safety (1) • Analyzing medicine labels (1) • Accessing support groups and treatment programs for drug addiction (4) • Accessing and analyzing reliable information about a medicine (BHS) • Advocacy skills to influence others not to use drugs (BHS)	• Influence of the media on tobacco use (2) (3) • Costs of tobacco use to society (2) • Influence of celebrities on tobacco use (3) • Accessing resources related to tobacco prevention and cessation (3) • Advocacy skills against tobacco use (BHS)
Injury Prevention and Safety	• Relationship of hallucinogens to injuries (3) • Risk of rape associated with club drugs (3)	
Tobacco, Alcohol, and Other Drugs	• Prescription versus OTC medicines (1) • Types of medicines and effects on body (1) • Side effects, tolerance, overuse, mixing of medicines (1) • Drug misuse, abuse, and addiction (2) • Narcotics, stimulants, and depressants (2) • Street drugs, inhalants, and anabolic steroids (3) • Psychological and physical dependence (3) • Benefits of not using illegal drugs (4) • Withdrawal (4)	• Risks of cigarettes, cigars, pipes, smokeless tobacco, and specialty cigarettes (1) • Harmful substances in tobacco (1) • Economic consequences of tobacco use (2) • Addictive effects of nicotine (2) • Dependence and withdrawal (2) • Identifying strategies for quitting (3)
Nutrition and Physical Activity		• Effects of tobacco use on fitness (1) (3)
Environmental Health		• Secondhand smoke contaminating the air (2)
Family Living	• Health consequences of illegal drug use (2) (3) • Adverse effect on normal body development by marijuana (3) • Height affected by misuse of steroids (3)	• Influence of families and peers on tobacco use (3) • Choosing friends who are tobacco free (3)
Growth and Development		• Damage to body and tobacco use (1) • Risk to unborn child from smoking during pregnancy (2)
Communicable and Noncommunicable Disease	• Relationship of injecting drug use to HIV/AIDS (2) • Marijuana use and increased risk of respiratory infection (3)	• Tobacco use and cancer, heart disease, allergies, and respiratory problems (1) • Secondhand smoke and acute and chronic illnesses (2)

KEY: (BHS)=Building Health Skills; (1)=Lesson 1; (2)=Lesson 2; (3)=Lesson 3, etc.

Scope and Sequence

Chapter 13 Alcohol	Chapter 14 Personal Care	Chapter 15 Your Body Systems
• Influence of personal factors on effects of alcohol (1) • Resisting peer pressure to use alcohol (3) • Choosing alternatives to using alcohol (3) • Decision-making skills to help someone with an alcohol problem (BHS)	• Practicing healthful behaviors for skin, hair, and nail care (1) • Taking care of hair and scalp problems (1) • Practicing healthful behaviors for teeth (2) • Causes of tooth decay (2) • Practicing healthful behaviors for eyes and ears (3)	• Practicing healthful behaviors to keep body systems healthy (1–8) (BHS) • Managing stress to maintain heart health (3) • Managing stress to prevent long-term health consequences (7)
• Services and support groups for addiction to alcohol (2) • Influence of the media on alcohol use (3) • Volunteering as alternative to alcohol use (3) • Advocacy skills in influencing others not to use alcohol (3) • Analyzing advertising that promotes alcohol use (BHS)	• Role of a dermatologist in skin care (1) • Choosing sunglasses and sunscreen for protection against the sun's rays (1) • Getting regular dental checkups (2) • Role of orthodontist in care of teeth (2) • Getting regular eye exams (3) • The influences of the media on body image (BHS) • Reducing noise pollution in the community (BHS)	• Accessing information on scoliosis (1) • Choosing shoes to support the feet (1) • Community blood donation • Citizenship skills by donating blood (3) • Advocacy skills to encourage healthy eating (6) • Importance of dental care to digestion (6) • Getting regular medical checkups (7) • Accessing information about the body (BHS)
• Teen alcohol use and traffic deaths, suicides, violent crimes, and date rape (1) • Unintentional injuries and alcohol use (2) (3) • Child abuse and spousal abuse related to alcohol (2)	• Wearing sports equipment to protect teeth (2) • Wearing protective eyewear (3) • Protecting eyes from eyestrain (3) • Protecting ears from injury (3)	• Types of injuries to the skeletal and muscular systems (1) (2) • Avoiding injuries to the nervous system (5)
• Drink equivalents and blood alcohol content (1) • Alcohol and addiction (2) • Stages of alcoholism (2) • Recognizing reasons teens drink alcohol (3) • Identifying benefits of not using alcohol (3)		• Avoiding tobacco use (3) (4) • Avoiding marijuana use (4) • Avoiding use of alcohol and other drugs (5)
	• Choosing healthful snacks for teeth (2)	• Importance of physical activity to healthy skeletal (1), muscular (2), circulatory (3), respiratory (4), and endocrine (7) systems • Importance of good nutrition to healthy skeletal (1), muscular (2), circulatory (3), digestive (6), excretory (6), and endocrine (7) systems
	• Protecting skin from the sun's rays (1) • Protecting eyes from the sun's rays (3)	• Avoiding polluted air (4)
• Communication skills to influence others to avoid alcohol (1) • Accessing treatment centers to help an addicted family member (2) • Supporting family members and friends in efforts to stop alcohol abuse (2)		
• Health consequences of alcohol on the body and on growth (1) (3) • Fetal alcohol syndrome (1)	• Parts and functions of the skin (1) • Wrinkling and aging because of sun exposure (1) • Effects of hormones on acne and hair during puberty (1) • Functions of the mouth and teeth (2) • Identifying parts of the eye and ear (3) • How vision problems are treated (3)	• Structure and function of each of the body systems (1–8) • Getting enough sleep (5) (7) • The role of endocrine system (7) • The menstrual cycle and fertilization (8) • Comparing changes in males and females (8)
• Alcohol use and chronic diseases (1) (3)	• Caring for acne, cold sores, and warts (1) • Relating sun exposure to skin cancer (1) • Avoiding tattoos and piercings (1) • Practicing eye care to prevent infection (3)	• Disorders of body systems (1–8) • Infections of the respiratory (4), nervous (5), digestive (6), and reproductive (8) systems • Reducing risk of infection to respiratory system (4) • Practicing sexual abstinence (8)

Scope and Sequence

Content Strands	Chapter 16 Growth and Development	Chapter 17 Communicable Diseases
Personal Health	• Recognizing developmental tasks (3) • Managing stress to cope with mood swings (3) • How differences in growth patterns may affect personal health (3) • Goal-setting skills to succeed at a developmental task (BHS)	• Self-inventory of personal habits (1) • Practicing healthful behaviors to reduce the risk of disease to self/others (1) (3) (BHS) • Taking care of a cold (3) • Avoiding sharing personal items (3) • Practicing sexual abstinence (4) (5)
Consumer and Community Health	• Role of an obstetrician in health care (2) • Accessing information on prenatal care (2) • Advocacy skills for good prenatal care (2)	• Accessing reliable information about communicable diseases (3) (BHS) • Seeking input from a trusted adult to handle difficult situations (4) • Seeking help for a suspected STD (4) • Advocacy skills for HIV prevention (5)
Injury Prevention and Safety		
Tobacco, Alcohol, and Other Drugs	• Adverse effects of tobacco, alcohol, and drugs to prenatal care and birth defects (2)	• Avoiding tobacco, alcohol, and other drugs to prevent disease (3) • Avoiding use of alcohol and other drugs to prevent HIV infection (5)
Nutrition and Physical Activity	• Nutrition, exercise, and prenatal care (2) • Relationship of nutrition to birth defects (2)	• Good nutrition and disease prevention (3) • Physical activity and disease prevention (3)
Environmental Health	• Healthy prenatal environment (2)	• Safe water and disease prevention (3)
Family Living	• How traits are inherited (2) • Genetic disorders and birth defects(2) • Using conflict resolution skills with parents (BHS)	• Choosing friends carefully (4) • Responsible behavior to avoid sexual behavior (4) • Resisting peer pressure to engage in sexual behavior (4)
Growth and Development	• Cells, tissues, organs, and systems (1) • Prenatal development and stages of birth (1) • Importance of prenatal care (2) • Erikson's eight stages of life (3) • Physical, mental/emotional, and social changes and development during adolescence (3) • The three stages of adulthood (4)	• How the immune system works (2) • The lymphatic system (2) • Natural and acquired immunity (2) • Adequate rest and disease prevention (3)
Communicable and Noncommunicable Disease	• Relationship of infections to birth defects (2) • HIV and the unborn child (2)	• Distinguishing communicable and noncommunicable diseases (1) • Types of pathogens and how they spread (1) • Importance of vaccinations (2) • Common communicable diseases and risk factors (3) • Facts about STDs (4) • Risk behaviors for spread of HIV (5) • Facts about HIV/AIDS (5)

KEY: (BHS)=Building Health Skills; (1)=Lesson 1; (2)=Lesson 2; (3)=Lesson 3, etc.

Scope and Sequence

Chapter 18 Noncommunicable Diseases	Chapter 19 Safety and Emergencies	Chapter 20 Environmental Health
• Managing stress to lower disease risk (1) (4) (BHS) • Decision-making to manage chronic conditions (2) • Recognizing the warning signs of cancer (3) • Conducting self-examinations for cancer (3) • Analyzing influences on personal risk of disease (BHS)	• Practicing safe habits for personal safety (1) • Refusal skills to resist peer pressure to engage in high-risk behavior or situations (1) (BHS) • Practicing healthful behaviors to recognize, respond to, and perform procedures in an emergency (BHS)	• Taking personal responsibility for cleaner air and water (2) • Practicing healthful behaviors by reducing and reusing (2) (BHS) • Reducing personal consumption of resources by precycling (2)
• Advocacy skills in promoting healthful lifestyle behaviors (1) • Accessing information on support groups (5)	• Following school safety rules (1) • Following vehicle/pedestrian safety rules (2) • Accessing information about a weather emergency (3) • Seeking help from community services for an emergency (4)	• Finding out how to dispose of hazardous waste (1) • Role of the federal EPA (2) • Environmentally conscious consumer (2) • Advocacy skills for environmental awareness (2) • Joining a conservation organization (2) • Advocacy skills to promote recycling (BHS)
	• Preventing accidents/injuries in the home (1) • Following precautions for gun safety (1) • Safety in a fire and preventing fires (1) • Using and wearing safety gear (1) (2) • Basic first-aid skills and supplies (4) • Four steps to take for emergencies (4) • Distinguishing minor and major injuries (5) (6) • First aid for emergencies, CPR (5) (6)	
• Alcohol use and fetal alcohol syndrome (1) • Avoiding use of tobacco, alcohol, and other drugs to lower disease risk (1) (3) (4) • Smoking as cause of lung cancer (3)	• Smoking and fire safety (1) • Avoiding riding with a driver who has been drinking alcohol (2) • Avoiding alcohol/drugs to prevent drowning (2)	• Walking and biking for cleaner air (2)
• Practicing good eating habits, physical activity, and maintaining healthy weight to lower disease risk (1) (3) (4) (5) • Diet and cancers of the colon and rectum (3)	• Following rules for recreational safety (2)	
• Avoiding secondhand smoke to lower disease risk (1) (4) • Environmental causes of serious health problems (1) (3) • Limiting sun exposure (3)	• Following weather-related safety rules (2) (3) • Following safety rules for natural disasters (3) • First aid for weather-related emergencies (5)	• Sources and effects of air pollution (1) • Ozone layer and skin cancer (1) • Causes and effects of water pollution (1) • Sources and disposal of solid waste (1) • Hazardous wastes (1)
• Genetic disorders (1) • Heredity and risk of cancer (3)	• Making the home safe from accidents (1) • Protecting children from accidents (1) • Practicing healthful behaviors to prepare a fire safety plan for the home and family (1) • Using the buddy system (2)	• Disposing of hazardous materials used in the home (1) • Conserving energy and water in the home (2) • Setting up a family recycling system (2)
• Birth defects linked to maternal lifestyle behaviors (1) • Getting enough rest to lower disease risk (1)		• Adverse effects of lead on growth and development (1)
• Causes of noncommunicable diseases (1) • Lifestyle behaviors and risk of disease (1) • Diagnosis and treatment of allergies (2) • Causes and management of asthma (2) • Types, causes, diagnosis, treatment, and prevention of cancer (3) • Causes and treatment of heart disease (4) • Causes, treatment, and prevention of diabetes and arthritis (5)	• Following universal precautions when giving first aid (4) (6)	• Smog and respiratory problems (1) • Diseases and conditions caused by contaminated drinking water (1) • Health consequences of asbestos exposure (1)

Glencoe Professional Health Series

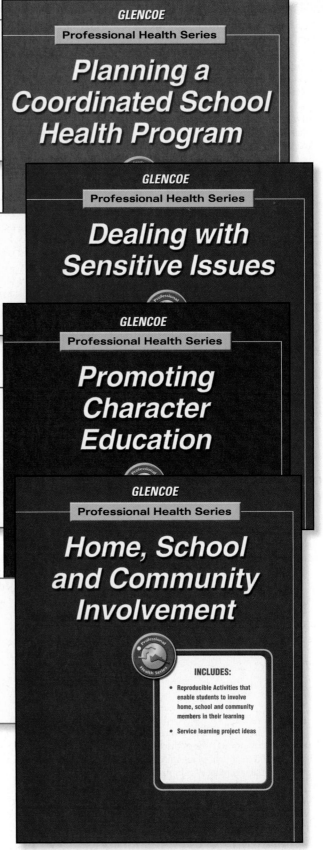

Planning a Coordinated School Health Program

What is coordinated school health? This booklet has been designed to answer that question and to increase awareness of the need for coordinated school health programs throughout the United States.

Dealing with Sensitive Issues

Health educators often need to discuss many sensitive issues with their students. To guide educators, this booklet provides background information and teaching strategies.

Promoting Character Education

This booklet outlines the principles of character education and strategies for developing a caring school community. It includes background information for the teacher and activity ideas designed to help students build good character.

Home, School, and Community Involvement

This guide has been designed to enable students to involve family and community members in their health education. Reproducible activities are provided, including great ideas for service learning projects.

Teen Health
Course 3

Mary H. Bronson, Ph.D.

Michael J. Cleary, Ed.D.

Betty M. Hubbard, Ed.D., C.H.E.S.

Contributing Author
Dinah Zike, M.Ed.

New York, New York   Columbus, Ohio   Chicago, Illinois   Peoria, Illinois   Woodland Hills, California

Meet the Authors

Mary H. Bronson, Ph.D., has taught health education in grades K–12, as well as health education methods classes at the undergraduate and graduate levels. As health education specialist for the Dallas School District, Dr. Bronson developed and implemented a district-wide health education program. She has been honored as Texas Health Educator of the Year by the Texas Association of Health, Physical Education, Recreation and Dance and selected Teacher of the Year twice, by her colleagues. Dr. Bronson has assisted school districts throughout the country in developing local health education programs. She is also the co-author of the *Glencoe Health* textbook.

Betty M. Hubbard, Ed.D., C.H.E.S., has taught health education in grades K–12 as well as health education methods classes at the undergraduate and graduate levels. She is a professor at the University of Central Arkansas, teaching classes in curriculum development, mental health, and human sexuality. Dr. Hubbard supervises student teachers and conducts in-service training for health education teachers in school districts throughout Arkansas. Her publications, grants, and presentations focus on research-based, comprehensive health instruction.

Michael J. Cleary, Ed.D., is Professor and School Health Education Coordinator at Slippery Rock University. Dr. Cleary taught at Evanston Township High School in Evanston, Illinois, and later became the Lead Teacher Specialist at the McMillen Center for Health Education in Fort Wayne, Indiana. Dr. Cleary has published and presented widely on curriculum development and portfolio assessment in K–12 health education. Dr. Cleary is the co-author of *Managing Your Health: Assessment for Action.* He is a Certified Health Education Specialist.

Dinah Zike, M.Ed., is an international curriculum consultant and inventor who has designed and developed educational products and three-dimensional, interactive graphic organizers for over thirty years. As president and founder of Dinah-Might Adventures, L.P., Dinah is the author of over 100 award-winning educational publications. Dinah has a B.S. and an M.S. in educational curriculum and instruction from Texas A&M University. Dinah Zike's *Foldables* are an exclusive feature of McGraw-Hill textbooks.

The McGraw-Hill Companies

Send all inquiries to:
Glencoe/McGraw-Hill
21600 Oxnard Street, Suite 500
Woodland Hills, California 91367

ISBN 0-07-861099-0 (Course 3 Student Text)
ISBN 0-07-861100-8 (Course 3 Teacher Wraparound Edition)

Printed in the United States of America.

1 2 3 4 5 6 7 8 9   071/043   08 07 06 05 04

Health Consultants

Christine A. Hayashi, M.A. Ed., J.D.
Attorney at Law, Special Education Law
Adjunct Faculty, Educational Leadership and Policy Studies Development
California State University, Northridge
Northridge, California

Patricia Sullivan, M.S., Special Education
Chair, Department of Language Arts
Meade Middle School
Fort Meade, Maryland

UNIT 1
Taking Charge of Your Health

Jill English, Ph.D., C.H.E.S.
Assistant Professor
California State University, Fullerton
Fullerton, California

Deborah A. Miller, Ph.D., C.H.E.S.
Professor and Health Coordinator
College of Charleston
Charleston, South Carolina

Alice Pappas, Ph.D., R.N.
Associate Professor/Associate Dean
Baylor University, Louise Herrington School of Nursing
Dallas, Texas

UNIT 2
Building Safe and Healthy Relationships

Kristin Danielson Fink
Executive Director
Community of Caring
Washington, DC

Jan King
Teacher
Neshaminy School District
Langhorne, Pennsylvania

J. Leslie Oganowski, Ph.D.
Professor of Health Education and Health Promotion
University of Wisconsin, La Crosse
La Crosse, Wisconsin

Howard S. Shapiro, M.D.
Associate Professor
University of Southern California School of Medicine
Los Angeles, California

UNIT 3
Physical Health and Fitness

Roberta Larson Duyff, R.D.
Food and Nutrition Consultant/President
Duyff Associates
St. Louis, Missouri

Mark L. Giese, Ed.D.
Chair, Health Science and Kinesiology Department
Northeastern State University
Tahlequah, Oklahoma

Tinker D. Murray, Ph.D.
Professor and Coordinator of the Exercise and Sports Science Program
Southwest Texas State University
San Marcos, Texas

Don Rainey
Instructor, Coordinator of the Physical Fitness and Wellness Program
Southwest Texas State University
San Marcos, Texas

UNIT 4
Making Safe and Drug-Free Decisions

Sally Champlin, C.H.E.S.
Faculty, Health Science
California State University, Long Beach
Long Beach, California

Taniesha Richardson, C.H.E.S.
Arkansas Department of Health
Office of Tobacco Prevention and Education
Little Rock, Arkansas

Peggy Woosley
Director of Curriculum
Stuttgart Public Schools
Stuttgart, Arkansas

UNIT 5
Understanding Your Body

Stephanie S. Allen
Senior Lecturer
Baylor University, Louise Herrington School of Nursing
Dallas, Texas

Victoria Bisorca, C.H.E.S.
Lecturer
California State University, Long Beach
Long Beach, California

Linda Stevenson, Ph.D., R.N.
Assistant Professor
Baylor University, Louise Herrington School of Nursing
Dallas, Texas

Health Consultants *(cont.)*

UNIT 6
Diseases and Disorders

Jennifer Weglowski, M.D.
Pediatrician/Senior Pediatric Resident
Children's Hospital of Pittsburgh
Pittsburgh, Pennsylvania

UNIT 7
Safety and Environmental Health

Jerry G. Hill
Agency Leadership Team
Arkansas Department of Health
Little Rock, Arkansas

David A. Sleet, Ph.D.
Associate Director for Science
Division of Unintentional Injury Prevention
Centers for Disease Control and Prevention (CDC)
Atlanta, Georgia

Reviewers

Beverly J. Berkin, C.H.E.S.
Health Education Consultant
Bedford Corners, New York

Donna Breitenstein, Ed.D.
Professor & Coordinator of Health Education
Director of North Carolina School Health
    Training Center
Appalachian State University
Boone, North Carolina

Julie Campbell-Fouch
Health Teacher, Department Chair
Stanford Middle School
Long Beach, California

Pamela R. Connolly
Subject Area Coordinator for Health and Physical
    Education, Diocese of Pittsburgh
Curriculum Coordinator for Health and Physical
    Education, North Catholic High School
Pittsburgh, Pennsylvania

Pat Freedman
Instructional Coordinator for Student Wellness
Humble Independent School District
Humble, Texas

Ginger Lawless, C.H.E.S.
Dyslexia and School Health Education Specialist
Fort Bend Independent School District
Sugar Land, Texas

Renee Rainey
Physical Education Teacher
Cowan Elementray School
Austin, Texas

James Robinson III, Ed.D.
Professor, Assistant Dean for Student Affairs
The Texas A&M University System
Health Science Center
School of Rural Public Health
College Station, Texas

Michael Rulon
Health/Physical Education Teacher
Johnson Junior High School
Adjunct Faculty, Laramie County Community
    College
Cheyenne, Wyoming

Jeanne Title
Coordinator, Prevention Education
Napa County Office of Education and Napa Valley
    Unified School District
Napa, California

Taking Charge of Your Health   1

Chapter 1 Understanding Your Health   2

Lesson 1   **What Is Health and Wellness?** 4
     ▶ HANDS-ON HEALTH: Wellness Survey 7

Lesson 2   **Changes During the Teen Years** 8
     ▶ HEALTH SKILLS: A Friend in Need 11

Lesson 3   **Taking Responsibility for Your Health** 14
     ▶ HEALTH SKILLS: Making Health a Habit 18

     TIME **Health**
     Teens with a Mission 20

     Building Health Skills
     Looking at Health Influences *(Analyzing Influences)* 22

Chapter 2 Health Skills: The Foundation   26

Lesson 1   **Making Decisions and Setting Goals** 28
     ▶ HEALTH SKILLS: What to Do? What to Do? 30

Lesson 2   **Practicing Communication Skills** 34
     ▶ HANDS-ON HEALTH: Sending "I" Messages 36

Lesson 3   **Managing Stress** 39
     ▶ HEALTH SKILLS: Balance Your Schedule 43

Lesson 4   **Developing Other Health Skills** 44
     ▶ HEALTH SKILLS: Personal Health Inventory 46

     TIME **Health**
     Under Pressure 50

     Building Health Skills
     Say No to Peer Pressure *(Refusal Skills)* 52

Chapter 3 Being a Health Consumer   56

Lesson 1   **Healthy Consumer Habits** 58
     ▶ HEALTH SKILLS: Know Your Rights 61

Lesson 2   **Choosing Health Services** 63
     ▶ HEALTH SKILLS: Health Care in the Community 66

Lesson 3   **Managing Consumer Problems** 68
     ▶ HANDS-ON HEALTH: Fact vs. Opinion 70

Lesson 4   **Public Health** 72
     ▶ HEALTH SKILLS: Public Health 74

     TIME **Health**
     Turn It Off! 76

     Building Health Skills
     Finding Reliable Sources *(Accessing Information)* 78

UNIT 2

Building Safe and Healthy Relationships 82

Chapter 4 Mental and Emotional Health 84

Lesson 1 **Your Mental and Emotional Health** 86
▶ HEALTH SKILLS: Improving Your Self-Esteem 89

Lesson 2 **Understanding Your Emotions** 91
▶ HANDS-ON HEALTH: Communicating Emotions 93

Lesson 3 **Mental and Emotional Problems** 96
▶ HEALTH SKILLS: If a Friend Seems Depressed 99

Lesson 4 **Getting Help** 101

Lesson 5 **Coping with Loss** 106
▶ HEALTH SKILLS: Writing a Sympathy Note 107

TIME Health
Dealing with Anxiety 110

Building Health Skills
Put Stress in Its Place *(Stress Management)* 112

Chapter 5 Promoting Social Health 116

Lesson 1 **Your Character and Your Relationships** 118
▶ HEALTH SKILLS: A Matter of Character 121

Lesson 2 **Getting Along with Your Family** 124
▶ HANDS-ON HEALTH: Positive Family Interactions 127

Lesson 3 **Marriage and Parenthood** 129
▶ HEALTH SKILLS: Identifying Role Models 131

TIME Health
Friendly Persuasion 134

Building Health Skills
Sending the Right Message *(Communication Skills)* 136

Chapter 6 Relationships: The Teen Years   **140**

Lesson 1   **Friendships: Growing and Changing** 142

Lesson 2   **Peer Pressure and Refusal Skills** 147

     ▶ HANDS-ON HEALTH: Recognizing Peer Pressure 149

Lesson 3   **Practicing Abstinence** 151

     ▶ HEALTH SKILLS: Supporting Abstinence 153

     TIME Health

     Cliques—Good or Bad? 156

     Building Health Skills

     Know Your Limits *(Goal Setting)* 158

Chapter 7 Conflict Resolution   **162**

Lesson 1   **The Nature of Conflict** 164

     ▶ HANDS-ON HEALTH: A Survey of Conflicts 165

Lesson 2   **Resolving Conflicts** 168

     ▶ HEALTH SKILLS: When to Suggest a Mediator 171

Lesson 3   **Avoiding and Preventing Violence** 172

     ▶ HEALTH SKILLS: Help Prevent School Violence 174

Lesson 4   **Preventing Abuse** 177

     ▶ HEALTH SKILLS: Helping a Victim of Abuse 180

     TIME Health

     Stopping Violence Before It Starts 182

     Building Health Skills

     Working Through Conflicts *(Conflict Resolution)* 184

UNIT 3

Physical Health and Fitness — 188

Chapter 8 Nutrition for Health — 190
Lesson 1 **The Importance of Nutrition** 192
Lesson 2 **Nutrients for Wellness** 196
   ▶ HANDS-ON HEALTH: Jars of Sugar 200
Lesson 3 **Following Nutrition Guidelines** 202
   ▶ HEALTH SKILLS: Reading a Food Label 206
Lesson 4 **Planning Meals and Snacks** 208
   ▶ HEALTH SKILLS: Choosing Healthful Snacks 210

TIME **Health**
   Teen Vegetarians 212

Building Health Skills
   Eating for Your Health (*Advocacy*) 214

Chapter 9 Physical Activity and Fitness — 218
Lesson 1 **The Benefits of Physical Activity** 220
   ▶ HEALTH SKILLS: Relaxation Exercises 222
Lesson 2 **Endurance, Strength, and Flexibility** 224
   ▶ HANDS-ON HEALTH: Your Target Pulse Rate 226
Lesson 3 **Setting Fitness Goals** 230
   ▶ HEALTH SKILLS: Activities for Fitness 231
Lesson 4 **Staying Fit and Avoiding Injury** 236
   ▶ HEALTH SKILLS: Abstaining from Drugs 240

TIME **Health**
   Are You A Good Sport? 242

Building Health Skills
   Warm Up! Work Out! Cool Down!
   (*Practicing Healthful Behaviors*) 244

Chapter 10 Your Body Image — 248
Lesson 1 **Maintaining a Healthy Body** 250
   ▶ HANDS-ON HEALTH: Calculating Fat Intake 252
Lesson 2 **Eating Disorders** 256
   ▶ HEALTH SKILLS: Helping a Friend 258

TIME **Health**
   Building a Better Body Image 260

Building Health Skills
   Sharpen Your Body Image (*Analyzing Influences*) 262

UNIT 4

Making Safe and Drug-Free Decisions — 266

Chapter 11 Medicines and Drugs — 268

Lesson 1 **Using Medicines Wisely** 270
▶ HEALTH SKILLS: Medicine Safety in the Home 274

Lesson 2 **Narcotics, Stimulants, and Depressants** 276

Lesson 3 **Marijuana and Other Illegal Drugs** 281
▶ HEALTH SKILLS: Refusing Drugs 284

Lesson 4 **Staying Drug Free** 286
▶ HANDS-ON HEALTH: Drug-Free Campaign 288

TIME Health
Marijuana Myths 290

Building Health Skills
Saying No to Drugs (*Advocacy*) 292

Chapter 12 Tobacco — 296

Lesson 1 **How Tobacco Affects the Body** 298
▶ HEALTH SKILLS: Choose to Refuse Tobacco 300

Lesson 2 **Tobacco and Society** 303
▶ HANDS-ON HEALTH: Tobacco Facts Pamphlets 306

Lesson 3 **Choosing to Be Tobacco Free** 308
▶ HEALTH SKILLS: Be Prepared 309

TIME Health
Smoke Signals 312

Building Health Skills
Steer Clear of Tobacco (*Goal Setting*) 314

Chapter 13 Alcohol — 318

Lesson 1 **What Alcohol Does to the Body** 320
▶ HEALTH SKILLS: Helping a Friend Stay Safe 324

Lesson 2 **Alcohol and Society** 325
▶ HANDS-ON HEALTH: Drunk-Driving Statistics 326

Lesson 3 **Choosing to Be Alcohol Free** 330
▶ HEALTH SKILLS: Saying No to a Drink 332

TIME Health
Getting MADD 334

Building Health Skills
Helping Someone Get Help (*Decision Making*) 336

Understanding Your Body — 340

Chapter 14 Personal Care — 342

Lesson 1 **Healthy Skin, Hair, and Nails** 344
   ▶ HEALTH SKILLS: Protect Yourself from the Sun 346

Lesson 2 **Healthy Mouth and Teeth** 349
   ▶ HANDS-ON HEALTH: Plaque Attack 352

Lesson 3 **Healthy Eyes and Ears** 354
   ▶ HEALTH SKILLS: Reducing Noise Levels 359

TIME Health
The Truth Behind Popular Health Tips 360

Building Health Skills
Seeing Beyond the Perfect Look *(Analyzing Influences)* . 362

Chapter 15 Your Body Systems — 366

Lesson 1 **Your Skeletal System** 368
   ▶ HEALTH SKILLS: Scoliosis Screening 370

Lesson 2 **Your Muscular System** 372
   ▶ HANDS-ON HEALTH: Stretch Out 374

Lesson 3 **Your Circulatory System** 376

Lesson 4 **Your Respiratory System** 381

Lesson 5 **Your Nervous System** 385

Lesson 6 **Your Digestive and Excretory Systems** 390
   ▶ HEALTH SKILLS: Encouraging Healthy Eating 394

Lesson 7 **Your Endocrine System** 396
   ▶ HEALTH SKILLS: Protecting Your Body 398

Lesson 8 **Your Reproductive System** 400

TIME Health
How Stress Takes Its Toll 406

Building Health Skills
Finding Facts About Your Body *(Accessing Information)* . 408

Chapter 16 Growth and Development — 414

Lesson 1 **The Beginning of Life** 416

Lesson 2 **Heredity and Environment** 421
   ▶ HANDS-ON HEALTH: Prenatal Care Brochure 423

Lesson 3 **From Childhood to Adolescence** 426
   ▶ HEALTH SKILLS: Coping with Mood Swings 430

Lesson 4 **Adulthood and Aging** 432

TIME Health
Can We Stay Young? 436

Building Health Skills
Resolving Conflicts with Parents *(Conflict Resolution)* . . 438

UNIT 6

Diseases and Disorders   442

Chapter 17 Communicable Diseases   444

Lesson 1 **Preventing the Spread of Disease** 446
   ▶ HANDS-ON HEALTH: Habits for Health 448

Lesson 2 **The Body's Defenses Against Infection** 450

Lesson 3 **Communicable Diseases** 454
   ▶ HEALTH SKILLS: Can I Catch What's in the News? ... 456

Lesson 4 **Sexually Transmitted Diseases** 458
   ▶ HEALTH SKILLS: Helping a Friend Choose Abstinence   460

Lesson 5 **HIV/AIDS** 464
   ▶ HEALTH SKILLS: Get the Message Out 466

TIME Health
Healthy Germs 468

Building Health Skills
Protecting Yourself and Others
(Practicing Healthful Behaviors) 470

Chapter 18 Noncommunicable Diseases   474

Lesson 1 **Noncommunicable Diseases** 476
   ▶ HEALTH SKILLS: Promoting a Healthful Lifestyle 478

Lesson 2 **Allergies and Asthma** 480
   ▶ HEALTH SKILLS: Managing Chronic Conditions 483

Lesson 3 **Cancer** 484

Lesson 4 **Heart and Circulatory Problems** 489
   ▶ HANDS-ON HEALTH: Measuring Blood Pressure 490

Lesson 5 **Diabetes and Arthritis** 494
   ▶ HEALTH SKILLS: Locating Support Groups 496

TIME Health
The Diabetes Explosion 498

Building Health Skills
Managing Teen Stress *(Stress Management)* 500

UNIT 7

Safety and Environmental Health 504

Chapter 19 Safety and Emergencies   506

Lesson 1   **Safety at Home and at School** 508
    ▶ HEALTH SKILLS: Preparing a Fire Safety Plan 512

Lesson 2   **Safety on the Road and Outdoors** 514

Lesson 3   **Safety in Weather Emergencies** 520
    ▶ HEALTH SKILLS: Local Weather Emergencies 522

Lesson 4   **Basic First Aid** 524

Lesson 5   **First Aid for Common Emergencies** 528

Lesson 6   **Life-Threatening Emergencies** 533
    ▶ HANDS-ON HEALTH: Locating Pressure Points 535

TIME Health
    Preventing Wildfires 538

Building Health Skills
    Avoiding Unsafe Behaviors *(Refusal Skills)* 540

Chapter 20 Environmental Health   544

Lesson 1   **Pollution and Health** 546
    ▶ HANDS-ON HEALTH: Effects of Water Pollutants 549

Lesson 2   **Preventing and Reducing Pollution** 552
    ▶ HEALTH SKILLS: Environment-Friendly Shopping . . . 556

TIME Health
    Mean Clean Machines 558

Building Health Skills
    Make the Most of It *(Practicing Healthful Behaviors)* . . . 560

Glossary 564

Glosario 579

Index 595

Hands-On Health

Wellness Survey 7

Sending "I" Messages 36

Fact vs. Opinion 70

Communicating Emotions 93

Positive Family Interactions 127

Recognizing Peer Pressure 149

A Survey of Conflicts 165

Jars of Sugar 200

Your Target Pulse Rate 226

Calculating Fat Intake 252

Drug-Free Campaign 288

Tobacco Facts Pamphlets 306

Drunk-Driving Statistics 326

Plaque Attack 352

Stretch Out 374

Prenatal Care Brochure 423

Habits for Health 448

Measuring Blood Pressure 490

Locating Pressure Points 535

Effects of Water Pollutants 549

Getting the most out of Teen *Health*

Making healthy and responsible decisions is easy with *Teen Health*. Follow the guidelines below to make the most out of each lesson.

Do the Quick Write

This feature will help you start thinking about the information in a lesson.

Preview the Lesson

Get a preview of what's coming by reading the lesson objectives in the **Learn About....** You can also use this feature to prepare for quizzes and tests.

Review Key Terms

Find each vocabulary term in the text and read its definition. The terms appear in blue so you can locate them easily!

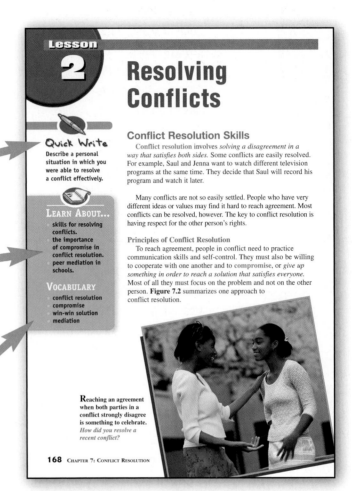

Lesson 2

Resolving Conflicts

Quick Write
Describe a personal situation in which you were able to resolve a conflict effectively.

LEARN ABOUT...
- skills for resolving conflicts.
- the importance of compromise in conflict resolution.
- peer mediation in schools.

VOCABULARY
- conflict resolution
- compromise
- win-win solution
- mediation

Conflict Resolution Skills

Conflict resolution involves *solving a disagreement in a way that satisfies both sides.* Some conflicts are easily resolved. For example, Saul and Jenna want to watch different television programs at the same time. They decide that Saul will record his program and watch it later.

Many conflicts are not so easily settled. People who have very different ideas or values may find it hard to reach agreement. Most conflicts can be resolved, however. The key to conflict resolution is having respect for the other person's rights.

Principles of Conflict Resolution
To reach agreement, people in conflict need to practice communication skills and self-control. They must also be willing to cooperate with one another and to compromise, or *give up something in order to reach a solution that satisfies everyone.* Most of all they must focus on the problem and not on the other person. **Figure 7.2** summarizes one approach to conflict resolution.

Reaching an agreement when both parties in a conflict strongly disagree is something to celebrate. *How did you resolve a recent conflict?*

168 CHAPTER 7: CONFLICT RESOLUTION

Use Glencoe's Health Web Site to Boost Your Health Smarts!

▶ Rate your health by taking the Health Inventory for each chapter. Jump-start your goals by filling out a Personal Wellness Contract.

▶ Check out Web Link Exercises for fun and interactive games and activities.

▶ Do some detective work on a particular health topic—Health Quests show you how.

▶ Get ready for tests by using the different Online Study Tools to review vocabulary terms and chapter content. E-flashcards, online quizzes, and interactive drag-and-drop games make studying fun!

▶ Building Health Skills features give you another chance to master important skills for wellness.

Study the Infographics

First, think about the overall message that the infographic is presenting. Then, read each callout carefully and determine what part of the image it is highlighting.

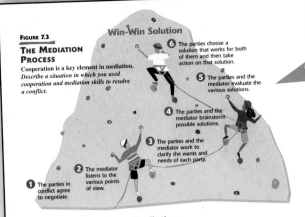

FIGURE 7.3

THE MEDIATION PROCESS

Cooperation is a key element in mediation. *Describe a situation in which you used cooperation and mediation skills to resolve a conflict.*

Win-Win Solution

6 The parties choose a solution that works for both of them and then take action on that solution.

5 The parties and the mediator evaluate the various solutions.

4 The parties and the mediator brainstorm possible solutions.

3 The parties and the mediator work to clarify the wants and needs of each party.

2 The mediator listens to the various points of view.

1 The parties in conflict agree to negotiate.

Peer Mediation

Many schools have peer mediation programs. In peer mediation, a student serves as the mediator for students who are involved in a conflict. Teens can be effective mediators because they understand their peers' attitudes and viewpoints. They can put the problem in language that students can relate to.

Students receive special training to become peer mediators. Training may be provided by teachers or by people from community mediation organizations. Training programs cover a number of topics that focus on the qualities, skills, and behaviors required of mediators. Here are some of the requirements of a peer mediator.

- Be trustworthy and keep the discussions confidential.
- Understand and analyze conflict.
- Listen carefully and express ideas clearly.
- Identify feelings.
- Remain completely neutral throughout the process.
- Handle anger in a positive way.
- Identify points of agreement.
- Brainstorm multiple solutions for a problem.
- Evaluate the consequences of various options.
- Take accurate notes.
- Once it has been agreed upon, describe a clear win-win agreement in writing.

170 CHAPTER 7: CONFLICT RESOLUTION

Try the Health Skills and Hands-On Health Activities

Develop valuable health skills by doing the Health Skills Activities that appear in each chapter. Conduct experiments, create ads, and try the other fun activities in the Hands-On Health features.

HEALTH SKILLS ACTIVITY

DECISION MAKING

When to Suggest a Mediator

Lisa, Tony, and Dave were all good friends until two weeks ago. After a serious argument, Tony and Dave stopped speaking to each other. Both are still speaking to Lisa, and each separately told Lisa his side of the conflict.

Dave told Lisa that Tony tries to copy Dave's school papers and tests. Dave explained that when he confronted Tony, Tony acted outraged and denied trying to copy anything. Later, Lisa listened to Tony's side of the story. Tony said that Dave is spreading lies about him, and that he will never be friends with Dave again. When Lisa suggested that Dave and Tony try to talk over their problem, Tony said, "Stay out of this! It's between Dave and me."

Lisa wonders if peer mediation would help settle their conflict. She thinks about suggesting it but is worried about Tony's warning. She decides to use the decision-making process to determine what she should do.

What Would You Do?

Apply the skills for decision making to Lisa's situation. Would you suggest mediation? Why or why not?

1. STATE THE SITUATION.
2. LIST THE OPTIONS.
3. WEIGH THE POSSIBLE OUTCOMES.
4. CONSIDER VALUES.
5. MAKE A DECISION AND ACT.
6. EVALUATE THE DECISION.

Complete the Lesson Reviews

Completing the lesson reviews can help you see how well you know the material you have just studied. It also gives you a chance to apply what you've learned to different situations, as well as practice a health skill.

Lesson 2 Review

Using complete sentences, answer the following questions on a sheet of paper.

Reviewing Terms and Facts

1. **Vocabulary** Define *win-win solution.*
2. **Summarize** In your own words, summarize conflict resolution/mediation skills.
3. **Explain** What makes students effective mediators for their peers?

Thinking Critically

4. **Apply** Relate conflict resolution/mediation skills to personal situations: How have you used these skills in your life?
5. **Explain** How can a peer mediation program help make your school safer?

Applying Health Skills

6. **Conflict Resolution** With a partner, write a skit in which a conflict is resolved peacefully. Perform your skit for the class to demonstrate strategies for coping with problems related to conflict.

LESSON 2: RESOLVING CONFLICTS **171**

UNIT 1

Taking Charge of Your Health

Unit Objectives

Students will learn about the concepts of health and wellness and how they are affected during the teen years. Strategies for developing health skills and wise consumer habits are also emphasized.

Unit Overview

Chapter 1
Understanding Your Health

Lesson
1 What Is Health and Wellness?
2 Changes During the Teen Years
3 Taking Responsibility for Your Health

Chapter 2
Health Skills: The Foundation

Lesson
1 Making Decisions and Setting Goals
2 Practicing Communication Skills
3 Managing Stress
4 Developing Other Health Skills

Chapter 3
Being a Health Consumer

Lesson
1 Healthy Consumer Habits
2 Choosing Health Services
3 Managing Consumer Problems
4 Public Health

DEALING WITH SENSITIVE ISSUES

The Bigger Picture When you deal with sensitive issues in the classroom, don't forget that parents, the school board, and the community may be concerned about what you teach and how you teach it. You can minimize their concerns by following these guidelines: Familiarize yourself with the regulations and guidelines in your school district about course content, parental permissions, and related issues. In your classes, emphasize abstinence from sexual activity before marriage, as well as from alcohol and illegal drugs. Avoid preaching to students about sensitive issues. Avoid classroom activities and behaviors that may be misinterpreted. Always thank parents for their concern.

Taking Charge of Your Health

Unit Introduction

Ask students to identify what they think they will learn in a health course. Encourage them to explain their responses with specific objectives; and coach them to include a broad range of areas that cover physical, mental/emotional, and social health.

List their responses on the board, and group them into categories that are the same as the three sides of the health triangle (physical, mental/emotional, and social). Ask students whether they were aware that health encompasses more than physical health and whether they can see any connections among the three categories.

Tell students that the chapters in this unit will explain more about the interrelationship of the three sides of the health triangle and the concepts of total health and wellness.

HEALTH in Action

The challenges you face in your teen years may seem bigger than an ocean, but you can develop the skills to meet them. You can learn to set goals, to make responsible decisions. You will be seeing many changes in the world around you— and in yourself—in the coming years. With the right skills and good habits on your side, however, you'll be prepared to make quite a splash!

How can taking care of yourself be like a day at the beach?

1

HEALTH in Action

Read the class the question on page 1. Ask students to name a few everyday choices that might affect health, either positively or negatively. You may need to make some suggestions yourself to get students started, such as "deciding what to have for lunch." Then lead the class in the following physical group activity:

Have each student write one decision that might affect health on a slip of paper. Collect slips in a container. Shake the container, then pass it around the class. Have each student remove a random entry and suggest a positive option for that decision. For example, a student who selects a piece of paper that says "deciding whether to skip breakfast when running late" might suggest having a piece of fruit or yogurt to go.

Planning Guide

Chapter 1	Skills/ Activities	Reproducible Resources	Assessment
Lesson 1 **What Is Health and Wellness?** *pages 4–7*	**Hands-On Health** ▲ Wellness Survey, page 7	*Student Activities Workbook available for use with each chapter* 📁 Parent Letter & Activities 1 📁 Concept Map 1 📁 Cross-Curriculum Activity 1 📁 Decision-Making Activity 1 📁 Enrichment Activity 1 📁 Health Lab 1 📁 Lesson Plan 1 📁 Reading Tutor Activity 1 📁 Reteaching Activity 1	📁 Lesson 1 Quiz
Lesson 2 **Changes During the Teen Years** *pages 8–13*	**HEALTH SKILLS ACTIVITY** ▲ A Friend in Need (*Communication Skills*), page 11	📁 Concept Map 2 📁 Enrichment Activity 2 📁 Lesson Plan 2 📁 Reading Tutor Activity 2 📁 Reteaching Activity 2	📁 Lesson 2 Quiz
Lesson 3 **Taking Responsibility for Your Health** *pages 14–19*	**HEALTH SKILLS ACTIVITY** ▲ Making Health a Habit (*Practicing Healthful Behaviors*), page 18	📁 Concept Map 3 📁 Cross-Curriculum Activity 2 📁 Decision-Making Activity 2 📁 Enrichment Activity 3 📁 Lesson Plan 3 📁 Reading Tutor Activity 3 📁 Reteaching Activity 3	📁 Lesson 3 Quiz 📁 Chapter 1 Test 📁 Performance Assessment 1

TIME HEALTH **Teens with a Mission** *pages 20–21*

BUILDING HEALTH SKILLS

Looking at Health Influences
(*Analyzing Influences*)
pages 22–23

📁 Building Health Skills Reproducible Master 26

Standards		Technology
National	**State/Local**	
National Health Education Standard **1.1, 1.2, 1.6, 1.8, 3.1, 3.2, 3.4**		Transparency 1 TeacherWorks™ Internet Activities
National Health Education Standard **1.1, 1.2, 1.3, 1.4, 1.6, 5.4, 5.5**		Transparency 2 TeacherWorks™
National Health Education Standard **1.1, 1.2, 1.6, 1.8, 3.1, 3.4, 2.1**		Transparency 3 TeacherWorks™ MindJogger Videoquiz **Exam**View® Pro Testmaker
National Health Education Standard **1.4, 4.1, 4.2, 4.3, 4.4**		Building Health Skills Transparency Master 4

TeacherWorks™

Glencoe's new and exclusive TeacherWorks™ is an all-in-one planner and resource center. Access the complete Teacher Wraparound Edition electronically. Find all your classroom resources with just a few easy clicks, and print them right from your computer. Connect directly to Glencoe's customized Health Web site. Access the National Health Education Standards correlations, or insert your own state standards and match them directly to the electronic Teacher Wraparound Edition.

Language Diversity

- English Audio Summaries
- Spanish Audio Summaries
- English Summaries, Quizzes, and Activities
- Spanish Summaries, Quizzes, and Activities
- Spanish Parent Letters and Activities

KEY TO ABILITY LEVELS

Teaching Strategies that appear throughout the chapters have been identified by one of four codes to give you an idea of their suitability for students of varying learning styles and abilities.

L1 **Level 1** strategies should be within the ability range of all students. Often full class participation is required.

L2 **Level 2** strategies are for average to above-average students or for small groups. Some teacher direction is necessary.

L3 **Level 3** strategies are designed for students able and willing to work independently. Minimal teacher direction is necessary.

INCL Strategies are appropriate for students with particular special needs in a general classroom setting.

Understanding Your Health

Chapter at a Glance

Lesson 1 defines health and wellness using the health triangle. It discusses how personal health choices affect total health and wellness.

Lesson 2 discusses adolescence and identifies the physical, mental/emotional, and social changes that take place during the teen years.

Lesson 3 discusses the risks that teens face and helps students understand what they can do to avoid high-risk behavior.

Health Skills
- A Friend in Need (*Communication Skills*), p. 11
- Making Health a Habit (*Practicing Healthful Behaviors*), p. 18
- Looking at Health Influences (*Analyzing Influences*), pp. 22–23

HANDS-ON ACTIVITY

Wellness Web Using three colors of yarn—red for physical health, blue for mental/emotional health, and yellow for social health—cut two- to six-foot sections. Tie the sections together and roll the yarn into a single ball. Ask students to sit in a circle on the floor. Anchor the end of the yarn ball within the circle, and roll the yarn ball to a student. As a student receives the yarn ball, he or she should, according to the color of the yarn, share a fact or ask a question that relates to that area of health. Keeping hold of the yarn, the student should then roll the yarn ball to another student who repeats the process. The pattern makes a web as it is rolled to each person in the class and keeps track of who has shared. It also facilitates a broader spectrum of discussion.

Understanding Your Health

Chapter Introduction

Use the options below to motivate students and preview chapter content.

HEALTH *Online*

What's the status of your health—fair, good, or very good? Find out how you rate by taking the Chapter 1 Health Inventory at health.glencoe.com.

HEALTH *Online*

Assign Health Inventory 1, or pick up some new teaching ideas at **health.glencoe.com**. Click on Teaching Today to download helpful tools such as graphic organizers and Webquest activities.

GLENCOE TECHNOLOGY

MindJogger Videoquiz

Use MindJogger to preview or review Chapter 1 content.

TIME HEALTH

Teens with a Mission
pages 20–21

FOLDABLES™ Study Organizer

Before You Read

Make this Foldable to record what you learn about health and wellness in Lesson 1. Begin with a plain sheet of 11″ × 17″ paper.

Step 1

Fold the short sides of the sheet of paper inward so that they meet in the middle.

Step 2

Draw two circles—one that covers both sides of the Foldable, and one that covers only one side of the Foldable. Label as shown.

As You Read

On the back of each panel of your Foldable, take notes, define terms, and record examples of health and wellness. In the middle section, draw your personal health triangle.

3

FOLDABLES™ Study Organizer

Dinah Zike Study Fold

Organizing Data Students will use this Foldable study guide to write about health and wellness. Under the appropriate tab of their completed Foldable, students will take notes, define terms, record examples, and draw their own personal health triangle. Encourage students to use what they learn to explain how the Venn diagram illustrates health as part of total wellness.

What Is Health and Wellness?

① Focus

Lesson Objectives

Students will be able to

- define *health* and *wellness*.
- identify the three sides of the health triangle.
- analyze the interrelationships of physical, mental/emotional, and social health.
- discuss how daily decisions contribute to wellness.

Motivators

 Quick Write
Copy the words *energy, strength,* and *confidence* on the board to get students started. Encourage them to think beyond physical health. Then add to the list as students share their responses.

Bellringer Activity

Ask students to write two choices they made in the last week that may have affected their health in either positive or negative ways.

VOCABULARY

Write the following scrambled words L-N-E-S-W-S-E-L and E-H-L-A-H-T. Have students unscramble the words, find their definitions in the Glossary in the back of the student text, and then use each word in an original sentence.

What Is Health and Wellness?

Quick Write

Jot down all the words that come to mind when you think of good health. Compare your list with those of your classmates.

LEARN ABOUT...

- keeping your physical, mental/emotional, and social health in balance.
- how daily decisions contribute to wellness.

VOCABULARY

- health
- wellness

Your Total Health

What do you think of when you hear the word *health*? Maybe you picture an athlete competing in a race. Perhaps you think of someone you know who never seems to get sick. Although being physically fit and being free from illness are important, there's much more to good health.

If you had a friend who was always putting herself down, would you think she was healthy? What about a classmate who was always picking fights with other students? Being healthy also involves feeling good about yourself and getting along with other people. **Health** is *a combination of physical, mental/emotional, and social well-being.*

You make choices every day that affect your health. You decide what to eat, how to spend your time, and who you will spend your time with. How can you tell which choices are best for your health? This book will help you recognize your health habits and decide whether you need to make any changes.

Deciding how to spend your time is one of many choices you make that affect your overall health. *What are some healthy ways to spend free time?*

4 CHAPTER 1: UNDERSTANDING YOUR HEALTH

Lesson 1 Resources

Teacher Classroom Resources

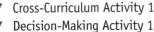 Parent Letter & Activities 1
Concept Map 1
Cross-Curriculum Activity 1
Decision-Making Activity 1
Enrichment Activity 1
Health Lab 1
Lesson Plan 1

Lesson 1 Quiz
Reading Tutor Activity 1
Reteaching Activity 1
Transparency 1

Student Activities Workbook
Chapter 1 Study Guide
Applying Health Skills 1

The Health Triangle

Like a triangle, your health has three sides: physical, mental/emotional, and social. All three sides are interrelated. For example, a teen who skips meals and doesn't get enough sleep may feel irritable and have trouble concentrating. A teen who doesn't express emotions in healthy ways may have difficulty getting along with family and friends.

The key to good health is keeping a balanced health triangle. To have a balanced triangle, you need to keep each side of your triangle healthy. **Figure 1.1** provides more information about the three sides of the health triangle.

FIGURE 1.1

The Health Triangle

The health triangle has three equally important sides.
Which side deals with managing stress?

Social
Social health involves getting along with other people. This includes being a caring family member, making and keeping friends, and giving and receiving support when it's needed. Social health also involves interacting effectively with many different types of people, including both males and females and members of different ethnic and cultural groups.

Mental/Emotional
Mental and emotional health involves liking and accepting yourself for who you are. This includes finding solutions to problems, expressing emotions in healthy ways, and finding positive ways to manage stress.

Physical
Physical health involves taking care of your body. This includes eating well-balanced meals and snacks, being physically active, avoiding disease, getting enough rest, and having regular medical and dental checkups.

② Teach

Discussing

Have students suggest five healthy ways to spend free time, and list their suggestions on the board. Then draw three columns labeled *physical health, mental/emotional health,* and *social health.* Ask how each activity might affect these areas of health, and jot down their responses in the appropriate columns. **L1**

Comparing

Ask students:

• How are your health-related responsibilities different from those you had five years ago?

• How do you expect your health-related responsibilities to change in the next five years? The next ten years? **L1**

VISUAL LEARNING

FIGURE 1.1 Guide students in reading and discussing the explanation of each side of the health triangle. Read aloud the caption for Figure 1.1, and have students answer the question. They should recall that the mental/emotional aspect of health deals with managing stress. **INCL** *English Language Learners, Special Learning Needs, Behavior Problems, Different Learning Styles* (*Visual*)

INCLUSION STRATEGIES

Special Learning Needs, Behavior Problems, English Language Learners, At-Risk, Different Learning Styles (Visual) To make the health triangle more meaningful, make a model of it using three strips of paper of the same length but of different colors. Label one strip *Physical Health,* another *Mental/Emotional Health,* and the third *Social Health.* Arrange the strips in a triangle shape. Tell students that the inside area of the triangle represents total health. By folding or cutting one of the strips, show them how the area of the triangle decreases if any side is shortened. Ask for volunteers to explain what the change in one side means in terms of total health.

6

VISUAL LEARNING

FIGURE 1.2 Ask students to describe each health triangle, explain why it is out of balance, and suggest what the teen could do to improve the balance of his or her health triangle.

Explain to students that temporary imbalances in the health triangle occur naturally. For example, people may develop faster physically than socially. **INCL** *English Language Learners, Special Learning Needs, Behavior Problems, Different Learning Styles (Visual)*

Hands-On Health

WELLNESS SURVEY

Time: 45 minutes; additional 30 minutes of class time about 1 week later

TEACHING THE ACTIVITY
- Read the introduction and activity instructions with students. Point out that the most useful survey questions usually call for simple responses such as yes or no.
- Let students work in pairs or small groups to compose and administer their surveys.
- Have each pair or group share their survey results with the rest of the class.

ASSESSMENT
Once the survey results have been tallied, have students write a paragraph identifying and discussing their most important findings.

Reading Check

Understand purpose and focus. Which paragraph on this page makes a statement and gives an example? Which defines a term? Which poses a question to think about?

Maintaining a Balance

Each side of your triangle is equally important to good health. By working to keep the sides balanced, you will be on your way toward being a healthy person. **Figure 1.2** shows the health triangles of four teens. Three of these teens have unbalanced health triangles. What could they do to balance all the sides?

What Is Wellness?

Wellness is much more than just being healthy. **Wellness** is *an overall state of well-being, or total health.* To achieve wellness you need to make good health a part of your daily routine.

Every decision you make can affect your wellness. For example, healthy snack choices, such as fruit or yogurt instead of potato chips or candy, will satisfy your hunger and contribute to your wellness. Doing your homework and riding your bike are healthier ways to spend your time after school than playing video games. Keep in mind that developing good daily habits now will have positive long-term effects on your health and wellness.

FIGURE 1.2

Four Health Triangles

Each triangle reflects choices each person has made. *What does your triangle look like?*

Matthew

Matthew is an excellent student. He spends most of his free time on his computer, so he doesn't have much time for his family or friends. Matthew keeps physically fit by jogging alone several times each week.

Karla

Karla spends a lot of time with her friends. They watch movies, listen to CDs, and go shopping. Karla gets good grades except in her physical education class. She doesn't get much physical activity and can't keep up with the rest of the class.

Raj

Raj loves sports and plays on the soccer and basketball teams. He doesn't do very well with his schoolwork, though. Raj tries to avoid his problems by playing video games with his friends.

Chantelle

Chantelle has a few close friends and sees them mostly on weekends. Most weeknights she is busy with homework and spending time with her family. She bikes to school every day, and twice a week she has gymnastics class.

6 CHAPTER 1: UNDERSTANDING YOUR HEALTH

Reading Check

Analyzing Text Thinking about the purpose or focus of a passage is an effective way for students to build comprehension skills. Point out that the final sentence of the first paragraph is a question intended to help the reader get the most out of Figure 1.2. The second paragraph defines wellness, and the third includes a statement about wellness supported by examples.

Have students complete this chart by adding other examples.

Statement	Examples
Every decision you make can affect your wellness	[Healthy snack choices will satisfy hunger and contribute to wellness.]

Hands-On Health

WELLNESS SURVEY

You may wonder why you should be concerned about staying healthy or becoming healthier. The reason is that the choices you make now could affect your health for years to come.

WHAT YOU WILL NEED
- pencil or pen
- sheet of paper

WHAT YOU WILL DO
1. With one or more classmates, develop a health survey. On a sheet of paper, list questions to find out how much students know about their physical, mental/emotional, and social health and the choices they make that affect their health triangles.
2. A few sample questions are: Is choosing nutritious foods important for good health? Are there healthy and unhealthy ways to express anger? Is physical activity necessary for good health? Do

you need to know how to communicate with others to be healthy?
3. With the help of your teacher, make copies of the survey and distribute them to a sample of students in your school. Ask the students to return the survey to your teacher.

IN CONCLUSION
Tally the survey responses. How much did students know about good health? Write an article about the results of the survey for the school newspaper.

Lesson 1 Review

Using complete sentences, answer the following questions on a sheet of paper.

Reviewing Terms and Facts

1. **Vocabulary** Define the term *health*. Use it in an original sentence.
2. **Identify** Which side of the health triangle is concerned with taking care of your body?
3. **List** Name three characteristics of mental/emotional health.
4. **Explain** What does social health involve?

Thinking Critically

5. **Analyze** In your own words, analyze the interrelationships of physical, mental/emotional, and social health.

Applying Health Skills

6. **Practicing Healthful Behaviors** Draw your own health triangle. If your triangle is balanced, describe how you keep the three sides equal. If the triangle is unbalanced, list specific ways you can help balance it.

LESSON 1: WHAT IS HEALTH AND WELLNESS? **7**

Discussing

Discuss with students how to make good health decisions a part of their daily routine. Ask: What everyday choices do you make that help you maintain your wellness? In what areas could you use improvement? **L1**

③ Assess

Evaluating

Assign the Lesson 1 Review; then assign the Lesson 1 Quiz in the TCR.

Reteaching

- Assign Concept Map 1 or Reteaching Activity 1 in the TCR.
- Have small groups of students draw health triangles on the board. Help them discuss each aspect of health represented in the drawing.

Enrichment

- Assign Enrichment Activity 1 in the TCR.
- Have pairs or groups of students plan and present skits that show teens making choices to promote a specific aspect of health.

④ Close

Ask each student to name one side of the health triangle and an example of a healthy lifestyle choice associated with it.

Lesson 1 Review

1. Health is a combination of physical, mental/emotional, and social well-being. Sentences will vary.
2. The physical side.
3. Any three: liking and accepting yourself for who you are, finding solutions to problems,

expressing emotions in healthy ways, finding positive ways to manage stress.
4. See copy under Social Health in Figure 1.1 on page 5.
5. Responses should accurately describe how the three parts of health are interrelated.

Changes During the Teen Years

Lesson 2

Changes During the Teen Years

① Focus

Lesson Objectives

Students will be able to

• describe physical growth that occurs during the early teen years.

• analyze the mental and emotional changes that occur.

• explain why relationships may change.

• explain how differences in growth patterns among adolescents, such as onset of puberty, may affect personal health.

Health Skills
• Communication Skills, p. 11

Motivators

Quick Write

Allow students to share from their lists of responses. Discuss how most things mentioned are common for individuals in their early teens.

Bellringer Activity

Have students identify three changes they may go through during their teen years. Encourage them to identify one change for each side of the health triangle.

VOCABULARY

Let volunteers find and read aloud the definition of each vocabulary term. Ask other volunteers to restate these definitions in their own words.

Lesson 2

Changes During the Teen Years

Quick Write

Divide a sheet of paper into two columns. In one column list the things that excite you about becoming a teen. In the other list the things that concern you.

LEARN ABOUT...

• the physical growth that occurs during the early teen years.
• the different ways you may begin to think and feel.
• why your relationships with others may change.

VOCABULARY

• adolescence
• hormones

Changing Times

The teen years involve changes that affect all sides of your health triangle. You might grow two inches, experience mood swings, and make new friends—all within a matter of months. Such changes can be challenging and even a bit scary, but they can also be exciting. These changing times signal that you're on your way to becoming an adult.

Adapting to and coping with changes during the teen years can make you feel physically tired and emotionally stressed. For these reasons, you need to pay careful attention to all sides of your health triangle:

• **Physical.** Be physically active, eat nutritious meals and snacks, and get enough sleep. Avoid tobacco, alcohol, and other drugs.
• **Mental/Emotional.** Use critical thinking skills. Find positive ways to express your feelings and manage stress. Ask for help and advice from trusted adults.
• **Social.** Do your best to get along well with others. Keep others' needs in mind and offer your support.

Your teen years are a time of growth and change. Remember to take care of your health and also take some time out to relax. *What do you like to do when you need to unwind?*

8 CHAPTER 1: UNDERSTANDING YOUR HEALTH

Lesson 2 Resources

Teacher Classroom Resources

 Concept Map 2

Enrichment Activity 2

Lesson Plan 2

Lesson 2 Quiz

Reading Tutor Activity 2

 Reteaching Activity 2

Transparency 2

Student Activities Workbook

 Chapter 1 Study Guide

 Applying Health Skills 2

Adolescence

At the beginning of the school year, did you notice that some of your classmates had grown much taller over the summer while others remained the same height? Next to infancy, the fastest period of physical growth is adolescence. **Adolescence** is *the time of life between childhood and adulthood.* It usually starts any time between the ages of 11 and 15.

In addition to growing taller, you also experience other physical changes associated with adolescence. For example, you may have noticed new hair beginning to appear on parts of your body. You may have started perspiring more than before. These changes are all part of a growth spurt that occurs during adolescence. They are related to the release of **hormones**, which are *chemical substances, produced in glands, that help to regulate many body functions.* These hormones and the changes they cause are preparing you for adulthood. During adolescence, growth isn't just physical. You grow mentally, emotionally, and socially as well. Develop and use effective communication skills to discuss with parents or other trusted adults any questions you have about the changes that occur during adolescence.

Physical Development

How do you know when you have reached adolescence? You will know when you begin to develop the physical traits of adults of your gender. For example, boys may notice that their voices get deeper, and girls may find their figures are developing. These physical changes begin at different ages in different people. There are also differences in growth patterns among adolescents. Many girls begin their growth spurt between the ages of 11 and 14 and add about 3 inches to their height. For boys, the growth spurt usually begins between the ages of 13 and 16. Boys may grow 6 or 7 inches during those years.

During the early teen years, you may grow at a faster or slower rate than your friends. *When do boys usually experience their first growth spurt?*

CONNECT TO

Social Studies

RITE OF PASSAGE
Many cultures and religions mark the beginning of adolescence with a special ceremony. In the Jewish faith, for example, boys and girls participate in a ceremony following their thirteenth birthday. For boys, it is called a bar mitzvah. For girls, it is called a bat mitzvah.

Lesson 2

② Teach

Discussing

Ask volunteers to tell what they like to do to relax. Ask: How do these activities benefit your physical, mental/emotional, and social health?

Then have volunteers identify some of the unhealthful activities teens sometimes try with the excuse of relaxing. (Examples may include smoking cigarettes and drinking alcohol.) Ask: How do these activities put all three aspects of health at risk? **L1**

Making Lists

Have each student divide a sheet of paper into thirds lengthwise and label the columns, from left to right, *Physical, Mental/Emotional,* and *Social.* Then have students list several examples of growth during adolescence under each heading. Draw a corresponding chart on the board. Have volunteers give examples from their work to be listed on the board. Now ask students to use the list on the board to explain how differences in growth patterns among adolescents such as onset of puberty may affect personal health. **L1**

Social Studies

Have students discuss how different cultures mark the passing from childhood to adolescence to adulthood. (*confirmations, Bar Mitzvahs, and sweet 16 parties are some examples*) **L1**

Finding Examples

Have students bring in newspaper or magazine features about teens. Ask if teens are shown positively or negatively and what opinions a reader would form about teens on the basis of the features. Ask students what they think of those opinions. **L2**

PROMOTING COORDINATED SCHOOL HEALTH

The Purpose The primary purpose of a coordinated school health program is to help your community's school tap into a system of health programming already in place. Most schools have health instruction and physical education classes, counselors, nurses, substance-abuse prevention programs, special education programs, and programs linked with state and local health agencies. Because learning is so closely tied to overall health, a student's physical and mental well-being will receive the priority attention it warrants. To help you develop such a program, or to strengthen an existing one, consult *Planning a Coordinated School Health Program* in the TCR. 📁

Interviewing

Ask students to examine physical and emotional development during adolescence by interviewing a parent, grandparent, or other close adult in his or her life about what it was like to be a teen.

• When each adult was a teenager, what were his or her feelings or concerns about appearance? Friends? Dating? Grades? Physical changes? Music? Recreation? Parents?

• What were his or her greatest fears? Joys?

You might list these questions on a sheet of paper and copy it for students to take home. Encourage students to share their findings with other members of their family. They can write down their findings and illustrate them as a memory book. Ask volunteers to share their findings with the class and describe personal health behaviors and knowledge unique to different generations. **L3**

VISUAL LEARNING

FIGURE 1.3 Have volunteers read aloud the information about each situation or problem and the teens' ideas about possible outcomes or solutions. Then let pairs of students act out various versions of the situation or problem, showing many different outcomes and solutions.

Then ask: How do these new ways of thinking make you more able to handle responsibilities? **INCL**
English Language Learners, Special Learning Needs, Behavior Problems, Different Learning Styles (Visual)

Reading Check

Think about these words from the chapter and what they have to do with stress and the changes of adolescence: *adapt, manage, coping.* Find two other words that fit with these to make a group.

Not only is physical development rapid during adolescence, but it is also uneven. Your hands and feet usually grow first, which may make them feel too big for the rest of your body. This makes some teens feel awkward or self-conscious. Keep in mind that every teen experiences these changes and they're completely normal.

Mental and Emotional Development

During adolescence, you also experience changes in the way you think and feel. As a child, you were able to solve only very basic kinds of problems. Now, you are able to solve increasingly complex problems.

Your new ability to reason and to think logically will enable you to think ahead and imagine possible outcomes of a situation. That way, you can weigh the consequences of a particular action. You will also be able to understand different points of view and see many possible solutions to a problem. **Figure 1.3** shows how new ways of thinking can help you with everyday situations.

FIGURE 1.3

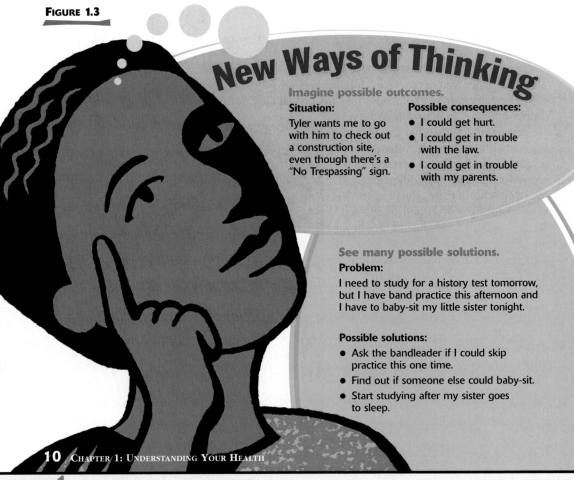

New Ways of Thinking

Imagine possible outcomes.

Situation:
Tyler wants me to go with him to check out a construction site, even though there's a "No Trespassing" sign.

Possible consequences:
● I could get hurt.
● I could get in trouble with the law.
● I could get in trouble with my parents.

See many possible solutions.

Problem:
I need to study for a history test tomorrow, but I have band practice this afternoon and I have to baby-sit my little sister tonight.

Possible solutions:
● Ask the bandleader if I could skip practice this one time.
● Find out if someone else could baby-sit.
● Start studying after my sister goes to sleep.

 Reading Check

List Group Label This activity draws on students' knowledge of a topic and invites them to organize that knowledge. Discuss with students that the three words in the list all name ways we handle change and stress in our lives. Ask them to add as many other words or phrases to the list as possible. Some possible words and phrases are: *put up with, control, muddle through, adjust, get* *used to, become accustomed to.* Encourage students to form a new group containing only those words or phrases that suggest a positive outcome. For example, *adapt, manage,* and *adjust* suggest positive ways to deal with stress, while *put up with* and *muddle through* do not. **INCL** *Special Learning Needs*

Adolescence is also a time of great emotional changes. These changes include:

- **Mood swings.** Have you ever felt very happy one minute and suddenly sad the next? Many teens find these mood swings confusing and even disturbing. However, they're a common part of adolescence, related to the release of hormones.
- **New feelings toward others.** Have you recently started to see your family and friends in a new way? During adolescence, you recognize that the people around you have needs, just as you do. You may take a more active interest in helping to meet the needs of others, such as a friend who has a problem.
- **Increased romantic interest.** Do you find that you want to spend more time with someone you find attractive? Romantic interest develops at different times for different teens. Some teens find the new feelings they have confusing at times. Having them, however, is a normal part of growing up.
- **Increased interest in what is important to you.** You may begin to realize how important your family, friends, physical activity, and education are to you. You may also be aware of your growing sense of responsibility to yourself and to others.

Your emotional growth helps you better understand what others are going through and to provide support. *How would you help a friend who is feeling sad?*

Lesson 2

Cross-Curriculum Activity

PERFORMING ARTS Divide the class into four groups. On slips of paper, write the following changes that teens experience:

1. Mood swings,
2. New feelings toward others,
3. Increased romantic interest, and
4. Growing importance of special interests.

Have each group pick a slip and then sketch out a situation comedy or drama with the phrase on the slip as the theme. Have groups stage their skits for the class. **L2 INCL** *Special Learning Needs, Behavior Problems, Different Learning Styles (Kinesthetic), English Language Learners*

HEALTH SKILLS ACTIVITY

COMMUNICATION SKILLS

Guide students in reading and discussing A Friend in Need. To help students use this story to examine emotional development during adolescence, ask:

- Why is Kyle "a friend in need"?
- What do you think Heather can do to change Kyle's situation? To help Kyle deal with the situation?
- What aspects of emotional development are illustrated in A Friend in Need?

Help students discuss the listed speaking and listening skills. Then have them work with partners to plan and present their role-plays.

Note: This skill is introduced in Chapter 2 on pages 34–38.

HEALTH SKILLS ACTIVITY

COMMUNICATION SKILLS

A Friend in Need

Recently, Heather has noticed that her friend Kyle seems unhappy. When Kyle's family moved into the apartment next door, Kyle and his brother Justin had to start sharing a bedroom. The two boys have not been getting along. Heather can see that Kyle is upset and frustrated with the situation. Heather wants to show Kyle that she supports him. What could she say to help him try to find a solution to his problem?

What Would You Do?

With a classmate, role-play a conversation between Heather and Kyle.

The teen taking the part of Heather should demonstrate good communication skills to help the teen playing Kyle.

Speaking skills:

- "I" messages
- Clear, simple statements
- Honest thoughts and feelings
- Appropriate body language

Listening skills:

- Appropriate body language
- Conversation encouragers
- Mirror thoughts and feelings
- Ask questions

LESSON 2: CHANGES DURING THE TEEN YEARS **11**

MORE ABOUT...

Adolescence During puberty the secondary sex characteristics begin to appear. These changes are caused by hormones. The male sex hormone is called testosterone; the female sex hormone is called estrogen—and both hormones are present in both sexes. Testosterone in the male is responsible for deepening of the voice, the appearance of facial hair, and muscle development. Estrogen in the female is responsible for breast development, widening of the hips, and the onset of menstruation. Emphasize that the changes do not occur at the same time in everyone.

Social Development

Social growth during the teen years affects the way you interact with your family, your friends, and your community. You may find, like many teens, that your friends become increasingly important to you during adolescence. As you begin to spend more time with friends, your relationship with your family could change. At the same time, you may begin to take a more active role in your community. Social growth involves relating to the people in your life in different ways:

• **Your Family.** During your childhood you were completely dependent on your parents or other family members. Now you are learning to act independently and to make decisions for yourself. It is only natural that this process may lead to differences between you and your family.

• **Your Friends and Peers.** During adolescence, you may prefer to share your thoughts and feelings with your friends rather than with family members. You may also find that your friends' opinions become more important to you. Your friendships may also change quite often, however, as you discover your own interests. If, for example, you become involved in soccer, you may make new friends on the team. That could leave less time for other friends who don't share your interest in soccer.

As a teen you will spend a great deal of time with your peers, or people your own age. Your peers will have a major effect on your social development. In fact, an important part of social growth is learning to benefit from the positive influence of peers while resisting any negative influence.

Spending quality time with your family is one way to develop mutual respect and maintain positive relationships. *What activities do you enjoy doing with your family?*

Health Literacy

Health Information Although nutrition is not a topic in this lesson, you might briefly discuss its relationship to adolescent development. Good nutrition helps teens reach their peak performance, whether they are studying, playing a sport, or creating art. Allow students to volunteer their preconceived ideas about the body's need for a well-balanced diet in order to function properly. In addition, ask them to identify foods that they think are healthful (and unhealthful) for mental development. Also, encourage them to discuss the relationship between eating and socializing. Be sure you tie their observations to the concept of adolescent growth.

- **Your Community.** During the teen years, you will begin to recognize your role in the larger community that includes your school and your neighborhood. Social growth involves contributing to your community in a meaningful way. At school, for example, you might clean up litter or help other students with schoolwork. In your neighborhood, you might donate used clothing to the needy or support a local environmental group.

Developing positive relationships with family, peers, and role models and avoiding negative relationships is an important part of social growth. Analyze the positive and negative relationships in your life to determine how they might influence both individual and community health.

Your friends may influence many of your decisions during your teen years. *How have your friends had a positive influence on your behavior or actions?*

Lesson 2 Review

Using complete sentences, answer the following questions on a sheet of paper.

Reviewing Terms and Facts

1. **Vocabulary** Define *adolescence.*
2. **List** Examine some signs of physical and emotional development that occur during adolescence.
3. **Explain** What new mental skills do you develop during adolescence?
4. **Recall** How do relationships with family and friends change during the teen years?

Thinking Critically

5. **Analyze** How can positive and negative relationships influence individual health?

6. **Describe** Explain how differences in growth patterns among adolescents may affect personal health.

Applying Health Skills

7. **Communication Skills** Develop a dialogue in which a teen uses effective communication skills to discuss with parents or other trusted adults a concern about the changes that occur during adolescence.

Lesson 2

Discussing

Have students describe the photograph on this page. Then ask:
- How have your friends influenced your behavior and habits in the past year or two?
- What does this change indicate about your social growth?

Then let volunteers read aloud the caption under the photograph and share their responses to the question.

③ Assess

Evaluating

📂 Assign the Lesson 2 Review; then assign the Lesson 2 Quiz in the TCR.

Reteaching

📂 Assign Concept Map 2 or Reteaching Activity 2 in the TCR.

Enrichment

- 📂 Assign Enrichment Activity 2 in the TCR.
- Let students work with partners to research Jean Piaget's theory of mental growth.

④ Close

Ask: What changes occur during adolescence? Go around the room asking each student to identify one change. List these changes on the board. Ask students to compare and contrast changes in males and females.

Lesson 2 Review

1. The time of life between childhood and adulthood.
2. Growing taller, new hair appearing on parts of the body, increased perspiration, developing traits of adults, mood swings, new feelings toward others, romantic interest, increased interest in what is important to you.
3. Possible response: new ability to reason and think logically.
4. See Social Development on page 12.
5. Responses should demonstrate an understanding that various relationships can have a positive or negative effect on one's health.
6. Responses may include how early or late growth and development might affect personal care practices.

Lesson 3

Taking Responsibility for Your Health

① Focus

Lesson Objectives

Students will be able to

- describe ways to develop positive health habits.
- explain what risks are, how they can be identified, and the consequences of risk behaviors.
- identify information relating to abstinence.
- discuss the importance of practicing abstinence from risk behaviors.

Health Skills
- Practicing Healthful Behaviors, p. 18

Motivators

Quick Write

Allow several volunteers to share their definitions. Discuss the ways they are currently responsible and the areas in which they would like to assume more responsibility.

Bellringer Activity

Have students sketch pictures of one or more teens in an unsafe, high-risk situation. Then have them sketch the same teens in a healthy, low-risk activity.

VOCABULARY

Refer to the vocabulary terms for this lesson. Ask students to write a definition for each term and use it in a sentence. Ask volunteers to share their responses. Correct any misconceptions.

Lesson 3

Taking Responsibility for Your Health

Quick Write

What does the word *responsibility* mean to you? Write a brief definition, then list the ways you show that you are responsible.

LEARN ABOUT...

- how you can develop positive health habits.
- ways to recognize and avoid risk behaviors.
- why abstinence is the most responsible choice for teens.

VOCABULARY

- lifestyle factors
- risk behaviors
- sedentary lifestyle
- cumulative risks
- precaution
- abstinence
- attitude
- self-control

Choosing a Healthy Lifestyle

Do you eat nutritious foods even when you're not at home? Do you get at least eight hours of sleep each night? Do you wear a safety helmet every time you ride your bike or skateboard? You might be surprised to learn how such lifestyle factors affect your health. **Lifestyle factors** are *behaviors and habits that help determine a person's level of health*. **Figure 1.4** illustrates certain positive lifestyle factors. How many of them do you practice regularly?

The health choices you make every day—such as eating plenty of fresh fruit and vegetables—are a major factor in your total health. *What healthy choices have you made today?*

14 CHAPTER 1: UNDERSTANDING YOUR HEALTH

Lesson 3 Resources

Teacher Classroom Resources

- Concept Map 3
- Cross-Curriculum Activity 2
- Decision-Making Activity 2
- Enrichment Activity 3
- Lesson Plan 3
- Lesson 3 Quiz
- Reading Tutor Activity 3

- Reteaching Activity 3
- Transparency 3

Student Activities Workbook

- Chapter 1 Study Guide
- Applying Health Skills 3
- Health Inventory 1

FIGURE 1.4

Positive Lifestyle Factors

Choosing positive lifestyle factors will help you avoid self-destructive behaviors, keeping you healthy both now and in the future.

Developing skills and talents

Eating nutritious foods, including a healthy breakfast

stay drug free

Avoiding tobacco, alcohol, and other drugs

Preventing injuries

Getting at least eight hours of sleep every night

Getting at least 60 minutes of physical activity every day

Spending time with friends

Recognizing Risk Behaviors

Risks are an unavoidable part of life. For example, you may need to cross a busy street on the way to school, or to use a sharp knife when preparing food. Such risks are not likely to injure you or someone else if you take reasonable care. Some actions, however, involve a high level of unnecessary risk. A **risk behavior** is *an action or behavior that might cause injury or harm to you or others.*

Some risk behaviors are obvious. Diving into a river when you don't know its depth is obviously risky. The chance of injury is great and immediate. Other risk factors, however, are not so obvious. For example, regularly eating foods high in fat and sugar is a risk behavior. Even though you may not notice any immediate effect, this unhealthy lifestyle factor may have a lasting negative impact on your health.

Lesson 3

② Teach

VISUAL LEARNING

FIGURE 1.4 Let volunteers describe each picture and read about the lifestyle factor. Have students identify specific ways in which they can practice each positive lifestyle factor. Then ask:

• How can this lifestyle factor affect your health now?

• How do you think it will affect your health in the future? **INCL** *English Language Learners, Special Learning Needs, Behavior Problems, Different Learning Styles* (*Visual*)

Critical Thinking

Encourage students to consider their own responsibility for choosing positive lifestyle factors:

• How can family members make it easier, or harder, for a teen to choose these lifestyle practices?

• At what age should individuals be considered responsible for choosing these practices for themselves? Why? **L1**

Cross-Curriculum Activity

SOCIAL STUDIES Have students find and bring to class newspaper stories about local accidents or crimes. Let them meet in groups to read and discuss the news articles. Have group members identify the lifestyle choices that might have led to each incident. **L2**

WHAT TEENS WANT TO KNOW

I'm young. Why should I care about my health?
Good health allows you to feel good and enjoy life. The choices and decisions you make today will also affect your health tomorrow. It is harder to break bad habits, such as overeating or physical inactivity, once they are established. Learn to make healthful decisions about the food you eat, the amount of physical activity you engage in, and the level of sleep you need. Develop a healthful lifestyle when you are young to prevent illnesses when you are an adult. Start taking positive actions now. For example, protect your skin from sun damage today to prevent the development of wrinkles and melanoma, a deadly skin cancer, later in life. Resist pressure to smoke cigarettes or experiment with alcohol or illegal drugs.

Listing

Let students work with partners to write two lists: one of unavoidable risks many teens take daily and another of avoidable risks that can cause problems for teens. Review the lists as a class, noting risks that appear on more than one list. **L1**

HEALTH SKILLS PRACTICE

Decision Making Read aloud the following for students to analyze: Here's a brief news item from the Northwest: "Three teenagers died, and two were injured when a car slammed into a bridge guardrail shortly after the grab-and-dash theft of a case of beer," police said. "Three of the teens were 17, and two were 16." List the decisions these five teens made, and identify the consequences. If you were a friend of theirs who had decided not to participate in this act, what values did you consider when you made your decision not to go?

Cooperative Learning

Divide students into small groups to discuss examples of teens taking cumulative risks. Then have the group members plan and put on a short skit about one of those situations. If students are uncomfortable acting in front of their classmates, have them use sock puppets to present their skits. **L1**

Reading Check

Understand word parts. Investigate the words *consequence* and *unhealthy*. What are their prefixes? What are their roots? What does each mean?

Risk Behaviors and Teens

Certain risk behaviors are strongly associated with teens, according to the Centers for Disease Control and Prevention (CDC). These include the use of tobacco, alcohol, and other drugs; an unhealthy diet; and a sedentary lifestyle. A **sedentary lifestyle** is *a way of life that involves little physical activity.* Another negative risk factor for teens is sexual activity. Other unsafe behaviors include riding a bike without a helmet. Developing a healthy lifestyle is an effective strategy for counteracting these risk factors.

Risk Behaviors and Consequences

All risk behaviors carry consequences—some minor and some major. Not getting enough sleep for only one night, for example, will probably just make you feel tired and grouchy the next day. Many risk behaviors, such as the use of tobacco, alcohol, or other drugs, result in much more serious and far-reaching consequences. These types of behaviors are self-destructive—that is, harmful to your physical, mental/emotional, and social health.

Consider Jason's story. He was running late for baseball practice, so he hopped on his bike without putting on his helmet. He took a shortcut on a busy street and crossed the road without looking first. A car hit him, causing a deep gash on his head and a concussion. Now he is angry with himself for taking an unnecessary risk, for ruining his bike, and for upsetting his parents. He won't be able to play baseball for the rest of the season.

This teen knows that a sedentary lifestyle is a risk behavior. By staying physically active, she protects her health. *What are some ways that you stay physically active?*

16 CHAPTER 1: UNDERSTANDING YOUR HEALTH

Reading Check

Prefixes and Roots Write the two words on the chalkboard. Have a student circle the prefix in each and ask the class to speculate about their meanings. Using a dictionary, students can discover that *con-* is a form of the prefix *com-* meaning *closely along, next to,* or *with. Un-* can mean various things including *not, the opposite of,* and *back.* Then have them look up the meanings of *sequence* and *healthy* and find other words with the same root. Point out that *sequence* and *sequel* are related because they share the same root. A *consequence,* then, is something that follows closely along after an event. *Healthy, heal, hale,* and *whole* are all similarly related. Being *healthy* is to be *whole,* or *hale* and *hearty. Unhealthy* is the opposite of *healthy.*

Jason's story is also an example of **cumulative risks**. These are *related risks that increase in effect with each added risk.* Jason's first risk behavior was not wearing a helmet. His second was riding his bike on a busy street. His third was crossing the street without looking. With each additional risk behavior, Jason's chances for serious consequences increased.

Abstaining from Risk Behaviors

How can you avoid serious consequences like Jason's? One effective strategy is taking precautions. A **precaution** is a *planned action taken before an event to increase the chances of a safe outcome.*

In addition to taking precautions, you can stay safe and avoid negative consequences by practicing healthful behaviors and abstinence. **Abstinence** is *not participating in high-risk behaviors.* You may be familiar with the word *abstinence* used to discuss avoiding sexual activity. Abstinence, however, means avoiding all high-risk behavior, including the use of tobacco, alcohol, and other drugs.

Abstinence from risk behavior is the wise choice for teens. It shows that you are responsible and that you respect yourself and others. By practicing abstinence, you protect all three sides of your health triangle. You protect your physical health by avoiding injury. You protect your mental/emotional health by avoiding the stress and worry involved with taking risks. In addition, you protect your social health by not disappointing family members and friends and by maintaining their trust.

This teen is protecting himself from injury by wearing protective gear. *How else can teens abstain from risk behaviors?*

LESSON 3: TAKING RESPONSIBILITY FOR YOUR HEALTH **17**

Developing Good Character ★

Self-discipline
Discuss with the class the idea that self-discipline is an important building block for developing a healthy, productive life. Brainstorm a variety of ways that people practice self-discipline every day. Ask students to write a short letter identifying one health-enhancing behavior they will commit to and practice for one month. Have them seal their letters in self-addressed envelopes. Invite students to open their letters one month later to reflect on their success.

Guest Speaker

Ask a family nurse practitioner or other health care provider to speak with the class about cumulative risks. **L1**

Cross-Curriculum Activity

VISUAL ARTS Have students work in small groups to plan, write, and illustrate magazine-style ads urging teens to avoid risk behaviors. **L2**

Interviewing

Have students interview someone they know who has done one of the following: stopped smoking, went on a weight-loss eating plan and lost substantial weight, became an avid jogger or swimmer, and so on. Ask students to record impressions of how the change has altered the person's outlook on life. **L3**

Health Literacy

Health Influences Ask students whether they are familiar with the expression, "Look on the bright side." The expression suggests that having a positive outlook protects and promotes health on all three sides of the health triangle. Laughter, in particular, can influence positive physiological changes as well as improve mental outlook or mood.

One scientific study found that laughter stimulates the production of endorphins, which help control pain. Another study demonstrated that stress-related hormones decreased during bouts of laughter. Humor and a positive outlook can help one cope with such life pressures as getting homework done on time, taking tests, and getting along with friends.

Lesson 3

Discussing

Ask students to share their ideas about the importance of a positive attitude:

- How can a positive attitude make life easier for you? For those around you?
- What are the most effective ways to develop a positive attitude? **L1**

Journal Writing

Ask students to write private journal entries about their own attitudes. Encourage them to respond to questions such as these:

- When am I likely to have a positive attitude? Why?
- In what situations is my attitude likely to be negative? Why?
- What can I do to improve my attitude? **L1**

HEALTH SKILLS ACTIVITY

PRACTICING HEALTHFUL BEHAVIORS

Have students meet in small groups to read and respond to Making Health a Habit. Ask group members to discuss how each listed activity demonstrates a teen's responsibility, and encourage them to add to the list.

Have students work independently at home to complete the On Your Own activity. Ask volunteers to share their records with the rest of the class.

Note: This skill is introduced in Chapter 2 on pages 46–47.

MEDIA WATCH

HEALTH IN THE NEWS

You've probably seen a headline like this: "Amazing pill lets you shed 10 pounds in 10 days!" *To protect your health, how would you determine if this information is true?*

Taking More Responsibility

Taking responsibility for your health involves more than just recognizing healthy choices and risk factors. Your personal **attitude**—your *feelings and beliefs*—also plays a role. You need to believe that making wise choices and developing good health habits can have a positive effect on your health.

Your attitude also includes the way you feel about yourself. If you like and respect yourself and believe that other people like and respect you, you will want to take care of yourself. To look, feel, and do your best, you will make choices that protect and promote your health. Taking responsibility for your health also requires **self-control**, or *restraint from your own emotions and desires*. For example, instead of slamming a door when you are angry, you could take a walk to cool off.

Having a positive attitude and using self-control will help show that you are ready to take on greater responsibility. Your family members can offer advice and support, but only your actions show that you're ready for more freedom. Being responsible for your own health is an important step toward becoming an adult.

HEALTH SKILLS ACTIVITY

PRACTICING HEALTHFUL BEHAVIORS

Making Health a Habit

A first step toward improving yourself and your total health is to take an honest look at your behavior. Do you feel that you're a responsible person? Do you show that you're ready for more responsibility? You can demonstrate your readiness in several ways. For example:

- Do your schoolwork and turn it in on time.
- Do your share of the household chores without being reminded.
- If you see something that needs to be done, do it without waiting to be asked.
- Be on time.
- Keep your promises.
- Finish tasks that you start, and clean up after yourself.

You can also improve yourself by following the positive lifestyle factors shown in **Figure 1.4** on page 15. Are all of those habits part of your current daily routine? If not, try the following:

- Identify a good health habit that you would like to develop. Write down the habit and the benefits that you could gain from making it part of your daily routine.
- Practice the habit several times during the next week. Each time, put a check mark next to the habit and the benefits you gained from practicing the habit.

ON YOUR OWN
Think about the ways that you demonstrated responsibility in the past week. Record the number of times you perform these actions during the week.

INCLUSION STRATEGIES

Special Learning Needs, Behavior Problems, English Language Learners Many students learn better with visual aids. Encourage them to present the concepts in this lesson in a graphic presentation. For example, they might show a series of stepping-stones on the pathway to good health.

Each stone could be labeled with a positive lifestyle factor such as *staying informed, eating a balanced diet,* or *physical activity.* Giving students the opportunity to work in small groups enhances their final presentation and promotes brainstorming possibilities and collective insights.

Staying Informed

How much do you really know about health? Where can you find more information? Because good health is part of a happy, satisfying life, learning how to get and stay healthy should be an important part of your life.

That's why health education is essential. Health education is more than just learning health facts. It can help you gain the tools you need to maintain and improve your total health and wellness. You can use health facts you learn in all areas of your life.

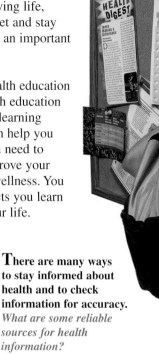

There are many ways to stay informed about health and to check information for accuracy. *What are some reliable sources for health information?*

Lesson 3 Review

Using complete sentences, answer the following questions on a sheet of paper.

Reviewing Terms and Facts

1. **Vocabulary** In the context of health, what are *lifestyle factors?*
2. **Vocabulary** Define *risk behaviors.*
3. **Give examples** What health risks are particularly associated with teens?
4. **Explain** How can you avoid the consequences associated with cumulative risks?
5. **Identify** Name two personal qualities that demonstrate that you are ready for more responsibility.

Thinking Critically

6. **Analyze** Look at the list of positive lifestyle factors in **Figure 1.4** on page 15. Choose one and think of ways you could develop it as a personal habit.
7. **Explain** Why is it important to be well informed about health?

Applying Health Skills

8. **Advocacy** Write a public service announcement that emphasizes the importance for teens of practicing abstinence.

Discussing

Ask students to name sources of information about health issues. (Examples might include specific magazines and TV shows, groups of books, and specific Web sites.) List students' ideas on the board. Then help students discuss the reliability of each source of information. **L1**

❸ Assess

Evaluating

🗂 Assign the Lesson 3 Review; then assign the Lesson 3 Quiz in the TCR.

Reteaching

🗂 Assign Concept Map 3 or Reteaching Activity 3 in the TCR.

Enrichment

• 🗂 Assign Enrichment Activity 3 in the TCR.
• Have students work together to plan, write, and create a short video about teens choosing abstinence.

❹ Close

Ask students to list at least two new lifestyle behaviors they would consider adopting to improve the quality of their health.

Lesson 3 Review

1. Behaviors and habits that help determine a person's level of health.
2. Actions or behaviors that might cause injury or harm to you or others.
3. Responses may include the use of tobacco, alcohol, and other drugs; an unhealthful diet; a sedentary lifestyle; sexual activity; other unsafe behaviors.
4. By planning ahead and taking precautions.
5. Possible response: having a positive attitude and using self-control.
6. Responses will vary.
7. Being informed helps you gain the tools you need to maintain and improve health and wellness.

Teens with a Mission

① Focus

Objectives

Students will be able to
- analyze one positive influence in their own lives.
- set a personal goal for community service.
- define the term *globalization* in relation to health issues.

Motivator

Quick Write

Tell students to write about two choices they have made this week that affected the lives of others in a positive way.

② Teach

Discussing

Ask students, "What influenced these three teens in pursuing their goals?" Write student answers on the board. (For instance, Alexandra was influenced by the personal experience of living in Zimbabwe. Roxanne was influenced by the high cancer rates in her hometown as well as her father's job as a physician.) Tell students to write about at least one strong positive influence in their own lives. Ask for volunteers to share their ideas with the class.

Cross-Curriculum Activity

SOCIAL STUDIES Have students work in small groups to research the country of Zimbabwe. Assign each group one of the following topics: history, geography, population, economy, and government. How does their assigned topic impact the AIDS epidemic in the country? Ask students to present their findings to the class.

TIME HEALTH

Teens with a Mission

Alexandra Govere
14, from Fullerton, California. Founder of Assisting AIDS Orphans

THE CHARITY: "I created the organization last year to provide clothing, toys, and school supplies to AIDS orphans in villages across Africa. With my younger sister, Saunsuray, I've brought together young people across the world to gather donations and send packages to kids in need."

WHY IT'S PERSONAL: "Zimbabwe is a peaceful place, but very poor. Living there until I was nine, I was extremely sad to see people in our village—even close friends and relatives—die of AIDS and leave their children behind. Many end up with no choice but to live in the streets and beg for money."

THE PAYOFF: "I was invited to speak at the first International Students Conference on HIV/AIDS and the Youth, but it was in Uganda and I couldn't afford to go. I was honored when one of the organizers wound up reading my speech for me. I felt that my effort to be an AIDS activist was finally being recognized."

HOW SHE'LL MAKE THE WORLD A BETTER PLACE: "The Assisting AIDS Orphans project is something I'd like to do for the rest of my life. I want to get more members and start helping worldwide. AIDS orphans aren't just in Africa, they're everywhere."

Beyond the Classroom

Community Divide students into small work groups. Tell each group that they will find someone in their own community who has done something to make the world a better place. Students will interview this individual and write his or her story, similar to those on this spread. Before students begin, brainstorm a list of interview questions as a class. Questions may include:

- How did you begin the work you do?
- Who benefits from your work?
- What personal benefits have you gained?
- How might others get involved in your cause?

Encourage students to incorporate original artwork, photos, newspaper clippings, testimonials, and other creative elements in their stories.

These three teens are out to make the world a better place.

Roxanne Tingir
17, from Port Washington, New York. Student cancer researcher

WHAT SHE DID: "I developed a diagnostic tool, called an ELISA, for a certain colon cancer treatment developed by the lab where I had an internship during high school. Basically my research will help doctors make sure that these colon cancer treatments are working."

WHY CANCER: "On Long Island, where I grew up, we have one of the highest breast cancer rates in the nation. Everyone knows of someone who's had it. My dad is a physician, and medical research has always interested me because you get such visible results."

ON HER ACCOMPLISHMENTS: "I really haven't done anything that extraordinary. When I read about what other teenagers have done, I'm absolutely amazed."

HOW SHE'LL MAKE THE WORLD A BETTER PLACE: "I really am not sure. I plan on attending Georgetown University. I'm leaning toward a major in government. I think our generation's biggest problem right now is globalization and how we're going to deal with September 11 and what's happened since. Everyone else's issues have really become our issues. The entire world is connected and we can't ignore that anymore."

Hans Lee
17, from Carmel, California. Inventor of a car safety system

THE INVENTION: "I built a safety system for a car that greatly improves its handling. [When a car goes out of control] the system will correct its trajectory and bring it back under control. I'm working at M.I.T. to implement the system in a full-size race car."

KEEPING AT IT: "I've always liked to build things. In sixth grade I decided to build a hybrid car from scratch. I worked on it in my garage for four years. Eventually it progressed into this project."

BEST MOMENT: "As I was walking up to receive my first award at the Intel International Science & Engineering Fair, I suddenly saw my face on two 40-foot screens on either side of the stage."

HOW HE'LL MAKE THE WORLD A BETTER PLACE: "I want all of my projects to improve people's lives, to make them easier and safer, and to advance society." ◢

TIME TO THINK...

About Teens Making a Difference

Pair off with a classmate and interview each other about your goals for the future. Using the style and format of the above article, write a brief description of your interview subject's goals. Read your article aloud.

③ Apply

Time to Think

Ask students to set their own goals for community service. First, have students write a clear goal statement. (I will volunteer at the library one afternoon each week. I will set up a schoolwide recycling program.) Ask, "Is your goal realistic? How will you meet this goal?" Have students develop a step-by-step plan, including several options for meeting their goal. They should also identify the rewards for meeting the goal. Check in with students in a few weeks to evaluate their progress. Do they need to adjust their goal or redo their plan?

VISUAL LEARNING

Ask students to analyze the photographs on this page. Does Alexandra look like an AIDS activist? Does Hans look like an award-winning engineer? Why or why not? Do the accomplishments of these young people change adults' assumptions about teenagers in general?

Health Literacy

Globalization Tell students that according to Roxanne, the biggest problem of her generation is *globalization*. Ask students:

1. What is globalization? (*Countries around the world are connected to each other in more ways than ever before.*)
2. Is this a relatively new issue? Why? (*global communications, world trade, transportation, and so on.*)
3. What are the health-related implications of globalization? (*Diseases spread from one nation to another more rapidly (SARS), medications developed in one country can assist patients in another, disparities in health between developed and developing nations are more obvious, and so on.*)

ANALYZING INFLUENCES

Objective

After completing the lesson, students will be able to analyze how internal and external influences affect their health.

Time: 45 minutes

Materials: notebook paper, pen or pencil

Teacher Classroom Resources

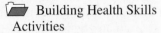 Building Health Skills Activities

- Transparency Master 4, "Analyzing Influences"

- Reproducible Master 26, "Looking at Health Influences"

---

1. Model

- Display Transparency Master 4. Remind students that internal and external influences affect their health.

- Have students work with a partner to read about Cassidy and note the influences on her physical health. (Examples include: *Athletics, physical activity, nutritious foods, a family who values sports.*)

- Ask volunteers to report the influences they noted to the class.

LOOKING AT HEALTH INFLUENCES

Model

Your friends and family are two of the many influences that affect the physical side of your health triangle. Other influences include your environment, your culture, the media, and your role models. Personal influences—such as what you know, your interests, and your hopes and fears—affect your physical health too. As you read about Cassidy, notice the influences that affect her physical health.

Cassidy has enjoyed being physically active since she was very young. She used to play soccer every weekend. Now she is more involved in track and bicycling.

Her best friend, Jacy, is a bicycling fanatic. Cassidy and Jacy often talk about becoming famous athletes. Cassidy knows that even if she never becomes famous, she wants to do something that involves sports.

Cassidy has learned a lot about sports from her family. Her sister is a high school athlete, and her dad played several sports in college. Around the dinner table, a common topic of conversation is healthful foods and training for competition.

22 CHAPTER 1: UNDERSTANDING YOUR HEALTH

Teaching Tips

Understanding Teens' Needs Although individual social influences will vary, all teens have a common set of social needs. The choices teens make in response to influences will reflect their efforts to get those needs met. Each teen needs to

- see himself or herself as a socially accepted person.

- have recognition and acceptance from peers.

- participate in congenial social situations.

- get along with members of the same and opposite gender.

| Standards | | Technology |
National	State/Local	
National Health Education Standard **1.1, 3.1, 3.4, 6.1, 6.2, 6.3, 6.4, 6.5**		Transparencies 4 & 5 Tape/DVD 3, Segment 3, "Taking Charge of Your Life" TeacherWorks™
National Health Education Standard **5.1, 5.3, 5.4, 5.5, 5.6**		Transparency 6 Tape/DVD 3, Segment 1, "Improving Your Communication Skills" TeacherWorks™
National Health Education Standard **1.1, 1.3, 1.6, 3.1, 3.4, 3.7**		Transparency 7 TeacherWorks™
National Health Education Standard **2.1, 2.2, 2.4, 3.1, 3.4, 4.1, 4.2, 4.3, 4.4**		Transparency 8 TeacherWorks™ MindJogger Videoquiz **Exam***View*® Pro Testmaker
National Health Education Standard **5.5, 5.6**		Building Health Skills Transparency Master 7

TeacherWorks™

Glencoe's new and exclusive TeacherWorks™ is an all-in-one planner and resource center. Access the complete Teacher Wraparound Edition electronically. Find all your classroom resources with just a few easy clicks, and print them right from your computer. Connect directly to Glencoe's customized Health Web site. Access the National Health Education Standards correlations, or insert your own state standards and match them directly to the electronic Teacher Wraparound Edition.

Language Diversity

- English Audio Summaries
- Spanish Audio Summaries
- English Summaries, Quizzes, and Activities
- Spanish Summaries, Quizzes, and Activities
- Spanish Parent Letters and Activities

KEY TO ABILITY LEVELS

Teaching Strategies that appear throughout the chapters have been identified by one of four codes to give you an idea of their suitability for students of varying learning styles and abilities.

L1 **Level 1** strategies should be within the ability range of all students. Often full class participation is required.

L2 **Level 2** strategies are for average to above-average students or for small groups. Some teacher direction is necessary.

L3 **Level 3** strategies are designed for students able and willing to work independently. Minimal teacher direction is necessary.

INCL Strategies are appropriate for students with particular special needs in a general classroom setting.

Health Skills: The Foundation

Chapter at a Glance

Lesson 1 introduces decision making as an everyday, necessary process. Students are introduced to the six-step decision-making process and to the skills involved in setting goals.

Lesson 2 focuses on healthy communication and offers strategies for refusal skills.

Lesson 3 discusses the effects of positive and negative stress and presents strategies for managing stress.

Lesson 4 introduces additional health skills that are beneficial throughout life.

Health Skills

- What to Do? What to Do? (*Decision Making*), p. 30
- Balance Your Schedule (*Stress Management*), p. 43
- Personal Health Inventory (*Practicing Healthful Behaviors*), p. 46
- Say No to Peer Pressure (*Refusal Skills*), pp. 52–53

26

HANDS-ON ACTIVITY

Beach Ball Pass This chapter introduces many skills necessary to keep the areas of the health triangle in balance. To find out how much your class already knows, pass a beach ball, or other soft object, like a beanbag, to various students around the room. When a student catches the ball, ask a question related to the chapter. Have him or her answer the question while tossing the ball back to you. Possible questions include: How do you make decisions? How many decisions have you made already today? What differences are there between making decisions and setting goals? What skills do you need for good communication? Is stress good or bad? How do you cope with stress? Where do you go to gather reliable health information? Make sure every student gets a chance to answer a question.

Health Skills: The Foundation

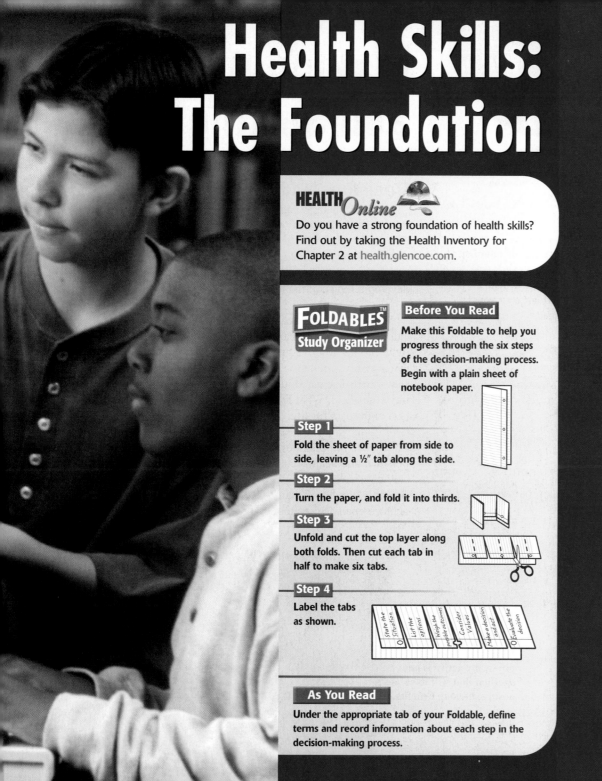

HEALTH *Online*

Do you have a strong foundation of health skills? Find out by taking the Health Inventory for Chapter 2 at health.glencoe.com.

FOLDABLES™ Study Organizer

Before You Read

Make this Foldable to help you progress through the six steps of the decision-making process. Begin with a plain sheet of notebook paper.

Step 1

Fold the sheet of paper from side to side, leaving a ½" tab along the side.

Step 2

Turn the paper, and fold it into thirds.

Step 3

Unfold and cut the top layer along both folds. Then cut each tab in half to make six tabs.

Step 4

Label the tabs as shown.

As You Read

Under the appropriate tab of your Foldable, define terms and record information about each step in the decision-making process.

27

Chapter Introduction

Use the options below to motivate students and preview chapter content.

HEALTH *Online*

Visit **health.glencoe.com**, and have students complete Health Inventory 2 to test their health skills. For other teaching strategies, explore the Lesson Plans and select from Cross-Curriculum, Reading, or Media Literacy activities.

GLENCOE TECHNOLOGY

Teen Health Video and DVD Series
(Each format available in both English and Spanish)

You may wish to use:

- Tape/DVD 3, Segment 1, "Improving Your Communication Skills"
- Tape/DVD 3, Segment 3, "Taking Charge of Your Life"

MindJogger Videoquiz

Use MindJogger to preview or review Chapter 2 content.

TIME HEALTH

Under Pressure
pages 50–51

FOLDABLES™ Study Organizer

Dinah Zike Study Fold

Using Flowcharts Students will use this flow chart Foldable to record the steps of the decision-making process and write about each step. You might ask students to make another flow chart Foldable as they progress through Lesson 1. As students read and discuss the lesson, they might use the front tabs of the first Foldable to record the six steps outlined on page 29, and take notes on each step under the appropriate tab. After students have been introduced to all steps, have them make another Foldable flow chart, once again recording the decision-making steps on the front tabs. Under the appropriate tab of this Foldable, however, students will write about how they used each step to make a decision they were faced with recently.

① Focus

Lesson Objectives

Students will be able to

- follow a six-step process to arrive at healthful decisions that affect themselves and others.
- discuss the benefits of setting health goals.
- follow the five-step goal-setting process to achieve their goals.

> **Health Skills**
> - Decision Making, p. 30

Motivators

Quick Write

Draw the health triangle on the board, labeling each side. List student responses on the appropriate side as they are identified.

> **VOCABULARY**
>
> Hand out four index cards to each student. On one side of each card, ask them to write one of the vocabulary terms from the lesson. On the other side of the card, have them describe an example or application of that term. Then ask them to shuffle the cards and choose a partner.
>
> Partners should take turns reading each other's examples and trying to identify the terms.

Making Decisions and Setting Goals

Quick Write

List the decisions you have made since you got up this morning. Place a check next to those that had an influence on your health.

LEARN ABOUT...

- how decisions affect your health and the health of others.
- ways to make healthy, responsible decisions.
- the benefits of setting health goals.

VOCABULARY

- decision making
- values
- evaluate
- goal setting

Decisions and Goals

Decision making and goal setting are two important health-related skills. Decision-making skills will help you make the best choices and find healthy solutions to problems. Goal-setting skills will help you take control over your life and give it purpose and direction. Making decisions and setting goals also help you to develop a focus on the future.

When it comes to health, even a decision that may seem small can have great significance. Daniel, for example, persuaded his older brother to drive him to the video store. Because they were driving only around the corner, Daniel did not bother to fasten his safety belt. The car skidded on ice and Daniel hit his head against the windshield. What Daniel thought was a minor decision has left him with scars for life.

It's also important to develop strategies for setting long-term personal and health-related goals. Achieving goals that help you stay physically active and prevent injury will provide health benefits throughout your life. Moreover, people who set and achieve goals feel better about themselves and about their lives.

Deciding to stay physically active is one decision that will have positive lifelong benefits. *Appraise the risks and the benefits of decision making about personal health.*

Lesson 1 Resources

Teacher Classroom Resources

- 📁 Parent Letter & Activities 2
- 📁 Concept Map 4
- 📁 Decision-Making Activity 3
- 📁 Enrichment Activity 4
- 📁 Reading Tutor Activity 4
- 📁 Lesson Plan 1

- 📁 Lesson 1 Quiz
- 📁 Reteaching Activity 4
- 📁 Transparencies 4 & 5

Student Activities Workbook

- 📁 Chapter 2 Study Guide
- 📁 Applying Health Skills 4

The Decision-Making Process

Decision making is *the process of making a choice or finding a solution.* It involves a series of six steps. **Figure 2.1** relates the practices and steps that are necessary for making decisions, including health decisions.

Step 1 is to identify the situation. What choice do you need to make? Steps 2 and 3 are to think through your options and consider the possible outcomes of each option. When evaluating your choices, follow the H.E.L.P. criteria to keep you focused on critical issues:

- **H (Healthful)** Will it contribute to your health?
- **E (Ethical)** Does it show respect for yourself and others?
- **L (Legal)** Is someone your age allowed by law to do this?
- **P (Parent Approval)** Would your parents approve?

FIGURE 2.1

The Decision-Making Process

What should Kendra do? Go through the six-step decision-making process to help her decide.

Kendra must make a decision. She and Michele have been best friends for a long time. Recently, Michele has been spending time with other students who ditch school. Michele has even boasted of going with them once. Now she wants Kendra to join them too. Kendra doesn't want to lose Michele's friendship, but she knows that her parents trust her to obey school rules.

1. **State the situation.**
2. **List the options.**
3. **Weigh the possible outcomes.**
4. **Consider values.**
5. **Make a decision and act.**
6. **Evaluate the decision.**

LESSON 1: MAKING DECISIONS AND SETTING GOALS **29**

② Teach

VISUAL LEARNING

FIGURE 2.1 Help students relate steps necessary for making health decisions. Ask them to read and discuss the information about Kendra's situation. Then have students meet in groups to apply the six steps of the decision-making process that Kendra might use. Encourage students to use the H.E.L.P. criteria to guide them in steps 2 and 3.

After about ten minutes, have each group share their decision with the rest of the class and explain their process. Ask:

- Did all the groups make the same decision? Why or why not?
- Which steps in the decision-making process differed most from group to group? Why? **INCL** *English Language Learners, Special Learning Needs, Behavior Problems, Different Learning Styles (Visual)*

Applying Skills

On index cards write brief descriptions of simple situations requiring decisions about personal health. Ask students to form groups. Have each group select a card at random. Give students ten minutes to work together, applying the six steps of the decision-making process to arrive at a decision. Have each group select a spokesperson to read the situation and explain to the rest of the class how they made their decision. As part of their presentations, have groups appraise the risks and benefits of decision making about personal health. **L2**

Health Literacy

Influencing Factors Because of their stage of cognitive development, young teens often have difficulty foreseeing how their decisions may affect others. To help them understand the role their decisions could play in the health of others and interpret critical issues related to solving health problems, describe to the class one or more examples such as the following: A teen decides to jaywalk instead of crossing the street at the light on the corner. That decision results in a driver swerving into the middle of the street to avoid hitting the teen. The swerving car is struck by a truck coming from the opposite direction. Even though the teen is unhurt, both drivers are seriously injured.

Lesson 1

HEALTH SKILLS ACTIVITY

DECISION MAKING

Help students read about Andy's situation, and discuss the steps in his decision-making process:

1. Andy has to decide how to balance swim team commitments and schoolwork.

2. Andy can quit the swim team or find a way to spend more time on schoolwork.

3. If he quits the team, he will feel less fit and be unlikely to make the local team again; all three aspects of his health may suffer. If he spends more time on schoolwork, his grades may improve but he may have less time to improve swimming skills.

4. Andy values physical fitness, good grades, and overall health.

5. Let students share their decisions for Andy.

6. Students should discuss long- and short-term consequences. **Note:** Asking questions such as "In six months (or 5 years) how will Andy know he made a good decision?" will guide students in this step.

Note: This skill is introduced in this chapter on pages 28–30.

Reading Check

Understand cause and effect. Complete this analogy: Showing respect is to earning trust as showing dis-respect is to _____.

In Step 4 you consider your values and the values of society. **Values** are *the beliefs and ideals that guide the way a person lives.* For example, keeping a positive relationship with your family is probably one of your personal values. You know that if you decide to stay out past your curfew, family members may lose trust in you. By considering your values, and getting home on time, you show respect and earn your family's trust. Respect and trust are also core ethical values, which means they are shared by people around the world.

Evaluating Your Decision

After Step 5—making your decision and taking action—Step 6 will have you evaluate the results. **Evaluate** means *to determine the value of something.* To evaluate your decision, ask yourself the following questions:

- What was the outcome of my decision? Was it what I expected?
- How did my decision make me feel about myself?
- How did my decision affect others?
- How did my decision affect each side of my health triangle?
- What did I learn? Would I make the same decision again?

As with any skill, decision making gets easier with practice. For example, you might think about some problems that you or your family may face. Think through all six steps of the decision-making process to find a healthy solution for each problem. This practice will help you with future decisions.

HEALTH SKILLS ACTIVITY

DECISION MAKING

What to Do? What to Do?

Andy has been swimming since he was five years old. He loves to swim because it's fun, it makes him feel healthy, and it helps him keep physically fit. Now he has a place on the local swim team, and that requires regular practice.

However, Andy has been so busy with his sport that his grades have begun to fall. If they slip too far, he could lose his place on the team, but cheating on homework and tests could also get him kicked off. What should Andy do?

WHAT WOULD YOU DO?

Apply the six steps of the decision-making process to Andy's situation. Compare your outcome to the solutions of your classmates.

1. STATE THE SITUATION.
2. LIST THE OPTIONS.
3. WEIGH THE POSSIBLE OUTCOMES.
4. CONSIDER VALUES.
5. MAKE A DECISION AND ACT.
6. EVALUATE THE DECISION.

Reading Check

Analogies Completing analogies can help students understand the relationships between words and concepts. Students will likely respond: Showing respect is to earning trust as showing disrespect is to losing trust. You might also offer this analogy: Setting goals is to focusing on behaviors you need to change as achieving goals is to obtaining a sense of accomplishment and pride.

Explain that the analogies presented here are formal statements of cause-and-effect relationships. Point out that the first element in each half of the analogy states a causal factor, and the second states its effect. Encourage students to find other cause-and-effect relationships in their reading and write their own analogies.

Why Set Goals?

Do you feel that you do all you can do to protect your health, or are you aware that there is room for improvement? Perhaps you need to work on family relationships, or ways to better protect yourself from injury or infection. Setting goals will help you focus on the behaviors you want to change. **Goal setting** is *the process of working toward something you want to accomplish.* Achieving a goal requires planning and effort, and it can give you a great sense of accomplishment and pride.

Goals that you set for one area of your life often lead to the achievement of goals in other areas. For example, if you work toward the goal of becoming a black belt in karate, you will achieve fitness goals, too. Along the way, you may also reach other goals such as making new friends, gaining more self-confidence, and learning more ways to manage stress.

The Benefits of Setting Goals

Goals help you identify what you want out of life. They also help you use your time, energy, and other resources wisely. Setting goals and working to reach them is an acceptable method of gaining attention. Your peers may admire your success and be inspired to set and achieve their own goals. Receiving positive attention and recognition from others can also encourage you to set new goals.

You will most likely have both long-term goals and short-term goals. Short-term goals often help you reach your long-term goals.

This teen wants to make the tennis team. *How will short-term goals help her achieve this long-term goal?*

Developing Good Character

Self-discipline

Setting goals and following through with a plan to achieve them requires self-discipline and motivation. *What health-related goal would you like to achieve?*

Developing Good Character

Self-discipline

Discuss the concept of self-discipline with students. Ask them why it is such a critical building block for health. Give examples of athletes who have succeeded because of their self-discipline. Have students identify the specific behaviors these athletes must have practiced in their lives to reach their level of success. Then have students think of examples in their own lives.

Analyzing

Have the class brainstorm a list of reasons goals are important, and record their ideas on the board. **L2**

Discussing

Ask students to discuss the possible long-term effects of not having any life goals. How might relationships be affected? How might this affect the decisions they make? **L1**

Critical Thinking

On the board write a list of goals that young teens might want to reach. Include goals based on negative values (such as winning a race against a friend) as well as goals based on positive values (such as improving a previous best time in a race). For each goal ask the class to identify the values that underlie it and decide whether the values are positive or negative. Then ask them to think of ways they could change the negative goals into positive ones. **L2**

MORE ABOUT...

Setting Goals Goals are important for mental health because setting and reaching goals improves self-esteem. Some people don't set goals because they see their lives as a series of events that just happen to them. Such people feel like they have little control over their futures, and that perception leads to low self-esteem. Other people see their lives as works of art they are con-stantly shaping by setting goals and working to achieve them. These people feel like they are in charge of their futures, and that perception leads to high self-esteem. Remind students that achieving goals doesn't "just happen." However, if they learn to follow the steps of goal-setting they can make them happen. **INCL** *At-Risk, Special Learning Needs, Behavior Problems*

Cross-Curriculum Activity

LANGUAGE ARTS Have students make posters that convey the benefits of goal setting, using an analogy to set goals in football, hockey, or other sports. Display some of the posters in class. **L2** **INCL** *At-Risk, Special Learning Needs, Different Learning Styles* (*Visual*)

Applying Skills

Tell students that the more specific their goals are, the more likely they will reach them. Ask the class to name several general goals, and write them on the board. (Examples might include getting better grades or learning to play the guitar.) Then have them reword the goals so that they are more specific and attainable. (For example, studying an extra hour each day or signing up for guitar lessons and practicing every day for half an hour.) **L2**

Interviewing

Have students interview several classmates or other acquaintances about setting and achieving goals. Each student should prepare a list of questions in advance. Questions might include:

- What goals have you set for yourself?
- If you don't set goals, why not?
- What are some goals you have reached?
- What did you do to reach your goals?
- How did reaching the goals make you feel? **L3**

MEDIA WATCH

GET INSPIRED

Your local newspaper may be a good place to learn about people who set and reach their goals. One community paper carried a photo of a teen presenting a check to a children's hospital. During the past year, the teen had organized bake sales, rummage sales, and car washes. Her goal was to raise $5,000 to refurnish the children's play area. Look for similar stories in your local paper and discuss the goals involved.

Short-Term Goals

Some short-term goals are just that: goals that you want to achieve in the next few days or weeks. Your short-term goals may, for example, include finishing a homework assignment and writing an e-mail to your grandfather.

Other short-term goals are stepping-stones to long-term goals. Suppose, for example, that your long-term goal is to take part in a local charity 5-K run. Your short-term goals might be to run several times a week, to gradually increase the distances that you run, and to eat more nutritious foods.

Long-Term Goals

Some goals take several weeks, months, or even years to achieve. For example, you might want to go on a rafting trip next summer, or to reach a vocational (career) goal such as becoming a professional baseball player. These are long-term goals. They will take time, planning, and dedication. Short-term goals will help you meet these long-term goals.

Building Goal-Setting Skills

Goal setting is a skill that will benefit you in many areas of life. A good way to ensure that you reach the goals you set for yourself is to make a plan. **Figure 2.2** shows the steps one teen used to reach his goal of making the school basketball team. Follow these steps to develop strategies for setting your own long-term personal and vocational goals.

It took many short-term goals along the way for this teen to reach her long-term goal of playing in front of an audience. *What are some of your long-term goals?*

32 CHAPTER 2: HEALTH SKILLS: THE FOUNDATION

INCLUSION STRATEGIES

English Language Learners Help students to develop strategies for setting long-term personal and vocational goals. Have students make a chart to reinforce their understanding of how to set and reach goals. Across the top of the chart, they should print the five steps of the goal-setting process. In each column, they should write at least one specific step an individual can make in order to reach the goal. Review their written statements, and provide suggestions for revisions where needed. Then have them illustrate each specific step of the chart, as it applies to the goal they selected, with drawings or clippings from newspapers and magazines.

FIGURE 2.2

The Goal-Setting Process

Here is one teen's plan to meet his goals.

1 Identify a specific goal and write it down.
Making the school basketball team.

2 List the steps you will take to reach your goal.
Run at least 2 miles four times each week.
Practice basketball every day.

3 Get help and support from others.
Ask my friends and my brother (who plays on the high school team) to play basketball with me whenever they can.
Get advice from the basketball coach about my training routine.

4 Set up checkpoints to evaluate your progress.
After 2 weeks of training, play a game of one-on-one against my brother.

5 Give yourself a reward once you have achieved your goal.
If I make the team, I will buy myself a new pair of basketball shoes.

Lesson 1 Review

Using complete sentences, answer the following questions on a sheet of paper.

Reviewing Terms and Facts

1. **Vocabulary** Define *decision making*.
2. **Relate** What are the necessary steps and practices of the decision-making process?
3. **Recall** What are three questions you can ask yourself when you evaluate a decision?
4. **Summarize** What are the benefits of setting goals?

Thinking Critically

5. **Analyze** Think of a personal health decision you made in the past month.
Appraise the risks and benefits of making that decision.
6. **Suggest** What are some goals that you could set to improve your level of health?

Applying Health Skills

7. **Goal Setting** Develop strategies for setting long-term personal and vocational goals: Think of one personal health goal and one career goal that you would like to achieve over the long term. Use the goal-setting steps to develop strategies for achieving each goal.

Lesson 1 Review

1. The process of making a choice or finding a solution.
2. State the situation; list the options; weigh the possible outcomes; consider values; make a decision and act; evaluate the decision.
3. Any three from the bulleted list under Evaluating Your Decision on page 30.
4. Goals help you identify what you want out of life and use time, energy, and other resources wisely.
5. Responses will vary, but should demonstrate understanding of the risks and benefits of a specific decision.
6. Responses will vary.

Lesson 1

VISUAL LEARNING

FIGURE 2.2 Guide students in reading and discussing the five steps in the goal-setting process. Ask:

• Why is each step important?

• How will this behavior help the teen reach his goal?

Then let students develop strategies for setting long-term personal and vocational goals. Ask them to choose a possible long-term goal and discuss how a teen might apply all five steps of the goal-setting process in that situation. **INCL** *English Language Learners, Special Learning Needs, Behavior Problems, Different Learning Styles (Visual)*

3 Assess

Evaluating

Assign the Lesson 1 Review; then assign the Lesson 1 Quiz in the TCR.

Reteaching

Assign Concept Map 4 or Reteaching Activity 4 in the TCR.

Enrichment

Assign Enrichment Activity 4 in the TCR.

4 Close

Ask students to explain why considering their values, and the values of their parents or guardians, when weighing their options is such an important step in the decision-making process.

Lesson 2

Practicing Communication Skills

① Focus

Lesson Objectives

Students will be able to

- discuss how body language can impact communication.
- explain why "I" messages are more effective than "you" messages.
- identify ways to improve their speaking and listening skills.
- use refusal skills effectively.

Motivators

Quick Write
Allow students to pair up with someone they don't know very well and ask their questions. Then discuss their experiences and the effectiveness of their questions.

Bellringer Activity

Play a game of "gossip." Write a sentence on a piece of paper, and give it to a student to read silently. Direct that student to whisper the sentence to the next student in his or her row. Continue until the end of the row. Ask the last person in each row to write down what he or she heard. Compare it with the original sentence.

VOCABULARY

Ask for volunteers to role-play situations that demonstrate any one of the terms. Instruct the rest of the class to identify which term is being acted out. Briefly discuss how each term is related to effective communication.

Quick Write

Write down five questions that you could use to start a conversation with someone you just met.

LEARN ABOUT...

- how body language can help you communicate.
- why "I" messages are more effective than "you" messages.
- how to improve your speaking and listening skills.
- how to use refusal skills.

VOCABULARY

- interpersonal communication
- body language
- mixed message
- eye contact
- active listening
- feedback
- refusal skills

Practicing Communication Skills

How Well Do You Communicate?

Some people are much better communicators than others. They have the ability to get their message across, listen to what others have to say, and keep the lines of communication open. In short, they have good interpersonal communication skills. **Interpersonal communication** involves *the exchange of thoughts, feelings, and beliefs between two or more people.*

Like other skills, interpersonal communication must be learned and practiced. It is an important skill because you use it in all of your relationships. Think about how often you talk with family members, friends, teachers, and classmates. Effective interpersonal communication involves body language and careful word choice as well as speaking and listening skills.

Team leaders, such as this soccer captain, use communication skills to get the best performance from their players. *Why are communication skills important for leadership?*

34 CHAPTER 2: HEALTH SKILLS: THE FOUNDATION

Lesson 2 Resources

Teacher Classroom Resources

📁 Concept Map 5

📁 Cross-Curriculum Activity 3

📁 Enrichment Activity 5

📁 Lesson Plan 2

📁 Lesson 2 Quiz

📁 Reading Tutor Activity 5

📁 Reteaching Activity 5

🗄 Transparency 6

Student Activities Workbook

📁 Chapter 2 Study Guide

📁 Applying Health Skills 5

Body Language

Interpersonal communication involves more than words. Your body helps to communicate your thoughts and feelings too. **Body language** is *a form of nonverbal communication.* For example, raised eyebrows might reflect curiosity, surprise, or interest. Drooping shoulders might indicate sadness, insecurity, or fear.

It is important for speakers and listeners to be aware of body language. Some forms of body language such as smiling and nodding encourage communication. Other forms such as frowning and crossing arms tightly across the chest discourage communication.

Sometimes your words and your body language don't communicate the same message. A **mixed message** occurs *when your words say one thing but your body language says another.* For example, you might say, "I'm not angry," but your frown and clenched jaw convey a different message. Your body language gives your true feelings away.

Using "I" Messages

Imagine your reaction if a friend said to you, "You're never on time!" or "You're so bossy!" These types of "you" messages place blame on the other person and often cause hurt or angry feelings. Using "I" messages instead is a much more effective way to communicate. An "I" message is a statement in which a person uses the pronoun I to express an opinion or comment.

A well-crafted "I" message is a powerful communication tool. It states the situation and how you feel about the situation. It also offers an explanation for your feelings. Finally, it states what you need. For example, you might say, "When you were late for the movie I felt disappointed. I'd heard that the opening sequence was funny and I didn't want to miss it. Next time we go to the movies let's make sure we're early so we don't miss anything."

Your body language and your words tell someone if you are interested in what he or she has to say. *What body language tells you that the teen on the right is interested in what the other teen is saying?*

❷ Teach

Examining the Issue

Discuss the effect that television viewing has on communication skills at home. Have students offer instances where they were unable to follow a conversation because the television was too great a distraction. Discuss the possibility of turning off the television during mealtime so that family communication can take place on a regular basis. **L1**

Finding Examples

Ask students to describe emotions that are expressed through a hug. (*affection, caring, concern, warmth*) Have them identify other gestures that communicate positive feelings as strongly as, or more strongly than, words. (*okay hand sign for approval, clapping hands for delight*) **L1**

Demonstrating

Write a variety of simple messages on slips of paper. Demonstrate the first message to the class using body language. The student who correctly identifies the message can pick a slip of paper and demonstrate the next message.

Then ask other volunteers to demonstrate mixed messages. Have students pick a slip of paper and use body language that contradicts their words. **L1** **INCL** *English Language Learners, Special Learning Needs, Behavior Problems, Different Learning Styles* (*Visual, Kinesthetic*)

Health Literacy

Interpersonal Skills Communication skills are vital to success in many areas of life. In fact, lack of communication skills has been reported by employers to be the primary deficiency of today's workers. Also, communication breakdown is said to be a major factor in marriage and family relationship problems. On the positive side, skillful communication enhances human interactions in nearly every circumstance. Developing a strong foundation of these skills in the teen years will provide many mental/emotional and social health benefits for years to come. Have students consider how good communication skills could enhance the student-teacher relationship.

Lesson 2

Synthesizing

Encourage students to illustrate appropriate body language:

- Have them demonstrate how an angry face can make even the nicest verbal message seem negative while a smile can make a serious message seem like a joke.
- Allow students time to practice maintaining eye contact in pairs or small groups. **L2**

Hands-On Health

SENDING "I" MESSAGES

Time: 30 minutes

TEACHING THE ACTIVITY

- As preparation for the activity, present a few "you" messages to the class:
  - You're always late!
  - You think only about yourself!
- Help students work together to suggest "I" messages that could be used in place of each.
- Have students work with partners to complete the activity.
- In a class discussion, have volunteers share their responses to the first In Conclusion question.

ASSESSMENT

Have students write their responses to the second In Conclusion question.

CONNECT TO

Social Studies

CULTURAL CONTEXTS

The use of eye contact varies among different cultures. In some cultures, eye contact means that the listener is interested in the speaker and that the message is getting across. In other cultures, however, eye contact is considered rude.

Speaking Skills

Interpersonal communication involves both giving and receiving messages. Speaking is the giving part. Good communication involves speaking clearly and carefully. Here are some tips for improving your speaking skills.

1. **Use "I" messages.** Consider how your words will affect the other person, and express your concerns in terms of your own feelings. You'll be less likely to make others feel defensive.
2. **Make clear, simple statements.** Stick to the point and be specific. Make sure the other person understands what you're saying.
3. **Be honest with thoughts and feelings.** Say what you want to say. Be truthful and direct about your values while showing respect for your listener's values.
4. **Use appropriate body language.** Make sure your facial expressions, gestures, and posture match your message. Use **eye contact**, or *direct visual contact with another person's eyes,* to show that you are sincere.

Hands-On Health

SENDING "I" MESSAGES

This activity will give you the opportunity to practice sending "I" messages. The more you practice this skill, the better communicator you will become.

3. Read each "you" message to the class. Then read the corresponding "I" message.

IN CONCLUSION

1. Which types of messages did you think were the most effective? Why?
2. Think of a recent disagreement that you had with a family member or friend. How could using "I" messages have helped resolve the conflict?

WHAT YOU WILL NEED

- pencil or pen
- index cards

WHAT YOU WILL DO

1. Working in pairs, imagine everyday situations in which "you" messages might occur. Write the situation across the top of the card. Then write the "you" message below on the left. Change that same message into an "I" message, and write the "I" version on the right. A sample card is shown here.
2. Here are a few sample situations:
   - Your older brother was an hour late in picking you up at the mall.
   - Your friend told a lie about you.

> **Situation:**
> Your friend always chooses what you'll do together
>
> **You** | **I**
> "You always get your own way." | "I'll go along with your choice this time if I can pick what we do the next time."

Beyond the Classroom

Community Being a part of a group makes us feel that we belong and that we fit in. Yet what happens when someone does not speak the same language as the rest of the people in the community? Such is the case with people who learned another language before they arrived in the United States. Students may be interested in learning more about volunteer literacy programs in their communities. To find out more about programs offered, suggest that students consult their local libraries and look for information on adult education classes offered at high schools and community colleges.

Listening Skills

Good listening skills are just as important to interpersonal communication as speaking skills. A speaker's message has meaning only if the listener receives it. Good communication involves active listening. **Active listening** means *hearing, thinking about, and responding to the other person's message.* Here are some effective listening skills.

1. **Use appropriate body language.** Pay attention to what the speaker has to say. Make eye contact, and use facial expressions and gestures that show that you are listening.
2. **Use conversation encouragers.** Show that you're listening by nodding or asking questions. Say things like "Really?" or "What happened next?" to show that you are paying attention.
3. **Mirror thoughts and feelings.** Repeat what the person said as a way of confirming what you heard. Offer feedback when appropriate. **Feedback** is *a response by the listener to what the speaker has said.*
4. **Ask questions.** After the person has finished speaking, ask questions or add your own comments or opinions.

Refusal Skills

During your teen years, there may be times when friends or acquaintances want you to do something that you do not want to do. Maybe you're just not interested. Maybe you don't have the time or the money. Maybe it's something that is unhealthy or that goes against your values. In these situations, refusal skills are useful. **Refusal skills** are *communication strategies that help you say no effectively.*

Using refusal skills will help you be true to yourself. You can resist without feeling guilty or uncomfortable. Other people will respect you for being honest about your needs and wants. An easy way to remember refusal skills is to keep in mind the letters in the word *stop.*

- **S**ay no in a firm voice.
- **T**ell why not.
- **O**ffer other ideas.
- **P**romptly leave.

Good communication skills help you form healthy relationships. *How do the speaking and listening skills apply when you talk on the telephone?*

Examining the Issue

Divide the class into groups of three or four, giving each group access to a video camera:

- Have each group member tape the other two members in normal conversation.
- After all three have made tapes, ask the group to play the tapes back and evaluate one another's listening skills using the list on this page.
- Then have students reevaluate the same tapes without sound, paying attention to how their facial expressions and body language indicate that they are or are not listening well.
- Aid students in drawing conclusions about good communication skills by asking them to distinguish between effective and ineffective listening skills, such as paying attention to the speaker versus not making eye contact. **L2**

HEALTH SKILLS PRACTICE

Refusal Skills Have students personalize refusal techniques. Assign the following: Your parents agreed to let you go out with a group of friends. A friend you know wants to go out with you, but just the two of you. It sounds like a great idea, but you know you're not ready. Plus your parents have said no dating yet. You want to say no and mean no, but you want the person to stay your friend. Write three possible no statements. Share them with a friend. Which one works best?

COOPERATIVE LEARNING ACTIVITY

Refusal Skills Have students form small groups and compile lists of other strategies, phrases, or behaviors that work when they want to say no. Have the groups analyze whether or not each of their techniques shows respect and understanding for both parties and their points of view. Techniques that do not show respect for both parties should be crossed off the list. Students can also design wallet cards with a collection of refusal techniques that they feel would work for them. Later, when students see a decision-making situation coming and cannot think of an effective way to say no, they can quickly refer to the wallet card. To conclude the activity, ask students to predict the consequences of refusal skills in various situations.

VISUAL LEARNING

FIGURE 2.3 Have students use their own words to explain why these teens' refusals are effective. Then ask students to give examples of body language that might not be as effective. **INCL** *English Language Learners, Special Learning Needs, Behavior Problems, Different Learning Styles (Visual)*

❸ Assess

Evaluating

📁 Assign the Lesson 2 Review; then assign the Lesson 2 Quiz in the TCR.

Reteaching

- 📁 Assign Concept Map 5 or Reteaching Activity 5 in the TCR.
- Ask students to define the term *communication* and list five guidelines each for effective verbal communication and good listening skills.

Enrichment

📁 Assign Enrichment Activity 5 in the TCR.

❹ Close

Ask students to explain how the lesson increased their ability to communicate effectively.

When you need to refuse someone, it is important to show that you mean what you say. Your body language, including eye contact, helps you to do this. **Figure 2.3** illustrates how body language can show refusal.

FIGURE 2.3

Say **NO** and mean it!

Your body language can speak as loudly as your words do. These teens are likely to be understood because of their strong body language.

This teen is showing his refusal with defiant body language. This refusal will be taken seriously.

This teen's crossed arms tell others that her refusal should be taken seriously.

Lesson 2 Review

Using complete sentences, answer the following questions on a sheet of paper.

Reviewing Terms and Facts

1. **Vocabulary** Define *interpersonal communication.*
2. **Recall** Give three examples of ways people use body language.
3. **Identify** List four tips for improving speaking skills.
4. **Explain** What is meant by *active listening?*

Thinking Critically

5. **Analyze** Choose someone you consider a particularly good communicator. Identify the skills that person uses to communicate so well.
6. **Compare** Distinguish between effective and ineffective listening, such as paying attention to the speaker versus not making eye contact.

Applying Health Skills

7. **Communication Skills** Make a videotape that demonstrates the power of nonverbal communication. Tape the body language of some volunteers and narrate the tape, explaining how body language sends messages. Ask the audience to interpret each person's message from his or her body language.

38 CHAPTER 2: HEALTH SKILLS: THE FOUNDATION

Lesson 2 Review

1. The exchange of thoughts, feelings, and beliefs between two or more people.
2. Any three: raised eyebrows, drooping shoulders, smiling, nodding, frowning, crossing arms across chest.
3. Use "I" messages; make clear, simple statements; be honest with thoughts and feelings; use appropriate body language.
4. Hearing, thinking about, and responding to the other person's message.
5. Responses will vary, but should include good communication skills.
6. Responses should effectively compare and contrast effective and ineffective listening skills, and include examples of each type.

Managing Stress

What Is Stress?

The teen years are a time of many changes. Your body is changing, you are gaining new responsibilities, and you are forming new kinds of relationships. Because of such changes, teens may experience stress. **Stress** is *your body's response to change* and is a normal part of life.

Stress is not necessarily bad. *Positive stress,* called **eustress**, can make your life more pleasurable. It can help you reach your goals and motivate you to do your best. Eustress is an exciting feeling. It might help you find the energy to score the winning goal in a soccer match or do exceptionally well on a school project.

Some stress can have a negative effect on personal health, however. This type of *negative stress* is called **distress**. You might react to distress by having an upset stomach before giving a report, or by losing sleep after you argue with your parents. You can't always avoid negative stress, but you *can* learn to manage it.

Quick Write

Jot down the types of situations that are most likely to cause you to feel stress.

LEARN ABOUT...

- the causes of stress.
- how your body responds to stress.
- positive ways to manage the stress in your life.

VOCABULARY

- stress
- eustress
- distress
- stressor
- fight-or-flight response
- adrenaline
- fatigue
- stress management skills
- time management

Learning to manage your time and planning ahead are coping strategies that can help you avoid stressful situations. *What steps do you take to manage stress in your life?*

LESSON 3: MANAGING STRESS **39**

---

① Focus

Lesson Objectives

Students will be able to

- explain the difference between positive and negative stress.
- identify the causes of stress.
- describe the effects of stress on the body.
- identify ways to manage stress.

> **Health Skills**
> • Stress Management, p. 43

Motivators

Quick Write
Encourage students to describe the situations that caused them to feel stress. Ask volunteers to describe what they feel when they experience stress.

Bellringer Activity

Have students write a definition for *stress.* Discuss ways they have handled stress in the past.

> ### VOCABULARY
>
> Explain to students that many words are created by combining roots with prefixes or suffixes. For example, *stress* (a response to change) and *-or* (the cause of something) form *stressor.* Have students write definitions of the terms. Then ask them to compare their definitions with those in the Glossary.

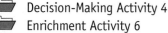

Lesson 3 Resources

Teacher Classroom Resources

- Concept Map 6
- Cross-Curriculum Activity 4
- Decision-Making Activity 4
- Enrichment Activity 6
- Health Lab 2
- Lesson Plan 3
- Lesson 3 Quiz

- Reading Tutor Activity 6
- Reteaching Activity 6
- Transparency 7

Student Activities Workbook

- Chapter 2 Study Guide
- Applying Health Skills 6

Analyzing

Have students think of the most stressful day they can remember:

- Have them list activities they engaged in that day, from the time they awoke to the time they went to bed.
- Instruct them to label any activity that was crucial (such as being on time for school) with the letter A, any activity that was not crucial (such as watching TV) with a C, and any activity that was in between (such as helping a friend study for a test) with a B.
- Have them make charts showing the amount of time expended on each activity.
- If there was a disproportionate amount of time spent on B and C activities, what conclusions can they draw about their time management skills and feeling stressed? **L2**

VISUAL LEARNING

FIGURE 2.4 Let volunteers read the lists of stressors aloud. Help students discuss what makes each situation stressful. Point out to students that many of these situations are stressful to adults as well. **INCL** *English Language Learners, Special Learning Needs, Behavior Problems, Different Learning Styles (Visual)*

Guest Speaker

Invite a well-known athlete from the community or a school coach to speak to the class about stress in sports. Ask him or her to talk about the effect of adrenaline on the body during sporting events. **L2**

What Causes Stress?

To handle stress, you need to know what causes it. *Anything that causes stress* is called a **stressor**. Stressors range from everyday annoyances to serious personal problems. They also affect different people in different ways. Whereas you might feel nervous about auditioning for the choir, your friend might find the same situation exciting. **Figure 2.4** shows some of the things that cause stress for teens.

FIGURE 2.4

Common Stressors for Teens

Although these events are common stressors, not everyone reacts to them in the same way.

Somewhat Stressful
- Arguing with a sibling or friend
- Moving to a new home
- Going to a new school
- Getting glasses or braces

- Arguing with a parent
- Worrying over height, weight, or acne
- Getting a lead role in the school play
- Being sick or injured

- Being suspended from school
- Starting to use alcohol or other drugs
- Loss or death of a pet
- Family member having a serious illness

Extremely Stressful
- Separation or divorce of parents
- Family member's alcohol or drug problem
- Getting arrested
- Failing classes at school

How Your Body Responds to Stress

When a person experiences a great deal of stress, the body reacts as though it is in danger. The natural way to deal with a danger is either to fight it or to flee from it. *The process by which the body prepares to deal with a stressor* is, therefore, known as the **fight-or-flight response**. One part of this response is the release of adrenaline. **Adrenaline** is *a hormone that gives the body extra energy*.

There's a limit to how much stress your body can handle. Too much stress can result in headaches, digestive problems, and high blood pressure. It can make you feel anxious, depressed, angry, or irritable. Over time, you might experience **fatigue**, or *exhaustion*, and a lower resistance to infection. This is your body's way of telling you that you need to rest and reduce your stress.

WHAT TEENS WANT TO KNOW

My palms sweat and my heart pounds before I take a test. Is this normal? Yes. Sweaty palms and pounding hearts are the physical symptoms of anxiety. It's perfectly normal and understandable to feel anxious before you take a test, speak in front of your class, or perform in a recital. When the situation passes, you feel relieved, and the symptoms disappear. A moderate amount of anxiety isn't necessarily bad. It can motivate you to finish your homework on time, study harder for a test, or kick a soccer ball farther. No one breezes through the teen years without some anxiety and fear. The key is to learn to control your anxiety. Use the anxiety to improve your performance rather than control you.

Ways to Manage Stress

To handle stress you need a variety of **stress management skills**, or *ways to deal with and overcome problems.* One of the basic ways to manage stress is to follow a healthy lifestyle. Problems are always easier to deal with if you feel well. More specific skills for dealing with stress include knowing how and when to relax, keeping a positive outlook, being physically active, and managing your time.

Relaxation

Relaxation reduces stress by slowing your heart rate and making you feel less tense. Try some of these strategies for coping with stress:

- **Relax your muscles.** Tighten and then relax one group of muscles at a time. Start at your toes and work your way up to your head.
- **Slow your breathing.** Take deep, even breaths for five minutes. Inhale through your nose and exhale through your mouth.
- **Get enough sleep.** Feeling tired can make a stressful situation seem worse. Everything looks better after a good night's sleep!

Keep a Positive Outlook

When you are under stress, it is easy to feel hopeless. In fact, stress can affect your emotions, causing you to feel depressed, anxious, or afraid. A minor problem can seem major. Remind yourself to look at the big picture and keep things in perspective. Is it *really* the end of the world if you don't get to stay out as late as some of your friends? Is your homework assignment *really* as difficult as you think? Following are some tips for keeping a positive outlook at times of stress.

Laughter is a great stress reliever. *Describe the relationship between emotions and stress.*

Lesson 3

Discussing

Discuss with students what physical and emotional signs of stress they sometimes see in themselves. Ask:

- How do these signs affect your ability to study?
- How do they affect your friendships?
- What do they do to family relationships? **L2**

Guest Speaker

Invite a counselor from school or from the community to speak to the class about stress and ways to deal with stressors. Afterward, have students write short papers summarizing the presentation. **L1**

Applying Knowledge

Let students discuss their own experiences with relaxation tapes. These tapes usually have music and/or nature sounds; some also include instructions for relaxing specific muscles. If possible, play a short portion of a relaxation tape for the class. Ask:

- Do you think this kind of tape could help you relax? Why or why not?
- Do you have a favorite song or piece of music that helps you to relax? **L1**

FYI

The six leading causes of death—heart disease, cancer, lung ailments, accidents, cirrhosis of the liver, and suicide—have all been linked to stress.

✓ Reading Check

Antonyms Working with antonyms can help students think about word relationships and build a strong vocabulary. Have students work individually, using dictionaries and thesauruses, to identify opposites, or close opposites, for words. Examples are: *stressor–reliever, helper, calming influence; fatigue–energy, liveliness; benefit–detriment, deficit; worry–to be unconcerned, untroubled, not bothered.* Encourage discussion by posing questions such as: What is the difference between something that is a *deficit* and something that is a *detriment*? How might someone who is *energetic* be different from a person who's *lively*?

Lesson 3

HEALTH Online

Encourage students to explore the Web Link for this chapter and complete the activity.

Discussing

Help students discuss the differences between deciding not to take difficult situations too seriously and refusing to acknowledge difficult situations. Emphasize that pretending a problem doesn't exist (repressing) usually leads to greater stress; recognizing a stressor and dealing with it realistically can reduce the level of stress. **L1**

Demonstrating

Explain to students that even light exercise or stretching can help a person relieve stress. Lead students in several stretching techniques. Have students stand up and reach for the sky to lengthen back and shoulder muscles. Then have them turn their heads from side to side to stretch their neck muscles. Ask them to demonstrate other stretches that can be done while sitting. Afterward, ask the students how they feel. **L1** **INCL** *English Language Learners, Special Learning Needs, Behavior Problems, Different Learning Styles (Visual, Kinesthetic)*

VISUAL LEARNING

FIGURE 2.5 Guide students in reading and discussing the listed benefits of physical activity. Then read aloud the caption for Figure 2.5, and have volunteers share their responses to the question. Students may suggest such benefits as improved fitness, better sleep, and contact with friends. **INCL** *English Language Learners, Special Learning Needs, Behavior Problems, Different Learning Styles (Visual)*

HEALTH Online

Topic: Reducing stress

For a link to more information on laughter and stress, go to **health.glencoe.com**.

Activity: Using the information provided at this link, create a comic strip that shows how a teen uses good humor to relieve stress.

- **Think positively.** If you tell yourself that you will fail at something, you will increase your stress. Instead, tell yourself that you will do a great job.
- **Keep your sense of humor.** Don't let stress prevent you from seeing the funny side of things. A good laugh is a great stress reliever.
- **Have some fun.** Take a little time out to do something enjoyable and relaxing. Listen to your favorite CD, read a book, or watch a funny video.

Remember that some stress can be helpful. It can motivate you to take action. Say, for example that you're nervous about doing well in team tryouts. The stress that you feel might motivate you to put in plenty of practice.

Physical Activity

Being physically active is one of the healthiest ways to manage stress. Physical activity can bring about physical and emotional changes that can offset the effects of stress and give you a more positive outlook. **Figure 2.5** shows some of these changes.

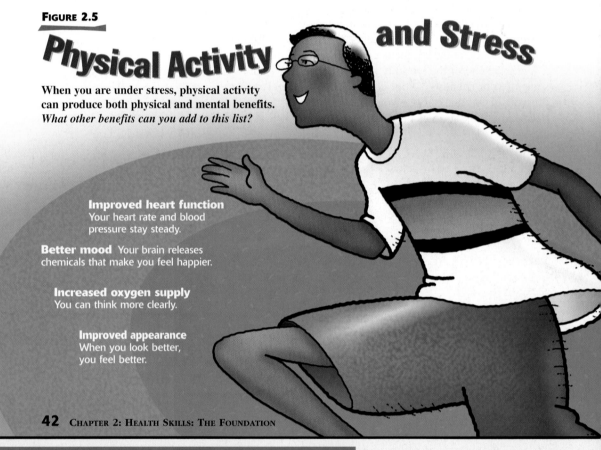

FIGURE 2.5

Physical Activity and Stress

When you are under stress, physical activity can produce both physical and mental benefits. *What other benefits can you add to this list?*

Improved heart function Your heart rate and blood pressure stay steady.

Better mood Your brain releases chemicals that make you feel happier.

Increased oxygen supply You can think more clearly.

Improved appearance When you look better, you feel better.

42 CHAPTER 2: HEALTH SKILLS: THE FOUNDATION

PROMOTING COORDINATED SCHOOL HEALTH

Adults as Models As an advocate for the health and well-being of students, you can use resources in the immediate school environment to stress the importance of lifelong responsibility for personal health. Since most school sites involve employees from a wide spectrum of age groups, students can witness how employees model good health behavior. For example, faculty and staff can be encouraged to participate in a student-teacher volleyball game. They might speak to your class about their personal evolution of maturity and intellect. Above all, everyone of all ages should be encouraged to recognize their role in making the school community function positively. For more information, consult *Planning a Coordinated School Health Program* in the TCR.

Managing Your Time

Learning time management skills can help you reduce stress and get more done. **Time management** means *using your time wisely*. It combines planning and self-discipline.

Managing your time involves figuring out which activities are most important to you. When you have a task to finish, stay focused. Avoid distractions such as phone calls and visitors until you are ready to take a break.

HEALTH SKILLS ACTIVITY

STRESS MANAGEMENT

Balance Your Schedule

One strategy for coping with stress is to use your time wisely and balance your schedule. Try these tips for managing a busy schedule.

- **SET PRIORITIES.** Figure out which tasks are required and which are optional.
- **PUT IT IN WRITING.** Include both required and optional tasks, but make sure you list (and do) the required tasks first.
- **PLAN YOUR TIME.** Allow enough time for each task, but also set aside some time for something you enjoy.

- **THINK AHEAD.** Think through all the details before you start a task.
- **USE REFUSAL SKILLS.** You won't always have time to do everything you want to do. Learn to say no to things you don't have time for.

WITH A GROUP
In small groups, devise your own list of time-management skills for busy teens. Demonstrate these time-management skills for the rest of the class.

Lesson 3 Review

Using complete sentences, answer the following questions on a sheet of paper.

Reviewing Terms and Facts

1. **Vocabulary** What is the difference between *eustress* and *distress?*
2. **Explain** What is the process known as the *fight-or-flight response*?
3. **Identify** Name four skills that can help you deal with stress.
4. **Summarize** What does time management involve?

Thinking Critically

5. **Interpret** Describe some possible effects of stress on personal and family health.
6. **Explain** Why are planning and self-discipline important to time management?

Applying Health Skills

7. **Stress Management** Choose one of the strategies for coping with stress described on pages 41–43. Create a skit about a teen who uses that strategy. Perform your skit for the class to demonstrate this strategy for coping with stress.

LESSON 3: MANAGING STRESS **43**

Lesson 3

HEALTH SKILLS ACTIVITY

STRESS MANAGEMENT
Help students read and discuss the listed tips. Then have students work in groups to list their own time-management strategies.

③ Assess

Evaluating

Assign the Lesson 3 Review; then assign the Lesson 3 Quiz in the TCR.

Reteaching

Assign Concept Map 6 or Reteaching Activity 6 in the TCR.

Enrichment

- Assign Enrichment Activity 6 in the TCR.
- Have students interview two people from different age groups. Ask students to find out what each person's greatest stressors are and what he or she does to manage stress. Have students make a chart comparing the stressors and conclusions about how stress varies with age.
- Ask volunteers to demonstrate time-management skills in a role-play for the class. Be sure students show the benefits of time management in their demonstration.

④ Close

Ask students to summarize the most important concepts learned in this lesson. Then have small groups of students create role-plays in which they demonstrate strategies for coping with stress.

Lesson 3 Review

1. Eustress is positive stress; distress is negative stress.
2. The process by which the body prepares to deal with a stressor.
3. Any four: relaxing muscles, slowing breathing, sleeping enough, thinking positively, keeping a sense of humor, making time for fun activities, being physically active.
4. Figuring out which activities are important to you, staying focused, using time wisely and without distraction.
5. Possible response: Stress can make you physically ill, anxious, depressed, or tired. It may cause you to become irritable or angry with family members.
6. They help you stay focused and set priorities.

Lesson 4

Developing Other Health Skills

1 Focus

Lesson Objectives

Students will be able to

- use critical thinking, such as interpreting media messages, to analyze health information.
- describe behaviors that enhance lifelong health and wellness.
- discuss and analyze internal and external influences on their health.

Health Skills
- Practicing Healthful Behaviors, p. 46

Motivators

Quick Write

Allow students to share their responses. Ask them to provide examples that demonstrate how each influence can affect their thinking in both positive and negative ways.

Bellringer Activity

Ask students: If you wanted to learn more about a specific health topic, such as the symptoms of measles, where would you look for the information? Have students review their answers at the end of the lesson.

Vocabulary

Have students find the definitions for the two vocabulary terms in the lesson. Ask students how the term *support system,* as identified in the lesson, can relate to support systems used in various structures like bridges and buildings.

Lesson 4 Developing Other Health Skills

Quick Write

What influences your decisions about health? List the people, media, and other factors that you think have the strongest influence on the decisions you make about your health.

Learn About...
- ways to get the health information you need.
- behaviors that enhance the way you look and feel.
- internal and external influences on your health.

Vocabulary
- support system
- environment

Health Skills: An Overview

Health skills are practices that help you maintain, protect, and improve your health. At the same time, they help you understand how and why your decisions, choices, and attitudes influence your health.

Health skills are also called life skills. That's because they will benefit you not only during the teen years but also throughout your life. The skills already discussed in this chapter—decision making, goal setting, communication skills, refusal skills, and stress management—are examples of health skills. **Figure 2.6** shows a complete list of health skills.

Figure 2.6

The Health Skills

Practicing these health skills will provide a lifetime of benefits.

- Accessing Information
- Self-Management
  - –Practicing Healthful Behaviors
  - –Stress Management
- Analyzing Influences
- Interpersonal Communication
  - –Communication Skills
  - –Refusal Skills
  - –Conflict Resolution Skills
- Decision Making/Goal Setting
- Advocacy

Lesson 4 Resources

Teacher Classroom Resources
- Concept Map 7
- Enrichment Activity 7
- Lesson Plan 4
- Lesson 4 Quiz
- Reading Tutor Activity 7
- Reteaching Activity 7
- Transparency 8

Student Activities Workbook
- Chapter 2 Study Guide
- Applying Health Skills 7
- Health Inventory 2

Accessing Information

This skill involves finding reliable health information and using health resources. "Reliable" means that the information comes from sources you can trust. Where can you find reliable information? Sources include parents, teachers, counselors, school nurses, and other trusted adults. You can also access printed and published information from a wide variety of sources available to the public. **Figure 2.7** shows some of these sources.

Analyzing and Using Health Information

Although you can obtain health information from a variety of sources, not all of it is accurate and reliable. Some information is misleading or even completely false. Sources that you should treat with caution include supermarket tabloids, advertisements, rumors, e-mail, and the Internet. Use critical-thinking skills to interpret media messages about health information.

FIGURE 2.7

Where to find Health Information

Which of these sources have you used recently? Explain the role of media and technology in influencing individual and community health.

Library
encyclopedias, nonfiction books, magazines, and health-related CD-ROMs

Print and Broadcast Media
newspaper articles, magazine articles, special interest magazines, health newsletters, television shows, and radio reports

Internet
Web sites for government agencies, health organizations, and educational institutions

Community Resources
government offices, such as the county health department, and health organizations, such as the American Heart Association

LESSON 4: DEVELOPING OTHER HEALTH SKILLS **45**

Lesson 4

② Teach

VISUAL LEARNING

FIGURE 2.6 Help students discuss the health skills listed in Figure 2.6:
- How does each relate to health and wellness?
- How are the two self-management skills alike? Different?
- How are the three skills of interpersonal communication alike? Different? **INCL** *English Language Learners, Special Learning Needs, Behavior Problems, Different Learning Styles (Visual)*

VISUAL LEARNING

FIGURE 2.7 Ask students to use critical thinking, such as interpreting media messages, to analyze health information. Begin by having volunteers read aloud the lists of resources. Encourage students to share their own experiences in using each kind of resource:
- Which specific sources do you consider most reliable? Why?
- Who can help you evaluate the reliability of sources? **INCL** *English Language Learners, Special Learning Needs, Behavior Problems, Different Learning Styles (Visual)*

MORE ABOUT...

Evaluating Health Information While there is a wealth of information available on the Web, not all of it is accurate or reliable. Internet resources maintained by government agencies, universities, and nonprofit organizations (addresses ending in .gov, .edu, or .org), are more likely to offer more objective, or unbiased, information than commercial sites such as health food stores.

Reputable sites list the names and credentials of the people who develop and review the site's content. Organizations with Web sites offering timely, accurate medical information include the American Medical Association, Centers for Disease Control and Prevention, and National Institutes of Health.

Applying Knowledge

Let students work in groups to use critical thinking, such as interpreting media messages, to analyze and use health information. Have group members compile a list of at least five Web sites they consider sources of reliable information. Then have students compare and discuss their lists, explaining why they chose specific sites. **L1**

Guest Speaker

Invite a school or community librarian to visit the class and discuss available sources of health-related information. In addition, ask the guest speaker to assist students in developing evaluation criteria for health information. **L1**

HEALTH SKILLS ACTIVITY

PRACTICING HEALTHFUL BEHAVIORS

In a class discussion, have students consider each practice listed in the personal inventory: How does it contribute to good health? Ask students to relate practices necessary for making health decisions. Then have students work independently to complete the inventory. Assure them that the results of this inventory are for their personal use; the results can be kept confidential.

 **MEDIA WATCH**

BE CAUTIOUS

Before buying any health product, use reliable sources to verify advertising claims. *Find an ad for a health product. Use critical thinking skills to analyze and interpret the health information in that ad. Verify the ad's claims using reliable sources.*

How can you tell the reliable information from the unreliable? You need to consider the source and make sure that it is trustworthy. Say, for example, that you read about a weight modification program on the Web. Check it out first. For accurate, up-to-date health information, you can count on agencies run by the government. Their Web addresses usually end in *.org* or *.gov*. Examples include the National Institutes of Health, the Food and Drug Administration, and the Centers for Disease Control and Prevention.

Practicing Healthful Behaviors

This skill applies to all sides of your health triangle—physical, mental/emotional, and social health. Practicing healthful behaviors involves taking care of yourself and avoiding risky situations. It means developing lifelong habits that increase your level of health and protect you from illness and injury.

Make Health a Habit

What health habits do you practice every day? Habits are things you do regularly and almost without even thinking about

---

HEALTH SKILLS ACTIVITY

PRACTICING HEALTHFUL BEHAVIORS

Personal Health Inventory

Take your personal health inventory by considering these lists of good habits for each area of your health triangle.

PHYSICAL HEALTH

- I eat well-balanced meals, including breakfast, and choose healthful snacks.
- I get regular physical activity and at least 8 hours of sleep each night.
- I avoid using tobacco, alcohol, and drugs.
- I stay within 5 pounds of my healthy weight.
- I practice good personal hygiene habits.
- I get regular physical checkups.

MENTAL/EMOTIONAL HEALTH

- I can name several things I do well.
- I generally keep a positive attitude.
- I express my emotions in healthy ways.

- I ask for help when I need it.
- I take responsibility for my actions.
- I take on new challenges to improve myself.

SOCIAL HEALTH

- I relate well to family, friends, and peers.
- I have several close friends.
- I can disagree with others without becoming rude.
- I treat others with respect.
- I use refusal skills to avoid risk behaviors.
- I get along with all kinds of people.

ON YOUR OWN

Give yourself 2 points for each habit that you always practice and 1 point for each one that you usually practice. If you scored 5 or less in any area, make a list of ways to improve your health habits.

Health Literacy

Health Influences Self-help is based on the premise that sharing problems with people who have lived through similar difficulties reduces isolation, enables exchange of ideas, and provides coping strategies. Groups support members to make positive changes in their lives. Self-help groups emphasize community, cooperation, and caring.

Groups offer opportunities for learned helpfulness, empowering people with similar problems to help one another. Today, online support groups extend the sense of community previously available only to those able to attend traditional, face-to-face group meetings. (Note: Remind students to ask a parent or trusted guardian for permission before attending a self-help group and before logging on to an Internet group.)

them. Making health a priority and establishing good habits are key elements for good health.

Do you understand the health benefits of brushing and flossing your teeth every morning after breakfast and every night before bedtime? Do you understand the benefit of putting on your safety belt every time you enter a car? Brushing your teeth and wearing a safety belt are habits that promote your physical health. You can also practice habits that promote the other areas of your health triangle. For example, managing stress in healthy ways and planning your time wisely are habits that promote mental/emotional health. Greeting people in a friendly manner and spending time with friends are good social health habits to develop.

Build a Support System

Having a solid support system is essential for good health. A **support system** is *a network of people available to help when needed.* If you have health questions or problems, the people in your support system can provide reliable information, advice, and encouragement. They care about you and your health. Your support system might include the following people.

- **Parents and other relatives,** such as grandparents and older brothers or sisters, are a built-in support system. Your family members can provide guidance and encouragement.
- **Teachers, coaches, and school counselors** whom you respect and trust can offer support and advice. School nurses can also help. These people are trained to understand situations faced by teens.
- **Health care providers,** such as doctors and nurses, are trained to deal with health-related issues and concerns. They can give you professional advice.
- **Religious leaders,** such as ministers, priests, mullahs, and rabbis, often are trained in counseling. They can listen to your questions and problems and offer answers and guidance.

This teen knows that she can always turn to her aunt when she needs advice and support. *Analyze other positive relationships that influence individual health, such as peers and role models.*

Lesson 4

Listing

Have students brainstorm a list of specific health habits they practice every day such as brushing and flossing teeth and wearing safety belts. Record their ideas on the board. Then help students briefly discuss each listed habit:

- To which aspect of health does it most closely relate?
- If this behavior is not a habit for you, how could you make it a habit? **L1**

Discussing

Help students discuss the importance of having support systems:

- Why are information, advice, and encouragement so important?
- How can you be part of a support system for other teens? **L1**

Journal Writing

Ask students write private journal entries about their own support systems:

- To whom can you turn for reliable information about a health concern?
- Which friends and family members encourage you to make positive choices?
- Who encourages you to care for all three aspects of your health?
- Using their journal entries, have students write a brief paragraph analyzing positive and negative relationships and how those relationships influence individual and community health. Have students consider the influence of families, role models, and peers. **L1**

MORE ABOUT...

Negative Peer Influence Negative peer influence is a powerful force contributing to initial experimentation with smoking, drinking alcohol, drug use, and other health-risk behaviors. However, teens who possess high self-esteem and self-reliance during their preteen years are less likely to associate with risk-taking peers. Supportive parents who are actively involved in teens' lives can help counteract the effects of negative peer influences. Parents who treat teens with respect, set firm expectations for behavior, and communicate openly are more likely to prevent teens from smoking and drinking alcohol. Similarly, teens who feel their parents respect them, like them, and listen to them are less likely to participate in these risk behaviors.

Discussing

Help students discuss the control they have over the internal influences on their health:

• Why do these influences sometimes seem fixed?

• What can you do to change your knowledge? Your likes and dislikes? Your fears?

Discuss internalization—moving an external influence to an internal one. Not everyone sees the same influence the same way. Why? **L2**

Critical Thinking

Help students discuss the influence of their values on their physical, mental/emotional, and social health:

• Think of one of your values. Now, analyze how that value influences your physical health.

• How do you develop your values? **L1**

Cooperative Learning

Let students work in small groups to list at least ten individuals many teens admire. Then have group members discuss the specific behaviors and attitudes each individual demonstrates: Which of these role models is truly worthy of admiration? Why? How are teens influenced by role models? Is the influence positive or negative? Explain.

Ask each group to share its conclusions with the rest of the class.

Analyzing Influences

This skill is based on an awareness of all the factors that affect your health. Understanding these internal or external factors enables you to choose behaviors that will contribute to improved health.

Internal Influences

Internal influences on your health come from within you. You have a great deal of control over these factors, which include:

● **Your knowledge.** How much do you know about health? The more knowledge you have, the better able you will be to make wise decisions and evaluate health information.

● **Your likes and dislikes.** What foods do you like and dislike? What types of activities do you enjoy in your free time? If you like fruits and vegetables and if you stay physically active, for example, you are well on your way to a healthy lifestyle.

● **Your values.** What beliefs and ideals are important to you? Placing value on good health can influence your decisions, such as avoiding drugs and practicing abstinence.

● **Your desires.** What are your plans and goals? If you hope to enjoy good health and to lead an active life, you will make decisions that lead you in that direction.

● **Your curiosity.** It's natural to be curious about things you haven't tried before. Be sure to focus your curiosity on healthful concerns, such as new sporting activities or foods that are unfamiliar to you, and to steer clear of harmful substances.

● **Your fears.** What health-related fears do you have? Concerns about the health of a relative who smokes cigarettes, for example, can influence your decision never to smoke.

A family that values physical activity and fitness will likely influence you to be active and fit. *Analyze how your family has a positive influence on your health.*

External Influences

External influences on your health come from outside sources. Being aware of these influences can help you make the right choices for you. External influences include:

● **Your family.** Your family influences what you do and how you behave. If family members help out in the community, for example, you will probably want to help others too. However, your health behaviors and knowledge may differ from those of your parents.

✔ Reading Check

If... , Then... Statements This activity will help students sort out cause-and-effect relationships and practice literal and inferential thinking. Point out to students that for most of the influences listed here, writing an If... , then... statement is easy because the cause-and-effect relationship is clearly stated in the paragraph. When the cause-and-effect relationship is not clearly spelled out, the students will have to use their inferential skills. For example, in the section on External Influences on page 49 a good If... , then... statement for the media and technology listing is: *If you evaluate the source before making a decision, then you will be less likely to make unhealthy purchases.*

- **Your friends and peers.** Your friends and classmates can have either a positive influence or a negative influence on your health. For example, a friend who encourages you to go bike riding instead of watching television has a positive influence.
- **Your environment.** Do you live in a house or an apartment? In a small town or a big city? In a warm or cold climate? Your *environment* is *the sum total of your surroundings.* It includes both physical and social factors. It includes your home and the school you attend. Your environment also includes such factors as the air quality, available recreational facilities, crime rate, and available health care.
- **Your culture.** What are your family's cultural background and traditions? Your culture can influence the way you live, the foods you eat, your values, and your goals.
- **Federal, state, and local laws.** What are the health-related federal, state, and local laws? For example, federal laws make buying cigarettes and drinking alcohol illegal for teens. Respecting these laws influences your decision not to use these substances.
- **The media and technology.** What TV shows do you watch? Which magazines and newspapers do you read? What Web sites do you visit? Media and technology can have a major influence on individual and community health. Just remember, though, to evaluate the source before making any decisions.
- **Your role models.** Who do you admire? Perhaps you look up to a favorite teacher or coach. Your role models show you how people with good character behave in situations that you might encounter.

Reading Check

Analyze the internal and external influences listed here and write an *If . . ., then. . .* statement for each. For example: *If you know a lot about health, then you will be better able to make decisions.*

Lesson 4 Review

Using complete sentences, answer the following questions on a sheet of paper.

Reviewing Terms and Facts

1. **List** Give four sources where you might find printed and published health information.
2. **Explain** What is a *support system?* How can a support system contribute to your health?
3. **Identify** What are six types of internal influences on your health?
4. **Vocabulary** Define the term *environment.*

Thinking Critically

5. **Describe** How are your personal health behaviors and knowledge different from those of your parents and grandparents? How might your behaviors and knowledge differ from a teen who lives in another part of the world?
6. **Relate** How does your physical environment influence your health?

Applying Health Skills

7. **Accessing Information** Prepare a survey of the available sources of health information in your community. Report your findings in the form of a pamphlet.

LESSON 4: DEVELOPING OTHER HEALTH SKILLS **49**

Lesson 4

③ Assess

Evaluating

Assign the Lesson 4 Review; then assign the Lesson 4 Quiz in the TCR.

Reteaching

- Assign Concept Map 7 or Reteaching Activity 7 in the TCR.
- Have students work with partners to write a sentence explaining each of these health skills: accessing information, practicing healthful behaviors, and analyzing influences.

Enrichment

- Assign Enrichment Activity 7 in the TCR.
- Have students review the internal and external influences in this lesson. Then have students relate how they influence community health. Have students consider other factors such as climate and gangs.

④ Close

Ask students to consider the categories of people identified on page 47. Then create a diagram that represents their own support system, filling in specific names of people they rely on. Explain that their lists of individuals will remain confidential.

Lesson 4 Review

1. Library, print media, Internet, and community resources.
2. A network of people available to help when needed. A support system can offer reliable information, advice, and encouragement.
3. Knowledge, likes and dislikes, values, desires, curiosity, fears.
4. The sum total of your surroundings.
5. Responses might include that older generations may have been less concerned with staying physically fit, watching fat and sugar consumption, and developing health skills. Health behaviors and knowledge for teens in other countries are affected by their influences and access to information, as well as culture.
6. Responses will vary.

Under Pressure

① Focus

Objectives

Students will be able to
- identify common sources of teen stress.
- list healthy ways to avoid or manage stress.
- locate community resources for stress management.

Motivator

Quick Write
Ask students to describe their stress level right now. What is going on in their lives to create stress? What are they doing to handle it?

② Teach

Analyzing

Tell students to draw a line down a piece of paper, creating two equal columns. Head one column "Stress Inducers" and the other column "Stress Busters." Have students read through the two case studies on this spread again. As they do so, they should write down everything that creates stress for these two teens and everything they do to fight it. Analyze the lists with students, dividing the entries into broad categories.

Stress inducers may include over-scheduling, high academic expectations, part-time work, and financial pressures.

Stress busters may include physical activity, working toward an identified goal, a positive support system, and enjoying a hobby.

Ask, "Are there other stress-busting strategies that neither of these teens mentions? What are some of these strategies?" *(eating right, avoiding drugs and alcohol, talking out their feelings, eliminating some activities, and so on.)*

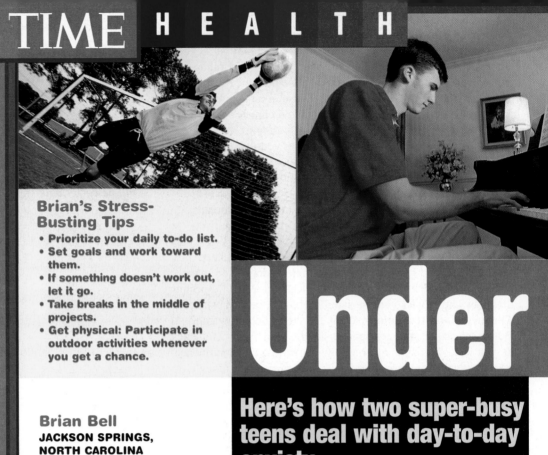

TIME HEALTH

Brian's Stress-Busting Tips
- **Prioritize your daily to-do list.**
- **Set goals and work toward them.**
- **If something doesn't work out, let it go.**
- **Take breaks in the middle of projects.**
- **Get physical: Participate in outdoor activities whenever you get a chance.**

Under

Here's how two super-busy teens deal with day-to-day anxiety.

Brian Bell
JACKSON SPRINGS, NORTH CAROLINA

Teen Brian Bell insists that other people have schedules that are just as hectic as his is. However, one look at his jam-packed plans makes that pretty hard to believe. Over the past three years, Brian has participated in 10 projects to help the elderly in his community and to raise funds for starving kids in third-world countries. "Knowing that what I'm doing will actually make a difference to someone is what keeps me motivated," he says.

Brian's motivation knows no limits. He played varsity soccer and also took part in his church's basketball league. All the activity proves to be a healthy distraction for him. "Getting out in the fresh air takes my mind off whatever I'm worried about," he says.

Physical activity isn't the only remedy for a stressed-out student: Playing the piano also helps. Brian says, "Playing it in a room where the lights are dim really relaxes me."

Brian designs Web sites and spends three or four nights a week working part-time at a computer store. On his evenings off, after he's finished his homework, Brian usually tinkers with his own Web site. "I certainly don't get to watch much television," he says, laughing.

These days, Brian does his best to hit the sack early. "There was a time when I was staying up until 3:00 A.M. every night, and I was so tired and worn out," he says. "My mom made a list of things for me to get done by a certain time. She showed me how to work toward a goal, which really helped. These days, I'm trying to focus on the long-term and not sweat the little stuff."

50 CHAPTER 2: HEALTH SKILLS: THE FOUNDATION

Health Literacy

Alcohol and Other Drugs Explain to students that sometimes alcohol or other drugs may seem like a good way to ease stress. Ask students why these are definitely *unhealthy* responses. What additional short- and long-term problems will alcohol or drug use create? List their answers on the board. Do these seem like problems that will reduce or increase an individual's overall stress load? Conclude with a strong message against substance use.

Pressure

Adriana's Tips to Axe Anxiety
- Escape with a good horror novel.
- Listen to relaxing music.
- Find a new hobby that makes you happy.
- Unwind by watching cartoons on television.
- Be sure to get enough sleep.

Adriana Cantu
MISSION, TEXAS

Ask Adriana Cantu to name her top priority in life and she'll answer, "I have to get an academic scholarship if I want to go to college." Adriana is faced with having to finance her own education. "My dad just retired, and that money isn't going to stretch for too long," she says. She adds that her parents' love and support is worth more to her than any amount of money.

"I get really frustrated when my grades start to sink," she says. "I just want to quit, but my mom sits with me while I do my homework."

To escape the tension, Adriana performs with a local theater company. "It takes you away from real life because you have to concentrate hard in order to become another person," says Adriana.

What happens when Adriana heads home after rehearsal? "I do my homework, then go to sleep by 10:30," she says. Adriana knows that lack of sleep can pose a problem, especially during football season. She plays flute in the school marching band, which means she gets up at 5:00 A.M. to make 6:45 practice.

Fortunately, Adriana has learned ways to maintain her energy. "Sometimes I read for a while, then take a nap," says Adriana, who enjoys books so much that she reads to children at her town's public library. She adds, "Other days I'll go for a run in the park, listen to Celtic music on my Walkman, or go shopping at the mall with friends." Adriana keeps it all together with one simple quote: "Believe and you can succeed."

TIME TO THINK...

About Managing Stress
How do you relieve stress in your life? Choose one or two of your own stress-busting tips and create an antianxiety ad campaign around them. Think of a catchy slogan that can help teens remember to stay calm when things get hectic. Create a visual aid, such as a poster, that features your slogan, and present your ad campaign to the class.

③ Apply

Time to Think

Have students work in groups to create their antianxiety ad campaigns. If possible, allow time for groups to present their campaigns to the class.

One of the best ways to manage stress is to identify its causes. Then individuals can learn strategies to avoid or minimize these causes. Ask students to keep a stress management journal for the next few days. Instruct them to record any stressful situations. (Where were they? Who were they with? What were they doing?) Is it possible to avoid this person, setting, or situation in the future? How? If not, what techniques can they use to help relieve the stress caused by this situation?

Ask students, "How might Brian or Adriana revise their daily plans to create a less stressful schedule?" Emphasize that it's perfectly okay for students to cut back on nonessential activities when they feel overburdened.

VISUAL LEARNING

Ask students to analyze the photographs on this spread. Ask, "What stress-busting techniques are Brian and Adriana demonstrating in these photos? Do they appear to be working? Are there any situations in which a stress-busting technique may actually increase a teen's stress load?" (For instance, when youth sports become too competitive.)

Beyond the Classroom

Community Resources Explain to students that while a certain level of stress is normal, too much can lead to serious health problems. If they experience ongoing symptoms, such as sleeplessness, lack of appetite, or depression, it may be time to seek help. Divide the class into small work groups. Have each group compile a list of people and places in the community where students can get help with stress management. Include contact information for resources at school, public and private health clinics, religious groups, neighborhood organizations, and so on. Compile the information into a resource guide to share with the fellow classmates.

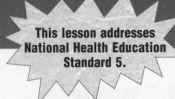
REFUSAL SKILLS

Objective

After completing the lesson, students will be able to examine the effects of peer pressure on decision making and demonstrate refusal skills for situations that involve risk behaviors.

Time: 45 minutes

Materials: None required.

Teacher Classroom Resources

📁 Building Health Skills Activities

• Transparency Master 7, "Refusal Skills"

• Reproducible Master 27, "Say No to Peer Pressure"

1. Model

• Have students examine the effects of peer pressure on decision making. Begin by asking students to brainstorm situations in which they would have difficulty refusing. Discuss common factors that make a refusal difficult.

• Have three students role-play the script of Laurel's refusal.

• Display Transparency Master 7, and have students identify the skills Laurel used. Ask: "How effective were her refusals?" "Are there ways she could improve her refusals?" "Was the situation realistic?"

BUILDING HEALTH SKILLS — **REFUSAL SKILLS**

SAY NO TO PEER PRESSURE

Model

Laurel knows that she must honor her own sense of right and wrong instead of just going along with her peers. She realizes that refusing to do things that don't feel right can protect her health. Read how Laurel used refusal skills to stand up for her own beliefs.

Sara and Bethany think it's fun to tease other students at school. They want Laurel to distract James so they can play a practical joke on him. Laurel knows that James would be upset by the joke.

SARA: Here's the plan. Laurel, you get James's attention and we'll take his math homework out of his backpack.

LAUREL: No, Sara. James would be upset when he gets to class and can't find his assignment. *(Say no in a firm voice; tell why not.)*

BETHANY: That's the point. Come on, it'll be funny, and James will get over it.

LAUREL: I'd rather do something else that won't get us in trouble. Why don't we go watch the guys try out for the basketball team? *(Offer another idea.)*

BETHANY: No, that's not the same.

LAUREL: I agree, it's not the same. It's better! Are you guys coming with me?

Teaching Tips

Using Role-Plays When introducing role-play to a class, it is helpful to begin with prescripted role-plays, move to partially scripted, and then finally use unscripted. Ask for volunteers, or select students who enjoy being the center of attention. Allow students to have you or other students check their role-plays for accuracy before they are presented in class.

Practicing Skills "Practice makes perfect" is true for every skill. We don't expect a student to shoot a perfect jump shot or solve an algebraic equation without errors on the first attempt. Students should understand that each skill becomes easier and more natural with practice—and the more practice, the better.

Standards		Technology
National	**State/Local**	
National Health Education Standard **2.1, 2.3, 2.5, 4.1, 4.2, 4.3, 4.4, 7.4, 7.5**		Transparency 9 TeacherWorks™
National Health Education Standard **1.6, 1.7, 2.1, 2.4, 2.6**		Transparency 10 TeacherWorks™
National Health Education Standard **2.1, 2.2, 2.3, 2.6**		Transparency 11 TeacherWorks™
National Health Education Standard **2.2, 2.4, 2.6, 7.4, 7.5**		Transparency 12 TeacherWorks™ MindJogger Videoquiz **Exam**View® Pro Testmaker
National Health Education Standard **2.1, 2.2, 2.4**		Building Health Skills Transparency Master 1

TeacherWorks™

Glencoe's new and exclusive TeacherWorks™ is an all-in-one planner and resource center. Access the complete Teacher Wraparound Edition electronically. Find all your classroom resources with just a few easy clicks, and print them right from your computer. Connect directly to Glencoe's customized Health Web site. Access the National Health Education Standards correlations, or insert your own state standards and match them directly to the electronic Teacher Wraparound Edition.

Language Diversity

- English Audio Summaries
- Spanish Audio Summaries
- English Summaries, Quizzes, and Activities
- Spanish Summaries, Quizzes, and Activities
- Spanish Parent Letters and Activities

KEY TO ABILITY LEVELS

Teaching Strategies that appear throughout the chapters have been identified by one of four codes to give you an idea of their suitability for students of varying learning styles and abilities.

L1 Level 1 strategies should be within the ability range of all students. Often full class participation is required.

L2 Level 2 strategies are for average to above-average students or for small groups. Some teacher direction is necessary.

L3 Level 3 strategies are designed for students able and willing to work independently. Minimal teacher direction is necessary.

INCL Strategies are appropriate for students with particular special needs in a general classroom setting.

Being a Health Consumer

Chapter at a Glance

Lesson 1 highlights the influences of teen buying decisions, the benefits of being an informed consumer, and the importance of health advocacy.

Lesson 2 describes various health care providers and explains how to shop and pay for health services.

Lesson 3 outlines how to deal with consumer problems including fraud.

Lesson 4 focuses on the roles that government and nongovernmental health organizations take in maintaining public health.

Health Skills
- Know Your Rights (*Advocacy*), p. 61
- Health Care in the Community (*Accessing Information*), p. 66
- Public Health (*Advocacy*), p. 74
- Finding Reliable Sources (*Accessing Information*), pp. 78–79

56

HANDS-ON ACTIVITY

Teen Buying Power Teens, especially between the ages of 11 and 15, are a major target for manufacturers and advertisers. To help students understand this idea, bring in a stack of teen magazines. Let students comb through them, cutting out all the ads they think are directed at them. Then, to emphasize their buying power, ask them to make a list of purchases they have made in the last month. Next to each item on their list, have them mark an "M" for items they purchased with their own money, a "D" for items that they made the sole decision to buy, and an "I" for any that they influenced someone else to buy for them. How many items are not marked? This illustrates how much buying power they are already exhibiting as consumers.

Being a Health Consumer

Chapter Introduction

Use the options below to motivate students and preview chapter content.

HEALTH *Online*

Are you a wise consumer? Find out by taking the Chapter 3 Health Inventory at health.glencoe.com.

HEALTH *Online*

Encourage students to take Health Inventory 3 at **health.glencoe.com**. Then brush up on health education by reading Professional Articles for health teachers. These articles can help keep you informed of national and state trends.

FOLDABLES™
Study Organizer

Before You Read

Make this Foldable to record what you learn in Lesson 1 about being a wise health consumer. Begin with two sheets of notebook paper.

Step 1

Fold one sheet in half from top to bottom. Cut about 1″ along the fold at both ends, stopping at the margin lines.

Step 2

Fold the second sheet in half from top to bottom. Cut or shave off the fold *between* the margin lines.

Step 3

Insert the first sheet through the second sheet and align folds.

Step 4

Fold the bound pages in half to make a booklet, and label the cover as shown. Then label each page as instructed by your teacher.

> Chapter 3,
> Lesson 1:
> Healthy Consumer
> Habits

As You Read

Define terms and take notes on being a health consumer on the appropriate page of your Foldable.

GLENCOE TECHNOLOGY

MindJogger Videoquiz

Use MindJogger to preview or review Chapter 3 content.

TIME HEALTH

Turn It Off!
pages 76–77

FOLDABLES™
Study Organizer

Dinah Zike Study Fold

Journal Writing Students will use this Foldable journal to write about healthy consumer habits. Have students label the six inside pages of their journal with the following titles: "What Influences My Buying Decisions?", "Understanding Advertising Appeals," "Identifying Hidden Advertising," "Comparing Choices," "Health Advocacy," and "New Consumer Options." As students read and study the information in Lesson 1, direct them to use their Foldable journal to take notes, define terms, and record personal experiences. Encourage students to list examples of ways in which they might use what they have learned about healthy consumer habits.

Lesson 1

Healthy Consumer Habits

① Focus

Lesson Objectives

Students will be able to
- discuss how to become an informed health consumer.
- describe the guidelines for becoming an effective health advocate.
- identify the options available to today's consumers.

Health Skills
- Advocacy, p. 61

Motivators

Quick Write

Discuss the influences that students identified. Encourage students to evaluate these influences.

Bellringer Activity

Ask each student to make a list of five products he or she buys or uses at least once a week. Then ask: What would you do if you bought one of the products and it didn't work or was defective?

VOCABULARY

Write the vocabulary terms on the board. Ask students to identify each term by listening carefully to these clues. Which terms are made up of three syllables? (*consumer, media, warranty*) Four syllables? (*advertising*) Compound term with five syllables? (*health advocacy*)

Lesson 1

Healthy Consumer Habits

Quick Write

Identify three health products you use. Explain what or who influenced you in choosing these products.

LEARN ABOUT...

- being an informed health consumer.
- effective health advocacy.
- new buying options for health consumers.

VOCABULARY

- consumer
- media
- advertising
- comparison shopping
- warranty
- health advocacy
- online shopping

You, the Health Consumer

Teen consumers in the United States spend millions of dollars every year. A **consumer** is *anyone who purchases products or services.* Many of the products and services that teens purchase can affect their health. Toothpaste, sunscreen, eyeglasses, sporting goods, food, and sports drinks are examples of health-related products. You purchase health-related services when you get your teeth cleaned or have a health screening.

Becoming an Informed Consumer

Informed consumers base their choices on reliable information. When shopping for health products they compare quality, effectiveness, and safety as well as cost. Informed consumers also know how to resolve problems with products or services that they buy.

Informed consumers compare products to find the one that best fits their needs.

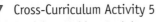

Lesson 1 Resources

Teacher Classroom Resources

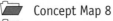

- Parent Letter & Activities 3
- Concept Map 8
- Cross-Curriculum Activity 5
- Decision-Making Activity 5
- Enrichment Activity 8
- Health Lab 3
- Lesson Plan 1

- Lesson 1 Quiz
- Reading Tutor Activity 8
- Reteaching Activity 8
- Transparency 9

Student Activities Workbook

- Chapter 3 Study Guide
- Applying Health Skills 8

FIGURE 3.1

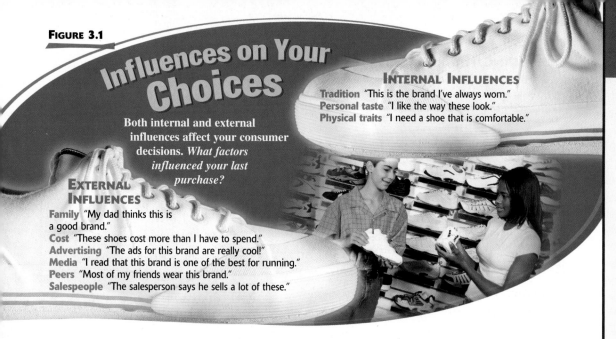

Influences on Your Choices

Both internal and external influences affect your consumer decisions. *What factors influenced your last purchase?*

INTERNAL INFLUENCES
Tradition "This is the brand I've always worn."
Personal taste "I like the way these look."
Physical traits "I need a shoe that is comfortable."

EXTERNAL INFLUENCES
Family "My dad thinks this is a good brand."
Cost "These shoes cost more than I have to spend."
Advertising "The ads for this brand are really cool!"
Media "I read that this brand is one of the best for running."
Peers "Most of my friends wear this brand."
Salespeople "The salesperson says he sells a lot of these."

What Influences Your Buying Decisions?

Many factors influence your buying decisions. Some are internal—they originate with you. Your personal taste is an example of an internal factor that influences your buying. External factors (those from outside sources) can also influence you. You may be influenced by what you see on TV, in newspapers and magazines, or on the Internet or billboards. Together, these *various methods for communicating information* are known as the media. Identifying the factors that influence you can help you understand why you buy a particular product or service. **Figure 3.1** illustrates the influences on one teen's purchasing decision.

Understanding Advertising Appeals

Many companies use advertising to promote health products and services. **Advertising** involves *sending out messages designed to interest consumers in buying a product or service.* Media advertising includes magazine and other print ads, TV and radio broadcast commercials, infomercials, and Internet advertising. Be aware that advertisers work closely with TV programmers and movie marketers to influence your buying decisions.

Ads let you know what products or services are available. Many ads provide good basic information. However, remember that the first goal of advertising is to get your attention and the second is to get you to buy. To reach these goals, advertisers use a variety of techniques to appeal to potential buyers. **Figure 3.2** on the next page explains some advertising techniques.

MEDIA WATCH

UNBIASED INFORMATION

Many people turn to Consumers Union for reliable information when planning a purchase. Consumers Union tests products and researches services. It reports its findings in various ways, such as in *Consumer Reports* magazine and *Consumer Reports* Online.

LESSON 1: HEALTHY CONSUMER HABITS **59**

Lesson 1

② Teach

Making Lists

Have students list as many health services as they can think of. Lists could include medical specialists, health club memberships, exercise classes, and so on. Ask students how a wise consumer would evaluate the services. (*by researching the service and training of the professional, the cost, advantages and disadvantages of the service, rules and regulations, safety precautions, and so on*) **L1**

VISUAL LEARNING

FIGURE 3.1 Ask students to describe the picture and read the two headings. Have volunteers explain how influences are related and how they are different. Have students read and discuss both lists of influences, offering other examples for each.

Read aloud the caption for Figure 3.1, and let students share their responses to the question. Ask: How do you think understanding these influences might change the choice you made? **INCL** *English Language Learners, Special Learning Needs, Behavior Problems, Different Learning Styles (Visual)*

Critical Thinking

Tell students that part of being a good consumer is the ability to evaluate health information. Have students develop evaluative criteria for health information and share their lists with the class.

MORE ABOUT...

Advertising and Health Popular media and advertising can affect our buying behavior and health decisions. For example, advertisers deliver an onslaught of messages urging us to eat convenience and fast foods that are high in calories and fat. Much of this advertising is directed at children and teens. Balancing ads for soft drinks and empty-calorie foods with pro-nutrition messages could have impact on health. One example of the positive effect of advertising is the recent campaign to encourage milk consumption. Advertising featuring celebrity endorsements is credited with a 30 percent increase in milk consumption.

FIGURE 3.2

DECODING HIDDEN MESSAGES IN ADVERTISING

Advertisements often include a hidden message designed to appeal to consumers' emotions. *How might these media messages influence a consumer's decision to purchase a health product?*

Technique	Example	Hidden Message
Bandwagon	Group of people using product or service.	Everyone is using it--don't be left behind.
Rich and famous	Expensive car driven by attractive person.	It will make you feel rich and famous.
Free rewards	Redeemable coupons for merchandise.	It offers great value because you get something for free.
Great outdoors	Scenes of nature.	It is associated with nature so it must be healthy.
Good times	People smiling and laughing.	It will add more fun to your life.
Testimonial	Celebrity	It will make you be like this person.

Identifying Hidden Advertising

Advertising is sometimes disguised as informative articles. A prominently displayed product logo worn by a sports figure during a media interview also sends consumers an advertising message. Increasingly, advertisers are getting their products into movies and TV programs in a process called product placement. Aware consumers ask: What is the message here? Who is creating it? What might advertisers want consumers to believe or do?

Comparing Choices

Comparison shopping is *a method of judging the benefits of different products or services by comparing several factors, such as quality, features, and cost.* The factors that are most important to you in a particular product will determine your choice.

When buying health-related products and services, safety should always be a priority. If you were buying sunglasses, for example, you might begin by comparing safety features. Find out if the lenses are unbreakable and protect from UV rays. Then you might compare other features, such as weight, durability,

60 CHAPTER 3: BEING A HEALTH CONSUMER

appearance, and cost. For some types of products you can compare warranties. A **warranty** is *a written promise to handle repairs if the product fails to work properly.*

Health Advocacy

Health advocacy involves *taking action to influence others to address a health-related concern or to support a health-related belief.* A major goal of health advocacy is to help friends, family, and members of the community to be healthy. Health advocates also help others become informed and aware consumers.

When you practice the skill of advocacy, you make a difference by taking action. Follow these guidelines to be an effective health advocate:

- **Identify your values.** Why are you proposing this action?
- **Understand the purpose of your message.** What result do you want to achieve?
- **Make your message appropriate to your audience.** What is important to the audience? What will appeal to them? What will make a difference to them?
- **Give convincing reasons why your message will benefit health.** How will your advice improve or protect the health of others?
- **Provide reliable supporting data to back up your proposal.** What facts and figures support your position?

Speaking for Students Against Destructive Decisions, this teen advocates for the health of others. *How can you help others make healthy decisions?*

Lesson 1

Using Technology

The photo on this page features Kyra White from S.A.D.D. You can find an interview with her on *Teen Health* Video/DVD 2, Segment 1. **L1 INCL** *English Language Learners, Special Learning Needs, Behavior Problems, Different Learning Styles (Visual)*

Discussing

Ask students to rate the stores where they shop regularly on the basis of specific product prices, quality of merchandise, convenience, and return policy. Encourage students to add other criteria to the comparison list, such as access for customers with disabilities, store hours, and customer service. **L1**

HEALTH SKILLS ACTIVITY

ADVOCACY

With students, read and discuss the list of consumer rights. Ask:

- Why is this right important?
- When and how can you exercise this right?

Then have students meet in cooperative learning groups to complete the With a Group assignment. Select a different right for each group. Suggest that some groups might prefer to present skits that demonstrate why their selected right is important and how it can be exercised.

Discussing

Encourage students to share their opinions about shopping online, from catalogs, and in stores. Ask: What are the advantages and disadvantages of each kind of shopping? Which do you prefer? Why? **L1**

HEALTH SKILLS ACTIVITY

ADVOCACY

Know Your Rights

Part of being a health advocate is knowing your consumer rights. When you know your rights, you can act on them to protect the health and safety of others. The list below summarizes your consumer rights.

- **THE RIGHT TO SAFETY.** You have the right to purchase products and services that will not harm you or other people.
- **THE RIGHT TO CHOOSE.** You have the right to select from many products at competitive prices.
- **THE RIGHT TO BE INFORMED.** You have the right to truthful information about products and services.

- **THE RIGHT TO BE HEARD.** You have the right to join in the making of the laws that govern buying and selling.
- **THE RIGHT TO HAVE PROBLEMS CORRECTED.** You have the right to seek compensation when you have been treated unfairly.

WITH A GROUP
Select one of the rights listed here. Discuss the meaning of the right and how you would exercise it. Then create a situation that demonstrates the need for, and use of, that right. Choose a spokesperson from your group to explain the situation to the rest of the class.

LESSON 1: HEALTHY CONSUMER HABITS **61**

INCLUSION STRATEGIES

Gifted Although no formal definition exists, gifted students can be described as having above-average ability, task commitment, and creativity. They usually finish work more quickly than other students and are capable of divergent thinking. Tips for instructing gifted students include the following:
- Make arrangements for students to work on independent projects.

- Encourage creative avenues of expression.
- Make resources (print, visual, and multimedia) available for additional investigation.
- Emphasize concepts, theories, ideas, relationships, and abstract thinking.

Critical Thinking

Ask students why it is important for teens to have the permission of an adult family member when they shop online. List their reasons on the board. Then ask students to rank these reasons, from most important to least important. **L1**

③ Assess

Evaluating

📁 Assign the Lesson 1 Review; then assign the Lesson 1 Quiz in the TCR.

Reteaching

- 📁 Assign Concept Map 8 or Reteaching Activity 8 in the TCR.
- Have students find the definitions of each of the vocabulary terms in the lesson. Then have them use each of the terms in an original sentence that states a main point of the lesson.

Enrichment

- 📁 Assign Enrichment Activity 8 in the TCR.
- Tell students to imagine that they are applying for a job as a salesperson in a drugstore. Have them state the skills and knowledge it would be useful to have, both for themselves and for their customers.

④ Close

Ask students to explain how programmers develop media to influence buying decisions.

New Consumer Options

Consumers have more shopping options than ever before. Catalog, or mail-order, shopping is a convenient way to shop, but it does involve some guesswork. You cannot touch, examine, or try the product before you buy. Moreover, the catalog may provide only limited information about the product.

Teens who shop online usually need their parents' permission since many online stores allow only credit card purchases.

Online shopping involves *using the Internet to buy products and services.* It has similar advantages and disadvantages to those of catalog shopping. Both mail-order and online shoppers often pay a lower price than they would pay in a store. However, that gain may be lost if shipping charges are added to the price. Additional shipping charges may be incurred if a product needs to be returned.

Lesson 1 Review

Using complete sentences, answer the following questions on a sheet of paper.

Reviewing Terms and Facts

1. **Vocabulary** Define the word *consumer.*
2. **List** Give two examples of internal influences on consumer choices and two examples of external influences.
3. **Recall** What is the purpose of comparison shopping?
4. **Explain** What is health advocacy?

Thinking Critically

5. **Apply** What criteria would you develop to select or reject a health product or service such as sunscreen or a dental exam?

6. **Analyze** Think about the last health care product you bought. Identify a variety of influences on that purchase. Analyze how each affected your decision.

Applying Health Skills

7. **Advocacy** Encourage others to become involved in health-promotion efforts at many different levels. Think of a health-related issue. Create a flyer that lists ways to advocate for that issue. For example, if you select tobacco-use prevention, your flyer might say that choosing not to smoke, supporting the school as a tobacco-free environment, and supporting local efforts to reduce smoking in the community are some ways to advocate for that issue.

Lesson 1 Review

1. Anyone who purchases products and services.
2. Two of each: Internal—tradition, personal taste, physical traits. External—family, cost, advertising, media, peers, salespeople.
3. To judge the benefits of different products or services by comparing several factors.
4. Taking action to influence others to address a health-related concern or to support a health-related belief.
5. Responses should include health and safety criteria.
6. Responses will vary.

Lesson 2

Choosing Health Services

The Role of Health Care

David is having a physical examination as required by his school. After checking David's immunization record, Dr. Lee gives him a booster shot for tetanus. When David tells her that he is having pain in his right knee, Dr. Lee carefully examines the knee. Then she writes out an order for tests on David's knee at the hospital X-ray department.

Dr. Lee, the hospital, and the X-ray technician are all part of the health care system. A **health care system** includes *all the medical care available to a nation's people, the way they receive the care, and the way the care is paid for.* The original role of the health care system in the United States was to treat people who were sick or injured. Today the role has expanded to include **preventive care**, which involves *keeping disease or injury from happening or getting worse.*

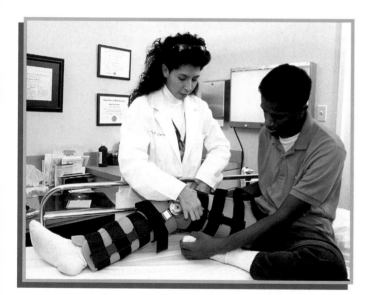

Quick Write

Make a list of the people who provide you and your family with health care. Beside each name, write what that person does.

LEARN ABOUT...

- **different kinds of health care providers.**
- **why teens need regular health screenings.**
- **how people pay for health care.**
- **trends in health care.**

VOCABULARY

- health care system
- preventive care
- primary care physician
- specialist
- health insurance
- health maintenance organization (HMO)
- preferred provider organization (PPO)
- point of service plan (POS)

A health care professional's responsibilites include treating many different types of injuries.

LESSON 2: CHOOSING HEALTH SERVICES **63**

Choosing Health Services

① Focus

Lesson Objectives

Students will be able to

- list people who provide health care services.
- discuss why teens need regular health screenings.
- discuss how people pay for health care.
- describe the new trends in health care.

Health Skills

- Accessing Information, p. 66

Motivators

Quick Write

Ask volunteers to share their lists. On the board, write the health care professions most often needed. Then add other professions that students can identify.

Bellringer Activity

Ask students to write four words, phrases, or sentences that describe the ideal doctor or clinic.

VOCABULARY

Draw a horizontal line across the board. Ask students for the term that names a person who has a general practice in medicine. (*primary care physician*) Write it above the line. Then ask for the name of a medical care worker with a specific practice, and write it below the line. (*specialist*)

Lesson 2 Resources

Teacher Classroom Resources

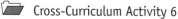 Concept Map 9

 Cross-Curriculum Activity 6

 Enrichment Activity 9

 Lesson Plan 2

 Lesson 2 Quiz

 Reading Tutor Activity 9

 Reteaching Activity 9

Transparency 10

Student Activities Workbook

 Chapter 3 Study Guide

 Applying Health Skills 9

63

② Teach

Analyzing

Ask students to analyze how health care workers can prepare themselves to address the special needs of adolescents. Begin by having students brainstorm a list of those special needs. Have students consider and then describe how geography, culture, and demographics might impact the needs of adolescents. Finish the discussion by asking how a health care facility would provide for such needs. **L1**

Discussing

Ask students to discuss why a person might choose to go to a family doctor with a specific problem rather than to a specialist. (*familiarity, physician's knowledge of family history, referral to a specialist, and so on*) Why might a person choose instead to go to a specialist? (*greater expertise about a specific condition, more sophisticated equipment, and so on*) **L1**

Discussing

Describe the goals of health care workers as: 1) to maintain good health, 2) to treat problems, 3) to prevent health problems. Have students brainstorm their ideas about the responsibilities each person should take in maintaining his or her own health care. Ask: What could you do to help workers in the health care system reach their goals? (*visit a dentist regularly, go to a doctor when symptoms first appear, visit a nutrition counselor.*) **L1**

The Health Care System

To be an informed consumer of health care services, you need to understand how the health care system works. Physicians, nurses, dentists, dental hygienists, optometrists, pharmacists, and laboratory technicians are just a few of the professionals who work in the health care system. Health care providers work in a variety of settings.

Who Provides Health Care?

Health care can be divided into general care and specialized care. **Primary care physicians** are *the medical doctors who provide physical checkups and general care.* School nurses, nurse practitioners, and physician's assistants are also part of primary care.

Patients who need a specific type of care are referred to specialists. **Specialists** are *doctors trained to handle particular kinds of patients or medical conditions.* Pediatricians (peed·ee·uh·TRISH·uhnz), for example, deal with infants and children, and dermatologists deal with problems and diseases of the skin. Have you had experience with a health specialist?

Nurse practitioners perform many routine medical examinations. *Explain the role of wellness exams in disease prevention.*

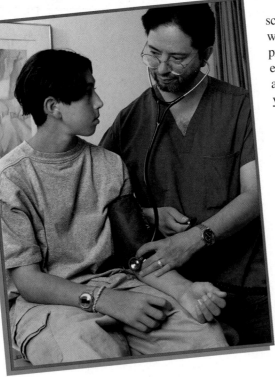

You and Your Health Care

It is recommended that teens get annual health screenings for preventive care. Sometimes called wellness exams, these screenings are designed to promote wellness and detect any health problems early. The recommended ages for these physicals are between 11 and 14 years, between 15 and 17 years, and between 18 and 21 years.

A wellness exam for teens might include:

- testing hearing and vision.
- checking for sports injuries, especially in the knee.
- checking for scoliosis, which is a disorder of the spine.
- screening for high blood pressure.
- screening for eating disorders and obesity.

In addition to the annual wellness exam, teens need to get other regular health screenings and to cooperate with the health care provider's recommendations for treatment. Types of health care teens might receive are listed in **Figure 3.3**.

64 CHAPTER 3: BEING A HEALTH CONSUMER

MORE ABOUT...

Scoliosis Scoliosis is a sideways curving of the spine. It is usually noticed between the ages of 10 and 14. The cause of 80 percent of cases is unknown. A scoliosis screening involves checking whether the patient's shoulders look level, the head is centered, and opposite sides of the body look level. While the patient bends over, the physician checks whether one side of the rib cage is higher than the other. X rays are sometimes performed. Many children have mild curves and need only periodic checkups to make sure the curve is not worsening. Of every 1,000 children screened, 6 require treatment. Braces are used to treat about 90 percent of children who require treatment, and the rest may require surgery.

FIGURE 3.3

Health Care for Teens

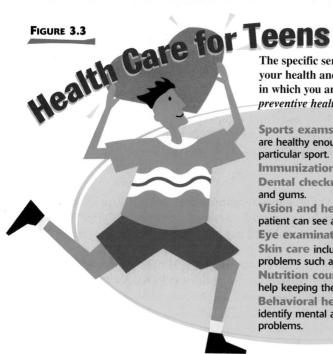

The specific services that you receive will depend on your health and, possibly, on the health care plan in which you are enrolled. *Explain the role of these preventive health measures in disease prevention.*

Sports exams ensure that teens are healthy enough to participate in a particular sport.

Immunizations protect against specific diseases.

Dental checkups determine the health of the teeth and gums.

Vision and hearing testing determine how well the patient can see and hear.

Eye examinations check for eye diseases and disorders.

Skin care includes screening and treatment for problems such as acne and skin cancer.

Nutrition counseling assists those who need help keeping their weight within a healthy range.

Behavioral health assessment helps identify mental and emotional problems.

Where Do You Go for Health Care?

Health care facilities provide inpatient care and outpatient care. Inpatient care is for patients who have a serious illnesses or injuries and who need to stay at the facility. A person recovering from major surgery, or one who needs constant monitoring, would receive inpatient care. Outpatient care is for less serious conditions or procedures. Examples are treating sprains, putting stitches on wounds, and extracting teeth. Patients get the care they need and then return home. Many routine tests are also provided on an outpatient basis.

Health services are available in most communities in a variety of forms. Facilities in your community may include the following:

- **Clinics.** Primary care physicians and specialists may provide outpatient care in a community clinic. Local clinics often receive government funding.
- **Private practice.** Primary care physicians and specialists who work in private practice work for themselves.
- **Group practice.** Often two or more physicians join together to offer health care in a group practice. Doctors in group practice share office space, equipment, and support staff.
- **Hospitals.** Most hospitals offer both inpatient and outpatient care. Some doctors work only in a hospital. Others have offices elsewhere and use the hospital facilities when their patients need them.

CONNECT TO

Science

MAGNETIC RESONANCE IMAGING
Modern technology plays an important role in medicine. Thanks to magnetic resonance imaging (MRI), doctors can now examine images of a patient's soft tissue. The images make it possible for doctors to detect tumors and other abnormalities. Finding such abnormalities early often makes it possible to treat them before they develop into serious problems.

Lesson 2

HEALTH SKILLS PRACTICE

Communication Read aloud the following to students: Visits with a doctor are usually brief, so it's necessary to focus only on the facts. When describing an illness, be specific regarding your symptoms and how long you've experienced them. Provide any information about medicines you are already taking. For physical exams, you may be asked to recall any illnesses, injuries, or changes you've noticed since your last exam. If you have questions about your health, write them down before your appointment so you're ready. Just list your top three health questions in your notebook to bring with you.

VISUAL LEARNING

FIGURE 3.3 Guide students in reading and discussing the explanation for each kind of health care service. Ask:

- Who needs this kind of exam or assessment?
- How often is an individual likely to need one?
- What problems might develop for a teen who skips this kind of service?
- Who probably provides this medical service? **INCL** *English Language Learners, Special Learning Needs, Behavior Problems, Different Learning Styles* (*Visual*)

Beyond the Classroom

Community One factor of concern for health insurance consumers is the choice of physicians. Students may benefit from examining lists of HMO and PPO providers in the community. Have students assess how much membership in managed care would restrict their choices. Provide PPO, POS, or HMO membership lists for students to examine. You may be able to use a list provided by your district plan. Let students compare the lists of providers for HMOs, POSs, and PPOs with the Yellow Pages list of physicians in the area. How many physicians are included on each list? Are students' family physicians on the lists? How many are excluded? Have students discuss their observations and whether they would feel restricted by managed care in your community.

Investigating

Ask a small group of volunteers to learn more about the three forms of private insurance: HMOs, PPOs, and POSs. Students can survey or obtain insurance plans from various companies in their area. Have them create a chart or table summarizing the similarities and differences.

HEALTH SKILLS ACTIVITY

ACCESSING INFORMATION

Guide students in reading and discussing the information about community health care services. Ask whether each listed service is available locally. If so, where? Then have students extend the list, naming other local community health care services.

Have students work in small groups to collect information about local health care resources. Have groups share and compare their lists, checking for accuracy and completeness. Then have the entire class (or a group of volunteers) work together to design and make a brochure.

Note: This skill is introduced in Chapter 2, on pages 45–46.

Reading Check

Brainstorm. Think about what *health care* means to you. List as many details as you can.

How People Pay for Health Care

Many people have some form of **health insurance**, which is *a plan in which private companies or government programs pay for part of a person's medical costs.*

With private insurance, a person pays a monthly fee to the insurance company. In return, the company pays part or most of that person's medical costs. Many people have private insurance through their employers. Common types of private insurance plans include:

- **Health Maintenance Organizations (HMOs).** An **HMO** is *an organization that provides health care for a fixed price.* People who belong to an HMO pay a monthly fee regardless of how much health care they need. Usually they must see only doctors who have signed a contract with the HMO.
- **Preferred Provider Organizations (PPOs).** A **PPO** is *a type of insurance in which medical providers agree to charge less for members of the plan.* Members who choose doctors outside the plan pay more.
- **Point of Service (POS) plans.** A **POS** is *a health plan that allows members to choose providers inside or outside the plan.* Choosing an outside provider often results in greater out-of-pocket costs to members.

HEALTH SKILLS ACTIVITY

ACCESSING INFORMATION

Health Care in the Community

Most communities have a variety of health care services. Examples include:

- home nursing care for patients who need medical help in their own home.
- relief support for people who are caring for an ill or injured family member.
- Alateen and Al-Anon groups for family members who live with alcoholics.
- community health screenings.
- flu shots for the elderly and other at-risk individuals.
- recreational sports and activity programs, providing supervised physical activity sessions.

WITH A GROUP
Make a list of health care resources offered at your school and in your community. You can obtain the information from parents and from local media. Then create a brochure that includes the name and number of each resource you found.

Reading Check

Concept Map This activity provides a format for students to organize new information about a topic in a meaningful way. A concept map is a visual representation of the definition of a concept or word. Begin by writing the term *Health Care* in the center of the board. Then ask students to provide details to fill in the corresponding blanks as shown here.

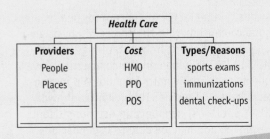

Health Care		
Providers	**Cost**	**Types/Reasons**
People	HMO	sports exams
Places	PPO	immunizations
_____	POS	dental check-ups

Trends in Health Care

The health care community is constantly looking for ways to improve the quality of health care or to reduce its cost. Here are some trends that reflect those goals.

- **Birthing centers** are homelike settings that involve the entire family in the delivery of the baby. Birthing centers are usually less expensive than hospitals.
- **Drug treatment centers** specialize in treating people with drug and alcohol problems.
- **Continuing care and assisted living facilities** provide care for people who need help with daily tasks but who do not require skilled medical care. Many older people need this kind of care.
- **Hospices** provide care for people who are terminally ill. Hospice workers are experts at managing pain and providing emotional support for the entire family.
- **Telemedicine** is the practice of medicine over distance through the use of telecommunications equipment. A specialist located hundreds of miles away can be brought electronically into an examination room via a live interactive system.

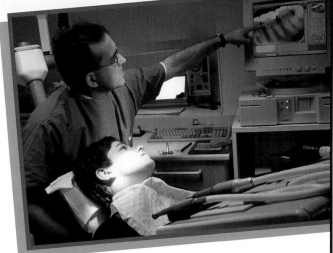

Computerized technology makes it possible for this teen to see images of the inside of his mouth as the dentist explains what he finds. *Explain the role of technology in influencing individual and community health.*

Lesson 2 Review

Using complete sentences, answer the following questions on a sheet of paper.

Reviewing Terms and Facts

1. **Vocabulary** Define the term *preventive care* and use it in an original sentence.
2. **Compare** What is the difference between a *primary care physician* and a *specialist*?
3. **Contrast** What are the differences in the ways HMOs, PPOs, and POS plans pay for health care?

Thinking Critically

4. **Hypothesize** Why do you think there is more emphasis on preventive care now than there was in the past?

5. **Summarize** Name four things a typical teen could expect his or her doctor to check for during a preventive medical checkup.

Applying Health Skills

6. **Advocacy** You've learned about the importance of preventive health measures. Prepare an announcement in which you explain why teens need to get regular health screenings. Be sure to mention wellness exams, dental checkups, immunizations, and treatment. If possible, arrange for your announcement to be delivered at school.

LESSON 2: CHOOSING HEALTH SERVICES **67**

Managing Consumer Problems

① Focus

Lesson Objectives

Students will be able to

- describe ways to protect themselves from health fraud.
- discuss how to resolve a consumer complaint about a defective product.
- identify consumer groups that protect the public against fraud.
- discuss problems people experience with health services.

Motivators

Quick Write

Allow students to form small groups to discuss how to resolve the problem. Ask representatives from each group to describe their problem-solving procedure.

Bellringer Activity

Ask students to write the names or descriptions of two products they bought that did not do what the advertisements promised. Discuss students' responses.

VOCABULARY

Ask students to write a short paragraph that incorporates each of the vocabulary terms. Then have students work in pairs to read one another's paragraphs, providing peer evaluations and checking for correct usage and meaning.

Managing Consumer Problems

Quick Write

Suppose you bought a new skateboard and a wheel fell off a week after you bought it. Explain how you would deal with the problem.

LEARN ABOUT...

- protecting yourself from health fraud.
- steps to take if you buy a defective product.
- consumer groups that protect the public from fraud.

VOCABULARY

- fraud
- health fraud

Let the Buyer Beware

You may have heard the saying "Let the buyer beware." It is used to warn people to watch out for products and services that don't do what sellers claim they will do. Most products *do* work, and most sellers *are* honest. Some individuals and businesses, however, sell faulty or useless products and services.

Health Fraud

Fraud is *deliberate deceit or trickery*. One of the worst types of fraud is **health fraud**, involving *the sale of worthless products or services claimed to prevent diseases or cure other health problems*. **Figure 3.4** illustrates some examples of health fraud.

To protect yourself from health fraud, watch for these signs:

- **Cure-all products.** There is no such thing as a product that cures everything.
- **Instant results.** The human body does not change appearance or shape overnight.
- **Suggestions that the usual treatment offered by doctors is wrong** and that this product or procedure is better.
- **Testimonials from "satisfied customers"** as proof of the effectiveness of the product or procedure.
- **Phony medical claims** such as "detoxify your body" and "boost nerve energy," which are impossible to measure.
- **Claims that the health care system is trying to keep this product or service off the market.**

Problems with Products

It is always a good idea to find out the seller's return policy before you buy. Follow these steps if you find you have bought a defective item.

1. Reread the instructions to make sure you followed them correctly and to ensure that the item is defective.
2. Decide whether you want a replacement or your money back.
3. Read the warranty that came with the product and follow the instructions in the warranty.

Lesson 3 Resources

Teacher Classroom Resources

- Concept Map 10
- Decision-Making Activity 6
- Enrichment Activity 10
- Lesson Plan 3
- Lesson 3 Quiz
- Reading Tutor Activity 10

- Reteaching Activity 10

- Transparency 11

Student Activities Workbook

- Chapter 3 Study Guide
- Applying Health Skills 10

FIGURE 3.4

EXAMPLES OF FRAUD

Type of Product	Typical Advertisement	Facts
Weight Management Products Pills Fad diets Exercise equipment	LOSE WEIGHT FAST! Get the slim body you want without changing what you eat. Just a few minutes a day with our Body Shaper will change fat into firm tissue. Why wait? Order now.	A good weight-management plan includes a sensible eating plan and regular physical activity. Losing weight takes time. False weight-loss programs and fad diets can damage your health.
Beauty Products Acne creams Hair enhancers Teeth whiteners	ERASE PIMPLES AND BLACKHEADS FOREVER. Don't hide behind makeup. With this breakthrough formula made from all-natural ingredients, you can have permanently clear skin in a few days. Send for a Free Sample. Enclose $10.00 shipping and handling.	Many products can help your skin temporarily. No product, however, can make your skin blemish-free permanently. Products that have not been approved by the FDA may actually harm your skin.
Miracle Cures Arthritis Cancer Depression	CONFUSED? DEPRESSED? IN PAIN? I can help! Benefit from the ancient healing techniques learned during 12 years of travel and study in remote areas of the Andes Mountains. Call today for a phone therapy session. Credit card required. Dr. Westfall, Healer.	Worthless products and phony cures often give seriously ill patients false hope. Using useless therapies may keep people from seeking the medical treatment they need.

"Let the Buyer Beware"

4. If you are to return the item to the store, take the item and your sales receipt back to the store. Ask a clerk to direct you to the returns department.

5. If you are to send the item to the manufacturer, repack the item in its original packaging and write a letter explaining the problem. Keep a copy of your letter.

6. If you are shipping the item to the manufacturer, get a shipping receipt to prove you sent it.

Reputable stores have policies that allow customers to return faulty products.

LESSON 3: MANAGING CONSUMER PROBLEMS **69**

MORE ABOUT...

Advertising Fraud The Better Business Bureau was started in the early 1900s in response to unrestrained commerce and free-wheeling advertising. The con artists of the day advertised products like "Complete Sewing Machines for 25 Cents." Then they mailed out 12 needles in packages. In 1910 a publisher and a lawyer drew up a model law concerning fraud and deception in advertising, which is now the law in most states. Meanwhile the Advertising Men's League of New York formed a committee to fight dishonesty in advertising. Within a year most big cities had formed similar groups. Local groups tested different names, and the name Better Business Bureau caught on.

Lesson 3

② Teach

Discussing

Help students discuss the saying, "Let the buyer beware":

• When and how have you heard it used?

• Do buyers need to "beware"? Why or why not?

• What organizations help protect buyers? **L1**

Listing

Divide the class into six groups, and assign each group one of the listed types of health fraud. (An example of instant results would be a weight-loss product claiming you will lose ten pounds in two weeks.) Have group members work together to list examples of that kind of fraud. **L1**

VISUAL LEARNING

FIGURE 3.4 Ask volunteers to read aloud the typical advertisements and the facts about each. Have students identify the specific clues that reveal health fraud in each ad. Then ask students to recall similar language in familiar radio, TV, print, and online banner ads. **INCL** *English Language Learners, Special Learning Needs, Behavior Problems, Different Learning Styles (Visual)*

Cross-Curriculum Activity

LANGUAGE ARTS Divide the class into small groups to create simple comic books to inform children about fraud. Display and discuss the completed projects. **L2** **INCL** *English Language Learners, Special Learning Needs, Behavior Problems, Different Learning Styles (Visual)*

Lesson 3

Hands-On Health

FACT VS. OPINION

Time: 1 hour

TEACHING THE ACTIVITY

- Have a volunteer read the introductory paragraph aloud, and let volunteers share examples of hype from familiar ads.
- Read and discuss the What You Will Do instructions with students. Then have them work with partners to complete the assignment.
- Have students meet in groups to compare and discuss their lists. Ask group members to work together in compiling a list of typical hype words and phrases.

ASSESSMENT

Have students write one or two sentences explaining what they learned from this activity.

Cooperative Learning

Have each student prepare a draft of a letter to a consumer advocate about a problem with a product or service. Then have students exchange papers with a partner and imagine they are the consumer advocate. Permit pairs to discuss the solutions they propose to each other's problems, and then compile a master list on the board. **L2**

Hands-On Health

FACT VS. OPINION

Some ads contain statements of fact and statements of exaggerated opinion, also called hype. In this activity, you will use critical-thinking skills to analyze marketing and advertising techniques and their influences on the selection of health-related services and products by separating fact from hype.

WHAT YOU WILL NEED

- two print ads for different health-related services or products
- paper and pencil

WHAT YOU WILL DO

1. Divide a sheet of paper vertically into two columns. In column 1, list the words used to describe the product (*great, smooth, breakthrough,* and so forth).
2. Still in column 1, skip two lines, then list the words that tell what the product claims to do (*stop dandruff, whiten, give shine,* and so forth).
3. Decide if each of the words listed in column 1 is fact or opinion. Is it something that can be verified, or proven to be a fact? Is it something that cannot be verified and that is,

therefore, an opinion? In column 2, write *fact* or *opinion* beside each word listed in column 1.
4. Write a brief summary of your findings. Compare your finished sheet with those of your classmates.

IN CONCLUSION

1. Remember that the goal of advertising is to get you to buy. With your classmates, prepare a master list of some typical hype words to watch out for.
2. Write a newspaper article warning against advertising hype aimed at teens.

Consumer Groups

Problems with defective products are usually not difficult to solve. Most businesses want their customers to be satisfied. Satisfied customers keep coming back. Sometimes, though, to get satisfaction, a consumer needs to take additional action. Several consumer groups can help.

- **Consumer advocates** are people or groups who help consumers with problems. The Consumers Union and local consumer groups are examples of such groups.
- **Business groups**, such as the Better Business Bureau, can help with disputes.

70 CHAPTER 3: BEING A HEALTH CONSUMER

 ## Reading Check

Synonyms Exploring word meanings through the use of synonyms (words that have a close meaning) helps readers understand new vocabulary and the subtleties of meaning. Have students work individually, using a dictionary or thesaurus, to identify as many synonyms as possible for the following terms on pages 68–70: *consumer, fraud, warranty, beware.* Examples are: *consumer—buyer, purchaser, shopper, customer; fraud—sham, fake; warranty—assurance, promise; beware—watch out, be careful.*

- **Government offices**, such as consumer affairs offices, make sure that consumers' rights are upheld in disputes.
- **Small claims courts** are state courts in which people can present their own cases without an attorney. A judge hears both sides and decides who wins.

Problems with Health Services

Some people experience problems with health services. If a person feels that a doctor does not spend enough time answering questions, he or she may simply decide to change doctors. Some concerns about the quality of health care are more complicated, however. One patient may feel that a doctor took too long to identify an illness. Another may think that the treatment the doctor recommends is not the best choice.

When patients have doubts about their doctor's diagnosis or about the treatment plan their doctor suggests, they should seek a second opinion. A second doctor will examine the patient, look over the patient's test results, and give an opinion about the patient and about the proposed treatment. Many insurance companies pay for a second opinion before major surgery.

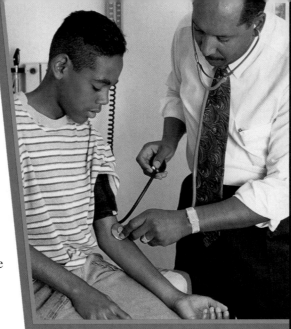

A patient who is unhappy about recommended treatment should request a second opinion.

Lesson 3 Review

Using complete sentences, answer the following questions on a sheet of paper.

Reviewing Terms and Facts

1. **Vocabulary** Define the term *fraud* and use it in an original sentence.
2. **Summarize** Briefly outline the steps to take when you buy a defective product.
3. **Describe** What happens in a small claims court?

Thinking Critically

4. **Apply** Imagine that you had a serious complaint about a local store that had sold

you defective products. What organization could you take your complaint to?

5. **Interpret** Suppose a doctor misdiagnosed a patient's illness. How might the patient solve this problem? What critical issues might arise?

Applying Health Skills

6. **Communication Skills** Write a dialogue in which a teen uses effective communication skills to return a faulty health product to a store.

LESSON 3: MANAGING CONSUMER PROBLEMS **71**

Lesson 3

Discussing

Have students discuss the types of consumer problems that may occur with health services (as opposed to products). List the types of problems on the board. Discuss how a consumer addresses those problems and the possible difference between solutions to service problems and solutions to product problems. **L1**

③ Assess

Evaluating

Assign the Lesson 3 Review; then assign the Lesson 3 Quiz in the TCR.

Reteaching

- Assign Concept Map 10 or Reteaching Activity 10 in the TCR.
- Ask students to write the main headings for this lesson on a sheet of paper along with their summaries of the sections.

Enrichment

- Assign Enrichment Activity 10 in the TCR.
- Have students formulate five laws that would make it harder for fraud to take place.

④ Close

Ask students to identify one important concept they learned in this lesson.

Lesson 3 Review

1. Deliberate deceit or trickery. Sentences will vary.
2. Reread instructions, decide between replacement or money back, read and follow warranty, take item and receipt to store, repack item with letter if sending to manufacturer, and get shipping receipt.
3. People present cases without an attorney. The judge decides who wins.
4. A local consumer group or the Better Business Bureau.
5. They can seek a second opinion. Critical issues that might arise could include how serious the illness is and the reason it was misdiagnosed.

Lesson 4

Public Health

① Focus

Lesson Objectives

Students will be able to

• discuss the role of government agencies in protecting public health.

• identify the health services provided by state and local agencies.

• identify the roles and services of nongovernmental health organizations.

Motivators

Quick Write

Poll the class to get students' general responses. Then ask several volunteers with different opinions to explain their reasoning.

Bellringer Activity

Ask students to write their personal definitions of *public health* and the role it plays in their lives. Use the responses to begin discussing the lesson.

VOCABULARY

On the board write the vocabulary term for the lesson. Have each student write a definition for the term and then use the term in a sentence.

Lesson 4

Public Health

Quick Write

Do you feel confident that your drinking water, foods, and medicines are generally safe? Explain why.

LEARN ABOUT...

• the role of government agencies in protecting public health.

• the public health role of state and local agencies.

• nongovernmental health organizations.

VOCABULARY

• public health

Government Health Services

Certain aspects of health need to be managed as part of a larger effort. This larger effort, managed by federal, state, and local governments, is referred to as public health. **Public health** involves *the protection and promotion of health at the community level.* In this context, the community may be a small town, a large city, a state, or even the nation. Many organizations are involved in administering public health at these different levels.

Federal Health Agencies

The main health organization of the federal government is the Department of Health and Human Services (HHS). HHS is responsible for more than 300 programs that protect the health of all Americans. These programs include two federal health insurance programs—Medicare and Medicaid. **Figure 3.5** lists some of the HHS public health divisions.

Making sure that milk is kept refrigerated in warehouses, during transport, and in stores is a public health responsibility. *What action can you take to ensure that the milk you buy is safe to drink?*

Lesson 4 Resources

Teacher Classroom Resources

📁 Concept Map 11

📁 Enrichment Activity 11

📁 Lesson Plan 4

📁 Lesson 4 Quiz

📁 Reading Tutor Activity 11

📁 Reteaching Activity 11

🔊 Transparency 12

Student Activities Workbook

📁 Chapter 3 Study Guide

📁 Applying Health Skills 11

📁 Health Inventory 3

Other federal agencies work to protect and enforce consumer rights. These include:

- **Consumer Product Safety Commission (CPSC).** The CPSC works to reduce the risk of injury or death from unsafe products. It can ban products it finds dangerous and can order manufacturers to notify people who have bought an unsafe product.
- **Food Safety and Inspection Service (FSIS).** The FSIS oversees the safety of meat and poultry.
- **Federal Trade Commission (FTC).** The FTC protects consumers from unfair trade practices. It also regulates advertising in order to prevent advertisers from presenting misleading information.

Reading Check

Which agency listed here would provide service for a teen with drug addiction? A doctor looking for information about a patient's unusual illness?

② Teach

Discussing

Discuss the health department's functions in relation to current health issues, such as the importance of immunizations and concern over AIDS and STDs. **L1**

Brainstorming

Have students brainstorm a list of criteria that could be used to judge a restaurant's cleanliness, safety, and overall concern for public welfare. **L1**

FIGURE 3.5

Federal Public Health Services

NATIONAL INSTITUTES OF HEALTH (NIH)
Supports about 35,000 research projects nationwide in cancer, diabetes, arthritis, heart disease, AIDS, and other diseases.

HEALTH RESOURCES AND SERVICES ADMINISTRATION (HRSA)
Provides access to essential health services for people who are uninsured, who have lower income, or who live in rural and urban neighborhoods where health care is scarce.

CENTERS FOR DISEASE CONTROL AND PREVENTION (CDC)
Monitors disease trends, investigates outbreaks of disease, promotes safe and healthful environments, and takes actions to prevent and control illness and injury.

THE DEPARTMENT OF HEALTH AND HUMAN SERVICES (HHS)

SUBSTANCE ABUSE AND MENTAL HEALTH SERVICES ADMINISTRATION (SAMHSA)
Works to improve the quality and availability of substance abuse prevention, addiction treatment, and mental health services.

INDIAN HEALTH SERVICES (IHS)
Provides medical and dental services through hospitals and health centers to nearly 1.5 million American Indians and Alaska Natives.

FOOD AND DRUG ADMINISTRATION (FDA)
Makes sure that foods and cosmetics are safe and that product labels are truthful. Makes certain that medicines and medical devices are safe and effective.

LESSON 4: PUBLIC HEALTH 73

VISUAL LEARNING

FIGURE 3.5 Divide the class into six groups, and assign each group one of the public health services divisions of the Department of Health and Human Services. Have group members read and discuss the information about their assigned department. Then have them explain it to the rest of the class, using their own words. You may also want to ask each group to learn more about their departments and discuss their findings with the rest of the class. **INCL** *English Language Learners, Special Learning Needs, Behavior Problems, Different Learning Styles (Visual)*

Reading Check

Analyzing Text The purpose or focus of this page is to provide information about a variety of public health agencies. The author organized the information in a manner which first states the agency and then follows with its primary function or goal. Have students complete a chart like the following by recording the main function of various public health agencies.

Agency	Purpose
National Institutes of Health	Medical research

Discussing

Ask students to recall recent news stories about natural disasters in the United States:

- How were people affected?
- How did government health workers assist the people affected by the disaster? **L1**

HEALTH SKILLS ACTIVITY

ADVOCACY

Work with the entire class to help students read and discuss the information about public-health advocacy. Have students brainstorm a list of local public-health issues, and record their ideas on the board. Then let students form groups by selecting one of the listed issues; each group should have no more than five members.

Provide class time for groups to create their advocacy plans. Carrying out their plans may require additional class time or might be better conducted outside of school. Ask groups to report on their progress at regular intervals.

Note: This skill is introduced in this chapter on page 61.

CONNECT TO

Social Studies

HEALTH-RELATED LAWS, POLICIES, AND PRACTICES
Public health laws, policies, and practices have had a positive impact on many health-related issues. For example, laws on the proper disposal of solid waste help keep drinking water safe. Policies such as requiring restaurant workers to wash their hands after using the restroom help prevent the spread of communicable diseases; so do practices such as regular inspections of restaurant kitchens. *Analyze local law, policy, or practice on a health-related issue.*

State and Local Health Agencies

State and community health organizations also offer services independently. All states and most cities have health departments. The work of these departments varies from place to place, but all help to control and prevent disease. Some of the tasks performed by local health departments include the following:

- Provide basic health care services to people with low incomes.
- Monitor the safety of water and sewage systems.
- Make sure that garbage is removed and properly handled and disposed of.
- Set standards of cleanliness and sanitation for restaurants.
- Offer health education and promotion programs.

HEALTH SKILLS ACTIVITY

ADVOCACY

Public Health

Use your advocacy skills to influence others to support a public health-related law, ordinance, goal, or project. Here are some of the many ways that teens can practice public health advocacy:

- Set an example by following health and safety laws and ordinances.
- Never take an action that could endanger the health or safety of others.
- Volunteer to help charitable organizations that sponsor public-health events.
- Learn which groups in your community deal with public-health issues. Identify their current goals and support them.
- If you notice a condition or activity that threatens public health, notify the proper authorities.

WITH A GROUP
Brainstorm a list of public health issues in your community. From your list, choose one issue to work on. Make an advocacy plan to bring about change. Interpret any critical issues related to solving this public health problem.

PROMOTING COORDINATED SCHOOL HEALTH

On-Site Health Services One characteristic of the successful coordinated school health program is an adequate amount of staff and personnel allotted to screening, surveillance, and managing of health problems. Traditionally, the school nurse serves as the primary health information resource both inside and outside the classroom with support from administration, parents, and community members. The nurse addresses the specific health needs of the students and reinforces positive health concepts. For more information about the program, consult *Planning a Coordinated School Health Program* in the TCR.

Nongovernmental Health Organizations

Governmental public health organizations are funded by the taxes people pay. Nongovernmental health organizations rely mostly on contributions and volunteers to provide important public health services. Some of these organizations focus on one type of disease. Examples are the American Heart Association, the Asthma and Allergy Foundation of America, and the American Cancer Society. They pay for research for ways to prevent and cure the disease. They also help people who have the disease, and they provide programs that teach ways to prevent it.

The American Red Cross is one of the first organizations on the scene after a natural disaster. Its workers are trained to respond quickly to a large-scale emergency. The Red Cross collects blood from volunteers and distributes it to hospitals for people who need transfusions. It also offers courses on first aid, safety, and health.

Race for the Cure is an example of a community-based event that raises money for cancer research. *What events like this take place in your community?*

Lesson 4

Discussing

Explain to students that both public and private health organizations are excellent sources of current, reliable health information. Many health organizations have local chapters or offices, and most maintain Web sites. **L1**

③ Assess

Evaluating

📁 Assign the Lesson 4 Review; then assign the Lesson 4 Quiz in the TCR.

Reteaching

- 📁 Assign Concept Map 11 or Reteaching Activity 11 in the TCR.
- Have students use the main headings of the lesson to summarize their new knowledge about consumer choices and public health.

Enrichment

- 📁 Assign Enrichment Activity 11 in the TCR.
- Direct students to learn more about important advances made in the field of medicine during the 1800s, such as antiseptic surgery and the use of X rays.

④ Close

Ask students to explain one element of public health that they did not know about before studying this lesson.

Lesson 4 Review

Using complete sentences, answer the following questions on a sheet of paper.

Reviewing Terms and Facts

1. **Vocabulary** Define the term *public health* and use it in an original sentence.
2. **Recall** What is the name of the main health organization of the federal government?
3. **Identify** Which federal agency is authorized to ban the sale of unsafe products?

Thinking Critically

4. **Apply** Name the HHS division you would contact for information on safe ways to store and prepare food.

5. **Investigate** Which nongovernmental health organizations would you contact for information on the latest cancer research? On where to find a safe place to stay after a serious storm?

Applying Health Skills

6. **Accessing Information** Interview the manager of your school cafeteria or the manager of a local public swimming pool. Find out what state and local health laws the manager must obey. Share your information with your classmates.

LESSON 4: PUBLIC HEALTH **75**

Lesson 4 Review

1. The protection and promotion of health at the community level. Sentences will vary.
2. Department of Health and Human Services (HHS).
3. Consumer Product Safety Commission (CPSC).
4. Food and Drug Administration (FDA).
5. American Cancer Society; American Red Cross.

Turn It Off!

① Focus

Objectives

Students will be able to

- analyze influences on their television viewing habits.
- practice the goal-setting process for TV-Turnoff Week.
- identify ways in which television has changed American life.

Motivator

Bellringer Activity

Ask students to imagine a world without television. How would American culture be different? How would their day-to-day lives change?

② Teach

Analyzing Influences

Explain to students that there are a variety of internal and external influences on their TV viewing habits. To help students identify some of these influences, have them answer the following questions:

- When and where do you do most of your TV viewing?
- How do you feel before you start watching?
- Do you turn on the TV or is it already on?
- Who are you with?
- What are you watching? Do you like the show? Are you really paying attention?
- Why do you stop watching?
- How do you feel afterward?

Ask students to analyze their replies. Understanding these influences will help them to develop a plan for living without TV during TV-Turnoff Week.

Turn It Off!

For one week, millions of people go TV-free. Here's why.

In April, millions of television sets around the world will go blank. Instead of fiddling with the remote or calling the cable company, those thwarted TV watchers will take drastic action. Entire families will go outside to ride bikes; groups of friends will play games. Will other television addicts turn off their sets and join in—or will they just watch?

TV-Turnoff Network, a nonprofit organization, has promoted the annual TV-Turnoff Week since 1995. In the beginning, only a few thousand people took part. Now there are participants in every state and in more than 12 countries.

TV and Violence

Each year, kids in the United States spend more time glued to the tube than doing anything else—except for sleeping! People have worried about the effects of TV ever since the 1940s, when television first became popular. Over the years, health-care groups like the American Academy of Pediatrics and the American Medical Association have voiced their concern. They point to studies that link excessive TV viewing to such problems as poor eating habits, a sedentary lifestyle, obesity, and violent behavior.

A study published in the journal *Science* claims that there is evidence of a connection between TV viewing and violence. Psychologist Jeffrey G. Johnson and his research team followed children in 707 families for 17 years. The researchers found that kids who watched more than one hour of television a day were more likely than other kids to show aggressive and violent behavior as they grew older.

Other TV Turnoffs

Others worry about the impact of commercials on kids. One study found that during four hours of Saturday-morning cartoons, television networks ran 202 ads for empty-calorie foods. The nonstop reminders to buy sugary sodas, cereals, and candy may be one reason that more than one in eight American kids is overweight. Long hours sitting in front of the tube is probably another reason. "Almost anything uses more

Beyond the Classroom

Home Ask students to interview a parent, grandparent, or other adult about their experiences with TV. Brainstorm interview questions beforehand as a class. They might include:

- What was life like before television? What did your family do for entertainment?
- What were some of your favorite shows?
- How has television changed since then?
- In general, do you think TV has been a positive or negative force in American life?

Have students share their interviews with the class.

TV By The Numbers

1,023 Hours per year the average American child watches television

900 Hours per year spent in school

1,180 Minutes per week the average kid watches TV

38.5 Minutes per week parents say they spend in meaningful conversation with their kids

41 Percent of U.S. households with three or more TV sets

49 Percent of Americans who say they watch too much TV

6 million Number of videos rented daily in the United States

3 million Public library items checked out daily

200,000 Average number of violent acts Americans see on TV by age 18

91 Percent of kids polled who said they felt upset by TV violence

Source: TV-Turnoff Network

③ Apply

Time to Think

Now students know the number of hours that they watch TV during an average week and some of the influences on their viewing habits. Using this information, ask students to plan a goal-setting process for TV-Turnoff Week. Students should

- write a clear goal statement. (I will try to cut my television viewing in half.)
- make a plan for meeting the goal. (When I feel stressed, I will go for a walk instead of turning on the TV.)
- identify barriers based on the influences they outlined earlier—and ways to overcome them. (If my brother is watching, I will go to a different room.)
- think of rewards for meeting the goal. (I will have more time to spend with my friends.)

Check in with students several days into TV-Turnoff Week. How are they doing? Do they need to revise their plans?

energy than watching TV," says Dr. William H. Dietz of the Centers for Disease Control and Prevention in Atlanta, Georgia.

Enjoying Life, Unplugged

TV-Turnoff Network wants to encourage life outside the box. "We're not anti-TV," says the group's director, Frank Vespe. The goal is to help kids tune in to real life so that "they won't have time for TV."

Is it really possible to live without your favorite TV shows? Sarah Foote, a middle-school student in Burke, Virginia, says she made it through TV-Turnoff Week last year—and actually enjoyed herself! Sarah says that after a few days without TV, "I thought, 'Why did I ever need TV?'" Her brother, Nathaniel, agrees: "There are about 8,000 other things you can do."

Still, some kids can't picture life without television. Christian Cardenas of New York City doesn't plan on tuning out. "It entertains you on rainy days," he says.

Could you go without TV for a whole week? Says TV-Turnoff veteran Carly Cara of Niles, Illinois: "You're doing so many fun things that before you know it, it's over!"

TIME TO THINK...

About Turning Off the TV

Figure out the number of hours that you watch television during an average week. Then, using a map and the map's scale, start at your hometown and see how far you could travel in that amount of time if you were moving 50 miles per hour. Report to your class what cities you could visit.

VISUAL LEARNING

Ask students to analyze the photograph on page 77. What are these students doing? Does it look more fun than watching television? According to a teen quoted in this spread, "There are about 8,000 other things you can do." Brainstorm at least a dozen activities teens can enjoy together instead of watching television.

WHAT TEENS WANT TO KNOW

TV isn't *all* bad, is it? Part of being a smart consumer is knowing how to compare choices. When television shows are chosen carefully and in moderation, they offer undeniable benefits. Television provides inexpensive entertainment for the whole family. It can be an effective tool for education, allowing viewers access to remote people and places. In emergency situations, TV is a critical method of disseminating information. Talk with your parents about appropriate programs for the whole family. Establish family viewing guidelines, such as "no TV on school nights" or "only half an hour of TV a day." Let this remarkable technology enhance your life, not take it over!

FINDING RELIABLE SOURCES

The extension ".gov" identifies a site run by a government agency. Glenn considers most information from these sites to be valid.

Model

Glenn is working on a report for health class about different kinds of pain relievers. He has decided to search the Internet for up-to-date information. Glenn knows, however, that not all information on the Internet is reliable. As he looks at different Web pages, he pays attention to their addresses, or URLs. Most URLs contain an extension that identifies the nature of the site. Glenn knows that some types of sites are more likely to be reliable than others.

U.S. DEPARTMENT OF HEALTH AND HUMAN SERVICES
FOOD AND DRUG ADMINISTRATION   **FDA**

Hot Topics
Buying Medicines Online
Antibiotic Resistance
BSE ("mad cow disease")
LASIK Surgery
Liver Toxicity

FDA NEWS

The purpose of most sites that end in ".com" is to sell a product or service. Glenn is always cautious when viewing these sites because he knows that companies may make false or exaggerated claims about their products. He does not use information from these sites unless he can find another source to support it.

Citizens for Accurate Labeling

Who We Are
Our Programs
Links
Site map

The ".org" extension is often used by nonprofit organizations. Some organizations, such as the American Cancer Society, are valid sources of health information. However, information from nonprofit organizations may be biased, or slanted toward a particular point of view. When Glenn views these pages, he looks for information about the organization and its purpose. He also checks to see whether a Web site is endorsed by public health and medical organizations. If it is, he considers it reliable.

Sayers Pharmaceuticals
"Healing the World through Science"

Our Products
Research
Investments
Job Opportunities

Buying Prescription Medicines Online: A Consumer Safety Guide

78 CHAPTER 3: BEING A HEALTH CONSUMER

Objective

After completing the lesson, students will be able to describe reliable sources of health information.

Time: two 40-minute periods

Materials: fitness and health magazines, general interest magazines, newspapers

Teacher Classroom Resources

📁 Building Health Skills Activities

• Transparency Master 1, "Accessing Information"

• Reproducible Master 28, "Finding Reliable Sources"

1. Model

• Ask students to brainstorm a list of sources of health-related information. (Answers may include *the Internet, product insert, pharmacist, Physicians' Desk Reference, library, magazine ad, TV/infomercial*.) Write the list on the board.

• Ask the class which sources in the list they think are more reliable than others. Why?

• Direct students to read about Glenn and how he determines which sources of health information on the Internet are reliable.

Teaching Tips

Brainstorming Brainstorming allows students to generate a list of decisions in a short time. Allot a brief period of time (e.g., two minutes) for brainstorming. Record the decisions without discussion or criticism. When time is up, invite comments about the decisions that have been recorded.

Teaching Health Skills Teaching skills is one of the best ways to affect students' behavior in healthy ways. Skills such as accessing information must be specifically taught. The *Teen Health* program will give you the tools you need to teach students skills.

Practice

Read the following scenario and answer the questions at the end. Share your answers with the class.

While watching television, Dawn sees an infomercial about a new weight-loss program. The creator of the program is a doctor who has written a book about his "medical breakthrough." He explains the basis for his program in technical-sounding language, but Dawn cannot tell whether his information is accurate.

1. Is this infomercial a valid source of health information? Why or why not?
2. What steps could Dawn take to verify the claims in the infomercial?

Apply

In a small group, look through several magazines for health-related claims in articles and advertisements. For example, an ad might claim that a particular food supplement will help prevent colds. Choose one of these claims to research, interpret, and analyze. As a group, discuss the sources you could use to verify the claim. You might start by checking the sources listed in the original article. You can also use reference works in the library, articles from other magazines and journals, and Internet sources.

Work as a group to develop evaluation criteria, then research your health claim. Try to find at least three reliable sources of information. Is the claim accurate? Why or why not? When you are done, present your findings to the class. List the sources you used and explain why you think they are reliable.

Accessing Information

When evaluating health information, ask yourself these questions:

- Is it based on scientific research?
- Does it give only one point of view?
- Is it trying to sell something?
- Does it agree with other reliable sources?

Self-√ Check

- Did we find at least three sources to support or contradict our health claim?
- Did we identify the sources we used and explain why they are reliable and valid?

2. Practice

- Display Transparency Master 1 to review the steps one can take to access reliable health information.
- Have students read about Dawn and answer the questions at the end of the scenario.
- As a class, discuss the answers to the questions.

3. Apply/Assess

- You may wish to distribute Building Health Skills Reproducible Master 28 in the TCR to guide students in completing this activity.
- Divide students into small groups. Provide each group with magazines and newspapers, and direct groups to locate health-related claims in articles and advertisements.
- Have each group choose one of the claims in an article or ad to research. Instruct each group to discuss the sources that could be used to verify the claim.
- Direct students to try to find at least three reliable sources for the claim to verify its accuracy.
- Allow time for each group to present its findings to the class.

Assessment Scoring

Using a rubric, student work should provide evidence of all criteria to achieve the highest score.

Skills

Student work demonstrates

- at least three reliable sources of health information.
- proper citation of the sources.

Concept

Student work provides

- clear explanations of why each source is reliable.

Checking Comprehension

Use the Chapter 3 Assessment to examine the most important ideas presented in the chapter.

Answers to Reviewing Vocabulary and Concepts

Lesson 1
1. advertising
2. warranty
3. comparison shopping
4. media
5. online shopping

Lesson 2
6. health care system
7. preventive care
8. health maintenance organization (HMO)
9. primary care physicians
10. health insurance

Lesson 3
11. true
12. false; health fraud
13. true

Lesson 4
14. true
15. false; meat and poultry
16. true

Thinking Critically

17. Responses should demonstrate an understanding of how programmers use media to target various groups and influence their buying decisions.
18. Responses should accurately describe and analyze the techniques and their influence on the selection of a health product or service.

After You Read

Use your completed Foldable to review the information on being an informed consumer.

FOLDABLES™
Study Organizer

Reviewing Vocabulary and Concepts

On a sheet of paper, write the numbers 1–10. After each number, write the term from the list that best completes each statement.

> - comparison shopping
> - advertising
> - health maintenance organization (HMO)
> - media
> - online shopping
> - health care system
> - health insurance
> - warranty
> - primary care physicians
> - preventive care

Lesson 1

1. Messages designed to interest consumers in buying a product or service are known as _____.
2. A written promise from a company to handle repairs if the product fails to work properly is a(n) _____.
3. _____ is a method of judging the benefits of different products or services by comparing several factors.
4. Together, various methods for communicating information are known as the _____.
5. If you buy products on the Internet, you are participating in _____.

Lesson 2

6. The U.S. _____ includes all the medical care available to Americans, the way they receive the care, and the way the care is paid for.
7. _____ involves keeping disease or injury from happening or getting worse.
8. An organization that provides health care for a fixed price is a(n) _____.
9. Medical doctors who provide physical checkups and general care are called _____.
10. _____ is a plan in which private companies or government programs pay for part of a person's medical costs.

On a sheet of paper, write the numbers 11–16. Write *True* or *False* for each statement below. If the statement is false, change the underlined word or phrase to make it true.

Lesson 3

11. <u>Fraud</u> is deliberate deceit or trickery.
12. <u>Second opinions</u> involve the sale of worthless products or treatments claimed to prevent diseases or cure other health problems.
13. People or groups who help consumers with problems are known as <u>consumer advocates</u>.

Lesson 4

14. The main federal health agency is the <u>Department of Health and Human Services</u>.
15. The Food Safety and Inspection Service oversees the safety of <u>milk and eggs</u>.
16. The <u>Centers for Disease Control and Prevention</u> monitor disease trends and investigate outbreaks of disease.

Thinking Critically

Using complete sentences, answer the following questions on a sheet of paper.

17. **Hypothesize** Explain how programmers develop media to influence purchasing decisions.

INCLUSION STRATEGIES

Special Learning Needs, Behavior Problems, English Language Learners The following suggestions are helpful for students with special learning needs, students with behavior problems, and ELL students:

- Pair these students with more proficient learners who can help summarize the main concepts of the chapter.

- 🎧 Direct these students to listen to the Teen Health Audio Summaries. This component provides an audio and written summary of the chapter in both English and Spanish.

- Use photographs, drawings, or magazine clippings whenever possible to help students visualize the important concepts of the chapter.

18. **Analyze** Select an ad for a health-related product or service. Use critical-thinking skills to analyze the marketing and advertising techniques used in the ad and their influence on the selection of the health-related service or product.
19. **Apply** Develop and apply criteria for the selection or rejection of health products, services, and information. Create a list of guidelines for consumers to follow.
20. **Judge** Should people who practice health fraud by selling worthless products or treatments be allowed to advertise in magazines and on television? Give reasons for your answer.

Career Corner

Health Services Administrator Nursing homes, hospitals and outpatient care facilities provide important community health services. It is the job of each facility's health services administrator to understand the needs of the consumer (the patient), while also maintaining and supervising health employees. Find out more about this challenging health career on Career Corner at health.glencoe.com.

Standardized Test Practice

Reading & Writing

Read the paragraphs below and then answer the questions.

Most fast-food choices tend to be high in fat, salt, or sugar, but low in vitamins and fiber. However, you don't have to give up fast food completely if you want to be healthy. You just need to be willing to make a few changes in the way you usually order.

First, look carefully at the menu before ordering. Burgers and fries are not the only items you will find there anymore. Fast-food restaurants are starting to offer healthier foods, such as salads and baked potatoes. Next, consider if you really need that jumbo portion. Big portions may seem like a great deal, but they can provide too many calories and contribute to unhealthful weight gain.

1. The author probably wrote this passage to
   Ⓐ explain how fast-food restaurants trick customers into ordering expensive food.
   Ⓑ persuade readers to change their eating habits at fast-food restaurants.
   Ⓒ describe the different types of food to be found in fast-food restaurants.
   Ⓓ persuade readers to give up eating at fast-food restaurants.

2. From the information in the second paragraph readers can conclude that
   Ⓐ people will always eat what they want.
   Ⓑ there are few choices at fast-food restaurants.
   Ⓒ it is up to you to decide what to eat.
   Ⓓ fast foods are always healthy.

3. Write a paragraph in which you try to persuade a friend or family member to take a specific action to improve his or her health.

 TH05_C3.glencoe.com/quiz

19. Criteria and guidelines will vary; accept all reasonable responses.
20. Students might argue for or against advertising freedom.

Test Practice
1. B
2. C
3. Answers should identify a specific healthful behavior and include persuasive arguments.

Reteaching
📁 Assign Study Guide 3 in the Student Activities Workbook.

Evaluate
• 📁 ⦿ Use the reproducible Chapter 3 Test in the TCR, or construct your own test using the **Exam***View*® Pro Testmaker.
• 📁 Use Performance Assessment 3 in the TCR.

Enrichment
Have students work together to write a short survey about the needs of health consumers. Let them use their survey to gather information from teens and/or adults. Then summarize their results.

Assessment

Self-Assessment Direct students to review the activities that are provided throughout the chapter. Encourage each student to select one finished product or activity that demonstrates his or her best work for the chapter. Have students explain what they learned and how the examples they selected show their progress.

Career Corner

Health Services Administrator After reviewing the career profile on the health Web site, write the following personal and career skills on the board: *leadership, organization, communication, multitasking*. Ask students to define each skill. Then ask them why each skill is important for a career as a health services administrator.

Building Safe and Healthy Relationships

Unit Objectives

Students will learn about developing positive mental/emotional health and issues affecting their social lives, such as building good character and establishing relationships. They will also examine conflict and violence and ways to deal with each.

Unit Overview

Chapter 4
Mental and Emotional Health

Lesson
1 Your Mental and Emotional Health
2 Understanding Your Emotions
3 Mental and Emotional Problems
4 Getting Help
5 Coping with Loss

Chapter 5
Promoting Social Health

Lesson
1 Your Character and Your Relationships
2 Getting Along with Your Family
3 Marriage and Parenthood

82

DEALING WITH SENSITIVE ISSUES

A General Approach As a health teacher, you have the opportunity to help students deal with sensitive issues in several ways. One way is by sharing accurate information and professional resources about the issues with students and doing so in ways that won't embarrass them, make them feel uncomfortable, or jeopardize their self-esteem. Knowledge alone is not enough, however. Experience shows that just conveying *information* is less effective in changing behaviors than teaching *skills*. For example, telling students to "just say no" to drugs is a less effective deterrent to drug use than teaching them *how* to say no. The chapters in this unit will guide you in teaching important life skills that promote mental/emotional and social health.

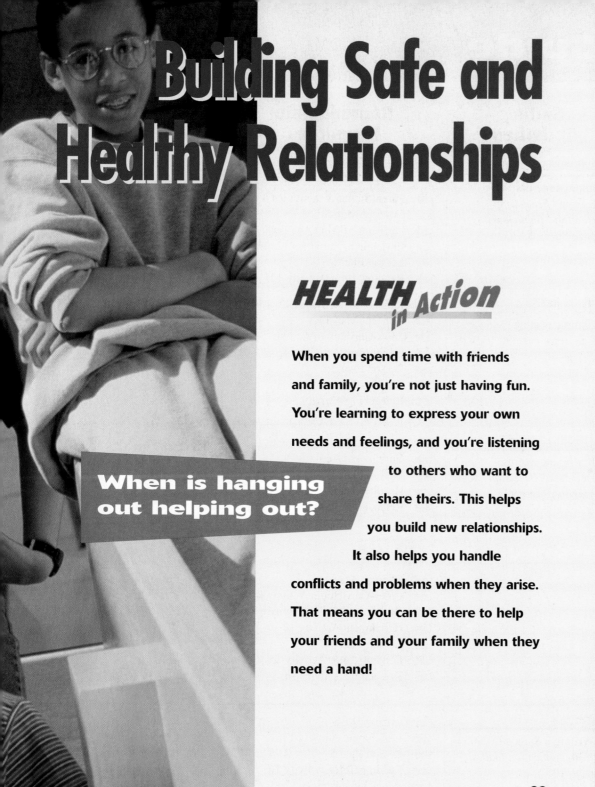

Building Safe and Healthy Relationships

HEALTH in Action

When is hanging out helping out?

When you spend time with friends and family, you're not just having fun. You're learning to express your own needs and feelings, and you're listening to others who want to share theirs. This helps you build new relationships. It also helps you handle conflicts and problems when they arise. That means you can be there to help your friends and your family when they need a hand!

Chapter 6
Relationships: The Teen Years

Lesson
1 Friendships: Growing and Changing
2 Peer Pressure and Refusal Skills
3 Practicing Abstinence

Chapter 7
Conflict Resolution

Lesson
1 The Nature of Conflict
2 Resolving Conflicts
3 Avoiding and Preventing Violence
4 Preventing Abuse

Unit Introduction

Write the following statement on the board: *A good relationship with another person starts with....* Ask students to copy the statement and complete the thought. When they have finished, ask volunteers to share their completed statements, and write their ideas on the board. Discuss the variety of responses received and encourage students to recognize what their ideas have in common.

Ask students whether they think there are differences between their relationships with family members and with friends. If so, what are they? If not, why not? Tell students that the chapters of Unit 2 will address the benefits of developing and maintaining healthy relationships with their families, friends, and other people.

83

HEALTH in Action

Read the class the question on page 83. Ask the class to give examples of ways that they have helped other people to solve problems. Then lead the class in the following physical group activity:

Have students line up against a wall. Name a common problem that teens might face. Starting at the front of the line, ask each student to state a possible solution. If the student names a workable solution, have him or her step forward. If the student can't offer a solution that hasn't already been named, he or she will stay in place. Once every student in the line has had a chance to offer a suggestion, start again at the beginning of the line with a new problem. The goal is to have each student standing in the new line at the activity's end.

Planning Guide

Chapter 4	Skills/ Activities	Reproducible Resources	Assessment
Lesson 1 **Your Mental and Emotional Health** *pages 86–90*	**HEALTH SKILLS ACTIVITY** ▲ Improving Your Self-Esteem (*Practicing Healthful Behaviors*), page 89	*Student Activities Workbook available for use with each chapter* 📁 Parent Letter & Activities 4 📁 Concept Maps 12, 13 📁 Decision-Making Activity 7 📁 Enrichment Activities 12, 13 📁 Lesson Plan 1 📁 Reading Tutor Activity 12	📁 Lesson 1 Quiz
Lesson 2 **Understanding Your Emotions** *pages 91–95*	**Hands-On Health** ▲ Communicating Emotions, page 93	📁 Reteaching Activities 12, 13 📁 Concept Map 14 📁 Cross-Curriculum Activity 7 📁 Enrichment Activity 14 📁 Lesson Plan 2 📁 Reading Tutor Activity 13 📁 Reteaching Activity 14	📁 Lesson 2 Quiz
Lesson 3 **Mental and Emotional Problems** *pages 96–100*	**HEALTH SKILLS ACTIVITY** ▲ If a Friend Seems Depressed (*Decision Making*), page 99	📁 Concept Map 15 📁 Enrichment Activity 15 📁 Lesson Plan 3 📁 Reading Tutor Activity 14 📁 Reteaching Activity 15	📁 Lesson 3 Quiz
Lesson 4 **Getting Help** *pages 101–105*		📁 Concept Map 16 📁 Cross-Curriculum Activity 8 📁 Decision-Making Activity 8 📁 Enrichment Activity 16 📁 Lesson Plan 4 📁 Reading Tutor Activity 15 📁 Reteaching Activity 16	📁 Lesson 4 Quiz
Lesson 5 **Coping with Loss** *pages 106–109*	**HEALTH SKILLS ACTIVITY** ▲ Writing a Sympathy Note (*Communication Skills*), page 107	📁 Concept Map 17 📁 Enrichment Activity 17 📁 Lesson Plan 5 📁 Reading Tutor Activity 16 📁 Reteaching Activity 17	📁 Lesson 5 Quiz 📁 Chapter 4 Test 📁 Performance Assessment 4
TIME **HEALTH** **Dealing with Anxiety** *pages 110–111*			
BUILDING HEALTH SKILLS **Put Stress in Its Place** (*Stress Management*) *pages 112–113*		📁 Building Health Skills Reproducible Master 29	

Standards		Technology
National	**State/Local**	
National Health Education Standard **1.6, 3.1, 3.2, 3.4, 5.4**		🖨 Transparency 13 📼 💿 Tape/DVD 3, Segment 2, "Building Confidence" 💿 TeacherWorks™
National Health Education Standard **3.1, 3.4, 5.3**		🖨 Transparency 14 📼 💿 Tape/DVD 1, Segment 2, "Dealing with Your Emotions" 💿 TeacherWorks™
National Health Education Standard **1.2, 1.3, 1.6, 2.6, 6.1, 6.2, 6.3**		🖨 Transparency 15 💿 TeacherWorks™
National Health Education Standard **1.6, 1.7, 2.4, 2.6, 3.1, 3.4**		🖨 Transparency 16 💿 TeacherWorks™
National Health Education Standard **1.6, 2.6, 5.1, 5.3, 5.4, 5.5**		🖨 Transparency 17 💿 TeacherWorks™ 📼 💿 MindJogger Videoquiz 💿 **Exam**_View_® Pro Testmaker
National Health Education Standard **1.6, 3.4, 3.7**		📁 Building Health Skills Transparency Master 3

TeacherWorks™

Glencoe's new and exclusive TeacherWorks™ is an all-in-one planner and resource center. Access the complete Teacher Wraparound Edition electronically. Find all your classroom resources with just a few easy clicks, and print them right from your computer. Connect directly to Glencoe's customized Health Web site. Access the National Health Education Standards correlations, or insert your own state standards and match them directly to the electronic Teacher Wraparound Edition.

Language Diversity

- 🎧 English Audio Summaries
- 🎧 Spanish Audio Summaries
- 📁 English Summaries, Quizzes, and Activities
- 📁 Spanish Summaries, Quizzes, and Activities
- 📁 Spanish Parent Letters and Activities

KEY TO ABILITY LEVELS

Teaching Strategies that appear throughout the chapters have been identified by one of four codes to give you an idea of their suitability for students of varying learning styles and abilities.

L1 **Level 1** strategies should be within the ability range of all students. Often full class participation is required.

L2 **Level 2** strategies are for average to above-average students or for small groups. Some teacher direction is necessary.

L3 **Level 3** strategies are designed for students able and willing to work independently. Minimal teacher direction is necessary.

INCL Strategies are appropriate for students with particular special needs in a general classroom setting.

Mental and Emotional Health

Chapter at a Glance

Lesson 1 examines self-concept and self-esteem and identifies ways to maintain good mental and emotional health.

Lesson 2 describes how to express emotions and meet emotional needs in healthy ways.

Lesson 3 highlights key types of mental health problems and common warning signs of suicide.

Lesson 4 helps students identify sources of help when an individual needs assistance with an emotional problem.

Lesson 5 discusses death and loss, explores Kübler-Ross's five stages of dying, and examines coping strategies and the stages of grief.

Health Skills

- Improving Your Self-Esteem (*Practicing Healthful Behaviors*), p. 89
- If a Friend Seems Depressed (*Decision Making*), p. 99
- Writing a Sympathy Note (*Communication Skills*), p. 107
- Put Stress in Its Place (*Stress Management*), pp. 112–113

84

HANDS-ON ACTIVITY

Interview a Classmate Divide the class into pairs. Ask one student in each pair to interview the other student for two minutes. Possible questions may include: Where did you grow up? What are your interests? (*movies, music, books, sports*) What school programs do you participate in and why? When the time is up, have students reverse roles. Then ask each interviewer to list as many positive attributes as possible about the person who was interviewed. Ask volunteers to read their lists aloud. After each list is read, ask the person whom the report was about to share how he or she felt during the reading.

Conclude by discussing the following questions: Why are we often uncomfortable when someone says nice things about us? How is self-concept related to what people say about us?

Mental and Emotional Health

Chapter Introduction

Use the options below to motivate students and preview chapter content.

HEALTH Online

Go to health.glencoe.com and take the Health Inventory for Chapter 4 to assess your mental and emotional health.

HEALTH Online

Have students take Health Inventory 4 or read extra credit articles at **health.glencoe.com.** By clicking on Health Updates, both students and teachers can discover the latest news on health topics.

FOLDABLES™ Study Organizer

Before You Read

Make this Foldable to help you organize the main ideas on mental and emotional health in Lesson 1. Begin with a plain sheet of 8½" × 11" paper.

Step 1

Line up one of the short edges of a sheet of paper with one of the long edges to form a triangle. Fold and cut off the leftover rectangle.

Step 2

Fold the triangle in half, then unfold. The folds will form an X dividing four equal sections.

Step 3

Cut up one fold line, and stop at the middle. This forms two triangular flaps. Draw an X on one tab, and label the other three as shown.

Step 4

Fold the X flap under the other flap, and glue together to make a three-sided pyramid.

As You Read

Write the main ideas on mental and emotional health on the back of the appropriate side of the pyramid.

GLENCOE TECHNOLOGY

Teen Health Video and DVD Series
(Each format available in both English and Spanish)

You may wish to use:
- Tape/DVD 1, Segment 2, "Dealing with Your Emotions"
- Tape/DVD 3, Segment 2, "Building Confidence"

MindJogger Videoquiz

Use MindJogger to preview or review Chapter 4 content.

TIME HEALTH

Dealing with Anxiety
pages 110–111

FOLDABLES™ Study Organizer

Dinah Zike Study Fold

Recording Main Ideas and Supporting Facts Students will use this Foldable study guide to help them understand what makes them who they are and to analyze the three main factors that affect their mental and emotional health. Have students write their names and something about themselves at the top of the pyramid. As students read and discuss the information in Lesson 1, have them take notes, write definitions, and record main ideas on the appropriate inside back of each of the labeled sides. To further illustrate factors that influence their mental and emotional health, students might convert their Foldable into a mobile by making and hanging small descriptive cards, photographs, or sketches from the appropriate sides of the pyramid.

Lesson 1

Your Mental and Emotional Health

1 Focus

Lesson Objectives

Students will be able to

- recognize the signs of good mental health.
- differentiate self-concept from self-esteem.
- explain ways to improve their self-esteem.
- discuss how their thoughts, behaviors, and attitudes affect the way they feel about themselves.

Health Skills
- Practicing Healthful Behaviors, p. 89

Motivators

Quick Write

Have students identify and explain traits of good mental and emotional health. Ask: How does good mental and emotional health affect you on a daily basis?

Bellringer Activity

Ask students: What are some of the problems caused by trying to be perfect and expecting others to be perfect?

VOCABULARY

On the board write the vocabulary terms for the lesson. Have each student write a definition for each term and then use the term in an original sentence. Ask students to share their definitions and sentences. Correct any misconceptions the answers reveal.

Lesson 1

Your Mental and Emotional Health

Quick Write

What do you think it means to be mentally and emotionally healthy? List at least three traits that suggest good mental and emotional health.

LEARN ABOUT...

- the signs of good mental and emotional health.
- ways to improve your self-esteem.
- how your thoughts, behaviors, and attitudes affect the way you feel about yourself.

VOCABULARY

- mental and emotional health
- personality
- self-concept
- self-esteem

Mental and Emotional Health

Think about some of the people whose company you most enjoy. It's likely that you enjoy being around them because you have fun with them, they make you laugh, and they listen to your concerns. They may also have a positive outlook on life. A positive outlook is just one of the signs of mental and emotional health. **Mental and emotional health** is *the ability to accept yourself and others, adapt to and cope with emotions, and deal with the problems and challenges you meet in life.*

There are several signs you can look for in yourself and in others that indicate good mental and emotional health.

- You see yourself, and life in general, in positive ways.
- You face life's challenges with confidence.
- You accept the fact that situations and events will not always go your way.
- You can motivate yourself to achieve goals.
- You understand and cope with your feelings.
- You can focus on your strengths.
- You accept constructive criticism and learn from your mistakes.
- You have a healthy sense of humor.
- You bounce back from disappointments.

Your mental and emotional health affects every aspect of your life—your happiness, your success in school, and your relationships with other people.

86 CHAPTER 4: MENTAL AND EMOTIONAL HEALTH

  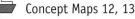   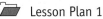

Lesson 1 Resources

Teacher Classroom Resources

- 📁 Parent Letter & Activities 4
- 📁 Concept Maps 12, 13
- 📁 Decision-Making Activity 7
- 📁 Enrichment Activities 12, 13
- 📁 Lesson Plan 1
- 📁 Lesson 1 Quiz

- 📁 Reading Tutor Activity 12
- 📁 Reteaching Activities 12, 13
- 🔦 Transparency 13

Student Activities Workbook

- 📁 Chapter 4 Study Guide
- 📁 Applying Health Skills 12, 13

What Makes You Who You Are?

The early teen years are a time to learn more about who you are. You find out about your physical and mental abilities. You discover the kinds of people you like to be with and the kinds of activities you enjoy and do well. You begin to determine what is really important to you.

Your Personality

Your personality has a big impact on your mental health. Your **personality** is *the unique combination of feelings, thoughts, and behavior that makes you different from everyone else.* Your personality helps determine how you react to problems, new situations, and other events. How would you feel about moving to a new school, for example? Would you feel excited and confident, or nervous and a little afraid? Different people react in different ways to the same situation.

Your Self-Concept

If you were asked to choose three words that best describe you, would you focus on your strengths? People who recognize their strengths and strong qualities generally have a positive self-concept. Your **self-concept** is *the view you have of yourself.* It is basically how you see yourself as the unique person you are.

Some teens and adults tend to focus on their limitations rather than on their strengths. People who focus on their limitations can begin to feel inadequate and can develop a negative self-concept. When teens who have a positive self-concept make a mistake, they are likely to say, "Okay, so I'm human." Those who have a negative self-concept might say, "I never do anything right." A positive self-concept is an important part of good mental and emotional health.

Your Self-Esteem and Self-Confidence

Your **self-esteem**, *the way you feel about yourself, and how you value yourself,* is closely related to your self-concept. Often a negative self-concept leads to low self-esteem. For example, if you aren't chosen for the track team after practicing for months, you might look upon yourself as a failure, even though you excel in other activities. This unrealistic picture of yourself could negatively affect your self-esteem.

Self-confidence, the belief you have in your abilities, is closely tied to self-esteem. People with good self-esteem usually have self-confidence. Characteristics that contribute to self-esteem and self-confidence include honesty, integrity (standing up for your values), responsibility, and respecting the dignity (worth) of other people.

LESSON 1: YOUR MENTAL AND EMOTIONAL HEALTH **87**

Developing Good Character

Caring

Everyone's self-concept gets a boost from a sincere compliment. You can give others that boost when you look for their strengths and tell them what you see. For example, if another student holds a door open for you when your hands are full, you could say: "Thanks—that's a big help." *What other examples can you suggest?*

Identifying

Tell students that messages affecting self-concept are sometimes unspoken. For example, a person's turning his or her back on another person might have a negative impact on that person's self-concept. Have students identify other unspoken messages: some positive, some negative. (*Positive examples include smiling, nodding in agreement, giving a slap on the back. Negative examples include laughing as a person passes, rolling one's eyes upward, sneering.*) **L1**

VISUAL LEARNING

FIGURE 4.1 Ask a volunteer to read aloud the title and the caption. Then guide students in reading and discussing the explanation of the cyclical relationship between high self-esteem and success. Ask students: How can understanding this relationship help you keep trying even when you don't succeed right away? **INCL** *English Language Learners, Special Learning Needs, Behavior Problems, Different Learning Styles* (*Visual*)

Cross-Curriculum Activity

LANGUAGE ARTS Ask students to think about the people who have had positive influences on their self-esteem. Ask them to choose a person and write a thank-you note to him or her, explaining how that person helped them. **L3**

FIGURE 4.1

How High Self-Esteem Leads to Success

If you have high self-esteem, you are more likely to try hard and succeed. This success, in turn, reinforces your self-esteem and leads you to make efforts in new areas.

High self-esteem leads you to make an effort.

Trying hard leads to success.

Success leads to praise from others.

Praise from others leads you to try harder and to make efforts in new areas.

New efforts lead to new successes, which lead to more praise, and so on.

How do you feel when you think about the kind of person you are? Do you like and respect yourself? Do you accept yourself for who you are? Do you have confidence to try new things even though you might fail? If you do, you have high self-esteem. **Figure 4.1** shows how high self-esteem leads to success.

Improving Your Mental/Emotional Health with Coping Skills

Mental/emotional health will go through ups and downs throughout life. Fortunately, you can apply the effective coping skills that follow to improve your self-esteem and your overall level of mental/emotional health.

88 CHAPTER 4: MENTAL AND EMOTIONAL HEALTH

MORE ABOUT...

Developing Good Mental and Emotional Health
Remind students that one of the keys to good mental and emotional health is to realize that they have no control over how others feel and act; they have control only over how they act. The next time they feel someone has not lived up to their expectations, encourage them to remem-ber the following: Everyone makes mistakes. Everyone has value even if they do not behave as others would like them to. Showing compassion will help the other person feel better about his or her mistake. Ask students to share techniques for responding to criticism.

Motivate Yourself

Being able to motivate yourself is a key to success. It means setting healthful, realistic goals and working to achieve them. Motivation helps you focus on your goals. You will be willing to set aside short-term pleasures to achieve important long-term goals. Imagine, for example, that your long-term goal is to play in your city's youth orchestra. Because you are motivated, you make time for lessons and for practice even though it means that you miss out on other activities with your friends. Motivating yourself to engage in healthful, rewarding activities is one of the best ways to combat boredom. Managing boredom effectively will contribute to your mental/emotional health.

Focus on Your Strengths

Seeing yourself in a more positive way can help improve your self-esteem. Start by listing all your strengths and your successes. Work to improve your talents and abilities. Recognize your limitations and develop realistic expectations—no one is perfect. All these actions are effective strategies for coping with feelings of inadequacy.

Understand and Manage Your Feelings

Managing your feelings is another important part of your mental and emotional health. For example, suppose that you find

Reading Check

Consider these words: *motivated, lazy, determined, doubting, confident, positive.* **What do they have to do with mental and emotional health? Categorize these words under high and low self-esteem.**

HEALTH SKILLS ACTIVITY

PRACTICING HEALTHFUL BEHAVIORS

Improving Your Self-Esteem
There are many ways to take action to improve your self-esteem.

- Make a list of your good qualities. Include adjectives such as *honest, kind, fair, hardworking,* and so on.
- Make a list of everything you do well. You may include sports, problem-solving skills, artistic abilities, academic skills, ability to get along with people, and so on.
- Find something you enjoy doing that gives you a feeling of success.

- Spend time with people who accept you as you are and who support you.
- Offer to help someone who needs help.
- Set realistic goals.

ON YOUR OWN
Choose one of the tips listed here. Demonstrate ways to use this health information to help yourself by putting this tip into action.

LESSON 1: YOUR MENTAL AND EMOTIONAL HEALTH **89**

Listing Examples

Divide the class into three groups with the following assignments about improving one's self-concept. Group one: List five ways you can make sure you finish a difficult term paper on time and receive an excellent grade. Group two: List five ways you can meet and make friends with someone who you really like but have been too shy to talk with all year. Group three: List five ways to cope when you didn't make a team when you really wanted to. Bring the groups together, and have a spokesperson read the group's responses to the entire class. **L2**

Cross-Curriculum Activity

PERFORMING ARTS Have students write song lyrics or a rap about feeling positive about themselves. **L2 INCL** *Special Learning Needs, Different Learning Styles (Kinesthetic)*

HEALTH SKILLS ACTIVITY

PRACTICING HEALTHFUL BEHAVIORS

Help students read and discuss the tips for improving self-esteem. Ask them to explain how and why they think each suggestion works to improve self-esteem.

Go over the On Your Own instructions. Suggest that students write private daily journal entries about their actions and feelings.

Note: This skill is introduced in Chapter 2 on pages 46–47.

Reading Check

List, Group, Label This activity encourages students to categorize words in meaningful ways. Point out that the words in the group are characteristics of self-esteem. Ask students to add as many other words or phrases to the list as possible. Accept all reasonable responses. Some possible words and phrases are *hardworking, focused,* *kind, depressed, considerate.* Next, ask students to group the terms as they are related to high or low self-esteem. For example, *motivated, confident,* and *positive* are all related to high self-esteem; *lazy* and *doubting* are related to low self-esteem. **INCL** *English Language Learners, Special Learning Needs*

Applying Knowledge

Advise students that another way to improve self-esteem is to learn how to handle constructive criticism:

- Focus on the problem, not on how the criticism makes you feel.
- Listen carefully to the criticism. Ask questions if you are not sure what the other person means.
- Ask yourself whether you should change your behavior.
- Consider the character of the person giving the criticism. Do you respect him or her? If so, take the comments seriously.

Have students summarize and share techniques for handling criticism.

❸ Assess

Evaluating

📁 Assign the Lesson 1 Review; then assign the Lesson 1 Quiz in the TCR.

Reteaching

📁 Assign Concept Maps 12, 13 or Reteaching Activities 12, 13 in the TCR.

Enrichment

- 📁 Assign Enrichment Activities 12, 13 in the TCR.
- Read this scenario: Pedro wishes he could look more muscular like other boys in his class. He has tried virtually everything, but nothing works. Ask students what mental health habit Pedro needs to work on and what solutions they might suggest.

❹ Close

Ask each student to identify one lifestyle behavior that promotes good mental and emotional health.

This teen's previous bicycle was stolen when he left it out unlocked. Now he is careful to lock his new bike whenever he has to leave it. *Which coping skill has he applied to his situation?*

yourself losing your temper with friends for no apparent reason. You may realize that you are nervous because you have a track meet coming up. Recognizing the cause of your anxiety will help you manage your interactions with friends.

Develop a Positive Attitude

Your thoughts and behavior have a strong influence on your mental and emotional health. If you believe that you cannot handle new situations, your mental and emotional health will suffer. If, on the other hand, you see challenges as obstacles that you can overcome, your mental health will be affected in a positive way.

Learn from Your Mistakes

You can also improve your self-esteem by learning from your mistakes. This means that you take responsibility for your actions and behavior and recognize when you are wrong. It also means that you see mistakes as opportunities to grow and improve.

Lesson 1 Review

Using complete sentences, answer the following questions on a sheet of paper.

Reviewing Terms and Facts

1. **Vocabulary** Define *self-concept* and *self-esteem.* Use both in a sentence that shows their relationship.
2. **Summarize** List four things you can do to improve your mental and emotional health.
3. **Describe** How does a positive attitude help you?

Thinking Critically

4. **Apply** Rebecca was so embarrassed when the teacher criticized her report that she

hardly listened to the criticism. Although she wasn't sure what the teacher meant, she said nothing. Describe some techniques Rebecca could have used to respond to the criticism.

Applying Health Skills

5. **Communication Skills** With a partner create a skit showing how a teen might demonstrate one of the characteristics that contribute to self-confidence and self-esteem: honesty, integrity, responsibility, and respecting others' dignity. Perform your skit for the class.

90 CHAPTER 4: MENTAL AND EMOTIONAL HEALTH

Lesson 1 Review

1. Self-concept is the view you have of yourself. Self-esteem is how you feel about yourself, or value yourself. The sentence should convey the idea that positive self-concept promotes healthy self-esteem.
2. Any four: Motivate yourself to set healthy, realistic goals and work to achieve them. Focus on your strengths. Understand and

manage your feelings. Develop a positive attitude. Learn from your mistakes.
3. It helps you overcome obstacles and improves mental and emotional health.
4. Responses will vary although they should be supportive of Rebecca.

Understanding Your Emotions

What Are Emotions?

Your **emotions** are your *feelings created in response to thoughts, remarks, and events*. The basic emotions are happiness, love, jealousy, sadness, anger, fear, anticipation, and joy. Emotions can influence most aspects of your life, including how you behave. For example, do sad movies make you cry? How do you react to being teased? How do you express extreme happiness?

Understanding Emotions

Emotions are neither good nor bad, right nor wrong. How you express your emotions is another matter. You can't always choose when an emotion will well up inside you, but you can choose how to handle it. People with good mental and emotional health seek healthy, responsible ways to express their emotions.

Important steps in learning how to express your emotions are described in **Figure 4.2** on page 92.

Expressing your happiness about an achievement is appropriate. *How do you celebrate your accomplishments?*

Quick Write

Briefly describe in writing two situations in which you experienced one of the following: fear, anger, love, guilt, mixed emotions.

LEARN ABOUT...

- expressing emotions in healthy ways.
- meeting emotional needs in healthy ways.

VOCABULARY

- emotions
- empathy
- anxiety
- panic
- resilience
- emotional needs

Lesson 2

Understanding Your Emotions

❶ Focus

Lesson Objectives

Students will be able to

- define *emotions* and explain how they can be expressed in healthy ways.
- name the three basic emotional needs of all humans.
- identify ways to meet their emotional needs in healthy ways.

Motivators

Quick Write
List the emotions on the board. Have students read their responses. As the students share, place a check mark by the appropriate emotion. Then rank the list in order of frequency.

Bellringer Activity
Tell students that colors are often used to signify emotional states. Ask students to name colors that signify emotions. (*red for rage, anger; blue for sadness; green for jealousy; yellow for cowardice; black for bitterness*)

VOCABULARY

Recite each vocabulary term, and instruct students to write the correct spellings for each. When finished, read the proper spellings, and have students correct their own work. Ask students to use each word in an original sentence.

Lesson 2 Resources

Teacher Classroom Resources

- Concept Map 14
- Cross-Curriculum Activity 7
- Enrichment Activity 14
- Health Lab 4
- Lesson Plan 2
- Lesson 2 Quiz

- Reading Tutor Activity 13
- Reteaching Activity 14
- Transparency 14

Student Activities Workbook

- Chapter 4 Study Guide
- Applying Health Skills 14

② Teach

Cross-Curriculum Activity

LANGUAGE ARTS Suggest that interested students write original poems about specific emotions. Encourage these students to share their compositions with the rest of the class. **L2**

Critical Thinking

Ask students to share their ideas about this statement: "Emotions are neither good nor bad, right nor wrong."

- What can make this statement difficult to accept?
- Why is it so important to remember that there are no "bad" emotions, only bad actions? **L1**

VISUAL LEARNING

FIGURE 4.2 Guide students in reading and discussing the stages in expressing emotions. Pose questions such as these:

- Why is it sometimes difficult to identify an emotion?
- Why is this step so important?
- Why do you think it is important to understand the cause of an emotion?
- What are some examples of healthy responses?

Following the discussion, have students describe some healthy methods of communicating emotions. **INCL** *English Language Learners, Special Learning Needs, Behavior Problems, Different Learning Styles (Visual)*

FIGURE 4.2

Expressing Your Emotions

Expressing your emotions in healthy ways helps improve your overall mental health.

1 Identify the Emotion Amy and Hannah used to be best friends. Now Amy feels angry with Hannah and avoids her. She realizes that it is because she is jealous of Hannah.

2 Understand the Cause Amy had expected to get the lead role in the school play. Instead Hannah got the lead, and Amy has just a small part.

3 Respond in a Healthy Way Amy recognizes that her jealousy is ruining a good friendship. She congratulates Hannah and offers to help her learn her lines.

Identifying Your Emotions

Recognizing the emotions that you experience will help you deal with them. Which emotions listed below are familiar to you?

- **Happiness** is a sense of well-being. When you are happy, you feel good about life in general.
- **Sadness** is a normal, healthy reaction to an unhappy event, such as a good friend moving away or a loved one dying. When you are sad, you may feel easily discouraged and have less energy.
- **Fear** is an emotion that can help keep you safe from danger. However, some fears, such as the fear of failure, may keep you from doing things you want or need to do.
- **Anger** is a common reaction to being emotionally hurt or physically harmed.
- **Love** is a combination of caring and affection that binds one person to another.
- **Empathy** affects your social health. **Empathy** is *the ability to understand and share another person's feelings.*
- **Sympathy** means understanding and sharing another's problems or sorrow.
- **Anxiety** can keep you from doing your best. **Anxiety** is *an overwhelming feeling of dread, much like fear.*
- **Jealousy** is a feeling of resentment or unhappiness at another's good fortune.

Reading Check

Complete a cause-and-effect chart listing emotions in the first column and possible effects of each emotion in the second column. In the third column, determine whether the effect was positive or negative.

92 CHAPTER 4: MENTAL AND EMOTIONAL HEALTH

Reading Check

Cause and Effect This reading check will help students identify various emotions as well as evaluate their possible effects. Ask students to fill in a three-column chart with the basic emotions and the effects they may cause. (Cause: Emotion; Effect: Reaction; and Result: Positive or Negative) Then, have the class evaluate the outcome of each emotional response. For example, if anger leads to physical fighting, the result would be negative. If the reaction or effect was to talk through the problem, the result may be a positive change in another's behavior. **INCL** *Special Learning Needs, Behavior Problems*

Expressing Emotions

People express emotions in different ways. We often learn how to express them from watching others who are close to us, such as family members. Learning to understand emotions and to express them in healthy ways is an important part of good mental and emotional health.

Expressing Anxiety and Fear

Have you ever felt anxious before giving a report or taking a test? When you are anxious or fearful, you take shorter breaths, your heart beats faster, and your muscles tense. Anxiety can help you accomplish more by releasing energy. However, too much anxiety and fear can cause you to lose sleep or even to panic. **Panic,** *a feeling of sudden, intense fear,* may be accompanied by physical symptoms such as dizziness and a pounding heart.

Hands-On Health

COMMUNICATING EMOTIONS

This activity will give you practice in communicating positive feelings.

WHAT YOU WILL NEED
- paper
- pen or pencil

WHAT YOU WILL DO
1. In a small group, develop a list of situations that could produce positive feelings for teens. An example might be receiving recognition from a coach after winning a track event.
2. Choose one of the situations on your list and write a skit in which someone expresses positive feelings to a friend.
3. Perform your skit for your classmates.
4. Have classmates evaluate your skit and, if necessary, describe a more effective method of communicating the positive emotions.

IN CONCLUSION
1. Draw conclusions from the skits. Were students comfortable expressing positive emotions? Did the audience have useful suggestions?
2. Overall, what did you learn from this activity? How will it affect your behavior in the future?

LESSON 2: UNDERSTANDING YOUR EMOTIONS **93**

Identifying Examples

Have students name specific emotions they consider positive. Ask: What thoughts, remarks, and events are most likely to create or trigger those feelings? **L1**

Cross-Curriculum Activity

LANGUAGE ARTS Bring to class an assortment of greeting cards, and read the messages on them about friendship and caring. Then have students compose an original greeting card that expresses a positive feeling about someone they care about. **L2**

Hands-On Health

COMMUNICATING FEELINGS

Time: 1 hour

TEACHING THE ACTIVITY
- Help students read and discuss the explanation and the activity directions.
- Have students form small groups in which to plan and perform their skits. Suggest that they focus on expressing pride in their accomplishments.
- Ask students to discuss their responses to the first two In Conclusion questions.

ASSESSMENT
Have students write their responses to the final In Conclusion questions. **INCL** *Different Learning Styles (Kinesthetic)*

MORE ABOUT...

Emotions Strong emotions such as anger can make us feel guilty and ashamed, especially if we have been brought up to believe that such feelings are wrong. Feeling guilty and ashamed, in turn, can erode our self-esteem and damage our mental health.

Be sure to tell students that no one can help how he or she feels; so they should never feel guilty or ashamed about their emotions. How they express their emotions is what matters, and that is something over which they *do* have control.

Lesson 2

Discussing

Ask students to consider the phrase "lose your temper." What does it imply? What usually happens when a person loses his or her temper? How can those outcomes be avoided? **L1**

Demonstrating

Help students discuss the importance of learning to acknowledge and express anger in healthy ways. Then ask volunteers to role-play situations in which teens express their anger clearly but without being threatening or hurtful. **L1**

Cooperative Learning

Guide students in discussing the benefits of volunteering. Ask: Which of your emotional needs are met when you volunteer to help others? How does volunteering improve the health of communities? Then have students work in cooperative groups to explore specific volunteer opportunities for teens in your community. **L2**

Listing

Ask each student to write a list of at least three groups whose members share her or his own values. The groups could have a social, religious, athletic, arts and crafts, or any other focus. Encourage students to consider joining one or more of these groups. **L1**

Sometimes just admitting to a family member or friend that you feel anxious helps. Other people may give you the reassurance and encouragement that you need. Overcoming your anxiety will help build your resilience. **Resilience** is *the ability to adapt to and recover from disappointment, difficulty, or crisis.* Resilience is also known as the "bounce-back" factor. People who develop resilience can bounce back from setbacks and disappointments.

Expressing Anger

It is normal to feel angry at times, but some people express their anger in unhealthy ways. Yelling, hitting, and threatening are not healthy ways to express anger. It is also not healthy to hold anger inside or to deny how you feel. Try these steps when you feel angry.

- Exercise self-control—take a deep breath and stay calm.
- Focus on exactly what made you angry.
- Think of words to communicate your true feelings.
- Calmly tell the other person how you feel and what action has caused you to feel this way.
- Tell the person what you expect from him or her in the future.

Understanding Your Emotional Needs

Everyone has physical needs, such as water, food, and sleep. You also have **emotional needs.** These are *needs that affect your feelings and sense of well-being.* Your basic emotional needs include the following:

- **The need to feel worthwhile.** You need to feel that you make a difference in the world—that you are making a contribution. Working toward short-term and long-term goals will give you a sense of accomplishment.
- **The need to love and be loved.** You need to feel that you are cared for and that you are special to people—family, friends, and classmates.
- **The need to belong.** You need to know that others accept and respect you as you are. Find friends who are accepting, reliable, and trustworthy.

Teens who participate in team sports often form strong bonds with coaches and teammates. The sense of belonging adds to their enjoyment of the sport.

What Teens Want to Know

Are fame and fortune the keys to personal satisfaction? For most people, fame and fortune are not the keys to personal satisfaction. Researchers have found that people were happy when they had the opportunity to choose what they did and when they were successful at what they did. People also rated having close relationships and high self-esteem as important for happiness and personal satisfaction. Happiness comes from having control of your life, participating in activities that allow you to express yourself, and becoming good at whatever you choose to do. Feeling connected to family and friends and feeling good about yourself are also important factors in personal satisfaction.

HEALTH SKILLS ACTIVITY

DECISION MAKING

If a Friend Seems Depressed

Leon has noticed that Keith just doesn't seem like Keith anymore. They have been friends since fifth grade. A month ago Keith's parents told him that the family will be moving to another state in the summer. At first Keith was excited about the move, but now he seems depressed about it. Nothing interests him, and he seldom smiles.

Leon is worried that Keith is showing the warning signs of suicide. However, he is afraid that if he says something, Keith might actually attempt it.

WHAT WOULD YOU DO?

Apply the decision-making skills to Leon's situation. Demonstrate the strategy that you would use to help Keith.

1. **STATE THE SITUATION.**
2. **LIST THE OPTIONS.**
3. **WEIGH THE POSSIBLE OUTCOMES.**
4. **CONSIDER VALUES.**
5. **MAKE A DECISION AND ACT.**
6. **EVALUATE THE DECISION.**

leading causes of death among young people. Every day, 14 young people between the ages of 15 and 24 years take their own lives.

Warning Signs of Suicide

You may know someone who has said things like: "The world would be better off without me," or "I'd be better off dead." Most people who commit suicide talk about it beforehand. Anyone who talks about suicide should be taken seriously. Tell a trusted adult immediately.

People who are thinking about suicide may show signs of depression at first. Once they decide to end their lives, they may feel better because they think that they have solved their problems. They may give away valued possessions. People who reach this point are in great danger. Other warning signs of suicide include:

- Lack of energy
- Withdrawal from friends and family
- No longer taking interest in favorite activities
- No longer taking interest in personal appearance
- Taking unnecessary risks
- Expressing suicidal thoughts or talking a lot about death

Family and friends can be a source of help and support for teens who are having difficulty handling their problems.

LESSON 3: MENTAL AND EMOTIONAL PROBLEMS **99**

Guest Speaker

Invite a counselor from a community mental health center to class to discuss suicide. Be sure to have the speaker reinforce the warning signs of depression and suicide and what someone should do if they suspect someone is considering suicide. Note: Be sure that students understand that any talk of suicide should always be reported. **L1**

HEALTH SKILLS ACTIVITY

DECISION MAKING

Discuss Leon's decision-making process:

1. **Leon is concerned that Keith is depressed and may even be considering suicide.**
2. **Leon can ignore his friend's problem, urge Keith to get help from an adult, or ask an adult to help Keith.**
3. **Keith might not get needed help if Leon ignores his problem. Keith might ignore Leon's suggestions that he get help. Keith might feel angry, but he is likely to get help if Leon talks with an adult.**
4. **Leon values his friendship with Keith. He also values Keith's health and his own.**
5. **Students may decide that Leon should talk to an adult. They should not choose to ignore the problem.**
6. **Remind students to evaluate both short- and long-term consequences.**

Health Literacy

Teen Depression Among teens, depressive symptoms, which include sad or hopeless moods, occur about eight times more often than serious depression. The key difference between depressed moods and serious depression is the intensity and duration of symptoms. Seriously depressed teens are profoundly pessimistic for prolonged periods and may be very self-critical and preoccupied with health, suicide, or death. Depressed teens may experience fatigue and changes in appetite and weight. Teens with depressive illness are more likely to have behavior and academic problems, attempt suicide, and use alcohol or other drugs.

HEALTH Online

Encourage students to explore the Web Links for this chapter and then complete the activity.

❸ Assess

Evaluating

📁 Assign the Lesson 3 Review; then assign the Lesson 3 Quiz in the TCR.

Reteaching

📁 Assign Concept Map 15 or Reteaching Activity 15 in the TCR.

Enrichment

• 📁 Assign Enrichment Activity 15 in the TCR.

• Tell students they have a talk show on a local radio station. A caller claims that he or she has had trouble sleeping, has been eating much more than usual lately, and suddenly dislikes being with people. What conclusion would students draw about the caller? What would they say to the caller? Ask volunteers to act out the talk-show scenario and demonstrate strategies for coping with problems.

❹ Close

Use the lesson objectives written on page 96 of the Teacher Wraparound Edition to review the main concepts of the lesson.

HEALTH Online

Topic: Mental and emotional problems

For a link to more information on mental and emotional problems, go to **health.glencoe.com.**

Activity: Using the information provided at this link, create a brochure that contains information on the different types of mental and emotional problems and how teens can get help.

What You Can Do

With most people, a suicide attempt is a cry for help. They don't really want to die, but they feel so much emotional pain that they can't see any other course of action. They need to be convinced that even though the pain seems unbearable, it will not last forever. If anyone you know talks of suicide:

• Try to react calmly and let the person talk out his or her feelings. Listen without interrupting.
• Don't make comments that challenge the person's intent, such as "You'd never have the nerve," or "You just want attention."
• Offer comfort and support. Tell the person how important she or he is to you and to other people.
• Urge the person to get help right away.
• Don't promise to keep a friend's talk of suicide secret. Tell an adult who will help. Telling could save a life.

Things to Remember When You're Down

Everyone has tough times and feels depressed now and then. Here are some points to remember next time you feel down.

• You are not alone. There are people who understand how you feel.
• Take care of your physical needs—get enough sleep, eat regular and healthful meals, and take time to relax.
• Participate in regular physical activity. Aerobic exercise is particularly effective in boosting mood.
• Avoid alcohol and other drugs, even caffeine. They will only add to your problems.
• Don't wait. Talk to someone about how you feel.

Lesson 3 Review

Using complete sentences, answer the following questions on a sheet of paper.

Reviewing Terms and Facts

1. **Vocabulary** Define *anxiety disorder*.
2. **Identify** What kind of mood disorder is characterized by extreme mood swings?
3. **Compare** What is the difference between clinical depression and the normal depression that most people feel from time to time?

Thinking Critically

4. **Restate** Explain why clinical depression is a serious mental disorder.
5. **Identify** Describe two lifetime strategies for the prevention of disorders such as depression and anxiety that may lead to long-term disability.

Applying Health Skills

6. **Communication Skills** With a classmate, role-play a situation in which one person is depressed and the other reaches out to help. The person offering help should use effective communication skills.

100 Chapter 4: Mental and Emotional Health

Lesson 3 Review

1. A condition in which intense anxiety or fear keeps a person from functioning normally.
2. Bipolar disorder.
3. Normal depression is a short-lived "down" feeling; clinical depression is a mood disorder in which a person loses interest in life and cannot find enjoyment in anything.
4. Clinical depression can disturb life and can lead to substance abuse and to suicide.
5. Responses will vary, but may include developing close relationships with others and working to improve self-esteem.

Getting Help

Knowing When to Get Help

Talking about your thoughts and feelings may be difficult at first. You may feel frightened or embarrassed. You may feel that the adult will be shocked or annoyed by what you have to say. Realize that most adults understand and want to help. Sometimes all you need to do is let someone know that you need help. Needing help is nothing to be ashamed of. It is a mistake *not* to ask for help.

Quick Write

List at least five adults to whom teens can go for help at your school or in your community.

LEARN ABOUT...

- **how to know if you need professional help for a mental or emotional problem.**
- **the kinds of treatments that are available.**
- **kinds of professionals who help people with mental health problems.**

VOCABULARY

- therapy
- family therapy
- psychologist
- psychiatrist

The first step toward solving a problem is to let someone know that you want help. *When was the last time you shared a problem with your parents, guardians, or a trusted adult?*

LESSON 4: GETTING HELP **101**

Lesson 4 Resources

Teacher Classroom Resources

- Concept Map 16
- Cross-Curriculum Activity 8
- Decision-Making Activity 8
- Enrichment Activity 16
- Lesson Plan 4
- Lesson 4 Quiz

- Reading Tutor Activity 15
- Reteaching Activity 16
- Transparency 16

Student Activities Workbook

- Chapter 4 Study Guide
- Applying Health Skills 16

Lesson 4

Getting Help

① FOCUS

Lesson Objectives

Students will be able to

- recognize whether they need professional help for a mental or emotional problem.
- identify the kinds of treatment that are available.
- list the kinds of people and professionals from whom a person can get help with mental health problems.

Motivators

Quick Write
Encourage volunteers to share their responses. Ask students: Which qualities set apart the professional from a good friend and listener?

Bellringer Activity

Ask students to identify the person or people they could go to for help if they had difficulty locating an item in a store, finding a specific room on the school campus, or learning the pronunciation of a foreign word. Encourage as many responses as they can give. Then ask: What do all these people have in common? (*They are sources of help in particular areas.*)

VOCABULARY

Write the vocabulary terms on the board. Ask volunteers to give a definition for each term in their own words. Then have students verify the definitions in the Glossary.

② Teach

Discussing

Ask students:

• What is the difference between discussing your feelings with another teen and talking to a trusted adult such as your parents about your feelings?

• Why is it important to be able to talk with both peers and trusted adults? **L1**

Journal Writing

Ask students to write private journal entries identifying at least four different trusted adults with whom they could discuss problems. For a visual aid, have students draw concentric circles starting with a small circle in the center. In this circle, they can name the adult with whom they can share almost any problem. Then add circles in a ripple effect, representing adults to whom they can tell personal issues, then general issues, and so on. **L1**

VISUAL LEARNING

FIGURE 4.5 Guide students in reading and discussing each of the signs that a person may need professional help. Help students identify the differences between experiencing such feelings occasionally and having them dominate one's outlook on life. **INCL** *English Language Learners, Special Learning Needs, Behavior Problems, Different Learning Styles (Visual)*

Seeking Professional Help

How can you tell if a problem is serious enough to discuss with a mental health professional? Learning the warning signs of mental health problems will help. **Figure 4.5** shows some signs that may indicate a mental health problem for which a professional's help is needed.

Therapy Methods

There are various methods of **therapy**, or *treatment*, for mental health problems. These fall into two broad types: talk therapy and biological therapy. Talk therapy includes a variety of counseling methods. Biological therapy involves using medication to treat mental health problems.

The goal of all mental health treatment is to help patients change so that they can handle their problems better. Some professionals use only counseling, others rely mostly on medication, and still others use both types of therapy. A teen who is clinically depressed after the death of a close friend may be given medication to help improve his or her mood. The teen may also receive counseling to help her or him deal with the loss.

FIGURE 4.5

SIGNS THAT YOU MAY NEED PROFESSIONAL HELP

If you experience several of these signs, and if they last a long time, you may need to talk to a professional. Getting help is an important lifetime strategy for early identification of mental health problems such as depression and anxiety.

- Feeling sad or angry for no reason
- Being tired all the time
- Finding it impossible to concentrate
- Getting lower grades than usual
- Having aches or pains for no reason
- Feeling hopeless, guilty, or ashamed
- Losing or gaining a lot of weight

- Waking up too early or sleeping too much
- Losing interest in activities you usually enjoy
- Avoiding friends or family and wanting to be alone
- Thinking that you just can't fit in anywhere
- Feeling that you can't deal with life
- Using alcohol or other drugs

102 CHAPTER 4: MENTAL AND EMOTIONAL HEALTH

Health Literacy

Personal/Interpersonal Skills Peer counseling has helped countless teens to become skilled listeners and to help their peers face difficult problems. First introduced in the 1960s, peer counseling programs can now be found in schools and youth organizations throughout the country. The teen counselors are trained in com-munication skills; handling emotions; dealing with topics such as depression and substance abuse; and making referrals to professionals for further, in-depth help. An adult coordinator oversees the program. Peer counselors are taught to keep all information confidential. They are also reminded that they are not professional counselors.

Counseling

In counseling, an individual talks with a mental health professional to learn new ways of thinking or behaving. Changing thoughts or behavior leads, in turn, to changes in feelings. By learning to think and behave in healthy ways, the person improves his or her mental and emotional health. Some people feel much better after just a few sessions with a mental health professional. Others may need months of counseling.

Some people choose to talk alone with a counselor. Others prefer to take part in group counseling. In group therapy, the counselor meets with several people at once who have the same or similar problems. Some people find that they benefit from the empathy and support that comes from other members of the group.

A variation on group therapy is family therapy. **Family therapy** is *counseling that seeks to improve troubled family relationships.* Family therapists are trained to help relieve family problems, strengthen family relationships, and solve small problems before they get bigger. The therapy sessions may involve all or some family members.

Counseling Methods

One form of counseling focuses on helping people think more positively about themselves. This kind of therapy can be especially helpful for people who experience depression. The professional helps the depressed person identify negative thoughts that are contributing to the depression. From that point, the person can be guided to more positive ways of thinking. Teens who are depressed because they focus on their weaknesses or mistakes, for example, can learn to focus on their strengths and achievements instead.

Family therapy is helping this family learn better ways to communicate with one another. *Describe how effective communication contributes to family health.*

Analyzing

Have students read several teen advice columns and make a list of the kinds of problems that are frequently presented. What kinds of problems could not be dealt with successfully in this format? (*urgent problems that require immediate attention, very personal problems*) **L3**

Cross-Curriculum Activity

VISUAL ARTS Assign students to create sketches, posters, murals, or other forms of art to represent signs of mental and emotional health problems, such as sadness, hopelessness, fear, and anger. **L1** **INCL** *English Language Learners, Special Learning Needs, Behavior Problems, Different Learning Styles* (*Visual*)

Guest Speaker

Invite a school counselor or a local mental health professional to discuss individual and group counseling with the class. Encourage students to ask general-interest questions after the presentation. You may also want the speaker to explain the process by which a student can seek counseling in the school or at community mental health centers. Emphasize that counseling sessions are confidential. **L1**

Comparing

Have students meet in groups to discuss the similarities and differences between individual counseling and group counseling. What are the advantages of each? **L1**

COOPERATIVE LEARNING ACTIVITY

Seeking Help After students have studied this lesson, ask them to list signs of mental and emotional health problems that teens, their friends, and/or their family members might experience. Record the list on the chalkboard. Assign students to small groups. Ask each group to select one of the signs from the list on the board. Have them identify possible causes and various sources of health care services that might be used to address the problem. Have them arrive at a consensus as to where someone might go to receive help. Ask each group to select a spokesperson to share the group's thinking with the class.

Comprehending

Ask students:

• Why is it important not to take another person's medicine?

• What consequences can result from taking antianxiety drugs or antidepressants that were not prescribed for you? **L1**

Providing Resources

Have students begin a "Yellow Pages Directory" of community resources for mental and emotional health. The directory should include the name of each program, a brief description of its services, an address, and phone number. Students probably will need to contact social workers, clergy, counselors, and public-health agencies to gather this information. Have students add other health services to this directory throughout the course. Ask volunteers to computerize the information, perhaps even creating a database. Make printouts for the class. **L3**

Cross-Curriculum Activity

LANGUAGE ARTS Write the types of professionals presented in the lesson on separate slips of paper. Place the slips in a box, and let every student draw one slip. Have students design a brochure that explains the training received and services offered by the type of professional written on their slip of paper. **L2**
INCL *English Language Learners, Special Learning Needs, Behavior Problems, Different Learning Styles (Visual)*

CONNECT TO
Language Arts

TALKING ABOUT
DEPRESSION
Imagine that you are depressed and feel that you need help. Consider how you would get a conversation started and how you would communicate your feelings. *What are three different ways in which you could tell someone that you need help?*

School psychologists are trained to listen to students and help them find a way of dealing with their problems. *How could teens and their families seek a cure for a mental or emotional problem from a school-linked service such as a school psychologist or a school nurse?*

Another form of counseling focuses on changing behavior. This type of therapy is especially helpful to people with anxiety disorders such as phobias. The individual learns to stay calm while facing the situation he or she fears. Imagine, for example, a girl who has a severe fear of giving speeches. She might begin by learning to stay calm while giving a brief talk to a few friends. Her therapist might then encourage her to speak for a little longer and to more people. Eventually, she might be able to speak in front of a large group without feeling any fear.

Drug Treatments

Some mental health disorders can be treated with drugs. Different types of drugs are used to treat different kinds of illnesses. People with anxiety disorders may take antianxiety drugs, which affect the central nervous system. Those who have clinical depression may take antidepressant drugs, which affect brain activity. Drug treatment is highly individual. A drug or dose that may help one person could seriously harm another. The medications used to treat mental disorders can be prescribed only by a medical doctor.

Sources of Help

People in a variety of roles and professions can help with mental health problems. Teens often seek help from the following people:

● **Parent or other adult family member.** You might be able to get all the help you need by talking with a parent or guardian, older brother or sister, or other adult family member. Family members have a special bond and care very deeply for one another.

Reading Check

Summarizing Have each student complete her or his own T-chart. Below are some sample elements to include:

Who: Teens can get help from family members, teachers, counselors, clergy, and medical professionals.

What: Therapy and counseling help to resolve issues and problems.

When: See signs listed in Figure 4.5 on page 102.

Where: School, home, medical facility, and so on.

How: Find someone you trust, and ask for help.

- **Clergy member.** A religious leader may have formal training in counseling. Even those who do not have such training usually have a lot of experience in counseling people of all ages.
- **Teacher or school counselor.** Many teachers and all school counselors are trained to help students with mental and emotional problems.
- **Family counselor.** Family counselors see family members together. Most family counseling sessions focus on improving communication among family members.
- **School nurse.** If you are not sure what kind of help you need, seek care from the school nurse with your family. School nurses are trained to deal with all types of health problems. A nurse can guide you to the help you need.
- **Social worker.** Many schools have social workers who help students and their families with social and personal problems that interfere with learning. Students experiencing these types of problems should seek care from school-linked services with their families when appropriate.
- **Psychologist.** A **psychologist** (sy·KAH·luh·jist) is *a mental health professional who is trained and licensed by the state to counsel.* Psychologists treat mental health problems by using one or several types of counseling.
- **Psychiatrist.** A **psychiatrist** (sy·KY·uh·trist) is *a medical doctor who treats mental health problems.* A psychiatrist is the only mental health professional who can prescribe drugs.

Reading Check

Increase comprehension. Complete a T-chart that shows what you know about getting help.

Lesson 4 Review

Using complete sentences, answer the following questions on a sheet of paper.

Reviewing Terms and Facts

1. **Identify** Name the two broad types of therapy for mental health problems.
2. **Recall** What are some of the benefits of group therapy?
3. **Vocabulary** Define the term *family therapy* and use it in a sentence.

Thinking Critically

4. **Compare** Compare and contrast thought and behavior therapy.

5. **Apply** What factors might determine which person an individual should talk to about a mental health problem?

Applying Health Skills

6. **Accessing Information** Research mental health disorders that are common in teens. In a report, identify and describe lifetime strategies for early identification and treatment of these disorders.

❸ Assess

Evaluating

📁 Assign the Lesson 4 Review; then assign the Lesson 4 Quiz in the TCR.

Reteaching

- 📁 Assign Concept Map 16 or Reteaching Activity 16 in the TCR.
- Have students use the information in the lesson to answer these questions: When should you get help? Where can you go for help? Whom can you talk to? Why is it important to get help?

Enrichment

- 📁 Assign Enrichment Activity 16 in the TCR.
- Have students construct flowcharts that show the course of action teens should take in helping troubled peers. If necessary, draw a flowchart model on the board.

❹ Close

Go around the room, and ask each student to name one place where a person with emotional problems could go for help.

Lesson 4 Review

1. Talk therapy, biological therapy.
2. Helps individuals receive empathy and support from other group members.
3. Counseling to restore troubled family relationships. Sentences will vary.
4. Thought therapy helps people identify harmful thoughts and develop more positive ways of thinking; behavior therapy encourages people to change behavior in small steps that do not threaten them.
5. Some possible answers may include who is available to help and how comfortable they feel with a particular person.

Lesson 5

Coping with Loss

① Focus

Lesson Objectives

Students will be able to
- identify the five stages people go through when they know they are dying.
- identify the five stages of grieving.
- list strategies for dealing with loss.

Health Skills
- Communication Skills, p. 107

Motivators

 Quick Write
Allow students to share their responses. Ask: Why is it sometimes difficult for people to step forward to comfort someone under these circumstances?

Bellringer Activity

Ask students to write about how they felt when they lost something of great value. After volunteers share their responses, explain that those common reactions are akin to what people feel when someone dies.

Lesson 5

Coping with Loss

Quick Write

Write about what you might do to help a close friend or relative deal with the loss of a loved one.

LEARN ABOUT...

- the stages people go through when they are dying.
- the stages of grieving.
- strategies for dealing with loss.

VOCABULARY

- grief
- hospice care
- grief counselor

Different Kinds of Loss

Have you ever lost something that was really important to you? Maybe a close friend moved away or a beloved family pet died. Whenever you experience loss, you feel sorrow.

The greatest sorrow usually occurs when a loved one dies. Although dying and death are part of the life cycle of human beings, at such times everyone experiences some kind of grief. **Grief** is *the sorrow caused by loss of a loved one.* The length of time a person grieves after a death depends on the individual.

Elisabeth Kübler-Ross, a noted Swiss-American doctor, studied the experiences of dying people and their families. Dr. Kübler-Ross identified five stages that people go through when they face death. Not all people experience all five stages, and some experience them in different sequences. The stages do, however, provide guidelines that help us understand how people experience dying.

- **Stage 1: Denial.** Refusing to accept that one is dying. Telling oneself that "it is all a mistake" and hoping to wake up from this "nightmare."

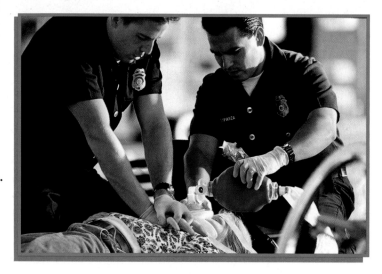

Rescue workers are among the first on the scene during emergencies. Their efforts can mean the difference between life and death.

Lesson 5 Resources

Teacher Classroom Resources
- Concept Map 17
- Enrichment Activity 17
- Lesson Plan 5
- Lesson 5 Quiz
- Reading Tutor Activity 16
- Reteaching Activity 17

 Transparency 17

Student Activities Workbook
- Chapter 4 Study Guide
- Applying Health Skills 17
- Health Inventory 4

- **Stage 2: Anger.** Angrily asking, "Why me?" Often directing the anger toward friends, family members, doctors, and nurses.
- **Stage 3: Bargaining.** Looking for ways to prolong life. Hoping for a medical miracle or praying to be spared in exchange for living a better life.
- **Stage 4: Depression.** Feeling deep sadness for loss of life and other losses. Realizing that one will not live to keep promises or realize goals.
- **Stage 5: Acceptance.** Accepting the reality of death and making peace with the world.

Hospice Care

Many dying people and their families choose to have hospice care during the last few weeks or months of the dying process. **Hospice care** is *care provided to the terminally ill that focuses on comfort, not cure.* The goal of hospice care is to provide support, relief from pain, and comfort for dying people and their families. Some people receive hospice care in a hospital, nursing home, or an inpatient hospice center. Most often, though, hospice care is provided in the patient's home to maintain peace, comfort, and dignity.

Hospice workers are specially trained to help people who are dying. *Where is hospice care provided?*

HEALTH SKILLS ACTIVITY

COMMUNICATION SKILLS

Writing a Sympathy Note

If a close friend or relative loses a loved one, you may wish to write a sympathy note. Your words will be a loving gift to your grieving friend and will also help you deal with the sorrow yourself.

Consider the following guidelines.

- Mention the special qualities of the person who died.
- Share a favorite memory about the person who died.
- Avoid comments such as: "Just be happy that he is out of pain," or "Think of all that you still have to be thankful for." Such comments can be hurtful and can make the grief process more difficult.

- Understand that your friend's grief is unique. Different people respond to death in different ways.
- Don't try to take away the hurt. You can't, but your sincere acknowledgment of your friend's sorrow can help.

ON YOUR OWN
Write a sympathy note to an imaginary friend who has suffered the loss of a loved one. Your note should be kind and comforting.

LESSON 5: COPING WITH LOSS **107**

---

② Teach

Examining the Issue

Direct students to recall any experiences with death they may have had as children. Ask:

- What feelings and events do they remember?
- Have those feelings changed as they grew older? If so, why? **L1**

Discussing

Ask students to describe the life cycle of human beings, including dying and death. Then ask students to discuss why teens seem to think death will never happen to them. (*It seems too far off. They haven't been exposed to death in most instances.*) Ask: Do you think children, teens, or senior citizens think about death most often? Why? **L1**

HEALTH SKILLS ACTIVITY

COMMUNICATION SKILLS

Help students read and discuss the suggestions for writing sympathy notes. Encourage students who have written (or received) sympathy notes to share their experiences, if they volunteer.

Then have students write sympathy notes as directed in On Your Own. Let them exchange notes with partners; have partners suggest changes, if appropriate.

Note: This skill is introduced in Chapter 2 on pages 34–38. **L2**

Beyond the Classroom

Community The need for hospice care in the United States is expected to rise. The hospice movement has always relied heavily on volunteers. Prompt students by asking: What qualities do you think a hospice volunteer would need? Then ask students to interview hospice staff and/or volunteers about their experiences with dying patients. Encourage students to learn about positive ways that the staff members and volunteers help the terminally ill patients and their families. As part of their research, students could learn more about the origin of the hospice program and its day-to-day operations. They could begin by contacting the nearest hospital or health care center.

Lesson 5

Examining the Issue

Ask students to think about instances in which they or someone close to them experienced a loss. Have students mention ways in which people helped them cope. Ask: What kinds of help seemed most effective? Encourage students to ponder the temporary or permanent changes that often accompany a loss, such as reluctance to take risks or fear of getting involved emotionally. Tell the class that certain feelings may become buried only to emerge later when a similar situation occurs. **L1**

Critical Thinking

Help students consider the role that funerals and memorial services play in the grieving process. How do these ceremonies help the living accept their loss? **L2**

The Grief Process

Understanding that death is part of the life cycle of human beings does not mean that the death of someone you care about won't be painful. Knowing how to grieve, however, can help you handle the hurt.

Grief often has stages similar to the stages of death. Like the stages of death, the stages of grief may be experienced in various orders. Not all people experience all of the following stages:

- **Shock.** Shortly after the death of a loved one, people tend to feel separated from their emotions. They may feel numb or empty or seem to have no feelings at all.
- **Anger.** Sometimes the survivors feel angry. The anger may even be directed at the dead person for leaving them.
- **Yearning.** The survivors ache. The loss of the loved one has left a great empty place in their lives. They wish that the loved one could come back.
- **Depression.** The survivors begin to accept the reality of their loss. The person has died and will not be coming back.
- **Moving on.** The survivors are able to go forward with their lives. They have not forgotten the one who died, but the deep pain over the loss has lessened.

In a national or local crisis in which people die, the community shares in the grieving process. *How does the bonding of communities provide support for individuals and families?*

DEALING WITH SENSITIVE ISSUES

Grief Sadly, today's teens may be faced with the grim realities of death. Making matters worse is the fact that they may be forced to cope with death from violent acts. While discussing the lesson, never force a student to participate. Reinforce the feelings of anger, disbelief, and sadness that are natural to the process of grieving. Remind students that grieving takes time and that each person will grieve in a unique way. Also, be sensitive to the fact that it may be too traumatic for students to revisit feelings of grief. Emphasize that this lesson will present ways to understand and cope with loss in the future.

Coping with the Death of a Loved One

Grieving people often need to share their feelings with others. Sometimes trained counselors help people cope with their loss. **Grief counselors** are *counselors who teach people coping strategies to deal with grief.* They often help whole communities cope with a disastrous event such as an airplane crash.

Coping strategies suggested by grief counselors include the following.

- **Remember what was good about the person.** Focus on happy times and on ways in which the person was special.
- **Don't run away from your feelings.** The hurt from the loss cannot be denied. It is best to let the feelings out.
- **Share your feelings with others.** Telling someone about the hurt you are feeling will remind you that you are not alone.
- **Join a support group.** Most communities offer support groups in which people who have suffered a loss can share their pain with others. These groups are usually sponsored by churches, synagogues, and other organizations.

Memorial services provide an opportunity to deal with loss and to start the healing process. *Have you attended a memorial service? How did it seem to comfort people?*

Lesson 5 Review

Using complete sentences, answer the following questions on a sheet of paper.

Reviewing Terms and Facts

1. **Vocabulary** Define the term *grief*.
2. **Explain** List and describe the five stages of dying.
3. **Recall** Describe three effective coping strategies for dealing with the loss of a loved one.

Thinking Critically

4. **Compare** How are the stages of dying and stages of grief similar? How are they different?

5. **Synthesize** How might you comfort a child whose pet had died?

Applying Health Skills

6. **Communication Skills** Active listening is important when you talk with a grieving person. With a classmate, write and perform a skit that demonstrates the use of listening skills to help a person who has lost a close friend. Demonstrate correct use of body language, conversation encouragers, mirroring thoughts and feelings, and asking questions.

LESSON 5: COPING WITH LOSS **109**

③ Assess

Evaluating

Assign the Lesson 5 Review; then assign the Lesson 5 Quiz in the TCR.

Reteaching

- Assign Concept Map 17 or Reteaching Activity 17 in the TCR.
- Have students identify the five stages a person may go through while dying and the five stages of grief, noting the similarities and differences between each parallel stage. Ask students to describe the application of effective coping skills.

Enrichment

- Assign Enrichment Activity 17 in the TCR.
- Ask students to imagine they have been asked to deliver a eulogy, a speech of remembrance, following the death of a friend. What words would they use that might help comfort the survivors?

④ Close

Go around the room, and ask each student to name one way he or she could show positive support for a person who is coping with death.

Lesson 5 Review

1. Sorrow caused by loss of loved one.
2. Denial, anger, bargaining, depression, acceptance.
3. Any three: Remember what was good about the person, don't run away from your feelings, share your feelings with others, join a support group.
4. Both include initial reactions of anger, but the dying process ends with acceptance while the grief process ends with moving on.
5. Possible answers include letting the child feel sad and encouraging the child to remember stories about the pet.

Dealing with Anxiety

1 Focus

Objectives

Students will be able to

- compare and contrast fears vs. phobias.
- define common specific phobias.
- communicate with a friend suffering from panic attacks.

Motivator
Quick Write

Ask students to write about the difference between a *fear* and a *phobia*. How are the two conditions the same? How are they different? Tell students to save their replies for later in the lesson.

2 Teach

Cross-Curriculum Activity

LANGUAGE ARTS Ask students to define each of the following common phobias:

- acrophobia (*fear of heights*)
- agoraphobia (*fear of leaving a safe place*)
- aviophobia (*fear of flying*)
- claustrophobia (*fear of confined spaces*)
- necrophobia (*fear of death or dead things*)
- pyrophobia (*fear of fire*)
- technophobia (*fear of technology*)
- xenophobia (*fear of strangers or foreigners*)

Have students come up with words that describe other, imaginary phobias. For instance, examophobia (fear of taking tests).

TIME HEALTH
Dealing with Anxiety

There's more than one kind of therapy when it comes to relieving anxiety.

Behavioral Therapy

When the brain sets off anxiety alarms, our first instinct is to find the off switch. Behavioral scientists (therapists who focus on changing a person's behavior) take the opposite approach. They want you to get used to the noise so that you don't hear it anymore. In this type of therapy, the standard treatment for anxiety conditions such as phobias is to expose patients to a tiny bit of the very thing that causes them anxiety. The exposure is increased over a number of sessions until the brain gets used to the fear.

A patient suffering from a blood phobia, or fear of blood, for example, might first be shown a picture of a scalpel or syringe, then a real syringe, then a vial of blood, and so on. The patient is taken up the anxiety ladder until there are no more rungs to climb. There is a risk that if treatment is cut short (before the patient has become used to the anxiety triggers), the anxious feelings could be made worse. Done right, however, behavioral therapy can bring relief from specific phobias in as little as two or three sessions. Social anxiety takes somewhat longer to treat, and other conditions may take a good deal longer still.

Cognitive Therapy

Cognitive therapists don't expect patients to surround themselves with anxiety. They ask patients to use the power of the mind to think their way through it. Cognitive therapy teaches people who are anxious or depressed to rethink their view of the world. This helps patients develop a more realistic idea of the risks or obstacles they face.

Patients suffering from social-anxiety disorder, for example, might see a group of people whispering at a party and assume the gossip is about them. A cognitive therapist would teach them to rethink that assumption.

WHAT TEENS WANT TO KNOW

I hate public speaking! Does that mean I have a phobia? In many studies, public speaking was cited as one of the most common fears in adults—more common than fear of heights, flying, and even death. This fear is perfectly normal and can even be positive. For instance, a fear of public speaking may motivate someone to prepare beforehand. First, recognize that your fear of public speaking is shared by many others. Remember that experience tends to make pubic speaking less stressful, so practice in front of friends or family members. If, however, the thought of public speaking incites a panic attack or extreme anxiety, you may well have a phobia and should seek treatment.

Physical Activity

Before turning to therapy, many people try to bring their anxiety under control on their own. Unlike most emotional or physical conditions, anxiety disorders can respond well to such self-medication. One of the most effective techniques is physical activity. It's no secret that a good workout or a brisk walk can take the edge off even the most severe anxiety. Scientists once believed that this positive effect was due to the release of natural chemicals known as endorphins. New research, however, has called this idea into question. Regardless, being physically active on a regular basis may well help ease the anxious brain.

Breathing Exercises

One way to quiet the mind is by focusing attention on breathing. Breathing exercises can help calm anxiety by slowing a racing heart and lengthening the short, shallow breaths of a panic attack.

Lifestyle Changes

If all else fails, go back to basics and try cleaning up your lifestyle. For starters, you can cut back on sugar and caffeine. Ask yourself: Am I eating right and getting enough physical activity, sleep, and time to relax? ▰

Generalized Anxiety Disorder

What it is: Excessive anxiety or worry, occurring regularly for at least six months.
What it isn't: Occasional serious worry that doesn't noticeably decrease quality of life.

Specific Phobia

What it is: Intense and exaggerated fear of a specific situation or object, often accompanied by extreme anxiety symptoms.
What it isn't: Strong dislike of certain places or things.

Panic Disorder

What it is: Recurrent, unexpected attacks of acute anxiety, peaking within 10 minutes. Such panic may occur in a familiar situation, such as a crowded elevator.
What it isn't: Occasional episodes of extreme anxiety in response to a real threat.

TIME TO THINK...

About Coping with Anxiety

People suffer from many different types of anxiety. This article mentions one specific example: blood phobia. Think of another kind of anxiety that a person might have. Now imagine that you are a behavioral therapist. Write down a step-by-step treatment plan for your patient's anxiety, using the method described in this article. Share your plan with the rest of the class.

③ Apply

Time to Think

Allow students to work in small groups to create their treatment plans. Review the plans to ensure that they're on target and have each group present their plan to the class.

Performing Role-Plays

Review with students the "Sources of Help" material on pages 104 and 105. Ask students to imagine the following scenario. Cecilia tells her friend Adriana that she is suffering from frequent panic attacks during which her palms sweat, her heart races, and she has trouble breathing. There is no pattern to the attacks and they occur in familiar situations at school, at home, and even on the bus. What should Adriana do? Divide students into pairs and have them role-play a scene in which Adriana listens to Cecilia and then advises her on ways to get help. Have students present their role-plays to the class.

Health Literacy

The Depiction of Fear in the Media Ask students to brainstorm movies and television shows that play upon common fears. (For instance, "Jaws" "Arachnophobia," and numerous fright films.) Ask students, "Why do you think these stories are popular? Do they alleviate people's fears or make them worse? Can you think of a situation in which this type of program may actually be therapeutic for someone?" For extra credit, ask students to sketch out the plot of their own fear-based movie or television show.

This lesson addresses National Health Education Standard 3.

STRESS MANAGEMENT

Objective

After completing the lesson, students will be able to demonstrate strategies for coping with stress and describe the relationship between emotions and stress.

Time: 45 minutes

Materials: video/audio recording equipment (optional)

Teacher Classroom Resources

📁 Building Health Skills Activities

• Transparency Master 3, "Stress Management"

• Reproducible Master 29, "Put Stress in Its Place"

---

1. Model

• Have students read about A.J. Conduct a brief discussion about the cause of his stress and the coping skills he used. Ask students to describe the relationships between emotions and stress.

• Ask students to brainstorm strategies they use for coping with stress. Classify these methods by referring to Transparency Master 3. Add other methods to the transparency, if indicated.

PUT STRESS IN ITS PLACE

Model

Teens experience many different and often conflicting emotions. These sudden emotional changes can become a source of stress. Read about a teen named A.J., who is trying to deal with many emotions at once.

A.J. has been friends with Paige for many years. Recently, he began to think of her as more than a friend. He wanted to tell her about his feelings but was afraid he might lose her friendship if he did. Then he found out that she was interested in another boy, Malcolm. Now he feels even more conflicting emotions. He still likes Paige and is happy when he's with her, but he feels angry about her feelings for Malcolm. He also feels jealous of Malcolm.

A.J. knows that he can't change his emotions, but he can deal with the stress they are causing in his life. He tries to think positively and keep matters in perspective. Paige is still his friend, and he is lucky to have her in his life. He also knows that Paige may not always like Malcolm as much as she does now. In the meantime he tries to ease the stress by spending time on activities he enjoys, such as listening to music. He also talks to other friends about his problems. This helps him feel better.

112 CHAPTER 4: MENTAL AND EMOTIONAL HEALTH

Teaching Tips

Incorporating Physical Activity Note that coping skills involving some form of physical activity are especially good for stress management. Coordinate with physical education teachers, yoga instructors, Tai Chi instructors, and providers of other community resources to demonstrate the benefits and techniques for different activities that incorporate body movement.

Posting Exemplars Posting anchor papers or exemplars is a good strategy for communicating expectations. The first time an assessment is given, you may need to outline an exemplar task. Any time there is more than one right answer for an assessment, exemplar tasks can be posted for all students to see.

Practice

The physical changes of adolescence can be a source of stress for teens. Rapid physical changes can lead to problems with body image, causing anxiety and low self-esteem. Read the scenario below, and answer the questions that follow. Compare answers with your classmates. How many stress management skills can you suggest?

Kelsey spends a lot of time looking in the mirror and worrying about her appearance. She feels that her feet are too big, her legs are too long, and her mouth is too small. Kelsey's mom keeps telling her, "You're beautiful the way you are." Kelsey knows that she has some attractive features, but she just can't seem to feel comfortable with her changing appearance.

1. What is the cause of Kelsey's stress?
2. Suggest three ways Kelsey can manage her stress.

Apply/Assess

Use what you've learned about emotional stress to develop a TV or radio announcement. Your announcement should tell teens what they need to know about managing emotional stress. Work with a small group to write an announcement between 30 and 60 seconds long. Describe some common emotions that teens experience, and explain how they can cause stress. Then suggest some strategies for coping with stress. If you have access to video or recording equipment, tape your announcement to demonstrate these strategies for other students.

Stress Management

Ways to manage stress include:
- Relaxing
- Connecting with others
- Keeping a positive outlook
- Staying physically active
- Managing your time

Self-Check

- Does our announcement describe emotions that teens experience?
- Do we explain how emotions can lead to stress?
- Do we suggest ways to manage stress?

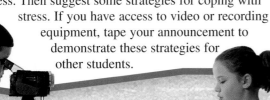

2. Practice

- Instruct students to read the scenario about Kelsey and answer the questions that follow.
- Provide an opportunity for students to compare their answers.
- Discuss the cause of Kelsey's stress and develop a class list of coping skills. Have students identify the skills that work best for them. Ask students to describe the relationships between emotions and stress.

3. Apply/Assess

- You may wish to distribute Building Health Skills Reproducible Master 29 in the TCR to guide students in completing this activity.
- Divide students into groups to develop their announcements. Allow time for volunteers to deliver their announcements to the class.
- If possible, provide video and/or recording equipment so students can record their announcements demonstrating strategies for coping with stress. Work with teachers in other grades or classes to view the announcements.
- Remind students to refer to the Self-Check before and after creating their announcements.

Assessment Scoring

Using a rubric, student work should provide evidence of all criteria to achieve the highest score.

Skills

Student work demonstrates

- the identification of emotions as causes of stress.
- a variety of coping skills to manage stress.

Concept

Student work provides

- accurate information about emotions teens experience.
- facts about stress management.
- conclusions about how stress management and health are interrelated.

Checking Comprehension

Use the Chapter 4 Assessment to examine the most important ideas presented in the chapter.

Answers to Reviewing Vocabulary and Concepts

Lesson 1
1. personality
2. self-concept
3. mental and emotional health

Lesson 2
4. resilience
5. panic
6. empathy
7. anxiety

Lesson 3
8. false; personality disorders
9. false; schizophrenia
10. true
11. true
12. false; mood disorders

Lesson 4
13. true
14. false; psychologist
15. true

Lesson 5
16. b
17. d

Thinking Critically

18. If you have high self-esteem, you believe in yourself and set challenging goals for yourself. This motivates you to do your best.
19. Responses will vary. Might set example by bouncing back after losing an important sporting competition or by showing humor after a disappointment.

After You Read

Use your completed Foldable to review the information on self-concept, self-esteem, and personality.

FOLDABLES Study Organizer

Reviewing Vocabulary and Concepts

On a sheet of paper, write the numbers 1–7. After each number, write the term from the list that best completes each sentence.

> - self-concept
> - empathy
> - resilience
> - anxiety
> - personality
> - panic
> - mental and emotional health

Lesson 1
1. Your _____ is the unique combination of feelings, thoughts, and behavior that makes you different from everyone else.
2. Your self-esteem is closely related to your _____.
3. A positive outlook is a sign of _____.

Lesson 2
4. Your ability to bounce back from disappointments and difficulties is called _____.
5. Dizziness and a pounding heart can accompany _____.
6. If you understand and share another person's feelings, you have _____.
7. _____ is an overwhelming feeling of dread, much like fear.

On a sheet of paper, write the numbers 8–15. Write *True* or *False* for each statement below. If the statement is false, change the underlined word or phrase to make it true.

Lesson 3
8. <u>Mood disorders</u> are a variety of psychological conditions that affect a person's ability to get along with others.
9. A person with <u>anxiety</u> loses contact with reality.
10. One of the warning signs of suicide is giving away <u>valued possessions</u>.
11. <u>Phobia</u> is an intense and exaggerated fear of a specific object or situation.
12. Bipolar disorder and depression are examples of <u>therapy</u>.

Lesson 4
13. There are two broad types of <u>therapy</u>, or treatment, for mental health problems.
14. A mental health professional who is trained and licensed by the state to counsel is a <u>hospice caregiver</u>.
15. The only kind of mental health professional who can prescribe drugs is a <u>psychiatrist</u>.

Lesson 5
On a sheet of paper, write the numbers 16 and 17. After each number, write the letter of the answer that best completes each statement.
16. Which of the following cares for the terminally ill?
    a. resilience
    b. hospice
    c. mood disorders
    d. heredity
17. What is the term for a person who teaches people coping strategies to deal with grief?
    a. therapist
    b. psychiatrist
    c. psychologist
    d. grief counselor

INCLUSION STRATEGIES

Special Learning Needs, Behavior Problems, English Language Learners The following suggestions are helpful for students with special learning needs, students with behavior problems, and ELL students:

- Pair these students with more proficient learners who can help summarize the main concepts of the chapter.

- Direct these students to listen to the Teen Health Audio Summaries. This component provides an audio and written summary of the chapter in both English and Spanish.

- Use photographs, drawings, or magazine clippings whenever possible to help students visualize the important concepts of the chapter.

Thinking Critically

Using complete sentences, answer the following questions on a sheet of paper.

18. Relate How is self-esteem related to self-motivation?

19. Hypothesize What are some ways you can show resilience that set an example for younger students to follow?

20. Compare How are anxiety disorders and mood disorders similar and different?

Career Corner

Mental Health Counselor Do you enjoy helping others solve personal problems? Then you might consider a career as a mental health counselor. These professionals have four years of college and a two-year advanced degree in counseling. They must also have supervised counseling experience to become licensed. Learn more by clicking on Career Corner at health.glencoe.com.

Standardized Test Practice

Math

Read the paragraph below and then answer the questions.

Teens who are severely depressed might consider suicide as a way out. What can you do to help someone before he or she reaches this point? Be aware of signs such as changes in sleeping and eating patterns and withdrawal from family and friends and activities that were once enjoyed. Tell the person that you care and listen to him or her. Encourage the person to get professional help.

1. Suicide is the third leading cause of death in the United States among people ages 15 to 24. In 1990, about 13 out of every 100,000 people in this age group committed suicide. According to this ratio, how many young people in a group of 525,000 young people would commit suicide? Use a proportion to solve.

(A) 9 young people

(B) 24 young people

(C) 53 young people

(D) 68 young people

2. Out of a group of 498 troubled young people, suppose 67 percent of them got counseling and medical help. How many of these young people received needed help?

(A) 33 young people

(B) 164 young people

(C) 334 young people

(D) 378 young people

3. What is meant by the statement that four times as many young males commit suicide as females, but young females attempt suicide four times more frequently than males?

---

20. Anxiety disorders involve fear or worry, whereas mood disorders involve a high or low mood. Both are common mental disorders that are less serious than schizophrenia.

Test Practice

1. D

2. C

3. More young females attempt suicide than young males, but their attempts are less likely to be successful.

Reteaching

📁 Assign Study Guide 4 in the Student Activities Workbook.

Evaluate

• 📁 💿 Use the reproducible Chapter 4 Test in the TCR, or construct your own test using the **Exam***View*® Pro Testmaker.

• 📁 Use Performance Assessment 4 in the TCR.

Enrichment

Direct interested students to learn more about traditional and contemporary theories of mental health treatment. They might contact a psychology teacher or a professional mental health counselor. Students should summarize the information they discover and present their findings to the class.

Assessment ✓

Self-Assessment Direct students to review the activities that are provided throughout the chapter. Encourage each student to select one finished product or activity that demonstrates his or her best work for the chapter. Have students explain what they learned and how the examples they selected show their progress.

Career Corner

Mental Health Counselor There are many different counseling fields. For example, one can study to be a school, family, career, or mental health counselor.

• Have students scan the help wanted ads in the local paper for counseling positions.

• Discuss the different areas of counseling that are listed and compare the job requirements.

Planning Guide

Chapter 5	Skills/ Activities	Reproducible Resources	Assessment
Lesson 1 **Your Character and Your Relationships** *pages 118–123*	**HEALTH SKILLS ACTIVITY** ▲ A Matter of Character (*Decision Making*), page 121	*Student Activities Workbook available for use with each chapter* 📁 Parent Letter & Activities 5 📁 Concept Map 18 📁 Cross-Curriculum Activity 9 📁 Decision-Making Activity 9 📁 Enrichment Activity 18 📁 Lesson Plan 1 📁 Reading Tutor Activity 17 📁 Reteaching Activity 18	📁 Lesson 1 Quiz
Lesson 2 **Getting Along with Your Family** *pages 124–128*	**Hands-On Health** ▲ Positive Family Interactions, page 127	📁 Concept Map 19 📁 Enrichment Activity 19 📁 Health Lab 5 📁 Lesson Plan 2 📁 Reading Tutor Activity 18 📁 Reteaching Activity 19	📁 Lesson 2 Quiz
Lesson 3 **Marriage and Parenthood** *pages 129–133*	**HEALTH SKILLS ACTIVITY** ▲ Identifying Role Models (*Analyzing Influences*), page 131	📁 Concept Map 20 📁 Cross-Curriculum Activity 10 📁 Decision-Making Activity 10 📁 Enrichment Activity 20 📁 Lesson Plan 3 📁 Reading Tutor Activity 19 📁 Reteaching Activity 20	📁 Lesson 3 Quiz 📁 Chapter 5 Test 📁 Performance Assessment 5

TIME HEALTH	**Friendly Persuasion** *pages 134–135*

BUILDING HEALTH SKILLS **Sending the Right Message** (*Communication Skills*) *pages 136–137*	📁 Building Health Skills Reproducible Masters 30a & 30b	

Standards		Technology
National	**State/Local**	
National Health Education Standard **1.2, 3.1, 3.4, 5.4, 6.1, 6.2, 6.3**		Transparency 18 Tape/DVD 3, Segment 5, "Developing Character" TeacherWorks™ Internet Activities
National Health Education Standard **1.2, 1.4, 3.4, 5.5**		Transparency 19 TeacherWorks™
National Health Education Standard **1.4, 1.6, 1.8, 2.6, 4.2, 5.4**		Transparency 20 TeacherWorks™ MindJogger Videoquiz **Exam***View*® Pro Testmaker
National Health Education Standard **3.4, 5.1, 5.5**		Building Health Skills Transparency Master 5

TeacherWorks™

Glencoe's new and exclusive TeacherWorks™ is an all-in-one planner and resource center. Access the complete Teacher Wraparound Edition electronically. Find all your classroom resources with just a few easy clicks, and print them right from your computer. Connect directly to Glencoe's customized Health Web site. Access the National Health Education Standards correlations, or insert your own state standards and match them directly to the electronic Teacher Wraparound Edition.

Language Diversity

- English Audio Summaries
- Spanish Audio Summaries
- English Summaries, Quizzes, and Activities
- Spanish Summaries, Quizzes, and Activities
- Spanish Parent Letters and Activities

KEY TO ABILITY LEVELS

Teaching Strategies that appear throughout the chapters have been identified by one of four codes to give you an idea of their suitability for students of varying learning styles and abilities.

L1 **Level 1** strategies should be within the ability range of all students. Often full class participation is required.

L2 **Level 2** strategies are for average to above-average students or for small groups. Some teacher direction is necessary.

L3 **Level 3** strategies are designed for students able and willing to work independently. Minimal teacher direction is necessary.

INCL Strategies are appropriate for students with particular special needs in a general classroom setting.

Promoting Social Health

Chapter at a Glance

Lesson 1 defines social health and identifies the skills essential to building character and healthy relationships.

Lesson 2 identifies the types of family units common in today's society, the changes families often face, and ways to strengthen family bonds.

Lesson 3 introduces the roles and responsibilities of marriage and parenting and the consequences of becoming teen parents.

Health Skills

- A Matter of Character (*Decision Making*), p. 121
- Identifying Role Models (*Analyzing Influences*), p. 131
- Sending the Right Message (*Communication Skills*), pp. 136–137

HANDS-ON ACTIVITY

The Top Ten As a class, have students create a top ten list of healthy relationships. Ask students to brainstorm qualities a person needs in order to have a successful relationship. Examples may include honesty, respect, and caring. Select the ten most important qualities offered by students and write them on the board, but do not number them. Have each student then write each term on a separate slip of paper and rank them in order of 1–10 (most important to least important.) Collect all of the papers, making sure that they are labeled and numbered. Ask two volunteers to count the votes. Have them calculate which quality came in first, second, third, and so on. Have a third volunteer read the top ten list to the class.

Promoting Social Health

HEALTH_Online_

Do you have a strong character? Find out by taking the Health Inventory for Chapter 5 at health.glencoe.com.

FOLDABLES™ Study Organizer

Before You Read

Make this Foldable to record what you learn in Lesson 1 about the six traits of good character. Begin with a plain sheet of 11″ × 17″ paper.

Step 1

Fold a sheet of paper into thirds along the short axis. This forms three columns.

Step 2

Open the paper and fold it in half along the long axis. Fold in half lengthwise two more times to form eight rows.

Step 3

Unfold and draw lines along the folds.

Step 4

Label the chart as shown.

Character Trait	My Traits	Others' Traits
Trustworthiness		
Respect		
Responsibility		
Fairness		
Caring		
Citizenship		
Additional Notes		

As You Read

Analyze and write about your own character traits and those of people you admire in the appropriate column of the chart.

Chapter Introduction

Use one or more of the options below to motivate students and preview chapter content.

HEALTH _Online_

Have students visit **health.glencoe.com.** and take Health Inventory 5 to rate their social health. For new teaching ideas, click on Teaching Today to download helpful tools such as graphic organizers and Webquest activities.

GLENCOE TECHNOLOGY

Teen Health Video and DVD Series
(Each format available in both English and Spanish)

📼💿 You may wish to use:

• Tape/DVD 3, Segment 5, "Developing Character"

MindJogger Videoquiz

📼💿 Use MindJogger to preview or review Chapter 5 content.

TIME HEALTH

Friendly Persuasion
pages 134–135

FOLDABLES™ Study Organizer **Dinah Zike Study Fold**

Organizing Data Using a Table
Students will use this Foldable table to write about their character traits and the character traits of someone they admire. As students read and study the information on the six traits of good character in Lesson 1, ask them to analyze and write about their own character traits in the second column of the chart. Then have them write about the character traits of someone they admire in the third column. Students might admire and describe different people for each of the traits listed. Encourage students to highlight traits that they would like to strengthen.

Lesson 1

Your Character and Your Relationships

① Focus

Lesson Objectives

Students will be able to
- identify different types of relationships.
- describe the traits of good character and explain why good character is important to relationships.
- identify ways to demonstrate good character.
- name ways to strengthen relationships.

Health Skills
- Decision Making, p. 121

Motivators

 Quick Write
Allow students to share their lists of qualities. Then ask: Why are these qualities important? Afterward, discuss ways to demonstrate those qualities.

Bellringer Activity

Ask: What are the benefits of having relationships with other people?

VOCABULARY

Write the lesson's vocabulary terms on six index cards. On six more cards, copy the definitions of each of the terms. Distribute one card to each of 12 students. Have them find a match for their word or definition. Then have each pair read the word and its matching definition.

Your Character and Your Relationships

Quick Write

Make a list of the qualities that you look for in a friend. How do you demonstrate those qualities to your friends?

LEARN ABOUT...

- different types of relationships.
- why character is important to relationships.
- the traits of good character.
- ways to demonstrate good character.
- ways to strengthen relationships.

VOCABULARY

- social health
- relationships
- character
- values
- character trait
- citizenship

Different Kinds of Relationships

One side of your health triangle is social health. **Social health** is *your ability to get along with the people around you.* Your social health is tied directly to your relationships. **Relationships** are *the connections you have with other people and groups in your life.*

People have many different kinds of relationships. As a teen, your relationships are mainly with family, friends, and peers. As you get older, you will develop other relationships, such as those you form at work.

A relationship with one person is distinct from those with others. For instance, you might have a closer bond with one cousin than with another cousin whom you don't see as often. No matter what kinds of relationships you have, they should be healthy and based on strong character traits.

Your relationships with family and friends contribute to your overall social health. *How can you demonstrate positive actions toward others?*

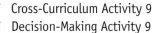

Lesson 1 Resources

Teacher Classroom Resources
- Parent Letter & Activities 5
- Concept Map 18
- Cross-Curriculum Activity 9
- Decision-Making Activity 9
- Enrichment Activity 18
- Lesson Plan 1
- Lesson 1 Quiz

- Reading Tutor Activity 18
- Reteaching Activity 18
- Transparency 18

Student Activities Workbook
- Chapter 5 Study Guide
- Applying Health Skills 18

118

Character—The Foundation of Relationships

How would you describe your character? **Character** is *the way in which a person thinks, feels, and acts.* Character is essential to all of your relationships and to your overall social health. It is the foundation of relationships. The greatest influence on the kinds of relationships you have with other people is your own character.

Whom do you enjoy spending time with? Whom do you trust in your everyday life? Perhaps you trust your parents or other family members, your friends, your teacher, and even your school bus driver. Why do you trust these people? Most likely, you trust them because, through their behavior and actions, they show that they understand, care about, and act upon what they believe is important.

Character, then, is concerned with understanding, caring about, and acting upon certain values. **Values** are *the beliefs and ideals that guide the way a person lives.* Certain core ethical values, such as trust, respect, responsibility, and fairness, are shared by people around the world.

What Is Good Character?

Many different character traits contribute to good character. A **character trait** is *a quality that demonstrates how a person thinks, feels, and acts.* **Figure 5.1** on the next page shows six primary traits of good character.

Your values guide your behavior and actions. By not cheating on tests or lying to your parents, you show that you are honest. *What are some other ways you show that you can be trusted?*

Fairness

When you show fairness, you treat others in the way you would want them to treat you. When you played with a sibling or a friend, you may have shared your toys or taken turns on a swing. As you got older and started participating in sports, you learned to play by the rules and be a team player. *How have you shown fairness in the past week?*

---

② Teach

Developing Good Character ★

Fairness

Invite students to brainstorm about the importance of fairness in relationships. Then have students pair up with one another to discuss and identify ways they could show fairness to one another. Be sure to discuss with students that "fair" isn't always "equal"—the concept of fair has to do with what is reasonable for the situation. This may be a good time to discuss special needs modifications. For example, if one student needs glasses to see clearly, it wouldn't be fair not to let him or her use them because other students didn't need them. Expand examples to other special needs you may have in your class. **INCL** *Special Learning Needs*

Analyzing

Help students develop strategies for monitoring positive and negative relationships that influence health. Begin by asking volunteers to describe a healthy relationship that he or she has with a family member or friend. Encourage discussion with the following questions:

• Has the relationship always been healthy?

• If so, what has made it healthy?

• If not, how was the relationship affected by troubled times?

Invite each student to examine how that positive relationship affects his or her physical, mental/emotional, and social well-being. **L1**

Health Literacy

Health Information Relationships provide the testing ground for teens to try out their emerging identities. They also serve as a bridge between childhood dependence and adult independence. When teens develop social relationships, they learn about trust, compromise, and the value of positive social health. Teens use their relationships with family members and friends to develop and practice positive life skills. For example, they learn empathy for people who may be excluded by a group. The biggest fear for many adolescents and teens is not being accepted into a social group.

Cross-Curriculum Activity

LANGUAGE ARTS Have students work in groups to look up the word *character* in a dictionary.

- How many definitions are given?
- How are all these meanings related?
- Which meaning is the one used in the lesson title? **L1**

Critical Thinking

Help students discuss the definition of values:

- Where do you think we get the beliefs and ideas that guide the way we live?
- Do you think it is possible to change your values? If so, how?
- Do you believe it is possible to have no values? Why or why not? **L1**

VISUAL LEARNING

FIGURE 5.1 Ask a volunteer to read aloud the title and caption for Figure 5.1. Then divide the class into six groups, and assign one of the listed character traits to each group. Have group members work together to read about and discuss their assigned trait. Ask them to brainstorm further examples of *What you might hear*. Then have each group present their character trait to the rest of the class. **INCL** *English Language Learners, Special Learning Needs, Behavior Problems, Different Learning Styles (Visual)*

FIGURE 5.1

Traits of GOOD Character

A person with these traits has good character. *How do you demonstrate these character traits?*

Trustworthiness
A trustworthy person is honest, loyal, and reliable. He or she has the courage to do the right thing and doesn't deceive, cheat, or steal.

What you might hear:
"I know that you can talk to the P.E. coach. She never lets me down."

Respect
Showing respect means being considerate of others and tolerant of differences. It also means using good manners and dealing peacefully with anger or disagreements. You make decisions that show you respect your health and the health of others. You treat people and property with care.

What you might hear:
"I'm getting along better with my parents since I stopped talking back to them."

Responsibility
Showing responsibility means using self-control, thinking before you act, and being accountable for your choices. It also involves doing what is expected of you and always doing your best.

What you might hear:
"I'm calling to let you know I'll be late."

Fairness
Being fair means playing by the rules and practicing good sportsmanship. Fairness also involves taking turns, sharing, and being open-minded.

What you might hear:
"We've been using this basketball court for a while now. Why don't we let those other kids have a turn?"

Caring
A caring person is kind and compassionate. If you care about others, you are sensitive to their needs.

What you might hear:
"She's my friend, so I'm going to be there to listen when she needs me."

Citizenship
The way you conduct yourself as a member of a community is called **citizenship**. Showing good citizenship means doing your part to advocate for a safe and healthy school and community. It also involves obeying the rules and laws and respecting authority.

What you might hear:
"We recycle in our house—I know my efforts can make a difference."

COOPERATIVE LEARNING ACTIVITY

Good Character Art Project Have groups of students work together to complete an art project on good character. Allow them to choose the focus of the project and choose any medium that is practical in the classroom. For example, the focus could be to select character traits that are valuable for different kinds of relationships. Caring would be a good trait to possess in family relationships or close friendships. The medium could be colored pens, pencils, crayons, charcoal, paint, magazine cutouts, and any combination of these. Once the groups have completed their projects, display the final results. **INCL** *English Language Learners, Special Learning Needs, Behavior Problems, Different Learning Styles (Visual)*

Character and Your Health

Your character affects all three sides of your health triangle—your physical, mental/emotional, and social health. Respecting yourself, for example, helps your physical health because you take care of your body by eating nutritious foods and keeping physically active. When you act responsibly and consider consequences, you protect your physical health by staying safe. Being kind and generous and helping people in need enhances your mental/emotional health because you feel good about yourself. When you treat people with respect and compassion, you get along well with others and improve your social health.

Character in Action

When you demonstrate good character traits, you promote not only your own health but also the health of other people. In addition, demonstrating good character through your actions is an acceptable method of gaining attention. You can make a difference in all areas of your life—at home, at school, and in your community.

When you practice healthful behaviors such as jogging, you show that you care about your health. *How can you show that you care about the health of others?*

HEALTH SKILLS ACTIVITY

DECISION MAKING

A Matter of Character

Jay met Brian a few months ago when Brian first moved into town, and the two teens hit it off right away. Today, Brian came over to Jay's house to work on a social studies report. When Jay suggested that they start with an outline, Brian said, "Hey, there's a much easier way to do this." Then he described how they could go on the Internet and find anything they might need on a subject without having to write the report themselves.

Jay likes Brian, but he knows that this is cheating and it's wrong. Besides, he could get in trouble if he goes along and his teacher finds out.

WHAT WOULD YOU DO?

Apply the six steps of decision making to Jay's situation. What are the possible outcomes? How might Jay's decision affect other people? How could he use this situation to demonstrate good character?

1. STATE THE SITUATION.
2. LIST THE OPTIONS.
3. WEIGH THE POSSIBLE OUTCOMES.
4. CONSIDER VALUES.
5. MAKE A DECISION AND ACT.
6. EVALUATE THE DECISION.

LESSON 1: YOUR CHARACTER AND YOUR RELATIONSHIPS **121**

Listing

Have students describe the photo on this page and discuss the teen's healthy behavior. Then have students share their responses to the photo caption. Ask a volunteer to list suggestions on the board. **L1**

HEALTH SKILLS ACTIVITY

DECISION MAKING

Have students meet in groups to discuss Jay's decision-making process.

1. Jay's friend Brian has suggested cheating on a school report.
2. Jay can go along with Brian or refuse to cheat. (Note: Students may come up with many different options.)
3. If Jay cheats, he may get into trouble at school and/or at home. He will feel bad about himself because he is doing something wrong. If he refuses, Brian may get angry and may even break off the friendship, but Jay will feel good about himself.
4. Jay values his own health, his parents' and teacher's trust, and Brian's friendship.
5. Students will likely decide that Jay should refuse, perhaps with a playful or joking response.
6. Remind students to evaluate both short- and long-term responses.

INCLUSION STRATEGIES

Behavior Problems, Special Learning Needs, English Language Learners Students with behavioral disorders deviate from standards or expectations of behavior and impair the functioning of others and themselves. These students may also be gifted or learning disabled. Guidelines that may assist you include the following:
- Provide a structured environment.

- Outline student expectations, and explain how you will help students meet the objectives.
- Reinforce and model appropriate behavior.
- Work for long-term, not short-term, improvement.
- Balance individual needs with group and class requirements.

HEALTH *Online*

Encourage students to explore the Web Links for this chapter and then complete the activity.

Cooperative Learning

Divide the class into three groups, and assign each group one of these sections: *Making a Difference at Home, Making a Difference at School, Making a Difference in Your Community.* Have group members read, discuss, and expand on the information in their assigned section by relating how physical and social environmental factors influence individual and community health. Then have group members share their ideas with the rest of the class. **L1**

Demonstrating

Ask pairs or small groups of students to role-play scenes in which teens try to improve negative relationships. To help prompt students, pass out index cards with various types of relationships written on them such as family, peers, and role models. Ask students how relationships can influence individual and community health. **L1**

Critical Thinking

Have students consider who is responsible for strengthening a relationship: Can one person succeed in improving, weakening, or even destroying a relationship? Why or why not?

HEALTH *Online*

Topic: Good character

For a link to more information on good character, go to **health.glencoe.com**.

Activity: Using the information provided at this link, write a short story about a teen who demonstrates a specific trait of good character.

When people care about their community, everyone benefits. *How do you show that you care for others in your community?*

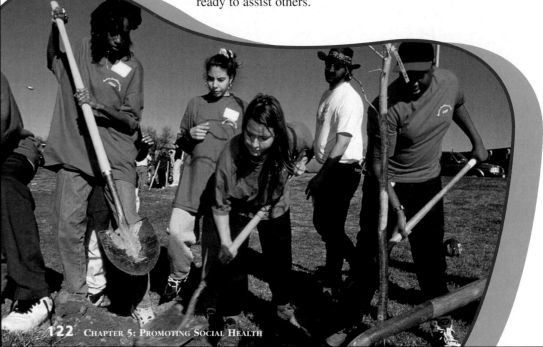

Making a Difference at Home

How do you demonstrate good character at home? You can show that you are responsible by getting up on time in the morning and telling your parents where you will be when you go out. You can also settle disagreements with your brother or sister without arguing. Doing your household tasks without being told and keeping your room neat are good ways to demonstrate responsibility at home. When you remember a family member's birthday or help make dinner, you show that you care about others.

Making a Difference at School

At school, you demonstrate good citizenship by understanding and following school rules and respecting teachers and other adults. You show caring by not bullying or harassing others. If you play a school sport, you can demonstrate fairness by being a responsible team player and a good sport. Refusing to use tobacco, alcohol, and other drugs shows that you are trustworthy.

Making a Difference in Your Community

There are many ways to demonstrate good character in your community. Some teens make a difference by participating in walkathons and supporting food drives. Many teens find ways to volunteer their time for such programs as the Special Olympics. By greeting your neighbors in a friendly manner or helping an older neighbor with her groceries, you show that you're a caring person. By reporting suspicious behavior and keeping a watchful eye on your neighborhood, you can help prevent crime and be ready to assist others.

122 Chapter 5: Promoting Social Health

✓ Reading Check

Synonyms and Antonyms Write the following word web on the board. Brainstorm antonyms and synonyms for *remember*. Have students list each of the following words in a similar web: *friendly, suspicious, honest, kind.* Encourage students to use a dictionary or thesaurus.

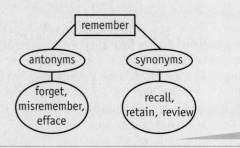

Relationships: The Teen Years

HEALTH Online

Before you begin Chapter 6, discover how well you rate as a friend. Take the Health Inventory at health.glencoe.com.

FOLDABLES Study Organizer

Before You Read

Make this Foldable to help you organize the information about friendships in Lesson 1. Begin with a plain sheet of 11″ × 17″ paper.

Step 1

Fold the short sides of a sheet of paper inward so that they meet in the middle.

Step 2

Fold the top to the bottom.

Step 3

Open and cut along the inside fold lines to form four tabs.

Step 4

Label the tabs as shown.

Who	When We Met
What I Admire	Why We're Friends

As You Read

Write down the qualities of a good friendship on the back of the Foldable. Then, describe the Who, What, When, and Why of a close friend under the appropriate tab.

141

Chapter Introduction

Use the options below to motivate students and preview chapter content.

HEALTH Online

Visit **health.glencoe.com**, and have students complete Health Inventory 6 to rate their peer relationships. For other teaching strategies, explore the Lesson Plans and select from Cross-Curriculum, Reading, or Media Literacy activities.

GLENCOE TECHNOLOGY

Teen Health Video and DVD Series
(Each format available in both English and Spanish)

You may wish to use:

- Tape/DVD 1, Segment 1, "Healthy Friendships"
- Tape/DVD 2, Segment 2, "Refusal Skills"
- Tape/DVD 3, Segment 4, "Resisting Negative Peer Pressure"

MindJogger Videoquiz

Use MindJogger to preview or review Chapter 6 content.

TIME HEALTH

Cliques—Good or Bad?
pages 156–157

FOLDABLES Study Organizer

Dinah Zike Study Fold

Descriptive Writing As students read and study the information in Lesson 1, direct them to take notes on the qualities of a good friendship on the back of their Foldable. Explain to students that note taking is a skill that is based upon listening or reading for main ideas and then recording those ideas for future reference. Under the appropriate tab of their Foldable, students can use what they have learned to describe the "Who, What, When, and Why" of a close friend.

Friendships: Growing and Changing

Lesson

Friendships: Growing and Changing

1 Focus

Lesson Objectives

Students will be able to

- discuss the qualities of a good friend.
- describe ways to meet new friends.
- define *clique*.
- discuss dating and the advantages of group dating.

Motivators

Quick Write

Encourage several students to read aloud their responses. Ask: How do friendships differ?

Bellringer Activity

Ask students to think about great times they have had with friends and to write a short paragraph describing two or three of those times.

VOCABULARY

Write each of the vocabulary terms on the board. Have students look up each term in the Glossary at the back of the student text. Direct students to use each of the terms in an original sentence.

Quick Write

There's a saying: "To have a friend, you must be a friend." Write what you think this saying means. Give examples.

LEARN ABOUT...

- the qualities of a good friend.
- how to make new friends.
- what a clique is.
- the advantages of group dating.

VOCABULARY

- empathetic
- clique

Friendships: Growing and Changing

Old Friends, New Friends

As you now move from childhood into your teen years, life starts to change. Friendships take on greater importance, and relationships with friends become deeper and more complex. You and your friends still talk about having fun, as you did when you were younger. However, you also begin to share thoughts and feelings about more serious matters.

You might also find that during the early teen years, friendships are often very changeable. Someone who was your best friend only a few months ago may not be your friend now. Teens grow and change at different rates, a fact that also affects their relationships. They often develop new interests and look for new friends to share these interests. They may see old friends less often in order to fit into a certain group. Changing relationships are a normal part of growing up.

Through your relationships with friends, you learn to understand yourself better. *What do you look for in a friend?*

Lesson 1 Resources

Teacher Classroom Resources

- Parent Letter & Activities 6
- Concept Map 21
- Cross-Curriculum Activity 11
- Enrichment Activity 21
- Health Lab 6
- Lesson Plan 1
- Lesson 1 Quiz

- Reading Tutor Activity 20
- Reteaching Activity 21
- Transparency 21

Student Activities Workbook

- Chapter 6 Study Guide
- Applying Health Skills 21

Qualities of a Good Friendship

All good friends share similar qualities:

- **Trust.** Good friends trust and believe in one another.
- **Reliability.** Good friends know that they can count on each other to keep their word.
- **Empathy.** Good friends are empathetic (em·puh·THE·tik), or *able to identify and share another person's feelings.*
- **Caring.** Good friends care for and about each other.
- **Respect.** Good friends respect each other's decisions and opinions.

The Changing Social Scene

Social groups can form and change throughout your life. For example, your school might have students who come from many different neighborhoods. That gives you the opportunity to meet new people and perhaps expand your circle of friends. By interacting with various social groups, you may learn new ideas, understand different perspectives, and gain important skills that will be helpful in adulthood.

Making New Friends

Making new friends is a skill that anyone can learn. Getting acquainted with new people is not easy for everyone, but it gets easier with practice. **Figure 6.1** shows four ways you could make new friends.

✓ **Reading Check**

Cause and effect relationships. Look for the connection between cause and effect in the paragraphs on these pages.

FIGURE 6.1

Ways to Make New Friends

It's important to know and use appropriate ways to make new friends. *Appraise the importance of social groups.*

Join a school club or community group that interests you.
Your school and community offer many activities for young people, such as sports teams, volunteer groups, and local plays.

Start a conversation.
Ask a question or give a compliment. You can always talk about school, sports, or movies.

Offer to help someone.
Show a classmate or neighbor how to solve a problem or fix something. Reaching out to others lets them know that you want to be friends.

Volunteer to work on a committee or project.
Join other teens who are planning an event. Working together on a project forms bonds among people.

LESSON 1: FRIENDSHIPS: GROWING AND CHANGING **143**

② Teach

Examining the Issue

Ask students to write paragraphs describing the kind of friend they are. Next, have them write paragraphs describing the type of person they would like to have as a friend. Collect the papers. Without revealing any names, read some of the paragraphs to the class. Discuss the similarities and differences among the qualities listed in the paragraphs read. **L2**

Discussing

Help students consider the importance of having friends of all ages.

- What can you learn from befriending a young child?
- What would you expect to gain, and give, in a friendship with an older adult? **L1**

Demonstrating

Let pairs of students role-play scenes in which teens demonstrate one or more of the qualities of a good friendship listed on this page. **L1**

VISUAL LEARNING

FIGURE 6.1 Direct students to study the suggestions for making new friends shown in Figure 6.1. Encourage pairs or small groups of students to role-play situations using each suggestion. Have groups brainstorm the situations and perform unscripted role-plays. **INCL** *English Language Learners, Special Learning Needs, Behavior Problems, Different Learning Styles (Visual)*

✓ **Reading Check**

Cause-and-Effect Relationships Explain to students that a common method of paragraph organization is a description of an effect or effects and an explanation of its cause or causes.

Draw students' attention to the second paragraph on page 142. Ask students what the paragraph is about (*changing friendships*). Ask: What is a cause of changes in relationships during the teen years? (*different rates of growing and changing*) What are some effects of these changes? (*new interests and new friends*) Ask students to identify causes and effects as they read the rest of the paragraphs on pages 142 and 143. **INCL** *At-Risk, Special Learning Needs, Behavior Problems*

Critical Thinking

Help students consider the importance of the skill of making new friends. Have them explain whether each of the following people needs the skill. Why or why not?

- A teen who seems to have lots of friends.
- A teen who seems happy with a single best friend.
- A teen who has had the same group of friends for years.
- A teen who insists he or she is not interested in having friends. **L1**

Discussing

Help students discuss cliques:

- How do cliques affect their members?
- How do they affect teens who don't belong?
- What can teens do to reduce the problems that cliques can cause?
- Why is belonging to a clique so important to its members? **L1**

Comparing

Have students meet in groups to discuss the similarities and differences between positive and negative relationships. Direct students to analyze positive and negative relationships that influence individual health such as families, peers, role models, and other social groups. Ask each group to share its conclusions with the rest of the class. As the groups share, write on the board the similarities and differences. Ask students to appraise the importance of social groups. **L1**

The desire for a sense of belonging is common to all teens. *How do cliques help fill this need? How can they be harmful?*

Cliques

A **clique** is *a group of friends who hang out together and act in similar ways.* Cliques are a common feature of the teen years. Members of a clique usually have certain things in common. For example, they might all play on the same team or belong to the same club or group, or they might all be good students. Membership in a clique is limited. Not everyone who wants to belong can join.

Cliques can have a positive or negative influence. Because most teens have a strong need to belong, they want to feel that they fit into a group. Cliques can help them meet this need. Sometimes teens feel unsure of themselves, and they use a clique to gain approval of what they wear or how they act.

Cliques can become harmful, however, if they pressure members to conform to the group in behavior that may damage their health. Cliques may discourage members from making their own decisions, presenting their own opinions, or having other friends who aren't accepted by the clique. Cliques may even pressure members to act in ways that go against their individual values and beliefs, such as lying to parents or teachers. Cliques can also hurt people outside the group. For example, members might make fun of a teen who isn't in the clique.

If you find yourself under this type of pressure from a clique, here are some actions you can take to improve your situation.

- **Suggest other activities.** Offer ideas that don't involve hurting others or putting anyone at risk.
- **Find new friends.** If staying in the clique is becoming a negative experience, you will be better off with new friends.

144 CHAPTER 6: RELATIONSHIPS: THE TEEN YEARS

MORE ABOUT...

Social Connections and Health Satisfying work, social activities, and personal relationships are important to physical and mental health. Family, friends, active interests, and community involvement may do more than simply help people enjoy life. During the past two decades, research has demonstrated that social experiences, activities, and relationships are related to health and well-being. The quality, not frequency, of social contacts is most important. People with infrequent, but satisfying, interactions with families and friends often feel better than those with unhappy or stressful relationships. Social interactions and activities may protect health because they offer opportunities for stimulation, involvement, and satisfaction.

Peer Relationships

In your early teen years, your relationships with both boys and girls may be changing. Some teens become interested in spending more time with people they find attractive.

However, not all young teens share these feelings of attraction. They might be shy and uncomfortable when they are around others of the opposite gender without the support of a group of friends. Still other teens have interests—such as sports, clubs, and hobbies—they prefer for the time being. Family customs and values also may influence with whom a teen is permitted to spend time. Whatever your situation, remember that you have options about how you spend your social time and with whom.

Going Out in a Group

Many teens prefer to go out in a mixed group of boys and girls. Going out in a group can be a good way to feel more comfortable with teens of both genders. For example, it may be more comfortable to go to parties, movies, and dances in groups. In those situations, you don't have to worry about making conversation. If you can't think of something to say, someone else in the group almost certainly will keep the conversation going. In a group you get an opportunity to practice social skills, and just being together can be lively and fun, too. **Figure 6.2** shows some ways to have fun with a group.

FIGURE 6.2

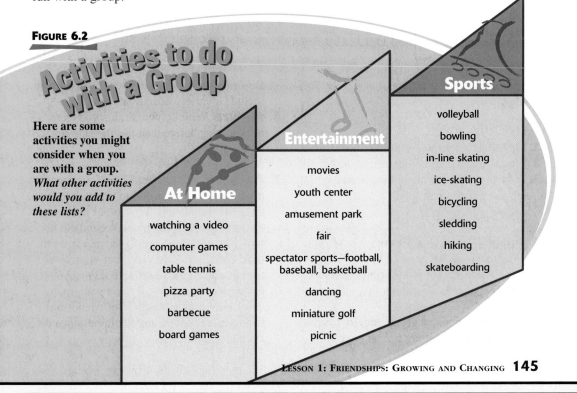

Activities to do with a Group

Here are some activities you might consider when you are with a group. *What other activities would you add to these lists?*

At Home
- watching a video
- computer games
- table tennis
- pizza party
- barbecue
- board games

Entertainment
- movies
- youth center
- amusement park
- fair
- spectator sports—football, baseball, basketball
- dancing
- miniature golf
- picnic

Sports
- volleyball
- bowling
- in-line skating
- ice-skating
- bicycling
- sledding
- hiking
- skateboarding

LESSON 1: FRIENDSHIPS: GROWING AND CHANGING **145**

Lesson 1

Cross-Curriculum Activity

SOCIAL STUDIES Dating customs vary from culture to culture. In some cultures an adult must accompany a young couple on a date. Other cultures don't allow dating at all—parents find marriage partners for their children. Have students research the dating customs of a culture different from their own. Encourage them to work in small groups and write up a short summary of their findings to present to the class. **L2**

 **Assess**

Evaluating

📁 Assign the Lesson 1 Review; then assign the Lesson 1 Quiz in the TCR.

Reteaching

• 📁 Assign Concept Map 21 or Reteaching Activity 21 in the TCR.

• Working in small groups, have students scan through the lesson, summarizing the information in each section.

Enrichment

• 📁 Assign Enrichment Activity 21 in the TCR.

• Have each student write a note to a special friend, thanking the person for his or her friendship or describing what that person's friendship means.

 **Close**

Ask each student to describe one way the lesson's content will help improve his or her peer relationships.

Individual Dating

Eventually you may begin to develop an interest in one person. Individual dating is a way to get to know that person better. Make sure that you go out on a date because you want to, and not because you feel pressured or because you want to win the approval of friends. This is part of responsible dating.

In a responsible dating relationship, you want to spend time with someone who demonstrates positive qualities. Here are some examples of traits to look for in a dating partner, with examples of actions and words that match those traits:

• **Respect.** "Your musical talents are really great! No wonder you made the choir."
• **Responsibility.** "We should call home and let our parents know that the game ran late, so they won't be worried."
• **Trustworthiness.** "I'll be there because I know how much this speech means to you."
• **Reliability.** "Don't worry—I'll make sure I'm on time so that you don't miss the bus."
• **Caring.** "I saved this seat for Janet because I knew she would be late getting out of practice."
• **Fairness.** "Before we decide to see this movie, let's make sure that the others agree on it."

Lesson 1 Review

Using complete sentences, answer the following questions on a sheet of paper.

Reviewing Terms and Facts

1. **Recall** List four ways to make new friends.
2. **Vocabulary** Define the term *clique*.
3. **Identify** What is the main advantage of going out in a group?

Thinking Critically

4. **Apply** Use the Qualities of a Good Friendship list on page 143 to develop three strategies for monitoring positive and negative peer relationships that influence health.
5. **Suggest** Choose a group activity from each column in Figure 6.2 on page 145.

Describe how you would adapt activities to include a variety of individuals.

6. **Analyze** Why do you think some teens begin dating before they feel they are ready?

Applying Health Skills

7. **Analyzing Influences** Draw four concentric circles (like a target) to represent your circle of friendships. Write your name in the innermost circle. In the second circle write the names of your best friends. In the third circle write the names of your good friends and in the fourth, the names of casual acquaintances. Write a paragraph describing how your circle of friends has changed and appraising the importance of friends and other social groups.

Lesson 1 Review

1. Start a conversation, join a school club or community group, offer to help someone, volunteer to work on a committee or project.
2. A group of friends who hang out together and act in similar ways.
3. It allows you to become more comfortable with teens of the opposite gender without the pressure of individual dating.
4. Strategies should involve determining if those qualities are evident in the relationship.
5. Responses will vary, but might include adapting physical activities to include those who are physically challenged.
6. They may feel pressured or want to win the approval of friends. Accept all reasonable responses.

Peer Pressure and Refusal Skills

Recognizing Peer Pressure

Relationships with peers are very important during the teen years. They begin to take on a special role, and as a group, your peers can also have a strong influence on you. **Peer pressure**, *the influence to go along with the beliefs and actions of your peers,* may come from the group either directly or indirectly. It can have a positive or negative effect on decision making.

Positive Peer Pressure

Peer pressure may be positive when it inspires you to do something worthwhile. For example, you may have acting talent but feel afraid to try out for the school play. Pressure from your friends may encourage you to audition for the play. A contest to see which classroom can bring the most canned food for a local charity can also create positive peer pressure. Positive peer pressure uses encouraging words and expressions.

Teens may use positive peer pressure to encourage others to engage in health-promoting behaviors. For example, someone who enjoys jogging may persuade a sedentary friend to try it.

Quick Write

Write a paragraph describing a time when someone your age tried to persuade you to do something that you felt was wrong or risky. Tell how this experience made you feel.

LEARN ABOUT...

- the difference between positive and negative peer pressure.
- the risks of negative peer pressure.
- how to develop and use refusal skills and assertiveness.

VOCABULARY

- peer pressure
- refusal skills
- assertive

Positive peer pressure can encourage you to acquire new skills, such as learning a new sport. *How can a teen promote positive behaviors among peers? Give two examples.*

LESSON 2: PEER PRESSURE AND REFUSAL SKILLS **147**

Lesson 2

Peer Pressure and Refusal Skills

❶ Focus

Lesson Objectives

Students will be able to

- differentiate between positive and negative peer pressure.
- describe the risks of negative peer pressure.
- describe strategies for using refusal skills.

Motivators

Quick Write
Encourage several volunteers to read their paragraphs aloud. Discuss how such pressure can affect a friendship.

Bellringer Activity

Have students write a paragraph describing ways they influence their friends. Encourage them to focus on the positive influence they exert.

VOCABULARY

Guide students in sharing what they already know about the vocabulary terms. Ask:

- Who can exert *peer pressure*?
- What does it mean to refuse something?
- How do you think the term *assertive* relates to saying no to something?

Lesson 2 Resources

Teacher Classroom Resources

📁 Concept Map 22

📁 Cross-Curriculum Activity 12

📁 Decision-Making Activity 11

📁 Enrichment Activity 22

📁 Lesson Plan 2

📁 Lesson 2 Quiz

📁 Reading Tutor Activity 21

📁 Reteaching Activity 22

🎮 Transparency 22

Student Activities Workbook

📁 Chapter 6 Study Guide

📁 Applying Health Skills 22

Developing Good Character ★

Responsibility

Divide the class into pairs of students. Have each pair write examples on index cards of negative peer pressure. Collect all cards and place them in a box. Pull out a card, read it to the class, and direct students to role-play resisting peer pressure with their partner. As an alternate activity, select two or three situations to be role-played in front of the whole class. Allow time for students' evaluation and feedback. **INCL** *At-Risk, Special Learning Needs, Behavior Problems, Different Learning Styles (Kinesthetic)*

VISUAL LEARNING

FIGURE 6.3 Have volunteers read aloud the title of Figure 6.3 and describe the picture. Have a few students describe, then list on the board what might be on the other side of the closed door. Then have students read and fully discuss each of the strategies. Have students meet in groups to role-play situations in which teens say no to negative peer pressure. **INCL** *English Language Learners, Special Learning Needs, Behavior Problems, Different Learning Styles (Visual)*

Discussing

Ask volunteers to identify specific skills they have developed through practice. Then ask them why it is important to practice refusal skills. **L1**

Developing Good Character ★

Responsibility

Working with your classmates, give examples of situations that involve negative peer pressure. Then brainstorm strategies for resisting the negative peer pressure. Practice these strategies in the form of role-plays or skits.

Negative Peer Pressure

Peer pressure becomes a negative social influence when people are trying to get you to do something that could hurt you or others. It could be something dangerous or illegal, something you're just not ready for, or something that goes against your values or your family's values. Teens who use tobacco, alcohol, or other drugs, for example, often do so because of negative peer pressure. Some peers may also pressure you to cheat, steal, lie, or show disrespect for others.

Negative peer pressure may involve threats, bribes, teasing, and name-calling. It may also take more subtle forms, such as facial expressions or gossip. When someone challenges your beliefs or encourages you to make an unhealthy or unsafe decision, it's important to know how to stand your ground and to resist negative peer pressure.

Learn to recognize and respond to negative peer pressure by avoiding this negative social influence. If you do find yourself in a situation in which you need to further resist negative peer pressure, you can use refusal skills. **Refusal skills** are *communication strategies that help you say no effectively.* **Figure 6.3** shows some refusal skills you can apply to effectively cope with negative peer pressure.

FIGURE 6.3

Closing the Door on Negative Peer Pressure

State reasons. You don't have to apologize or defend your position, but if you wish to, state your reasons clearly. You might practice saying no in front of a mirror so that you are ready to be firm and confident.

Don't agree to meet the other person halfway. You have the right to say no. Giving in a little is still giving in, and it leaves you open to continued pressure.

Use strong body language. Look the person in the eye when you're speaking to show that you're serious.

Suggest alternatives. Try to interest the other person in doing something else with which you're comfortable. Make sure that your suggestion takes you away from the risky situation.

Walk away. If all else fails, walk away. Your actions will match your words and make it clear that you mean no.

Plan ahead. Talk to someone you trust—a parent or counselor— about the people who pressure you. Trusted adults can help you avoid these pressure situations in the future.

148 CHAPTER 6: RELATIONSHIPS: THE TEEN YEARS

MORE ABOUT...

Peer Influences A teen's peers come from many backgrounds and have diverse cultural heritages. Students should have an opportunity to interact with teens who represent this diversity. To help students understand teens from different cultures, you may want to establish a pen pal program. Select a school in a different community, a different state, or a different country and begin corresponding with a teacher in that school. Together, try to match pairs of students who have similar interests, and let them introduce themselves as pen pals. Pen pals may want to e-mail one another, send postcards or letters, and/or exchange photographs and artwork. Parents should be informed of this activity. Also, ensure that student privacy is addressed.

Effective Refusal Skills

When you feel pressured to do something you don't want to do, you need to use effective refusal skills. Effective refusal skills let others know that you mean what you say. Like other skills, they take practice.

It's important to be assertive when you use refusal skills. **Assertive** means *behaving with confidence and clearly stating your intentions.* Show with words and actions that you mean what you say. Speak clearly, calmly, and in a firm tone of voice.

Be sure that your body language and gestures match your words. If you stare at the floor or shift your weight from one leg to another, you won't seem very assertive. If you have a smile on your face and a teasing look in your eyes, the person pressuring you won't believe that you're serious. Instead, use eye contact, put a serious or neutral look on your face, and stand or sit up straight.

Lesson 2

Demonstrating

Ask volunteers to do some role-playing with you. Have a student demonstrate the four steps of effective refusal skills (S.T.O.P.). Pause to announce each step as the student demonstrates it. Ask the class to predict the consequences of refusal skills in various situations. **L1** **INCL** *At-Risk, Special Learning Needs, Behavior Problems, Different Learning Styles (Kinesthetic)*

Hands-On Health

RECOGNIZING PEER PRESSURE

Learning to recognize peer pressure will help you decide whether to go along with the group or to act as an individual.

WHAT YOU WILL NEED
- pencil or pen
- several sheets of paper

WHAT YOU WILL DO
1. During the next week, observe peer pressure around you. Try to identify one example of peer pressure in your life, one in the lives of others in your family, and one on television or in other media.
2. For each observation, divide a sheet of paper into two columns. Head the columns with the words *Observation* and *Analysis.*
3. In the Observation column, describe the situations you observed.

4. In the Analysis column, write your interpretation of the event. Describe how peer pressure was involved. Differentiate between positive and negative peer pressure. Note how the person handled the pressure. If the pressure was handled poorly, what could the person have done?

IN CONCLUSION
At the end of the week, share your observations and analyses with your classmates. Discuss the consequences of giving in to negative pressure and ways of resisting it.

Hands-On Health

RECOGNIZING PEER PRESSURE

Time: 30 minutes divided between two class sessions a week apart

TEACHING THE ACTIVITY
- Read the introduction and directions. Have volunteers suggest incidents that might be appropriate.
- Give students a week to make their observations and write their analyses.
- Have volunteers share their records, and help students discuss their conclusions.

ASSESSMENT
Have each student write one or two sentences explaining the main purpose of this activity.

COOPERATIVE LEARNING ACTIVITY

Refusal Skills Have students form small groups and compile lists of other strategies, phrases, or behaviors that work when they want to say no. Have groups analyze whether or not each of their techniques shows respect and understanding for both parties and their points of view. Techniques that do not show respect for both parties should be crossed off the list. Encourage the groups to keep working until they can come up with a top five or top ten list. Emphasize that sometimes humor can be very effective. Students can also design wallet cards with a collection of refusal techniques that they feel would work for them. Students may want to keep cards on their persons in case they need them.

Lesson 2

③ Assess

Evaluating

📁 Assign the Lesson 2 Review; then assign the Lesson 2 Quiz in the TCR.

Reteaching

- 📁 Assign Concept Map 22 or Reteaching Activity 22 in the TCR.
- Have students write one-page essays telling what peer pressure is and differentiating between positive and negative peer pressure.

Enrichment

- 📁 Assign Enrichment Activity 22 in the TCR.
- Have students examine the effects of peer pressure on decision making. Ask each student to select a short story or novel in which peer pressure is depicted. Have students give oral reports on those works, discussing how peer pressure is exerted and how characters respond to it.

④ Close

Have students list at least eight healthy, safe activities they enjoy participating in with friends.

Teens can have fun together in ways that do not involve risky situations. *What are some ways you and your friends have fun together safely?*

The next time you're in a pressure situation, think of the word *stop*. It will help you remember the four steps of effective refusal skills. Here's what the letters represent:

- **S**ay no in a firm voice.
- **T**ell why not.
- **O**ffer other ideas.
- **P**romptly leave.

More Ways to Refuse

Peers who try to persuade you to act against your judgment often use pressure lines such as "Everybody's doing it." To resist negative peer pressure, you should be ready with responses to these pressure lines. Here are some examples.

Pressure Lines	What You Can Say
"Everybody's going."	"Well, I'm not everybody. Besides, I don't believe that everybody's going."
"If you're my friend, you'll do it."	"I am your friend. If you were my friend, you wouldn't ask me to do it."
"Oh, come on—just this once."	"It only takes once to get into trouble."

Effective refusal skills can earn you the respect of others. You certainly will be able to respect yourself. Remember, you have the right to make safe and healthful choices for yourself and others.

Lesson 2 Review

Using complete sentences, answer the following questions on a sheet of paper.

Reviewing Terms and Facts

1. **Vocabulary** Define the term *peer pressure*.
2. **Compare** Differentiate between positive and negative peer pressure.
3. **List** Give three examples of refusal skills.
4. **Describe** How can you be assertive in using refusal skills?

Thinking Critically

5. **Describe** Examine and describe the effects of peer pressure on decision making.

6. **Analyze** Predict the consequences of using refusal skills in various situations.

Applying Health Skills

7. **Advocacy** In a small group, decide on a worthwhile improvement for your school. For example, you might want trash-free school grounds, new sports equipment, or a recycling program. Plan a campaign to achieve your goal. Include ways to use positive peer pressure to persuade other students to join your campaign. If possible, put your plan into action.

150 CHAPTER 6: RELATIONSHIPS: THE TEEN YEARS

Lesson 2 Review

1. The influence to go along with the beliefs and actions of your peers.
2. Positive peer pressure inspires you to do something worthwhile; negative peer pressure tries to get you to do something that could hurt you or others.
3. Any three from Figure 6.3 on page 148.
4. By speaking clearly and calmly and with a firm voice, using eye contact, having a serious look on your face, sitting or standing straight.
5. Responses will vary, but might include both positive and negative decisions.
6. Accept all reasonable responses.

Practicing Abstinence

Setting Limits

Limits are *invisible boundaries that protect you.* Setting limits protects you from risky or unhealthy behavior. There may be limits, for example, on the amount of television you are allowed to watch or on how late you can stay up on a school night. That's because if you watch too much television, you don't have time for anything else. If you stay up too late, you can't stay awake in school the next day.

Limits are important when it comes to dating. As a young teen, you need limits on the kinds of people you date, the places you go, your activities, and even the transportation you take. Such limits protect you from getting hurt. They also help you avoid sexual activity. Parents or guardians set limits because they love their children and want them to be safe.

Quick Write

List examples of limits your parents or other adults place on you or limits you place on yourself. Explain at least one health-related benefit of these limits.

LEARN ABOUT...

- the importance of setting limits in dating situations.
- ways to practice abstinence.
- the benefits and rewards of abstinence.

VOCABULARY

- limits
- self-respect
- consequences

Trust your judgment and spend your time with people who share your values. *Who are the people you trust and like to go out with?*

Lesson 3

Practicing Abstinence

1 Focus

Lesson Objectives

Students will be able to

- describe the importance of setting limits in dating situations.
- explain ways to practice abstinence.
- identify the benefits and rewards of abstinence.

Health Skills
- Advocacy, p. 153

Motivators

Quick Write

List the limits identified by the students on the board. Ask students to share the benefits of these limits. Then identify the area of health benefited by each limit that was set.

Bellringer Activity

Ask students: What would motivate a person to set his or her own limits?

VOCABULARY

Ask students to explain the relationships among each of the vocabulary terms. Have volunteers use each term in an original sentence.

Lesson 3 Resources

Teacher Classroom Resources
- Concept Map 23
- Decision-Making Activity 12
- Enrichment Activity 23
- Lesson Plan 3
- Lesson 3 Quiz
- Reading Tutor Activity 22
- Reteaching Activity 23
- Transparency 23

Student Activities Workbook
- Chapter 6 Study Guide
- Applying Health Skills 23
- Health Inventory 6

② Teach

Making Lists

Ask students to make a list of adults they could talk to about setting limits in dating relationships. Have students suggest other ways they can demonstrate affection than sexual contact. See Showing Affection on page 153 for a few ideas. **L2**

Listing

Have students work in groups to write a list of "planning ahead" questions teens should ask before a party or other date. Then have the groups share, compare, and revise their lists. **L1**

Discussing

Encourage students to discuss the importance of commitments in their personal and public lives. Help them see that making commitments to physical, social, and emotional health will influence their choices in positive ways. **L1**

Discussing

Ask students to review what they have learned in Lesson 3, and then to analyze the importance of abstinence from sexual activity for unmarried persons of school age. Students' discussion should include the legal implications of sexual activity among minors.

MEDIA WATCH

AVOIDANCE TECHNIQUES

Avoidance techniques are actions or phrases you can use to avoid risky situations. With your classmates, recall successful avoidance techniques you have seen in movies or on television. *How many of them involved humor? Role-play some avoidance techniques that use humor to deal with a difficult situation.*

Some guidelines for setting limits include:

- **Plan ahead.** Planning ahead can help make dating safe and fun. For example, if you're going to a party, find out who will be there and whether adults will be present to supervise. For any date, decide ahead of time what you will do and how long the date will last. This will make it easier to stay in control of a situation.
- **Avoid risky situations.** Teens need to be able to recognize and avoid situations that may place them at greater risk of participating in sexual activity. For example, a party where there will be alcohol or drugs is a risky situation. These substances impair judgment and reduce inhibitions. A teen who gives in to peer pressure to use alcohol or drugs might end up engaging in sexual activity. It is also wise to avoid being home alone or in an isolated spot with a date.

Practicing Abstinence

You've learned that *abstinence* means not participating in high-risk behaviors, including sexual activity. Responsible teens abstain from sexual activity before marriage.

Practicing sexual abstinence shows that you respect your health and the health of others. You may begin to experience strong physical attraction to another person. Sexual feelings are normal and healthy, and they can be managed. Use effective communication skills to discuss with parents or other trusted adults any questions you have about sexual feelings or other aspects of sexuality. Adults can offer useful suggestions for dealing with these issues. Exercise self-control by setting limits, planning ahead, and avoiding risky situations.

These teens have made a conscious decision to practice abstinence and to give themselves time for their friendship to develop. *Discuss why abstinence from sexual activity is the only method that is 100 percent effective in preventing the emotional trauma associated with adolescent sexual activity.*

152 CHAPTER 6: RELATIONSHIPS: THE TEEN YEARS

DEALING WITH SENSITIVE ISSUES

Discussing Dating While some of your students might be very interested in dating, others are not. In addition, some may be allowed to date while others may not. Consequently, the level of interest in this issue will vary. However, those who are experienced may be willing to volunteer their perspectives on dating, which may one day help others. For example, have them offer advice about dealing with rejection by another person. What is most helpful at that time? What is least helpful? Talk about the reasons a person might be turned down for a date. Also, discuss the feelings a rejected person might have and how a teen copes with those feelings.

Showing Affection

Some teens may think that they must engage in sexual activity to show that they love or care for someone. This isn't true. Sexual activity isn't the same as love. It is one way to express love, but it isn't the only way. Here are a few ways to be close to someone and show affection without being sexually active.

- Listen to each other's problems.
- Give or get a hug.
- Study together at the kitchen table.
- Go for a long walk and hold hands.
- Do something nice for each other.
- Put affectionate notes in each other's locker or books.

You can show someone that you care in hundreds of different ways. *What are some ways in which you would show your affection for a special person?*

HEALTH SKILLS ACTIVITY

ADVOCACY

Supporting Abstinence

You can be an advocate for sexual abstinence by telling other teens why you've made a decision to protect your health in this way. Being an advocate for abstinence strengthens your own commitment. At the same time, you can be a role model to friends who are looking for ways to make abstinence easier. Here are a few ideas.

- Join a program or group that supports teen abstinence.
- Socialize with other teens who share your beliefs.
- Talk to parents and other trusted adults about your decision to be abstinent.
- Find out the facts about pregnancy and sexually transmitted diseases so that you are informed.
- Participate in group dates.

ON YOUR OWN
In a paragraph, analyze why abstinence from sexual activity is the preferred choice of behavior for unmarried persons of school age. Then list ways to practice abstinence.

LESSON 3: PRACTICING ABSTINENCE **153**

Lesson 3

Brainstorming

Have students brainstorm a list of some of the "nice things" teens can do for one another to show affection without engaging in sexual activity. Ask a volunteer to record students' ideas on the board.

Discussing

Ask students to identify familiar TV shows with teen characters. Help students discuss the actions of those characters and the messages the shows send viewers:

- How do the characters show affection without engaging in sexual activity?
- Can students find and identify information relating to abstinence in these shows?
- If the characters engage in sexual activity, what messages are they sending to teen viewers? How do the characters' actions affect their lives?

HEALTH SKILLS ACTIVITY

ADVOCACY

Read and discuss the introduction, and encourage students to share what they know about local programs that support teen abstinence. Have students write lists as directed in On Your Own. Lists are confidential, but encourage students to share their ideas with close friends and family members.

Note: This skill is introduced in Chapter 3 on page 61.

INCLUSION STRATEGIES

Ability Levels Students with various reading and organizational difficulties may have problems relating pictures and captions to the main text, especially when the text focuses on a complex issue such as social health. Before assigning the text in a lesson, ask students to look at the tables and pictures. Have them describe what the pictures illustrate. Next, have students read the lesson, and explain again how the pictures and the text are related. Ask students to explain why the visuals were included in the lesson.

Lesson 3

Critical Thinking

Ask students to evaluate the usefulness of teen abstinence programs:

- Do you think that participating in an abstinence program helps teens practice abstinence? Why or why not?

- What are the most important advantages of abstinence programs?

Discussing

Inform students that most sexually transmitted diseases occur in teens and young people up to about age 25. Ask students how their lives would change if they were diagnosed with a sexually transmitted disease. Further explain that, although it is sometimes difficult to avoid catching the common cold and flu, there is an easy way to avoid catching sexually transmitted diseases. Then ask students to discuss abstinence from sexual activity as the only method that is 100 percent effective in preventing sexually transmitted diseases and the sexual transmission of HIV or AIDS.

Researching

Have students research and write reports on the incidence and consequences of teen pregnancies. In the reports, students should discuss abstinence from sexual activity as the only method that is 100 percent effective in preventing pregnancy and the emotional trauma associated with adolescent sexual activity. The reports should also include how their own lives would change if they became teen parents.

Discussing

Discuss with students the legal implications regarding sexual activity as it relates to minors.

✓ Reading Check

List the contractions on these pages and explain what the apostrophe indicates. Then list possessive forms and explain what the apostrophe shows.

Practicing abstinence enables you to focus on your friends and the ways in which they are special. *How could a sexual relationship with a boyfriend or girlfriend interfere with other friendships?*

154 CHAPTER 6: RELATIONSHIPS: THE TEEN YEARS

Reasons to Practice Abstinence

More and more teens are choosing to abstain from sexual activity. These teens also are willing to talk about their decision. They want others to know that abstinence makes it easier for them to remain physically and emotionally healthy.

Respect for Self and Others

Teens who practice sexual abstinence gain self-respect. **Self-respect** is *the positive feeling you have about yourself when you live up to your beliefs and values.* We learn our beliefs and values from our families, through religious instruction, and in school. Many teens have been taught that sexual intimacy should be postponed until a couple is married. They also strongly believe that a relationship should be based on trust, caring, and friendship, not on physical attraction alone. Teens who are abstinent for these reasons honor their ideals.

Teens also may decide on abstinence to show respect for the beliefs and values of their parents and other family members. They may feel that sexual activity would disappoint or hurt people who are important to them. In addition, there are legal implications regarding sexual activity as it relates to minor persons.

Avoiding Possible Consequences

Consequences are *outcomes or effects that may occur as a result of a decision or an action.* Sexual activity among teens is likely to have several consequences, any of which may have a serious and long-lasting impact on a teen's life:

- **Unplanned pregnancy.** Most teens who are sexually active don't use birth control, or they use it inconsistently. Pregnancy and childbearing can damage a teen mother's physical health. Teens generally aren't prepared emotionally or financially to raise a child. These situations can also prevent or hinder future goals, such as going to college.

- **Sexually transmitted diseases (STDs).** Teens who are sexually active often fail to protect themselves against STDs. STDs can lead to lifelong health problems, and in the case of HIV/AIDS, even death. They can cause sterility, increase the risk of some cancers, and pose serious health risks to future children.

✓ Reading Check

Apostrophes in Contractions and Possessives
Students of all ages have difficulty using the apostrophe correctly.

Ask students to locate the first contractions on page 154 (*don't*) and explain the function of the apostrophe in the word. (*The apostrophe replaces the o in* not *and joins the words* do *and* not *into the contraction* don't.)

Next, have students find the first possessive form with an apostrophe. (*teen's*) Ask a volunteer to explain the purpose of the apostrophe (*The apostrophe indicates possession.*) Have students list the rest of the contractions and possessive forms on these pages and explain how the apostrophe is used.

- **Emotional trauma.** Sexual activity affects emotional as well as physical health. The stress of lying and the guilt caused by behavior that must be hidden from parents is painful. Teens also might regret behavior that doesn't bring them love, respect, or acceptance.

Rewards of Abstinence

Abstinence from sexual activity provides teens with many rewards. Here are just a few of the many benefits of deciding to be sexually abstinent:

- **Peace of mind.** Abstinence is the only method that is 100 percent effective in preventing pregnancy; sexually transmitted diseases, including HIV infection; and the emotional trauma associated with adolescent sexual activity.
- **Self-respect.** Abstinence allows you to be in control of your own body. Others will know you as a confident, responsible person.
- **Time for personal growth.** A sexual relationship can complicate life and keep teens from achieving their goals. Abstinence gives you more time to pursue your interests and develop your talents and skills.
- **Healthy relationships.** Abstinence lets you avoid the pressure of a sexual relationship. Teens who are abstinent can develop meaningful relationships based on mutual respect and shared interests.

Developing Good Character

Responsibility

One way to show responsibility is to think before you act and consider the possible results of your actions. *Why is it particularly important to think ahead when it comes to sexual activity?*

Lesson 3 Review

Using complete sentences, answer the following questions on a sheet of paper.

Reviewing Terms and Facts

1. **Explain** Why does setting limits in dating help teens to show responsibility?
2. **Recall** Give an example of a risky dating situation.
3. **Vocabulary** Define *self-respect*.
4. **List** Describe three possible consequences of failure to practice abstinence.

Thinking Critically

5. **Evaluate** List the advantages of abstinence. Then study your list and determine which items you consider most important. Explain your choices.

6. **Apply** Discuss the legal implications regarding sexual activity as it relates to minor persons.

Applying Health Skills

7. **Goal Setting** Having clear goals for your future can help you practice abstinence. Make a list of goals you want to accomplish. Then write a paragraph describing how early sexual activity might keep you from reaching your goals.

LESSON 3: PRACTICING ABSTINENCE 155

Lesson 3 Review

1. It protects them from risky or unhealthy behavior.
2. Any of the following: going to a party where there will be alcohol or other drugs, being in an isolated setting, viewing suggestive movies.
3. The positive feeling you have about yourself when you live up to your beliefs and values.
4. Unplanned pregnancy, sexually transmitted diseases, emotional distress.
5. Responses will vary, but may include peace of mind, self-respect, time for personal growth, or healthy relationships.
6. Responses should mention that it is illegal for unmarried minors to engage in sexual activity.

Lesson 3

Developing Good Character

Responsibility

Have students write for five minutes without stopping. Prompt them by asking: Can a person really show their love for another person by doing something that might hurt them? What are ways to be close to someone and show affection without being sexually active?

3 Assess

Evaluating

Assign the Lesson 3 Review; then assign the Lesson 3 Quiz in the TCR.

Reteaching

- Assign Concept Map 23 or Reteaching Activity 23 in the TCR.
- Ask students: What diseases and problems can be avoided entirely, 100 percent, when abstinence is practiced? (Answers should include STDs, teen pregnancy, emotional trauma)

Enrichment

Assign Enrichment Activity 23 in the TCR.

4 Close

Ask students to write a paragraph or two in which they analyze the importance of abstinence from sexual activity for unmarried persons of school age.

Cliques—Good or Bad?

1 Focus

Objectives

Students will be able to

- compare and contrast *clique* with similar words.
- practice the decision-making process in relation to a clique.
- access sources of information and guidance about friendship.

Motivator

Bellringer Activity

Write the word *clique* on the board. Ask students to free-associate, calling out the first ten words they think of when they see this word.

2 Teach

Cross-Curriculum Activity

LANGUAGE ARTS Remind students that a *synonym* is a word that has the same, or nearly the same, meaning as another word. Ask students to call out a few examples of synonyms (joyful/elated, hot/warm, sad/blue). Ask students if they can list some synonyms for the word *clique*. (Answers may include group, gang, friends, team, club, and so on.) Review the list together, discussing how the various words are the same or different. Explain that sometimes slight variations in meaning have to do with a word's *connotation*. While *annotation* means a word's explicit or primary meaning, *connotation* means "an associated meaning of a word or expression." Go through the list of words again and talk about each word's connotation. For instance, the word *club* has a positive and inclusive connotation while the word *gang* has a negative, violent connotation. Ask students, "Does the word *clique* have a positive or negative connotation? How do you think this connotation developed?"

Cliques
—Good or Bad?

What do you think about cliques? Join the debate!

Pro

"Too many people hear about cliques and immediately think of a social circle that's as secure as Fort Knox, where only the most beautiful, rich, and popular kids can be included. I think this idea is totally false and extremely outdated. Teenagers are looking for somewhere to belong. The word 'clique' is simply a label that gets attached to a circle of friends as soon as they find a few people who they're comfortable around. In my opinion, finding that niche is a very positive thing and an important element of being a teenager. For me, being in a group is part of what makes school so great—through thick and thin, 'my girls' and I are always there for one another. I believe that today's teens are forming cliques not for the purpose of exclusivity, but to find other kids who they can connect with. As far as I'm concerned, there's absolutely nothing wrong with that."

—*Kerisha Harris, 15
Paterson, New Jersey*

Con

"While Hollywood tends to make cliques seem fashionable, the truth is, there's nothing glamorous about them. For kids who can't seem to fit in anywhere (and whose self-esteem gets shattered in the process), cliques are one of the most devastating parts of school. Granted, it's normal for teens to be drawn to people who are like them, and that may automatically make a group of friends seem like a clique. I'm not saying it's bad to have close friends, but that stops being OK when you're not accepting of others. If you're hurting your peers or putting them down just because they're not as 'cool' or they're different from you, that's when it's time to take a closer look at yourself. Most likely there's something wrong with you, not the other people."

—*Nick Casey, 15, Brentwood, California.*

Health Literacy

Accessing Information Where can teens turn when they are having trouble with cliques or other social issues? Working independently, have students come up with a confidential list of at least ten sources of information and guidance. Resources may include a parent, school counselor, sibling, other friends, religious leader, coach or club leader, book, magazine, Web site, and so on. Ask students to write a one- or two-sentence description of each source, what they offer, and how they differ from other sources. (For instance, a parent may have experience, but a magazine offers confidentiality.) Then have students prioritize the list, from sources they are most likely to use to those they are least likely to use.

Making Things "Click"

School violence has raised people's awareness of the problems cliques can cause—and moved more teens to find ways to help turn things around. That's where SHINE365 (Seeking Harmony in Neighborhoods Everyday) comes in. The youth organization's Get Yourself Connected Speak Outs, held at malls nationwide, are getting teens talking about what causes clique intolerance and how to solve it. Inspired, young people have also formed school-based diversity organizations and channeled aggressive energy into art projects. "The mall forums get a whole cross section of teens," says SHINE365 coexecutive director Jennifer Kahn. "If we can expose [them] to different points of view, hopefully we can start making a difference in their lives."

Many teens think overcoming barriers starts with acceptance. "When you see someone [all alone], go up and ask about something that happened that day. It makes them feel more accepted," says SHINE365 member Melissa Mercier, 14, of Springfield, Massachusetts. Kahn suggests "embracing uniqueness," instead of passing judgment on people who are not like you.

Other Teens Speak Up

"Some people believe that being dependent on a small group of people is harmful or can create peer pressure. I think trusting and knowing someone well is exactly what makes friends into best friends."
—*Maria Marchenkova, 16, Columbus, Ohio*

"[At my school] everyone watches out for each other, so we are in essence one big clique."
—*Katie Chamberlain, 16, Huntsville, Alabama*

"A clique, by definition, is a group of friends, so I don't think that they're necessarily bad. However, the 'group-think' mentality of cliques concerns me."
—*Tony Pham, 16, Bellevue, Washington*

"Cliques tend to discriminate against other cliques or individuals. I've seen situations where people join a clique simply to be part of the crowd and end up hurting themselves or their true friends in the end."
—*Amanda Hughes, 14, Goshen, Ohio*

TIME TO THINK...

About Cliques

Hold a class debate on whether cliques have a positive or negative influence on teens. Start by defining the term *clique* on the board. Your teacher will then divide the class in half, assigning one half to argue for cliques, the other against them. Before the debate, each group—through research and discussion—should develop at least five strong arguments to support its position.

③ Apply

Time to Think

Allow time for groups to formulate their arguments either for or against cliques. Hold the actual debate the next time the class meets.

Case Study

Present students with the following case study:

The first week at her new school, Sonia is approach by several girls who seem friendly and welcoming. She is grateful for their attention and quickly becomes a part of the group. Gradually, Sonia notices her new friends spreading hurtful gossip and snubbing other students. What should Sonia do? As a class, go through the steps of the decision-making process.

- Clarify the decision Sonia needs to make.
- Identify at least four of Sonia's options and the possible outcomes of each.
- Choose a decision for Sonia.
- Evaluate and reflect on the decision.

VISUAL LEARNING

Ask students to analyze the photograph on page 157. Is this a realistic depiction of the social scene at their school? Why or why not?

DEALING WITH SENSITIVE ISSUES

Cliques Cliques and the associated issue of exclusion can be an emotionally loaded topic for students. The following guidelines will help all students to feel comfortable during classroom discussions:
- Enforce all standard class ground rules, including no put-downs, no name-calling, and so forth.

- Give students the right to pass during discussions that involve personal opinions, feelings, or experiences.
- Keep the discussion general, avoiding the names of specific people or known school groups and organizations.
- Avoid judgmental language and correct students when they use judgmental statements.

GOAL SETTING

Objective

After completing the lesson, students will be able to demonstrate how to set a goal for abstinence.

Time: 45 minutes

Materials: None

Teacher Classroom Resources

📁 Building Health Skills Activities

• Transparency Master 9, "Goal Setting"

• Reproducible Master 31, "Know Your Limits"

---

1. Model

• Instruct students to read about Claudia and how she set firm limits to remain abstinent.

• Brainstorm rewards (benefits) for staying abstinent; then conduct a class discussion about future plans that could be altered by the risks of sexual activity (e.g., pregnancy, STDs).

KNOW YOUR LIMITS

Model

Claudia recently began dating. She knows that she does not want to become sexually active, and she wants to avoid situations where she might be pressured. Claudia decides to set some firm limits for herself. She uses the goal-setting steps to plan ahead.

1. **Identify a specific goal.** "I want to avoid being pressured to be sexually active."

2. **List the steps you will take.** "I will insist that my first date with anyone be a group situation. I will always let my parents know where I am and when I will be home. I will not go to parties or other places where alcohol is present."

3. **Get help and support from others.** "My older sister can help me decide how to tell my dates about my limits. I will ask my parents to come pick me up if I ever need to leave in the middle of a date."

4. **Set up checkpoints.** "Each time I begin dating someone, I will tell that person what my limits are. I will not go out with anyone who does not agree to respect them."

5. **Reward yourself.** "I will feel good about myself because I am sticking to my limits."

Teaching Tips

Honoring Family Values The students that comprise any class are a part of diverse family units with differing sexual values. While schools present information and skills, it is up to the family to supply the values for student-based decisions.

Sexuality education in schools can provide opportunities for students to interact with their families about sexual issues. Encourage students to take their contracts home and share them with the adults in their lives.

Practice

Read the paragraph below. Then show how Lawrence could use the goal-setting steps to structure the time he spends with Mimi. Write your plan on a separate piece of paper.

Lawrence has been dating Mimi for several months, and he likes her very much. He also finds her very attractive. He values their relationship and wants it to last for a long time. Lawrence feels that in order to practice abstinence with Mimi, he must set limits for himself. He decides to use the goal-setting steps to help him plan for the time he spends with Mimi.

Apply/Assess

Make a contract with yourself in which you set a goal to remain abstinent. Remember to include limits that you set for yourself. Use the goal-setting steps to write your contract. First, state your goal. Then list the limits you will set to help you reach your goal. Include the names of people who can help you stick to your limits, and describe checkpoints you can use to make sure that you are staying on target. Finally, describe the rewards you will gain by choosing these limits. Use the sample contract here as a model.

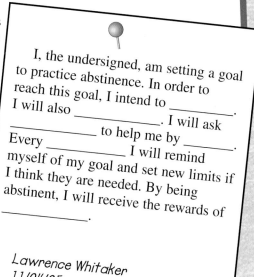

I, the undersigned, am setting a goal to practice abstinence. In order to reach this goal, I intend to _____. I will also _____. I will ask _____ to help me by _____. Every _____ I will remind myself of my goal and set new limits if I think they are needed. By being abstinent, I will receive the rewards of _____.

Lawrence Whitaker
11/04/05

2. Practice

- Discuss the importance of having a plan for remaining abstinent.
- Have students work with a partner to develop a plan for Lawrence. Display Transparency Master 9 to remind students of the steps to use in their plans.
- Provide an opportunity for partners to compare their plan with others in the class.

3. Apply/Assess

- 📁 You may wish to distribute Building Health Skills Reproducible Master 31 in the TCR to guide students in completing this activity.
- Refer to the list of rewards that were generated by the class for staying abstinent. Ask each student to choose the reward(s) that is most important to her or him.
- 📁 Direct students' attention to the sample contract on the page. Then have students create their own contracts by filling in the blanks on Reproducible Master 31.
- Allow students to share their contracts with others in the class.

Assessment Scoring

Using a rubric, student work should provide evidence of all criteria to achieve the highest score.

Skills

Student work demonstrates

- a clear goal statement.
- steps that lead to achievement of the goal.
- resources that support achievement of the goal.

- a strategy that evaluates progress.
- a healthy reward.

Concepts

Student work provides

- accurate information about setting limits.
- conclusions about abstinence.

Checking Comprehension

Use the Chapter 6 Assessment to examine the most important ideas presented in the chapter.

Answers to Reviewing Vocabulary and Concepts

Lesson 1
1. empathetic
2. clique
3. group date
4. volunteer
5. individual date

Lesson 2
6. peer pressure
7. positive peer pressure
8. negative peer pressure
9. refusal skills
10. assertive

Lesson 3
11. b
12. a
13. c
14. d
15. a

Thinking Critically

16. Teens might need refusal skills if an older teen or adult pressures them to do something wrong or something that makes them uncomfortable. Predictions will vary.

17. Possible response: accomplishing the goal may be put off for an extended period of time, or you may never be able to accomplish it because your situation and/or physical condition will have changed.

After You Read

Use your completed Foldable to review the information on the qualities of a good friendship.

FOLDABLES™
Study Organizer

Reviewing Vocabulary and Concepts

On a sheet of paper, write the numbers 1–10. After each number, write the term from the list that best completes each statement.

> - individual date
> - assertive
> - clique
> - volunteer
> - negative peer pressure
> - peer pressure
> - positive peer pressure
> - refusal skills
> - group date
> - empathetic

Lesson 1

1. Friends are said to be _____ when they are able to identify and share another person's feelings.
2. A group of friends who hang out together and act in similar ways are a(n) _____.
3. One way to feel more comfortable around teens of both genders is to go out on a(n) _____.
4. One way to make new friends is to _____ to work with others.
5. When you go on a(n) _____, you get to know one person better.

Lesson 2

6. _____ is the influence other teens have on you to act and think like them.
7. Classmates who encourage another student to stop smoking are using _____.

8. _____ occurs when other teens ask you to do something that will hurt you or others.
9. _____ can help you get out of uncomfortable situations.
10. When you behave with confidence, you are being _____.

Lesson 3

On a sheet of paper, write the numbers 11–15. After each number, write the letter of the answer that best completes the sentence or answers the question.

11. Which of the following is another word for invisible boundaries that protect you?
    a. distress   c. crowd
    b. limits   d. clique
12. Living up to your values and beliefs helps you have
    a. self-respect.
    b. sympathy.
    c. peer pressure.
    d. guilt.
13. Having an accident or getting a speeding ticket because of driving too fast would be a
    a. limit.
    b. group date.
    c. consequence.
    d. conversation.
14. Which of the following might be a consequence of early sexual activity?
    a. refusal skills
    b. group dating
    c. trust
    d. a sexually transmitted disease
15. The only method that is 100 percent effective in preventing pregnancy and STDs is
    a. abstinence from sexual activity.
    b. going on group dates.
    c. responding to peer pressure.
    d. being assertive.

INCLUSION STRATEGIES

Special Learning Needs, Behavior Problems, English Language Learners The following suggestions are helpful for students with special learning needs, students with behavior problems, and ELL students:
- Pair these students with more proficient learners who can help summarize the main concepts of the chapter.

- 🎧 Direct these students to listen to the Teen Health Audio Summaries. This component provides an audio and written summary of the chapter in both English and Spanish.
- Use photographs, drawings, or magazine clippings whenever possible to help students visualize the important concepts of the chapter.

Thinking Critically

Using complete sentences, answer the following questions on a sheet of paper.

16. Hypothesize When might a teen need to use refusal skills with someone other than a peer? Predict the consequences of refusing in this situation.

17. Apply How would one of your long-term goals be negatively affected by an unplanned pregnancy or an STD?

18. Explain How can you determine if relationships are a positive or negative influence on your health? Develop strategies for monitoring these relationships.

Career Corner

School Counselor Many teens will go to a school counselor for help in handling emotions or resolving conflicts. School counselors help students with school, family, or personal problems. They also work with students to help plan their futures.

This profession requires a four-year degree and two years of graduate training in counseling. If you think you might like to help young people solve problems, visit the Career Corner at health.glencoe.com to find out more about this career.

Standardized Test Practice

Math

Read the paragraph below and then answer the questions.

Surveys have shown that many teens don't wear safety belts when riding in a car. One of the main reasons that teens gave for not wearing safety belts was peer pressure.

1. In 2001, more than 5,000 teens were killed in traffic accidents. Two-thirds of these teens were not wearing safety belts. How many of the teens were not wearing safety belts?

- (A) 1,667 teens
- (B) 2,500 teens
- (C) 3,333 teens
- (D) 4,500 teens

2. Of the students surveyed, 32 percent of students who didn't wear safety belts said that they did not wear them because of peer pressure. Suppose there are 194 students in your school who say they don't wear safety belts. How many of these students do not wear safety belts because of peer pressure?

- (A) 45 students
- (B) 62 students
- (C) 132 students
- (D) 149 students

3. Suppose you surveyed teens who rode with adults and those who rode with teen drivers about safety belt use. For which group do you think the percentage of teens not wearing a safety belt is higher? Explain.

 TH05_C3.glencoe.com/quiz

18. Possible responses include: determine whether the relationship is based on trust, caring, respect, communication, and avoiding risky behavior. Strategies will vary.

Test Practice

1. C

2. B

3. Sample answer: The percentage would be higher in the group riding with the teen drivers because of peer pressure to not wear a safety belt.

Reteaching

📁 Assign Study Guide 6 in the Student Activities Workbook.

Evaluate

- 📁 ⊙ Use the reproducible Chapter 6 Test in the TCR, or construct your own test using the **Exam**View® Pro Testmaker.

- 📁 Use Performance Assessment 6 in the TCR.

Enrichment

Have students work together to make a video about healthy friendships and dating practices. (If video equipment is not available, suggest that they plan and perform a play or a series of skits.)

Assessment

Self-Assessment Direct students to review the activities that are provided throughout the chapter. Encourage each student to select one finished product or activity that demonstrates her or his best work for the chapter. Have students explain what they learned and how the examples they selected show their progress.

Career Corner

School Counselor School counselors must have strong communication skills and enjoy working with young people. Invite the school counselor to your class, and have him or her discuss the responsibilities of the job. Encourage students to ask questions about how one prepares for a career as a school counselor.

161

Planning Guide

Chapter 7	Skills/ Activities	Reproducible Resources	Assessment
Lesson 1 **The Nature of Conflict** *pages 164–167*	**Hands-On Health** ▲ A Survey of Conflicts, page 165	*Student Activities Workbook available for use with each chapter* 📁 Parent Letter & Activities 7 📁 Concept Map 24 📁 Decision-Making Activity 13 📁 Enrichment Activity 24 📁 Lesson Plan 1 📁 Reading Tutor Activity 23 📁 Reteaching Activity 24	📁 Lesson 1 Quiz
Lesson 2 **Resolving Conflicts** *pages 168–171*	**HEALTH SKILLS ACTIVITY** ▲ When to Suggest a Mediator (*Decision Making*), page 171	📁 Concept Map 25 📁 Cross-Curriculum Activity 13 📁 Enrichment Activity 25 📁 Lesson Plan 2 📁 Reading Tutor Activity 24 📁 Reteaching Activity 25	📁 Lesson 2 Quiz
Lesson 3 **Avoiding and Preventing Violence** *pages 172–176*	**HEALTH SKILLS ACTIVITY** ▲ Help Prevent School Violence (*Advocacy*), page 174	📁 Concept Map 26 📁 Cross-Curriculum Activity 14 📁 Decision-Making Activity 14 📁 Enrichment Activity 26 📁 Health Lab 7 📁 Lesson Plan 3 📁 Reading Tutor Activity 25 📁 Reteaching Activity 26	📁 Lesson 3 Quiz
Lesson 4 **Preventing Abuse** *pages 177–181*	**HEALTH SKILLS ACTIVITY** ▲ Helping a Victim of Abuse (*Communication Skills*), page 180	📁 Concept Map 27 📁 Enrichment Activity 27 📁 Lesson Plan 4 📁 Reading Tutor Activity 26 📁 Reteaching Activity 27	📁 Lesson 4 Quiz 📁 Chapter 7 Test 📁 Performance Assessment 7

TIME HEALTH | **Stopping Violence Before It Starts** *pages 182–183*

BUILDING HEALTH SKILLS

| **Working Through Conflicts**
(*Conflict Resolution*)
pages 184–185 | | 📁 Building Health Skills
Reproducible Masters 32a & 32b | |

Standards		Technology
National	**State/Local**	
National Health Education Standard **1.4, 3.1, 3.3, 3.4, 5.2, 5.5, 5.7**		Transparency 24 Tape/DVD 1, Segment 2, "Dealing with Your Emotions" TeacherWorks™ Internet Activities
National Health Education Standard **3.4, 5.4, 5.5, 5.6, 5.8, 6.1, 6.2, 6.3**		Transparency 25 Tape/DVD 1, Segment 4, "Resolving Conflicts Through Healthy Communication;" Tape/DVD 2, Segment 4, "Resolving Conflicts in Nonviolent Ways" TeacherWorks™
National Health Education Standard **1.4, 3.5, 3.6, 5.7, 7.2, 7.4, 7.5**		Transparency 26 Tape/DVD 2, Segment 5, "Avoiding Potentially Dangerous Situations" TeacherWorks™
National Health Education Standard **1.4, 2.6, 3.3, 5.1, 5.2, 5.4, 5.5**		Transparency 27 TeacherWorks™ MindJogger Videoquiz **Exam***View*® Pro Testmaker
National Health Education Standard **5.4, 5.5, 5.8**		Building Health Skills Transparency Master 6

TeacherWorks™

Glencoe's new and exclusive TeacherWorks™ is an all-in-one planner and resource center. Access the complete Teacher Wraparound Edition electronically. Find all your classroom resources with just a few easy clicks, and print them right from your computer. Connect directly to Glencoe's customized Health Web site. Access the National Health Education Standards correlations, or insert your own state standards and match them directly to the electronic Teacher Wraparound Edition.

Language Diversity

- English Audio Summaries
- Spanish Audio Summaries
- English Summaries, Quizzes, and Activities
- Spanish Summaries, Quizzes, and Activities
- Spanish Parent Letters and Activities

KEY TO ABILITY LEVELS

Teaching Strategies that appear throughout the chapters have been identified by one of four codes to give you an idea of their suitability for students of varying learning styles and abilities.

L1 **Level 1** strategies should be within the ability range of all students. Often full class participation is required.

L2 **Level 2** strategies are for average to above-average students or for small groups. Some teacher direction is necessary.

L3 **Level 3** strategies are designed for students able and willing to work independently. Minimal teacher direction is necessary.

INCL Strategies are appropriate for students with particular special needs in a general classroom setting.

CHAPTER
7

Conflict Resolution

Chapter at a Glance

Lesson 1 discusses conflict and its effects. It describes ways teens can manage anger constructively.

Lesson 2 focuses on conflict resolution skills, discusses the mediation process, and shows teens how peer mediation can work in schools.

Lesson 3 examines factors that contribute to teen violence and identifies what teens and schools can do to prevent and protect individuals against violence.

Lesson 4 explains the forms and negative effects of abuse. It also shows teens how to avoid abuse and where to get help.

Health Skills
- When to Suggest a Mediator (*Decision Making*), p. 171
- Help Prevent School Violence (*Advocacy*), p. 174
- Helping a Victim of Abuse (*Communication Skills*), p. 180
- Working Through Conflicts (*Conflict Resolution*), pp. 184–185

HANDS-ON ACTIVITY

Tell How You Feel Using "I" statements is an effective way to let people know how you feel without blaming or accusing them. A good "I" message states the situation, tells how you feel about it, explains your feelings, and affirms what you need. "I" statements begin with, "I feel...," "I think...," or "I am angry because..." "You stole my favorite CD from my locker" can be changed to "I think you borrowed my favorite CD without asking me first." Have students practice changing "you" statements to "I" statements. Ask them to generate ideas for "you" statements, and write them on the board. Afterward, change the "you" statements to "I" statements. Practice as a class; then pair students together to write other "you" and "I" statements. Have them act out the scenes if time allows.

Conflict Resolution

 **HEALTH** *Online*

Discover what you know about the nature of conflicts and violence prevention. Go to health.glencoe.com and take the Chapter 7 Health Inventory.

FOLDABLES™
Study Organizer

Before You Read

Make this Foldable to help you organize what you learn in Lesson 1 about the nature of conflict. Begin with a plain sheet of 8½″ × 11″ paper or notebook paper.

Step 1

Fold the sheet of paper from top to bottom, leaving a 2″ tab at the bottom.

Step 2

Fold in half from side to side.

Step 3

Unfold the paper once. Cut along the center fold line of the top layer only. This makes two tabs.

Step 4

Label the tabs as shown.

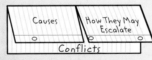
Causes | How They May Escalate
Conflicts

As You Read

Under the appropriate tab, record information on some common causes of conflict and the factors that may cause them to escalate.

163

Chapter Introduction

Use the options below to motivate students and preview chapter content.

HEALTH *Online*

Encourage students to take Health Inventory 7 at **health.glencoe.com**. Then brush up on health education by reading Professional Articles for health teachers. These articles can help keep you informed of national and state trends.

GLENCOE TECHNOLOGY

Teen Health Video and DVD Series
(Each format available in both English and Spanish)

 You may wish to use:

- Tape/DVD 1, Segment 2, "Dealing with Your Emotions," or Segment 4, "Resolving Conflicts Through Healthy Communication"
- Tape/DVD 2, Segment 4, "Resolving Conflicts in Non-violent Ways"

MindJogger Videoquiz

Use MindJogger to preview or review Chapter 7 content.

TIME HEALTH

Stopping Violence Before It Starts
pages 182–183

 **FOLDABLES™**
Study Organizer

Dinah Zike Study Fold

Analyzing Cause and Effect As students read and discuss the material on conflict presented in Lesson 1, ask them to record what they learn about the causes of conflict under the appropriate tab of their Foldable. Guide them as they record and analyze factors that may cause conflict to escalate. Have students give specific examples of conflicts that have escalated. As a class, discuss why conflicts may escalate and what can be done to prevent it. Guide students in discussing why it is important to prevent conflicts from escalating.

Lesson 1

The Nature of Conflict

① Focus

Lesson Objectives

Students will be able to

- define *conflict* and explain how it occurs.
- explain why some conflicts become violent.
- discuss positive ways of managing anger.
- identify factors that cause conflicts to escalate.

Motivators

Quick Write

Encourage students to share their responses. Ask: What was prevented by resolving the conflict peacefully?

Bellringer Activity

Ask students to think about any argument they have had recently. Have them try to remember what caused the arguments.

VOCABULARY

Ask volunteers to read the definitions of *conflict*, *escalate*, and *prejudice* given in the lesson. Ask students to recall a broad range of instances, such as World War II, and the prejudices that may underlie those conflicts.

Lesson ① The Nature of Conflict

Quick Write

Describe an incident that you witnessed in which someone's words or actions resolved a conflict peacefully.

LEARN ABOUT...

- how conflicts occur.
- why some conflicts get out of hand.
- positive ways to manage anger.
- factors that can cause conflicts to escalate.

VOCABULARY

- conflict
- escalate
- prejudice

How Conflicts Occur

Conflict is *a disagreement between people with opposing viewpoints, ideas, or goals.* It is a normal part of life. Conflict can arise among friends, family members, and groups in a community. Sometimes a conflict can be positive and can produce needed change. A conflict does not have to be a contest in which one side wins and the other loses. The best solution is a fair one, in which both sides win. There are many reasons for conflict, but the three major ones are competition for resources, clashes over values, and exchanges involving emotional needs.

- **Conflicts over Resources.** You can peacefully handle conflict over resources by sharing. To share resources without conflict, the people involved must respect one another's needs. For example, two sisters argued daily because they both borrowed each other's clothing without asking permission. Eventually each girl realized that the best way to gain respect was to show respect. The sisters agreed not to borrow again without asking.
- **Conflicts over Values.** Your values are the beliefs and ideals that guide your decisions and behavior. A conflict over values, for example, may involve you and your parents disagreeing about what you wear, how you spend your money, or who you spend your time with.

Conflicts often begin over competition for resources, differences in values, and emotional needs. *What caused a recent conflict you had with a friend?*

Lesson 1 Resources

Teacher Classroom Resources

 Parent Letter & Activities 7

Concept Map 24

Decision-Making Activity 13

Enrichment Activity 24

 Lesson Plan 1

Lesson 1 Quiz

Reading Tutor Activity 24

Reteaching Activity 24

 Transparency 24

Student Activities Workbook

 Chapter 7 Study Guide

Applying Health Skills 24

A Survey of Conflicts

Analyzing conflicts you have had in the past can give you insight into effective ways to manage future conflicts.

WHAT YOU WILL NEED
- notebook paper
- pen or pencil

WHAT YOU WILL DO
1. Use the paper to create a record sheet. Make four columns and label them *Location, Number of People Involved, Problem, What Happened.*

2. In the next two days, observe one conflict in school or among friends and write your observations on the record sheet.

IN CONCLUSION
In a small group, discuss what you observed with your classmates. Choose conflicts that were not resolved or that were poorly managed. Brainstorm ideas for ways in which they could have been managed better. Write a new plan for a healthier resolution.

- **Conflicts Involving Emotional Needs.** People's basic emotional needs include the need to belong and the need to feel respected and worthwhile. Conflicts may arise when people are excluded from groups they would like to join. Also, when someone shows disrespect to another person or group, disagreements are bound to occur. A frequent source of conflict for teens is spreading rumors about others.

Why Some Conflicts Get Out of Hand

The best time to resolve a conflict is in its early stages. If a disagreement isn't managed peacefully, the conflict can **escalate**, or *become more serious.* Certain factors, such as anger, bullying, and group pressure, can increase the chance that a minor argument will escalate into a major dispute.

Anger

People become angry when they are frustrated or believe that they are being mistreated. Everyone feels angry now and then. When you are angry, your heart beats faster than usual. Blood rushes to your face and your muscles tense as your body prepares for action. If you can channel your energy into something positive, you have a better chance of avoiding violence.

Vigorous physical activity is a positive way to release your anger.

LESSON 1: THE NATURE OF CONFLICT **165**

② Teach

Cross-Curriculum Activity

LANGUAGE ARTS Tell students that a conflict that escalates grows more intense—it goes up a level. Explain that *escalate* comes from a Latin word *scalae,* meaning "a flight of stairs." Ask students to use a dictionary to find out what *de-escalate* means. Discuss its importance in conflict resolution. **L2**

Hands-On Health

A Survey of Conflicts

Time: 30 minutes during two class sessions, two days apart

TEACHING THE ACTIVITY
- Help students read and discuss the activity introduction and directions. Draw a sample record sheet on the board, and have volunteers fill it in.
- Have students prepare and fill in their own record sheets.
- Have students meet in groups to share and discuss their observations.

ASSESSMENT
Ask each student to evaluate his or her own record sheet and group participation.

Health Literacy

Health Influences How people express anger and other strong emotions can affect not only their relationships with others but also their self-esteem. For example, people who don't express their anger and keep it bottled up inside tend to feel frustrated and resentful. Those who take their anger out on others tend to feel guilty and negative toward themselves. In both cases, self-esteem suffers a blow. Emphasize that students need to learn positive ways to express their anger for the sake of their self-esteem and overall mental/emotional health.

Cross-Curriculum Activity

LANGUAGE ARTS Ask students to write short fictional dialogues in which two characters have a conflict over a difference in values and then resolve their differences. Ask volunteers to read their dialogues to the rest of the class. Have the class explain the particular strategies used to resolve the conflict. Revisit this activity after reading Lesson 2. **L2**

VISUAL LEARNING

FIGURE 7.1 Ask students to speculate about why they think each strategy for managing anger can be effective, depending on the circumstances. Have students match these strategies with possible scenarios. For example, which strategy should one use to handle an insult from a classmate? **INCL** *English Language Learners, Special Learning Needs, Behavior Problems, Different Learning Styles (Visual)*

Demonstrating

Ask several volunteers to demonstrate an effective posture and gait to use when walking away from a bully. **L1** **INCL** *English Language Learners, Different Learning Styles (Kinesthetic)*

Cross-Curriculum Activity

SOCIAL STUDIES Have volunteers find and read news articles about bullying in schools. Ask these students to summarize the articles for the rest of the class.

Guest Speaker

Invite a police officer or social services worker to speak to the class about the relationships among alcohol, drugs, and violence. **L1**

Reading Check

Understand suffixes. The suffix *-ing* can be used to turn a verb into the subject of a sentence. Find as many examples as you can on this page.

Anger that is not managed well can make a conflict worse. It's important to exercise self-control so that your anger does not get out of hand. One strategy is to stop focusing on how angry you are. Dwelling on whatever is making you angry can build anger into rage. Rage, in turn, can lead to violence. Fortunately, there are several effective ways to manage anger. **Figure 7.1** shows some positive strategies for dealing with anger.

Bullying and Teasing

Some people seek power and attention by bullying. Bullies can be males or females of any age. Groups sometimes bully individuals or even whole neighborhoods. Bullying may take the form of pushing, shoving, or other physical abuse. Teasing, taunting, using ethnic slurs, and making sexual comments or gestures are other forms of bullying.

One way to deal with bullies is to walk away with your head held high. Bullies want victims to react with fear or anger. Walking away sends the message that you don't care. Ignoring the bully or pretending the bully doesn't exist are other ways to stop aggressive behavior. Bullying is serious and no one needs to put up with it. If you become aware of bullying in your school or neighborhood, talk with a school counselor, parent, or other adult.

Group Pressure

When Tanya found out that Alison had started a rumor about her, she was furious. She confronted Alison, and as they argued, their voices became louder. A crowd gathered. Someone began to shout, "Fight! Fight!" Although Tanya and Alison had been ready to stop, both now felt pressured to keep the argument going.

FIGURE 7.1

Positive Ways to Manage Anger

You don't have to give in to anger. Coping skills can help you manage anger. *Describe some strategies you have applied to effectively manage anger.*

- Take time to cool down.
- Walk, run, swim, or do something active.
- Listen to music, or just sit quietly.
- Identify exactly what triggered your anger.
- Attack the problem, not the person.

- Brainstorm ways to handle the situation.
- Ask yourself if you have taken the situation too personally.
- Explain to the other person how you feel.
- Try to imagine the other person's point of view.
- Talk over the situation with a parent, friend, or trusted adult.

166 CHAPTER 7: CONFLICT RESOLUTION

Reading Check

How Words Function Reviewing parts of speech and the function of words in sentences can help students improve comprehension of text. Draw students' attention to the fourth sentence in the paragraph headed Bullying and Teasing. Point out that the subject of the sentence is *bullying* and that the *-ing* form of a verb is called a gerund when it is used as a noun. Encourage students to find other examples of gerunds used as the subjects of sentences in the text on these two pages. For example, in the last sentence of the same paragraph, the words *teasing, taunting, using,* and *making* are gerunds.

HEALTH SKILLS ACTIVITY

DECISION MAKING

When to Suggest a Mediator

Lisa, Tony, and Dave were all good friends until two weeks ago. After a serious argument, Tony and Dave stopped speaking to each other. Both are still speaking to Lisa, and each separately told Lisa his side of the conflict.

Dave told Lisa that Tony tries to copy Dave's school papers and tests. Dave explained that when he confronted Tony, Tony acted outraged and denied trying to copy anything. Later, Lisa listened to Tony's side of the story. Tony said that Dave is spreading lies about him, and that he will never be friends with Dave again. When Lisa suggested that Dave and Tony try to talk over their problem, Tony said, "Stay out of this! It's between Dave and me."

Lisa wonders if peer mediation would help settle their conflict. She thinks about suggesting it but is worried

about Tony's warning. She decides to use the decision-making process to determine what she should do.

What Would You Do?

Apply the skills for decision making to Lisa's situation. Would you suggest mediation? Why or why not?

1. **STATE THE SITUATION.**
2. **LIST THE OPTIONS.**
3. **WEIGH THE POSSIBLE OUTCOMES.**
4. **CONSIDER VALUES.**
5. **MAKE A DECISION AND ACT.**
6. **EVALUATE THE DECISION.**

Lesson Review

Using complete sentences, answer the following questions on a sheet of paper.

Reviewing Terms and Facts

1. **Vocabulary** Define *win-win solution*.
2. **Summarize** In your own words, summarize conflict resolution/mediation skills.
3. **Explain** What makes students effective mediators for their peers?

Thinking Critically

4. **Apply** Relate conflict resolution/mediation skills to personal situations: How have you used these skills in your life?
5. **Explain** How can a peer mediation program help make your school safer?

Applying Health Skills

6. **Conflict Resolution** With a partner, write a skit in which a conflict is resolved peacefully. Perform your skit for the class to demonstrate strategies for coping with problems related to conflict.

LESSON 2: RESOLVING CONFLICTS **171**

HEALTH SKILLS PRACTICE

Conflict Resolution Invite students to practice their mediation skills by reading aloud the following: Do your family members disagree about friends, makeup, music, or something else? Agree to be the mediator. Name the problem. Listen to both sides, summarize, and suggest a compromise everyone can agree upon. For example, your parents think your brother plays the music too loudly and too long. Your brother thinks it's just right. Write down a summary of comments from both sides, and suggest a compromise for your family to try.

③ Assess

Evaluating

📁 Assign the Lesson 2 Review; then assign the Lesson 2 Quiz in the TCR.

Reteaching

📁 Assign Concept Map 25 or Reteaching Activity 25 in the TCR.

Enrichment

📁 Assign Enrichment Activity 25 in the TCR.

④ Close

Ask volunteers to summarize and relate conflict resolution and mediation skills to personal situations.

Lesson 2 Review

1. An agreement that gives each party something they want.
2. Responses should include the steps listed in Figure 7.2 on page 169 and Figure 7.3 on page 170.
3. They understand their peers' attitudes and viewpoints and speak the same language.
4. Responses will vary.
5. Peer mediation can help keep conflicts at school from escalating into violence.

Avoiding and Preventing Violence

① Focus

Lesson Objectives

Students will be able to
- identify factors that contribute to teen violence.
- identify policies to prevent violence in schools.
- describe ways to protect themselves from violence.

Health Skills
- Advocacy, p. 174

Motivators

Quick Write
Have several students read their paragraphs aloud. List the reasons that are stated on the board. Then ask the class to add to the list of reasons.

Bellringer Activity

Tell students that TV programs, movies, and video/computer games are thought to contribute to violence in our society. Ask: What evidence have you seen to support this theory?

VOCABULARY

Have students use each vocabulary term in a sentence. Divide the class into groups of three students. Ask them to share their sentences with the group. Have the group rate the sentences and share their best sentences with the class. Correct any misconceptions the responses reveal.

Quick Write

Write a short paragraph explaining why you think some young people resort to violence to settle differences.

LEARN ABOUT...

- factors that contribute to teen violence.
- policies to prevent violence in schools.
- ways to protect yourself from violence.

VOCABULARY

- violence
- homicide
- gang
- zero tolerance policy
- rape

Violence in Our Society

Hitting someone is clearly an example of violence, but what about *threatening* to hit or hurt someone? Is that violence? What about destroying property or yelling mean and hurtful words at someone? Is that violence? The answer is yes. **Violence** is *any act that causes physical or psychological harm to a person or damage to property.* **Homicide**, *the killing of one human being by another,* is violence at its worst. In recent years the numbers of homicides and other violent acts have declined in the United States. The rates are still unacceptably high, however, and homicide remains a leading cause of death among teens.

Various factors have been suggested as causes for the high rates of violence. Some people point to the violent acts shown on television and in movies as contributing factors. Others cite changes in family structure that tend to leave children unsupervised for hours at a time. Many also believe the availability of a variety of weapons, including guns, is a major cause of violence.

Incidents of violence have led communities to establish public curfews. *Analyze how this strategy can prevent the deliberate injuries that can result from violence.*

Lesson 3 Resources

Teacher Classroom Resources

- Concept Map 26
- Cross-Curriculum Activity 14
- Decision-Making Activity 14
- Enrichment Activity 26
- Health Lab 7
- Lesson Plan 3
- Lesson 3 Quiz

- Reading Tutor Activity 26
- Reteaching Activity 26
- Transparency 26

Student Activities Workbook

- Chapter 7 Study Guide
- Applying Health Skills 26

Violence and Teens

Much of the recent violence has involved teens. In 1998, about one-third of all victims of violent crime were ages 12 to 19. Teens are not just victims, however. Each year more than 120,000 youths are arrested for committing violent crimes. Teen violence often involves gangs, weapons, and drugs.

Gangs

Although gang activity was once associated with large cities, it is now a national problem. A **gang** is *a group of people who associate with one another to take part in criminal activity.* Typical gang activities include vandalism, graffiti, robbery, and drug dealing.

Because gang members often carry weapons, they make an environment unsafe for everyone. In addition, some of their actions, such as random shootings, are unpredictable. As a result, innocent people are injured or killed. The presence of gangs in a school or community causes people to live in fear instead of in security.

Weapons

Firearm injuries are the second leading cause of death for young people ages 10 to 24. For every one person killed by a firearm, four are wounded. A survey of young people who had been shot revealed that 35 percent of them were carrying guns when they were wounded. Strategies to prevent firearm accidents include controlling gun ownership and installing safety devices on guns. Gun owners are advised to keep their firearms unloaded and to store ammunition in a separate locked place.

Drugs

Drugs and violence tend to go hand in hand. Drug users who are desperate for money to support their drug habit often turn to illegal and violent behavior. Drugs also affect a user's ability to think clearly and have good judgment. While under the influence of drugs, a person might shoplift, steal a car, or commit a violent crime.

Violence is prevalent in the media. *How do you think the media's portrayal of violence influences individual and community health?*

Reading Check

Analyze word structure. Find the compound word in this list: *random, ammunition, ownership, firearms.* **Locate other compound words on pages 172 and 173.**

② Teach

Applying Knowledge

Have students apply what they are learning about preventing violence to problems with the community. Brainstorm ways the community could be made safer. Have students plan ways to make the changes. Help students present their plans to local civic officials. **L2**

Cross-Curriculum Activity

VISUAL ARTS Have students create posters that suggest alternatives to gangs for teens who want to feel that they belong to a group of peers. (Possibilities include school clubs, neighborhood youth groups, church or synagogue groups, and sports teams.) **L1** **INCL** *English Language Learners, At-Risk, Special Learning Needs, Behavior Problems, Different Learning Styles* (*Visual*)

Critical Thinking

Ask students whether they think violent acts shown on television, in movies, and in computer games contribute to the high rates of violence. Have students explain why or why not. **L1**

Critical Thinking

Ask students to share their ideas about safe storage for firearms:

- Where and how should owners store guns if there are children or teens in the home?

- What else do you think gun owners should do to keep their firearms away from others?

- Why is it important to comply with rules prohibiting possession of weapons? **L1**

Cross-Curriculum Activity

SOCIAL STUDIES Have volunteers use online sources or library resources to learn about state or federal legislation related to hate crimes. Have students find out whether a particular incident initiated the legislation. Ask these volunteers to define hate crimes and share their findings with the rest of the class. **L3**

Discussing

Ask students:

- Does our school have a zero tolerance policy regarding drugs, weapons or weapon look-alikes, and violent behavior? If so, do you think the policy is effective?
- What are the specific rules and consequences outlined in the school's policy?
- If the school does not have such a policy, do you think one should be adopted? Why?
- Explain the importance of complying with rules prohibiting possession of drugs and weapons.

HEALTH SKILLS ACTIVITY

ADVOCACY

Guide students to ensure that they apply strategies for avoiding violence and weapons. Read and discuss the activity with students. Ask:

- Why is each action an important contribution to school safety?
- Which actions may be especially difficult? Why?
- How can joining with other teens make those actions easier?

Then have students work in cooperative groups to plan, write, and illustrate their brochures.

Note: This skill is introduced in Chapter 3 on page 61.

Violence in Schools

Incidents of violence in schools have led to increased security measures. Many schools now keep all or most doors to the school locked. In some schools, students must pass through metal detectors to enter the school. School officials may search lockers and students' belongings if they have reasonable suspicion that someone is planning a violent act.

To further increase safety, many schools have also adopted a zero tolerance policy for weapons or weapon look-alikes, drugs, and violent behavior. A **zero tolerance policy** is *a policy that makes no exceptions for anybody for any reason.* Any student found guilty of bringing any prohibited items to school, or of violent behavior, is automatically expelled.

To do your part to prevent school violence, follow the tips listed in the Health Skills Activity on this page. Understand and follow school rules related to health, including rules prohibiting the possession of weapons at school.

School violence gets a lot of publicity, but the vast majority of schools experience little or no violence. *Do you think most students feel safe in your school?*

HEALTH SKILLS ACTIVITY

ADVOCACY

Help Prevent School Violence

You can help prevent school violence by acting safely and by encouraging others to play their part. Here are some actions that you can take and advocate.

- Refuse to bring a weapon or weapon look-alike to school, to carry a weapon for another person, or to keep silent about those who carry weapons.
- Immediately report any violent incidents or threats of violence to school authorities or the police.

- Learn how to manage your own anger.
- Help others settle arguments peaceably.
- Welcome new students and get to know students who are often left out.
- Sign (or start) a Peace Pledge in which students promise to settle disagreements peaceably and to work toward a safe campus.

WITH A GROUP
Work with classmates to create a brochure that encourages all students to play their part in keeping the school safe.

174 CHAPTER 7: CONFLICT RESOLUTION

COOPERATIVE LEARNING ACTIVITY

Role-Playing As a class, brainstorm a list of incidents of teen violence against persons that have occurred or could occur in their school or community. Write the list on the board. Then, divide the class into small groups. Direct each small group on one side of the room to choose a situation and analyze strategies for preventing deliberate injuries. Direct each group on the other side of the room to choose another situation and analyze strategies for responding to deliberate injuries. Each group will use its analyses of strategies for preventing or responding to deliberate injuries to write a skit that they will perform for the class.

FIGURE 7.4

Shield Yourself from Violence

Follow these precautions to protect yourself from violence. *What other strategies could you use to avoid violence, gangs, and weapons?*

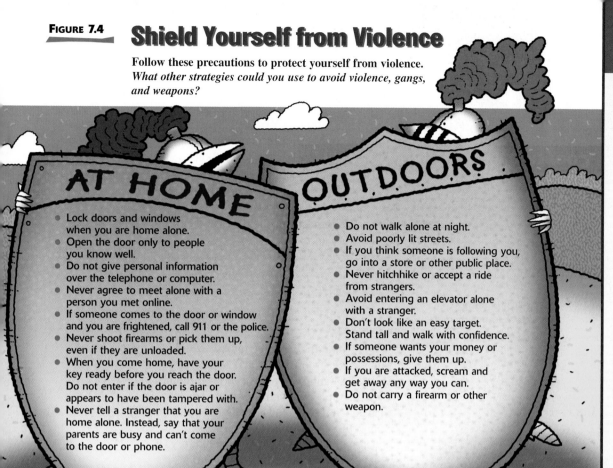

AT HOME

- Lock doors and windows when you are home alone.
- Open the door only to people you know well.
- Do not give personal information over the telephone or computer.
- Never agree to meet alone with a person you met online.
- If someone comes to the door or window and you are frightened, call 911 or the police.
- Never shoot firearms or pick them up, even if they are unloaded.
- When you come home, have your key ready before you reach the door. Do not enter if the door is ajar or appears to have been tampered with.
- Never tell a stranger that you are home alone. Instead, say that your parents are busy and can't come to the door or phone.

OUTDOORS

- Do not walk alone at night.
- Avoid poorly lit streets.
- If you think someone is following you, go into a store or other public place.
- Never hitchhike or accept a ride from strangers.
- Avoid entering an elevator alone with a stranger.
- Don't look like an easy target. Stand tall and walk with confidence.
- If someone wants your money or possessions, give them up.
- If you are attacked, scream and get away any way you can.
- Do not carry a firearm or other weapon.

Protecting Yourself from Violence

Protect yourself from violent crime by avoiding unsafe situations. Develop self-protection habits by being alert to what is going on around you and trusting your instincts. If a situation feels dangerous, it probably is. Be ready for threatening situations before they happen by planning ahead. With the adults in your family, identify some potential dangers. Figure out what you could do to get out of those situations safely. If you suspect or hear a student talking about violence, report it to school authorities.

Choosing your friends wisely is another way to protect yourself. Avoid people who have a low commitment to school, participate in illegal activities, or use alcohol or drugs. **Figure 7.4** suggests other ways to protect yourself from violence.

LESSON 3: AVOIDING AND PREVENTING VIOLENCE **175**

WHAT TEENS WANT TO KNOW

How do I avoid gangs? Enable and encourage students to apply strategies for avoiding violence, gangs, weapons, and drugs. Tell students that gangs tend to recruit, confront, and harass teens who are alone and unoccupied. If possible, leave school with a group of friends. Limit the opportunities for gang members to approach you by practicing a sport, rehearsing for a play, or studying in an organized group. Never confront a gang member. Gang members may be involved with drugs, may be armed with weapons, or may be seeking opportunities for violent conflict. If you are threatened or you see gang activity, report it to your school, parents, and local law enforcement officials.

Lesson 3

Discussing

Help students identify specific unsafe situations that might arise in their school or community.

- What are the early warning signs of these unsafe situations?
- What are the best ways to avoid or leave these situations? **L1**

Applying Knowledge

Have students apply strategies for avoiding violence, gangs, weapons, and drugs. If your school has a violence hot line, ask the students to explain how to access it. If your school does not already have or promote a bully-proofing program, suggest that interested students work with school officials to start one. **L1**

VISUAL LEARNING

FIGURE 7.4 Read aloud the title and the caption for Figure 7.4. Ask students to keep the caption question in mind as they read and discuss the precautions for use at home and outdoors. Then have students identify other actions they can take to protect themselves from violence, gangs, and weapons. **INCL** *English Language Learners, Special Learning Needs, Behavior Problems, Different Learning Styles (Visual)*

Investigating

Help students discuss what to do and whom to notify if a rape does take place. Then ask volunteers to collect and share rape-information brochures from the local police department and rape crisis center. **L3**

Lesson 3

Discussing

Students who watch television have probably viewed programs in which a variety of weapons are used in violent acts. Have these students discuss with the class the dangers associated with these weapons.

③ Assess

Evaluating

📁 Assign the Lesson 3 Review; then assign the Lesson 3 Quiz in the TCR.

Reteaching

• 📁 Assign Concept Map 26 or Reteaching Activity 26 in the TCR.
• Ask students to identify several methods that have been used by schools to reduce school violence.

Enrichment

• 📁 Assign Enrichment Activity 10 in the TCR.
• Have students make posters depicting several ways teens can protect themselves from violence on the street, such as avoiding dark alleys and staying with a group.

④ Close

Go around the room and ask each student to identify one new idea they learned from this lesson. Encourage a variety of answers to avoid repetition.

Many communities have worked together with local law enforcement agencies to make their neighborhoods safer. *What is being done to protect your community?*

Protecting Yourself from Rape

Rape is *any kind of sexual intercourse against a person's will.* Over half of all rape victims know their attackers. Whenever a person is forced to have sex, whether with someone he or she knows or with a stranger, a rape has occurred. Rape is always an act of violence, and it is illegal. To protect yourself from rape, you need to recognize and avoid situations that might increase the risk of an attack. Here are some suggestions.

• If you go out alone with someone, make it clear that you're not interested in any sexual activity.
• Avoid secluded places.
• Don't drink alcohol or use other drugs or date people who do.
• Always carry money so you can call home or take a cab or bus if you feel unsafe.

Preventing Violence

People across the nation are making an effort to reduce and prevent violence. Here are some of the actions they have taken:

• Holding stop-the-violence rallies
• Supporting stronger gun laws
• Installing lighting in parks and playgrounds
• Breaking up gang control of public parks
• Starting Neighborhood Watch programs
• Supporting teen curfews
• Teaching nonviolent conflict resolution
• Assigning more police to street patrols

Lesson 3 Review

Using complete sentences, answer the following questions on a sheet of paper.

Reviewing Terms and Facts

1. **Vocabulary** Define *violence* and *homicide.*
2. **Explain** What is the purpose of a zero tolerance policy?
3. **Identify** What are three basic ways you can protect yourself from violence?

Thinking Critically

4. **Explain** Why is it important to follow the rules prohibiting possession of weapons at school?

5. **Apply** What strategies could help teens in your community avoid violence and gangs?
6. **Analyze** Describe the dangers associated with weapons and strategies for avoiding weapons.

Applying Health Skills

7. **Practicing Healthful Behaviors** With a partner, write a skit in which a teen helps a peer avoid or cope with a potentially dangerous situation involving violence. Perform your skit for the class to demonstrate strategies for preventing deliberate injuries that may result from violence.

176 Chapter 7: Conflict Resolution

Lesson 3 Review

1. Violence is any act that causes physical or psychological harm to a person or damage to property. Homicide is the killing of one human being by another.
2. To prevent anyone from breaking the rules for any reason.
3. Any three: avoid unsafe situations, develop self-protection habits, be alert, trust instincts, choose friends wisely.
4. Responses should include the idea that this helps maintain health and safety.
5. Students may suggest providing more recreational facilities or sports programs so that teens have safe places to hang out.
6. Accept all reasonable responses.

Preventing Abuse

Forms of Abuse

Abuse takes many forms and is a significant problem in the United States. In general, **abuse** can be defined as *the physical, emotional, or mental mistreatment of one person by another.* Abuse occurs among all ages, in all racial and ethnic populations, and in all economic groups. There is no situation in which abuse is okay. Abuse is damaging to everyone involved and is illegal.

Abuse occurs mostly in close relationships. Parents or guardians may abuse children, siblings may abuse each other, and friends may abuse friends. Many abusers are more powerful than their victims and try to make them feel that they deserve to be treated harshly. Abuse is not an acceptable form of discipline. No one ever deserves abuse, and it is never the victim's fault.

Physical Abuse

Physical abuse includes hitting, slapping, kicking, pushing, shoving, punching, choking, and other ways of doing physical harm to a person. An abuser could use a weapon, belt, or other item to harm the victim. Shaking is also abuse. Shaking a baby or young child is especially dangerous because it can cause brain damage. A legal term used to describe physical abuse is battery. **Battery** is *the beating, hitting, or kicking of another person.* Battery, like all other forms of abuse, is against the law.

Quick Write

What does the term *abuse* mean to you? Who would you talk to if you thought a friend was being abused?

LEARN ABOUT...

- forms of abuse and their effects on victims.
- the cycle of abuse.
- ways to avoid abuse.
- where to get help if you are abused.

VOCABULARY

- abuse
- battery
- sexual harassment
- neglect
- cycle of abuse

In most communities, help is available for victims of abuse and for those who abuse. *Where can students in your school report abuse?*

LESSON 4: PREVENTING ABUSE **177**

Lesson 4

Preventing Abuse

1 Focus

Lesson Objectives

Students will be able to

- define abuse and describe the different forms of abuse that can occur.
- explain the cycle of abuse.
- list ways to avoid abuse.
- identify where to go for help if they are abused.

Health Skills
- Communication Skills, p. 180

Motivators

 **Quick Write**
Have students read their responses aloud. Ask: Would you first get approval from your friend before talking with someone about the abuse? Why or why not?

Bellringer Activity

Have students recall the health triangle. Ask them to list at least one type of abuse for each aspect of health.

VOCABULARY

Ask volunteers to read the vocabulary terms and give definitions in their own words. Have other volunteers read the definition provided in the chapter. Correct any misconceptions.

Lesson 4 Resources

Teacher Classroom Resources

- Concept Map 27
- Enrichment Activity 27
- Lesson Plan 4
- Lesson 4 Quiz
- Reading Tutor Activity 27
- Reteaching Activity 27

 Transparency 27

Student Activities Workbook

- Chapter 7 Study Guide
- Applying Health Skills 27
- Health Inventory 7

Lesson 4

② Teach

Guest Speaker

Invite the director of a shelter for battered women or a police officer who deals with spousal abuse to speak to the class. Ask the speaker to address such issues as the causes of abuse, forms of spousal or family abuse, characteristics of abusers and their victims, and sources of help for abused spouses. Encourage the speaker to address the impact of spousal abuse on the entire family, particularly the children. Have students prepare questions in advance. **L1**

Discussing

Initiate a discussion on what constitutes sexual harassment. Ask:

• What are some examples of behavior that would be considered sexual harassment? (Note: You may want to provide examples instead of having students provide them.)

• How does a person know when certain behavior is sexual harassment? (*The behavior creates a hostile environment for the victim, is not wanted, and continues to occur even after the victim has requested that it stop.*) **L1**

Emotional abuse can make a person feel isolated and unwanted. *How might you reach out to someone who needs help?*

Emotional Abuse

Emotional abuse is the use of words or gestures to mistreat another person. It occurs when a person is made fun of, yelled at, bullied, and made to feel stupid, worthless, or helpless. Threats of physical violence are emotional abuse. If a male teen threatens his girlfriend when he sees her talking with another male teen, he is committing emotional abuse.

Sexual Abuse

Sexual abuse occurs when a person is forced to participate in a sexual act against his or her will. It is sexual abuse any time an adult commits a sexual act with a child or young person below the age of consent. Often the sexual abuser of children and teens is an adult family member or friend. Sexual abusers don't always use physical force. Young people are often persuaded, bribed, tricked, or bullied into performing sexual acts. All sexual abuse is illegal.

One kind of sexual abuse that may happen at school is **sexual harassment**, which is *uninvited and unwelcome sexual conduct directed at another person.* Sexual harassment includes words, touching, jokes, looks, notes, or gestures with sexual meaning. When confronted, many people claim they meant it as a joke, but sexual harassment is not funny. It is illegal and must be reported to school personnel.

Neglect

People need love and encouragement, nourishing food, clothing, adequate housing, education, safety, and medical and dental care. Children, elderly people, and people with disabilities depend on other people to help them meet these needs. **Neglect** is *the failure to meet a person's basic physical and emotional needs.* Neglect causes physical and emotional harm. Children who are neglected may grow up feeling worthless and have difficulty setting and achieving goals. Neglect is a form of abuse and is against the law.

178 Chapter 7: Conflict Resolution

MORE ABOUT...

Abusive Dating Relationships In this type of relationship, the abuser (usually male, but not always) tries to control the victim. He or she may humiliate the victim, tell the victim what to wear, and choose his or her friends. Physical abuse may also occur. The victim may withdraw from activities or regular friends and have bruises or sprains. Share with students that it is never okay to be threatened, intimidated, or put down. They should not mistake excessive jealousy and controlling behavior for affection. It is possible to break out of these relationships with the help of counselors and health professionals. Teens who suspect a friend is being abused should encourage the person to talk to a trusted adult.

Effects of Abuse

The effects of abuse are long term and serious. In many cases, the mental and emotional effects remain long after any physical injuries have healed. Victims often blame themselves and are too afraid or too embarrassed to seek help. Yet if a person does not receive help, the effects of abuse can last a lifetime. Long-term effects of abuse include the following:

- Self-neglect or self-injury
- Depression, anxiety, panic attacks, and sleep disorders
- Violent and criminal behavior
- Chronic pain
- Abuse of alcohol and other drugs
- Eating disorders
- Inappropriate sexual conduct
- Suicide attempts
- Poor personal relationships

The Cycle of Abuse

A person who was abused as a child or who witnessed abuse of others may see abuse as a normal way of life. As adults, such people are more likely to abuse children. This *pattern of repeating abuse from one generation to the next* is known as the **cycle of abuse**. One key to stopping all forms of abuse is to break the cycle of abuse. That starts with getting help from someone you trust.

If you or someone you know is being abused, tell a parent, other family member, teacher, school nurse, doctor, or trusted adult. If you do not get the help you need from this adult, tell someone else. Abused people need help and so do abusers. Their past experience does not make it acceptable for them to abuse others. Abuse is never acceptable and is always illegal.

People who were abused as children are at risk of becoming abusers. *What can a person do to break the cycle of abuse?*

LESSON 4: PREVENTING ABUSE **179**

Applying Knowledge

Ask volunteers to collect brochures, posters, and information packets from local centers that provide help for victims of abuse. Display these in the classroom. Have each volunteer give the name, address, and telephone number of the center. **L1**

Discussing

Have students discuss why abuse is a significant problem in the United States today. Write the following reasons on the board: the cycle of abuse, emotional problems that go untreated, and a lack of communication skills. Ask:

- How could each of these possible reasons lead to an increase of violence in relationships?
- How can your knowledge about the forms and effects of abuse help you identify strategies for prevention of emotional, physical, and sexual abuse?
- How can that knowledge help you avoid becoming a victim? **L2**

Critical Thinking

Ask students:

- Over time, how might a person's self-confidence and self-esteem be affected by an abusive relationship?
- What could a person do to get out of such a relationship? **L2**

Health Literacy

Health Information Properly taught, discipline in home and school helps teens learn to work productively within the limits of society's laws. When parents or teachers discipline a child, they should follow these guidelines to avoid damaging a child's self-esteem:

- Be consistent so that the child knows what to expect.
- Distinguish between the misbehavior and the child so that the child realizes that the behavior is bad, not he or she as a person.
- Remain friendly, fair, and firm.
- Give children choices whenever possible.
- Avoid physical punishments.

Analyzing

Ask students to analyze why abuse damages the abuser as well as the victim. (*The abuser is likely to feel guilty and ashamed because of the abusive acts. This sense of guilt, in turn, decreases his or her self-esteem.*) **L2**

HEALTH SKILLS ACTIVITY

COMMUNICATION SKILLS

Guide students in reading about Alex's situation and in discussing his concerns. Also, help students review the listed speaking and listening skills.

Then have students work with partners to write out a conversation between Alex and Lauren. Ask each pair to perform their dialog for the rest of the class.

Note: This skill is introduced in Chapter 2 on pages 34–38.

Cooperative Learning

Have groups of students use telephone books to find the numbers for local shelters, support groups, and crisis hot lines. Have each group analyze strategies they would use to respond to deliberate violent injuries and then present a skit in which they demonstrate those strategies. Assign each member of the group an individual role. For example, one member can be the leader, one the recorder or compiler of information, and one the reporter. **L1**

How to Avoid Abuse

To avoid abuse and to help prevent it, remember the three Rs:

- **Recognize.** Learn to recognize and avoid situations that can increase the risk of abuse.
- **Resist.** If someone tries to abuse you physically or sexually, resist. Fight back any way you can. Be assertive.
- **Report.** Tell someone about the incident as soon as you can.

Where to Get Help

Teens who are abused need help to get out of their situation. Asking for help is not a sign of weakness. Instead, it shows courage and a willingness to stand up for yourself. Seeking help can break the cycle of abuse.

Many helpful resources are available in your school and community. Ask a teacher or counselor about school resources for victims of abuse and abusers. Many religious organizations have counselors who can help with abuse problems. Also look for teen help lines, abuse hot lines, and crisis centers in your local phone

HEALTH SKILLS ACTIVITY

COMMUNICATION SKILLS

Helping a Victim of Abuse

When Alex noticed bruise marks on Lauren's arm, she said it happened when her boyfriend was just "goofing around." Later, Alex noticed other bruises, and one day Lauren came in with a black eye. Lauren's explanation of how she got it didn't make sense, and she seemed ashamed of the injury.

Alex thinks that Lauren might be in an abusive relationship. He knows that if Lauren is being abused, the one thing she needs most is for someone to hear and believe her. On the other hand, Lauren has brushed off Alex's questions before. Alex wants to talk to Lauren about her injuries, but he isn't sure how to handle the conversation. He decides to use the speaking and listening skills he has learned to help her cope with this dangerous situation.

WHAT WOULD YOU DO?

With a classmate, write and perform a skit to demonstrate how Alex could use the communication skills below to help his peer cope with this dangerous situation in a healthy way.

SPEAKING SKILLS

- "I" messages
- Clear, simple statements
- Honest thoughts and feelings
- Appropriate body language

LISTENING SKILLS

- Appropriate body language
- Conversation encouragers
- Mirror thoughts and feelings
- Ask questions

180 CHAPTER 7: CONFLICT RESOLUTION

INCLUSION STRATEGIES

Gifted Suggest to gifted students that they present a debate to the rest of the class. Each student should adopt one of the following points of view in the debate:

- Violence should be permitted at any time on television because censoring violence would be a violation of the freedom of speech.

- The networks should reduce violence during prime-time hours, but it is up to parents to control their children's exposure to violence on television at other times.

- The networks should take an active role in protecting children from violence by keeping violence to a minimum in all television programming.

book. Most centers offer help for both the abused and the abuser. General resources are described below:

- **Police department.** Call here if someone is in immediate danger. In many communities the emergency number for the local police department is 911.
- **Hospital.** Hospitals provide emergency medical treatment.
- **Shelters.** Family members in danger of being abused can stay in shelters while they get help putting their lives in order.
- **Support or self-help groups.** In these groups, people have a chance to discuss their situation with others who have experienced similar problems.
- **Crisis hot lines.** These are telephone services that parents and abused children can call to get help. Hot line workers receive special training. All conversations are kept confidential, and the caller does not have to give his or her name.

Families that experience abuse need the help of an experienced counselor. *Why must both the abuser and the victim get help?*

Explain to students that both public and private health organizations are excellent sources of current, reliable health information. Many health organizations have local chapters or offices, and most maintain Web sites. **L1**

❸ Assess

Evaluating

📁 Assign the Lesson 4 Review; then assign the Lesson 4 Quiz in the TCR.

Reteaching

- 📁 Assign Concept Map 27 or Reteaching Activity 27 in the TCR.
- Work with small groups of students to review the definition of abuse, the forms of abuse, and the sources of help for victims of abuse.

Enrichment

- 📁 Assign Enrichment Activity 27 in the TCR.
- Ask groups of students to gather national, state, or local statistics on abuse over the past ten years. Have them draw graphs or prepare other visual presentations of their findings.

❹ Close

Ask each student to identify the most important concept she or he learned about abuse.

Lesson 4 Review

Using complete sentences, answer the following questions on a sheet of paper.

Reviewing Terms and Facts

1. **Vocabulary** Define *abuse* and use it in a sentence that shows that you understand its meaning.
2. **List** Give three examples of behaviors that could be viewed as sexual harassment.
3. **Explain** What is the *cycle of abuse?*
4. **Identify** What do the three Rs for avoiding abuse stand for?

Thinking Critically

5. **Explain** Why do you think some people are reluctant to report incidents of abuse?

6. **Evaluate** Analyze strategies for responding to deliberate injuries that may result from abuse. Which ones do you think would be the most effective? Why?

Applying Health Skills

7. **Advocacy** Identify several strategies for prevention and intervention of physical, emotional, and sexual abuse. Create a flyer that features these strategies and tells teens where they can go for help.

Lesson 4 Review

1. The physical, emotional, or mental mistreatment of one person by another. Sentences will vary.
2. Any three: words, touching, jokes, looks, notes, gestures with sexual meaning.
3. The pattern of repeating abuse from one generation to the next.
4. Recognize, resist, report.
5. They may be too embarrassed or ashamed, or they may feel that they are somehow to blame for the abuse.
6. Responses will vary, but should include getting medical help.

Stopping Violence Before It Starts

① Focus

Objectives

Students will be able to

- discuss safety issues at their own school.
- analyze various approaches to increasing school safety.
- advocate for students to report potentially violent situations.

Motivator

Bellringer Activity

Ask students, "Do you think safety is an issue at our school? On a scale of 1 to 10, with 1 being "I feel 100 percent safe at school" and 10 being "I am extremely concerned about my safety," how would you rate our school?

② Teach

Discussing

Ask students, "What are some steps a school might take to increase safety?" Have students review the spread again, calling out various options mentioned. These include peer-mediation programs, crime-stopper hot lines, patrols by uniformed officers, metal detectors, and antiviolence pledges.

Encourage students to brainstorm other ideas. These might include random locker searches, surveillance cameras, rules about gang clothing/colors and family/community outreach.

Ask students, "What are the positives and negatives of these options? Should students be asked to give up their privacy or other rights in the name of increased safety? Which of these options might be effective at our school?"

Stopping Violence Before It Starts

Teens are finding ways to make their classrooms safer.

182 CHAPTER 7: CONFLICT RESOLUTION

Beyond the Classroom

Community Ask students, "How are the strategies we've discussed for school safety the same as or different from strategies used in other settings?" Divide students into small work groups. Direct each group to pick one familiar setting in the community, such as a shopping mall or a baseball stadium. Direct each group to do the following:

- Visit their chosen site.
- Research the various safety strategies in place.
- Interview an employee about these strategies. Are they effective? Have there been problems?

Have groups present their findings to the class. Ask: What can school administrators learn about safety strategies from these other sites?

Teen Brandon Boxler doesn't want anyone in his school to get hurt by violence—so he's doing something to prevent it. Brandon had heard that two of his classmates at Northern High in Durham, North Carolina, were moving from a war of words to physical fighting. So Brandon, president of his school's Students Against Violence Everywhere (SAVE) chapter, convinced the pair to participate in his group's peer-mediation program. Now, when the girls see each other in the hall, they just say hello and move on. "Everybody gets mad," Brandon says, "but how you deal with it is the difference between violence and a peaceful resolution."

Unfortunately, more students seem to be resorting to guns to solve problems. According to the National School Safety Center, there were 13 school shooting incidents during one recent school year—almost twice as many as the year before. Alarmed, school officials nationwide have started programs to help ensure safety.

Teens Stopping Crime

Palm Beach County, Florida, has had great success with its Student Crime Stoppers hotline. Over a five-month period, tips from young people led to 14 arrests—eight of which involved students with weapons. In Texas, each of Houston's 23 high schools has uniformed officers who patrol the halls and give metal detector tests to students in random classrooms. Violent crime in Houston schools dropped 20 percent. Nicole Vazquez, a student at Lamar High, is glad the officers are around: "[Their presence] prevents people from taking extreme actions."

Promoting School Safety

Many students aren't waiting for schools to make changes. Like Brandon and his fellow SAVE participants—80,000 total in 34 states—they're taking violence prevention into their own hands. Teen Monti Murphy and more than a dozen classmates started an antiviolence organization called Keep It Real at Woodrow Wilson Senior High in Washington state. After two

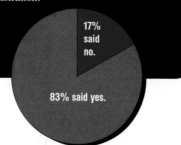

What Would You Do?

Take a look at the pie chart below to see how 5,000 teens responded to this question: If you suspected someone might commit a violent act, would you notify the school administration?

17% said no.

83% said yes.

students were shot following a fight at a school basketball game, Monti decided to try to stop the violence. Through the nonprofit group, 400 students have signed an antiviolence pledge. Now teen mentors talk to grade-school students about alternatives to fighting. Working with young people helps Monti understand the importance of nonviolence. "This eight-year-old girl told me about being scared to walk home, and we exchanged phone numbers. She calls me and we talk about her fear," Monti says. "We try to reach one person at a time."

About Preventing School Violence

Study the pie chart above. About how many teens said that they would report a potential problem to the school administration? About how many said they'd keep the information to themselves? With your classmates, respond to the poll question on slips of paper. Your teacher will tally the results. How do they compare with the results above? As a class, discuss possible barriers to reporting potential violence and how these obstacles might be overcome.

③ Apply

Time to Think

Once students have identified barriers to reporting potential violence at school, ask them to create an advocacy campaign that tries to change peer norms and encourages teens to report potential problems. Campaign elements may include essays or editorials in the school paper, posters, pamphlets, a music video, a play or puppet show, and so on. Make sure that student work

- takes a clear stand for a healthy choice.
- uses information to support the choice.
- shows awareness of the audience.
- is persuasive.
- shows conviction about the message.

VISUAL LEARNING

Ask students to analyze the photograph on page 182. Ask, "How would you feel in this young man's position? Would the addition of a metal detector at school make you feel safer? Why or why not?"

WHAT TEENS WANT TO KNOW

Isn't it illegal for school administrators to search my locker without my permission? The issue is controversial, with some students and their parents arguing that random searches are an invasion of privacy and amount to "illegal search and seizure." Proponents argue that these searches provide greater safety for all pupils and personnel. In fact, school lockers are temporarily assigned to students for their convenience and remain the property of the school or district. In numerous cases, locker searches have been legally defended based on "reasonable" circumstances within the school environment (including violence or illegal drug activity). Many schools, districts, and states have a written policy about locker searches. You may want to research the guidelines in your state and present your findings to students and their parents.

CONFLICT RESOLUTION

Objective

After completing the lesson, students will be able to demonstrate steps for conflict resolution in reaching a win-win situation.

Time: 45 minutes

Materials: none

Teacher Classroom Resources

📁 Building Health Skills Activities

• Transparency Master 6, "Conflict Resolution"

• Reproducible Master 32a, "Working Through Conflicts"

• Reproducible Master 32b, "T.A.L.K."

1. Model

• Review the T.A.L.K. steps with the class.

• Have students read about Sophia and Nathan's solution to their conflict. Discuss the steps they used to reach a win-win solution. (*Steps they used: 1. Sophia went out to "cool off." 2. They talked about the situation. 3. They negotiated a compromise.*)

WORKING THROUGH CONFLICTS

Model

Sophia and her brother Nathan often disagree over how to share household tasks. Read about how they compromised to resolve their conflict.

Sophia and Nathan are responsible for cleaning the house. Both teens prefer to vacuum. Neither likes to dust or clean the bathrooms. One Saturday, when Nathan rushed to get the vacuum first, Sophia became angry. She went for a bike ride to "cool off." When she returned, Sophia told Nathan she wanted to talk about their problem. She asked him to explain his side of the story.

Nathan said he thought cleaning the bathrooms was disgusting and dusting took too long. He liked to get his part of the cleaning done so he could do other things. Sophia said she didn't like cleaning the bathrooms either, but she would be willing to dust if Nathan would vacuum and clean the bathrooms. Nathan said that wasn't fair, since dusting didn't take as long as both of the other chores. He said that he would clean the bathrooms and vacuum most of the house if Sophia would dust the house and vacuum her bedroom. Sophia and Nathan agreed to try this solution.

184 CHAPTER 7: CONFLICT RESOLUTION

Teaching Tips

Reaching a Win-Win Solution When conflict arises, the best outcome is a win-win solution. Consider an outcome in which one person wins and the other loses (a win-lose situation). The person who loses feels bad, and the winner also loses in an indirect way. For example, the loser may feel the need to retaliate. In friendships or family relationships, a win-lose situation may damage the relationship. It is important to remember that the goal of conflict resolution is not to win but to improve the relationship; then everyone wins.

Practice

Work with a partner to write a conversation based on one of the situations shown below. Each of you will take the part of one of the characters involved in the conflict. Have one partner begin the conversation by stating his or her character's point of view about the conflict. Pass the paper back and forth and take turns responding to each other's comments. Don't speak to each other or try to pre-plan your conversation. As you write, use the steps for conflict resolution to reach a win-win situation. When you're done, read your conversation to the class. Ask the other students to identify the T.A.L.K. steps that you used.

Elliot and Spencer share a bedroom. Elliot likes to listen to music while he studies. Spencer prefers peace and quiet when he's working.

Annabel wants to wear a new trendy outfit to a family celebration. Her father thinks it is entirely inappropriate for this event.

Kayla and Jeremy have been friends for a long time. This morning, Kayla heard from another friend that Jeremy was spreading rumors about her.

COACH'S BOX

Conflict Resolution

T   Take a time out, at least 30 minutes.
A   Allow each person to tell his or her side uninterrupted.
L   Let each person ask questions.
K   Keep brainstorming to find a solution.

Apply/Assess

Write a story about two characters who are having a conflict. State the reason for their conflict and show how the characters use the T.A.L.K. steps to reach a win-win solution. You can use one of the ideas below or choose a situation that has created conflict for you or someone you know. When you are finished, read your story aloud to the class.

Self-√Check

- Does my story show how to use the T.A.L.K. steps to resolve conflict?
- Did I show a win-win solution?

CONFLICT:
Someone approaches you when you're sitting on a school bench and tells you that this is his "turf."

CONFLICT:
Another classmate pushes ahead of you in the cafeteria line.

CONFLICT:
You and a friend like the same person as a girlfriend or boyfriend.

BUILDING HEALTH SKILLS: WORKING THROUGH CONFLICTS **185**

2. Practice

- Discuss the importance of a win-win solution in resolving conflict.
- Display Transparency Master 6 as a reminder of the T.A.L.K. steps. Instruct students to work with a partner to have a conversation on paper. Have students incorporate the T.A.L.K. steps to reach a win-win solution.
- Ask volunteers to read their conversations to the class. Following each conversation, have the class identify the T.A.L.K. skills that were used.

3. Apply/Assess

- You may wish to distribute Building Health Skills Reproducible Master 32a in the TCR to guide students in completing this activity.
- Have students choose one of the conflicts or create their own. Instruct them to write a story that incorporates how to use the T.A.L.K. steps to reach a win-win solution.
- Distribute Reproducible Master 32b to each student. Have them mark the steps that are used as classmates read their stories.
- Discuss each story, including the win-win solution and the steps that were identified.

Assessment Scoring ✓

Using a rubric, student work should provide evidence of all criteria to achieve the highest score.

Skills

Student work demonstrates

- a time-out from the situation.
- both persons' points of view.
- questions to clarify the conflict.
- brainstorming to find a solution.

Concept

Student work provides

- accurate information about issues that create conflict.
- an understanding of a win-win solution.

Checking Comprehension

Use the Chapter 7 Assessment to examine the most important ideas presented in the chapter.

Answers to Reviewing Vocabulary and Concepts

Lesson 1
1. conflict
2. values
3. escalate
4. prejudice

Lesson 2
5. win-win solution
6. mediation
7. peer mediation
8. compromise

Lesson 3
9. b
10. a
11. c
12. d

Lesson 4
13. false; battery
14. false; the cycle of abuse
15. true

Thinking Critically

16. Responses will vary, but should include reporting the violence or abuse.
17. Examples will vary, but might include avoiding situations involving alcohol or drug use.

After You Read

Use your completed Foldable to review the information on the nature of conflict.

FOLDABLES™
Study Organizer

Reviewing Vocabulary and Concepts

On a sheet of paper, write the numbers 1–8. After each number, write the term from the list that best completes each statement.

> - escalate
> - conflict
> - mediation
> - peer mediation
> - compromise
> - win-win solution
> - prejudice
> - values

Lesson 1

1. A disagreement between people with opposing viewpoints, ideas, or goals is a(n) _____.
2. The beliefs and ideals that you consider important are your _____.
3. Poorly managed conflicts can _____, or become more serious.
4. A negative and unjustly formed opinion, usually against people of a different racial, religious, or cultural group, is called _____.

Lesson 2

5. A(n) _____ resolves a conflict by giving both parties something they want.
6. The process in which a third person helps those in conflict find a solution is called _____.
7. In _____, a student serves as the mediator for students involved in a conflict.

8. When you _____, you give up something in order to reach a solution that satisfies everyone.

Lesson 3

On a sheet of paper, write the numbers 9–12. After each number, write the letter of the answer that best completes each statement.

9. A group of people who associate with one another to take part in criminal activity is a
   a. clique.
   b. gang.
   c. circle.
   d. club.
10. Any act that causes physical or psychological harm to a person or damages property is
    a. violence.
    b. battery.
    c. prejudice.
    d. cowardice.
11. A zero tolerance policy means that exceptions to school rules are made for
    a. good students.
    b. first-time offenders.
    c. no one.
    d. anyone.
12. Another word that means the killing of one human being by another is
    a. suicide.
    b. hate crime.
    c. battery.
    d. homicide.

Lesson 4

On a sheet of paper, write the numbers 13–15. Write *True* or *False* for each statement below. If the statement is false, change the underlined word or phrase to make it true.

13. A legal term used to describe physical abuse is <u>sexual harassment</u>.

INCLUSION STRATEGIES

Special Learning Needs, Behavior Problems, English Language Learners The following suggestions are helpful for students with special learning needs, students with behavior problems, and ELL students:

- Pair these students with more proficient learners who can help summarize the main concepts of the chapter.

- Direct these students to listen to the Teen Health Audio Summaries. This component provides an audio and written summary of the chapter in both English and Spanish.

- Use photographs, drawings, or magazine clippings whenever possible to help students visualize the important concepts of the chapter.

14. The process of an abused child growing up and abusing his or her children is known as <u>bullying</u>.

15. The failure to meet a person's basic physical and emotional needs is <u>neglect</u>.

Thinking Critically

Using complete sentences, answer the following questions on a sheet of paper.

16. **Identify** List three healthy ways that peers can help each other avoid and cope with potentially dangerous situations involving violence or abuse.

17. **Recognize** Give two examples of how a teen might avoid situations that can increase the risk of abuse.

Career Corner

Professional Mediator Are you a good listener and able to see both sides of a disagreement? If so, then you may have what it takes to be a professional mediator. These professionals work in corporations, government agencies, and schools, helping people solve problems peacefully. To enter this career, you'll need a four-year college degree and training in mediation. If you think this career might match your skills, read more about it in Career Corner at health.glencoe.com.

Standardized Test Practice

Math

Read the paragraph below and then answer the questions.

Overcrowding can cause conflict to erupt. To minimize conflict, it is essential for each individual to have enough space to avoid the stress of overcrowding.

1. A school district determined that each student needs 12 square feet of space in a class. According to this guideline, how many students can occupy a classroom that measures 20 feet by 25 feet, if an area 5 feet by 25 feet is kept empty at the front of the room?
   - (A) 25 students
   - (B) 31 students
   - (C) 41 students
   - (D) 60 students

2. The classrooms in a certain school are different sizes. The numbers of students that can occupy the eighth-grade classrooms without being too crowded are 23, 30, 24, 21, 26, and 21. What is the mean of these numbers?
   - (A) 21 students
   - (B) 23 students
   - (C) 24 students
   - (D) 25 students

3. Explain why area instead of volume is used to determine the space needed to avoid overcrowding.

 TH05_C3.glencoe.com/quiz

Test Practice

1. B
2. C
3. Sample answer: More people can be added to the side of other people, but only one person is present in a vertical space.

Reteaching

📁 Assign Study Guide 7 in the Student Activities Workbook.

Evaluate

- 📁 💿 Use the reproducible Chapter 7 Test in the TCR, or construct your own test using the **Exam**View® Pro Testmaker.

- 📁 Use Performance Assessment 7 in the TCR.

Enrichment

Have students write short essays in response to the following prompt: How can an understanding of violent behaviors and their destructive effects help reduce their impact on your life?

Assessment

Self-Assessment Direct students to review the activities that are provided throughout the chapter. Encourage each student to select one finished product or activity that demonstrates his or her best work for the chapter. Have students explain what they learned and how the examples they selected show their progress.

Career Corner

Professional Mediator After reviewing the career profile on the health Web site, students might:

- Describe the skills, training, and education needed.

- Discuss why a corporation or government agency might need the services of a professional mediator.

Physical Health and Fitness

Unit Objectives

Students will examine the factors that contribute to good nutrition and learn the importance of engaging in regular physical activity to maintain health. Body image and eating disorders will also be addressed.

Unit Overview

Chapter 8
Nutrition for Health

Lesson
1 The Importance of Nutrition
2 Nutrients for Wellness
3 Following Nutrition Guidelines
4 Planning Meals and Snacks

Chapter 9
Physical Activity and Fitness

Lesson
1 The Benefits of Physical Activity
2 Endurance, Strength, and Flexibility
3 Setting Fitness Goals
4 Staying Fit and Avoiding Injury

Chapter 10
Your Body Image

Lesson
1 Maintaining a Healthy Body
2 Eating Disorders

3

UNIT

188

DEALING WITH SENSITIVE ISSUES

Nonverbal Communication Much of what people communicate to others—especially when the issue at hand is difficult to talk about—is communicated through nonverbal cues. In fact, nonverbal cues may be more important than verbal ones. Sympathetic words spoken in a demeaning tone of voice, for example, are unlikely to be sincere. Body movements send important messages to the listener. People who avert their eyes may be showing shyness or nervousness. Folded arms or clenched fists may indicate anger, discomfort, or nervousness. Being aware of such nonverbal cues in yourself and your students is fundamental to good communication about sensitive issues.

Physical Health and Fitness

HEALTH *in Action*

How can eating breakfast get you to the finish line?

Choosing the right foods at every meal is just as important as staying active. Nutrition and physical activity work hand in hand to keep you alert, fit, and energetic. Healthy foods give you the fuel you need for your favorite sport, for a day at school, or for just hanging out with your friends. Daily physical activity is healthful, fun, and can keep you at the front of the pack, on or off the field. If you eat smart and keep moving, you'll always be on track!

189

Unit Introduction

Ask students to describe the characteristics of a physically fit teen. They will probably volunteer a person with energy, vitality, and stamina. Encourage them to put themselves in the role of this fictitious teen and tell what he or she does in his or her spare time. Ask them to describe a typical day's food intake.

Next, ask them to describe a physically unfit teen, and their responses will probably be extreme (*overweight, lacking in energy, inclined to sit for long periods of time, and eats unhealthy food*).

Finally, ask them how they think fitness and nutrition influence the three sides of the health triangle. Tell students that the chapters in this unit will acquaint them with the value of healthy nutrition and fitness choices.

HEALTH *in Action*

Read the class the question on page 189. Have students share their thoughts on body image, diet, and physical activity. Then lead the class in the following physical group activity:

Have the students stand and jog in place for two minutes. Give them a moment or two to rest and catch their breath. Ask students to name the things they noticed happening to their bodies. For example, students may note that their hearts began to beat more quickly, that they began to breathe more heavily, and that they became tired. Ask volunteers to name what foods they ate that day and to evaluate whether that meal made jogging in place easier or more difficult, and why. Emphasize to students the concept of food as fuel.

Planning Guide

Chapter 8	Skills/ Activities	Reproducible Resources	Assessment
Lesson 1 **The Importance of Nutrition** *pages 192–195*		*Student Activities Workbook available for use with each chapter* 📁 Parent Letter & Activities 8 📁 Concept Map 28 📁 Enrichment Activity 28 📁 Lesson Plan 1 📁 Reading Tutor Activity 27 📁 Reteaching Activity 28	📁 Lesson 1 Quiz
Lesson 2 **Nutrients for Wellness** *pages 196–201*	**Hands-On Health** ▲ Jars of Sugar, page 200	📁 Concept Map 29 📁 Decision-Making Activity 15 📁 Enrichment Activity 29 📁 Lesson Plan 2 📁 Reading Tutor Activity 28 📁 Reteaching Activity 29	📁 Lesson 2 Quiz
Lesson 3 **Following Nutrition Guidelines** *pages 202–207*	**HEALTH SKILLS ACTIVITY** ▲ Reading a Food Label (*Accessing Information*), page 206	📁 Concept Map 30 📁 Cross-Curriculum Activity 15 📁 Decision-Making Activity 16 📁 Enrichment Activity 30 📁 Health Lab 8 📁 Lesson Plan 3 📁 Reading Tutor Activity 29 📁 Reteaching Activity 30	📁 Lesson 3 Quiz
Lesson 4 **Planning Meals and Snacks** *pages 208–211*	**HEALTH SKILLS ACTIVITY** ▲ Choosing Healthful Snacks (*Decision Making*), page 210	📁 Concept Map 31 📁 Cross-Curriculum Activity 16 📁 Enrichment Activity 31 📁 Lesson Plan 4 📁 Reading Tutor Activity 30 📁 Reteaching Activity 31	📁 Lesson 4 Quiz 📁 Chapter 8 Test 📁 Performance Assessment 8
TIME HEALTH	**Teen Vegetarians** *pages 212–213*		
BUILDING HEALTH SKILLS **Eating for Your Health** (*Advocacy*) *pages 214–215*		📁 Building Health Skills Reproducible Master 33	

Standards		Technology
National	**State/Local**	
National Health Education Standard **1.1, 1.4, 1.8, 3.1, 3.4**		Transparency 28 TeacherWorks™ Internet Activities
National Health Education Standard **1.1, 1.8, 3.1, 3.4**		Transparency 29 TeacherWorks™
National Health Education Standard **1.1, 1.8, 2.1, 2.2, 3.1, 3.4**		Transparency 30 Tape/DVD 1, Segment 6, "Nutrition and Physical Activity" TeacherWorks™
National Health Education Standard **1.1, 1.8, 3.1, 3.4, 6.1, 6.2, 6.3**		Transparency 31 TeacherWorks™ MindJogger Videoquiz **Exam**View® Pro Testmaker
National Health Education Standard **7.2, 7.4, 7.5**		Building Health Skills Transparency Master 10

TeacherWorks™

Glencoe's new and exclusive TeacherWorks™ is an all-in-one planner and resource center. Access the complete Teacher Wraparound Edition electronically. Find all your classroom resources with just a few easy clicks, and print them right from your computer. Connect directly to Glencoe's customized Health Web site. Access the National Health Education Standards correlations, or insert your own state standards and match them directly to the electronic Teacher Wraparound Edition.

Language Diversity

- English Audio Summaries
- Spanish Audio Summaries
- English Summaries, Quizzes, and Activities
- Spanish Summaries, Quizzes, and Activities
- Spanish Parent Letters and Activities

KEY TO ABILITY LEVELS

Teaching Strategies that appear throughout the chapters have been identified by one of four codes to give you an idea of their suitability for students of varying learning styles and abilities.

L1 **Level 1** strategies should be within the ability range of all students. Often full class participation is required.

L2 **Level 2** strategies are for average to above-average students or for small groups. Some teacher direction is necessary.

L3 **Level 3** strategies are designed for students able and willing to work independently. Minimal teacher direction is necessary.

INCL Strategies are appropriate for students with particular special needs in a general classroom setting.

Nutrition for Health

Chapter at a Glance

Lesson 1 highlights the benefits derived from eating a variety of nutritious foods.

Lesson 2 pinpoints the nutrients necessary for good health and the foods from which they can be derived.

Lesson 3 instructs students on how to put together a healthful eating plan based on the Food Guide Pyramid.

Lesson 4 emphasizes the importance of establishing a healthful pattern of meals and snacks.

Health Skills

- Reading a Food Label (*Accessing Information*), p. 206
- Choosing Healthful Snacks (*Decision Making*), p. 210
- Eating for Your Health (*Advocacy*), pp. 214–215

190

HANDS-ON ACTIVITY

Creating a Snack Bar Students often have difficulty choosing snack foods that satisfy their hunger yet do not add unnecessary fat and sugar to their diets. Ask students to collect and bring in empty boxes and other containers for snacks they like to eat. (You may also want to keep a few empty boxes in your classroom.) For foods that don't come in containers, have students draw pictures of the foods on pieces of cardboard folded in half (so that they can be displayed on a table). Have students discuss which food groups are represented by the snacks. Ask which ones they think make healthy snacks. Then have students create a classroom "snack bar" with the containers and cardboard displays.

Nutrition for Health

HEALTH *Online*

Do you practice healthy nutrition habits? Go to health.glencoe.com and take the Health Inventory for Chapter 8 to find out how you rate.

FOLDABLES™
Study Organizer

Before You Read

Make this Foldable to record what you learn in Lesson 1 about the body's need for nutrients. Begin with two plain sheets of 8½" × 11" paper.

Step 1

Collect two sheets of paper and place them 1" apart.

Step 2

Fold up the bottom edges, stopping them 1" from the top edges. This makes all tabs the same size.

Step 3

Crease the paper to hold the tabs in place. Staple along the fold.

Step 4

Turn and label the tabs as shown.

The Importance of Nutrition
Why You Need Nutritious Foods
Influences on Your Food Choices
Getting the Nutrients You Need

As You Read

Under the appropriate tab of your Foldable, define terms and record information on nutrients and influences on food choices.

191

Chapter Introduction

Use the options below to motivate students and preview chapter content.

HEALTH *Online*

Have students take Health Inventory 8 or read extra credit articles at **health.glencoe.com**. By clicking on Health Updates, both students and teachers can discover the latest news on health topics.

GLENCOE TECHNOLOGY

Teen Health Tape and DVD Series
(Each format available in both English and Spanish)

 You may wish to use:

• Tape/DVD 1, Segment 6, "Nutrition and Physical Activity"

MindJogger Videoquiz

Use MindJogger to preview or review Chapter 8 content.

TIME HEALTH

Teen Vegetarians
pages 212–213

FOLDABLES™
Study Organizer

Dinah Zike Study Fold

Recording Main Ideas and Supporting Facts Students will use this Foldable study guide to write about the importance of eating nutritious foods. After students have made their Foldable, point out that the first tab is labeled with the title of Lesson 1, and the three remaining tabs are labeled with the main ideas of the lesson. As students read and discuss the information on the importance of nutrition in Lesson 1, guide them in recording the supporting facts on this topic under the appropriate tabs of their Foldable. Ask students to describe on the back of their Foldable whether they feel they are or are not getting the nutrients they need.

Lesson 1

The Importance of Nutrition

1 Focus

Lesson Objectives

Students will be able to

- explain why the body needs nutritious food.
- discuss what influences their food choices.
- differentiate between hunger and appetite.
- define *nutrient deficiency*.

Motivators

Quick Write
Have students share their responses. List the influences on the board as they are revealed. Then poll the class to determine the three strongest influences on food choices of those mentioned.

Bellringer Activity

Ask students to list at least five foods they like and five foods they dislike. At the end of the chapter, have them determine which of these foods are nutritious.

VOCABULARY

Have students use each of the vocabulary terms in a sentence. Suggest students use a dictionary or the Glossary in the student text if they do not know the meaning of a word.

Quick Write

Write down six items that you've eaten recently, and list the factors that influenced your decision to eat each food. Determine the strongest influences on your food choices.

LEARN ABOUT...

- why your body needs nutritious food.
- what influences your food choices.
- the difference between appetite and hunger.
- getting the nutrients you need.

VOCABULARY

- calories
- nutrients
- nutrition
- appetite
- hunger
- nutrient deficiency

The Importance of Nutrition

Why You Need Nutritious Food

When you drink a cold glass of milk or bite into a crisp apple, you probably are thinking about the taste and texture of the foods. Yet while you're enjoying the pleasures of eating, the foods you eat are influencing your overall health and wellness. When you make healthy choices about foods, you're more likely to look your best and perform at your peak.

One important reason you eat is to take in calories. **Calories** are *units of heat that measure the energy used by the body and the energy that foods supply to the body.* You need this energy for everything you do—from running laps to doing your homework. Food also provides **nutrients**, *substances in food that your body needs.* Nutrients have many important roles, including

- giving you energy.
- building new tissues and repairing cells.
- helping your body's processes and systems run smoothly.

Different foods contain different types and amounts of nutrients. You need a wide variety of healthful foods to get all the nutrients your body needs.

Nutrition is *the process of using food and its substances to help your body have energy, grow, develop, and work properly.* Good nutrition is one of the main factors in building and maintaining good health.

Eating also offers an opportunity to spend time with friends and family. *What types of food do you choose when you eat out with friends?*

 Lesson 1 Resources

Teacher Classroom Resources

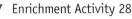 Parent Letter & Activities 8

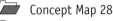 Concept Map 28

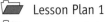 Enrichment Activity 28

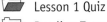 Lesson Plan 1

 Lesson 1 Quiz

Reading Tutor Activity 28

 Reteaching Activity 28

Transparency 28

Student Activities Workbook

 Chapter 8 Study Guide

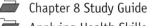 Applying Health Skills 28

FIGURE 8.1

FACTORS THAT INFLUENCE FOOD CHOICES

Factors	Description
Family and friends	You may prefer certain foods, like burritos or vegetable stir-fry, because you have grown up eating them at home. At the same time, your friends may persuade you to try new and different foods.
Cultural background	Different cultures have different traditions about what they eat, and perhaps where, how, and with whom they eat. For example, Mexican American families may eat beans, corn, and tortillas, while Italian American families may favor pasta dishes. Many Americans enjoy trying a variety of ethnic foods. What cultural foods are part of your eating pattern?
Food availability	Some foods are regional, growing only in certain areas. Some are seasonal and available only in certain months. Fresh blueberries, for example, are plentiful in summer but hard to find in the winter months. Still, modern transportation and growing methods have expanded the food supply. Many foods that were once regional or seasonal are now available in many areas year-round.
Time and money resources	Schedules and budgets affect a family's food choices. Eating fast foods or convenience foods often takes less time. Some families may look for bulk foods that provide more for the dollar.
Advertising	Have you ever tried a food because you heard about it from a television or magazine ad? Ads can influence our choices of certain brands and products and may persuade us to try new foods.
Knowledge of nutrition	The more you know about the nutrients in different foods, the better able you are to choose foods that supply the health benefits that you need.
Personal preferences	Your personal likes and dislikes and overall health goals contribute to your food choices. Some people have allergies or other medical conditions that affect their food choices. Among the foods that most often cause allergic reactions are milk, peanuts, wheat, and shellfish.

What Influences Your Food Choices?

What are your favorite foods? Do you know why you make these food choices? Chances are that you eat a variety of foods and that your food choices are influenced by many different factors. **Figure 8.1** describes some of these factors.

Appetite and Hunger

When you smell popcorn, do you want to try some? Does the sight of fresh strawberries make your mouth water? Do you love to crunch on fresh carrots? These are signs of your appetite at work. Your **appetite** is *the psychological desire for food.* It may be stimulated by the smell, sight, or texture of food.

LESSON 1: THE IMPORTANCE OF NUTRITION **193**

Lesson 1

② Teach

Discussing

Have students talk about the eating habits they had as children (*being a picky eater, eating only peanut butter and jelly for lunch*) and how those eating habits may have changed. Do they eat different foods and healthier ones? Have students discuss changes that they think they should consider making. **L1**

Critical Thinking

Ask students to identify the leading factors that affect their food choices. Have them consider whether they really love pizza or whether they eat it because their friends do. Do they choose easy foods for breakfast when they prepare it themselves? Is cost a factor when eating out? **L1**

VISUAL LEARNING

> **FIGURE 8.1** Have students describe and react to the chart. Then have volunteers read aloud the listed factors and their descriptions. Ask students to give specific examples of how each factor influences their own food choices. **INCL** *English Language Learners, Special Learning Needs, Behavior Problems, Different Learning Styles (Visual)*

CULTURAL PERSPECTIVES

Cultural Awareness Many families have unusual recipes or foods that they serve only on special occasions. Sometimes, these food choices stem from particular tastes of individuals within the family. More often, specific ingredients, recipes, serving styles, or food lore hold valuable family history. A family's food choices often have strong ties to the culture of their ancestors or relatives. Encourage students to learn to grow, prepare, and cook some of these foods as a way of learning about their cultural heritage. It also can be an effective way to preserve and pass on family traditions. ■ ■ ■

Comparing

Ask students to explain, in their own words, the difference between appetite and hunger.

• How are the two related?

• Why is it important to recognize the difference between your appetite and your hunger?

• Why do you think that even after you eat a meal and are full, you still want dessert? **L1**

Journal Writing

Suggest that students keep private food journals for one week. Have them record each meal or snack and note their emotions at the time they begin to eat (*e.g., anxious, happy, angry*). At the end of the week, ask students to review their entries, looking for relationships between their emotions and their eating patterns. **L1**

Researching

Have several volunteers work together to learn more about the importance of calcium in the diet of teens. They should learn about recommended daily intake, good food sources of calcium, and the pros and cons of taking calcium supplements. Ask these volunteers to share their findings with the rest of the class. **L3**

Reading Check

Build vocabulary. Write sentences using these words from the chapter: *calories, nutrients, appetite, hunger, nutrient deficiency.*

Appetite is different from hunger. **Hunger** is *the physical need for food.* When you are hungry, your brain sends a signal to find food. You may hear your stomach growl, or feel it contract. You may also feel tired or light-headed. These signs indicate that your body's supply of food energy and nutrients is running low.

When you eat, the hunger gradually goes away. Your stomach needs about 20 minutes to send a message back to the brain to turn off the hunger switch. Eating slowly allows time for your brain to receive the message. Many people overeat when they eat too fast.

Food and Emotions

Food can meet emotional needs too. Do certain foods that you associate with special events bring you happy memories? Perhaps you have favorite foods that comfort you when you are feeling ill or sad. Using food as a way of dealing with negative emotions is not a healthy way to respond to these feelings. People who eat to relieve stress or boredom need to develop more appropriate coping skills.

Getting the Nutrients You Need

Everyone needs the same nutrients to maintain good health, but the amount of nutrients needed depends on a person's age, gender, state of health, and level of activity. When you do not get enough of

Nutrients are like team members. They work together to promote good health. *How can you make sure you have a strong nutrient team working for you?*

Reading Check

Possible Sentences Discuss with students that each vocabulary word is related to the importance of nutrition. List each word on the board. Once students have written sentences containing the words, have students share some of their sentences with the class. Students should discuss the possible veracity, or truth, of each sentence. Point out the differences between such terms as *appetite* and *hunger* and *calories* and *nutrients.* Have students rewrite the sentences to make them more specific. Discuss the changes necessary to fix each sentence. This exercise provides an excellent opportunity for students to distinguish subtle differences in the meanings of vocabulary words.

a particular nutrient, you could have a **nutrient deficiency,** *a shortage of a nutrient.*

As a teen, you need more calcium than you did before for building strong and growing bones. However, suppose you don't eat enough foods that supply calcium. Over time, the calcium deficiency could affect the strength of your teeth and bones. A food plan that includes calcium-rich foods helps prevent osteoporosis, a disease in which bones become brittle and more liable to break. You also need more iron because your body makes more red blood cells as you grow. A shortage of iron can lead to a blood disease called anemia. In general, teens need more of most nutrients to support growth and satisfy energy needs.

Most people in the United States get plenty of food, yet many still do not get the nutrients they need. This is partly the result of lifestyles that tend to encourage fast foods and promote foods that are high in fat and sugar. Eating low-nutrient, high-fat foods, along with overeating, can lead to long-term health problems such as obesity, heart disease, cancer, and diabetes. Your nutritional knowledge and healthful eating habits are your best defense against poor nutrition.

CONNECT TO

Math

UNIT PRICING
Calculating the unit prices of food products and comparing them can help you determine the most economical purchases. To compute the unit price, locate the weight or volume on a packaged food product. Divide the price of the product by its weight or volume. The result will be the unit price. *At the supermarket, find three sizes of the same packaged food. Calculate the unit price of each and compare to determine which product is the most economical purchase.*

Lesson 1 Review

Using complete sentences, answer the following questions on a sheet of paper.

Reviewing Terms and Facts

1. **Vocabulary** What are *calories?* What do they measure?
2. **Recall** What is *nutrition?* What is the relationship between nutrition and health?
3. **Compare** What is the difference between appetite and hunger?
4. **Explain** Why are calcium-rich foods an important part of a teen's food choices?

Thinking Critically

5. **Evaluate** Explain the role of media and technology in influencing food choices.

6. **Analyze** How is it possible to have plenty of food and yet be poorly nourished?

Applying Health Skills

7. **Analyzing Influences** Find an advertisement for a specific food product. Use critical-thinking skills to analyze the marketing and advertising techniques in the ad and their influence on food selection. Report your findings to the class.

③ Assess

Evaluating

Assign the Lesson 1 Review; then assign the Lesson 1 Quiz in the TCR.

Reteaching

- Assign Concept Map 28 or Reteaching Activity 28 in the TCR.
- Have students work with partners to write, in their own words, a definition of *nutrition* and to list five examples of good nutrition.

Enrichment

- Assign Enrichment Activity 28 in the TCR.
- Have students work in groups to create booklets with foods, preparation tips, and recipes that reflect specific cultural backgrounds.

④ Close

Have each student write a paragraph about one new fact he or she learned about factors that influence his or her food choices.

Lesson 1 Review

1. Units of heat; they measure the energy used by the body and the energy that foods supply to the body.
2. See the last paragraph on page 192.
3. Appetite is the psychological desire for food; hunger is the physical need for food.
4. For building strong and growing bones; over time calcium deficiency could affect the

strength of teeth and bones.
5. Responses will vary, but might include the influence of TV commercials and the increased availability of foods due to advances in technology.
6. The foods eaten may not contain sufficient amounts of nutrients.

① Focus

Lesson Objectives

Students will be able to

• list the six types of nutrients and explain how the body uses them.

• identify the sources of different nutrients.

• discuss the daily need for water and fiber.

• identify the substances in food that need to be limited.

Motivators

Quick Write

Allow students to form groups to compare their menus. Ask: Which foods were common among your menus?

Bellringer Activity

Ask: If you had a choice between eating fruit or potato chips, which would you choose? Encourage students to consider why they would make their choices.

VOCABULARY

Write the vocabulary terms on the board. Display a label from a food product. Challenge students to find the terms on the label. When students have finished, point out that some words appear indirectly. For example, while the word *minerals* does not appear, *iron, calcium, sodium,* and *potassium,* which are minerals, do appear.

Quick Write

What's your idea of a healthful meal or snack? Create a menu for what you consider a day of healthful foods you would enjoy.

LEARN ABOUT...

• how your body uses different nutrients.
• the sources of different nutrients.
• the need for water and fiber in your meals and snacks.
• substances in food that should be limited.

VOCABULARY

• carbohydrates
• proteins
• amino acids
• saturated fats
• unsaturated fats
• vitamins
• minerals
• fiber

Most of your body's energy supply should come from carbohydrates. *What foods do you enjoy that are good sources of simple and complex carbohydrates?*

Nutrients for Wellness

The Six Types of Nutrients

Food nourishes you with more than 40 different nutrients. These nutrients are grouped into six categories: carbohydrates, proteins, fats, vitamins, minerals, and water. Eating a variety of foods to provide these nutrients is essential to good health.

Carbohydrates

Carbohydrates are *the sugars and starches that provide your body with most of its energy.* Carbohydrates can be either simple or complex. Simple carbohydrates, or sugars, are found in fruit, milk, and honey. Sugar is also added to candy, cookies, and other foods. Complex carbohydrates, or starches, are found in breads, cereals, pasta, rice, potatoes, dry beans, corn, and other starchy vegetables. As your body digests complex carbohydrates, it breaks them down into simple sugars, which are absorbed into the bloodstream to provide energy. Nutritionists recommend that 45 to 65 percent of your daily calories come from carbohydrates.

Lesson 2 Resources

Teacher Classroom Resources

📁 Concept Map 29
📁 Decision-Making Activity 15
📁 Enrichment Activity 29
📁 Lesson Plan 2
📁 Lesson 2 Quiz
📁 Reading Tutor Activity 29

📁 Reteaching Activity 29
🕹 Transparency 29

Student Activities Workbook

📁 Chapter 8 Study Guide
📁 Applying Health Skills 29

Proteins

Proteins are *nutrients your body uses to build, repair, and maintain cells and tissues.* They also help your body fight disease, and they provide energy when your body doesn't get enough from other sources.

Amino acids are *small units that make up protein.* Your body can produce most amino acids on its own. The remaining ones, called essential amino acids, must come from food you eat.

Foods from animal sources, such as meat, fish, poultry, eggs, milk, and yogurt, contain complete proteins. They provide all the essential amino acids. Foods from plant sources, such as soybeans, nuts, peas, and dry beans contain incomplete proteins. They lack one or more of the essential amino acids. Vegetarians can combine foods from plant sources to make complete proteins. Consuming a variety of plant foods, such as beans, rice, nuts, and peas, gives you complete protein and provides the essential amino acids. You don't need to eat these foods at the same meal to get the benefit. Just have a good variety throughout the whole day.

Meals that include a variety of plant-based foods can provide all the essential amino acids. *What are some of your favorite sources of protein?*

Fats

Fats are nutrients that provide energy and perform many functions for your body. They carry fat-soluble vitamins and promote healthy skin and normal growth. Foods that are high in fats tend to be high in calories. For this reason, health experts generally recommend that your eating plan include only moderate amounts of fat.

Saturated fats are *fats that are solid at room temperature.* They are found mostly in animal and dairy products, such as butter, red meat, cheese, and whole milk. An eating pattern that includes too many saturated fats can increase a person's risk of heart disease.

Unsaturated fats are *fats that remain liquid at room temperature.* They come mainly from plant sources. Foods containing mostly unsaturated fats include vegetable oils, nuts, avocados, and olives. Unsaturated fats lower cholesterol levels and are considered healthier than saturated fats. Trans fats are a type of fat produced when hydrogen atoms are added to unsaturated fats to make them solid. Trans fats have been linked to heart disease.

✓ Reading Check

Study the words *saturated* and *unsaturated*. What difference does the prefix make in their meanings? What does the root mean?

② Teach

Making Lists

Have students make individual lists of the carbohydrates they commonly eat. Form two composite lists on the board, simple and complex. Discuss the types of carbohydrates that appear on each list. Ask students: How could you reduce the number of simple carbohydrates that you consume? **L1**

Discussing

Have students discuss sources of protein for vegetarians. (*eggs, cheese, beans combined with grains, tofu and other forms of soy protein*) **L1**

Cross-Curriculum Activity

FAMILY AND CONSUMER SCIENCES Team up with a foods class for a demonstration of healthful cooking techniques. For example, a demonstration of low-fat cooking might show trimming the fat from meat, skimming the fat from homemade soups or sauces, and stir-frying. **L1** **INCL** *Different Learning Styles* (*Kinesthetic*)

The FDA has standardized fat-related terms on labels. *Fat free* means the food has less than one-half gram of fat per serving. *Low fat* indicates the food has three grams or less of fat per serving.

✓ Reading Check

Prefixes, Roots, and Suffixes Knowing the meaning of a prefix will enable readers to begin to decode unfamiliar words. Write the words *saturated* and *unsaturated* on the board. Have a student divide the words with slashes between their parts. For example, *saturat/ed* and *un/saturat/ed.* Then discuss the meaning of each part of the word and how it affects the meaning of the word as a whole.

Using a dictionary, students will find *un-* means *not, saturate* means *soaked* or *drenched,* and *-ed* means *to have the characteristics of.* Ask students to name other words that have the same prefix or root and discuss the connections among the words' meanings.

SCIENCE Divide the class into small groups and assign each group a vitamin. Have each group investigate the benefits of that vitamin, the problems caused by a lack of it, and the foods rich in it. Have each group report to the class. Note: To make this activity more challenging, have students research vitamins not listed in this lesson. **L2**

Discussing

Ask students to discuss why vitamin and mineral supplements should never substitute for a varied eating plan. (*Foods offer other nutrients beyond vitamins and minerals, as well as needed calories and fiber, and the pleasure of flavor.*) **L1**

VISUAL LEARNING

FIGURE 8.2 Have a volunteer read aloud the title and information in Figure 8.2. Then let volunteers share their ideas about foods they need to add to their eating plans. **INCL** *English Language Learners, Special Learning Needs, Behavior Problems, Different Learning Styles* (*Visual*)

Debating

Have a group of interested volunteers research the pros and cons of taking vitamin and mineral supplements. Then have these students present a brief debate. **L3**

Vitamins

Vitamins are *substances needed in small quantities to help regulate body functions*. Vitamins help your body fight infections, use other nutrients, and perform other tasks. Water-soluble vitamins, such as vitamin C and B vitamins, dissolve in water, cannot be stored in your body, and should be part of your daily eating pattern. Fat-soluble vitamins, including vitamins A, D, E, and K, dissolve in fat and can be stored in body fat until needed. See **Figure 8.2** for more information about functions and sources of selected vitamins.

FIGURE 8.2

VITAMINS AND MINERALS: FUNCTIONS AND SOURCES

Functions	Sources
Vitamin A Promotes healthy skin and normal vision	Dark green leafy vegetables (such as spinach); dairy products (such as milk); deep yellow-orange fruits and vegetables (such as carrots, winter squash, apricots); eggs; liver
B Vitamins Needed for a healthy nervous system; help in energy production	Poultry; eggs; meat; fish; whole-grain breads and cereals
Vitamin C Needed for healthy teeth, gums, and bones; helps heal wounds and fight infection	Citrus fruits (such as oranges and grapefruit); cantaloupe, strawberries, mangoes; tomatoes; cabbage and broccoli; potatoes
Vitamin D Promotes strong bones and teeth and the absorption of calcium	Fortified milk; fatty fish (such as salmon and mackerel); egg yolks; liver
Vitamin K Helps blood clot	Dark green leafy vegetables (such as spinach); egg yolks; liver; some cereals
Calcium Needed to build and maintain strong bones and teeth	Dairy products (such as milk, yogurt, cheese); dark green leafy vegetables (such as spinach); canned fish with edible bones (such as sardines)
Fluoride Promotes strong bones and teeth; prevents tooth decay	Fluoridated water; fish with edible bones
Iron Needed for hemoglobin in red blood cells	Red meat; poultry; dry beans (legumes); fortified breakfast cereal; nuts; eggs; dried fruits; dark green leafy vegetables
Potassium Helps regulate fluid balance in tissues; promotes proper nerve function	Fruits (such as bananas and oranges); dry beans and peas; dried fruits
Zinc Helps heal wounds; needed for cell reproduction	Meat; poultry; eggs; dry beans and peas; whole-grain breads and cereals

198 CHAPTER 8: NUTRITION FOR HEALTH

Health Literacy

Health Information Science and technology have greatly improved the efficiency of agriculture and the quality and quantity of our food supply. However, there have been drawbacks as well as benefits. Among the benefits are increased food production, upgrading of livestock health, improvement of hygiene and sanitation, extension of food freshness, and greater ease of preparation. Among the drawbacks are commercial fertilization, chemicals and artificial hormones in foods, highly processed and irradiated foods, and loss of nutritional value and flavor.

Minerals

Minerals are *elements needed in small quantities for forming healthy bones and teeth, and for regulating certain body processes.* Calcium, phosphorus, and magnesium help build strong bones and teeth. Iron plays a vital role in making red blood cells. See **Figure 8.2** for more information about functions and sources of selected minerals.

Water

Water is a nutrient that is vital to your life and health. It makes up over half of your body and serves many important functions. Water transports nutrients through your body, helps you digest food, lubricates your joints, removes wastes, and helps regulate body temperature.

You lose water every day in urine and sweat, and you need to replace it continually. Nutritionists generally recommend that you consume at least eight 8-ounce cups of fluids a day, and even more during hot weather. Choose liquids such as plain drinking water, fruit juices, milk, and soup. Beverages with caffeine or added sugar are not the best choices.

Other Substances in Food

Food contains many substances in addition to the major nutrients. Some of these substances, such as fiber, are important to your health and should be part of your everyday food choices. For good health, try to limit fats, cholesterol, added sugars, and salt. Go easy on drinks with caffeine, too.

Fiber

Fiber is *the part of fruits, vegetables, grains, and beans that your body cannot digest.* It helps move food particles through your digestive system. Including high-fiber foods in your eating plan may help lower your risk of certain types of cancer and reduce your risk of heart disease. Foods high in fiber include whole-grain breads and cereals, fruits and vegetables, and dry beans and peas.

Hidden Fats

Health experts recommend that no more than 35 percent of your daily calories come from fat. It's easy to cut down on the fats you can see. For example, put a smaller amount of butter on your baked potato, or trim fat from meat. Fats are often hidden in processed and prepared foods. It's harder to cut down on hidden fats, but it can be done. Go easy on fried foods and switch from whole to low-fat milk. Read the labels on packaged foods to check for fats and oils.

The fiber found in raw vegetables and fruit plays an important role in protecting your health. *What are some high-fiber foods that you like?*

Lesson 2

Critical Thinking

Ask students to think about the foods they eat. Ask:

- Do you eat foods that contain all six types of nutrients, or do you favor only a few types?
- Do you notice a lack of certain nutrients in your eating plans?
- Ask students to consider their answers and write which new food they would be willing to try in each nutrient group. **L1**

Analyzing

Many foods that are naturally low in fat are often prepared with considerable added fat. Fried or creamed dishes, dressings, and condiments often make some of the lowest-fat foods into some of the highest-fat meals. Ask students to suggest at least one high-fat and one low-fat method of preparing each of the following: chicken, fish, potatoes, and broccoli. **L1**

Applying Skills

Point out to students that they need 25–30 grams of fiber each day. Have them check the nutritional labels on breakfast cereals to calculate how many bowls of each cereal they would have to eat to meet that requirement. Make sure students understand that you are not suggesting they meet their daily need for fiber by eating only breakfast cereal. **L2**

Health Literacy

Health Information Drinking plenty of water before, during, and after participating in sports or other activities is important for all ages. However, specific fluid needs vary depending on several factors including age. Teens in general share the water needs of adults, but young teens might require extra water during sports activities.

Students may have heard that drinking water, especially cold water, during a workout or a competition can cause stomach cramps. For most people, this isn't true. In fact, an athlete is much more likely to suffer stomach cramps as a result of dehydration than as a result of drinking cold water.

Cross-Curriculum Activity

LANGUAGE ARTS Have students discuss and compile a list of the various names for sugar and sugar products. What word part do these names share? Have students look up the definition of the suffix *-ose* in the dictionary. **L2**

JARS OF SUGAR

Time: 30 minutes

TEACHING THE ACTIVITY

- With students, read the activity introduction and instructions. Note: As an alternative, you may wish to measure out the sugar in advance and bring the filled jars to class. Each group can then guess which jar goes with each food item.
- Divide the class into seven groups, and assign each group one of the listed foods. Have group members fill their jar to show the amount of sugar in their assigned food.
- Ask each group to show its filled jar to the rest of the class. Have students discuss their reactions.

ASSESSMENT

Ask: What is the most important lesson you learned from this activity? Have students write one-sentence responses.

Cholesterol

Cholesterol is a waxy substance used by the body to build cells and hormones and to protect nerve fibers. Most cholesterol is produced in your liver and circulates in the blood. Cholesterol is also found in foods of animal origin, including meats, chicken, egg yolks, and dairy products. Eating high-cholesterol foods can affect the levels of cholesterol in your blood. There are two types of cholesterol in your blood. Low-density cholesterol, or LDL, is a "bad" form that can leave deposits on the walls of your blood vessels. This buildup raises the risk of heart attack or stroke. High-density cholesterol, or HDL, is a "good" form that can help lower LDL levels. To help reduce LDL levels in your blood, limit your intake of foods that are high in fat and cholesterol. Regular physical activity also helps prevent LDL buildup.

Added Sugar

You may be surprised to learn that the average American eats about 100 pounds of sugar a year! Sugar occurs naturally in fruit

Hands-On Health

JARS OF SUGAR

Do you know how much sugar you consume when you grab a quick drink or snack? The following table lists the amount of sugar, in grams, that you might find in several popular foods.

FOOD	GRAMS OF SUGAR
Cola (12 oz.)	42
Fat-free, fruit yogurt (8 oz.)	35
Light popcorn (1 c.)	0
Fruit punch drink (8 oz.)	27
Sweetened breakfast cereal (¾ c.)	15
Three reduced-fat chocolate sandwich cookies	14
Chocolate candy bar (1.55 oz.)	40

WHAT YOU WILL NEED

- seven empty baby food jars
- container of sugar
- set of measuring spoons

WHAT YOU WILL DO

1. Note that 5 grams of sugar is equivalent to 1 level teaspoon of sugar; 1 gram is just under ¼ teaspoon; 2 grams is a little under ½ teaspoon.
2. Calculate how many teaspoons of sugar each listed product contains.
3. Using the spoons, measure the amount of sugar in each product. Place that amount in a jar and label the jar.

IN CONCLUSION

1. Evaluate your findings.
2. Take time out to determine the nutrient content of the foods in each list. Which foods offer the best nutritional value?

200 CHAPTER 8: NUTRITION FOR HEALTH

WHAT TEENS WANT TO KNOW

Should teens be concerned about cholesterol?
Yes. Teens with high cholesterol tend to have high cholesterol into adulthood. Cholesterol is a fatty substance that is made by the body and is found in certain foods. Many factors affect cholesterol level, including diet, exercise, age, weight, gender, genetics, diseases, and lifestyle. An easy way to reduce cholesterol in your diet is to limit the amount of high-fat foods you eat. Fatty meats, cheeses, butter, and whole milk are high in saturated fats, which are linked to the production of cholesterol in the body. You should eat only small amounts of these foods. Instead, eat foods such as fish, skinless chicken, egg whites, and skim milk. Physical activity also helps lower the amount of cholesterol in the blood.

and milk, and it provides food energy. It is also added to many prepared foods, such as soft drinks, cookies, candy, breakfast cereal, and even spaghetti sauce. Sugar is not harmful in moderate amounts. However, you might develop health problems if you eat too many foods high in added sugar.

Sodium

Sodium is a necessary nutrient that helps control the balance of fluids in the body. It occurs naturally in salt, in various foods, and in many prepared sauces. It is also used extensively in processed foods to flavor or preserve the food.

Most Americans eat much more sodium than they need. For some people, too much sodium may contribute to high blood pressure and fluid retention. You can lower your sodium intake by using spices instead of salt, and by using food labels as a guide.

Caffeine

Caffeine is a substance that stimulates the nervous system and can become habit-forming. It is an ingredient in "power drinks," cola, some other soft drinks, coffee, tea, and chocolate. Caffeine stimulates the heart rate and the appetite. It can perk you up, but then it makes you feel drowsy so that you want more. For this reason it's best to limit your intake of products containing caffeine.

 **MEDIA WATCH**

NUTRITION FACTS VS. FALLACIES

Not all information about the nutritional value of foods and food supplements is correct. Use critical-thinking skills to distinguish facts from fallacies concerning the nutritional value of foods and food supplements. *List claims you've heard about a food product or supplement, such as a multivitamin. Distinguish the claims that are true from those that are false.*

Lesson 2 Review

Using complete sentences, answer the following questions on a sheet of paper.

Reviewing Terms and Facts

1. **Vocabulary** Define *carbohydrates*. Give two examples of foods that contain simple carbohydrates and two examples of foods that contain complex carbohydrates.
2. **Explain** Why does your body need protein?
3. **Compare** What is the difference between saturated fats and unsaturated fats?
4. **Summarize** What kinds of foods contain added sugars?

Thinking Critically

5. **Hypothesize** Why do you think people tend to eat too much fat and too much sugar? What might be done to change this situation?
6. **Summarize** Select two of these four food substances: fiber, sodium, caffeine, and sugar. Explain whether or not they are components of your daily food and drink choices.

Applying Health Skills

7. **Accessing Information** Use reliable resources to determine when it might be appropriate to take a vitamin or mineral supplement. Develop and apply criteria for the selection or rejection of this health product. Report your criteria to the class.

LESSON 2: NUTRIENTS FOR WELLNESS **201**

Lesson 2

③ Assess

Evaluating

Assign the Lesson 2 Review; then assign the Lesson 2 Quiz in the TCR.

Reteaching

- Assign Concept Map 29 or Reteaching Activity 29 in the TCR.
- Have students list the six groups of nutrients, their major functions, and two good food sources for each. Have students trade papers with a partner and check each other's answers.

Enrichment

- Assign Enrichment Activity 29 in the TCR.
- Have students work together to compare the sugar, sodium, and fiber content of popular breakfast cereals.

④ Close

Use the Lesson Objectives on page 196 of the Teacher Wraparound Edition to review students' understanding of the lesson content.

Lesson 2 Review

1. Sugars and starches that provide the body with most of its energy. See Carbohydrates on page 196.
2. To build, repair, and maintain cells and tissues; to help fight disease; to provide energy.
3. Saturated fats are solid at room temperature; unsaturated fats are liquid at room temperature.
4. Prepared foods such as soft drinks, cookies, candy, breakfast cereals, and spaghetti sauce.
5. Responses may mention easy availability and low cost of fast foods and processed foods. Solutions may include educating public about nutrition and fast-food establishments providing healthier meals.
6. Responses should demonstrate clear understanding of each food substance.

Following Nutrition Guidelines

① Focus

Lesson Objectives

Students will be able to

- identify and discuss resources that can help them make wise food choices.
- discuss ways to balance the different foods they eat.
- describe how to use the nutrition information on food labels.

Health Skills
- Accessing Information, p. 206

Motivators

Quick Write

Discuss students' responses. Draw a bar graph on the board that illustrates the food-choice tendency of the class.

Bellringer Activity

Ask students to identify their favorite *empty-calorie food.* Establish the need for objective measures of food value as provided in this lesson.

VOCABULARY

Scramble the letters for each vocabulary term and write each of the scrambled words on index cards. Have students form small groups. Give each group a set of scrambled words to unscramble and combine to identify the vocabulary terms. Once identified, have students use the Glossary to define the terms.

Quick Write

List the foods that you eat most often. Then describe why you choose them. Do you consider their nutritional value? How they look and taste? Their convenience?

LEARN ABOUT...

- resources that can help you make wise food choices.
- balancing the different foods you eat.
- using the nutrition information on food labels.

VOCABULARY

- Dietary Guidelines for Americans
- foodborne illness
- Food Guide Pyramid
- Percent Daily Value

Following Nutrition Guidelines

Three Nutrition Guides

How do you know you're getting the nutrients you need? The U.S. government has developed three nutrition tools to help Americans make wise food choices. They are the Dietary Guidelines for Americans, the Food Guide Pyramid, and the Nutrition Facts panel.

The ABCs of Nutrition

The **Dietary Guidelines for Americans** are *recommendations about food choices for all healthy Americans age two and over.* The booklet has three sections, labeled A, B, and C: **A**im for fitness, **B**uild a healthy base, and **C**hoose sensibly.

Aim for Fitness

Fitness involves both healthful eating and regular physical activity. Follow these guidelines to keep healthy and fit.

- **Aim for a healthy weight.** Maintaining your weight helps you look and feel good. It also lowers your risk of heart disease, some cancers, and diabetes. Check with your health care provider to determine if you are at a healthy weight for your height and age.
- **Be physically active each day.** Physical activity can be almost any activity that keeps you moving. Try to include 60 minutes of moderate physical activity in your daily routine.

Build a Healthy Base

"Build a healthy base" refers to the base of the Food Guide Pyramid, which you'll learn more about later in the lesson. You'll learn that the foods located at the base of the Pyramid—grains, fruits, and vegetables—form the foundation of a healthful eating plan. Follow these guidelines to build a healthy base.

- **Let the Pyramid guide your food choices.** Eat the recommended number of servings from the five food groups.
- **Choose a variety of grains daily, especially whole grains.** You need the largest number of daily servings from the grains group. Whole-grain foods include whole-wheat bread, brown rice, and oatmeal.

Lesson 3 Resources

Teacher Classroom Resources

 Concept Map 30
Cross-Curriculum Activity 15
Decision-Making Activity 16
Enrichment Activity 30
Health Lab 8
Lesson Plan 3
Lesson 3 Quiz

Reading Tutor Activity 30
Reteaching Activity 30

Transparency 30

Student Activities Workbook
Chapter 8 Study Guide
Applying Health Skills 30

- **Choose a variety of fruits and vegetables daily.** Eat all kinds and colors of fruits and vegetables to get the full range of vitamins and minerals, as well as fiber.
- **Keep food safe to eat.** Making sure that foods are safe from harmful bacteria and other contaminants will reduce the risk of **foodborne illness,** *a sickness that results from eating food that is not safe to eat.* Developing basic food-preparation skills, including sanitary food preparation and storage, will help keep food safe to eat. For example, wash your hands before and after handling foods, especially raw meat, poultry, and fish. Cook foods thoroughly and refrigerate perishable foods promptly.

Choose Sensibly

Sensible choices include foods that are low in fats, sugars, and salt. Follow these guidelines:

- **Choose foods that are low in saturated fat and cholesterol and moderate in total fat.** Foods high in saturated fats, such as butter and whole milk, raise blood cholesterol levels. Eat wisely by getting most of your calories from plant foods and by choosing nonfat or low-fat dairy products and lean meats.
- **Choose beverages and foods to moderate your intake of sugars.** Soft drinks provide many calories but few nutrients. They can also contribute to tooth decay. Limit your intake of drinks and foods containing added sugar. Check the ingredient list on packaged foods. If sucrose, corn syrup, honey, fructose, or other sweeteners are listed first or second, these foods are high in sugars.
- **Choose and prepare foods with less salt.** High salt or sodium intake can contribute to high blood pressure and cause calcium loss. Season foods with herbs or spices instead.

When shopping for foods, buy perishable foods last, take them straight home, and refrigerate them promptly. *List three sanitary food preparation and storage skills that can make food safe to eat.*

HEALTH *Online*

Topic: Food safety

For a link to more information on keeping foods safe, go to **health.glencoe.com.**

Activity: Using the information provided at this link, prepare a fact sheet on food safety.

Lesson 3

② Teach

Discussing

Help students consider the intended audience of the Dietary Guidelines for Americans:

- Who is included?
- Who is not included? Why?
- How do these guidelines take individual differences into account? (*They allow individuals to make their own choices within broad categories, such as which types of physical activities to engage in and which grains to eat.*) **L1**

Applying Knowledge

Ask each student to bring to class a fruit or vegetable (cooked, if appropriate) that he or she considers unusual. Then have a "fruit-and-vegetable tasting." Encourage students to try at least one new food. Note: Be sure to consult your school policy about food in the classroom. **L2 INCL** *English Language Learners, Special Learning Needs, At-Risk, Different Learning Styles (Kinesthetic)*

Demonstrating

Bring to class empty containers for soft drinks, power drinks, fruit juices, and other popular beverages. Have students study the labels to evaluate the health benefits or risks of the beverages. **L2**

HEALTH *Online*

Encourage students to explore the Web Links for this chapter and then complete the activity.

Health Literacy

Health Information Illustrate how eating healthful foods contributes to the physical health side of the health triangle. For example, explain the role of antioxidants. Tell students that these chemical compounds, which include vitamins C and E, rid the body of free radicals. Explain that free radicals, which are formed in numerous metabolic reactions, trigger destructive chemical reactions, damage genes, and destroy cells. Add that scientists believe damage by free radicals is one cause of cancer and of aging. Ask students whether they know what foods are rich in antioxidants (*primarily fruits and vegetables*).

Cross-Curriculum Activity

FAMILY AND CONSUMER SCIENCES

Have students gather recipes for vegetarian sandwiches and meals. Remind students to think about complete proteins and the five basic food groups as they look for recipes. **L2**

Cooperative Learning

Bring to class magazine photos of meals or casserole-style main dishes. Have students form cooperative groups, and give each group one picture. Have them work together to identify the food groups represented in their pictured meal or dish. **L2** **INCL** *English Language Learners, Different Learning Styles* (*Visual*)

Comparing

Ask students to compare the calories, fat grams, and calcium provided in one cup each of homogenized, low-fat, and nonfat milk or other dairy product. **L2**

Evaluating

Distribute copies of the school lunch menu. Ask students to evaluate lunches for a week according to the Food Guide Pyramid.

• How do they rate?

• What changes or substitutes do students recommend?

Suggest that students compile their recommendations and present them to the school menu planner. **L2**

CONNECT TO

Math

HEALTHY FOODS ON A BUDGET

Use these effective consumer skills to purchase nutritious foods within budget constraints:

• **Make a list so that you buy only what you need.**

• **Look for coupons for foods you buy regularly.**

• **Compute and compare unit prices (see Connect to Math on page 195).**

The Food Guide Pyramid

The **Food Guide Pyramid** is *a guide for making healthful daily food choices*. **Figure 8.3** gives the sizes of the servings listed in **Figure 8.4**, the Food Guide Pyramid. The Food Guide Pyramid provides recommendations for the number of daily servings from each food group.

Following the Food Guide Pyramid is the easiest way to build a balanced eating plan. The following recommendations will help you follow advice from the Food Guide Pyramid and avoid overusing fat and added sugars.

• **Pay attention to serving sizes.** It is just as important to eat reasonable portions as it is to eat the right *number* of servings.

• **Keep meats lean.** Remove skin from poultry and visible fat from meat.

• **Read the labels on dairy products.** Choose nonfat or low-fat milk, cheese, and yogurt most of the time.

• **Use whole-grain or enriched grain products.** Check package labels and choose at least three servings of whole-grain breads and cereals each day. The rest should be enriched.

• **Cook it right.** Food preparation techniques make a difference. Baked or broiled foods have less fat than fried foods. Steamed vegetables retain more nutrients than vegetables cooked in water.

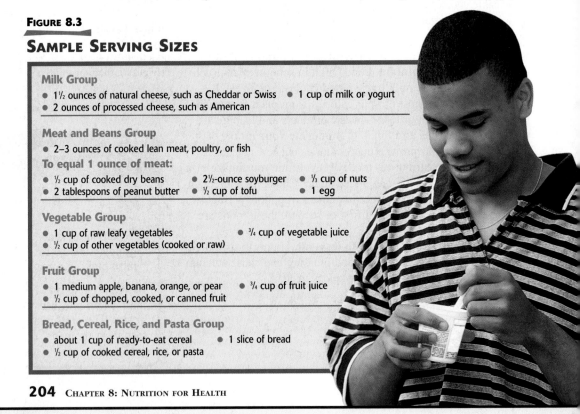

FIGURE 8.3

SAMPLE SERVING SIZES

Milk Group
• 1½ ounces of natural cheese, such as Cheddar or Swiss   • 1 cup of milk or yogurt
• 2 ounces of processed cheese, such as American

Meat and Beans Group
• 2–3 ounces of cooked lean meat, poultry, or fish

To equal 1 ounce of meat:
• ½ cup of cooked dry beans   • 2½-ounce soyburger   • ⅓ cup of nuts
• 2 tablespoons of peanut butter   • ½ cup of tofu   • 1 egg

Vegetable Group
• 1 cup of raw leafy vegetables   • ¾ cup of vegetable juice
• ½ cup of other vegetables (cooked or raw)

Fruit Group
• 1 medium apple, banana, orange, or pear   • ¾ cup of fruit juice
• ½ cup of chopped, cooked, or canned fruit

Bread, Cereal, Rice, and Pasta Group
• about 1 cup of ready-to-eat cereal   • 1 slice of bread
• ½ cup of cooked cereal, rice, or pasta

Beyond the Classroom

Community In the past, meats with a lot of marbling were preferred. Today, many consumers prefer lean meats. Agriculture and the food industry have responded to consumer demand by raising leaner animals. Now muscle replaces much of the body fat. For example, cooked pork has an average of 31 percent less total fat and 29 percent less saturated fat than pork eaten in the 1970s and 1980s. Also, supermarkets are now trimming the outside fat layer of meats to less than 1/8 inch, down from about 1/2 inch a decade ago. In these ways, the food industry has helped consumers reduce their intake of saturated fats. Ask students to think of other health behaviors or knowledge that has changed in the last few decades.

FIGURE 8.4

THE FOOD GUIDE PYRAMID

By following the recommended number of daily servings and serving sizes from each group, you will have a balanced eating plan.

Fats, Oils, and Sweets
USE SPARINGLY
Foods: butter, salad dressing, sugar, candy, soft drinks

Milk, Yogurt, and Cheese Group (Milk Group)
3–4 servings for teens; 2–3 servings for adults
Foods: Milk, yogurt, cheese

Meat, Poultry, Fish, Dry Beans, Eggs, and Nuts Group (Meat and Beans Group)
2–3 servings
Foods: Beef, pork, veal, lamb, chicken, turkey, fish, shellfish, liver, eggs, beans, nuts, peanut butter

Vegetable Group
3–5 servings
Foods: Green beans, broccoli, dark green leafy vegetables, cabbage, carrots, corn, potatoes

Fruit Group
2–4 servings
Foods: Citrus fruits, apples, bananas, peaches, pears

Bread, Cereal, Rice, and Pasta Group (Grains Group)
6–11 servings
Foods: Whole-grain or enriched breads, cereals, rice, pasta

LESSON 3: FOLLOWING NUTRITION GUIDELINES **205**

Lesson 3

VISUAL LEARNING

FIGURE 8.4 Guide students in reading and discussing the recommendations in the Food Guide Pyramid. Have students identify their favorite foods from each group. Point out that many foods (*e.g., hamburgers and pizza*) contain ingredients from several different groups. If possible, have foods from each group available, and demonstrate the recommended serving sizes. Encourage students to share their reactions to these sizes. **INCL** *English Language Learners, Special Learning Needs, Behavior Problems, Different Learning Styles* (*Visual*)

Cooperative Learning

Ask students to name their favorite foods, and record the names of those foods on the board. Then have students form cooperative groups, and divide the listed foods among the groups. Ask the members of each group to evaluate the foods they have been assigned, identify where they fit in the Food Guide Pyramid, and decide how frequently they should be eaten. Have each group discuss its evaluations with the rest of the class. **L1**

Discussing

Ask students to discuss what variables make the field of nutritional requirements in humans an inexact science. (*Reasons may include variations in age, gender, weight, genetic makeup, diet, medications, and so on. Also, several nutrients have only recently been discovered, and there may be more to come.*) **L2**

Beyond the Classroom

Community Teens may often have difficulty achieving balanced diets because of circumstances or conditions beyond their control. For teens and their families who frequent fast-food restaurants, for instance, avoiding fatty, salty foods is practically impossible. Invite a restaurant owner or manager to speak to the class about ways she or he is encouraging consumers to avoid unhealthy foods, especially those high in fat, sodium, cholesterol, caffeine, or sugar. Ask students to suggest ways restaurants can help teens make healthful food choices.

Lesson 3

Discussing

Tell students that Americans are buying more processed foods and fewer fresh foods than ever before. Ask:

- What do you think are the reasons for the change? (*More processed foods are available, they take less time to cook, they can be stored longer.*)
- What effect does the increased consumption of processed foods have on the American diet? (*In some cases, it means a poorer diet, one with added fat, salt, and sugar.*) L1

HEALTH SKILLS ACTIVITY

ACCESSING INFORMATION

Guide students in reading and discussing the information presented in the activity introduction. Then go over the activity instructions. If possible, distribute empty food packages. Let students read the package labels and refer to them in answering the On Your Own questions. Have students refer to the food label on the next page and write their answers to the questions about that food.

Note: This skill is introduced in Chapter 2 on pages 45–46.

Reading Check

Increase comprehension. Brainstorm the key concepts and ideas of this lesson. Jot down terms or phrases that you recall.

- **Consider nutritive values.** Choose foods that supply plenty of nutrients for the calories. Go easy on foods from the tip of the Pyramid, which have few or no nutrients, and on fatty and sugary foods within the five food groups.
- **Eat enough high-protein foods.** Sources include foods from the milk group and the meat and beans group.

Using Food Labels

Perhaps you have noticed that all packaged foods carry a label titled "Nutrition Facts." These labels provide valuable information for making healthful food choices. Food labels compare products to the **Percent Daily Value**. This figure is *the percent of the recommended daily amount of a nutrient provided in a serving of food.* The Percent Daily Value is based on an intake of 2,000 calories per day. Understanding how to read a food label, like the one shown in **Figure 8.5**, can help you select nutritious foods and balance your eating pattern.

HEALTH SKILLS ACTIVITY

ACCESSING INFORMATION

Reading a Food Label

The following information is provided on all Nutrition Facts panels. Use this information to compare foods and choose wisely.

- **SERVING SIZE.** The serving size is the portion that most people eat. Portion sizes allow for easy comparison of similar foods.
- **CALORIES.** Female teens should consume 2,200 calories per day, and male teens should have 3,000. Consider what percentage of this amount one serving of the food provides for you. Also consider how many of the calories in a serving come from fat.
- **NUTRIENTS.** Use the nutrient information to limit your intake of total fat, saturated fat, cholesterol, and sodium. Get enough dietary fiber, vitamins A and C, calcium, and iron.
- **PERCENT DAILY VALUE.** Determine how much the nutrients in a serving contribute

to your total daily eating plan. Use the "5–20 rule." Look for foods that provide 5 percent Daily Value or less of fat, cholesterol, and sodium. Choose foods that provide 20 percent Daily Value or more of dietary fiber, vitamins, and minerals.

1. How many grams of fat does one serving of the product contain? How much saturated fat does it have?
2. What percentage of your total daily sodium allowance does one serving contain?
3. What Percent Daily Value of vitamin A does one serving provide? Vitamin C? Is the product a good source of these vitamins?

ON YOUR OWN
Use the sample label in Figure 8.5 to help answer these questions. Assume that you take in about 2,500 calories a day.

Reading Check

Guided Reading Procedure Ask students to brainstorm on their own, jotting down the main ideas or terms that they recall from reading the lesson. Then compile a list of information on the board as a class. Once the students feel that they cannot recall anything else, allow them to review the lesson. Have students search for information that they missed while brainstorming. Then as a class, have them revise their information on the board for the purpose of creating an outline. They might find that some information was recalled incorrectly or that they missed important points that need to be added. Challenge students to come to an agreement on which points need revision.

FIGURE 8.5

WHAT THE FOOD LABEL TELLS YOU

Food labels provide important nutritional information that can help you make sensible food choices.

A The nutrient content of the food is calculated according to its serving size. The serving size on the food label may differ from sizes shown on the Food Guide Pyramid.

B The amount of total fat in one serving is listed, followed by the amount of saturated fat. The calories from fat are shown to the right of the total calories per serving.

C Major vitamins and minerals are shown, along with their Percent Daily Value.

Nutrition Facts

Serving Size 1/2 cup (114g)
Servings Per Container 4

Amount Per Serving	
Calories 90	Calories from Fat 30

	% Daily Value*
Total Fat 3g	5%
Saturated Fat 0g	0%
Cholesterol 0mg	0%
Sodium 300mg	13%
Total Carbohydrate 13g	4%
Dietary Fiber 3g	12%
Sugars 3g	
Protein 3g	

Vitamin A	80% •	Vitamin C	60%
Calcium	4% •	Iron	4%

* Percent Daily Values are based on a 2,000 calorie diet. Your daily values may be higher or lower depending on your calorie needs:

Calories	2,000	2,500
Total Fat	Less Than 65g	80g
Sat Fat	Less Than 20g	25g
Cholesterol	Less Than 300mg	300mg
Sodium	Less Than 2,400mg	2,400mg
Total Carbohydrate	300g	375g
Dietary Fiber	25g	30g

Calories per gram:
Fat 9 • Carbohydrate 4 • Protein 4

D Major nutrients are listed in milligrams (mg) or grams (g) and as a percentage of the recommended amount for a person consuming 2,000 calories per day.

E Dietary fiber and sugar are given under Total Carbohydrate.

F Information provided on the lower part of the Nutrition Facts panel is the same from product to product. It contains advice about the amounts of certain nutrients that should be eaten each day. Amounts are given for both a 2,000-calorie and a 2,500-calorie diet.

Lesson 3 Review

Using complete sentences, answer the following questions on a sheet of paper.

Reviewing Terms and Facts

1. **List** What are the three tools developed by the government to help Americans make wise food choices?
2. **Recall** What are the ABCs outlined in the Dietary Guidelines for Americans?
3. **Vocabulary** Define *foodborne illnesses.* How can foodborne illness be prevented?
4. **Give Examples** Name two foods in each of the five food groups that make up the Food Guide Pyramid.

Thinking Critically

5. **Analyze** Explain how the shape of the Food Guide Pyramid makes it easier to choose a balanced eating plan.

6. **Evaluate** Think about your own food choices. What food groups do you need to eat more from in your eating plan? What food groups do you need to cut down on?

Applying Health Skills

7. **Accessing Information** Use reliable resources to find out more about developing basic food-preparation skills, including sanitary food preparation and storage techniques that help prevent foodborne illness. Then, find recipes for a healthy breakfast and lunch that you would like to prepare. Write down the steps you would take to properly store the ingredients and prepare each meal safely.

VISUAL LEARNING

FIGURE 8.5 Have students point to the correct section of the sample label as volunteers read aloud each explanation. Help students discuss how they can use each fact on a label to evaluate their food choices. **INCL** *English Language Learners, Special Learning Needs, Behavior Problems, Different Learning Styles* (*Visual*)

3 Assess

Evaluating

📁 Assign the Lesson 3 Review; then assign the Lesson 3 Quiz in the TCR.

Reteaching

- 📁 Assign Concept Map 30 or Reteaching Activity 30 in the TCR.
- Have students write a two- or three-sentence summary of the information in the Food Guide Pyramid.

Enrichment

- 📁 Assign Enrichment Activity 30 in the TCR.
- Have groups of students plan and present skits about teens making healthy food choices in a school cafeteria or fast-food restaurant.

4 Close

Ask students to identify and summarize the three nutrition guides discussed in the lesson.

Lesson 3 Review

1. Dietary Guidelines for Americans, Food Guide Pyramid, Nutrition Facts on food labels.
2. Aim for fitness, Build a healthy base, Choose sensibly.
3. Sicknesses resulting from eating unsafe food; washing hands before and after handling foods, cooking foods thoroughly, refrigerating perishable foods promptly.
4. Each set of two should come from these groups: milk, meat, vegetable, fruit, grains.
5. The shape helps people remember that most of the servings should come from the widest part and the fewest servings should come from the tip.
6. Responses will vary.

Planning Meals and Snacks

Lesson 4

Planning Meals and Snacks

1 Focus

Lesson Objectives

Students will be able to

- describe how to use the Food Guide Pyramid to plan meals and snacks.
- identify the benefits of a healthful breakfast.
- explain the importance of eating regular meals.
- explain how to choose nutritious snacks.

Health Skills
- Decision Making, p. 210

Motivators

Quick Write
Discuss the students' responses. List the snack favorites on the board. Have students save their lists to evaluate at the end of the lesson.

Bellringer Activity

Ask students to list the foods they ate for breakfast that morning. Then have them describe what they ate and explain why they chose to eat what they did.

VOCABULARY

Write both vocabulary terms on the board. Have students look up each term in the Glossary at the back of the text. Ask students to write sentences for each term and define the term in their own words.

Quick Write

When do you generally reach for a snack? What types of snacks do you usually choose?

LEARN ABOUT...

- how to use the Pyramid to plan daily meals and snacks.
- the benefits of a healthful breakfast.
- the importance of eating regular meals.
- how to choose nutritious snacks.

VOCABULARY

- empty calories
- nutrient density

Planning Meals and Snacks

Plan Ahead

The Food Guide Pyramid is a great planning tool! Use it every day to plan your food choices and meet your goals for healthy eating. Remember that your daily food choices include not only regular meals but also snacks. The goal is to eat a variety of foods and to achieve the number of servings recommended by the Pyramid.

Start with Breakfast

You have probably heard people say that breakfast is the most important meal of the day. It's true! When you wake in the morning, you most likely haven't eaten for 10 to 12 hours. While you sleep, your body uses energy for breathing, keeping your heart beating, and growing and repairing cells. By morning, your body needs food to replenish its energy supply.

Studies have shown that eating breakfast regularly helps teens perform better in school. Teens who eat breakfast regularly tend to earn higher test scores and grades and have better school attendance. They are also more likely to maintain a healthy weight and have better muscle coordination.

Keep in mind that you can make breakfast quickly and take it with you. For example, you could grab a granola bar and an apple to eat at the bus stop.

A healthful breakfast gives you energy to start the day. *What other benefits result from eating breakfast regularly?*

208 CHAPTER 8: NUTRITION FOR HEALTH

Lesson 4 Resources

Teacher Classroom Resources

 Concept Map 31

Cross-Curriculum Activity 16

Enrichment Activity 31

Lesson Plan 4

Lesson 4 Quiz

Reading Tutor Activity 31

 Reteaching Activity 31

Transparency 31

Student Activities Workbook

Chapter 8 Study Guide

Applying Health Skills 31

Health Inventory 8

You can choose from a wide variety of foods for a nutritious breakfast. *What is your favorite breakfast food?*

② Teach

Cooperative Learning

Have students meet in groups to plan breakfast menus. Challenge the groups to think of nutritious, balanced breakfasts that might be both unusual and appealing. Then have each group describe its breakfast menu to the rest of the class. **L1**

Demonstrating

Changing eating patterns within a family can be a challenge. Ask students to consider the kinds of changes they would like to see their families make. Then ask them to think about the best approaches to discussing those changes with parents and other family members. Have volunteers role-play effective family discussions about meals and snacks. **L1**

HEALTH SKILLS PRACTICE

Practicing Healthful Behaviors
Read aloud the following to students: Skipping a meal may seem easy, but it is hard on your growing body. To get the balanced nutrition you need, plan ahead. Make a list of at least five healthy food choices you can eat "on the run" or carry in your backpack to add to a meal. You're looking for a balance of nutrients with less than 35 percent of your daily calories from fat. Read food labels, and write down three choices.

Plan Meals Wisely

In any family, planning meals can be a challenge. Different people may have different needs. For example, you may be hungry for dinner before other family members get home. Try to work with your family to find an eating pattern that is right for you. Eating regular meals is important. When you eat regularly, you are less likely to get strong hunger pangs that can lead to overeating. You also maintain a balanced blood sugar level.

Choose Sensible Snacks

What do you think of when you hear the word *snack?* For many people, snacks mean candy bars, potato chips, and other foods with few nutrients. If you eat too many of these foods, you may consume excess calories, sodium, and fat.

As you learned earlier, the amount of energy that is available in foods is measured in calories. *Calories that come from foods that offer few, if any, nutrients* are called **empty calories**. They usually come from foods at the tip of the Food Guide Pyramid—fats, oils, and sweets.

MEDIA◉WATCH

EXTRA-LARGE PORTIONS

Ads for extra-large portions may tell you about the value of bigger sizes. However, nutritional information is often omitted. *Use critical-thinking skills to analyze the influence of this advertising technique on food selection.*

COOPERATIVE LEARNING ACTIVITY

Cereal Content Divide students into groups of four. Explain that nutritionists recommend that for each serving, a cereal should have at least 5 grams of fiber, less than 8 grams of sugar, and no more than 2 grams of fat. Have each group examine six labels from empty cereal boxes and make bar graphs as follows: Graph 1—grams of fiber on the vertical axis, cereal names on the horizontal axis (each cereal is a separate bar); Graph 2—grams of sugar on the vertical axis, cereal names on the horizontal axis; Graph 3—grams of fat on the vertical axis, cereal names on the horizontal axis. Each group should prepare three graphs. Which cereals meet nutritionists' recommendations?

Lesson 4

Guest Speaker

Invite the school dietitian or nutritionist to class to explain how meals are planned for the school lunchroom. **L1**

Making Lists

Some of the healthy snacks mentioned in the lesson could be brought to school. Expand the list with the class, and plan for a "healthy snack day,"when each student will bring in a healthy snack to eat. Each student should be prepared to explain why his or her snack is healthy. **L1**

HEALTH SKILLS ACTIVITY

DECISION MAKING

Have volunteers read aloud the description of Rosalie's situation. Guide students in discussing the choices Rosalie has to make, and brainstorm a list of her options.

Then have students meet with partners to discuss the possible outcomes of Rosalie's options, consider her values, and make a decision for Rosalie. Also have them evaluate the likely consequences, both short- and long-term, of their decision. Finally, have each pair role-play their ideas for the conversation between Rosalie and Corey.

Reading Check

Understand cause and effect. Complete this analogy: *Healthy snacks are to high nutrient density as _____ are to low nutrient density.*

How can you tell which snacks have a lot of nutrients and which provide only empty calories? One way is to compare their **nutrient density**, or *the amount of nutrients relative to the number of calories they provide.* A typical candy bar, for example, has low nutrient density. It provides about 250 calories but few nutrients. **Figure 8.6** provides suggestions for nutrient-dense snacks.

Eating Out, Eating Right

Eating out can present a challenge if you're trying to maintain a healthful eating plan. Many menu items are fried or served with butter, mayonnaise, gravy, or other high-fat toppings. By making wise choices, however, you can eat out but still eat healthful foods. Order food that is grilled, broiled, or baked, rather than fried. Ask for sauces and other toppings to be served on the side. Eat a sensible serving, and take the rest home to enjoy the next day.

HEALTH SKILLS ACTIVITY

DECISION MAKING

Choosing Healthful Snacks

Rosalie knew that she had developed some unhealthful eating habits. She often snacked on potato chips after school. On days when she had band practice, she would grab a candy bar. Rosalie snacked so much that she didn't eat all the nutrient-rich foods her parents provided for dinner.

Rosalie decided to change her eating habits and become more active. She began choosing nutrient-dense snacks like peanut butter on whole wheat crackers and carrot sticks. Rosalie also increased her physical activity by walking her dog every day and swimming several times a week.

Rosalie is proud of her healthier lifestyle. Now her friend Corey has called to suggest that they go to the movies with Josh and Molly. Rosalie wants to go, but her friends usually stop for fast food and ice cream after the movies. She wants to stick with her eating plan, but she's afraid of falling into old habits.

What Would You Do?

Apply the steps of the decision-making process to Rosalie's situation. With a partner, role-play a conversation in which Rosalie suggests some options to Corey.

1. **STATE THE SITUATION.**
2. **LIST THE OPTIONS.**
3. **WEIGH THE POSSIBLE OUTCOMES.**
4. **CONSIDER VALUES.**
5. **MAKE A DECISION AND ACT.**
6. **EVALUATE THE DECISION.**

Reading Check

Analogies Completing analogies can help students understand the relationships between words and concepts. For example, healthy snacks are to high nutrient density as *empty calories* are to low nutrient density.

Explain that the analogy presented here is a formal statement of a cause-and-effect relationship.

If students need further help completing them, note that the example comes from the first paragraph on page 210. Point out that the first half of the statement states the cause and the second half states its effect. Challenge students to explore other cause-and-effect relationships and to practice writing their own analogies.

FIGURE 8.6

Sensible Snacks

Sensible snacks, such as those shown and listed here, can be an important part of a healthful eating plan.

Milk, Yogurt, and Cheese Group
Nonfat or low-fat milk, yogurt, cheese

Vegetable Group
Celery or carrot sticks, sliced peppers, broccoli or cauliflower spears, salad

Meat, Poultry, Fish, Dry Beans, Eggs, and Nuts Group (Meat and Beans Group)
Slices of lean turkey, ham, or roast beef, hard-cooked egg, peanut butter, dry-roasted peanuts

Fruit Group
Any raw fruits, dried fruits such as raisins

Bread, Cereal, Rice, and Pasta Group
Air-popped popcorn without butter, graham crackers, plain bagel, instant oatmeal, rice cakes, tortillas

Lesson 4 Review

Using complete sentences, answer the following questions on a sheet of paper.

Reviewing Terms and Facts

1. **Recall** What are three benefits of eating a nutritious breakfast?
2. **Vocabulary** What are *empty calories?* What kinds of foods provide empty calories?
3. **Explain** How does knowledge of nutrient density help you choose sensible snacks?
4. **Give Examples** Suggest a healthful snack from each of the five food groups.

Thinking Critically

5. **Explain** Why might air-popped popcorn be a smarter snack choice than other types of popcorn?

6. **Analyze** David went to a fast-food restaurant for lunch. He ordered a cola drink; a taco with chicken, cheese, shredded lettuce, and tomato; and ice cream. Which of these items have high nutrient density? Which have low nutrient density?

Applying Health Skills

7. **Accessing Information** Find three recipes—one for a high-fat dish, one for a dish that calls for a large amount of salt, and one for a sugary dessert. Adapt each recipe to make it healthier by lowering the fat, salt, or sugar content and increasing the fiber content. Present your ideas to the class.

LESSON 4: PLANNING MEALS AND SNACKS **211**

Lesson 4 Review

1. Any three: replenishes energy, improves grades, helps maintain healthy weight, improves muscle coordination.
2. Calories that come from foods that offer few, if any, nutrients; any foods at the tip of the Pyramid: fats, oils, and sweets.
3. You can compare the nutrient densities of snacks and choose the snack with the most

nutrition for the number of calories it provides.
4. See Figure 8.6 above for possible answers.
5. Air-popped popcorn is lower in fat.
6. High nutrient-density: the taco. Low nutrient-density: cola drink, ice cream.

Lesson 4

VISUAL LEARNING

FIGURE 8.6 Have volunteers describe the snack foods in the photos and read aloud the names of the food groups and the examples from each group. Ask:

• Which group from the Food Guide Pyramid is not included?

• Why do you think that food group has been left out? **INCL** *English Language Learners, Special Learning Needs, Behavior Problems, Different Learning Styles (Visual)*

③ Assess

Evaluating

📁 Assign the Lesson 4 Review; then assign the Lesson 4 Quiz in the TCR.

Reteaching

• 📁 Assign Concept Map 31 or Reteaching Activity 31 in the TCR.

• Have students review and discuss the snacks they usually choose as listed in response to the Quick Write assignment. What changes should they make in their snack choices?

Enrichment

• 📁 Assign Enrichment Activity 31 in the TCR.

• Have each student work with a partner to write a plan of balanced meals and snacks for an entire week.

④ Close

Have students summarize strategies for making healthful food choices for meals and snacks.

Teen Vegetarians

① Focus

Objectives

Students will be able to
- identify influences that might lead a person to become a vegetarian.
- identify challenges to maintaining a vegetarian eating plan.
- plan a healthy vegetarian meal.

Motivator
Bellringer Activity

Ask students, "Imagine that you decide to become a vegetarian. How would your eating habits have to change? Would it be a simple change for you? Why or why not?"

② Teach

Discussing

Ask students, "What are some of the influences that might lead a person to become a vegetarian?" Have students review the lesson again, noting the various influences mentioned (*love of animals, concern for the environment, peer norms, and so on.*) Then ask students, "What are some of the challenges to enjoying a vegetarian diet?" List student answers on the board (*family diet, health concerns, and so on.*). Ask students to consider how one's environment acts as a positive or negative influence on their ability to be a vegetarian, asking, "Where can you buy vegetarian foods in our community? Are there any restaurants in our town that cater to vegetarian diets? Does our school cafeteria offer vegetarian options? What about the local movie theater, mall, and sports arena?" Ask students to consider how the answers to these questions might influence one's decision to become or remain a vegetarian.

Teen Vegetarians

More kids are saying no to meat. Is this a healthy option?

Lauren Butts, a high-school student from Medford, Oregon, recalls the moment she became a vegetarian. At age 13, Lauren, a horse owner, accidentally ordered horsemeat at a restaurant in France. Although she avoided eating the burger, something clicked. "It made sense then," Lauren says. "There was no way I was going to eat the relatives of my horses."

Lauren is the author of *OK, So Now You're a Vegetarian,* the first vegetarian cookbook by a teen for teens. She is part of a small but fast-growing movement among young people ages 6 to 18 to cut out all meat. Inspired by everything from a love of animals to trendiness to a concern for the environment, young people are becoming vegetarians at higher rates than ever—often independent of their meat-eating parents.

Still, people who consider themselves vegetarians make up only about 6 percent of the population. Moreover, the definition of "vegetarian" can vary. (See "A Veggie Guide.") The number of those who just cut out red meat—or who refuse any animal products except eggs and dairy—is far greater than the number of strict vegans, who eat no animal products at all.

Whatever the definition, a recent poll found that 8- to 12-year-olds were signing on to vegetarianism at twice the rate of adults. "The jump among young people is clear," says Dennis Bier of the Children's Nutrition Research Center at Baylor College of Medicine in Houston, Texas. This raises an important question: Is vegetarianism a healthy choice? Bier says, "Concerns about proper growth and bone density should exist whether one's diet is vegetarian or not. However, there's no question that if it's well planned, a vegetarian diet is perfectly healthy for kids." A teen who is thinking about becoming a vegetarian should consult a doctor or a registered dietitian before changing his or her eating habits.

A Veggie Good Diet

Since beef, chicken, and fish are all good sources of protein and vitamins, nutritionists stress that a vegetarian diet requires research and careful meal planning. This is especially true during the growth spurts that occur in adolescence.

Beyond the Classroom

Home Tell students that they are going to plan a nutritional dinner that will satisfy everyone in their family. First, they should interview family members to learn about food restrictions or preferences. Is anyone a vegetarian? Is anyone on a low-sodium or low-fat diet? Are there any allergies? What are family members' favorite foods? Based on this information, what challenges do students face? Students should use this information, facts from Chapter 8, and additional research to plan a meal that is healthy and appetizing for all family members. For extra credit, ask a few interested students to shop for, prepare, and serve the meal. Have students share their experiences with the class.

A Veggie Guide

Did you know that there are different kinds of vegetarians? Here are a few:

VEGAN: No animal products of any kind, including dairy products, eggs, and honey, are eaten. A vegan lifestyle often involves more than just avoiding all animal products; it's a philosophy that emphasizes reverence for all forms of life.
Keep in mind: Vegans need to eat foods that contain some fat (beans), iron (broccoli), calcium (fortified soy milk or orange juice), and zinc (whole grains). Vitamin B12, found only in foods of animal origin, can be taken in supplement form.

LACTO-OVO: These types of vegetarians don't eat meat, chicken, or fish, but do eat eggs and dairy products.
Keep in mind: Eggs, milk, yogurt, and cheese are all good sources of important nutrients, but contain a lot of fat and cholesterol. Lacto-ovo vegetarians should opt for low-fat products.

PESCO: The largest group of vegetarians, pesco-vegetarians eat fish, dairy products, and eggs but not chicken or red meat.
Keep in mind: The key nutrients are all there—pesco-vegetarians just need to make sure to include lots of fruits and vegetables in their dietary plan.

VEGGIE-LITE: This is an unofficial term that embraces pollo vegetarians (those who eat chicken) and others who eat meat occasionally but consider themselves vegetarians.
Keep in mind: Eat a variety of fruits and vegetables. Eating mostly pasta, pizza, and bagels will not provide the optimal amount of nutrients.

Strict vegans have to be very careful to make sure they get enough iron, zinc, calcium, and vitamin B12. (B12 is found only in animal products.) Yet most experts agree that a vegetarian eating style can be managed. Beans, tofu, peanut butter, broccoli, milk, eggs, and whole grains can provide protein, iron, calcium, and zinc.

Challenges of a New Lifestyle

Both parents and their children say the vegetarian lifestyle has its challenges. Eating out at restaurants, friends' houses, and school can be tricky. Worse, it sometimes encourages consumption of empty-calorie foods or even abstaining from eating. Meat-eating parents may disapprove of their child's new eating style, causing tension at mealtimes. Parents also worry about their children getting proper nutrition. "But kids need to watch what they're eating regardless," says Bier.

"Keep in mind, most Americans need to be eating more fruits and vegetables anyway. It's good stuff!"

TIME TO THINK...

About Vegetarianism

Write down everything that you ate and drank yesterday. Now imagine that you are a vegan. (Use the information from this article and do your own research to find out more about what a vegan eating plan does and does not include.) How many things on your food list would you need to cross off if you were a vegan? Suppose you *had* subtracted those foods from what you ate that day: What vegan foods would you add to the list to ensure that you were getting the nutrients you need?

③ Apply

Time to Think

Allow time for students to complete their lists of vegan items, and have volunteers present their lists to the class. Explain that being a vegetarian is not always as simple as crossing one food off a list and replacing it with another. Vegetarian cooking has been raised to a gourmet level by dietitians and chefs across the country. Divide the class into small groups. Assign each group the task of turning a common meat-based dish into a vegetarian alternative. Students are free to use existing recipes in vegetarian cookbooks, magazines, and other sources, or create their own. Have students serve their recipe to the class. You might even gather the recipes into a vegetarian cookbook.

VISUAL LEARNING

Ask students to analyze the photograph on page 212. Ask, "Does this food look appetizing to you? Does the food on this plate represent an entire meal or just a snack? What might you add to this plate to create a more well-rounded vegetarian meal?"

Health Literacy

Food Choices Tell students that this feature mentions some of the influences on an individual's choice to become a vegetarian. However, some people argue that our food choices have implications for social, ecological, and economic issues worldwide. Ask students, "How might a plant-based diet be different from a meat-centered diet in terms of the global production, harvest, and transportation of food? Which type of diet do you think takes more water, land, and other natural resources to develop and bring to market? Why do you think these issues are considered controversial by some people?" Encourage a few interested students to research this issue and present their findings to the class.

ADVOCACY

Objective

After completing the lesson, students will be able to advocate healthful food choices for teens.

Time: 45 minutes

Materials: drawing paper, colored markers

Teacher Classroom Resources

📁 Building Health Skills Activities

• Transparency Master 10, "Advocacy"

• Reproducible Master 33, "Eating for Your Health"

---

1. Model

• Have students work with partners to identify the ways in which Grace advocates for eating breakfast.

• Conduct a class discussion based on these questions: 1) Is there additional information Grace could give to Caitlyn? If so, what is it?

• 2) Are there other statements that Grace should include to be more convincing? If so, what are they?

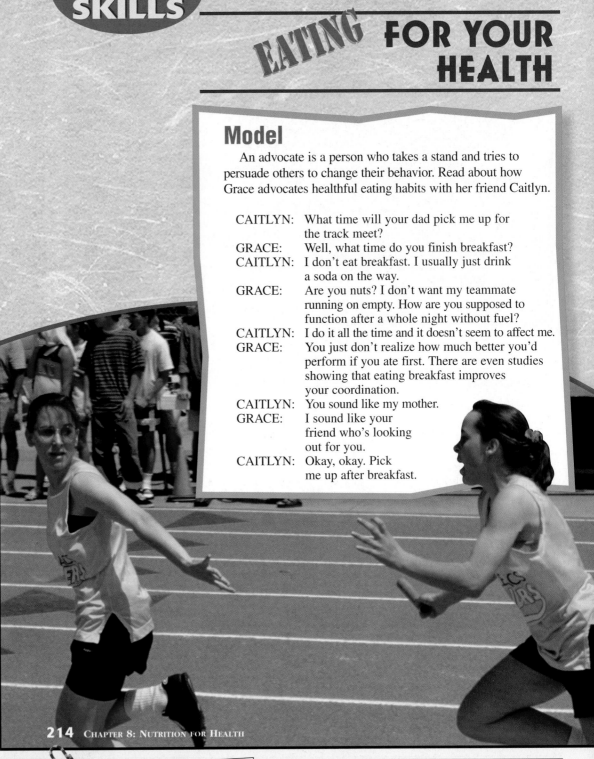

BUILDING HEALTH SKILLS

EATING FOR YOUR HEALTH

Model

An advocate is a person who takes a stand and tries to persuade others to change their behavior. Read about how Grace advocates healthful eating habits with her friend Caitlyn.

CAITLYN:	What time will your dad pick me up for the track meet?
GRACE:	Well, what time do you finish breakfast?
CAITLYN:	I don't eat breakfast. I usually just drink a soda on the way.
GRACE:	Are you nuts? I don't want my teammate running on empty. How are you supposed to function after a whole night without fuel?
CAITLYN:	I do it all the time and it doesn't seem to affect me.
GRACE:	You just don't realize how much better you'd perform if you ate first. There are even studies showing that eating breakfast improves your coordination.
CAITLYN:	You sound like my mother.
GRACE:	I sound like your friend who's looking out for you.
CAITLYN:	Okay, okay. Pick me up after breakfast.

214 CHAPTER 8: NUTRITION FOR HEALTH

Teaching Tips

Creating Artwork Using this Building Health Skills feature provides an opportunity for students to use their artistic skills. Some students may complain that they can't draw. Explain that anything goes— stick figures included. The point is to develop the skill of advocacy. The ability to draw is just an added benefit and is not graded in this activity.

Understanding Advocacy An advocate feels strongly, even passionately, about an issue that requires action. Ask the following questions to raise students' consciousness and engage their interest: How do you feel about diets? What has happened in your family or among your peers that makes you feel strongly?

Standards		Technology
National	**State/Local**	
National Health Education Standard **1.1, 1.2, 1.3, 1.8, 3.1, 3.4, 3.7**		Transparency 32 Tape/DVD 1, Segment 6, "Nutrition and Physical Activity" TeacherWorks™ Internet Activities
National Health Education Standard **1.1, 1.3, 1.8, 3.1, 3.2, 3.4**		Transparency 33 TeacherWorks™
National Health Education Standard **1.1, 1.8, 3.1, 3.4, 3.5, 6.4, 6.5, 6.6**		Transparency 34 TeacherWorks™
National Health Education Standard **1.1, 1.6, 1.8, 3.1, 3.4, 3.5, 5.6**		Transparency 35 TeacherWorks™ MindJogger Videoquiz **Exam**_View_® Pro Testmaker
National Health Education Standard **3.1, 3.4, 3.5**		Building Health Skills Transparency Master 2c

TeacherWorks™

Glencoe's new and exclusive TeacherWorks™ is an all-in-one planner and resource center. Access the complete Teacher Wraparound Edition electronically. Find all your classroom resources with just a few easy clicks, and print them right from your computer. Connect directly to Glencoe's customized Health Web site. Access the National Health Education Standards correlations, or insert your own state standards and match them directly to the electronic Teacher Wraparound Edition.

Language Diversity

- English Audio Summaries
- Spanish Audio Summaries
- English Summaries, Quizzes, and Activities
- Spanish Summaries, Quizzes, and Activities
- Spanish Parent Letters and Activities

KEY TO ABILITY LEVELS

Teaching Strategies that appear throughout the chapters have been identified by one of four codes to give you an idea of their suitability for students of varying learning styles and abilities.

L1 Level 1 strategies should be within the ability range of all students. Often full class participation is required.

L2 Level 2 strategies are for average to above-average students or for small groups. Some teacher direction is necessary.

L3 Level 3 strategies are designed for students able and willing to work independently. Minimal teacher direction is necessary.

INCL Strategies are appropriate for students with particular special needs in a general classroom setting.

Physical Activity and Fitness

Chapter at a Glance

Lesson 1 defines physical activity and provides strategies for increasing one's level of fitness.

Lesson 2 examines the elements of fitness: heart and lung endurance, muscle strength and endurance, body composition, and flexibility.

Lesson 3 discusses how to set and achieve fitness goals and describes the three stages of an exercise session.

Lesson 4 emphasizes the benefits of both individual and team sports and discusses sports conditioning and safety considerations.

Health Skills

- Relaxation Exercises (*Stress Management*), p. 222
- Activities for Fitness (*Practicing Healthful Behaviors*), p. 231
- Abstaining from Drugs (*Refusal Skills*), p. 240
- Warm Up! Work Out! Cool Down! (*Practicing Healthful Behaviors*), pp. 244–245

218

HANDS-ON ACTIVITY

Pulse Comparisons Let students form small groups in which to check, compare, and graph their pulse rates. Have each group member take and record his or her own pulse three times: while sitting relaxed in a chair, while standing, and then again after running in place for two minutes. Encourage students to discuss how their pulse rates compare in each situation. What do the differences indicate? Then have group members work together to plan and draw an appropriate graph (such as a multiline graph) that shows the pulse rates of all group members in all three situations. (This activity is best used to reinforce/extend the Hands-On Health activity on page 226.)

Physical Activity and Fitness

HEALTH *Online*

Do you get enough physical activity? Find out how you rate by taking the Health Inventory for Chapter 9 at health.glencoe.com.

FOLDABLES™ Study Organizer

Before You Read

Make this Foldable to help you organize the informa-tion on physical activity, exercise, and physical fitness presented in Lesson 1. Begin with a plain sheet of 11″ × 17″ paper.

Step 1

Fold the sheet of paper in half along the short axis, then fold in half again. This forms four columns.

Step 2

Open the paper and refold it in half along the long axis, then fold in half again. This forms four rows.

Step 3

Unfold and draw lines along the folds.

Step 4

Label the chart as shown.

Chapter 9	Definition	Examples	Impact on my life
Physical Activity			
Exercise			
Physical Fitness			

As You Read

In the appropriate section of the chart, write down definitions and examples of physical activity, exercise, and physical fitness, as well as the impact each has on your daily life.

Chapter Introduction

Use the options below to motivate students and preview chapter content.

HEALTH *Online*

Have students visit **health.glencoe.com** and take Health Inventory 9 to rate their physical activity and fitness levels. For new teaching ideas, click on Teaching Today to download helpful tools such as graphic organizers and Webquest activities.

GLENCOE TECHNOLOGY

Teen Health Video and DVD Series
(Each format available in both English and Spanish)

📼 💿 You may wish to use:

• Tape/DVD 1, Segment 6, "Nutrition and Physical Activity"

MindJogger Videoquiz

📼 💿 Use MindJogger to pre-view or review Chapter 9 content.

TIME HEALTH

Are You a Good Sport?
pages 242–243

FOLDABLES™ Study Organizer

Dinah Zike Study Fold

Organizing Data Using a Table As students read and study the material in Lesson 1, direct them to fill in the appropriate section of their Foldable table with definitions and examples of the terms. Then have them list the short- and long-term benefits of physical activity, exercise, and physical fitness, and describe how each has had an impact on their lives. Encourage students to determine their current level of physical fitness and guide them as they set realistic goals for improvement.

Lesson 1

The Benefits of Physical Activity

The Benefits of Physical Activity

Quick Write

Describe in a sentence or two what it means to be physically fit.

LEARN ABOUT...

- what it means to be physically fit.
- the benefits of physical activity.
- kinds of activities that will help you stay fit.

VOCABULARY

- physical activity
- exercise
- physical fitness
- balance
- coordination
- aerobic exercise
- anaerobic exercise

Physical Activity, Exercise, and Physical Fitness

The terms *physical activity, exercise,* and *fitness* are closely related, but each has a particular meaning. **Physical activity** refers to *any kind of movement that uses up energy.* Physical activity includes exercising and playing sports. It also includes the movements associated with an active lifestyle, such as biking to the store, raking leaves, and walking up and down the stairs. **Exercise** is *a specifically planned and organized session of physical activity that you do to improve or maintain your physical fitness.* By combining regular exercise with an active lifestyle and sound nutrition, you can be fit. **Physical fitness** is *the ability to handle the physical demands of everyday life without becoming overly tired.*

When you're physically fit, you have enough energy to do the things you want to do, plus energy in reserve for the unexpected.

Some forms of physical activity let you enjoy the company of other people while helping you stay in shape. *What outdoor activities do you like?*

Lesson 1 Resources

Teacher Classroom Resources

- Parent Letter & Activities 9
- Concept Map 32
- Decision-Making Activity 17
- Enrichment Activity 32
- Lesson Plan 1
- Lesson 1 Quiz

- Reading Tutor Activity 31
- Reteaching Activity 32
- Transparency 32

Student Activities Workbook

- Chapter 9 Study Guide
- Applying Health Skills 32

FIGURE 9.1

Benefits of Physical Activity

Mental/Emotional Benefits
- Feel more alert and energetic
- Reduce stress
- Learn new things
- Get a sense of accomplishment
- Lessen mental fatigue
- Build a positive self-image
- Increase self-confidence and self-esteem

Physical Benefits
- Strengthen heart and lungs
- Strengthen bones
- Manage weight
- Control blood sugar
- Control blood pressure
- Increase strength and stamina
- Improve flexibility and muscle tone
- Improve **balance**, *the feeling of stability and control over your body*
- Develop **coordination**, *the smooth and effective working together of your muscles and bones*
- Improve reaction time
- Increase body's defense against diseases
- Improve sleep

Social Benefits
- Engage in enjoyable activities
- Meet and interact with new people
- Work with others as a team
- Get support from friends
- Share goals and achievements with others

Benefits of an Active Lifestyle

Physical activity benefits you in both body and mind. Besides promoting your overall health, physical activity helps you look and feel better. Since many physical activities involve other people, you'll also get social benefits.

Physical activity provides mental and emotional benefits, too. Being active lets you clear your mind and "burn off" stress. In addition, the physical and social benefits that you get help you feel good about yourself as a person. **Figure 9.1** shows some of the mental/emotional, physical, and social benefits of physical activity.

Increasing Your Level of Fitness

How can you increase your level of physical fitness? The first step toward physical fitness is to recognize that physical activity is important to your lifelong health and well-being. The next step is to move more! Make physical activity part of your daily life.

LESSON 1: THE BENEFITS OF PHYSICAL ACTIVITY **221**

---

② Teach

Debating

Have students develop lists of labor-saving devices used in our country today. (*washers/dryers, dishwashing machines, cars, and so on*) Ask students to debate the benefits of convenience versus the increase in sedentary lifestyles such devices encourage. **L2**

Examining the Issue

Ask students who exercise regularly to raise their hands. Then call on those students to describe how they feel after a good workout. How do they feel later in the day? (*Students will probably say that they feel refreshed and invigorated after a workout.*) Tell students that those are natural responses. Lead the class to a recognition of the cause-and-effect relationship between vigorous exercise and a person's physical and mental well-being. **L1**

VISUAL LEARNING

FIGURE 9.1 Guide students in reading and discussing the listed benefits of physical activity. Then let volunteers name specific activities and identify the most important benefits from each group. Ask: How do the benefits on one side of the health triangle improve the other sides? Have students analyze the interrelationships of physical, mental/emotional, and social health. **INCL** *English Language Learners, Special Learning Needs, Behavior Problems, Different Learning Styles* (*Visual*)

Beyond the Classroom

Home To help students understand the many benefits of physical fitness, suggest that they each make a fitness contract with family members or friends. To do so, they will choose an exercise or sport in which everyone in the family or group is willing and able to take part. Then they write a contract that spells out when, where, and how they will exercise together. They should also list fitness goals, benefits, and rewards as part of the contract. Remind them to review the contract periodically with the other participants and modify goals or conditions as necessary.

Lesson 1

Cross-Curriculum Activity

LANGUAGE ARTS Ask students to write short essays in which they address these questions:

- What activity would I probably enjoy doing as a regular part of my life, now and in the future?
- How might my ability to perform the activity change as I grow older?
- How might I adapt to this change?

Ask volunteers to read their original compositions to the class. **L2**

HEALTH SKILLS ACTIVITY

STRESS MANAGEMENT

Guide students in reading and discussing the instructions for relaxation exercises. Ask volunteers to share what they already know about these and similar exercises. Also, ask students when, where, and why people might want to use them.

Have students try the relaxation exercises at home. The next day, let students meet in groups to discuss their experiences. If your students know how to take their pulses, have them do so before and after the exercises.

Note: This skill is introduced in Chapter 2 on pages 39–43.

✓ Reading Check

Categorize words. Sort these words into categories: *biking, dancing, curl-ups, swimming, soccer, stretching, weightlifting, playing catch, tai chi, roller-blading.* **Add more words to each list.**

Becoming more active is as easy as seeing the opportunities for physical activity that are all around you. Instead of using elevators and escalators, take the stairs. Walk or ride a bike to the mall rather than asking your parents for a lift.

In addition to looking for everyday opportunities, plan regular sessions of exercise. Aim for at least three to five sessions a week. Start by exercising 10 to 15 minutes at a time and gradually work up to about 30 minutes or more. If you feel that you do not have time to spare, try breaking your physical activity down into smaller sessions during the day. Three 10-minute sessions provide the same benefit as one 30-minute activity.

Choosing the Right Activities

It is important to choose activities that give you the benefits you want. There are two main types of exercise: aerobic and anaerobic. **Aerobic exercise** is *rhythmic, nonstop, moderate to vigorous activity that requires large amounts of oxygen and works the heart.* Running, biking, and swimming are forms of aerobic exercise. **Anaerobic exercise** is *intense physical activity that requires little oxygen but uses short bursts of energy.* Sprinting and gymnastics are examples of anaerobic exercise.

Each type of exercise benefits the body in a particular way. You can combine both types of exercise to achieve optimum fitness. By choosing a variety of activities, you can receive the benefits of both types of exercise.

HEALTH SKILLS ACTIVITY

STRESS MANAGEMENT

Relaxation Exercises

Physical activity is an effective way to relieve stress and help you unwind. You might also do relaxation exercises to reduce feelings of stress. Here are some examples:

- **LIE ON YOUR BACK.** Make fists and tense your arms. Hold for a moment, then relax. In turn, tense and then relax your neck, shoulders, legs, feet, and abdomen.
- **LIE ON YOUR SIDE, WITH BOTH ARMS ABOVE YOUR HEAD.** Tense your whole body, then completely relax, letting your arms and legs fall where they may, as though you were a rag doll. Turn to your other side and repeat.
- **SIT QUIETLY.** Close your eyes, take a slow, deep breath, and let it out slowly. Repeat two more times. Open your mouth, move your jaw to the right, and hold for a few seconds. Then move it to the left and hold. Repeat several times.

ON YOUR OWN
Try each of these exercises. Did they reduce your body tension? Which exercise had the greatest effect?

✓ Reading Check

List/Group/Label Categorizing key words can aid students in understanding concepts and vocabulary. Have students work in pairs to brainstorm categories for the words in the list. Possible groupings include aerobic exercise, anaerobic exercise, activities needing equipment, activities needing no equipment, team sports, individual sports, physical activities I (we) prefer, physical activities I (we) dislike, and so on. Have the partners work together to list the words under their category headings and then add other words to their lists. Allow the partners to share their categories and lists with the class. **INCL** *English Language Learners, Special Learning Needs, Behavior Problems*

Monitoring Your Progress

As you work toward your fitness goals, you'll want to monitor your progress. Remember that change comes gradually. Don't expect to cut 30 seconds off your mile time after a week of working out. Here are some suggestions for monitoring your progress.

- Keep an exercise log or journal. Making performance notes after each workout will help you keep track of exercise sessions.
- After four to eight weeks of workouts, you should observe some improvement in your overall fitness. Depending on the exercises you've been doing, you should feel stronger, have more endurance, and have greater flexibility. You may also find that you feel better overall, look fitter, and have more energy.
- If you see no significant change after eight weeks, you need to evaluate the situation. Have you been exercising regularly? Do you need to modify your fitness goals?
- Another measure of fitness is your resting heartbeat rate, the number of times per minute your heart beats when your body is at rest. The average heartbeat rate ranges from 72 to 84 beats per minute. A resting heartbeat rate less than 72 is generally associated with physical fitness.
- Once you reach your fitness goals, consider setting new goals for yourself.

Recording your performance in an exercise log will help you assess your progress. *What system would you use to record your progress?*

Lesson 3 Review

Using complete sentences, answer the following questions on a sheet of paper.

Reviewing Terms and Facts

1. **Summarize** What should you keep in mind when preparing an activity plan?
2. **Recall** What are the three stages of an exercise workout?
3. **Vocabulary** Define *warm-up* and *cool-down*. What are their similarities and differences?
4. **Explain** Why would it be unwise to skip the cool-down stage?

Thinking Critically

5. **Apply** What adjustments do you need to make in frequency, intensity, and time to meet your personal workout needs?
6. **Explain** Why is it important to set fitness goals before starting an exercise program?

Applying Health Skills

7. **Practicing Healthful Behaviors** Make a weekly activity plan like the one shown in Figure 9.7 on page 232. Exchange plans with another student and offer suggestions to each other.

LESSON 3: SETTING FITNESS GOALS **235**

Lesson 3 Review

1. Balance your schedule, be flexible about what you can do on any given day.
2. Warm up, work out, cool down.
3. Both involve low to moderate activity. Warming up prepares you for working out; increases heartbeat, body temperature, and flexibility. Cooling down helps circulation and body temperature return to normal after exercise.
4. Your muscles may tighten up. You may feel dizzy or faint.
5. Students should recognize that frequency, intensity, and time can all be adjusted to suit individual needs.
6. Setting goals helps ensure that you balance your activities in order to increase your overall fitness.

Lesson 3

Discussing

Emphasize to students that keeping an exercise journal can be very useful. Encourage them to write down little cues like how they eat and sleep. They might see patterns developing. **L1**

❸ Assess

Evaluating

📁 Assign the Lesson 3 Review; then assign the Lesson 3 Quiz in the TCR.

Reteaching

- 📁 Assign Concept Map 34 or Reteaching Activity 34 in the TCR.
- Have students work with partners to write informal outlines of the facts and suggestions in Lesson 3.

Enrichment

- 📁 Assign Enrichment Activity 34 in the TCR.
- Have students write three or four suggestions they might give a friend who is starting a fitness program.

❹ Close

Discuss the relationship between personal freedom and the additional responsibilities that come as a result of making one's own decisions.

Lesson 4

Staying Fit and Avoiding Injury

① Focus

Lesson Objectives

Students will be able to

- compare the benefits of individual sports with those of team sports.
- discuss ways to become physically fit in order to participate in a sport.
- identify ways to minimize the risk of injury when participating in a sport.

Health Skills
- Refusal Skills, p. 240

Motivators

Quick Write
Allow time for students to share their preferences and explanations.

Bellringer Activity

Ask students to name sports or physical activities at which they are good or at which they would like to be good. Direct them to explain in one sentence why the sport or activity is important to them.

VOCABULARY

Have students write the definitions for each vocabulary term in their health notebooks. Then quiz the class on each term's correct spelling and definition.

LESSON 4

Staying Fit and Avoiding Injury

Quick Write

Some people love playing team sports. Others prefer to exercise on their own. Many enjoy doing both. Which group do you fit in? Explain your preference.

LEARN ABOUT...

- choosing sports activities that are right for you.
- preparing yourself to take part in sports.
- minimizing your risk of injury in sports.

VOCABULARY

- individual sports
- team sports
- sports conditioning
- dehydration
- anabolic steroids

Choosing Sports Activities

To choose the right sports for you, consider the kinds of activities you enjoy most. While both individual and team sports provide personal satisfaction and a way to stay active, one sport may suit your needs better than others. Of course, many teens take part in both individual *and* team sports.

Individual Sports

Individual sports are *physical activities that you can do on your own or with a friend.* You don't need to be part of a team to participate in individual sports. For example, biking, running, swimming, and skating are all sports you can do by yourself.

What are the advantages of individual sports? They are more flexible than team sports. You can do them whenever you feel like it, and you can do them for as long as you wish.

That's also one possible disadvantage to individual sports. You have to find the time and the motivation to take part in your chosen sport. Some people find it hard to stick to a plan if they have to do it on their own.

One advantage of individual sports is that you can set your own schedule. *What are other advantages?*

236 CHAPTER 9: PHYSICAL ACTIVITY AND FITNESS

Lesson 4 Resources

Teacher Classroom Resources
 Concept Map 35
Cross-Curriculum Activity 18
Decision-Making Activity 18
Enrichment Activity 35
Lesson Plan 4
Lesson 4 Quiz
Reading Tutor Activity 34

Reteaching Activity 35
Transparency 35

Student Activities Workbook
Chapter 9 Study Guide
Applying Health Skills 35
Health Inventory 9

Team Sports

Many teens enjoy **team sports**—*organized physical activities with specific rules in which groups of people play together against other groups.* There are many different team sports to choose from, including baseball, soccer, basketball, volleyball, and football. Dual sports, requiring only two to four players, include tennis and racquetball. Team sports may be offered by

- schools.
- city or town recreation departments.
- community centers.
- teen clubs and organizations.
- sports and fitness centers.
- church and synagogue youth programs.

Playing on a team can be a positive and enjoyable experience. Many teens like the excitement of competition. Whether or not your team wins, you have the companionship and support of your teammates and coaches as you work together toward a common goal. Playing on a team also gives you an opportunity to develop communication and social skills. You learn about cooperation, compromise, and good sportsmanship.

Of course, team sports are not suitable for everyone. Some teens don't like having a set schedule, which typically requires them to attend several practices and games a week, after school and on weekends. Perhaps their family circumstances prevent them from committing themselves to a team. For these people, individual sports offer a better fitness alternative.

Team sports give you an opportunity to exercise, have fun, and make friends. *What are other benefits of team sports?*

Developing Good Character

Sportsmanship

Being a good sport means treating others fairly and respectfully. It means playing by the rules and accepting both victory and defeat graciously. It can include helping a less-talented athlete by giving him or her pointers for a better game. *What real-life examples can you think of that show good sportsmanship?*

Lesson 4

② Teach

Developing Good Character

Sportsmanship

Encourage students to think of either professional or amateur athletes who exhibit good sportsmanship and are great role models for others. Ask: What other qualities of good character are important in a top athlete?

Discussing

Ask students to consider why bicycling has become a popular competitive sport in the United States in recent years. Why can bicycling be considered a sport you can participate in throughout your life? **L1**

Applying Skills

Ask volunteers to follow a bicycling program for three weeks. Have them keep daily logs of their progress and feelings. At the end of three weeks, discuss their reactions to the program. **L3**

Analyzing

Ask students who are members of sports teams to share with the class the physical, mental/emotional, and social benefits they gain from being a part of the team. Then ask the same of students who participate in individual sports. Discuss the similarities and differences among the responses. **L1**

Health Literacy

Health Information Weight training is an individual sport that builds muscle strength and endurance. It is popular because the benefits are attainable without access to a set of barbells or fitness center equipment. The following two types of weight training are healthy alternatives to pumping iron.

- *Isotonic exercise* develops strength by relying on repetitions, or reps. Push-ups, pull-ups, and sit-ups are all isotonic exercises.

- *Isometric exercise* uses muscle tension to build strength and endurance. Pushing against a wall with all your might is an example of an isometric exercise.

Lesson 4

Recalling

Ask students to recall recommendations for making water an important element in a balanced diet. Then ask:
- Why is it important to drink more water when participating in sports?
- Why does your need for water increase when the weather is hot? **L1**

Investigating

Let interested students identify and learn about fruit-flavored waters and high-energy waters that are now being sold. What advantages and disadvantages do these new drinks offer? How much sugar do they contain? Ask these students to discuss their findings with the rest of the class. **L3**

Researching

Ask a pair of interested volunteers to research the causes, symptoms, and treatment of dehydration or heatstroke. Then have them plan and present a skit, a demonstration, or an oral report to share the results of their research with the rest of the class. **L3**

MEDIA WATCH

SPORTS DRINKS

Sports drinks are advertised on TV and in magazines. The ads suggest that the drinks will improve athletic performance. Use your critical-thinking skills to interpret media messages and determine whether these claims are true. *Write a paragraph summarizing your conclusions.*

These teens know the importance of avoiding dehydration. *How many glasses of water a day are recommended for athletes?*

Sports Conditioning

Whether you choose an individual sport or a team sport, you need to be physically fit to do your best. **Sports conditioning** is *regular physical activity or exercise to strengthen and condition muscles for a particular sport.* It takes time and effort. You'll also need to eat healthful foods, learn safety rules, and obtain appropriate equipment.

Sports and Nutrition

An important part of sports conditioning is eating a balanced, nutritious diet. Your choices should include a variety of foods from the different food groups and a limited amount of fat. Here are other guidelines.

- **Get enough carbohydrates.** Your body needs extra energy to play sports. Fruits, vegetables, pasta, and whole-grain breads provide carbohydrates, an excellent energy source.
- **Get enough vitamins and minerals.** These nutrients are essential to a balanced diet and to sports conditioning. Calcium, for example, strengthens bones, while iron helps provide muscles with oxygen during physical activity.
- **Don't eat too much protein.** Athletes need protein, but no more than anyone else, provided they are eating enough nutritious foods. Even though protein helps to build muscle tissue, it is only through exercise and training that you can develop your muscles.
- **Drink water!** If you play sports, your body will lose water through perspiration. To maintain fluid balance, drink a total of 9 to 13 glasses a day, especially when it is hot outside, and take a drink every 15 minutes. Your goal is to avoid **dehydration**, *excessive water loss from the body*, which can lead to dizziness, muscle cramps, and heatstroke.

WHAT TEENS WANT TO KNOW

What's the difference between "conditioning" and "training?" Conditioning involves exercises to build stamina, strength, and speed. It combines aerobic exercises, such as running, and anaerobic exercises, such as diving. Conditioning aims to improve athletes' overall energy efficiency, flexibility, muscle tone, and strength. Conditioning programs also include warm-up and cool-down routines to improve flexibility and keep athletes supple and limber. Training is different from conditioning. It teaches sport-specific skills like pitching, batting, swinging a golf club, and using a balance beam for gymnastics. Professional teams and school physical education programs combine conditioning and training to help professional and student athletes achieve peak performances.

Safety First

Whenever you exercise or participate in sports, you increase your risk of injury. The three basic aspects of safety are safe behavior, safe and proper equipment, and knowing your limits.

Safe Behavior

Many sports-related injuries can be prevented by thinking ahead. Here are some tips.

- **Exercise where and when it's safe.** A soft, even surface is easier on your legs, knees, and feet than a hard or uneven surface. Exercise with another person and avoid deserted places. Protect yourself during hot weather by exercising in the cooler mornings or evenings. Remember to wear sunscreen outdoors.
- **Always warm up and cool down.** Gradually get your body ready to begin exercising. End your workout by cooling down.
- **Practice your sport regularly.** Team practices help you maintain your physical fitness levels and help you and your teammates learn to work together effectively and safely.
- **Learn the proper techniques and rules of the game.** Following the rules and regulations of a sport promotes both safety and good sportsmanship.
- **Keep your emotions under control.** Anger or frustration can lead to unsafe or unwise actions. Try to stay calm and relaxed.

Safe Equipment

What you wear when you exercise or play sports is important to your safety. Here are some clothing and equipment guidelines.

- **Wear loose-fitting or stretchable clothes.** For some sports, clothing that fits loosely gives you freedom of movement and helps you stay cooler. For other sports, tight, stretchable clothes are more appropriate.
- **If you exercise outdoors, make yourself visible.** Wear light-colored and reflective clothing so you'll be visible to drivers.
- **When exercising in cold weather, dress in layers.** You can easily add or remove layers as needed during your workout.
- **Wear protective equipment.** Different sports require protection for different parts of the body. Always wear the necessary gear.
- **Choose shoes carefully.** Shoes should fit properly, feel comfortable, provide adequate support, and be suitable for the activity you have chosen.
- **Select your equipment wisely.** Whether you're picking skates, a helmet, or a baseball glove, take the time to make a wise choice.

LESSON 4: STAYING FIT AND AVOIDING INJURY **239**

Protective equipment that is properly sized and correctly worn helps prevent injury. *What protective gear is this hockey player wearing?*

Lesson 4

Discussing

Guide students in discussing the importance of listening to their own bodies when exercising and playing sports. Ask:

• How can teammates help one another pay attention to their own limits?

• What do you think you should say to a friend who appears to have an injury or a cramp but who wants to continue competing? **L1**

At the 1988 Olympics, Canadian sprinter Ben Johnson ran 100 meters in an amazing 9.79 seconds. However, that world record was nullified and Johnson was stripped of his gold medal when he tested positive for stanozolol, an anabolic steroid.

HEALTH SKILLS ACTIVITY

REFUSAL SKILLS

Guide students in discussing the activity introduction. Ask:

• How do you think Ben feels about Scott's offer?

• Why should Ben not try Scott's pills?

Then have students work with partners to role-play a conversation between Ben and Scott.

Note: This skill is introduced in Chapter 6 on pages 149–150.

This teen was able to compete because she trained properly and knew her limits. *What strategies help you know your limits?*

Know Your Limits

When exercising or playing sports, it's important to recognize your limits. Here are some suggestions that will help.

• **Listen to your body.** Exercise can cause discomfort, like mild breathlessness or tired muscles, but pain is not normal. If you're feeling pain, your body is telling you to slow down, rest, or stop completely. If pain persists, see a doctor.

• **Stop if you get injured or feel ill.** If you get hurt while exercising or while playing in a game, don't continue until someone checks you out. Consult a coach, fitness instructor, or doctor. Also, don't play sports if you're not feeling well.

• **Use the R.I.C.E. formula.** If you have a minor sports injury such as a sprained ankle, follow the Rest, Ice, Compression, Elevation formula. See Chapter 19 for details.

HEALTH SKILLS ACTIVITY

REFUSAL SKILLS

Abstaining from Drugs

Ben enjoys being part of his school's traveling track team. In his last race, Ben came in second, a half step behind the lead runner. After the race, one of his teammates, Scott, came over and said, "You know, you could have won." When Ben asked what he meant, Scott smiled and held up a small bottle. "These pills will increase your speed like you won't believe!"

Ben wants to increase his speed, but he knows that taking a drug is not only cheating, it's also dangerous. He uses his refusal skills to let Scott know how he feels.

WHAT WOULD YOU DO?

Suppose you were Ben. Describe how you would apply the S.T.O.P. refusal skills in your conversation with Scott. With a partner, role-play the interaction between Ben and Scott.

SAY NO IN A FIRM VOICE.
TELL WHY NOT.
OFFER OTHER IDEAS.
PROMPTLY LEAVE.

MORE ABOUT...

Sports Safety Concussions are brain injuries resulting from blows to the head. They are routine sports injuries, occurring in as many as 20 percent of all high school football players each year. Along with headache, dizziness, and light-headedness, concussions may cause memory loss and disorientation. Concussions may not involve loss of consciousness, but there's a risk of amnesia. Symptoms can last from minutes to weeks. Athletes are usually advised to wait seven days after symptoms have cleared before returning to competition. Adolescents who suffer more than two concussions should be excluded from further hard-collision sports since multiple concussions may be associated with injury to the brain and nervous system.

Avoiding Harmful Substances

Anabolic steroids are *drugs that cause muscle tissue to develop at an abnormally fast rate.* Although steroids and certain other drugs may increase strength, the use of these drugs is both dangerous and illegal. Here are some of the side effects users may experience:

- Liver and brain cancers
- Weakening of tendons, leading to joint or tendon injuries
- Cardiovascular damage and high blood pressure, raising the risk of heart attack
- Mental and emotional effects, such as anxiety, severe mood swings, uncontrolled rage, and delusions
- Severe acne
- Trembling
- Bone damage
- Facial hair growth in females and breast development in males

Using steroids can seriously damage a person's health, even later in life. Avoid harmful substances to perform well and stay healthy.

Anabolic steroids and other performance-enhancing drugs have no place in a healthy fitness plan. Besides damaging your body, they can destroy your athletic career.

Lesson 4 Review

Using complete sentences, answer the following questions on a sheet of paper.

Reviewing Terms and Facts

1. **Vocabulary** Explain the meaning of *sports conditioning.*
2. **Explain** What is *dehydration*? Why is it dangerous?
3. **Give Examples** List three ways to practice safe behavior in sports.
4. **Recall** What are the dangers of using anabolic steroids?

Thinking Critically

5. **Suggest** What advice would you give to a teammate who often misses practice or arrives late?

6. **Analyze** Carlton borrows his older brother's protective gear and his sports shoes, even though his brother is much bigger. How is he risking injury?

Applying Health Skills

7. **Accessing Information** With a partner, make a list of all the places in your community that provide opportunities to join a sports team. Include on your list information about the hours they are open and fees they charge. Share your list with your classmates.

Lesson 4 Review

1. See definition on page 238.
2. Excessive water loss from the body, which can lead to dizziness, muscle cramps, and heatstroke.
3. Any three from the list under Safe Behavior on page 239.
4. Responses should include side effects from the list provided on this page.
5. Practice keeps players in shape and helps teammates work together effectively and safely. Missing practice or arriving late increases risk of injury if the teammate isn't warmed up or conditioned.
6. In order to be safe and comfortable, protective gear must be properly sized for each individual.

Are You a Good Sport?

❶ Focus

Objectives

Students will be able to
- list the rules of good sportsmanship.
- analyze society's views on sportsmanship.
- discuss whether or not professional athletes demonstrate good sportsmanship.

Motivator

Quick Write

Ask students whether or not they have ever experienced bad sportsmanship or behaved in a way that might be perceived as bad sportsmanship. Have them write their answers anonymously on a sheet of paper. What was the situation? How did those involved respond?

❷ Teach

Cross-Curriculum Activity

MATH On a second piece of paper, have students answer the quiz questions. Remind them that this is an anonymous quiz, and to answer the questions truthfully instead of choosing what they "should" do. Have them score their own work using the score chart on page 243, and ask them to hand in their work. Write on the board the four categories of sportsmanship: "All-Star Sport," "First-String Good Sport," and so on, and tally the student's answers. Graph the results of the class as a whole; the x-axis being the categories of sportsmanship, and the y-axis being the number of students. Discuss the results. What is the number of students per category of sportsmanship? What percentage of the class does this represent? Is the graph an accurate reflection of sportsmanship in our society? Why or why not?

TIME HEALTH

Are You A Good Sport?
Take this quiz to find out if you need to work on the way you play.

What does it mean to be a "good sport"? HINT: It's not about how many points you put up on the scoreboard. Answer yes or no to the questions below, then use the scoring chart on the next page to grade yourself.

1. Do you shake hands with your opponent after a game?
2. If you know you're out but the umpire calls you safe, do you tell the umpire the truth?
3. Do you talk trash?
4. Do you ever encourage kids standing on the sideline to join the game?
5. If your team is losing by a lot, do you still try your hardest on every play?
6. Do you yell at your teammates for making a mistake?
7. If you think the referee made a bad call, do you argue with him?
8. Do you arrive for practices and games on time?
9. If an opponent falls down, do you help him or her get up?
10. Did you ever write a thank-you note to your coach at the end of the season?
11. If a kid on the other team makes a good play, do you compliment him or her?
12. Have you ever donated your used sports gear to charity?
13. If you see trash on the playing field, do you pick it up?
14. If kids are arguing during a game, do you try to get them to stop?
15. Do you always play your hardest, but never so hard that you injure someone?

COOPERATIVE LEARNING ACTIVITY

Letter Writing Have students brainstorm a list of professional sports figures. Discuss whether or not the individuals demonstrate good sportsmanship. Ask students to provide examples to support their position. Divide students into small work groups. Ask each group to write a letter to one of the sports figure expressing appreciation for his/her behavior on the playing field, or encouraging improvement. Stress that the letters should be cordial and professional. Student letters should be persuasive and take a clear stand for a healthful position.

A Good Sport With a Great Idea!

Mark Guterman of Short Hills, New Jersey, celebrated his bar mitzvah recently. (At age 13, a Jewish boy often celebrates a bar mitzvah, a ceremony to commemorate the acceptance of religious duty and adult responsibility.)

To show that he was ready for his bar mitzvah, Mark did something to help other people: He sent letters to friends and relatives asking if they could donate used sports equipment to kids in need.

Mark and his family collected hundreds of pieces of equipment, such as in-line skates, baseball mitts, skateboards, tennis rackets, and footballs. Then they gave all the equipment to kids at a homeless shelter and a foster home.

"It lit up their faces. They were thrilled," says Mark. "It made me feel good to help. I wanted to give to people who are less fortunate than I am."

Scoring Chart

Give yourself 1 point for every "yes" answer that you gave to questions 1, 2, 4, 5, 8, 9, 10, 11, 12, 13, 14, and 15.

Give yourself 1 point for every "no" answer that you gave to questions 3, 6, and 7.

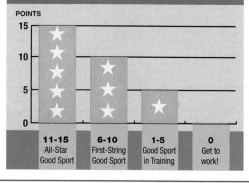

See how you scored by using the bar graph below.

POINTS			
15			
10			
5			
0			
11-15 All-Star Good Sport	6-10 First-String Good Sport	1-5 Good Sport in Training	0 Get to work!

TIME TO THINK...

About Being a Good Sport

Imagine that you're playing basketball. You take a shot and—wham! A player on the other team hits your arm so hard that you miss the shot. Amazingly, the referee does not call a foul. What would you do? Write down your thoughts in a brief paragraph. Then, as a class, discuss different options on what to do in this situation.

❸ Apply

Time to Think

Have volunteers share their paragraphs with the class. Then ask students what their favorite professional sports figure might do in a similar situation. Would he/she identify the options and consequences before taking action? Why or why not? Discuss the fact that while good sportsmanship is highly touted in professional sports, it isn't always practiced. Hockey, for example, is notorious for fights on the ice, yet the situation is not only ignored, but subtly encouraged. Ask students, "What does this tell us about society's views of sportsmanship? What influences these views (*television, the media, high salaries*)?" Have students chose a sport and use online or print resources to research what rules apply in relationship to sportsmanship. Is poor sportsmanship often part of the game? What are the consequences? What are the rules professional athletes overlook without being penalized? Have the students write a one-page essay describing their findings.

VISUAL LEARNING

Ask students to analyze the drawing on pages 242–243. What examples of good sportsmanship do they see? Is this a realistic representation of a football game? Why or why not?

Health Literacy

Good Sportsmanship In 1997, the NCAA (National Collegiate Athletic Association) created a Committee on Sportsmanship and Ethical Conduct for intercollegiate athletics. This committee's goal is to improve sportsmanship and ethical conduct through the values of respect, fairness, civility, honesty and responsibility. Every year, the NCAA sponsors a Good Sports Contest to promote good sportsmanship at an early age. Often, the contest involves making posters or writing essays on sportsmanship. Log on to the NCAA Website to find contest details. Then, have students enter the competition. First, brainstorm a list of the rules of good sportsmanship. Have students incorporate some or all of these guidelines into the project.

PRACTICING HEALTHFUL BEHAVIORS

Objectives

After completing the lesson, students will be able to

- describe the benefits of warming up and cooling down.

- create a personal workout that includes warming up and cooling down.

Time: 40 minutes

Materials: paper, pen or pencil, construction paper, markers

Teacher Classroom Resources

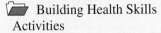 Building Health Skills Activities

- Transparency Master 2c, "Practicing Healthful Behaviors"

- Reproducible Master 34, "Warm Up! Work Out! Cool Down!"

---

1. Model

- Display Transparency Master 2c, and discuss its content with the class.

- Direct students to read the scenario about Ryan and Amber. Have volunteers explain the differences in the siblings' approaches to exercise. Ask: Why did Ryan get injured?

- Lead a class discussion on the importance of warming up before engaging in physical activity and cooling down afterward.

WARM UP! WORK OUT! COOL DOWN!

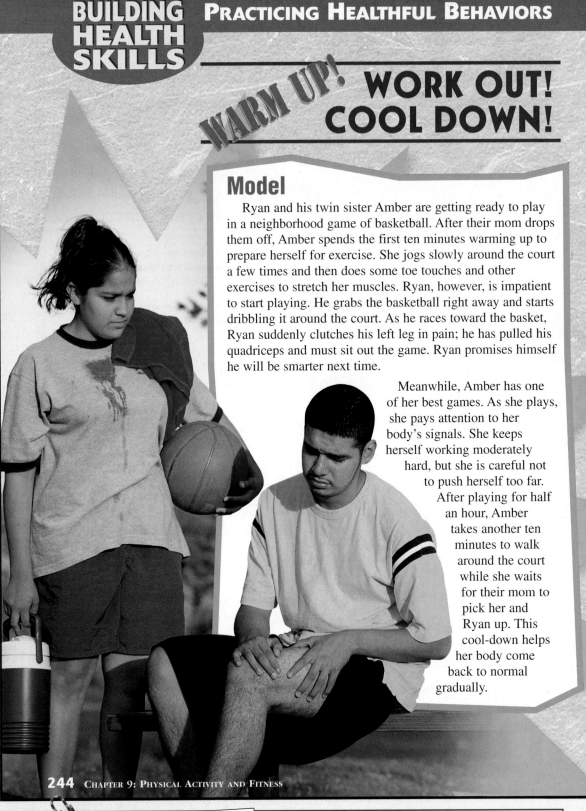

Model

Ryan and his twin sister Amber are getting ready to play in a neighborhood game of basketball. After their mom drops them off, Amber spends the first ten minutes warming up to prepare herself for exercise. She jogs slowly around the court a few times and then does some toe touches and other exercises to stretch her muscles. Ryan, however, is impatient to start playing. He grabs the basketball right away and starts dribbling it around the court. As he races toward the basket, Ryan suddenly clutches his left leg in pain; he has pulled his quadriceps and must sit out the game. Ryan promises himself he will be smarter next time.

Meanwhile, Amber has one of her best games. As she plays, she pays attention to her body's signals. She keeps herself working moderately hard, but she is careful not to push herself too far. After playing for half an hour, Amber takes another ten minutes to walk around the court while she waits for their mom to pick her and Ryan up. This cool-down helps her body come back to normal gradually.

244 CHAPTER 9: PHYSICAL ACTIVITY AND FITNESS

Teaching Tips

Converting Rubric Scores to Letter Grades Rubric scores are an especially useful tool for reporting students' performance on assessment activities. Often, however, students and their parents expect evaluations in the form of letter grades. Many individual school districts have their own conversion policies. In other cases, teachers use this basic conversion table:

Rubric Score	Letter Grade Range
4	A to A−
3	B+ to C
2	C− to D
1	F

Practice

Form groups of two or three. Tell the members of your group about your favorite way to work out. You may name more than one type of exercise if you wish. Write your choice or choices at the top of a sheet of paper. Then, as a group, discuss each of the exercises you have named. Try to think of appropriate ways to warm up for that type of exercise and to cool down afterward. Write down the group's ideas on your paper.

1. Did you think of at least one way to warm up and cool down for your favorite exercise?
2. Do you usually warm up and cool down when you do this activity? Why or why not?

Apply/Assess

Now that you know how to include warm-up and cool-down activities in a workout, use your knowledge to create your own workout plan. Use the chart below as a model. Fill in the activities you plan to do during each part of your workout. Include at least 10 minutes to warm up, 20 to 25 minutes to work out, and 10 minutes to cool down. If you include more than one type of activity in your workout, put aerobic activities before strength-building activities. Display your charts in the classroom.

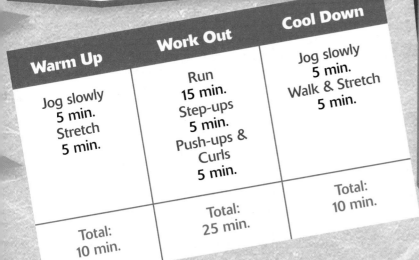

Warm Up	Work Out	Cool Down
Jog slowly 5 min. Stretch 5 min.	Run 15 min. Step-ups 5 min. Push-ups & Curls 5 min.	Jog slowly 5 min. Walk & Stretch 5 min.
Total: 10 min.	Total: 25 min.	Total: 10 min.

Practicing Healthful Behaviors

A healthy workout includes a warm-up and a cool-down period.
- A good warm-up should include about ten minutes of light exercise and gentle stretching.
- Ten minutes of moderate activity and gentle stretching is a good way to cool down.

Self-Check
- Did my fitness plan include a warm-up and a cool-down?
- Did my fitness plan put aerobic activities before any strength-building activities?
- Did I make a realistic plan for a busy teen?

2. Practice

- Divide students into groups of two or three, and have each group discuss their favorite ways to exercise and list them on a sheet of paper.
- Instruct each group to think of appropriate warm-ups and cool-downs for each exercise on their list.
- After each group has generated several warm-up and cool-down ideas, ask the groups to share their ideas with the class. Write them on the board.

3. Apply/Assess

- You may wish to distribute Building Health Skills Reproducible Master 34 in the TCR to guide students in completing this activity.
- Distribute markers and construction paper to each student.
- Direct students to create their own exercise plans, using the one depicted in the Apply/Assess section as a model.
- Ask volunteers to name the warm-ups and cool-downs that they chose for their workouts and discuss them as a class.
- Display completed charts in the classroom.
- Remind students to refer to the Self-Check before and after they create their workout plans.

Assessment Scoring

Using a rubric, student work should provide evidence of all criteria to achieve the highest score.

Skills

Student work demonstrates
- the steps of a workout plan.
- steps in the correct sequence.

- sufficient time for each part of the workout plan.

Concept

Student work provides
- accurate information about warming up and cooling down.

Checking Comprehension

Use the Chapter 9 Assessment to examine the most important ideas presented in the chapter.

Answers to Reviewing Vocabulary and Concepts

Lesson 1
1. balance
2. coordination
3. aerobic
4. anaerobic

Lesson 2
5. muscle strength
6. muscle endurance
7. skinfold test
8. flexible

Lesson 3
9. activity plan
10. stretching exercises
11. intensity
12. heartbeat rate

Lesson 4
13. d
14. c
15. d

Thinking Critically

16. When you are physically fit, you have more energy, better balance and coordination, and a more positive self-image.
17. Should make a plan; consider current level of fitness, kind of exercise/sports enjoyed, and overall health.
18. Responses will vary.
19. Possible responses: warming up and cooling down, wearing protective gear, following rules and procedures, drinking liquids, controlling emotions, dressing appropriately.

After You Read

Use your completed Foldable to review the information on physical activity, exercise, and physical fitness.

FOLDABLES
Study Organizer

Reviewing Vocabulary and Concepts

On a sheet of paper, write the numbers 1–12. After each number, write the term from the list that best completes each sentence.

- heartbeat rate
- anaerobic
- muscle strength
- skinfold test
- intensity
- muscle endurance
- balance
- stretching exercises
- aerobic
- flexible
- coordination
- activity plan

Lesson 1

1. _____ is the feeling of stability and control over your body.
2. _____ is the smooth and effective working together of your muscles and bones.
3. _____ exercise works the heart.
4. Gymnastics is an example of _____ exercise.

Lesson 2

5. _____ measures the most weight you can lift or the most force you can exert at one time.
6. The greater your _____, the longer your muscles can exert their strength.
7. The _____ involves pinching and measuring folds of skin on your arm and calf.
8. The more _____ you are, the easier it is to bend, turn, and stretch your body.

Lesson 3

9. A weekly _____ can help you schedule your activities.
10. Warm-ups should start with light activity, followed by _____.
11. When developing an exercise program, consider the frequency, _____, duration, and order of your workouts.
12. The most common way to measure exercise intensity is by checking your _____.

Lesson 4

On a sheet of paper, write the numbers 13–15. After each number, write the letter of the answer that best completes each statement.

13. The advantage of individual sports is that
    a. it is more flexible than a team sport.
    b. you can do them whenever you wish.
    c. you can do them for as long as you wish.
    d. all of the above.
14. Good nutrition for athletes includes
    a. eating only high-protein foods.
    b. drinking a limited amount of water in order to prevent nausea.
    c. eating enough carbohydrates to give the body extra energy.
    d. cutting back on some minerals, especially calcium.
15. Many sports injuries can be prevented by
    a. becoming very emotional during competition so you don't build up anger.
    b. skipping some team practices so you don't overexert yourself.
    c. borrowing someone's safety gear.
    d. wearing shoes that are suitable for the activity or sport.

Thinking Critically

Using complete sentences, answer the following questions on a sheet of paper.

16. **Interpret** Explain how being fit can improve the quality of your everyday life.

INCLUSION STRATEGIES

Special Learning Needs, Behavior Problems, English Language Learners The following suggestions are helpful for students with special learning needs, students with behavior problems, and ELL students:

• Pair these students with more proficient learners who can help summarize the main concepts of the chapter.

• ⌒ Direct these students to listen to the Teen Health Audio Summaries. This component provides an audio and written summary of the chapter in both English and Spanish.

• Use photographs, drawings, or magazine clippings whenever possible to help students visualize the important concepts of the chapter.

17. Apply If you decided to raise your level of physical fitness, how would you proceed? What factors would you consider?

18. Analyze Participation in individual sports requires self-discipline. Do you think someone who doesn't have self-discipline can develop it? Why or why not?

19. Explain What actions can you take before, during, and after a game to protect yourself against a sports injury?

20. Discuss Your friend eats two steak sandwiches every day, claiming that protein develops muscles. What would you tell him?

Career Corner

Athletic Trainer Athletes often consult athletic trainers for advice on fitness programs. These professionals help athletes maintain their physical fitness by supervising nutrition and exercise. They also treat sports injuries. Athletic trainers need at least one to two years of community college, vocational/technical school, or an apprenticeship. Find out more about this and other health careers by clicking on Career Corner at health.glencoe.com.

Standardized Test Practice

Reading & Writing

Read the paragraphs below and then answer the questions.

Baseball, football, basketball—these sports were all invented in the United States, right? Wrong. Of these three, only basketball was invented and first played in the United States.

In 1891 a physical education teacher in Springfield, Massachusetts was asked to create a sport for students to play indoors during the cold New England winters. Using a soccer ball and two peach baskets attached to the balcony railing of the gym, he invented basketball. He wrote 13 rules for the game, taught them to his class, and the first game of basketball took place later that year. The new game required teamwork, quick reaction time, and endurance. Basketball caught on and was soon being played by YMCA, high-school, college, and professional teams across the United States. Today, it is the most popular indoor sport, with millions of fans crowding gyms and arenas to cheer their favorite teams. Millions more watch on television.

1. The author begins the passage with a question and answer in order to

  A introduce the topic of basketball.

  B inform readers about the rules of basketball.

  C explain the difference between three sports.

  D encourage readers to think about sports.

2. Which of the following best describes the organization of the second paragraph?

  A presenting events in the order in which they occurred

  B comparing sports as they developed

  C explaining a problem and telling how to solve it

  D ranking events in order of importance

3. Write a paragraph explaining the rules for playing a particular sport.

 TH05_C3.glencoe.com/quiz

---

20. People who are trying to build muscle do not need more protein than anyone else.

Test Practice
1. A
2. A
3. Answers should include specific steps, rules, scoring, and appropriate behavior for a certain sport.

Reteaching
Assign Study Guide 9 in the Student Activities Workbook.

Evaluate
Use the reproducible Chapter 9 Test in the TCR, or construct your own test using the **Exam**View® Pro Testmaker.

Enrichment
Ask volunteers to visit bookstores or the school library to survey types of books available on physical fitness and sports. Have them write the title, author, subject area, date of publication, and author's credentials for each book. Ask the students to share what they learned in class.

Assessment

Self-Assessment Direct students to review the activities that are provided throughout the chapter. Encourage each student to select one finished product or activity that demonstrates his or her best work for the chapter. Have students explain what they learned and how the examples they selected show their progress.

Career Corner

Athletic Trainer The National Athletic Trainers Association certifies trainers who have college degrees and have completed educational programs and exams. Some states require that athletic trainers obtain certifications or licenses. Have students do research to determine whether their state requires athletic trainers to be certified or licensed. If so, what is the process?

Planning Guide

Chapter 10	Skills/ Activities	Reproducible Resources	Assessment
Lesson 1 **Maintaining a Healthy Body** *pages 250–255*	**Hands-On Health** ▲ Calculating Fat Intake, page 252	*Student Activities Workbook available for use with each chapter* 📁 Parent Letter & Activities 10 📁 Concept Map 36 📁 Cross-Curriculum Activity 19 📁 Decision-Making Activity 19 📁 Enrichment Activity 36 📁 Health Lab 10 📁 Lesson Plan 1 📁 Reading Tutor Activity 35 📁 Reteaching Activity 36	📁 Lesson 1 Quiz
Lesson 2 **Eating Disorders** *pages 256–259*	**HEALTH SKILLS ACTIVITY** ▲ Helping a Friend (*Decision Making*), page 258	📁 Concept Map 37 📁 Cross-Curriculum Activity 20 📁 Decision-Making Activity 20 📁 Enrichment Activity 37 📁 Lesson Plan 2 📁 Reading Tutor Activity 36 📁 Reteaching Activity 37	📁 Lesson 2 Quiz 📁 Chapter 10 Test 📁 Performance Assessment 10
TIME HEALTH	**Building a Better Body Image** *pages 260–261*		
BUILDING HEALTH SKILLS **Sharpen Your Body Image** (*Analyzing Influences*) *pages 262–263*		📁 Building Health Skills Reproducible Master 35	

Planning Guide

Standards		Technology
National	**State/Local**	
National Health Education Standard **1.1, 1.6, 1.8, 3.1, 3.4, 4.2**		Transparency 36 Tape/DVD 1, Segment 5, "Body Image and Media Influences" TeacherWorks™
National Health Education Standard **1.6, 1.8, 2.6, 5.4, 6.1, 6.2, 6.3**		Transparency 37 TeacherWorks™ MindJogger Videoquiz **Exam**_View_® Pro Testmaker
National Health Education Standard **4.1, 4.2, 4.4**		Building Health Skills Transparency Master 4

TeacherWorks™

Glencoe's new and exclusive TeacherWorks™ is an all-in-one planner and resource center. Access the complete Teacher Wraparound Edition electronically. Find all your classroom resources with just a few easy clicks, and print them right from your computer. Connect directly to Glencoe's customized Health Web site. Access the National Health Education Standards correlations, or insert your own state standards and match them directly to the electronic Teacher Wraparound Edition.

Language Diversity

- English Audio Summaries
- Spanish Audio Summaries
- English Summaries, Quizzes, and Activities
- Spanish Summaries, Quizzes, and Activities
- Spanish Parent Letters and Activities

KEY TO ABILITY LEVELS

Teaching Strategies that appear throughout the chapters have been identified by one of four codes to give you an idea of their suitability for students of varying learning styles and abilities.

L1 **Level 1** strategies should be within the ability range of all students. Often full class participation is required.

L2 **Level 2** strategies are for average to above-average students or for small groups. Some teacher direction is necessary.

L3 **Level 3** strategies are designed for students able and willing to work independently. Minimal teacher direction is necessary.

INCL Strategies are appropriate for students with particular special needs in a general classroom setting.

Your Body Image

Chapter at a Glance

Lesson 1 explains to students the concept of body image and how to determine their appropriate weight. It also discusses ways to reach or maintain a healthy weight.

Lesson 2 examines the dangers of anorexia nervosa, bulimia, and binge eating disorder and tells students where to turn for help with such eating disorders.

Health Skills

- Helping a Friend (*Decision Making*), p. 258
- Sharpen Your Body Image (*Analyzing Influences*), pp. 262–263

248

HANDS-ON ACTIVITY

Countering Media Stereotypes Mental health professionals argue that dieting and exercising by teen girls to achieve the perfect body are strongly correlated with reading fashion magazines. The media typically portray the standard for men in terms of power and independence and for women in terms of thinness, femininity, and beauty. In this activity, students identify messages that counter media stereotypes and promote or rein-force healthy lifestyles. Ask students to bring in magazines that they and adults in their family read. Have small groups identify advertisements or articles that portray males and females realistically (e.g., a woman who is fit participating in a healthful activity or a man who does not have bulging muscles). Groups should explain to the class why the people they chose represent healthy lifestyles and attitudes.

Your Body Image

HEALTH *Online*

Do you manage your weight in a healthy way? Find out by taking the Health Inventory for Chapter 10 at health.glencoe.com.

FOLDABLES™
Study Organizer

Before You Read

Make this Foldable to help you record what you learn about body weight in Lesson 1. Begin with a plain sheet of 8½" × 11" paper.

Step 1

Fold the sheet of paper in half along the long axis.

Step 2

Turn the paper and fold it into thirds.

Step 3

Unfold and cut the top layer along both fold lines. This makes three tabs.

Step 4

Turn the paper vertically and label the tabs as shown.

Overweight

Appropriate Weight

Underweight

As You Read

Under the appropriate tab of your Foldable, record definitions and take notes on each term relating to body weight.

Chapter Introduction

Use the options below to motivate students and preview chapter content.

HEALTH *Online*

Visit **health.glencoe.com** and have students complete Health Inventory 10 to rate their body images. For other teaching strategies, explore the Lesson Plans and select from Cross-Curriculum, Reading, or Media Literacy activities.

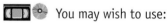

GLENCOE TECHNOLOGY

Teen Health Video and DVD Series
(Each format available in both English and Spanish)

You may wish to use:

- Tape/DVD 1, Segment 5, "Body Image and Media Influences"

MindJogger Videoquiz

Use MindJogger to preview or review Chapter 10 content.

TIME HEALTH

Building a Better Body Image
pages 260–261

FOLDABLES™
Study Organizer

Dinah Zike Study Fold

Formulating Questions Before beginning Lesson 1, have students think of one question about overweight, appropriate weight, and underweight and record the question under the appropriate tab of their Foldable. As students read and study the information in Lesson 1, direct them to use their Foldables to take notes, define terms, and answer the questions they asked prior to reading.

Lesson 1

Maintaining a Healthy Body

① Focus

Lesson Objectives

Students will be able to

- explain the relationships among weight, growth, and health.
- explain how eating and physical activity habits affect weight.
- describe ways to maintain a healthy weight.

Motivators

Quick Write

Encourage volunteers to share their responses. Ask: Why do you think such expectations are perpetuated?

Bellringer Activity

Have students identify familiar dieting tips from magazines and newspapers. Ask: Does any of the advice seem dangerous? Which of the plans seem most sensible?

VOCABULARY

Write the term *weight* on the board. Ask students to think of words they associate with weight. Draw a concept map of their responses on the board. Then display the vocabulary terms. Ask volunteers to read those words. Then ask the class to find relationships among the words on the map and the new words.

Lesson

① Maintaining a Healthy Body

Quick Write

How are teens' body images portrayed in magazines and other media? Are they realistic? Write down your opinions on this issue.

LEARN ABOUT...

- the relationship between weight, growth, and health.
- how eating and physical activity habits affect weight.
- ways to maintain your healthy weight.

VOCABULARY

- body image
- appropriate weight
- Body Mass Index (BMI)
- overweight
- underweight

Body Image

How do you feel about your appearance? *The way you see yourself* is called your **body image**. A person who feels good about the way she or he looks is more likely to have a positive self-image.

Trying to look the same as a model, an athlete, or anyone else is not a healthy approach to body image. It's important to recognize and accept that there are differences in body type—no individual weight or body type is ideal at any age. Your body will grow and change throughout your teen years. A few extra pounds now, for example, could disappear in a few months as you grow. Someone who feels too skinny may fill out after he or she stops growing taller.

Your Appropriate Weight

Many factors influence your **appropriate weight**, or *the weight that is best for your body*. These factors include your gender, height, age, and body frame (small, medium, or large), and, during your teen years, your growth pattern. At your appropriate weight, you are more likely to feel good about yourself and have the energy you need for peak performance.

Images in advertising, entertainment, and electronic media sometimes cause teens to develop a distorted body image. *Explain why this might be so.*

Lesson 1 Resources

Teacher Classroom Resources

 Parent Letter & Activities 10

Concept Map 36

Cross-Curriculum Activity 19

Decision-Making Activity 19

Enrichment Activity 36

Health Lab 10

Lesson Plan 1

 Lesson 1 Quiz

Reading Tutor Activity 35

Reteaching Activity 36

 Transparency 36

Student Activities Workbook

Chapter 10 Study Guide

Applying Health Skills 36

FIGURE 10.1

Body Mass Index

To find your place on the chart, first calculate your BMI by following the formula given below. Then trace an imaginary line straight up from your age to the BMI you calculated. The point where your age and BMI meet tells you the approximate weight range you fall into. However, since people grow at different rates, this is only an estimate.

To calculate your BMI:

❶ Multiply your weight in pounds by 0.45.

❷ Multiply your height in inches by 0.025. Square the result.

❸ Divide your answer to step 1 by your answer to step 2. The answer is your BMI.

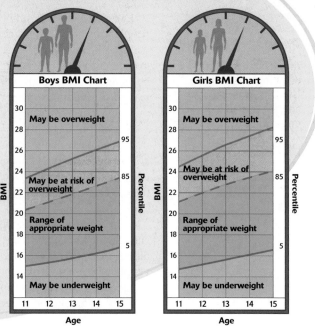

You can find out if your weight is appropriate by using the Body Mass Index chart in **Figure 10.1**. The Body Mass Index **(BMI)** is *a measurement that allows you to assess your body size, taking your height and weight into account.*

Weight Problems

Being overweight or underweight is unhealthy. People who are overweight are *more than the appropriate weight for gender, height, age, body frame, and growth pattern.* People who are underweight are *less than the appropriate weight for gender, height, age, body frame, and growth pattern.* Many teens are concerned that they have a weight problem. In reality, most teens don't need to lose or gain weight. In fact, unwise dieting can interfere with normal growth and development.

Overweight

Eating empty-calorie foods or eating more food than needed leads to weight gain. Busy teens on the run tend to grab food from fast-food places and convenience stores. Much of this food is high in fat and calories. Some food comes in supersize portions, which attract consumers with a bargain price. Weight gain is also linked to a sedentary, or inactive, lifestyle. Many people spend their days sitting at desks. At home they may watch television, play video games, or use a computer. These activities burn fewer calories than those involving movement.

WHAT TEENS WANT TO KNOW

Why is it so bad to want to look like the models in magazines? Most models in magazines are unusually tall and born with structural features that can't be obtained through diet and physical activity alone. Professional models often appear better looking in magazines than they do in person. Skillful makeup artists, flattering lighting, expert photography, and computer-based graphics programs are used to improve a model's natural good looks. Besides eliminating flaws, photo retouching may be used to improve a model's appearance. Some models are underweight and have eating disorders, which threatens their health.

Lesson 1

❷ Teach

Discussing

Ask students to identify some of the positive and negative ways our attitudes toward body weight are influenced by television, movies, and other media. (*Positive: greater acceptance of fitness and reducing excess body fat. Negative: overemphasis on being thin.*) **L1**

VISUAL LEARNING

FIGURE 10.1 Ask students to make up the height and weight of a hypothetical teen and write those figures on the board. Ask volunteers to read aloud the instructions for calculating BMI. Then have students work together to find the BMI and the healthy weight range for the hypothetical teen. **INCL** *English Language Learners, Special Learning Needs, Behavior Problems, Different Learning Styles* (*Visual*)

According to the National Health and Nutrition Examination Survey, more than half of all American adults are overweight.

Brainstorming

Ask students to brainstorm a list of active alternatives to such sedentary pastimes as watching TV and using a computer. Then challenge students to include an extra hour or two of these physical activities in their weekly schedules. **L1**

Lesson 1

Discussing

Have students discuss how a person can be both overweight and undernourished. (*A high proportion of caloric intake is from foods poor in nutrient value.*) **L1**

Applying Knowledge

Have students use what they already know about nutrition to suggest how an underweight teen might gain weight in a healthy way. Ask:

• What changes do you think an underweight teen should make in his or her eating habits? Why?

• What type and amount of physical activity would you recommend? Why? **L1**

Hands-On Health

CALCULATING FAT INTAKE

Time: 30 minutes, in two separate class sessions

TEACHING THE ACTIVITY

• With students, read and discuss the activity introduction and instructions.

• If food packages are available, let volunteers calculate several examples on the board.

• Have students complete the activity at home.

• Have students meet in groups to compare and discuss their results.

ASSESSMENT

Use students' In Conclusion paragraphs to assess their learning.

✓ Reading Check

Identify the effects of being overweight. Then list the causes and effects of being underweight.

Excess weight puts strain on the heart and lungs. Overweight people have an increased risk of developing high blood pressure, diabetes, heart disease, cancer, and stroke. If you think that you are overweight, check with your health care professional. You may just be gaining a few pounds before getting taller. This is the body's way of storing up extra energy for growing.

Underweight

If you appear skinny during your teenage growth years, you are not necessarily underweight. You may simply be growing taller first. After reaching a certain height, your body may take time to catch up and add shape and muscle.

Some people are underweight because they do not consume enough nutrients. Others are underweight because of extreme dieting or excessive exercise. Both reasons pose serious health risks. People who are underweight may not have enough body fat to cushion the body's organs and bones. They may often feel tired due to insufficient food energy, and they have little body fat as an energy reserve. Underweight people are also more likely to develop disorders related to a low food intake, such as anemia.

Hands-On Health

CALCULATING FAT INTAKE

The Dietary Guidelines recommend that you receive no more than 35 percent of your calories from fat. In this activity, you will learn how to calculate the percentage of calories from fat in a given food.

WHAT YOU WILL NEED
• pencil and notebook
• calculator (optional)
• 3 Nutrition Facts food labels

WHAT YOU WILL DO
1. Choose one of your food labels. Divide the amount in the "calories from fat" category by the amount in the "total calories" category. For example, a 200-calorie granola bar might contain 80 calories from fat. Divide 80 by 200 and you get 0.4.

2. Multiply the result by 100 to express the figure as a percentage. 0.4 times 100 is 40. The granola bar derives 40 percent of its calories from fat.

3. Repeat this procedure with your other food labels and record the results.

IN CONCLUSION
1. Which, if any, of the foods provides over 35 percent of its calories from fat?

2. Save labels from as many foods you eat in a day as possible. Use the formula to determine the percentage of calories from fat of each.

3. How can you use the formula to make healthy choices about your daily food intake?

✓ Reading Check

Cause-and-Effect Relationships Remind students that the information in many paragraphs, including the ones on page 252 of their textbooks, is organized into causes and effects. Note that some effects have many causes and some causes have many effects. Emphasize that either causes or effects may be described first. Ask students to identify the causes and effects that are described in the paragraphs on this page. Have students reread the first paragraph and identify the cause that is mentioned and the effect(s) this cause has. (*Cause: being overweight, might have several effects: high blood pressure, diabetes, heart disease, increased risk of cancer or stroke.*)

Most people with anorexia nervosa eat very little. Some develop **malnutrition**, *a condition in which the body doesn't get the nutrients it needs to grow and function properly.* They may also develop shrunken organs, bone loss, low body temperature, low blood pressure, and a slowed metabolism. In some people with anorexia, an irregular heartbeat may lead to cardiac arrest.

Treatment for anorexia nervosa sometimes requires a stay at a hospital or clinic. There the person will get the nutrients needed to restore physical health. She or he will also receive counseling to address the underlying problems causing the disorder.

Bulimia

Another type of eating disorder is bulimia, or bulimia nervosa. **Bulimia** is *a condition in which a person eats large amounts of food and then tries to purge.* Many people with bulimia force themselves to vomit. Others take laxatives to force the food quickly through their body. Although bulimia is most common among young women and teenage girls, young men and teenage boys can also develop the disorder.

People with bulimia are extremely concerned about being thin and attractive. They have an overwhelming need to maintain control over their bodies. They might gorge on large amounts of food. Then, fearing that they are losing control of their bodies, they may take drastic steps to regain control. Some go on crash diets, including fasting, to try to make up for overeating.

Bulimia damages the body in many ways. Stomach acids from frequent vomiting can damage teeth and injure the mouth and throat. Vomiting can also cause the stomach to rupture. Repeated use of laxatives can damage the kidneys and liver, causing long-term health problems. Many people with bulimia suffer from malnutrition as a result of emptying the body of nutrients.

People with bulimia often eat large amounts of food high in calories and fat. Then they try to purge. *How does this eating pattern damage the body?*

Lesson 2

② Teach

Applying Skills

Many people respond to stress or anxiety by not eating or by overeating. Such actions can ultimately result in long-term eating disorders. Explain to students that such actions do not eliminate stress. Explore with them ways of effectively reducing or eliminating stress—ways that they may already practice. (If needed, refer students to Chapter 2, pages 41–43, to review stress-management techniques.) **L1**

The National Institute of Mental Health estimates that 0.5 to 3.7 percent of American females suffer from anorexia nervosa at some point in their lifetimes. It also estimates that 1.1 to 4.2 percent of American females suffer at some point from bulimia.

Critical Thinking

Have students identify and then describe eating disorders such as bulimia, anorexia, and compulsive overeating. Help students discuss the diagnosis and treatment of eating disorders. Ask:

• What makes early diagnosis difficult?

• Why is early treatment so important? **L1**

MORE ABOUT...

Eating Disorders Eating disorders often appear during adolescence. More than 90 percent of affected teens are female, but more males are becoming affected. Anorexia nervosa is more common in young teens; bulimia is more common in older adolescents and young adults. Both eating disorders involve obsessions with food and weight, but neither is purely about eating and body weight.

Eating disorders are attempts to control and resolve emotional pressures and psychological conflicts. Since eating disorders have psychological and medical origins, they require integrated medical and psychotherapeutic treatment. Untreated, eating disorders may be life threatening. Prompt recognition, accurate diagnosis, and immediate treatment are very important.

Developing Good Character

Respect

Sometimes being a good friend means talking to parents, health professionals, or the school guidance counselor about a friend's behavior. Have students work in groups of four to generate ideas on situations that require talking to an adult. Have them identify criteria they can use to help them make decisions. (*The behavior is risky, dangerous, unethical, illegal, hurtful to self or others, and so on.*)

Cross-Curriculum Activity

LANGUAGE ARTS Have volunteers look up and read aloud the dictionary definitions of *binge* and *compulsive*. Ask: How do these definitions help you understand binge eating disorder? **L1**

HEALTH SKILLS ACTIVITY

DECISION MAKING

Have volunteers read aloud Jasmine's situation. Ask students to discuss the situation and the choice Jasmine has to make. Have students brainstorm options and record them on the board. Emphasize that anorexia is a dangerous disorder and should be taken very seriously.

Guide students in discussing the option they consider best and in evaluating the short- and long-term consequences of that decision.

Developing Good Character

Respect

It is important to value people for who they are on the inside, and to appreciate differences in body size and shape. If you are worried about the health of a friend, talk to a parent, a health professional, or a guidance counselor. However, be sure to do it with kindness and respect.

Binge Eating Disorder

Another eating disorder is **binge eating disorder**, or *compulsive overeating*. This disorder may be the most common eating disorder, affecting between 1 million and 2 million Americans. People with binge eating disorder eat unusually large amounts of food at a time. Unlike people with bulimia, though, they do not rid their bodies of the food. Afterward, they often feel a sense of guilt and shame.

People with binge eating disorder may use food as a way of coping with depression and other mental/emotional problems. However, the guilt and shame they feel after bingeing adds to the depression. This creates a cycle that can be difficult to break without professional help. Because binge eating disorder often leads to excess weight, it contributes to many health problems such as obesity, diabetes, and heart disease.

Help for People with Eating Disorders

People who have eating disorders usually need professional help. Sometimes this help can come from a counselor or psychologist. Help is also available through clinics and support groups such as Overeaters Anonymous, which are found in many communities. If a friend develops an eating disorder, you might want to speak to a school nurse or counselor. It is natural to want

HEALTH SKILLS ACTIVITY

DECISION MAKING

Helping a Friend

Recently, Jasmine has become concerned about her best friend Maria. At lunch, Maria barely touches her food. She doesn't have the energy for riding her bike anymore. She has become very thin. Yet when Jasmine and Maria went shopping recently, Maria complained about being fat, even though small-sized clothes were too big for her.

Jasmine is worried that Maria may have anorexia nervosa. Jasmine has tried to share her concerns with Maria, but Maria denies that she has a problem. Jasmine has thought about talking to Maria's mother, but she doesn't want to make Maria angry by going behind her back.

WHAT WOULD YOU DO?

Apply the decision-making process to Jasmine's situation. With a classmate, role-play a conversation in which Jasmine expresses her concerns to Maria. Then role-play a conversation between Jasmine and Maria's mother. What other options does Jasmine have?

1. **STATE THE SITUATION.**
2. **LIST THE OPTIONS.**
3. **WEIGH THE POSSIBLE OUTCOMES.**
4. **CONSIDER VALUES.**
5. **MAKE A DECISION AND ACT.**
6. **EVALUATE THE DECISION.**

Beyond the Classroom

Community People who have eating disorders often seek the support of self-help organizations. Overeaters Anonymous (OA) helps people who eat compulsively get control of their lives. The OA program relies on the same 12 steps of recovery followed by groups such as Alcoholics Anonymous. Like those programs, it respects confidentiality. More information regarding such organizations is available in the white pages of your local phone book. You may also contact the National Eating Disorders Association by calling (800) 931–2237.

to solve your friend's problem by yourself. However, you can help most by showing support and guiding him or her to a health professional.

Family and friends can also provide much-needed support for a person with an eating disorder. Often their role is to encourage the person to seek help. **Figure 10.3** takes a closer look at the role that family and friends can play.

FIGURE 10.3

HELPING SOMEONE WITH AN EATING DISORDER

Someone you know may have an eating disorder. Following these steps may enable you to help him or her.

A Encourage the person to seek help.
A person with an eating disorder may not be aware of the seriousness of the condition. The person may also deny that the problem exists and may not want to be helped.

B Tell an adult.
You can talk to your parent or guardian, the school nurse, a counselor, or another trusted adult to see if they can help the person.

C Get professional help.
Psychological problems are usually the cause of eating disorders. The person with the disorder requires professional help. Sometimes family members are also encouraged to meet with the counselor.

D Encourage the person to join a support group.
Support groups provide encouragement to people with eating disorders and help them on the road to recovery.

E Recommend a follow-up.
Eating disorders can recur and could become lifelong problems. Follow-up visits to counselors and support groups are an important part of the recovery process.

VISUAL LEARNING

FIGURE 10.3 Guide students in reading and discussing the steps for helping someone with an eating disorder. Ask:

• Why is a person with an eating disorder not likely to seek help?

• Do you think you could help an acquaintance, rather than a close friend, deal with an eating disorder? Why or why not? **INCL** *English Language Learners, Special Learning Needs, Behavior Problems, Different Learning Styles (Visual)*

③ Assess

Evaluating

📁 Assign the Lesson 2 Review; then assign the Lesson 2 Quiz in the TCR.

Reteaching

📁 Assign Concept Map 37 or Reteaching Activity 37 in the TCR.

Enrichment

📁 Assign Enrichment Activity 37 in the TCR.

④ Close

Review the factors that lead to eating disorders and ask students to identify places where people with those disorders can find help.

Lesson Review

Using complete sentences, answer the following questions on a sheet of paper.

Reviewing Terms and Facts

1. **Vocabulary** What is an *eating disorder?*
2. **List** Name four ways in which anorexia and bulimia can harm the body.
3. **Recall** Identify and describe the three types of eating disorders.
4. **Give Examples** What kinds of people can help a person with an eating disorder?

Thinking Critically

5. **Hypothesize** Why are many people with eating disorders unwilling to seek help?

Applying Health Skills

6. **Analyzing Influences** Find a magazine article or book about someone with bulimia or anorexia nervosa. Read the article or book and write a brief summary of it. What influences or pressures contributed to the disorder? Were the influences internal or external?

LESSON 2: EATING DISORDERS **259**

Lesson 2 Review

1. Extreme and damaging eating behavior that can lead to sickness and even death.
2. Any four of each. Anorexia: malnutrition, shrunken organs, bone loss, low body temperature, low blood pressure, slowed metabolism, cardiac arrest; bulimia: damaged teeth, mouth, throat, kidneys, liver; stomach rupture; malnutrition.
3. Responses should include the information given on pages 256–258.
4. A counselor or psychologist, clinics and support groups, family and friends.
5. They may not think they have an eating disorder, or they may be unwilling to discuss their problems.

Building a Better Body Image

1 Focus

Objectives

Students will be able to

- analyze influences on a young person's body image.
- turn negative body thoughts into positive ones.
- identify gender differences in body image.

Motivator

Bellringer Activity

Give students five minutes to draw and/or describe the "perfect" body. Tell them that their work will remain private. How old is this body? What size and shape is it? Is it thin, muscular, rounded, tall? Tell students to hold on to their work until later in the lesson.

2 Teach

Discussing

Tell students to look at the so-called "perfect" bodies that they have created. Ask, "Where did your assumptions about these bodies come from? What factors influence a young person's opinion about the ideal body?" List student answers on the board. (*Answers may include TV, magazines, movies, sports stars, family, peers, and so on.*) Stress that mass media is an extremely strong influence on how young people view their bodies. Ask students, "Do most teens look like movie stars? Do most teens have the time and resources to exercise like professional athletes? Are these 'ideal' images realistic for the average person? What affect might they have on a person's identity and self-esteem?"

BUILDING A BETTER BODY IMAGE

Making positive life changes can boost how people think about themselves. Here are a few ideas.

1. Remind yourself that you're a work in progress.

The more you know about puberty and how your body is growing (read books, pay attention in health class, ask your doctor questions), the more you'll understand that it's a time of tremendous change. For instance, even though it's normal to experience about a 25 to 30 percent weight gain during puberty, that doesn't mean you need to prepare for a lifetime of sudden weight gain. "The body you have at fourteen is not necessarily the body you will have at nineteen," says Dr. L. Kris Gowen, an adolescent–body-image expert at Stanford School of Education. "Your body is a long-term project," she adds. "Think of puberty as the first-draft phase of writing a term paper."

2. Be good to your body.

It works hard for you, so be sure to take time out to pamper your body. You don't have to do anything complicated. Sometimes the tiniest

---

DEALING WITH SENSITIVE ISSUES

Body Image Students spend a significant amount of time in the school setting. Teachers, coaches, and administrators can all guide students towards a healthy acceptance of their own bodies and those of others.

- Show diversity as an integral part of the everyday school experience. The classroom environment (posters, artwork), teaching materials (textbooks, videos), and lesson content (examples, case studies) should reflect a variety of ages, races, genders, body shapes and sizes.
- Enforce all standard class ground rules (no put-downs, no name-calling, and so forth.)
- Give students the right to pass during discussions that involve personal feelings or experiences.
- Focus on students' interests and abilities, not their appearance.

thing can make you feel better about yourself, such as using a new shampoo, going for a walk after school with a friend, or taking time out to relax. The most harmful thing you can do to your body is hate it, Dr. Gowen says.

3. Learn to love being healthy.

"People who are healthy feel good and look good," says Dr. Gowen. "Being beautiful isn't necessarily about being thin or buff." To get on the right track, try to eat sensibly, make physical activity a habit, and get plenty of sleep. Avoid any extreme behaviors (such as crash diets or working out to the point of injury), which are always unhealthy.

4. Compare yourself with...you.

Competing with the entire world is exhausting and destructive—though understandable. "Our culture encourages us not to be satisfied with what we have—especially girls, who are considered stuck up if they regard themselves as beautiful," says Dr. Gowen. "As a result, everyone is insecure—even the person you think you want to look like." Your goal should be like a runner who's trying to achieve a personal best instead of trying to beat the pack.

5. Practice zero tolerance toward teasing.

The amount of teasing that goes on in locker rooms and school hallways has reached destructive levels. Stick up for yourself and stick up for each other when you hear your friends or classmates making petty comments about the way someone looks.

6. Spend time on activities that have nothing to do with appearance. Do more of what you excel at and love.

You'll be reminded that there's more to you—and others—than mere looks. Sing, play guitar, hike, paint, design a Web site, or write a poem. Challenge yourself with new projects. Do them with other people if you can. Not only will you appreciate your own talents, regardless of your appearance, but you'll also begin to appreciate, value, and possibly learn from others.

Stay Positive!

If you're a teen and you've got a body, you might have very mixed feelings about it. Too often these feelings are negative, as you can see from the answers to the poll question below. After you check out the results (based on the responses of 4,000 young people), think about ways you might put a more positive spin on the way you think about your body.

Which of the following makes you unhappy with the way you look?

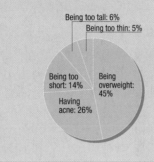

Being too tall: 6%
Being too thin: 5%
Being too short: 14%
Being overweight: 45%
Having acne: 26%

7. Recognize serious body-image problems.

Teens might try to cope with their body-image problems by engaging in harmful behaviors such as overexercising, binge eating, smoking, or drug and alcohol abuse. Destructive behaviors such as these require immediate professional help. If you're hurting, talk to an experienced professional about what you're going through and the way you're feeling. ▪

TIME TO THINK...

About Body Image

With the poll results above in mind, create a pamphlet entitled "Five Ways to Feel Better about Your Body." What are the top five tips you would offer your readers? What practical ways can you suggest to make it easy for the reader to use each tip in his or her life? Share the completed pamphlet with the rest of the class.

③ Apply

Time to Think

Ask students to review the section entitled "Stay Positive!" What do they think "a positive spin" means? How can they incorporate this idea into their pamphlets? Explain that when it comes to their changing bodies, students can learn to focus on positive traits such as comfort and ability rather than perceived negative traits. As an example, write the phrase, "My legs are too heavy," on the board. Ask students, "What might be a more positive thought about someone's legs?" Write their answers on the board. (*Answers may include: My legs are strong and powerful, My legs take me where I need to go, My legs can run, jump, bike, and swim, and so on.*) Practice this activity with several other gender-neutral body parts (eyes, hair, feet, and so forth.) Encourage students to use this strategy when they are tempted to judge their own body or those of others.

Have volunteers present their completed pamphlets to the rest of the class.

VISUAL LEARNING

Ask students to analyze the photograph on page 260. Ask, "Do you think male teens are as concerned about body image as female teens? Why or why not? Are the factors that influence male body image the same or different than for females?"

WHAT TEENS WANT TO KNOW

How can I respond to mean comments about the way someone looks? Try one of the following responses:
- Be direct. Say, "That's not a very nice thing to say. Don't you know comments like that can hurt someone's feelings?"
- Question the speaker's motivation. Say, "Hmm...why would you say something like that?" or "Why are you spending so much time worrying about what someone else looks like?"
- Turn the tables. Ask, "How would you feel if someone said that about you?"
- Make a positive observation about the person's interests or abilities, such as, "I hear she's a great basketball player."

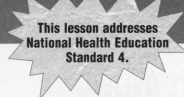
ANALYZING INFLUENCES

Objective

After completing the lesson, students will be able to analyze the influences that affect their body images.

Time: 45 minutes

Materials: none

Teacher Classroom Resources

📁 Building Health Skills Activities

• Transparency Master 4, "Analyzing Influences"

• Reproducible Master 35, "Sharpen Your Body Image"

---

1. Model

• Review influences that affect teens by displaying Transparency Master 4.

• Have students work with partners to identify the positive and negative influences on Blair and her peers. Write the influences on the board. Put a "+" by positive influences and a "−" by negative influences. (*Negative influences: wanting to look like the super-thin women they see in magazines, on TV, and in films; fad diets or pills. Positive influences (internal): she knows she's growing and changing and that these changes are normal, she is knowledgeable about health and knows her body weight is healthy.*)

BUILDING HEALTH SKILLS   **ANALYZING INFLUENCES**

SHARPEN YOUR BODY IMAGE

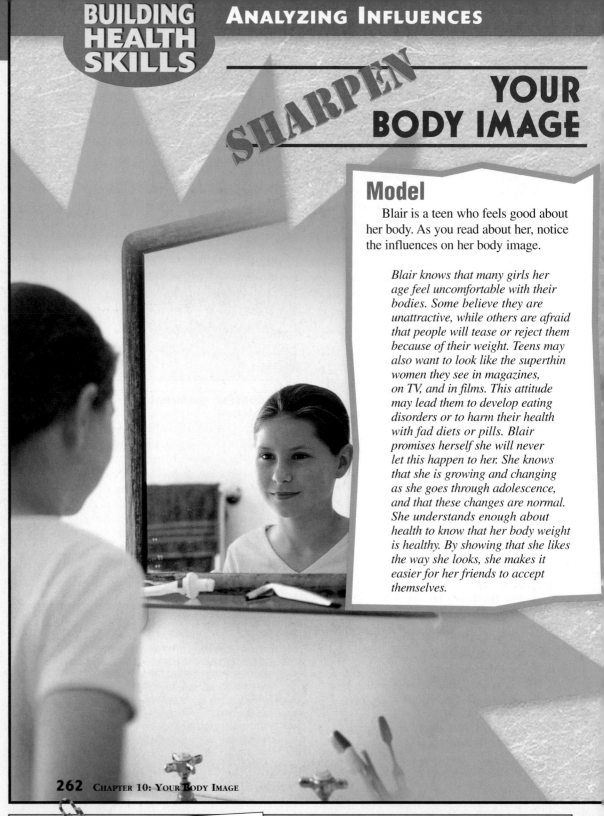

Model

Blair is a teen who feels good about her body. As you read about her, notice the influences on her body image.

Blair knows that many girls her age feel uncomfortable with their bodies. Some believe they are unattractive, while others are afraid that people will tease or reject them because of their weight. Teens may also want to look like the superthin women they see in magazines, on TV, and in films. This attitude may lead them to develop eating disorders or to harm their health with fad diets or pills. Blair promises herself she will never let this happen to her. She knows that she is growing and changing as she goes through adolescence, and that these changes are normal. She understands enough about health to know that her body weight is healthy. By showing that she likes the way she looks, she makes it easier for her friends to accept themselves.

262   CHAPTER 10: YOUR BODY IMAGE

Teaching Tips

Considering Influences Teens have an important influence on other teens. A comment or joke about another's appearance can be devastating. A compliment can brighten someone's day and improve a relationship. Compliments should be sincere and provided with "no strings attached." Compliments should be received with a simple "thank you." There is no need to "downplay" a compliment. Accept it in the spirit in which it is given.

Practice

Read the following scenario and answer the questions below.

Kirk is dissatisfied with his body. All his friends seem to be growing faster than he is, and he is now the shortest boy in his class. He also thinks his muscles are not big enough. Kirk wishes he could look like his older brother, who is on the high school football team and is very popular. Sometimes Kirk watches sports events on TV and imagines himself looking like the star athletes he sees.

1. What influences affect Kirk's body image?
2. What could help Kirk feel better about how he looks?

COACH'S BOX

Analyzing Influences

Influences on your body image may include

Internal
- knowledge.
- values.
- desires.
- fears.

External
- family and friends.
- media and culture.
- role models.

Apply/Assess

What influences your body image? Copy the list in the Coach's Box onto a separate sheet of paper. Then think of ways that each item influences your body image. For example, if one of your role models is someone with a healthy, but not "perfect," body, you could write this down under "role models." If you do not believe that a factor influences you in any way, write down "not an influence" under that factor.

When you are finished, look at each item on your list. If it describes something that makes you feel good about your body, write "+" next to the statement. If it describes something that makes you feel bad about your body, write "-." Identify the factor that has the most positive influence on your body image and the one that has the most negative influence. Then, at the bottom of your paper, write a statement about what you could do to improve your body image.

Self-√ Check

- Did I identify influences on my body image?
- Did I show the most positive and the most negative influences on my body image?
- Did I describe how to improve my body image?

BUILDING HEALTH SKILLS: SHARPEN YOUR BODY IMAGE **263**

2. Practice

- Instruct students to read about Kirk and answer the questions that follow.
- Ask small groups of students to work together to compare their answers. Answer questions and solicit comments as a full-class activity.

3. Apply/Assess

- 📁 You may wish to distribute Building Health Skills Reproducible Master 35 in the TCR to guide students in completing this activity.
- Conduct a class discussion on ways teens can improve their body images.
- Remind students to refer to the Self-Check before and after they create their lists of positive and negative influences on their body images.

Assessment Scoring

Using a rubric, student work should provide evidence of all criteria to achieve the highest score.

Skills

Student work analyzes

- internal and external influences that affect body image.
- positive and negative influences on body image.

- influences that have the most effect.

Concepts

Student work provides

- accurate information about body image.
- conclusions about ways to improve body image.

263

Checking Comprehension

Use the Chapter 10 Assessment to examine the most important ideas presented in the chapter. Encourage students to ask questions and add details as appropriate.

Answers to Reviewing Vocabulary and Concepts

Lesson 1

1. body image
2. appropriate weight
3. Body Mass Index
4. overweight
5. underweight
6. calories
7. nutrient density
8. supersize
9. Food Guide Pyramid

Lesson 2

10. c
11. b
12. b
13. c
14. d

Thinking Critically

15. It is important to obtain calories from foods that offer a large amount of nutrients.
16. Responses will vary.
17. Physical activity helps people who want to gain weight, add muscle, lose weight, and burn calories.
18. Possible response: He or she may feel pressure to remain thin in order to compete.

After You Read

Use your completed Foldable to review the information on body weight.

FOLDABLES™ Study Organizer

Reviewing Vocabulary and Concepts

On a sheet of paper, write the numbers 1–9. After each number, write the term from the list that best completes each sentence.

- appropriate weight
- nutrient density
- body mass index
- body image
- calories
- **Food Guide Pyramid**
- supersize
- overweight
- underweight

Lesson 1

1. When you have a positive _____, you feel good about the way you look.
2. Your _____ is influenced by your gender, height, age, body frame, and growth pattern.
3. You can use the _____ chart to determine if you are at an appropriate weight.
4. _____ is a condition in which people weigh more than their appropriate weight.
5. Someone who is _____ is less than the appropriate weight for his or her gender, height, age, body frame, and growth pattern.
6. When you take in the same number of _____ that your body burns, your weight remains the same.
7. A healthful eating plan is based on foods with high _____.

8. Foods with _____ portions may contribute to weight problems.
9. Using the _____ will help you develop healthful eating habits.

Lesson 2

On a sheet of paper, write the numbers 10–14. After each number, write the letter of the answer that best completes each statement.

10. Anorexia nervosa is an eating disorder characterized by
    a. overeating.
    b. binge eating.
    c. self-starvation.
    d. laxative abuse.
11. Which of the following best describes the disorder of a person who eats huge amounts of food but does not purge?
    a. anorexia nervosa
    b. binge eating disorder
    c. bulimia
    d. malnutrition
12. A condition in which the body does not get the nutrients it needs to grow and function properly is called
    a. overnourishment.
    b. malnutrition.
    c. obesity.
    d. low blood pressure.
13. Which of the following usually involves vomiting and abuse of laxatives?
    a. anorexia nervosa
    b. binge eating disorder
    c. bulimia
    d. obesity
14. You can help a person with an eating disorder by
    a. encouraging the person to seek help.
    b. telling a trusted adult that you believe the person needs help.
    c. encouraging the friend to join a support group.
    d. all of the above.

264 CHAPTER 10: YOUR BODY IMAGE

INCLUSION STRATEGIES

Special Learning Needs, Behavior Problems, English Language Learners The following suggestions are helpful for students with special learning needs, students with behavior problems, and ELL students:

- Pair these students with more proficient learners who can help summarize the main concepts of the chapter.

- Direct these students to listen to the Teen Health Audio Summaries. This component provides an audio and written summary of the chapter in both English and Spanish.

- Use photographs, drawings, or magazine clippings whenever possible to help students visualize the important concepts of the chapter.

Thinking Critically

Using complete sentences, answer the following questions on a sheet of paper.

15. Evaluate Why should people who want to manage their weight be aware of the nutrient value of foods?

16. Hypothesize Why do you think magazines feature very thin models even though extreme thinness is unhealthy?

17. Explain Why is physical activity an important part of weight management?

18. Suggest Why might an athlete such as a gymnast develop an eating disorder?

Career Corner

Psychologist Are you fascinated by how the mind works? Do you wonder why people behave the way they do? Then consider a career as a psychologist. Psychologists study human behavior. In practice, they help people understand and improve their behaviors. A doctoral degree in psychology is required to enter this profession. Find out more about this and other health careers by visiting the Career Corner at health.glencoe.com.

Standardized Test Practice

Reading & Writing

Read the paragraphs below and then answer the questions.

I urge you to support the school uniform proposal. I believe that it will benefit everyone at school if uniforms are worn here. Wearing uniforms will save money, improve students' grades and behavior, and reduce competition among students.

Uniforms will save money since they are less expensive than regular clothing. Students who are not distracted by what they or others are wearing can focus more on their schoolwork and behavior. Fewer behavior problems will make learning easier for students; better grades will improve the school's reputation. Uniforms will also reduce the stress of competition among students. If everyone wears a uniform, students will not feel that they have to have certain clothes or wear something different each day.

1. Which sentence expresses an opinion?
- **A** I believe that it will benefit everyone at school if uniforms are worn here.
- **B** I urge you to support the school uniform proposal.
- **C** Uniforms will also reduce the stress of competition among students.
- **D** Fewer behavior problems will make learning easier for students.

2. Which sentence in the speech best summarizes the speaker's argument?
- **A** I believe that it will benefit everyone at school if uniforms are worn here.
- **B** I urge you to support the school uniform proposal.
- **C** Fewer behavior problems will make learning easier for students.
- **D** Wearing uniforms will save money, improve students' grades and behavior, and reduce competition among students.

3. Write a paragraph that features your views on the issue of school uniforms and give reasons for your opinion.

Test Practice
1. A
2. D
3. Answers should include an opinion on either side of the issue and specific reasons that support that opinion.

Reteaching
📁 Assign Study Guide 10 in the Student Activities Workbook.

Evaluate
- 📁 💿 Use the reproducible Chapter 10 Test in the TCR, or construct your own test using the **Exam**View® Pro Testmaker.
- 📁 Use Performance Assessment 10 in the TCR.

Enrichment
Have students work in groups to plan and make banners, posters, or other kinds of ads to promote healthy body image.

Assessment ✓

Self-Assessment Direct students to review the activities that are provided throughout the chapter. Encourage each student to select one finished product or activity that demonstrates her or his best work for the chapter. Have students explain what they learned and how the examples they selected show their progress.

Career Corner

Psychologist After reviewing the career profile on the health Web site, students might:
- Describe the skills, training, and education needed.
- Write short paragraphs describing a day in the life of a psychologist.

Making Safe and Drug-Free Decisions

Unit Objectives

In this unit, students explore the dangers of using drugs, tobacco, and alcohol as well as reasons and strategies to refuse these substances if they are offered. The chapters repeatedly emphasize the value of using refusal skills and the decision-making process when a teen is confronted with these substances.

Unit Overview

Chapter 11
Medicines and Drugs

Lesson
1 Using Medicines Wisely
2 Narcotics, Stimulants, and Depressants
3 Marijuana and Other Illegal Drugs
4 Staying Drug Free

Chapter 12
Tobacco

Lesson
1 How Tobacco Affects the Body
2 Tobacco and Society
3 Choosing To Be Tobacco Free

Chapter 13
Alcohol

Lesson
1 What Alcohol Does to the Body
2 Alcohol and Society
3 Choosing To Be Alcohol Free

266

DEALING WITH SENSITIVE ISSUES

Sharing Knowledge Sharing knowledge with students about sensitive issues will give them the information they need to make informed decisions and to solve problems wisely. Unless students know that using tobacco, alcohol, or other drugs can harm not only their physical health but also their mental/emotional and social health as well, they may not have the knowledge they need to make informed decisions about refusing these substances. Sharing accurate information about sensitive issues will also help make students aware that many other youths face similar challenges and have similar concerns. As a result, students will feel less isolated and less different from their peers.

Making Safe and Drug-Free Decisions

Unit Introduction

Divide the class into three groups, and assign one of the following substances to each group: drugs, tobacco, alcohol. If your class is large, you might divide them into six groups and assign one substance to two different groups.

In a timed period of five to ten minutes, ask students to brainstorm as many reasons as possible for avoiding their assigned substance. Ask for a student from each group to share the group's findings with the class. Discuss the similarities and differences among the responses.

Tell students that the chapters in Unit 4 will help them understand why a wise, healthy teen is one who chooses to be substance free.

HEALTH in Action

Whether you're planning a pick-up football game or planning your future, avoiding tobacco, alcohol, and other drugs will ensure that you'll be able to follow through on those

How does staying drug free help you plan?

plans. By following your doctor's orders with regard to prescriptions and being careful with over-the-counter medications, you can maintain the physical, mental/emotional, and social health you need to set and meet your goals.

267

HEALTH in Action

Read the class the question on page 267 and discuss the dangers of substance use. Then lead the class in the following physical group activity:

Divide the class in two; assign one half to be the "cause" side, and the other the "effect" side. Ask the "cause" students to think of a behavior that could affect health, either positively or negatively. Have them write that behavior on a piece of paper. Then, ask the "effect" students to think of a possible outcome of such behaviors and to write that outcome down on a piece of paper. Then have all the students stand and locate their "partner"—each cause matched to a likely effect. Ask paired or grouped students to share their causes and effects with the rest of the class.

Planning Guide

Chapter 11	Skills/ Activities	Reproducible Resources	Assessment
Lesson 1 **Using Medicines Wisely** *pages 270–275*	HEALTH SKILLS ACTIVITY ▲ Medicine Safety in the Home (*Practicing Healthful Behaviors*), page 274	*Student Activities Workbook available for use with each chapter* 📁 Parent Letter & Activities 11 📁 Concept Map 38 📁 Enrichment Activity 38 📁 Health Lab 11 📁 Lesson Plan 1 📁 Reading Tutor Activity 37 📁 Reteaching Activity 38	📁 Lesson 1 Quiz
Lesson 2 **Narcotics, Stimulants, and Depressants** *pages 276–280*		📁 Concept Map 39 📁 Decision-Making Activity 21 📁 Enrichment Activity 39 📁 Lesson Plan 2 📁 Reading Tutor Activity 38 📁 Reteaching Activity 39	📁 Lesson 2 Quiz
Lesson 3 **Marijuana and Other Illegal Drugs** *pages 281–285*	HEALTH SKILLS ACTIVITY ▲ Refusing Drugs (*Refusal Skills*), page 284	📁 Concept Map 40 📁 Cross-Curriculum Activity 21 📁 Decision-Making Activity 22 📁 Enrichment Activity 40 📁 Lesson Plan 3 📁 Reading Tutor Activity 39 📁 Reteaching Activity 40	📁 Lesson 3 Quiz
Lesson 4 **Staying Drug Free** *pages 286–289*	**Hands-On Health** ▲ Drug-Free Campaign, page 288	📁 Concept Map 41 📁 Cross-Curriculum Activity 22 📁 Enrichment Activity 41 📁 Lesson Plan 4 📁 Reading Tutor Activity 40 📁 Reteaching Activity 41	📁 Lesson 4 Quiz 📁 Chapter 11 Test 📁 Performance Assessment 11

TIME HEALTH **Marijuana Myths** *pages 290–291*

BUILDING HEALTH SKILLS

Saying No to Drugs
(*Advocacy*)
pages 292–293

📁 Building Health Skills Reproducible Master 36

Standards		Technology
National	**State/Local**	
National Health Education Standard **1.3, 2.2, 2.6, 3.1, 3.4**		Transparency 38 TeacherWorks™ Internet Activities
National Health Education Standard **1.3, 1.6, 1.8, 2.2, 2.6, 3.1, 7.4, 7.5**		Transparency 39 TeacherWorks™
National Health Education Standard **1.3, 1.6, 1.8, 3.1, 5.6**		Transparency 40 TeacherWorks™
National Health Education Standard **1.1, 1.2, 1.6, 1.8, 2.6, 3.1, 3.4, 7.1**		Transparency 41 Tape/DVD 2, Segment 1, "Teen Advocacy"; Segment 2, "Refusal Skills" TeacherWorks™ MindJogger Videoquiz **Exam**_View_® Pro Testmaker
National Health Education Standard **1.8, 7.4, 7.5**		Building Health Skills Transparency Master 10

Teacher Works™

Glencoe's new and exclusive TeacherWorks™ is an all-in-one planner and resource center. Access the complete Teacher Wraparound Edition electronically. Find all your classroom resources with just a few easy clicks, and print them right from your computer. Connect directly to Glencoe's customized Health Web site. Access the National Health Education Standards correlations, or insert your own state standards and match them directly to the electronic Teacher Wraparound Edition.

Language Diversity

- English Audio Summaries
- Spanish Audio Summaries
- English Summaries, Quizzes, and Activities
- Spanish Summaries, Quizzes, and Activities
- Spanish Parent Letters and Activities

KEY TO ABILITY LEVELS

Teaching Strategies that appear throughout the chapters have been identified by one of four codes to give you an idea of their suitability for students of varying learning styles and abilities.

L1 **Level 1** strategies should be within the ability range of all students. Often full class participation is required.

L2 **Level 2** strategies are for average to above-average students or for small groups. Some teacher direction is necessary.

L3 **Level 3** strategies are designed for students able and willing to work independently. Minimal teacher direction is necessary.

INCL Strategies are appropriate for students with particular special needs in a general classroom setting.

Medicines and Drugs

Chapter at a Glance

Lesson 1 draws a distinction between medicines and other drugs and describes the role of the FDA in ensuring medicines' safety. It also describes types of medicines and how medicines affect the body.

Lesson 2 distinguishes between drug misuse and drug abuse and highlights the use and dangers of narcotics, stimulants, and depressants.

Lesson 3 focuses on marijuana and other illegal drugs and highlights the dangers of using hallucinogens, inhalants, and club drugs.

Lesson 4 provides ways and reasons to avoid drugs and lists alternatives to drug use and resources to help drug abusers.

Health Skills

- Medicine Safety in the Home (*Practicing Healthful Behaviors*), p. 274

- Refusing Drugs (*Refusal Skills*), p. 284

- Saying No to Drugs (*Advocacy*), pp. 292–293

268

HANDS-ON ACTIVITY

Packaging of Medicines Let groups of students work together to examine different kinds of over-the-counter medicine packaging. Have group members bring to class (or provide for them) a variety of empty over-the-counter medicine packages. As group members examine each type, let them decide the purpose of the type of packaging: Whom is it intended to protect? How well does it succeed? What problems might be associated with the packaging? Then ask group members to design a new kind of packaging that will provide safety and convenience. Let group members draw and label their packaging design, or have them write a description of it. Assign one student in each group to present the design.

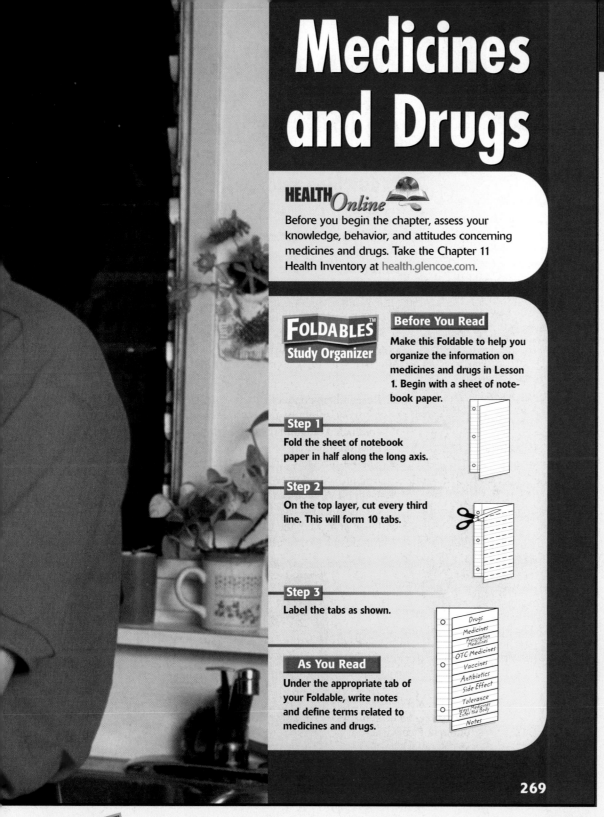

Medicines and Drugs

HEALTH *Online*

Before you begin the chapter, assess your knowledge, behavior, and attitudes concerning medicines and drugs. Take the Chapter 11 Health Inventory at health.glencoe.com.

FOLDABLES™ Study Organizer

Before You Read

Make this Foldable to help you organize the information on medicines and drugs in Lesson 1. Begin with a sheet of notebook paper.

Step 1

Fold the sheet of notebook paper in half along the long axis.

Step 2

On the top layer, cut every third line. This will form 10 tabs.

Step 3

Label the tabs as shown.

Drugs
Medicines
Prescription Medicines
OTC Medicines
Vaccines
Antibiotics
Side Effect
Tolerance
Ways Medicines Enter the Body
Notes

As You Read

Under the appropriate tab of your Foldable, write notes and define terms related to medicines and drugs.

269

Chapter Introduction

Use the options below to motivate students and preview chapter content.

HEALTH *Online*

Encourage students to take Health Inventory 11 at health.glencoe.com. Then brush up on health education by reading Professional Articles for health teachers. These articles can help keep you informed of national and state trends.

GLENCOE TECHNOLOGY

Teen Health Video and DVD Series
(Each format available in both English and Spanish)

▭▭ ⊙ You may wish to use:

- Tape/DVD 2, Segment 1, "Teen Advocacy"; Segment 2, "Refusal Skills"

MindJogger Videoquiz

▭▭ ⊙ Use MindJogger to preview or review Chapter 11 content.

TIME HEALTH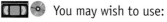

Marijuana Myths
pages 290–291

FOLDABLES™ Study Organizer Dinah Zike Study Fold

Defining Terms and Descriptive Writing Students will use their Foldable to describe the terms and concepts presented in this lesson. As students read and study the information on using medicines wisely in Lesson 1, have them define terms, take notes, and list examples under the appropriate tab of their Foldable. Foldable vocabulary books make great study guides because students can review important terms, recall what they know, and check their responses by looking under the tabs.

Lesson 1

Using Medicines wisely

① Focus

Lesson Objectives

Students will be able to

- discuss how medicines differ from drugs.
- identify the various types of medicines.
- explain how medicines affect the body.

Health Skills

- Practicing Healthful Behaviors, p. 274

Motivators

Quick Write

Make two columns on the board labeled *Helpful* and *Harmful*. List students' responses in the appropriate column.

Bellringer Activity

Ask students whether they have ever received a medicine by injection. Ask whether they have ever taken a medicine by mouth. Ask: Why are some medicines given by injection and some by mouth?

VOCABULARY

Copy each of the vocabulary terms on an index card. Write each term's definition on nine more cards. Mix up the cards, and give one to each of 18 students. At your signal they should try to find a match for their terms or definitions. After they have finished, each pair of students should read the term and its matching definition.

270

Lesson 1

Using Medicines Wisely

Quick Write

List three medicines you have used, and briefly describe the intended use of each. How might the medicines cause harm?

LEARN ABOUT...

- how medicines differ from drugs.
- types of medicines.
- how medicines are used.
- how medicines affect the body.

VOCABULARY

- drugs
- medicines
- prescription medicines
- over-the-counter (OTC) medicines
- vaccine
- antibiotics
- side effect
- tolerance

Medicines and Drugs

What do you think of when you hear the words *medicines* and *drugs?* Many people use the terms interchangeably. However, there is a difference. **Drugs** are *substances other than food that change the structure or function of the body or mind.* **Medicines** are *drugs that are used to treat or prevent diseases and other conditions.* All medicines are drugs, but not all drugs are medicines.

Medicine Safety

In the United States, the Food and Drug Administration (FDA) is responsible for ensuring that all medicines are safe and effective. The FDA approval process includes the following steps.

1. A potential new medicine is discovered.
2. Researchers conduct experiments to help decide how the new medicine might be used to treat an illness. Early testing is conducted on animals to determine if the medicine has any harmful effects.
3. The FDA reviews the preliminary research and test results. If approved, the new medicine is studied in humans.
4. If the FDA decides that the medicine is safe and effective for its intended use, the FDA approves it.
5. Once approved, the medicine can be made available for physicians to prescribe or for consumers to purchase.

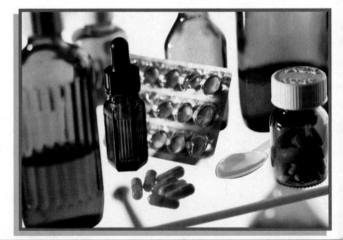

Medicines come in many different forms. *What medicine did you take the last time you had a cold?*

270 CHAPTER 11: MEDICINES AND DRUGS

 **Lesson 1 Resources**

Teacher Classroom Resources

- Parent Letter & Activities 11
- Concept Map 38
- Enrichment Activity 38
- Health Lab 11
- Lesson Plan 1
- Lesson 1 Quiz

- Reading Tutor Activity 37
- Reteaching Activity 38
- Transparency 38

Student Activities Workbook

- Chapter 11 Study Guide
- Applying Health Skills 38

FIGURE 11.1

PRESCRIPTION MEDICINE LABEL

Medicine labels provide important information. *How many times can this prescription be refilled?*

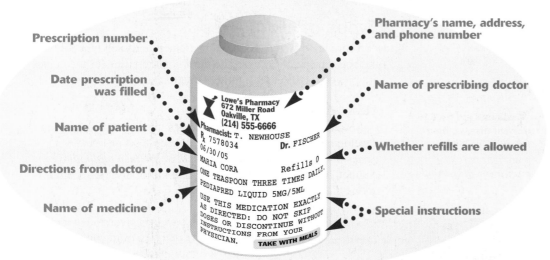

Prescription number

Date prescription was filled

Name of patient

Directions from doctor

Name of medicine

Pharmacy's name, address, and phone number

Name of prescribing doctor

Whether refills are allowed

Special instructions

Lowe's Pharmacy
672 Miller Road
Oakville, TX
(214) 555-6666
Pharmacist: T. NEWHOUSE
R 7578034
06/30/05   Dr. FISCHER
MARIA CORA   Refills 0
ONE TEASPOON THREE TIMES DAILY.
PEDIAPRED LIQUID 5MG/5ML
USE THIS MEDICATION EXACTLY
AS DIRECTED: DO NOT SKIP
DOSES OR DISCONTINUE WITHOUT
INSTRUCTIONS FROM YOUR
PHYSICIAN.   TAKE WITH MEALS

Prescription Medicines

Some medicines are very strong and potentially harmful, so doctors must write special orders for them. These **prescription medicines** are *medicines that can be sold only with a written order from a physician.* **Figure 11.1** shows the information that must appear on all prescription medicine labels. Before you take a prescription medicine, read the label carefully and make sure that you are interpreting the instructions correctly.

Over-the-Counter (OTC) Medicines

Have you ever used cough syrup or nasal spray when you had a cold? These **over-the-counter (OTC) medicines** are *medicines that are safe enough to be taken without a written order from a physician.* OTC medicines may cause harm if not used as directed.

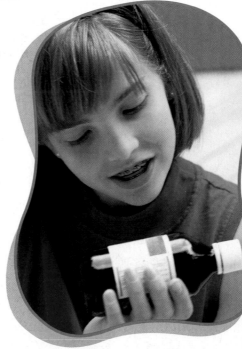

Potential side effects are listed on medicine container labels. *Why should you read the label carefully before taking any medication?*

LESSON 1: USING MEDICINES WISELY **271**

Lesson 1

② Teach

Critical Thinking

Discuss the reasons for the length of time it takes for the Food and Drug Administration to approve a new drug. Ask students:

- Do you think all the steps of the approval process are necessary?
- Would you feel differently if someone you know was dying from a disease and a new drug promised possible help? **L1**

VISUAL LEARNING

FIGURE 11.1 Have students locate information provided on the prescription medicine, including that there are no refills. Then ask: Why do you think it is important for a prescription label to give information about the pharmacy? (*So that a patient can call with questions about usage or reactions.*) **INCL** *English Language Learners, Special Learning Needs, Behavior Problems, Different Learning Style* (*Visual*)

Critical Thinking

Explain that labels on OTC medicines give information about ingredients, amount of active ingredient, name and address of the manufacturer, and the control number. Ask:

Why is such information important? (*It allows the consumer and/or retailer to check against known allergies, to contact the manufacturer if a problem arises, and to trace drugs that might have been tampered with or recalled.*) **L2**

Health Literacy

Health Information Clinical drug trials on humans, the third step in the FDA testing process, are designed to distinguish the actual effects of the drug from the possible psychological effects. Two groups are used for the test; one group is given the experimental drug while the other group, called the control group, is given a *placebo* (a substance containing no active ingredients). In blind studies, only the researchers know which group is the control group. In double-blind studies, neither the subjects nor the researchers know which group is the control group. An independent third person monitors and records the results.

Discussing

Discuss ways in which medicines that fight diseases have helped society. Talk about the need for such medications and for vaccines in developing nations today. Then ask: What changes result from the introduction of medications and vaccines into a country? (*Fewer people die, healthier people can work to produce more food and goods, and so on.*) **L1**

Comprehending

Guide students in understanding the role of antibiotics in fighting bacteria. Ask: Why is penicillin, an antibiotic, not effective when the body is fighting a cold or flu? (*Both are caused by viral infections, and antibiotics cannot fight viruses.*) **L1**

Analyzing

Have each student write about one instance when he or she took aspirin or an aspirin substitute such as acetaminophen. Then ask students to discuss in writing any other ways they might have tried to deal with the problem or the pain without using medicine (*going for a walk when you have a slight headache, soaking in a hot bath when you have stiff muscle.*) Discuss the concept of aspirin as a quick cure. **L2**

OTC medicines are available at pharmacies, supermarkets, and other stores that sell medicine. Always check with an adult before using any OTC or other medicine. Be sure to read and interpret correctly the information provided on an OTC medicine container label.

Types of Medicines

There are different types of medicines, and each type affects the body in specific ways. The most common uses for medicines are preventing disease, fighting infection, and relieving pain.

Medicines are used to prevent disease, fight infection, and relieve pain. *Why are some medicines available only by prescription?*

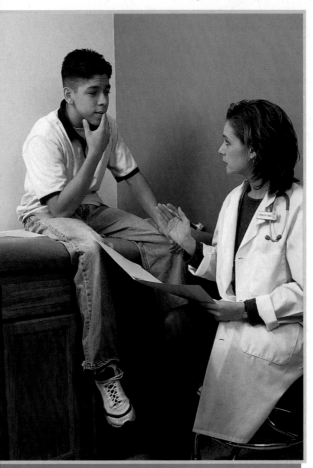

Medicines to Prevent Diseases

Some medicines, known as vaccines, prevent a disease from developing. A **vaccine** is *a preparation of dead or weakened germs that causes the immune system to produce antibodies.* Antibodies are proteins that attack and kill or disable specific germs that cause disease.

Common vaccines given today include those that protect you from communicable diseases (those that can spread), such as diphtheria, whooping cough, measles, mumps, rubella, chicken pox, pneumonia, and hepatitis A and B. These vaccines provide long-lasting protection. Others, such as the flu vaccine, must be administered periodically.

Medicines to Fight Infection

Many communicable diseases cannot be prevented with vaccines. Instead, certain medicines are used to restore health. **Antibiotics** (an·ti·by·AH·tiks) are *medicines that reduce or kill harmful bacteria in the body.* Each type of antibiotic fights only certain types of bacteria. For example, penicillin (pen·uh·SI·luhn) is highly effective in killing the bacteria that cause strep throat and pneumonia.

Medicines to Relieve Pain

Many people take medicines to relieve pain. When the body feels pain, such as that from a headache or toothache, pain messages travel along the nerves and spinal cord to the brain. Pain medicines block these pain messages or lessen their effect.

272 CHAPTER 11: MEDICINES AND DRUGS

MORE ABOUT...

The Food and Drug Administration (FDA) As a division of the United States Department of Health and Human Services, the FDA is charged with ensuring the purity and safety of foods, drugs, and cosmetics. It is also responsible for regulating levels of radiation emission of electronic products and the sanitary standards of restaurants. The federal government maintains regional FDA offices in each federal district. The telephone directory in your area will provide the number for the nearest FDA office. Have a volunteer call the office to determine what services the regional offices provide to the public.

Aspirin is one of the most commonly used medicines for treating minor pain. Aspirin substitutes such as acetaminophen and ibuprofen are also popular. These pain medicines are widely available and do not require a doctor's prescription. Occasionally a serious illness or a chronic disease will cause serious pain. In this case a doctor may prescribe stronger medicines such as codeine or morphine.

Other Medicines

A variety of medicines is available to treat people with certain health problems or conditions. Specific medicines are used by people with chronic conditions including heart and blood pressure problems, diabetes, and allergies.

Medicine in the Body

The effects of a medicine in the body depend on the type and amount of medicine taken. The way a medicine is taken will also affect how quickly it begins to work in the body. **Figure 11.2** illustrates the four main ways in which medicines can enter the body.

Medicines will affect each person differently. That is why it is important for medicine to be used only as prescribed or directed, and only by the person who needs the medicine.

Reading Check

Investigate word parts. Analyze the words *injection* and *ingestion*. What does the prefix *in-* mean? What is the root of each word? What do the roots mean?

FIGURE 11.2

HOW MEDICINES ENTER THE BODY

The way medicines enter the body depends on their form.

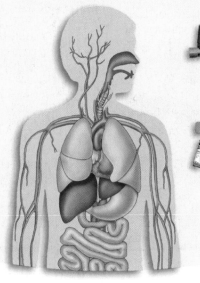

Ingestion
Medicine in the form of pills, tablets, capsules, and liquids is ingested, or swallowed. The medicine moves through the stomach and small intestine and is absorbed into the bloodstream and circulated throughout the body. You can take cold medicines this way.

Injection
Medicine given through injection goes directly into the blood. Some injections are given in a vein, others under the skin or into a muscle. If you have diabetes, you may need to give yourself daily injections.

Inhalation
When a liquid medicine is changed into a fine mist, it can be inhaled, or breathed in. If you have asthma, you may need an inhaler.

Absorption
Creams and ointments are applied to the skin or scalp and absorbed by the body. Skin patches are applied to the skin and release medicine over time. If you have a cold, you may rub ointment on your chest to clear your lungs.

LESSON 1: USING MEDICINES WISELY 273

Lesson 1

Comprehending

Explain to students that some therapies, including drug therapies, may have to be administered for long periods, sometimes even for the rest of the patient's life. Have someone who takes insulin or asthma or allergy medicine come to class to talk about his or her therapeutic routine. **L1**

VISUAL LEARNING

FIGURE 11.2 Have volunteers read aloud the title and caption for Figure 11.2. Then have other volunteers read aloud the explanations of how medicines enter the body. Ask students to identify other examples of each method. **INCL** *English Language Learners, Special Learning Needs, Behavior Problems, Different Learning Style (Visual)*

FYI

Like infants and young children, teens should avoid using aspirin and aspirin-combination medicines. Aspirin use has been linked to Reye's syndrome, a rare but dangerous disease that can be fatal. The U.S. Surgeon General, the Federal Drug Administration, the Centers for Disease Control and Prevention, and the American Academy of Pediatrics all recommend that anyone under the age of 19 not take aspirin during fever-causing illnesses.

Reading Check

Affixes and Roots Identifying word parts and recognizing common meanings help students build vocabulary skills. Write the words *injection* and *ingestion* on the board. Have a student divide the words into their separate parts (*in/ject/ion, in/gest/ion*). Then discuss the meaning of each part and how it affects the meaning of the word.

Using a dictionary, students will find in- means "into," -ject means "to force," -gest means "to carry in," and -ion means "the result of an act or process." Ask students to name other words that have the same prefix or root and discuss the connections among the words' meanings. Some possible answers are *reject* and *digest*.

Debating

Write the following on the board, and ask students to write their responses: *Should all drugs (even aspirin) carry a warning label that states the possible problems of tolerance?* Divide the class into two teams, and have the teams debate the issue. To help students remember, write on the board their statements for or against the idea. Note: Students may need time to research the topic before the team debate. You could assign the topic as homework and hold the debate the next day. **L2**

HEALTH SKILLS ACTIVITY

PRACTICING HEALTHFUL BEHAVIORS

Ask volunteers to read the activity introduction aloud, and help students discuss each of the tips for storing, using, and disposing of medicine. Have students form small groups to plan and create their checklists. Have groups compare and revise their lists so that all are complete.

Note: This skill is introduced in Chapter 2 on pages 46–47.

Side Effects

In addition to the intended effect, some medicines also cause one or more side effects. A **side effect** is *any effect of a medicine other than the one intended.* Common side effects include headaches, an upset stomach, and drowsiness. If you have side effects with a medicine, talk to your doctor, nurse, or pharmacist. Some side effects, such as kidney failure, can be serious. Others may stop after the body adjusts to the medicine. Some people may be allergic to certain medicines and may need to see a doctor about a replacement.

Tolerance

When used over a long period of time, certain medicines can cause a person to develop a tolerance. **Tolerance** is *a condition in which a person's body becomes used to the effect of a medicine and needs greater and greater amounts of it in order for it to be effective.* In some cases, the medicine ceases to be effective and the doctor must prescribe a different type of medicine.

HEALTH SKILLS ACTIVITY

PRACTICING HEALTHFUL BEHAVIORS

Medicine Safety in the Home

How much do you know about medicine safety? Follow these tips to store, use, and dispose of medicines safely.

- Store medicines in a cool, dry place.
- Keep medicines safely sealed in childproof containers, and keep them out of the reach of children.

- Do not share prescription medicines. They could cause serious harm to someone else.
- Do not use nonprescription medicines for more than ten days at a time unless you check with your doctor.
- Before taking two or more medicines at the same time, get your doctor's approval.
- Know what medicines are in your home and what they are used to treat. Keep only those that are currently needed.
- Do not use medicines that have passed their expiration date.
- To safely dispose of outdated or unused liquids or pills, flush them down the toilet.

WITH A GROUP
Create a "Medicine Safety Checklist" suitable for home use. Review the completed checklist with your family. Post the list in an appropriate place in your home.

274 CHAPTER 11: MEDICINES AND DRUGS

Beyond the Classroom

Home Safe storage of medicines in the home is crucial to the health and well-being of every family member. Ask each student to look at the medicine chest in his or her home and come up with a list of questions that a person might answer to determine whether the medicine chest is safely located, secured, and organized. (*Is the cabinet difficult for small children to reach? Do medicines have childproof caps? Have any prescriptions expired?*) If any students report that there are no medicine chests in their homes, encourage them to discuss an effective substitute with their families. Also, ask students where else medicines are kept in their homes. Then ask them to assess whether these are safe storage areas.

Overuse of Medicines

If medicines are overused, they can lose their ability to fight diseases. For example, the use of penicillin became widespread in the 1940s. Within just a few years, new strains of bacteria had developed. The new bacteria were resistant to penicillin. The more often antibiotics are used, the more likely it is that bacteria will develop a resistance to them. This is another reason why medicines must always be used wisely and in moderation.

Mixing Medicines

When two or more medicines are taken at the same time, the combined effects may be dangerous. The following reactions are possible.

- Each medicine may have a stronger effect than it would have if taken alone.
- The medicines may combine to produce unexpected effects.
- One medicine may cancel out the expected effects of the other.

Because mixing medicines can produce unpredictable and sometimes even deadly results, it is vital to let your physician know about all medicines you are presently taking.

MEDIA WATCH

MEDICINE ADS

Find several magazine ads for medicines. Look for common information in the ads. *Use critical-thinking skills to interpret the ads' messages. What conclusions can you draw about the legal requirements for medicine ads?*

Lesson 1

Critical Thinking

Ask students: Who should be responsible for reporting to the physician all medicines a teen takes? Why? **L2**

❸ Assess

Evaluating

Assign the Lesson 1 Review; then assign the Lesson 1 Quiz in the TCR.

Reteaching

- Assign Concept Map 38 or Reteaching Activity 38 in the TCR.
- Have students list the three main types of medicines and their uses.

Enrichment

- Assign Enrichment Activity 38 in the TCR.
- Ask students to research and write short reports about medicines currently being considered for approval by the FDA.

❹ Close

Ask each student to write a brief explanation of why it is important to know the difference between medicines and other drugs.

Lesson 1 Review

Using complete sentences, answer the following questions on a sheet of paper.

Reviewing Terms and Facts

1. **List** Give three reasons people take medicines.
2. **Relate** How can medicines be used to prevent or treat communicable disease?
3. **Vocabulary** What is a *side effect?*
4. **Give Examples** List the three possible reactions that can result from taking more than one medicine at the same time.

Thinking Critically

5. **Contrast** Explain the difference between prescription medicines and over-the-counter medicines.

6. **Draw Conclusions** Every day, Rose took the same dose of the same medicine to manage her arthritis pain. After taking the medicine for two years, it no longer helped. What might have happened?

Applying Health Skills

7. **Advocacy** Write a letter to the editor of your school or community newspaper promoting the responsible use of antibiotics. Be sure to mention the problems caused by overuse of antibiotics.

LESSON 1: USING MEDICINES WISELY 275

Lesson 1 Review

1. To prevent diseases, to fight infection, to relieve pain.
2. Possible response: Vaccines can prevent communicable diseases by causing the immune system to produce antibodies; antibiotics can treat communicable diseases by killing harmful bacteria.
3. Any effect of a medicine other than the one intended.

4. A medicine may have a stronger effect than if taken alone; may produce unexpected effects; one may cancel out the expected effects of the other.
5. Prescriptions require a doctor's written permission; OTC medicines can be obtained without a doctor's written order.
6. Rose's body may have developed a tolerance for the drug.

Lesson

Narcotics, Stimulants, and Depressants

① Focus

Lesson Objectives

Students will be able to

• explain the difference between drug misuse and drug abuse.

• discuss the effects of narcotics, stimulants, and depressants on the body.

• define narcotics, stimulants, and depressants.

• explain the impact of addiction to drugs.

Motivators

Quick Write

List the reasons on the board as volunteers share their responses. Then ask students to create categories for the reasons. (*possible categories: Side effects, addiction, personality changes, behavior changes, misuse/abuse, crime, risks to individual/society*)

Bellringer Activity

Ask students to list all the uses they can think of for a pencil and to label each with a G for *good* or a B for *bad*. Have students share their responses; then discuss that many items have good as well as bad uses.

VOCABULARY

Write the definitions of the vocabulary terms on the board. Then instruct each student to write each term along with its definition on a sheet of paper. Call on students to supply the correct definition for each term.

Quick Write

Why do you think some drugs are illegal?

LEARN ABOUT...

• the difference between drug misuse and drug abuse.

• how narcotics affect the body.

• the effects of stimulants on the body.

• what depressants do to the body.

VOCABULARY

• narcotics
• addiction
• stimulants
• amphetamine
• methamphetamine
• depressants

Drug Misuse and Abuse

People can harm themselves by not using drugs properly. Drug misusers take legal drugs in an improper way. Drug abusers take substances that are against the law or are not supposed to be taken into the human body. They may also use legal drugs for nonmedical purposes. The following are forms of drug misuse and drug abuse.

Drug Misuse

• Using a drug without following the directions
• Combining medicines without a physician's advice
• Taking more of a drug than the doctor ordered
• Using a drug prescribed for someone else
• Giving your prescription to someone else
• Using a drug for longer than a physician advises

Drug Abuse

• Using any illegal drug
• Using a medicine when you do not need it
• Taking a substance that was not meant to enter the body
• Using a drug for purposes other than medical treatment
• Faking health problems to obtain or renew a prescription

Teens who use illegal drugs face serious consequences. Getting dropped from the school team is an immediate one. *What might be some longer-term consequences of drug abuse?*

Lesson 2 Resources

Teacher Classroom Resources

 Concept Map 39

 Decision-Making Activity 21

Enrichment Activity 39

 Lesson Plan 2

 Lesson 2 Quiz

 Reading Tutor Activity 38

 Reteaching Activity 39

 Transparency 39

Student Activities Workbook

 Chapter 11 Study Guide

 Applying Health Skills 39

Narcotics

Narcotics are *specific drugs that are obtainable only by prescription and are used to relieve pain.* Doctors may prescribe the narcotics morphine or codeine, for example, to treat extreme pain. Narcotics can be safe when taken under a physician's supervision, but they are so addictive that their sale and use is controlled by law. People with an **addiction** have a *physical or psychological need for a drug.* Another name for drug addiction is chemical dependency. Pharmacists must keep records of all sales of narcotics.

Heroin

Heroin (HEHR·uh·win) is an illegal narcotic that is made from morphine. It is the most commonly abused narcotic and is highly addictive. When users do not get the heroin they need, they feel severe pain. Heroin depresses the central nervous system and can lead to coma or death.

Because drug users often share dirty needles, users of heroin and other injected drugs are at increased risk of contracting HIV. According to recent CDC data, half of all new infections with HIV occur among abusers of injected drugs.

Stimulants

Stimulants (STIM·yuh·luhnts) are *substances that speed up the body's functions.* Stimulants make the heart beat faster, increase breathing rate, and raise blood pressure. The effects of some stimulants are so mild that people may not even realize they are using a drug. Caffeine is a stimulant found in cocoa, coffee, tea, and many soft drinks.

Some stimulants may be prescribed to help people with certain physical or emotional problems. Stimulant abuse can be very dangerous, however. High doses of strong stimulants may cause blurred vision, dizziness, anxiety, loss of coordination, or collapse. Stimulants such as amphetamine, cocaine, and crack can also become habit-forming, and users can become addicted quickly. **Figure 11.3** on the next page describes some common stimulants and their harmful effects.

Once a person develops an addiction, he or she constantly needs to find and use more of the drug. *Explain how chemical dependency and addiction to a drug might impact a person's life.*

Reading Check

Three paragraphs on this page present a definition of a term, followed by characteristics of it. For each term, write the definition followed by at least one of its characteristics.

Discussing

Ask students to discuss the difference between drug misuse and drug abuse. (*Note that both can lead to harm.*) **L1**

Speculating

Ask students whether they agree that drugs are the number-one issue among teens today. Ask students to name other current issues that are related to drugs (*communicable disease, foreign policy, poverty, crime, education, health care*). Discuss with them how drugs relate to these other issues. **L1**

Critical Thinking

Briefly explain to students the concept of supply and demand. Tell them that drug enforcement policies are aimed at reducing both the supply of drugs to a community and the demand for drugs in the community. Ask them to think about effective ways of reducing the drug supply and the drug demand. Ask them whether they think the supply or the demand comes first and encourages the other. **L2**

Analyzing

Have each student write two facts about narcotics in general and two facts about heroin specifically. Discuss the facts chosen, noting each on the board. Which items did students consider most important? **L1**

Reading Check

Analyzing Text Have students search for and identify key words in the reading that indicate the pattern of definition and characteristics, such as *for example.* Lead students to discover each of the definitions followed by characteristics throughout this lesson. Have students create charts with the headings *Term, Definition,* and *Characteristics* to organize their notes. For example, under *Term* list *Narcotics.* Under *Definition* list *specific drugs that are obtainable only by prescription and are used to relieve pain.* Under *Characteristics* list *doctors prescribe, can be addictive, pharmacists keep records.*

FIGURE 11.3 Read aloud the caption for Figure 11.3, and emphasize the serious dangers posed by stimulants. Have all students follow the chart as volunteers read aloud information about each stimulant. Have students identify other names for these stimulants. Ask: Why is it important to know the current or local names for drugs? **INCL** *English Language Learners, Special Learning Needs, Behavior Problems, Different Learning Style (Visual)*

Cross-Curriculum Activity

SOCIAL STUDIES Ask volunteers to investigate and share with the class the legal consequences of possessing, using, and selling cocaine and crack cocaine. As part of their reports, students should explain the importance of complying with rules prohibiting possession of drugs. **L2**

Developing Good Character

Citizenship

Have students brainstorm a list of their favorite school or community activities. Ask: What do you value most about these activities? How would alcohol and drug use get in the way of enjoying these activities? How would one's alcohol and drug use hurt the other people involved?

FIGURE 11.3

EFFECTS OF STIMULANTS

Stimulants come in a variety of forms, all of which can be very dangerous if abused.

Substance	Other Names	Forms	Methods of Use	Harmful Effects
Amphetamine	Crystal, ice, glass, crank, speed, uppers	Pills, powder, chunky crystals	Swallowed, snorted up the nose, smoked, injected	Uneven heartbeat, rise in blood pressure, physical collapse, stroke, heart attack, and death
Methamphetamine	Meth, crank, speed, ice	Pills, powder, crystals	Swallowed, snorted up the nose, smoked, injected	Memory loss, damage to heart and nervous system, seizures, death
Cocaine	Coke, dust, snow, flake, blow, girl	White powder	Snorted up the nose, injected	Damage to nose lining, liver, and heart; heart attack, seizures, stroke, and death
Crack	Crack, freebase rocks, rock	Off-white rocks or chunks	Smoked, injected	Damage to lungs if smoked, seizures, heart attack, and death

Developing Good Character

Citizenship

Find out about organizations in your school or community that promote a drug-free environment and sponsor drug-free events. Identify the organizations' goals and how students can participate. *Which organization would you be interested in joining? Why?*

Amphetamine

Amphetamine (am·FE·tuh·meen) is *a drug that stimulates the central nervous system.* Doctors may prescribe amphetamines to treat hyperactive children. Amphetamines are highly addictive, however. People who use or abuse amphetamines can develop a dependence on the drugs, needing larger and larger doses to get the desired effect.

Methamphetamine

Methamphetamine is *a stimulant similar to amphetamine.* Doctors prescribe methamphetamines to treat diseases such as narcolepsy, Parkinson's disease, and obesity. In recent years, methamphetamines have appeared in "club drugs"—dangerous, illegal substances available at dance clubs and all-night parties.

Cocaine

Cocaine is a powerful, illegal stimulant. Its abuse has become a major health problem in the United States. Among teens, cocaine abuse increased during the 1990s. However, studies showed a significant drop in teen cocaine use in 1999.

278 CHAPTER 11: MEDICINES AND DRUGS

MORE ABOUT...

Ephedrine Advise students of the risks of another stimulant—ephedrine. This substance is derived from the plant ephedra, a shrub found in desert regions in central Asia. Ephedrine is also the active element of ma huang, an herb used in Chinese medicine. It stimulates the cardiovascular and central nervous system. Ephedrine is found in OTC weight-loss products, energy-boosting supplements, and "herbal ecstasy." The substance has also been used by athletes to enhance athletic performance. The Food and Drug Administration (FDA) has received reports of adverse reactions, including memory loss, nerve damage, liver failure, elevated blood pressure, strokes, and deaths.

Some people use cocaine because it makes them feel happy and energetic. This feeling is short-lived, however, and is followed by depression as the drug wears off. Users often take more cocaine to relieve the depression, thus forming an addiction to it. Cocaine is a dangerous drug, and an overdose can be fatal.

Crack

Crack is a concentrated form of cocaine that can be smoked. Smoking crack has the same effects on the body as using cocaine, only stronger. Crack reaches the brain within seconds and produces an intense high. The high lasts only for a few minutes, though, and is followed by an equally intense low. The user then craves more of the drug to relieve the intense bad feelings. For these reasons, crack is one of the most addictive and dangerous drugs used in the United States today.

Depressants

Depressants are *substances that slow down the body's functions and reactions.* These substances, which are often called sedatives, lower blood pressure and slow down heart rate and breathing. Doctors sometimes prescribe depressants for relief of anxiety, tension, nervousness, and sleeplessness. There are three main kinds of depressants.

- **Tranquilizers** (TRAN·kwuh·ly·zerz), when used as prescribed by a physician, can help reduce anxiety and relax muscles.
- **Barbiturates** (bar·BI·chuh·ruhts) are powerful sedatives that produce a feeling of relaxation.
- **Hypnotics** (hip·NAH·tiks) are very strong drugs that bring on sleep.

A teen with strong values will choose healthful behaviors and avoid the use of drugs.

Analyzing

Ask students to discuss why crack is probably the most dangerous and addictive drug used in this country today. (*Crack reaches the brain just seconds after being taken; addiction can occur after just one use.*) **L1**

Cross-Curriculum Activity

SCIENCE Have students read about sleeping pills. Ask:

- What kinds of drugs do they contain?
- Why are they dangerous when used for long periods of time?
- What happens when an addicted person tries to give them up?

Have students make public service announcements about the dangers of sleeping pills. Ask them to include ways to get to sleep that do not involve drugs. **L2**

Cross-Curriculum Activity

LANGUAGE ARTS Have students write editorials about the extent of student drug use at your school. The editorial should contain factual information and suggestions for parents, the school, and the community at large to combat the problem. Submit the best editorial to the school newspaper as well as to the local newspaper. **L3**

LESSON 2: NARCOTICS, STIMULANTS, AND DEPRESSANTS **279**

MORE ABOUT...

What is ecstasy, and is it dangerous? MDMA (also known as ecstasy, E, X, Adam) is a stimulant with mildly hallucinogenic and amphetamine-like effects. It is not a harmless drug. In fact, taking it may prove fatal. Users may experience high body temperature and potentially fatal dehydration, some users experience confusion, depression, anxiety, and paranoia. Studies of long-term effects of MDMA on rats and other animals indicate that MDMA damages the brain nerve cells (neurons), which produce serotonin, a neurotransmitter. Serotonin influences mood, appetite, sleep, and memory. In the studies, damaged neurons had regrown abnormally or failed to regrow at all.

❸ Assess

Evaluating

📁 Assign the Lesson 2 Review; then assign the Lesson 2 Quiz in the TCR.

Reteaching

• 📁 Assign Concept Map 39 or Reteaching Activity 39 in the TCR.

• Have each student divide a sheet of paper in thirds vertically and write *Narcotics, Stimulants,* and *Depressants* at the top of the columns. Ask students to list four important facts about each.

Enrichment

📁 Assign Enrichment Activity 39 in the TCR.

❹ Close

Ask students for healthy suggestions on how they can get extra energy when they feel listless.

Depressants should be taken only under a doctor's supervision. If taken over an extended period, they can cause dependence and a need for more and more of the drug.

Depressants produce effects similar to those produced by alcohol, which itself is a form of depressant. When depressants are combined with alcohol, the effects increase and the risks multiply. The results can be deadly. **Figure 11.4** provides more information about depressants and their effects on the body.

FIGURE 11.4

EFFECTS OF DEPRESSANTS

If abused, depressants can have many harmful effects on the body, up to and including death.

Substance	Other Names	Forms	Methods of Use	Harmful Effects
Tranquilizer	Valium, Librium, Xanax	Pills or capsules	Swallowed	Anxiety; reduced coordination and attention span. Withdrawal can cause tremors and lead to coma or death.
Barbiturate	Downers, barbs, yellow jackets, reds	Pills or capsules	Swallowed	Causes mood changes and excessive sleep. Can lead to coma.
Hypnotic	Quaaludes, Ludes, Sopor	Pills or capsules	Swallowed	Impaired coordination and judgment. High doses may cause internal bleeding, coma, or death.

Lesson 2 Review

Using complete sentences, answer the following questions on a sheet of paper.

Reviewing Terms and Facts

1. **Recall** What are three forms of drug misuse and three forms of drug abuse?
2. **Vocabulary** What is *addiction?* Use it in a complete sentence.
3. **Explain** How is heroin use related to the spread of HIV?
4. **Give Examples** List two types of stimulants, and describe their effects on the body.

Thinking Critically

5. **Contrast** How do the effects of stimulants differ from those of depressants?
6. **Apply** How would you refuse an offer to try crack?

Applying Health Skills

7. **Stress Management** Some people use illegal drugs because they think that drugs will help them manage stress. Write down five examples of healthful ways to manage stress without using drugs.

280 CHAPTER 11: MEDICINES AND DRUGS

Lesson 2 Review

1. Any three of each of the bulleted items on page 276.
2. A physical or psychological need for a drug. Sentences will vary.
3. Users may share dirty needles and become infected.
4. See Figure 11.3 on page 278.

5. Stimulants speed up body's functions; depressants slow them down.
6. Responses will vary, but should include the use of effective refusal skills.

Marijuana and Other Illegal Drugs

Street Drugs

Companies that manufacture drugs sold as medicines must follow strict government regulations. These laws ensure that the medicines are pure and consistent in strength, known risks, and side effects.

Any drug that is made or sold outside of these laws is considered a street drug. Street drugs include illegally made, packaged, or sold legal drugs, such as amphetamines. Street drugs also include illegal drugs, such as heroin and marijuana. There are no laws to protect the purity and content of street drugs. People who use them don't know how much of the drug they are taking. As a result, they risk being poisoned and dying of accidental overdose.

Marijuana

Marijuana is the most commonly used street drug. The main active chemical in marijuana is THC (tetrahydrocannabinol), which affects the brain. Hashish, which is made from the same plant, is much stronger than marijuana because it contains more THC. **Figure 11.5** lists the effects of marijuana.

FIGURE 11.5

EFFECTS OF MARIJUANA

Common street names for marijuana include pot, grass, weed, joint, and herb.

- Reduces memory, reaction time, and coordination, and impairs judgment
- Reduces initiative and ambition
- Increases heart rate and appetite and lowers body temperature
- Damages heart and lungs
- Interferes with normal body development in teens by changing hormone levels
- May cause addiction

Quick Write

List at least two dangers of illegal drug use.

LEARN ABOUT...

- the risks of using marijuana.
- the dangers of hallucinogens.
- how inhalants affect the body.
- what club drugs and steroids do to the body.

VOCABULARY

- hallucinogens
- psychological dependence
- inhalant
- physical dependence

Lesson 3

Marijuana and Other Illegal Drugs

❶ FOCUS

Lesson Objectives

Students will be able to

- outline the risks of using marijuana.
- explain the dangers of hallucinogens.
- describe how inhalants affect the body.
- discuss the risks of using club drugs and steroids.

Health Skills

- Refusal Skills, p. 284

Motivators

Quick Write
Ask volunteers to share their responses. Then ask: How could such dangers affect the illegal drug user's daily responsibilities and future goals?

Bellringer Activity
Ask students to write any changes they would make to current laws pertaining to drugs. Ask: Why would you make the changes?

VOCABULARY

Scramble the letters for each of the vocabulary terms, and write each of the scrambled words or phrases on an index card. Display one of the cards, and read to the class the definition of that term as it appears in the lesson. Have students try to guess the term.

Lesson 3 Resources

Teacher Classroom Resources

 Concept Map 40

 Cross-Curriculum Activity 21

 Decision-Making Activity 22

Enrichment Activity 40

Lesson Plan 3

 Lesson 3 Quiz

 Reading Tutor Activity 39

Reteaching Activity 40

 Transparency 40

Student Activities Workbook

 Chapter 11 Study Guide

Applying Health Skills 40

Lesson 3

② Teach

VISUAL LEARNING

FIGURE 11.5 Have volunteers read aloud the title and caption for Figure 11.5 on page 281 and then the listed effects of marijuana. Help students discuss each effect by asking:

- How would this affect a teen's physical health?
- How would this affect a teen's mental/emotional and social health? **INCL** *English Language Learners, Special Learning Needs, Behavior Problems, Different Learning Styles* (*Visual*)

Critical Thinking

Ask students why many teens mistakenly believe marijuana is a harmless drug. (*It does not create effects as dramatic as those of some hallucinogens. It is associated with smoking cigarettes, a habit accepted by many segments of society. Its reputation as a safe drug prevails among the uninformed.*)

Discussing

Remind students that a person can become addicted to behaviors as well as drugs. Some behavioral addictions are food, shopping, and gambling. An addiction to a drug or other substance is called chemical dependency. Ask students to explain the impact chemical dependency and addiction would have on an addict's life.

Synthesizing

Separate the class into groups of two to four students. Ask each group to decide on a specific description of how marijuana use might be harmful to a football player, an office worker, an auto mechanic, a builder, and a student. Have groups share their answers and discuss them briefly. **L2**

CHEMICAL MESSAGES
Your brain communicates with the rest of your body by sending chemical messages along nerve cells. This communication system can be interrupted, changed, or damaged by hallucinogens.

Although some users mix marijuana with food and eat it, most choose to smoke it. As a result, marijuana smokers experience many of the same lung problems as tobacco smokers. These include persistent coughing, bronchitis symptoms, and frequent colds. Marijuana smoke contains three to five times the amount of tar and other cancer-causing substances found in tobacco smoke.

Hallucinogens

Hallucinogens (huh·LOO·suhn·uh·jenz) are *drugs that distort moods, thoughts, and senses.* Physical effects of hallucinogens include increased heart rate and blood pressure and lack of muscle coordination. Hallucinogens can also cause decreased sensitivity to pain, which can result in serious self-injury.

Taking a hallucinogen may cause the user to hallucinate, or see things that are not really there. Sometimes it can trigger uncontrolled, violent behavior. Hallucinogens also cause people to lose their sense of direction, distance, and time. These effects often lead to misjudgments that result in serious injuries and death.

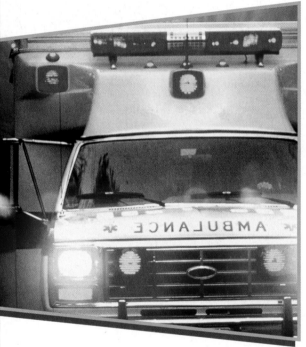

People cannot always predict how their bodies might react to drugs. *How might drug use and the abuse of medicines lead to health problems in later life and other adverse consequences?*

PCP

Phencyclidine (fen·SI·kluh·deen), commonly called PCP, is a powerful and dangerous hallucinogen whose effects last a long time. PCP produces strange, destructive behavior, which causes many users to end up in hospital emergency rooms. PCP use often leads to **psychological dependence**, *an addiction in which the mind sends the body a message that it needs more of a drug.* **Figure 11.6** provides more information about PCP.

LSD

LSD is an abbreviation for lysergic (luh·SER·jik) acid diethylamide (dy·e·thuh·LA·myd), another powerful hallucinogen. Use of LSD often produces rapid mood swings and hallucinations. Some users have terrifying thoughts and feelings, such as fear that they are dying or going crazy. Many LSD users experience flashbacks. During a flashback, the effects of LSD may recur days, months, or years after the drug was taken. **Figure 11.6** gives additional information about LSD.

DEALING WITH SENSITIVE ISSUES

Confidentiality The results of surveys, inventories, and personal behavior analyses that students will take during a health class are always confidential. Never should a student's privacy be invaded for the sake of a class lesson. One valuable way to discuss behaviors and attitudes in connection with any lesson or activity is to create fictional profiles of teens and discuss how the teens would, or should, handle specific lifestyle behaviors. Students who have tried drugs because they couldn't say no to peer pressure may feel guilty or ashamed when the issue is raised. Be sure to emphasize that saying yes to drugs is a bad decision, but that making a bad decision doesn't mean that a person is bad. Also, point out that saying no to drugs shouldn't make someone feel left out—more teens don't do drugs than do.

FIGURE 11.6

EFFECTS OF HALLUCINOGENS

Hallucinogens can have many harmful effects on the body, up to and including death.

Substance	Other Names	Forms	Methods of Use	Harmful Effects
PCP	Angel dust, supergrass, killer weed, rocket fuel	White powder; liquid	Applied to leafy materials and smoked	Loss of coordination; increase in heart rate, blood pressure, and body temperature; convulsions, heart and lung failure, or broken blood vessels; bizarre or violent behavior; temporary psychosis; false feeling of having super powers.
LSD	Acid, blotter, microdot, white lightning	Tablets; squares soaked on paper	Eaten or licked	Increase in blood pressure, heart rate, and body temperature; chills, nausea, tremors, and sleeplessness; unpredictable behavior; flashbacks; false feeling of having super powers.

Inhalants

Any substance whose fumes are sniffed and inhaled to produce mind-altering sensations is considered an **inhalant**. Household products that come in aerosol spray cans are commonly used as inhalants. These products include spray paint, cleaning fluid, lighter fluid, hair spray, nail polish remover, and other harmful substances. These substances are not meant to be taken into the body and can be very dangerous.

When inhalants are breathed in, their harmful fumes go directly to the brain. These fumes commonly cause headache, nausea, vomiting, and loss of coordination. A single use can result in sudden death. Inhalant use can lead to **physical dependence**, *a type of addiction in which the body itself feels a direct need for a drug.* Long-term inhalant use can damage the liver, kidneys, and brain.

Club Drugs

Club drugs are drugs that are associated with nightclubs, concerts, and all-night dance parties called raves. Other terms for drugs associated with these activities are designer drugs and look-alike drugs. The term *designer drug* often refers to a synthetic version of a natural drug. Look-alike drugs are drugs that resemble and are passed off as another drug.

Lesson 3

VISUAL LEARNING

FIGURE 11.6 Ask two small groups of students to study the information in the chart. Have one group focus on PCP and the other on LSD. After reading and discussing the material, have the members of each group present their assigned hallucinogen to the rest of the class. **INCL** *English Language Learners, Special Learning Needs, Behavior Problems, Different Learning Style* (*Visual*)

Analyzing

Ask students:

- Why is PCP especially dangerous as a street drug? (*The user never knows the concentration of the drug, the total amount, or the purity.*)
- Why is it especially dangerous when smoked with marijuana? (*When smoked, it passes rapidly to the brain, causing severe physical and mental effects. It gets mixed with over 400 other drugs in unknown proportions.*) **L1**

Discussing

Discuss the dangers of inhalants. Emphasize the destruction of brain cells. Ask:

- How does the availability of inhalants make them especially dangerous?
- What could you do to warn others about the dangers of inhalants? **L1**

MORE ABOUT...

Inhalant Dangers Inhaled fumes act like anesthesia, replacing oxygen in the blood. Users are intoxicated and may vomit, hallucinate, become dizzy, and lose consciousness. Death can result from suffocation, dangerous behavior, aspiration (removal of liquids or gases), and sudden sniffing death syndrome. Suffocation occurs when users lose consciousness while inhaling from a plastic bag, that blocks the nose and mouth. Dangerous behavior can lead to motor vehicle accidents, drowning, falls, and fires caused by highly flammable inhalants. Aspiration deaths occur when users choke on their own vomit. Sudden sniffing death, from cardiac arrest, can occur with the first use, or after months of abuse.

Lesson 3

According to the National Institute on Drug Abuse, ecstasy causes injury to the brain, especially affecting neurons. Damage to neurons can negatively affect mood, sleep, and sensitivity to pain.

HEALTH SKILLS ACTIVITY

REFUSAL SKILLS

Guide students in applying strategies for avoiding drugs. Have students read the activity introduction and discuss Megan's situation. Also, help students review and discuss the S.T.O.P. refusal skills.

Divide the class into groups. Have partners within each group role-play their scenario for the other group members.

Note: This skill is introduced in Chapter 6 on pages 149–150.

Some club drugs are colorless, tasteless, and odorless. These properties have led to the dangerous practice of drug slipping. Drug slipping occurs when a drug is placed in someone's food or beverage without that person's knowledge. Because drug slipping has been used to aid in committing rape, some club drugs are sometimes called date rape drugs. Commonly used club drugs include:

- **Ecstasy**, also called E, X, and XTC, is a stimulant and a hallucinogen in pill form. Users may experience confusion, depression, anxiety, nausea, faintness, chills, or sweating. Ecstasy can cause permanent brain damage.
- **GHB** is a depressant, and its street names include Liquid Ecstasy, Liquid X, Georgia Home Boy, and Grievous Bodily Harm. Available in powder and liquid form, GHB is especially dangerous when taken with alcohol or other drugs. The combination may result in sleep, coma, and death.
- **Rohypnol** is a powerful sedative. It's also called the date rape drug, Roofies, and R-2. Rohypnol is typically a small white tablet which, when dissolved in liquid, has no taste or odor. The drug's short-term effect is a sleepy, relaxed feeling that lasts two to eight hours. The user might also black out.
- **Ketamine** is an anesthetic used for medical purposes, mostly in treating animals. Misused as a club drug, ketamine is often sold as a white powder to be snorted, like cocaine, or injected. The drug is also smoked with marijuana or tobacco products. Ketamine causes hallucinations and dreamlike states. Its use may result in death through respiratory failure.

HEALTH SKILLS ACTIVITY

REFUSAL SKILLS

Refusing Drugs

Megan is thrilled when Nina invites her to "join the crowd" at her home after school. It isn't often that a junior like Nina would even talk to Megan, a freshman.

When Megan gets to Nina's house, she sees that there are five or six girls from school but no adults. Nina brings out a little bag of tablets and tells the girls that the pills are a cool new club drug. She says that all the kids are taking the pills at dance parties. She starts to pass the pills around. Megan sits frozen in her chair.

WHAT WOULD YOU DO?

Apply refusal skills to Megan's situation. With a classmate, role-play a scenario in which Megan used S.T.O.P. to refuse Nina's offer of a club drug.

SAY NO IN A FIRM VOICE.
TELL WHY NOT.
OFFER OTHER IDEAS.
PROMPTLY LEAVE.

284 CHAPTER 11: MEDICINES AND DRUGS

COOPERATIVE LEARNING ACTIVITY

Practicing Refusal Skills Ask for student volunteers to act out situations in which two students try to persuade two other students to use drugs. Have the pro-drug group leave the room while the anti-drug group and the rest of the class prepare a list of ways and reasons to say no. Once both groups are ready, the interaction begins. Limit the time to three or four minutes. Have new volunteers take over the roles but never allow the pro-drug group to be seen as winners. Prevent that result by cutting the time allowance or asking for stronger class support for not using drugs. Conclude the activity by having the class develop a strong, positive no-use statement.

The best way to improve your athletic performance is to practice. *How could drug use ruin, rather than help, an athlete's career?*

❸ Assess

Evaluating

📁 Assign the Lesson 3 Review; then assign the Lesson 3 Quiz in the TCR.

Reteaching

• 📁 Assign Concept Map 40 or Reteaching Activity 40 in the TCR.

• Have students explain the impact of addiction to drugs and other substances discussed in this lesson.

Enrichment

• 📁 Assign Enrichment Activity 40 in the TCR.

• Help students list ideas for sharing drug awareness with elementary-school children. Then have them work together to develop and carry out one of their ideas.

❹ Close

Ask students to identify the important concepts in this lesson using the major divisions or headings in the text. Then have students use what they have learned in Lessons 1, 2, and 3 to relate medicine and other drug use to problems in later life and other adverse consequences.

Anabolic Steroids

Some athletes mistakenly believe that drugs will improve their performance. They may start using steroids, which bulk up muscle at an abnormally fast rate. In time, the harmful effects of steroids become obvious. They include acne, mood swings, nausea, liver damage, brain cancers, and shorter adult height when taken by children and teens. Athletes are routinely tested for illegal drugs. If they have been using steroids or other drugs, they face stiff penalties and may lose their right to compete.

Lesson 3 Review

Using complete sentences, answer the following questions on a sheet of paper.

Reviewing Terms and Facts

1. **Vocabulary** Define the terms *hallucinogen* and *inhalant*. Explain the relationship between the two terms.
2. **List** Name two hallucinogens known by their initials.
3. **Compare** What is the difference between *psychological dependence* and *physical dependence?*
4. **Explain** Why are club drugs especially dangerous?

Thinking Critically

5. **Apply** Explain the impact of chemical dependency and addiction to illegal drugs and other substances.
6. **Analyze** Why are teens more likely than adults to abuse inhalants?

Applying Health Skills

7. **Accessing Information** Use reliable resources to research marijuana's harmful effects on body systems. Report your findings to the class.

LESSON 3: MARIJUANA AND OTHER ILLEGAL DRUGS **285**

Lesson 3 Review

1. Hallucinogens are drugs that distort moods, thoughts, and senses. Inhalants are substances whose fumes are inhaled for mind-altering sensations. Inhalants are hallucinogens.
2. PCP, LSD.
3. Psychological dependence is a sense of need that comes from the mind; physical dependence is a sense of need that comes from the body.
4. Some club drugs are colorless, tasteless, and odorless. When placed in a drink, they cannot be detected.
5. Responses should detail the harmful impact of chemical dependency and addiction to illegal drugs on physical, mental/emotional, and social health.
6. They are easy and inexpensive to obtain.

① Focus

Lesson Objectives

Students will be able to

- identify ways to avoid using drugs.
- summarize how drug users can kick the habit.
- discuss places where people who abuse drugs can get help.
- describe alternatives to using drugs.

Motivators

Quick Write
List students' responses on the board. Then poll the students to determine which one the class considers to be the most important reason.

Bellringer Activity

Ask each student to think about a time when she or he had to refuse a friend's request or suggestion. Ask volunteers to share their responses. Tell students not to use names to respect privacy.

VOCABULARY

Remind students that a synonym is a word that has the same or nearly the same meaning as another. Have students look up the two vocabulary terms and create synonyms for each.

Lesson ④

Staying Drug Free

Quick Write

Briefly describe the most important reason teens should avoid drug use.

LEARN ABOUT...

- ways to avoid drugs.
- how drug users can kick the habit.
- where people who abuse drugs can get help.
- alternatives to using drugs.

VOCABULARY

- withdrawal
- detoxification

Avoiding Drugs

You have the responsibility to be the healthiest person you can be. The best way to meet that responsibility is to make wise choices that have a positive effect on your health. One of the most important decisions you can make is to be drug free. **Figure 11.7** shows some of the many advantages of avoiding drugs. What can you add to the list?

FIGURE 11.7

Reasons to Be Drug Free

- You will not be breaking the law.
- You will have better concentration and memory.
- You will make wiser decisions.
- You will be able to focus on improving your talents and enjoying your interests.
- You will have more natural energy.
- You can reach your full growth potential.
- You can be as healthy as possible.
- You will look better because drugs will not ruin your appearance.
- You will have better control of your feelings and actions.
- You will not regret foolish actions caused by drug-impaired judgment.
- You will not waste money on drugs.
- You will have better relationships with family members.
- You will respect yourself for taking care of your body and mind.
- You will be able to succeed in education.
- Your mental and emotional development will be on time, not delayed.

286 CHAPTER 11: MEDICINES AND DRUGS

Lesson 4 Resources

Teacher Classroom Resources
 Concept Map 41
 Cross-Curriculum Activity 22
 Enrichment Activity 41
 Lesson Plan 4
 Lesson 4 Quiz
 Reading Tutor Activity 40

 Reteaching Activity 41
Transparency 41

Student Activities Workbook
 Chapter 11 Study Guide
 Applying Health Skills 41
 Health Inventory 11

Marijuana by the Numbers

Match the numbers at the bottom with the correct description.

1. **The number of cigarettes a person has to smoke to do the kind of damage to his or her lungs that smoking one joint does.**

2. **The approximate percentage of teens who have used marijuana at least once in the past year.**

3. **The number of times more potent today's marijuana is than it was a few decades ago. (Newer, stronger types of marijuana are being grown, so it's more harmful to your body and brain than ever before.)**

A. 30 B. 20 C. 5

Answers: 1. C., 2. A., 3. B.

MYTH "Marijuana is not addictive—users can stop whenever they want."

FACT Marijuana *is* an addictive drug. Some people claim that they only use marijuana when they're stressed or depressed. Martha Gagné, director of the American Council for Drug Education, says that even occasional use can lead to a bad situation: "Suddenly, when people want to escape their problems, or even to feel good about themselves, they need to use marijuana." That's called a psychological addiction. Worse, marijuana might also be physically addictive. After a marijuana user hasn't smoked it in a while, he or she may experience such withdrawal symptoms as sweating, jitteriness, and nausea. One recent study has shown that marijuana has the same addictive effect on the brain as heroin.

MYTH "Marijuana is natural—it can't harm the body."

FACT Wrong! In males, heavy marijuana smoking can delay the onset of puberty, decrease sperm count, and make sperm abnormal. In girls, marijuana use can disturb menstrual cycles and decrease fertility. It may also raise levels of the hormone testosterone, which can increase the growth of facial and body hair and cause acne. Also, when people smoke marijuana, their responses are slower and they can't think as clearly, which can lead to serious, or even fatal, accidents.

MYTH "Smoking marijuana is safer than using other drugs."

FACT There's no way to tell if the marijuana is laced with another drug, such as cocaine, crack, or heroin. So a marijuana smoker might sample another dangerous drug without knowing it and become physically addicted to it.

MYTH "Getting caught with marijuana is no big deal."

FACT Marijuana is illegal. If someone gets caught using the drug, he or she can go to jail. Depending on the state where they live, marijuana users risk landing themselves sentences ranging from probation to something more severe—like time at a residential drug-treatment center or a juvenile detention center. ◼

TIME TO THINK...

About Marijuana's Harmful Effects

Review the information presented in this article and in the sidebar. Then, create several bumper stickers that feature antimarijuana slogans. Each slogan should focus on a different harmful effect of the drug. Slogans should be brief, as well as catchy and thought provoking.

❸ Apply

Time to Think

To make student slogans more persuasive, put the harmful effects of marijuana use into context. For instance, how might marijuana use effect one's ability to play sports? (*loss of coordination, increased heart rate*). How might smoking marijuana impair one's ability to take an important test? (*problems with memory, trouble problem solving*). What might be the deadly result of smoking marijuana before driving? (*distorted perception, slow reaction time*). Tell students to pick a specific situation that is familiar to their peers. Slogans based on these situations will make marijuana's harmful effects more relevant to young people.

TIME HEALTH: MARIJUANA MYTHS **291**

WHAT TEENS WANT TO KNOW

What are blunts? Blunts are cigars containing a mixture of marijuana and tobacco. Some people smoke blunts because they appear to be cigars – a legal tobacco product for people over 18. However, don't be fooled into thinking this combination makes blunts "better for you" than straight marijuana. The negative health effects of tobacco use are widely known. Plus, you never know exactly what is in a blunt. They can be laced with other dangerous drugs including cocaine, crack, or heroine. Blunts are dangerous and illegal.

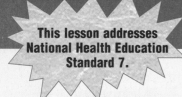

ADVOCACY

Objectives

After completing the lesson, students will be able to persuade other teens to avoid drugs.

Time: two to three 35-minute periods

Materials: unlined paper, markers, scissors, glue/tape, magazines

Teacher Classroom Resources

📁 Building Health Skills Activities

• Transparency Master 10, "Advocacy"

• Reproducible Master 36, "Saying No to Drugs"

---

1. Model

• Ask students to read the scenario about Steve and J.R.

• Display Transparency Master 10, and review the skill of advocacy with the class.

• As a class, identify which of Steve's statements demonstrates his ability to advocate a drug-free lifestyle to his younger brother. (*Steve tells J.R. that he is worried about him spending time with Lucas because he uses drugs. Steve then gives a personal example of someone who suffered the negative consequences of using drugs. He also expresses concern about his younger brother's future.*)

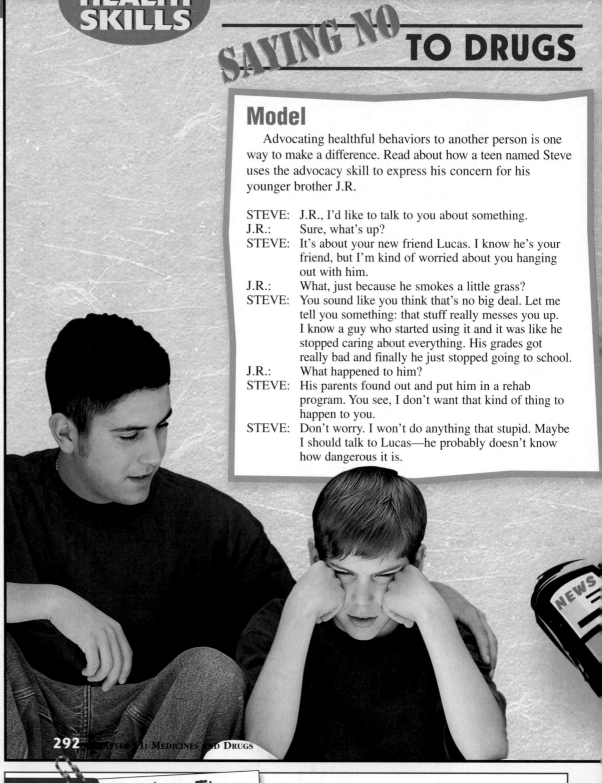

BUILDING HEALTH SKILLS

ADVOCACY

SAYING NO TO DRUGS

Model

Advocating healthful behaviors to another person is one way to make a difference. Read about how a teen named Steve uses the advocacy skill to express his concern for his younger brother J.R.

STEVE: J.R., I'd like to talk to you about something.

J.R.: Sure, what's up?

STEVE: It's about your new friend Lucas. I know he's your friend, but I'm kind of worried about you hanging out with him.

J.R.: What, just because he smokes a little grass?

STEVE: You sound like you think that's no big deal. Let me tell you something: that stuff really messes you up. I know a guy who started using it and it was like he stopped caring about everything. His grades got really bad and finally he just stopped going to school.

J.R.: What happened to him?

STEVE: His parents found out and put him in a rehab program. You see, I don't want that kind of thing to happen to you.

STEVE: Don't worry. I won't do anything that stupid. Maybe I should talk to Lucas—he probably doesn't know how dangerous it is.

292 CHAPTER 11: MEDICINES AND DRUGS

Teaching Tips

Exploring Attitudes About Drug Use The lesson provides an opportunity to discuss how some teens believe their peers are casual about others' use of drugs such as marijuana. Point out that not only do most teens *not* use drugs, they prefer that others abstain as well. Advocacy allows these teens to find their voices.

Facilitating Creativity Creative expression, such as developing a brochure, provides an opportunity for students to demonstrate knowledge in an innovative way. It integrates language arts, fine arts, and personal experience. These activities can be done individually or in groups.

Practice

Read the scenario below about a teen named Marnie who wants to advocate avoiding drugs to her friends. What are some of the ways Marnie could take a stand on this issue? What approach do you think would be most effective? Write a dialogue in which Marnie shares her views with her friends. Show how she uses advocacy skills to take a clear position and be convincing.

Marnie is having lunch with some friends. A few of the other girls start talking about a party they went to where some people were using drugs. They are talking about it as if they think it's normal. Marnie is worried about her friends. She wants to make sure they understand about the dangers of using drugs.

Apply/Assess

Work with a group to create an illustrated brochure that will convince other teens to remain drug free. Use three or four blank sheets of unlined paper. On them, provide information about how drug use can harm physical, mental/emotional, and social health. Your brochure should also include information about the many benefits of a drug-free lifestyle. Use design features such as color, highlighting, and bulleted lists to make your main points stand out. Illustrate your brochure with your own drawings or with photographs cut out of magazines and newspapers. Finally, make an attractive cover for your brochure and give it a catchy, health-promoting title.

Advocacy

Using the skill of advocacy means you
- take a clear stand on an issue.
- persuade others to make healthy choices.
- are convincing.

Self-✓Check

- Did our brochure take a clear stand against drugs?
- Did we give reasons for avoiding drugs?
- Would our message persuade others to stay drug free?

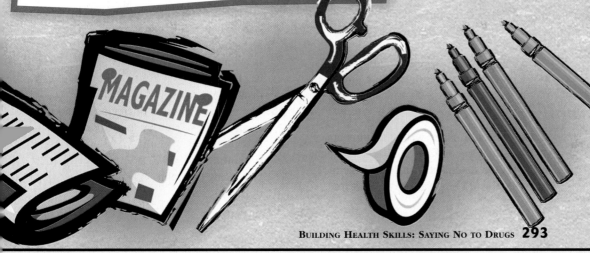

BUILDING HEALTH SKILLS: SAYING NO TO DRUGS **293**

2. Practice

- After students have read the scenario, have them brainstorm ways in which Marnie could advocate effectively for avoiding drug use. Ask: Which approaches do you think would work best?

- Have students write a dialogue in which Marnie demonstrates ways to use health information to help others. By using the skill of advocacy, she helps her friends understand the dangers of drug use and remain drug free.

- Keep Transparency Master 10 displayed to help students incorporate key elements of the advocacy skill into their dialogues.

3. Apply/Assess

- 📂 You may wish to distribute Building Health Skills Reproducible Master 36 in the TCR to guide students in completing this activity.

- Divide the class into groups, and distribute materials to each group.

- Have students create illustrated brochures to persuade other teens to stay drug free. Content should include the dangers of drug use on all three aspects of health and the many benefits of a drug-free lifestyle. Keep Transparency Master 10 displayed for reference.

- Emphasize that brochures should be visually attractive and should appeal to a teen audience.

- If time permits, encourage groups to present and explain their brochures to the class.

- Remind students to refer to the Self-Check before and after they create their brochures.

Assessment Scoring

Using a rubric, student work should provide evidence of all criteria to achieve the highest score.

Skills
Student work
- takes a clear stand against drugs.
- is persuasive and convincing.
- shows awareness of a teen audience.

Concept
Student work provides
- accurate information about the effects of drug use.
- a connection between drug use and health.

Checking Comprehension

Use the Chapter 11 Assessment to examine the most important ideas presented in the chapter.

Answers to Reviewing Vocabulary and Concepts

Lesson 1
1. drugs
2. vaccines
3. prescription medicine
4. medicines
5. tolerance
6. over-the-counter (OTC) medicine

Lesson 2
7. false; stimulants
8. false; depressants
9. true
10. true

Lesson 3
11. b
12. a
13. d

Lesson 4
14. d
15. a

Thinking Critically

16. Responses might say that the label indicates proper dosage, provides warnings, and explains the medicine's purpose.

After You Read

Use your completed Foldable to review the information on medicines and drugs.

FOLDABLES™ Study Organizer

Reviewing Vocabulary and Concepts

On a sheet of paper, write the numbers 1–6. After each number, write the term from the list that best completes each sentence.

- medicines
- over-the-counter (OTC) medicine
- prescription medicine
- drugs
- tolerance
- vaccines

Lesson 1

1. _____ change the structure or function of the body or mind.
2. _____ cause the immune system to produce antibodies.
3. A type of medicine that requires a physician's written order is _____.
4. To treat or prevent diseases, you might take _____.
5. _____ occurs when a person's body becomes used to the effects of a substance.
6. Medicine that is safe enough to be taken without a written order from a physician is _____.

Lesson 2

On a sheet of paper, write the numbers 7–10. Write *True* or *False* for each statement below. If the statement is false, change the underlined word or phrase to make it true.

7. Substances that speed up body functions are called <u>depressants</u>.
8. <u>Stimulants</u> are substances that slow down the body's functions and reactions.
9. Physicians may prescribe <u>narcotics</u> such as morphine to treat extreme pain.
10. <u>Hypnotics</u> are very strong drugs that bring on sleep.

On a sheet of paper, write the numbers 11–15. After each number, write the letter of the answer that best completes each statement.

Lesson 3

11. PCP and LSD are examples of
    a. narcotics.
    b. hallucinogens.
    c. inhalants.
    d. stimulants.
12. An addiction in which the body feels a direct need for a drug is
    a. physical addiction.
    b. abusive addiction.
    c. psychological addiction.
    d. dependent addiction.
13. Which is associated with club drugs?
    a. bulking up muscles
    b. inhaling harmful fumes
    c. increased acne
    d. drug slipping

Lesson 4

14. Someone who stops using an addictive substance may experience symptoms such as
    a. hallucinations.
    b. vomiting.
    c. chills.
    d. all of the above.
15. The physical process of freeing the body of an addictive substance is called
    a. withdrawal.
    b. quitting.
    c. kicking the habit.
    d. detoxification.

INCLUSION STRATEGIES

Special Learning Needs, Behavior Problems, English Language Learners The following suggestions are helpful for students with special learning needs, students with behavior problems, and ELL students:

- Pair these students with more proficient learners who can help summarize the main concepts of the chapter.

- 🎧 Direct these students to listen to the Teen Health Audio Summaries. This component provides an audio and written summary of the chapter in both English and Spanish.

- Use photographs, drawings, or magazine clippings whenever possible to help students visualize the important concepts of the chapter.

Thinking Critically

Using complete sentences, answer the following questions on a sheet of paper.

16. Suggest Give three examples to show how reading the label of an OTC medicine and interpreting the instructions correctly can help you use it safely.

17. Evaluate Why would it be dangerous to ride in a car with a driver who has been smoking marijuana?

18. Apply How could a teen use positive peer pressure to help counteract the negative effects of living in an environment where drug abuse exists?

Career Corner

Medical Record Technician If you like managing information, consider a career as a medical record technician. These professionals maintain patients' records in hospitals, clinics, and doctor's offices. They track health information to ensure that patients receive the right treatments and medications.

A medical record technician has an associate's degree in information management. Find out more about this and other health careers by clicking on Career Corner at health.glencoe.com.

17. Marijuana delays reaction time and impairs coordination. These effects increase the chances of a car accident.

18. Responses might include encouraging the user to get help.

Test Practice

1. B

2. B

3. The drops should be good until they are gone unless the expiration date on the bottle comes first. One hundred days from August 12 is November 20, so the drops are good for 100 days from August 12. They will be gone before the expiration date on the bottle.

Reteaching

Assign Study Guide 11 in the Student Activities Workbook.

Evaluate

Use the reproducible Chapter 11 Test in the TCR, or construct your own test using the **Exam** *View*® Pro Testmaker.

Enrichment

Have students work in cooperative groups to plan and make flip books warning of the dangers of particular drugs.

Standardized Test Practice

Math

Read the paragraph below and then answer the questions.

Over-the-counter medicines have an expiration date printed on them. These dates tell you the last date that you can assume that the medicine is safe to use. Prescription medicines have a date printed on the label. This is the date that the prescription was filled. According to the instructions of how much to take and for how long, the medication will be fresh for the length of time of its use.

1. Gina had a bacterial infection and was given 30 antibiotic tablets to take. She is to take one pill three times a day. The date on the prescription bottle is April 23, 2005. What is the last date she should use the medication?

A April 30, 2005
B May 3, 2005
C May 23, 2005
D May 30, 2005

2. Marcus bought some cough syrup dated January 14, 2005. He is to take two teaspoons twice a day and expects to take the medicine for a week. What is the last day he should use this cough syrup?

A January 7, 2005
B January 14, 2005
C January 21, 2005
D January 28, 2005

3. Kai bought some prescription eye drops for his allergies on August 12. They had an expiration date on the label of November 28 of the same year. There are enough drops in the bottle to last for 100 days. Identify the date that Kai should use to determine when he should stop using the drops.

TH05_C3.glencoe.com/quiz

Assessment

Self-Assessment Direct students to review the activities that are provided throughout the chapter. Encourage each student to select one finished product or activity that demonstrates his or her best work for the chapter. Have students explain what they learned and how the examples they selected show their progress.

Career Corner

Medical Record Technician After reviewing the career profile on the health Web site, students might:

• Describe the skills, training, and education needed.

• Do research to identify schools in the area that offer accredited programs for record technicians.

Planning Guide

Chapter 12	Skills/Activities	Reproducible Resources	Assessment
Lesson 1 **How Tobacco Affects the Body** *pages 298–302*	HEALTH SKILLS ACTIVITY ▲ Choose to Refuse Tobacco (*Refusal Skills*), page 300	*Student Activities Workbook available for use with each chapter* 📁 Parent Letter & Activities 12 📁 Concept Map 42 📁 Cross-Curriculum Activity 23 📁 Enrichment Activity 42 📁 Lesson Plan 1 📁 Reading Tutor Activity 41 📁 Reteaching Activity 42	📁 Lesson 1 Quiz
Lesson 2 **Tobacco and Society** *pages 303–307*	**Hands-On Health** ▲ Tobacco Facts Pamphlets, page 306	📁 Concept Map 43 📁 Decision-Making Activity 23 📁 Enrichment Activity 43 📁 Health Lab 12 📁 Lesson Plan 2 📁 Reading Tutor Activity 42 📁 Reteaching Activity 43	📁 Lesson 2 Quiz
Lesson 3 **Choosing to Be Tobacco Free** *pages 308–311*	HEALTH SKILLS ACTIVITY ▲ Be Prepared (*Analyzing Influences*), page 309	📁 Concept Map 44 📁 Cross-Curriculum Activity 24 📁 Decision-Making Activity 24 📁 Enrichment Activity 44 📁 Lesson Plan 3 📁 Reading Tutor Activity 43 📁 Reteaching Activity 44	📁 Lesson 3 Quiz 📁 Chapter 12 Test 📁 Performance Assessment 12
TIME HEALTH	**Smoke Signals** *pages 312–313*		
BUILDING HEALTH SKILLS **Steer Clear of Tobacco** (*Goal Setting*) *pages 314–315*		📁 Building Health Skills Reproducible Master 37	

Standards		Technology
National	**State/Local**	
National Health Education Standard **1.1, 1.3, 1.4, 1.6, 1.8, 5.5, 5.6**		Transparency 42 TeacherWorks™ Internet Activities
National Health Education Standard **1.1, 1.2, 1.3, 1.5, 1.6, 1.8, 4.2, 7.2, 7.4**		Transparency 43 TeacherWorks™
National Health Education Standard **1.4, 1.6, 1.8, 4.1, 4.2, 4.4, 5.6**		Transparency 44 Tape/DVD 2, Segment 1, "Teen Advocacy"; Segment 2, "Refusal Skills TeacherWorks™ MindJogger Videoquiz **Exam**View® Pro Testmaker
National Health Education Standard **1.8, 6.4, 6.6**		Building Health Skills Transparency Master 9

TeacherWorks™

Glencoe's new and exclusive TeacherWorks™ is an all-in-one planner and resource center. Access the complete Teacher Wraparound Edition electronically. Find all your classroom resources with just a few easy clicks, and print them right from your computer. Connect directly to Glencoe's customized Health Web site. Access the National Health Education Standards correlations, or insert your own state standards and match them directly to the electronic Teacher Wraparound Edition.

Language Diversity

- English Audio Summaries
- Spanish Audio Summaries
- English Summaries, Quizzes, and Activities
- Spanish Summaries, Quizzes, and Activities
- Spanish Parent Letters and Activities

KEY TO ABILITY LEVELS

Teaching Strategies that appear throughout the chapters have been identified by one of four codes to give you an idea of their suitability for students of varying learning styles and abilities.

L1 **Level 1** strategies should be within the ability range of all students. Often full class participation is required.

L2 **Level 2** strategies are for average to above-average students or for small groups. Some teacher direction is necessary.

L3 **Level 3** strategies are designed for students able and willing to work independently. Minimal teacher direction is necessary.

INCL Strategies are appropriate for students with particular special needs in a general classroom setting.

Tobacco

Chapter at a Glance

Lesson 1 identifies the types of tobacco and the toxic substances in tobacco and tobacco smoke. It also explains how these substances harm the body.

Lesson 2 focuses on the personal and social costs of tobacco dependency and addiction.

Lesson 3 examines reasons teens try tobacco and offers them strategies to quit using tobacco and to refuse when tobacco is offered.

Health Skills

- Choose to Refuse Tobacco (*Refusal Skills*), p. 300
- Be Prepared (*Analyzing Influences*), p. 309
- Steer Clear of Tobacco (*Goal Setting*), pp. 314–315

296

HANDS-ON ACTIVITY

Anti-Tobacco Graffiti Wall Dedicate a bulletin board or specific wall space in your classroom to be a very visible focus on the cost of tobacco products and alternatives to spending money on them. Have students identify the average cost of a pack of cigarettes or other tobacco products in your community. Write that cost on the Graffiti Wall. Use that cost, and add the calculations for a week and a year. Invite your students to write their ideas of things they'd rather buy with the money than buy tobacco. Keep writing their ideas throughout the tobacco unit. Have students illustrate those ideas with pictures from magazines or their own original drawings.

Tobacco

12

Chapter Introduction

Use the options below to motivate students and preview chapter content.

HEALTH Online

Have students take Health Inventory 12 or read extra credit articles at **health.glencoe.com**. By clicking on Health Updates, both students and teachers can discover the latest news on health topics

GLENCOE TECHNOLOGY

Teen Health Video and DVD Series
(Each format available in both English and Spanish)

 You may wish to use:

- Tape/DVD 2, Segment 1, "Teen Advocacy"; Segment 2, "Refusal Skills"

MindJogger Videoquiz

Use MindJogger to preview or review Chapter 12 content.

TIME HEALTH

Smoke Signals
pages 312–313

HEALTH Online

Do you know the truth about how tobacco damages lifelong health? To find out, take the Health Inventory for Chapter 12 at health.glencoe.com.

FOLDABLES™ Study Organizer

Before You Read

Make this Foldable to record what you learn in Lesson 1 about tobacco's harmful effects. Begin with a plain sheet of 8½" × 11" paper.

Step 1

Fold a sheet of paper in half along the short axis.

Step 2

Open and fold the bottom edge up to form a pocket. Glue the edges.

Step 3

Label the front of the booklet as shown. Label the pockets "Tobacco Products" and "Harmful Effects." Place an index card or quarter sheet of notebook paper into each pocket.

How Tobacco Affects the Body

As You Read

On index cards or quarter sheets of notebook paper, take notes on the different types of tobacco products and how they harm the body. Store these cards in the appropriate pocket of your Foldable.

FOLDABLES™ Study Organizer

Dinah Zike Study Fold

Researching and Observing

Students will use this pocket Foldable to collect and organize their notes on tobacco's harmful effects on the human body. For study cards, students will need 3"× 5" index cards or sheets of notebook paper cut into quarter sections. As students read and study the information on tobacco products in Lesson 1, have them record and define terms, list main ideas and supporting facts, outline cause-and-effect relationships, and give examples of how tobacco affects health. Guide students as they sort and store these study cards in the appropriate pocket of their Foldable, and encourage them to use their study cards to review what they have learned.

Lesson

How Tobacco Affects the Body

① Focus

Lesson Objectives

Students will be able to
- identify several forms of tobacco.
- identify the harmful substances in tobacco.
- list the harmful effects of tobacco on the body.
- explain the impact of addiction to tobacco.

Health Skills
- Refusal Skills, p. 300

Motivators

Quick Write
Write student responses on the board. Then ask: Do you think the person who smokes is aware of these telltale signs? Why or why not?

Bellringer Activity

Ask students to list reasons they have heard people give for smoking or chewing tobacco. Then ask: What reasons have you heard for not using tobacco?

VOCABULARY

For each term, have a student write the correct definition and two false ones on a piece of paper. Ask volunteers to read the three definitions for each term. Have students vote for the definition they think is the correct one and verify their responses by checking the Glossary.

Quick Write

Tobacco use is hard to hide. List telltale signs that help you identify a person who smokes or chews tobacco.

LEARN ABOUT...

- the different forms in which tobacco is sold and consumed.
- the harmful substances in all forms of tobacco.
- the damage tobacco does to body systems.
- the negative effects that tobacco may have on appearance.

VOCABULARY

- nicotine
- addictive
- tar
- cilia
- carbon monoxide

What Is Tobacco?

Tobacco is a plant that grows best in warm, humid climates. The leaves of a tobacco plant are dried, aged for two or three years, mixed with chemicals, and then used to make various products for smoking or chewing.

Tobacco contains a powerful drug that changes the brain's chemistry. This change makes the tobacco user want more and more tobacco. Tobacco use is harmful to people's health and is a major cause of early and preventable death. Nonetheless, many people use some form of tobacco on a regular basis.

Different Tobacco Products

Tobacco products come in many different forms, including cigarettes, cigars, and smokeless tobacco. Regardless of the form, all tobacco products are harmful. That's why there are laws to control the advertising and sale of tobacco products.

Despite the fact that tobacco use is harmful, tobacco companies continue to produce billions of tobacco products every year. *What creates the demand for tobacco products?*

298 CHAPTER 12: TOBACCO

Lesson 1 Resources

Teacher Classroom Resources
- 📁 Parent Letter & Activities 12
- 📁 Concept Map 42
- 📁 Cross-Curriculum Activity 23
- 📁 Enrichment Activity 42
- 📁 Lesson Plan 1
- 📁 Lesson 1 Quiz

- 📁 Reading Tutor Activity 41
- 📁 Reteaching Activity 42
- 🖨 Transparency 42

Student Activities Workbook
- 📁 Chapter 12 Study Guide
- 📁 Applying Health Skills 42

Cigarettes

Cigarettes are the most common form of tobacco. In the United States, millions of people smoke cigarettes. Cigarettes put smokers at risk for emphysema and other lung and heart diseases, cancer, infertility, and stroke. Each year more than 430,000 people in the U.S. die from diseases caused by cigarette smoking.

Cigars and Pipes

Cigars contain the same dangerous substances as cigarettes but in much larger quantities. One large cigar can contain as much tobacco as a pack of cigarettes. Cigar smokers are four to ten times more likely to contract cancer of the mouth, larynx, and esophagus than nonsmokers, and they have a greater risk of dying from heart disease.

Some people smoke pipes, using loose tobacco. Pipe smokers usually inhale less than cigarette smokers, but they still increase their risk of cancer. Cancers of the lip, mouth, and throat are common among pipe smokers.

Smokeless Tobacco

Smokeless tobacco is tobacco that is chewed or sniffed. Common names for it are spit, chew, and snuff. Many people believe that smokeless tobacco is safer than other tobacco products because the user doesn't inhale tobacco smoke. This is not true. Users of smokeless tobacco still absorb poisonous substances through the mouth or nose. Smokeless tobacco has been linked to cancers of the mouth, esophagus, larynx, stomach, and pancreas. Chewing tobacco also stains the teeth and causes tooth loss and gum disease. Moreover, tobacco chewers need to spit out tobacco juice from time to time—a habit that many people find offensive.

Specialty Cigarettes

The use of bidis and cloves has increased in the United States. Bidis are flavored, unfiltered cigarettes from India. Clove cigarettes, which are made in Indonesia, contain tobacco and ground cloves. Bidis and cloves are often sold in health food stores, which may give people the impression that they are safe to smoke. These specialty cigarettes can, however, be even more dangerous than regular cigarettes. Some bidis contain pure tobacco with seven times as much nicotine and twice as much tar as regular cigarettes.

✔ **Reading Check**

Synonyms are words that have similar meanings. Identify synonyms for the following words: *smokeless tobacco, cigarette.*

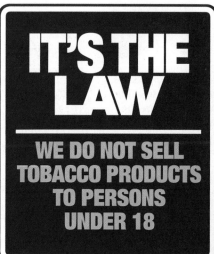

IT'S THE LAW

WE DO NOT SELL TOBACCO PRODUCTS TO PERSONS UNDER 18

State governments have strict laws to keep tobacco out of the hands of anyone under 18. *Why do states specifically regulate teen smoking?*

② Teach

Discussing

Have students name places they know of that have banned smoking either partially or completely. Discuss why those places would consider the substances in tobacco smoke harmful enough to ban smoking. **L1**

Analyzing

Bring several magazine ads for smokeless tobacco to class. (Most will feature athletes using the product.) Have students discuss ways in which those images can have an even greater impact on teen audiences than other cigarette ads. (*Teens may identify more with athletes.*) **L2**

Cross-Curriculum Activity

SOCIAL STUDIES Have students research laws regarding tobacco in your state. They may also want to research the reasons the government allows tobacco to be grown at all. **L3**

Cross-Curriculum Activity

SCIENCE Tell students that nicotine is used in many insecticides because it is lethal. Ask students to determine some of the other industrial uses of this chemical. **L3**

LESSON 1: HOW TOBACCO AFFECTS THE BODY **299**

✔ **Reading Check**

Synonyms Exploring word meanings through the use of synonyms helps readers understand new vocabulary and the subtleties of word meanings. Have students work individually using dictionaries and thesauruses to identify as many synonyms or close synonyms as possible for *smokeless tobacco* and *cigarette*. Examples are *smokeless tobacco—spit, chew, dip, chaw;* *cigarette—light, smoke, drag, cig*. Spark additional discussion by asking students to consider the differences in meanings of the following restaurant terms that are close synonyms: *smoke free* and *designated nonsmoking*. Have students research the terms to determine the slight differences.

Demonstrating

To demonstrate the harmful effects of chemicals in tobacco, find a plant infested with aphids and cut off a twig or leaf cluster that has many insects on it. Remove the paper from several cigarettes. Boil the tobacco in a cup of water for 15 minutes. Strain the solution by pouring it through filter paper or a paper towel into a glass jar. Add a pinch of soap detergent to this tobacco solution to make it easier to spray. Pour the solution into an atomizer or other spray can. Spray the leaves on top and bottom. Do not breathe the spray. Observe what happens to the aphids. (*The solution kills the aphids because nicotine, a chemical in tobacco, is poisonous.*) **L1**

HEALTH SKILLS ACTIVITY

REFUSAL SKILLS

Have students read the activity introduction, and guide them in discussing Elena's situation and her reactions to it. Ask:

• Why does Elena want to say no to Phoebe's offer?

• Why is it hard for her?

• What approach will be most effective?

Then have pairs of students role-play the conversation.

Note: This skill is introduced in Chapter 6 on pages 149–150.

What Is in Tobacco?

Tobacco and tobacco smoke contain approximately 4,000 chemicals. Over 200 of them are known to be dangerous to humans, especially nicotine, tar, and carbon monoxide.

Nicotine is *an addictive drug found in tobacco leaves and in all tobacco products.* An **addictive** drug is one that is *capable of causing a user to develop intense cravings for it.* When smoked or chewed, nicotine takes less than 7 seconds to reach the brain, where it creates a feeling of stimulation. About 30 minutes later, when the chemicals have left the brain, the user begins to feel discomfort. The desire to recapture the feeling and avoid the feeling of discomfort causes the user to crave more tobacco. The user is chemically dependent on the nicotine in tobacco.

Tar is *a dark, thick, sticky liquid that forms when tobacco burns.* When smokers inhale, tar gets into their lungs. It leaves a residue that destroys **cilia**, the *tiny, hairlike structures that protect the lungs.* Over time, it also destroys the air sacs in the lungs. The presence of tar can make breathing difficult. It is known to cause emphysema, lung cancer, and other lung diseases.

Carbon monoxide is *a colorless, odorless, poisonous gas that is produced when tobacco burns.* The carbon monoxide in smoke passes through the lungs into the bloodstream. There it reduces the amount of oxygen the blood cells can carry. A reduced oxygen supply weakens muscles and blood vessels, which, in turn, may lead to heart attacks and stroke.

To understand the damage that smoking can do, compare the healthy lung (top) with the diseased lung (bottom).

HEALTH SKILLS ACTIVITY

REFUSAL SKILLS

Choose to Refuse Tobacco

Elena, an eighth grader, attends a school that includes grades seven through twelve. One day Phoebe, a popular junior, stops to talk to her on the way home from school. Elena feels flattered by the older girl's attention. Her good mood turns to alarm, however, when Phoebe offers her a bidi.

Elena's health class has just finished a unit on tobacco, and she knows that bidis are harmful. She decides to use the S.T.O.P. refusal skills to deal with the situation.

WHAT WOULD YOU DO?

Apply the S.T.O.P. refusal skills to Elena's situation. With a classmate, role-play a conversation between Elena and Phoebe. Reverse roles and do the role-play again. Were you comfortable using the S.T.O.P. refusal skills? Why or why not?

SAY NO IN A FIRM VOICE.
TELL WHY NOT.
OFFER OTHER IDEAS.
PROMPTLY LEAVE.

300 CHAPTER 12: TOBACCO

DEALING WITH SENSITIVE ISSUES

Raising Student Awareness You may find that students often have difficulty understanding why tobacco use is dangerous if so many people smoke or chew tobacco regularly. Have guest speakers, who suffer from chronic diseases, discuss the negative physical effects of tobacco use. Usually, such speakers are eager to tell students how they themselves ignored, or were ignorant of, the long-term dangers when they started using tobacco. Encourage them to discuss their efforts to quit the tobacco habit. Were they successful? What health problems do they still suffer from despite quitting? How has using tobacco affected each aspect of their health? If they could change anything about their past behavior or decisions, what would it be and why?

How Tobacco Affects the User's Body

The chemicals in tobacco and tobacco smoke cause damage to most of the body's systems. Tobacco use is particularly damaging to teens because their bodies are still growing and developing. Some of the effects of tobacco use are evident almost immediately. Others become apparent over time. **Figure 12.1** shows both the short-term and the long-term harmful effects of tobacco use on body systems.

FIGURE 12.1

SHORT-TERM AND LONG-TERM EFFECTS OF TOBACCO USE

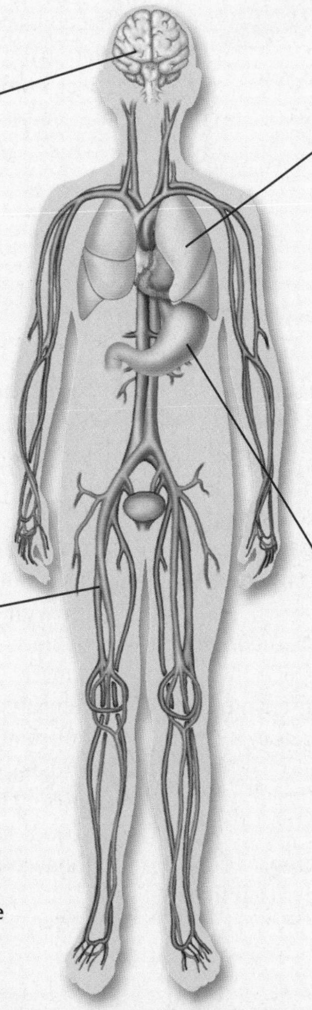

A Nervous System
Short-term effects: Changes take place in brain chemistry. Withdrawal symptoms (nervousness, shakes, headaches) may occur as soon as 30 minutes after the last cigarette. The heart rate and blood pressure increase.
Long-term effects: There is an increased risk of stroke due to decreased flow of oxygen to the brain.

B Circulatory System
Short-term effects: Heart rate is increased. Energy is reduced because less oxygen gets to body tissues.
Long-term effects: Blood vessels are weakened and narrowed. Cholesterol levels increase. Blood vessels are clogged due to fatty buildup. Oxygen flow to heart is reduced. Risk of heart disease and stroke is greater.

C Respiratory System
Short-term effects: User has bad breath, shortness of breath, reduced energy, coughing, and more phlegm (mucus). Colds and flu are more frequent. Allergies and asthma problems increase. Bronchitis and other serious respiratory illnesses increase.
Long-term effects: Risk of lung cancer, emphysema, and other lung diseases increases.

D Digestive System
Short-term effects: User has upset stomach, bad breath, stained teeth, dulled taste buds, and tooth decay.
Long-term effects: Risk of cancer of the mouth and throat, gum and tooth disease, stomach ulcers, and bladder cancer increases.

Lesson 1

Analyzing

Ask students to write three goals they have set for their lives. Discuss how the use of tobacco could hinder students in achieving their goals. For more information on the harmful effects of tobacco use, see Figure 12.1. **L1**

VISUAL LEARNING

FIGURE 12.1 Divide the class into four groups, and assign each group one of the body systems shown in Figure 12.1: nervous, circulatory, respiratory, or digestive. Instruct the members of each group to read and discuss the information presented. Then have them explain that information to the rest of the class. **INCL** *English Language Learners, Special Learning Needs, Behavior Problems, Different Learning Styles* (*Visual*)

Critical Thinking

Emphasize that the effects of tobacco are particularly damaging to teens because their bodies are still developing. Ask students: If you damage your body as it is still developing, what activities or sports may it be hard to do or play? **L1**

COOPERATIVE LEARNING ACTIVITY

The Effects of Tobacco Arrange students into small groups. Ask each group to draw the outline of a human figure on a large piece of drawing paper. Each group will then diagram the parts of the body affected by smoking or chewing tobacco. They can draw specific organs or just circle the parts of the body. (Refer to Figure 12.1 above.) Explanations can be placed beside the body, and arrows can be drawn to the affected area. Ask representatives from each group to present their drawings and summarize their explanations to the class. Display completed work on the wall or on a bulletin board. Remind students to refer to the completed diagrams when they are studying for the lesson or chapter test. **INCL** *English Language Learners, Special Learning Needs, Behavior Problems, Different Learning Styles* (*Visual*)

The benefits of healthy habits that you develop in your teen years will last a lifetime. *How does staying tobacco free help you maintain a healthy appearance?*

Tobacco and Appearance

Most of the damage caused by tobacco use occurs inside the body. However, tobacco use also harms a person's outer appearance. Every time a person uses a tobacco product, the smell of tobacco lingers on his or her hands, breath, hair, and clothing.

Over time, tobacco use can lead to stained teeth and fingers. Tobacco users often look older more quickly because their skin wrinkles. With shortness of breath and frequent coughing, smokers are generally less physically fit than nonsmokers. Smokeless tobacco users often develop cracked lips, inflamed gums, and sores in their mouths.

A tobacco user's appearance can affect his or her social relationships. Many people are offended by a tobacco user's smelly breath, hair, and clothing, and they don't want to get close to him or her.

Lesson 1 Review

Using complete sentences, answer the following questions on a sheet of paper.

Reviewing Terms and Facts

1. **Recall** Name five forms of tobacco.
2. **Explain** Why is smoking cigars or using smokeless tobacco just as harmful as smoking cigarettes?
3. **Vocabulary** Define the terms *nicotine* and *addictive*.
4. **Restate** Describe some long-term effects that tobacco has on the respiratory system and the digestive system.

Thinking Critically

5. **Hypothesize** Why do you think cigarettes are more commonly used than other forms of tobacco?

6. **Synthesize** Explain why tobacco use can negatively affect a person's social relationships.

Applying Health Skills

7. **Advocacy** Demonstrate ways to use health information to help others: Find a local chapter of the American Cancer Society, American Heart Association, American Dental Association, or American Lung Association on the Internet. Request information about the effects of smoking or using smokeless tobacco. Use this information to prepare a display for the school library or nurse's office on what tobacco does to the body.

302 CHAPTER 12: TOBACCO

Tobacco and Society

Who Buys Tobacco?

Tobacco is a big business in the United States. In one year, tobacco companies spend over $6.8 billion on marketing and advertising campaigns. That's more than $18.5 million every day! In spite of all this advertising, tobacco use among adults has declined over 40 percent since 1965. Today, the majority of adults—about 75 percent—don't use tobacco.

Tobacco companies want to attract new users to replace those who have either quit or died. In the eyes of the tobacco industry, children and teens represent the most profitable market. People who become addicted to nicotine as teens are likely to spend thousands of dollars on tobacco products in their lifetime. As a result of lawsuits settled in 1998, tobacco companies have agreed not to use cartoon characters and other advertising methods that might attract children and teens. Nevertheless, the industry continues to find ways to lure young smokers.

Antitobacco advertisements tell another side to the tobacco story. *Explain how billboards like this one can positively influence individual and community health.*

Quick Write

What can be done to reduce the number of people in your community who use tobacco?

LEARN ABOUT...

- why people become addicted to tobacco.
- how tobacco use harms other people.
- the costs to society of tobacco use.

VOCABULARY

- addiction
- physical dependence
- psychological dependence
- withdrawal
- secondhand smoke
- mainstream smoke
- sidestream smoke

---

1 Focus

Lesson Objectives

Students will be able to

- discuss both physical and psychological addiction to tobacco.
- list the harmful effects of secondhand smoke on nonsmokers.
- describe the costs of tobacco on society.

Motivators

Quick Write

Allow time for students to share and discuss their responses. List each idea on the board. Then have the class vote on the one action that they think would be most effective.

Bellringer Activity

Ask students to describe, in their own words, what the term *addiction* means. Then ask them to think about how addiction could affect one's physical, mental/emotional, and social health.

VOCABULARY

Instruct students to find definitions for the vocabulary terms. In the process they might locate other terms with which they are not familiar. Encourage students to learn the definitions of those new terms as well. Ask students to explain how the terms they have learned relate to the use of tobacco.

Lesson 2 Resources

Teacher Classroom Resources

- Concept Map 43
- Decision-Making Activity 23
- Enrichment Activity 43
- Health Lab 12
- Lesson Plan 2
- Lesson 2 Quiz

- Reading Tutor Activity 42
- Reteaching Activity 43
- Transparency 43

Student Activities Workbook

- Chapter 12 Study Guide
- Applying Health Skills 43

Lesson 2

② Teach

HEALTH Online

Encourage students to explore the Web Links for this chapter and then complete the activity.

Comprehending

Display several tobacco ads cut from magazines. Ask:

• Who is the intended audience for each ad?

• What message does the ad communicate?

• How do you think the ad tries to lure young smokers? **L2**

Discussing

Ask students: Why would a cigarette company give away sample packages of cigarettes? Do they have an obligation to only hand these out to adults? Should this practice be allowed? Are there any laws regulating this practice? **L1**

Interviewing

Ask volunteers to interview tobacco users and former tobacco users. Have the students ask the tobacco users how easy it would be for them to quit if they wanted to. Have the students also ask the former tobacco users how easy it was for them to quit. How were they successful? Ask the students to share their findings with the class. **L3**

HEALTH Online

Topic: Tobacco

For a link to more information on tobacco use, go to **health.glencoe.com.**

Activity: Using the information provided at this link, prepare an oral report that includes statistics on tobacco use. Make sure you emphasize the importance of a tobacco-free lifestyle.

An Expensive Habit

Tobacco use is not only an unhealthy habit but also an expensive one. People who use tobacco frequently pay higher health insurance rates. They generally have more doctor and dental bills because of tobacco-related illnesses. There is also the cost of the tobacco product itself. A pack of cigarettes costs around $3.25. At that rate, smokers who smoke a pack a day will spend over $1,100 each year just on cigarettes.

Tobacco Addiction

Despite the high personal costs and health risks of tobacco use, a number of people continue to smoke or chew tobacco. They may want to stop but find it difficult or frustrating. This is because they have formed a chemical dependency on, or addiction to, the nicotine in tobacco. An **addiction** is *a physical or psychological need for a drug.* Addiction develops from regular use of a drug. Nicotine addiction can occur in a short amount of time. Nicotine causes two types of addiction.

• **Physical dependence** is *a type of addiction in which the body itself feels a direct need for a drug.* Nicotine affects body temperature, heart rate, digestion, and muscle tone. Once the nicotine level drops or the nicotine leaves the body's systems, the body craves more. Tobacco users don't feel normal unless their bodies are under the influence of nicotine.

• **Psychological dependence** is *an addiction in which the mind sends the body a message that it needs more of a drug.* Certain events, situations, and habits trigger a desire to use tobacco. Teens might think they need to smoke a cigarette to help them relax at a party or to help them be more alert before a test. Many smokers feel the need for a cigarette every time they talk on the telephone or finish a meal.

According to the Centers for Disease Control and Prevention, nicotine addiction is the most common form of drug addiction in the United States. Nicotine is more addictive than heroin or cocaine. Teens are more likely to develop a severe level of addiction than people who begin to use tobacco at a later age.

You Can Quit!

Two-thirds of the adults who smoke say that they would like to quit, and teen smokers are as eager to quit as adults are. In the year 2000, 70 percent of teen smokers said they regretted having started. Despite the difficulties associated with quitting, approximately 44 million American adults are now former smokers. **Figure 12.2** shows the number of former smokers in the United States population between 1970 and 1998.

MORE ABOUT...

Nicotine It only takes less than 10 seconds for nicotine to reach the brain after a person inhales tobacco smoke. In that short amount of time, the nicotine is absorbed into the bloodstream through the lining of the mouth and through the lungs. The smoker's blood pressure goes up; heart rate increases by 33 beats per minute; oxygen supply for body circulation to the arms, hands, legs, and feet decreases. Then, as the text states, the first "rush" of stimulation of the brain is followed by depression and fatigue, leading the smoker to seek even more nicotine—another cigarette.

Withdrawal

In order to quit, tobacco users have to go through **withdrawal**, *the physical and psychological symptoms that occur when someone stops using an addictive substance.* Physical symptoms of nicotine withdrawal include the craving to use nicotine, headaches, shakiness, fatigue, increased appetite, and nausea. Psychological symptoms include feeling irritable, nervous, anxious, and sad. People going through withdrawal may have trouble thinking during the day and sleeping during the night. The intensity of withdrawal symptoms and the length of time they last vary from person to person. An inability or reluctance to cope with withdrawal is often the main obstacle to quitting tobacco use.

FIGURE 12.2

LOOK WHO'S NOT SMOKING

The number of Americans who don't smoke, either because they never started or because they quit, has been rising steadily.

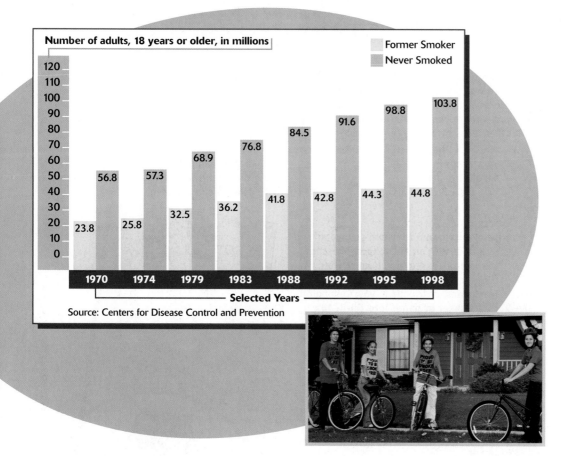

Source: Centers for Disease Control and Prevention

LESSON 2: TOBACCO AND SOCIETY **305**

Lesson 2

Guest Speaker

Invite an addiction specialist to speak to the class about addiction to nicotine. Suggest that the speaker address issues such as chemical and psychological dependence on nicotine and how nicotine compares with other addictive drugs in its health impact, economic costs, and addictive potential. After the speaker has concluded his or her presentation, ask students to use what they have learned to write brief essays in which they explain the impact of chemical dependency and addiction to tobacco. **L1**

VISUAL LEARNING

FIGURE 12.2 Help students study and discuss the information in the graph. Ask:

• Are the numbers of former smokers and nonsmokers increasing or decreasing? How can you tell?

• In 1992, how many people were former smokers? How many had never smoked? **INCL** *English Language Learners, Special Learning Needs, Behavior Problems, Different Learning Styles (Visual)*

PROMOTING COORDINATED SCHOOL HEALTH

The Cost of Prevention Many believe that a person's lifestyle cannot be influenced by schools and social agencies. Still others believe that schools cannot afford the costs of problems stemming from the following: low self-esteem; dropout rate from school; participation in high-risk behaviors, sexually transmitted diseases, and teen pregnancy; health costs associated with poor prenatal care; ineffective parenting practices; malnutrition; and poor mental health. One mechanism for schools to improve the health of their students, faculty, and staff is through a coordinated school health program. For more information, consult *Planning a Coordinated School Health Program* in the TCR.

Lesson 2

Developing Good Character ★

Citizenship

Discuss with students the idea of "the common good." Ask: In the United States, what are our processes for making decisions that affect everybody? In addition to banning smoking in public areas, what are other health-related issues where decisions have been made for "the common good"?

Hands-On Health

TOBACCO FACTS PAMPHLETS

Time: 1 hour (more if students do all writing and drawing during class sessions)

TEACHING THE ACTIVITY

- Guide students in reading and discussing the activity introduction and instructions.
- Ask each student to identify the group to which he or she will direct the anti-tobacco message.
- Have students work independently to plan and create their pamphlets.

ASSESSMENT

Have students share copies of their pamphlets and discuss the reactions of teens who received them.

Developing Good Character ★

Citizenship

A ban on smoking in public places such as malls, restaurants, and theaters helps protect the health of nonsmokers. *What are the nonsmoking policies in your community?*

The Costs to Society

Individuals who use tobacco are not the only ones harmed by its effects. Smoke from cigarettes, cigars, and pipes also threatens the health of nonsmokers. In addition, the harm tobacco causes adds up to serious costs for families and society.

Secondhand Smoke

Secondhand smoke is *air that has been contaminated by tobacco smoke.* There are two kinds of secondhand smoke. **Mainstream smoke** is *smoke that a smoker inhales and then exhales.* **Sidestream smoke** is *smoke given off by the burning end of a cigarette, cigar, or pipe.* Sidestream smoke contains twice as much tar and nicotine as mainstream smoke.

Hands-On Health

TOBACCO FACTS PAMPHLETS

Antitobacco programs in schools have been very successful in reducing tobacco use among young people. In this activity you will use your health knowledge to help other teens stay away from tobacco.

WHAT YOU WILL NEED
- sheet of paper
- pen and colored markers

WHAT YOU WILL DO
1. Think of a group to whom you would like to deliver an antitobacco message. It should be a group you know well, such as your scout troop, your soccer teammates, or friends in your community.
2. Fold a sheet of paper into thirds to make a six-page pamphlet.
3. Put a catchy title for your pamphlet on the cover.
4. Use the other pages to list facts that may persuade the group to stay tobacco free.
5. Illustrate your pamphlet with antitobacco drawings, cartoons, or logos.
6. Photocopy your pamphlet so you have enough copies for everyone in the group.

IN CONCLUSION
Give your pamphlet to the members of the group. Ask them to share the pamphlet with other groups of teens.

306 CHAPTER 12: TOBACCO

WHAT TEENS WANT TO KNOW

What can I do to promote a smoke-free environment? Suggest the following activities for students to strengthen their resolve not to smoke and assist others in doing so. (1) Encourage students to do volunteer work for the American Lung Association, American Cancer Society, or the American Heart Association. (2) Encourage students to organize and conduct presentations for elementary school students in order to help prevent young children from becoming future smokers. (3) Suggest that students organize peer-support groups to help students stop smoking. (4) Suggest that students brainstorm ways to create a smoke-free school or public environment. (5) Have students analyze how smoking affects their lives.

Nonsmokers can develop respiratory illnesses such as pneumonia and bronchitis as a result of secondhand smoke. Infants and young children who are constantly exposed to secondhand smoke have more colds, ear infections, allergies, and asthma than children who grow up in smoke-free homes. Secondhand smoke can also lead to lung disease, heart disease, and cancer in nonsmokers.

Public Health Costs

Tobacco-related illnesses increase the cost of medical care for everyone. Consumers must pay higher rates for health care insurance in order to cover these costs. Taxpayers must also pay the medical bills of patients who lack health insurance.

Costs to the Nation's Economy

People who miss work because of tobacco-related illnesses produce fewer goods and services. As a result, companies earn less money. Productive time is also lost when tobacco users leave their workstations to have a cigarette. Tobacco use costs the United States almost $100 billion each year in health care costs and lost productivity.

Pregnancy and Tobacco

Females who smoke during pregnancy increase their risk of having a low birth weight baby and a premature delivery. Nicotine and carbon monoxide keep needed nutrients and oxygen from the fetus. The incidence of Sudden Infant Death Syndrome (SIDS) is also higher in homes where parents smoke.

Because smoking can harm a fetus and a young baby, pregnant females should never smoke. *What other healthful behaviors can pregnant females practice?*

Lesson 2 Review

Using complete sentences, answer the following questions on a sheet of paper.

Reviewing Terms and Facts

1. **Vocabulary** Define the term *addiction*. Use it in an original sentence.
2. **Contrast** How do physical dependence and psychological dependence differ?
3. **Recall** What are three symptoms of nicotine withdrawal?
4. **Describe** Identify the two types of smoke that nonsmokers might inhale.

Thinking Critically

5. **Apply** Explain the impact of chemical dependency and addiction to tobacco.
6. **Summarize** Why are pregnant women advised not to smoke?

Applying Health Skills

7. **Advocacy** Make a poster showing the effects of secondhand smoke on non-smokers. Your poster should express a point of view about the rights of non-smokers. Be sure to include the facts to support your point of view. Display your poster in the classroom.

LESSON 2: TOBACCO AND SOCIETY **307**

Lesson 2 Review

1. A physical or psychological need for a drug. Sentences should reflect definition.
2. Physical dependence is when the body feels a direct need for a drug; psychological dependence is when the mind sends a message to the body that it needs more of a drug.
3. Any three: the craving to use nicotine, headaches, shakiness, fatigue, increased appetite, nausea, irritability, nervousness, anxiety, sadness.
4. Mainstream smoke and sidestream smoke.
5. Possible response: Chemical dependency and addiction to tobacco cause many health problems because it is difficult to quit, and regular use of tobacco harms the body.
6. Smoking increases risk of low birth weight babies, premature births, and SIDS.

① Focus

Lesson Objectives

Students will be able to

- discuss why some teens start using tobacco.
- identify strategies for avoiding tobacco use.
- explain ways smokers can quit.

Health Skills

- Analyzing Influences, p. 309

Motivators

Quick Write
Call on students to read one of the reasons they listed. Then ask whether the reasons given are worth the health risks.

Bellringer Activity

Have each student write five ways to refuse something they don't want. Encourage them to use humor in some of their refusal statements.

VOCABULARY

Direct students to find the definitions for the vocabulary terms in the lesson. Then have them explain how each term relates to being tobacco free.

Quick Write

Why do some teens begin using tobacco? List all the reasons you can think of.

LEARN ABOUT...

- reasons some teens start using tobacco.
- strategies for avoiding tobacco use.
- ways to quit using tobacco.

VOCABULARY

- cold turkey
- nicotine patch

Why Some Teens Start to Use Tobacco

The good news is that the majority of young teens—about 65 percent—don't smoke. In addition, smoking among high school students began to decline in 1998. The bad news is that each day, 4,800 teens smoke their first cigarette. Of this group, 2,000 will become regular smokers. One-third of these will eventually die of smoking-related illnesses.

Internal Influences

Teens may start using tobacco because of internal influences.

- **Stress.** Teens may think that tobacco will help them relax and cope with stress. They don't realize that the symptoms of withdrawal from nicotine, which occur as often as every 30 minutes, will add to their daily stresses.
- **Weight.** Some teens wrongly believe that using tobacco will help them maintain a healthy weight. In reality, its use reduces a person's capacity for aerobic exercise and sports.
- **Image.** Using cigarette lighters and blowing smoke makes some teens feel grown up. Teens who are really mature know that they don't want to give up lifelong health just to look "cool."

The best way to maintain a healthy weight is to stay active and eat a healthful diet. *Why doesn't tobacco fit into a healthy weight-management plan?*

Lesson 3 Resources

Teacher Classroom Resources

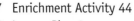 Concept Map 44

Cross-Curriculum Activity 24

Decision-Making Activity 24

Enrichment Activity 44

Lesson Plan 3

Lesson 3 Quiz

Reading Tutor Activity 43

 Reteaching Activity 44

 Transparency 44

Student Activities Workbook

 Chapter 12 Study Guide

Applying Health Skills 44

Health Inventory 12

Explanations

1. **Damage to the lungs, heart, and circulation occurs within days after a person starts smoking,** says Jack Fincham, Ph.D., of the University of Kansas. That's because cigarette smoke contains a lethal list of toxins: cyanide, methanol (wood alcohol), ammonia, and poisonous gases like carbon monoxide. In addition, check out this scary statistic: The younger a person is when he or she starts smoking, the more likely lung growth will be stunted for life.

2. According to Fincham, nearly 50 percent of all previous nonsmokers who smoke more than two cigarettes go on to become regular smokers within a year. **What's more, of those new smokers, nearly 90 percent are under age 21.** (Most smokers start their habit between the ages of 10 and 18.)

3. As surprising as it may sound, **cigarettes are considered as addictive as drugs like cocaine and even heroin,** according to Saul Shiffman, Ph.D., of the Smoking Research Group at the University of Pittsburgh. That's because nicotine, which occurs naturally in tobacco, is very addictive. Also, cigarette smoking is associated with other drug use. According to a recent Surgeon General's report, teens who smoke are three times more likely to use alcohol, eight times more likely to use marijuana, and 22 times more likely to use cocaine than teens who don't smoke.

4. According to the Centers for Disease Control and Prevention (CDC), **teens often underestimate the addictiveness of nicotine.** Seventy-five percent of people who were daily smokers in high school but planned to quit were still smoking six years later. Also, even after quitting, former smokers have a permanent physical tolerance to nicotine. That means even one cigarette smoked years later could be enough to get a person hooked again.

5. **According to reports by the CDC, lifelong smokers who die from a smoking-related disease have probably lost about 12 years of their typical life span.** The upside: Fifteen years after smokers quit, their life expectancy reverts to nearly the same as that of lifelong nonsmokers. ◼

New Names, Same Danger

Are "herbal" cigarettes just as dangerous as regular cigarettes? You bet. Here are the facts:

BIDIS: These small, unfiltered cigarettes are imported from India. Aside from added flavorings, they're nothing more than tobacco leaves rolled in a cigar-like casing. They have three times the nicotine of regular cigarettes and, because they have no filter, a lot more of the tar that causes lung damage.

CLOVES: These are typically two-thirds tobacco and one-third ground cloves. When people inhale, an ingredient deadens sensation in the throat, allowing them to inhale more deeply and hold the smoke in for a longer period. This makes clove cigarettes especially harmful to the lungs.

About the Dangers of Smoking

Brainstorm with your classmates to create an original antismoking ad campaign. What new angle can you take? Use reliable online and print resources to research the subject and to find statistics and facts that will enhance your campaign. Use images from the Internet or from newspapers and magazines to increase the impact of your message. With your teacher's permission, create posters and flyers and distribute them throughout your school.

③ Apply

Time to Think

Instead of (or in addition to) an anti-smoking ad campaign, give students the option of creating a board game. The game should present information on the dangers of smoking and advocate for a tobacco-free lifestyle. Encourage students to be creative in presenting persuasive information in a fun, unique manner. (For instance, correct answers to questions about tobacco move players around a board shaped like lungs.) Other alternatives to posters and flyers include

- a children's book.
- a collection of jokes.
- a music video.
- a song or poem.

VISUAL LEARNING

Ask students to quickly brainstorm words to describe this photograph of cigarette butts. (*gross, ugly, nasty, and so on.*) Discuss the fact that cigarette butts are a major source of pollution littering our streets, parks, and beaches. Just one more way tobacco use harms our health.

Beyond the Classroom

Community Explain to students that as we learn more about the harmful effects of tobacco, social norms about cigarette smoking are gradually changing. Not very long ago, smoking was allowed in restaurants, offices, and bars without restriction. Smoking was allowed on airplanes and trains. Many high schools even had designated smoking areas for students who smoked. Ask students to interview a parent, grandparent, or other person over the age of 40 about attitudes toward smoking when they were younger. How have these attitudes changed over time? Have students present their findings to the class.

GOAL SETTING

Objective

After completing the lesson, students will be able to describe how their goals could be affected by tobacco use.

Time: 40 minutes

Materials: pen or pencil, paper

Teacher Classroom Resources

📁 Building Health Skills Activities

- Transparency Master 9, "Goal Setting"

- Reproducible Master 37, "Steer Clear of Tobacco"

---

1. Model

- Display Transparency Master 9, and review the steps of goal setting with the class.

- After students have read the scenario, ask volunteers to describe how avoiding tobacco use will help Jackson reach his long-term goal. (*He will be able to stay in good shape so that he will have the energy to walk lots of dogs; he will have money to promote his business.*)

BUILDING HEALTH SKILLS

GOAL SETTING

STEER CLEAR OF TOBACCO

Model

Jackson is an ambitious teen. One of his goals is to start his own business walking dogs in his neighborhood. This is a long-term goal that will require a lot of effort to achieve.

Jackson knows that using tobacco will make it much more difficult for him to achieve his goal. Chemicals in tobacco could harm his health, making it harder for him to find the energy he needs to walk the dogs. Using tobacco would also cost him a lot of money that he could be spending to promote his business. So Jackson has made avoiding tobacco one of the steps in his plan to achieve his long-term goal. He makes a conscious effort, not only to be tobacco free himself, but also to avoid secondhand smoke. He politely asks others not to smoke near him when they are in a car or any other enclosed space. With his worries about tobacco out of the way, Jackson can move on to the other steps in his plan to get his business started.

📎 Teaching Tips

Using Scoring Guides Scoring guides are the teacher's version of rubrics. They are designed to help you evaluate and score each student's work fairly and accurately. *Teen Health* provides a task-specific description of the highest score, 4, for each assessment; these descriptions can be found in the Assessment Scoring box. Each rubric presents a specific set of criteria for each scoring level. It is important to remember that all criteria must be met if a specific score is given. For example, if the rubric states that the student's response at the highest level should demonstrate breadth and depth and show relationships between concepts, a response must meet all three of those criteria to receive the highest score.

Planning Guide

Standards		Technology
National	**State/Local**	
National Health Education Standard **1.1, 1.3, 1.6, 1.8, 3.1, 3.4, 5.4, 7.4**		Transparency 45 TeacherWorks™ Internet Activities
National Health Education Standard **1.1, 1.2, 1.3, 1.6, 1.8, 2.6, 5.2, 5.4**		Transparency 46 TeacherWorks™
National Health Education Standard **1.1, 1.4, 1.6, 1.8, 3.1, 4.1, 4.2, 4.4, 5.6**		Transparency 47 Tape/DVD 2, Segment 1, "Teen Advocacy"; Segment 2, "Refusal Skills" TeacherWorks™ MindJogger Videoquiz **Exam***View*® Pro Testmaker
National Health Education Standard **6.1, 6.2, 6.3**		Building Health Skills Transparency Master 8

TeacherWorks™

Glencoe's new and exclusive TeacherWorks™ is an all-in-one planner and resource center. Access the complete Teacher Wraparound Edition electronically. Find all your classroom resources with just a few easy clicks, and print them right from your computer. Connect directly to Glencoe's customized Health Web site. Access the National Health Education Standards correlations, or insert your own state standards and match them directly to the electronic Teacher Wraparound Edition.

Language Diversity

- English Audio Summaries
- Spanish Audio Summaries
- English Summaries, Quizzes, and Activities
- Spanish Summaries, Quizzes, and Activities
- Spanish Parent Letters and Activities

KEY TO ABILITY LEVELS

Teaching Strategies that appear throughout the chapters have been identified by one of four codes to give you an idea of their suitability for students of varying learning styles and abilities.

L1 **Level 1** strategies should be within the ability range of all students. Often full class participation is required.

L2 **Level 2** strategies are for average to above-average students or for small groups. Some teacher direction is necessary.

L3 **Level 3** strategies are designed for students able and willing to work independently. Minimal teacher direction is necessary.

INCL Strategies are appropriate for students with particular special needs in a general classroom setting.

Alcohol

Chapter at a Glance

Lesson 1 emphasizes the harmful effects of alcohol on the body and describes dangers facing teens who use alcohol.

Lesson 2 describes the dangers of drinking, the three stages of alcoholism, the steps to recovery, and where people with drinking problems can turn for help.

Lesson 3 explores factors that underlie teen alcohol use and provides students with ways to say no and healthy alternatives to drinking.

Health Skills
- Helping a Friend Stay Safe (*Communication Skills*), p. 324
- Saying No to a Drink (*Refusal Skills*), p. 332
- Helping Someone Get Help (*Decision Making*), pp. 336–337

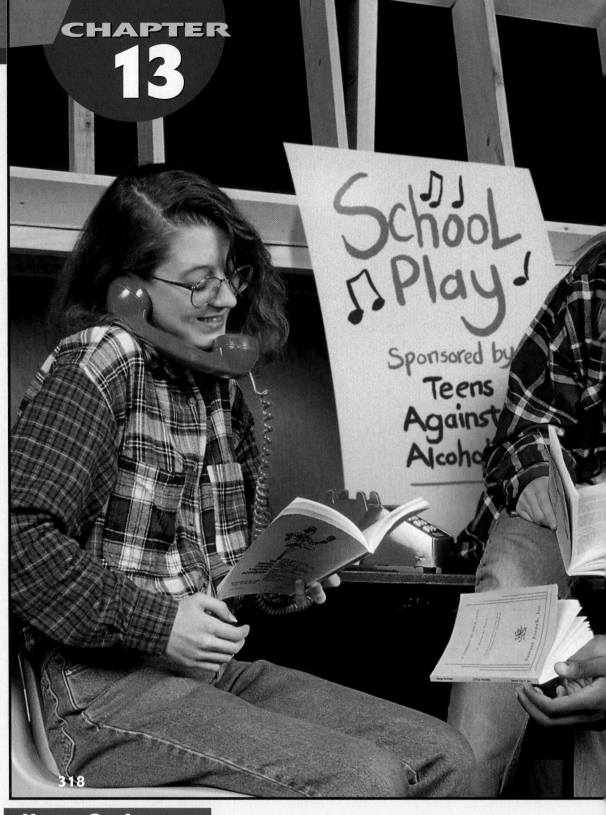

CHAPTER
13

318

HANDS-ON ACTIVITY

Alcohol and the Media Provide students with a selection of popular magazines and ask them to determine which ones have the most advertisements for alcohol. As part of their study, have them determine the target audience for each magazine. Ask them to draw conclusions about the way alcohol is advertised and the people likely to read the magazine. Prompt students by asking: Are the people in the ads having fun? Do they seem sophisticated or not? Are they athletic? As a class, cut out the ads students selected. Place the ads into plastic sleeves and then into a binder. Have the classes' comments added to the binder. Discuss what other possible destructive behaviors are promoted through the media and by which means they are promoted.

Alcohol

Chapter Introduction

Use the options below to motivate students and preview chapter content.

HEALTH *Online*

Do you know how to help someone who has a problem with alcohol? You can find out more by taking the Chapter 13 Health Inventory at health.glencoe.com.

FOLDABLES™ Study Organizer

Before You Read

Make this Foldable to organize the information in Lesson 1 on alcohol and its effects on the body. Begin with a plain sheet of 11″ × 17″ paper.

Step 1

Fold the sheet of paper into thirds along the short axis. This forms three columns.

Step 2

Open the paper and refold into thirds along the long axis, then fold in half lengthwise. This forms six rows.

Step 3

Unfold and draw lines along the folds.

Step 4

Label the chart as shown.

Effects	Short Term	Long Term
Mouth and Esophagus		
Heart and Blood Vessels		
Brain and Nervous System		
Liver		
Stomach and Pancreas		

As You Read

In the appropriate section of the chart, take notes on the short- and long-term effects of drinking alcohol.

319

HEALTH *Online*

Have students visit **health.glencoe.com** and take Health Inventory 13 to rate their knowledge of alcohol and its effects on the body. For new teaching ideas, click on Teaching Today to download helpful tools, such as graphic organizers and Webquest activities.

GLENCOE TECHNOLOGY

Teen Health Video and DVD Series
(Each format available in both English and Spanish)

You may wish to use:

- Tape/DVD 1, Segment 1, "Teen Advocacy"; Segment 2, "Refusal Skills"

MindJogger Videoquiz

Use MindJogger to preview or review Chapter 13 content.

TIME HEALTH

Getting MADD
pages 334–335

FOLDABLES™ Study Organizer

Dinah Zike Study Fold

Organizing Data Using a Chart

As students read and study the material presented in Lesson 1, ask them to record information on the short- and long-term effects of alcohol in the appropriate section of their chart. On the back of their chart, have students describe one of the consequences of teen alcohol use and draw a graph illustrating one of the percentages given on page 323.

What Alcohol Does to the Body

① Focus

Lesson Objectives

Students will be able to

- describe the effects of alcohol on the body.
- explain why alcohol affects each individual differently.
- discuss the effects of alcohol on a fetus.
- identify the special problems alcohol causes in teens.

> **Health Skills**
> - Communication Skills, p. 324

Motivators

 Quick Write
Have students share their lists. Clarify any misperceptions they may have. Ask students to add to their lists as they read the chapter.

Bellringer Activity

Ask students to name two ways that alcohol is like other beverages and two ways that it is not (*liquid, might quench thirst; impair functions, addictive*).

> #### VOCABULARY
> Have students use each of the vocabulary terms in a sentence. Suggest that students look up the definition in a dictionary or in the Glossary in the student text if they do not know the meaning of a term.

Quick Write

List two or three ways that you think alcohol negatively affects the body.

LEARN ABOUT...

- the effects of alcohol on the body.
- why alcohol affects each individual differently.
- the effects of alcohol on a fetus.
- the problems alcohol causes in teens.

VOCABULARY

- alcohol
- cirrhosis
- blood alcohol concentration (BAC)
- intoxicated
- binge drinking
- fetal alcohol syndrome (FAS)

What Alcohol Does to the Body

Alcohol and the Body

Alcohol is *a drug that is produced by a chemical reaction in fruits, vegetables, and grains.* It is a depressant that has powerful effects on the body. In the United States, the law prohibits alcohol use by minors. Adults, however, can choose whether or not to drink alcohol. To make responsible decisions about alcohol use, people need to understand how alcohol affects the body.

Alcohol, like other depressant drugs, slows down the functions of the brain and other parts of the nervous system. It also affects the digestive and urinary systems. Excessive use of alcohol over a long period can damage almost every organ in the body. **Figure 13.1** shows some of the short-term and long-term effects of alcohol consumption.

Avoiding alcohol will help you concentrate and stay focused. *What day-to-day activities in your life require precision and skill?*

Lesson 1 Resources

Teacher Classroom Resources

- Parent Letter & Activities 13
- Concept Map 45
- Cross-Curriculum Activity 25
- Decision-Making Activity 25
- Enrichment Activity 45
- Health Lab 13
- Lesson Plan 1

- Lesson 1 Quiz
- Reading Tutor Activity 44
- Reteaching Activity 45
- Transparency 45

Student Activities Workbook

- Chapter 13 Study Guide
- Applying Health Skills 45

FIGURE 13.1

EFFECTS OF ALCOHOL ON THE BODY

Short-term effects occur within minutes of drinking alcohol. Long-term effects develop over time.

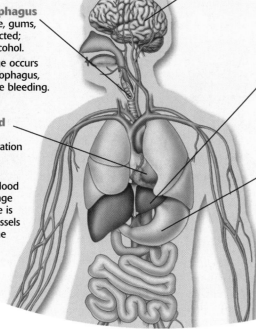

Mouth and Esophagus
Short term: Tongue, gums, and throat are affected; breath smells of alcohol.
Long term: Damage occurs to tissues of the esophagus, resulting in possible bleeding.

Heart and Blood Vessels
Short term: Perspiration increases and skin becomes flushed.
Long term: High blood pressure and damage to the heart muscle is common. Blood vessels harden and become less flexible.

Brain and Nervous System
Short term: Speech is slurred and vision is blurred. Drinker has difficulty walking.
Long term: Brain cells, many of which cannot be replaced, are destroyed. Damage occurs to nerves throughout the body, resulting in numbness in the hands and feet.

Liver
Short term: Liver changes alcohol into water and carbon dioxide.
Long term: Liver is damaged, possibly resulting in **cirrhosis** (suh·ROH·sis), *scarring and destruction of the liver.*

Stomach and Pancreas
Short term: Stomach acids increase, which often results in nausea and vomiting.
Long term: Irritation occurs in the stomach lining, causing open sores called ulcers. Pancreas becomes inflamed.

Alcohol and the Individual

The effect that alcohol has on a person is influenced by a number of factors, including:

- **Body size.** The same amount of alcohol has a greater effect on a small person than it does on a larger person.
- **Gender.** In general, alcohol moves into the bloodstream faster in females.
- **Time frame.** A person who drinks a lot in a short period of time is more likely to become intoxicated. Rapid drinking overwhelms the liver's ability to break down the alcohol.
- **Amount.** Drinking a large quantity of alcohol causes alcohol levels in the bloodstream to rise. If the levels become too high, alcohol poisoning can occur. **Figure 13.2** on the next page shows the alcohol content of some common alcoholic beverages.
- **Food.** Food in the stomach slows down the passage of alcohol into the bloodstream.
- **Medicine.** Alcohol can interfere with the effects of medicines, and medicines can intensify the effects of alcohol.

LESSON 1: WHAT ALCOHOL DOES TO THE BODY **321**

WHAT TEENS WANT TO KNOW

Is it safer to drink beer and wine coolers than to drink hard liquor? No. Beer and wine coolers are not safer than hard liquor. Some teens think these drinks are safer because ounce for ounce, they contain less alcohol than hard liquor. A can of beer or a wine cooler contains as much alcohol as a shot of whiskey. Wine coolers are dangerous because they don't taste like alcohol, so teens may be unaware of the alcohol content. A couple of beers or wine coolers will have the same effect on your body and judgment as the alcohol in two shots of hard liquor. You can prevent alcohol-related accidents and injuries by not drinking, and discouraging your friends from drinking.

FIGURE 13.2

ALCOHOL CONTENT OF DIFFERENT DRINKS

Each of the following contains the same amount of alcohol—about 0.5 oz. of pure alcohol. Beer and wine contain a lower percentage of alcohol by volume than distilled liquors such as vodka or whiskey.

VISUAL LEARNING

FIGURE 13.2 Help students read and discuss Figure 13.2. Be sure all students recognize that beer and wine are alcohol and can be as dangerous as mixed drinks. **INCL** *English Language Learners, Special Learning Needs, Behavior Problems, Different Learning Styles (Visual)*

Investigating

Ask volunteers to learn about alcohol poisoning. In an oral presentation, have them discuss the answers to these questions:

• What is alcohol poisoning?

• What can cause alcohol poisoning?

• What are the symptoms of alcohol poisoning?

• What should be done if a person appears to have alcohol poisoning? Why? **L2**

Developing Good Character ★

Responsibility

Have students imagine a situation in which they are pressured to ride in a car with a driver who is under the influence. As a class, brainstorm refusal statements. Remind students to evaluate whether their decisions are rooted in respect for themselves and others.

Developing Good Character ★

Responsibility

One sign of responsibility is thinking before you act. For example, never put yourself in danger by riding with a driver who has been drinking. Instead, look for a safe alternative for getting home. You might prepare a list of people you could call for a ride.

Blood Alcohol Concentration

The amount of alcohol in a person's bloodstream is referred to as the **blood alcohol concentration (BAC)**. BAC is expressed as a percentage of total blood volume. For example, if a person's BAC is 0.1 percent, then 1/10 of 1 percent of the fluid volume of his or her blood is actually alcohol. A person's BAC depends on the amount of alcohol consumed as well as body size and the other factors discussed on page 321.

A person with a BAC of 0.1 percent—or in some states, 0.08 percent—is considered legally **intoxicated**, or *physically and mentally impaired by the use of alcohol*. Driving while intoxicated can result in a jail term and, in some states, loss of driver's license. For anyone under 21, a BAC above 0 percent is illegal.

Binge drinking—*the consumption of several alcoholic drinks in a very short period of time*—is especially dangerous. Because alcohol is a depressant, it slows body systems down. If the BAC of a binge drinker rises sharply enough, the person will stop breathing and will die.

Fetal Alcohol Syndrome

When a pregnant female drinks alcohol, it passes from her body into her developing baby's bloodstream. A fetus exposed to alcohol in this way may be born with fetal alcohol syndrome.

MORE ABOUT...

Blood Alcohol Concentration One drink is .05 percent blood alcohol concentration (BAC), which can cause sedation and reduced self-control. Two to three drinks is .14 percent BAC, which causes loss of coordination and judgment. Four drinks is .18 percent BAC, which induces intoxication and very slow reaction time. Five to six drinks is .27 percent BAC, which results in a stupor. Seven to eight drinks is .36 percent BAC, which leads to unconsciousness and may cause death. Nine or more drinks is .41 percent BAC, which will lead to death.

Share this information with students. Ask: If a 120-pound teen drank two beers in an hour, what BAC would he or she likely have?

Fetal alcohol syndrome (FAS) is *a group of alcohol-related birth defects that include both physical and mental problems.*

FAS is the leading known cause of mental retardation in the United States. The good news is that it is entirely preventable. Since even small amounts of alcohol can harm a fetus, the only safe decision for a pregnant female is not to drink any alcohol at all.

Alcohol and Teens

Alcohol can interfere with a teen's growth process. Studies show that teens who abuse alcohol have poorer language skills than other teens. New research also suggests that exposure to alcohol during the teen years reduces levels of certain hormones essential to normal development. It may also delay the onset of the menstrual cycle and affect other aspects of sexual maturity.

Teen alcohol use also has many other adverse consequences:

- Up to two-thirds of suicides on college campuses involve alcohol.
- Almost one-half of all traffic deaths of people under age 25 involve alcohol.
- Nearly a quarter of all violent crimes committed by teens involve alcohol.
- Between one-third and two-thirds of date rape cases among teens and college students involve alcohol.

✔ **Reading Check**

Build your vocabulary. Consider what the term *alcohol* means to you. Relate as many details as you can.

Avoiding alcohol helps prevent injuries and builds a better foundation for life. *How might alcohol use contribute to a drowning accident?*

LESSON 1: WHAT ALCOHOL DOES TO THE BODY **323**

Lesson 1

Critical Thinking

Fetal alcohol syndrome is one example of a way in which one person's drinking can hurt another. Ask students to identify other ways in which a person's drinking can negatively affect others, either directly or indirectly. **L1**

Comparing

Discuss the effects of alcohol on teens. Ask:

- How are these effects different from the effects of alcohol on adults?
- How does alcohol use relate to communicable disease?
- What do you consider the most serious danger of teen alcohol consumption? Why?

HEALTH SKILLS ACTIVITY

(*See Student page 324.*)

COMMUNICATION SKILLS

Guide students in discussing Leah's situation. Review and discuss speaking and listening skills. Then have students brainstorm possible sentences Leah might use to begin a conversation with Becky. For example:

- Did you know that Mike's parents aren't going to be home?
- I'm worried about this party. Some of the other kids might be drinking.
- Let's think of something else fun to do that night.

Have students work with partners to role-play possible conversations between Leah and Becky.

✔ **Reading Check**

Concept Map This activity provides a format for students to organize new information about a topic in a meaningful way. Creating a visual display for a complex term helps readers see connections between a word and its meaning. A concept map is a visual representation of the definition of a concept or word. Begin by writing the term *alcohol* in the center of the board. Then ask students to provide details to fill in the corresponding blanks below.

Lesson 1

3 Assess

Evaluating

 Assign the Lesson 1 Review; then assign the Lesson 1 Quiz in the TCR.

Reteaching

- Assign Concept Map 45 or Reteaching Activity 45 in the TCR.
- Have students list five parts of the body and alcohol's effect on each.
- Have students explain the impact of chemical dependency to alcohol.

Enrichment

- Assign Enrichment Activity 45 in the TCR.
- Have students write paragraphs describing relationships, activities, and goals that are most important to them and how alcohol could put these things at risk.

4 Close

Ask students to identify as many negative effects of alcohol on the body as they can.

HEALTH SKILLS ACTIVITY

COMMUNICATION SKILLS

Helping a Friend Stay Safe

Leah and Becky both read the open invitation to an end-of-school party tacked up in the locker room. Becky asks Leah if she wants a ride. Leah hesitates before answering. She had heard the party's host, Mike, say that his parents would be out of town. He bragged about his father's bar.

Leah does not want to go to Mike's party—it seems like trouble. Leah wants to help Becky change her mind about going to the party. What could she say to Becky?

What Would You Do?

Apply the skills for good communication to this situation. With a classmate, role-play a conversation between Leah and Becky.

The teen taking the part of Leah should state facts that Becky should consider before making her decision.

Speaking Skills

- Use "I" messages.
- Make clear, simple statements.
- Be honest with thoughts and feelings.
- Use appropriate body language.

Listening Skills

- Use appropriate body language.
- Use conversation encouragers.
- Mirror thoughts and feelings.
- Ask questions.

Lesson 1 Review

Using complete sentences, answer the following questions on a sheet of paper.

Reviewing Terms and Facts

1. **Vocabulary** Define the term *alcohol*. Use it in an original sentence.
2. **Recall** What kind of drug is alcohol? How does it affect the nervous system?
3. **Give Examples** List three factors that will influence the way an individual is affected by alcohol.
4. **Vocabulary** What is *BAC* short for? What does it measure?

Thinking Critically

5. **Apply** Why is a small female who drinks the same amount of alcohol as a large male more likely to experience a stronger effect from the alcohol?
6. **Explain** Why are pregnant females generally advised to avoid all alcohol during their pregnancies?

Applying Health Skills

7. **Advocacy** Do your part to advocate against binge drinking. Prepare a public service announcement in which you emphasize the extreme dangers of binge drinking by teens. If possible, record your announcement and arrange to have it played at school.

324 Chapter 13: Alcohol

Lesson 1 Review

1. A drug that is produced by a chemical reaction in fruits, vegetables, or grains. Sentences will vary.
2. Alcohol is a depressant; it slows the working of the nervous system.
3. Any three: body size, gender, time frame, amount consumed, presence of food in the stomach, and presence of medicine in body.
4. Blood alcohol concentration; the amount of alcohol in a person's bloodstream.
5. Alcohol moves more quickly through the bloodstream of females; smaller people are more affected than larger people by the same amount of alcohol.
6. Alcohol can pass from mother to baby's bloodstream; baby may be born with fetal alcohol syndrome.

Alcohol and Society

Alcohol: A Threat to Everyone

Alcohol use is widespread in American society. Nearly 14 million adult Americans have physical, social, and psychological problems related to alcohol use. It causes premature death from a variety of diseases. It also contributes to unnecessary deaths and injuries on the roads and in the home.

Drinking and Injuries

Drinking and driving are a dangerous, and potentially deadly, combination. Drinking alcohol impairs a person's vision, reaction time, and physical coordination. Consequently, a person who has been drinking should never get behind the wheel of a car.

Alcohol causes other kinds of unintentional injuries as well. It impairs a person's ability to ride a bicycle, skateboard, or scooter. About one-third of all bicyclists and pedestrians who die in motor vehicle collisions have been drinking. Alcohol is also linked to about one-third of all drowning deaths and about half of all deaths by fire.

Quick Write

Write a short note to an older person, over 21, persuading him or her not to drink and drive.

LEARN ABOUT...

- the dangers of drinking.
- the disease called alcoholism.
- how alcoholics can recover.
- sources of help for alcohol addiction.

VOCABULARY

- alcoholism
- recovery
- detoxification
- sobriety

More than half of the drivers killed in nighttime automobile collisions are legally drunk. *What could be done to prevent drunk driving in your community?*

LESSON 2: ALCOHOL AND SOCIETY **325**

Lesson 2

Alcohol and Society

① Focus

Lesson Objectives
Students will be able to

- discuss the serious dangers of drinking.
- describe the three stages of alcoholism.
- explain how alcoholics can recover.
- identify support groups that help the alcohol-dependent person and her or his family members.

Motivators

Quick Write
Ask a few volunteers to read their notes. List the reasons they offered on the board. Then have the class add to the list from their own responses. Discuss why alcohol is not just a teen issue.

Bellringer Activity
Ask students to write five sentences describing how an alcoholic looks and acts. After responses have been shared, point out that while some alcoholics fit these descriptions, most do not.

VOCABULARY
Write the definitions of the four vocabulary terms on the board. Then instruct each student to write each term along with its definition on a sheet of paper. Call on students to supply the correct definition for each term.

Lesson 2 Resources

Teacher Classroom Resources
 Concept Map 46
Decision-Making Activity 26
Enrichment Activity 46
Lesson Plan 2
Lesson 2 Quiz
Reading Tutor Activity 45

Reteaching Activity 46
Transparency 46

Student Activities Workbook
Chapter 13 Study Guide
Applying Health Skills 46

② Teach

Discussing

Discuss with students how many studies have been done to find out why some people use alcohol to escape their problems. Environmental factors and/or genetic factors may play a role. Researchers agree, however, that children of alcoholic parents do not automatically become alcoholics themselves. Likewise, children of parents who do not drink alcohol can become addicted to it. **L1**

Hands-On Health

DRUNK DRIVING STATISTICS

Time: 45 minutes

TEACHING THE ACTIVITY

- With students, read and discuss the activity introduction and instructions. Let volunteers draw an outline of a line graph on the board and chart several points on it.
- Have students work with partners to draw their own graphs.
- Then have partners write their responses to the In Conclusion questions.
- Have students share and compare their responses.
- As students respond that the percentage has leveled out, challenge them to discuss how that percentage can be further lowered.

ASSESSMENT

Use students' bar graphs and paragraphs to assess their learning.

CONNECT TO
Social Studies

ALCOHOL AND THE LAW
From 1920 to 1933, the sale of alcohol to all age groups was illegal throughout the United States. Today the sale of alcohol to people under 21 is illegal in all states. *Why do you think the government enacts such laws?*

Alcoholism

Alcohol can become addictive. **Alcoholism** is *a progressive, chronic disease involving a mental and physical need for alcohol.* People with this disease are called alcoholics. Alcoholics cannot control their drinking. They drink even when they know they are harming their health and hurting others.

A chemical dependency, or addiction to, alcohol is both psychological and physical. With psychological addiction, the mind sends the body a message that it needs more and more alcohol. With physical addiction, the body develops a direct need for the drug. Either way, an alcoholic feels very uncomfortable when alcohol is withheld for even a brief period.

Hands-On Health

DRUNK-DRIVING STATISTICS

You probably have seen public service announcements about drunk driving on television and billboards. Find out whether these campaigns help reduce alcohol-related collisions.

WHAT YOU WILL NEED
- pencil
- ruler
- sheet of graph paper

WHAT YOU WILL DO
Study the following statistics from the National Highway Traffic Safety Administration. The statistics show the percentage of people killed in traffic accidents involving a person who was legally drunk, out of the total number of people killed in all traffic accidents.
Create a line graph to examine the data. Divide the horizontal x-axis into ten one-year segments, and label each year from 1990 to 1999. Label the vertical y-axis with percent values in increments of 5, ranging from 25 percent at the bottom to 45 percent at the top. Graph the data. Then answer the questions that follow.

YEAR	PEOPLE KILLED IN ALCOHOL-RELATED ACCIDENTS
1990	39.6 percent
1991	38.4 percent
1992	36.3 percent
1993	34.9 percent
1994	32.2 percent
1995	32.5 percent
1996	32.0 percent
1997	30.3 percent
1998	30.0 percent
1999	30.0 percent

IN CONCLUSION
Examine your graph and determine how the data changed over a ten-year period. Did alcohol-related fatalities increase, decrease, or stay the same? What factors may have caused a change in the rate of alcohol-related fatal collisions?

INCLUSION STRATEGIES

Physically Impaired Students who are physically challenged fall into two categories, those with orthopedic impairments (restricted use of one or more limbs) and those with other health impairments (respirators or other medical equipment are required). To assist those students, use the following guidelines:

- Openly discuss with the students any uncertainties you have about when to offer assistance.
- Allow those students to do everything their peers do.
- Help nonimpaired students and adults understand the needs of individuals who have physical impairments.

Stages of Alcoholism

Alcoholism develops in three stages. These stages develop over time and are not the same for each alcoholic.

- **Stage 1.** A person starts using alcohol to relieve stress or to relax. Soon the person needs alcohol to cope with daily life. He or she begins to lie or make excuses about drinking.
- **Stage 2.** As the person continues to drink, the body develops a need for more and more alcohol. The drinker may be absent from school or work but continues to deny that there is a problem.
- **Stage 3.** In the final stage of alcoholism, the problem is clear to other people. The drinker's body is strongly addicted, and the drinking is now out of control.

Help for the Dependent Person

A person who is addicted to alcohol is dependent on it. The addiction can be treated, however. *The process of learning to live an alcohol-free life* is called **recovery**. The steps of recovery are shown in **Figure 13.3**.

Recovering from alcoholism is difficult, but it can be done. Many alcoholics join support groups to help them be successful. One of the best known is Alcoholics Anonymous (AA). AA is an organization of recovering alcoholics who know firsthand the difficulty of beating alcohol addiction. Maintaining **sobriety**, which is *living without alcohol,* is a lifelong struggle.

FIGURE 13.3

STEPS TO RECOVERY

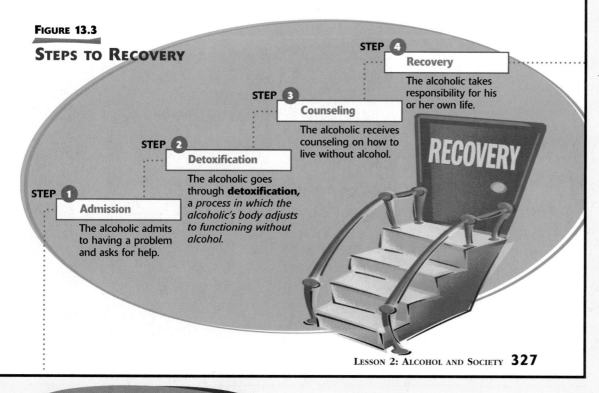

STEP 1 Admission
The alcoholic admits to having a problem and asks for help.

STEP 2 Detoxification
The alcoholic goes through **detoxification,** *a process in which the alcoholic's body adjusts to functioning without alcohol.*

STEP 3 Counseling
The alcoholic receives counseling on how to live without alcohol.

STEP 4 Recovery
The alcoholic takes responsibility for his or her own life.

LESSON 2: ALCOHOL AND SOCIETY **327**

Lesson 2

Critical Thinking

Help students consider the stages in the development of alcoholism. Ask:

- Who do you think would be most likely to recognize these stages of developing alcoholism: the alcoholic, a family member, a friend, or an acquaintance? Why?
- Who could intervene most successfully? How? **L1**

Applying Life Skills

Divide the class into pairs. Instruct each pair to rehearse a situation in which a person is helping a friend with a drinking problem. Every student should have a turn at both parts in the situation. Then have students discuss various tactics used in the activity. What approaches or particular ways of phrasing advice were especially helpful? **L2**

VISUAL LEARNING

FIGURE 13.3 Guide students in reading and discussing the steps to recovery from alcoholism. Ask:

- Why is each step necessary?
- What particular problems do you think are associated with each step?
- How does each step help make the next step possible?
- How could you support a friend or family member during each step? **INCL** *English Language Learners, Special Learning Needs, Behavior Problems, Different Learning Styles (Visual)*

MORE ABOUT...

Teen Drinking In an average month, 9 million American teens drink alcohol. In a nationwide survey, 32 percent of students in grades 9 through 12 reported that they had first drunk alcohol (more than a few sips) before age 13. Among eighth graders, 8 in 1,000 drink every day. Signs of a problem with drinking (besides seeing the person drinking or drunk) include lying about things, avoiding friends, giving up activities, taking risks, and feeling depressed. People with a drinking problem often deny it and don't get help on their own. Teens who suspect a friend has a problem should tell a trusted adult. They can let the friend know they care and encourage the person to talk to a trusted adult.

Lesson 2

HEALTH
Online

Encourage students to explore the Web Links for this chapter and then complete the activity.

Discussing

To provide a safe context for discussing families with members who suffer from alcoholism, have students describe and discuss depictions they have seen on TV or in movies. **L1**

Investigating

Ask a group of interested volunteers to gather information about local Al-Anon and Alateen programs. Have them share this information with the rest of the class. Also, ask the volunteers to bring to class any available schedules or brochures for the programs; make them available in the classroom. **L2**

Critical Thinking

Ask students to interpret critical issues related to solving health problems by considering the situation of a teen who lives with an alcoholic parent or other adult. Ask:

• Do you think the teen should try to help the adult recognize his or her problem with alcohol?

• If not, why not?

• If so, what do you think the teen should say and do? What do you think the teen should avoid saying and doing? Why? **L1**

HEALTH
Online

Topic: Alcohol

For a link to more information on the dangers of alcohol use, go to **health.glencoe.com.**

Activity: Using the information provided at this link, create a flyer that encourages teens to avoid alcohol.

Help for the Family

The harmful effects of alcohol do not affect only the drinker. The drinker's family members and friends suffer as well. One in four families in the United States is affected by alcoholism. Alcohol abuse is a factor in the breakup of many families. Many cases of spousal abuse and child abuse involve someone who has been drinking.

A growing number of young people are living with a person who is addicted to alcohol. These teens may not realize that they need help for themselves as well as for the problem drinkers in their lives. The first step to take is to admit that the problem exists. The second is to reach out for help.

Many alcohol treatment centers offer help to family members of the alcoholic. These programs teach family members about alcoholism and provide individual and family therapy. Some family members join support groups where they can talk with other people who have faced the same problems. Two of these support groups are described here.

• **Al-Anon** helps family members and friends of alcoholics. Al-Anon members learn how to help themselves as well as the person dependent on alcohol.

• **Alateen** helps young people cope with having a family member or friend who is an alcoholic. Its members share their experiences and work together to improve their lives.

Support groups can help teens who have an alcoholic in their family. *What are the benefits of joining a support group?*

328 CHAPTER 13: ALCOHOL

Health Literacy

Health Information For years it was widely believed that a recovery program would not be effective until the substance abuser recognized her or his problem and accepted the need to seek professional help. Now, intervention offers a chance to help substance abusers enter treatment before they hit bottom. A skilled intervention counselor works with the family, friends, teacher and/or employer to develop a plan to reach the substance abuser and motivate her or him to accept help. Intervention emphasizes positive motivation and negotiation rather than negative confrontation.

How You Can Help

If a friend or family member has a problem with alcohol, he or she needs help. Always remember, however, that your most important responsibility is to yourself. If you are close to an alcoholic, try not to let that person's drinking problem change your own behaviors and attitudes. Here are some ways you may be able to help an alcoholic.

- When the drinker is sober, talk calmly with him or her about the harm that alcohol does.
- Tell the drinker how concerned you are, and encourage her or him to seek help. Let the person know that the drinking worries you.
- Help the drinker feel good about quitting, and provide information about groups that can help.

Using positive peer pressure may help counteract the negative effects of living in an environment where alcohol abuse exists.

Gathering information is a good way to help someone with a drinking problem. *Where would you find information in your community?*

Lesson 2

③ Assess

Evaluating

 Assign the Lesson 2 Review; then assign the Lesson 2 Quiz in the TCR.

Reteaching

- Assign Concept Map 46 or Reteaching Activity 46 in the TCR.
- Have students describe in their own words the symptoms of the three stages of alcoholism. Have them name two organizations devoted to solving alcohol-related problems for family members and friends of an alcohol-dependent person.

Enrichment

- Assign Enrichment Activity 46 in the TCR.
- Have groups of students plan and perform skits that dramatize and explain the impact of addiction to alcohol.

④ Close

Ask students to write one or two paragraphs in which they explain the impact of addiction to alcohol. Have students include in their work a summary of the dangers of alcohol use and the harmful effects of alcoholism.

Lesson 2 Review

Using complete sentences, answer the following questions on a sheet of paper.

Reviewing Terms and Facts

1. **Explain** In what ways does alcohol impair a person's ability to drive?
2. **Vocabulary** Define the term *alcoholism*. Use it in an original sentence.
3. **Recall** Name the two kinds of addiction involved in alcoholism.
4. **Describe** What happens during the first stage of alcoholism?

Thinking Critically

5. **Suggest** What could be done to reduce the number of collisions resulting from drinking and driving?

6. **Apply** Explain the impact of chemical dependency and addiction to alcohol.

Applying Health Skills

7. **Advocacy** Play your part to stamp out drunk driving. Check out the Web site for Students Against Destructive Decisions (SADD). Use some of the information and ideas you find there to prepare your personal campaign to advocate against drinking and driving.

LESSON 2: ALCOHOL AND SOCIETY 329

Lesson 2 Review

1. Impairs vision, reaction time, physical coordination, all of which will affect a person's ability to drive.
2. A progressive, chronic disease involving a mental and physical need for alcohol. Sentences will vary.
3. Physical and psychological.
4. First, a person starts drinking to relieve stress or relax. Soon the person needs alcohol to cope with daily life. Then he or she begins to make excuses about drinking habits.
5. Responses will vary but may discuss having designated drivers and making tougher laws.
6. Responses will vary but link chemical dependency and addiction to alcohol to serious health problems.

Lesson 3

Choosing to Be Alcohol Free

① Focus

Lesson Objectives

Students will be able to

• discuss why some teens use alcohol.

• identify reasons to refuse alcohol.

• explain how the media influences our view of alcohol.

• describe alternatives to alcohol for fun and relaxation.

Health Skills

• Refusal Skills, p. 332

Motivators

Quick Write

Ask volunteers to read their statements aloud. Discuss the fact that some teens who start drinking do so because they do not have firm refusal statements in mind before their first encounters with alcohol.

Bellringer Activity

Have students write four healthful ways that teens can have a good time without spending any money. After responses are shared, point out that such activities are not only free but also safe.

VOCABULARY

Tell students that the term *alternatives* is used to indicate activities to do instead of drinking. Have them develop lists of alternatives other than those listed in the lesson.

Choosing to Be Alcohol Free

Why Some Teens Drink Alcohol

You have learned that alcohol will harm your physical and mental/emotional health, and that drinking alcohol is against the law for teens. Why, then, do some young people experiment with alcohol? Here are some statements teens may give, followed by what they should know about alcohol.

What Teens May Say	What Teens Should Know
• "I'll look more grown-up with a drink in my hand."	• You won't look mature getting in trouble for illegal underage drinking.
• "If I drink, I'll be able to forget my problems."	• The problems will still be there when the effects of the alcohol wear off.
• "I'm stressed out about this test. A drink will help me relax."	• Alcohol does not relieve stress; it disrupts sleep and can create more stress.
• "My friends keep pressuring me to try alcohol."	• Real friends won't pressure you to do something harmful.
• "The ads make drinking look like fun."	• Alcohol companies want people to spend money on their products.

You do not need to use alcohol to relax. *List three healthy alternative ways to relax.*

Quick Write

Write a refusal statement that you can use to avoid the pressure to use alcohol.

LEARN ABOUT...

• the reasons some teens use alcohol.
• the reasons to avoid alcohol use.
• how the media influence our view of alcohol.
• alternatives to alcohol for fun and relaxation.

VOCABULARY

• alternatives

Lesson 3 Resources

Teacher Classroom Resources

📁 Concept Map 47

📁 Cross-Curriculum Activity 26

📁 Enrichment Activity 47

📁 Lesson Plan 3

📁 Lesson 3 Quiz

📁 Reading Tutor Activity 46

📁 Reteaching Activity 47

🔊 Transparency 47

Student Activities Workbook

📁 Chapter 13 Study Guide

📁 Applying Health Skills 47

📁 Health Inventory 13

"First we learned about the overall drinking and driving issue and how each of us could make a difference back home. These messages came from leaders like former attorney general Janet Reno. We also broke into smaller workshops to brainstorm possible solutions for reducing teen drinking. At the end of the conference, we recommended that Congress increase the tax on alcoholic beverages and use that money to fund youth substance-abuse awareness and prevention programs. We also suggested that the federal government lower the blood-alcohol limit while driving from .10 percent to .08 percent.

"What I'll remember most are the stories many attendees shared about why they got involved. Cody Cowan, a teen delegate from Murray, Utah, joined MADD after a drunk driver severely injured one of his friends and killed two others. '[At first], I fell into a deep depression,' Cody said. Later, on a friend's advice, Cody said, 'I took all my negative energy and turned it into positive. I focused on changing the community and helping them realize that we really do have a problem with drinking.'

"Cody's story—and those of many others— reminded me of what might happen if I don't stand up and express my beliefs. Without my voice, underage drinking really could endanger the lives of people I care about. That would be something I couldn't live with."

Danger on the Road

As the statistics show, drinking and driving don't mix.

- In 2002, car crashes killed 42,850 people; 42% of those who died were involved in alcohol-related crashes.
- Almost a third of all Americans will be in a traffic accident that involves alcohol.
- In 2002, 30% of 15- to 20-year-old drivers who were killed in car crashes had been drinking.

Alcohol causes more problems than just auto accidents. In the United States, drinking alcohol is a factor in
- 40% of all suicide attempts.
- 50% of all boating accidents.
- 54% of all violent crimes.
- 80% of all domestic disputes.

Source: MADD

TIME TO THINK...

About Alcohol's Harmful Effects

Using reliable sources on the Internet and in your school's media center, conduct research to learn more about alcohol's effects on a person's perception, judgment, coordination, reaction time, and balance. Then, make a list of five common activities (for example, riding a bike or walking down stairs) and describe how drinking alcohol might negatively affect the performance of those activities, sometimes dangerously so. Share your findings with the class.

3 Apply

Time to Think

Have students refer back to the Drunk-Driving Statistics on page 326. Using online and print resources, ask students to find more targeted statistics relating to drinking and driving. For instance, are males or females more likely to drive drunk? Are there state variations in DUI? At what age are DUI deaths most likely? What is the average fine for driving under the influence? Have students share their findings with the rest of the class. Then ask, "Do you think the development of MADD has affected these statistics? Is MADD an effective way of preventing drinking and driving? Why or why not?" Students may also choose to research more about MADD and the steps the organization takes to educate against drunk driving.

VISUAL LEARNING

Ask students to analyze the photographs on pages 334 and 335. Explain that these buttons all advocate saying no to drinking and driving. Ask students to come up with other creative slogans designed to stop people from drinking and driving.

TIME HEALTH: GETTING MADD **335**

COOPERATIVE LEARNING ACTIVITY

Role-Plays Divide students into small groups. Ask each group to role-play one of the following scenarios involving drinking and driving. Role-plays should demonstrate a variety of communication skills, including "I" messages, refusal skills, and appropriate body language.

- Lucia got a ride to a party with her friend Devon. Now it's past Lucia's curfew and Devon

has been drinking. How can she get home safely?

- Rob feels like a baby walking home from school each day when all the other seniors drive. One afternoon a gang of football players offer Rob a ride home. He can tell that they have been drinking. What should he do?

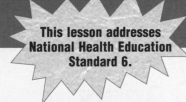

This lesson addresses National Health Education Standard 6.

DECISION MAKING

Objective

After completing the lesson, students will be able to decide how to help a friend who may have an alcohol problem.

Time: 35–40 minutes

Materials: index cards, pen or pencil

Teacher Classroom Resources

📁 Building Health Skills Activities

• Transparency Master 8, "Decision Making"

• Reproducible Master 38, "Helping Someone Get Help"

1. Model

• Display Transparency Master 8, and review the steps of the decision-making process.

• Have students read the scenario. As a class, go over each step of Carly's decision. (*Carly states the situation, lists options, weighs the possible outcomes, considers her values, makes a decision and acts. Then she evaluates her decision.*)

• Assign disruptive students to separate groups.

• Explain to students how using the decision-making steps can help them make more thoughtful, responsible decisions.

HELPING SOMEONE GET HELP

Model

Carly is worried about her friend Sandy. Sandy's grades have gone down and she has recently dropped out of all school activities. When Carly tries to make plans to study with Sandy, Sandy says she's too tired or has too much to do at home. Carly has seen Sandy hanging out with a group of older teens known for their drinking parties. She's concerned that Sandy might be drinking too. Carly wants to help Sandy but doesn't want her to stop being her friend. She uses the decision-making process to decide what to do.

1. STATE THE SITUATION
I'm worried that my friend is developing a drinking problem.

2. LIST THE OPTIONS
I could say nothing.
I could confront Sandy with my concerns.
I could talk to Sandy's parents.

3. WEIGH THE POSSIBLE OUTCOMES
If I say nothing, Sandy could get worse.
If I confront her, she might get angry and not be my friend anymore.

4. CONSIDER VALUES
Sandy is my friend; sometimes you have to tell friends things they don't want to hear.

5. MAKE A DECISION AND ACT
I will tell Sandy my concerns and let her know there are many people who can help.

6. EVALUATE YOUR DECISION
Sandy and I had a long talk; she will see the school counselor on Monday; I think I made a good decision.

336 CHAPTER 13: ALCOHOL

📎 Teaching Tips

Reviewing Student Work For this activity to be most effective, carefully monitor the development of each group's scenario. Before collecting and redistributing scenarios, do another quick review to make sure that they are appropriate and complete. Allow a few extra minutes for students to revise their work, if necessary.

Using Role-Plays Effectively Here are some tips for using role-plays effectively:

• Keep role-plays short.

• Involve observers by giving them tasks.

• Assign disruptive students to separate groups.

Practice

Using the decision-making process, write a paragraph in response to Drew's situation.

One day Drew goes to visit his older sister Stacey, who has a baby. When Drew lets himself into the apartment, he sees the baby crying in the crib and Stacey asleep on the couch. There are several empty beer bottles on the counter. Drew has long suspected that his sister has a drinking problem. He is worried for his sister and his little niece. What could he say or do?

Apply/Assess

In groups, develop two scenarios involving teens and alcohol use. Write them on index cards. The scenarios will be collected by your teacher and distributed to other groups to role-play for the class. Your scenario should have at least two characters and should describe a realistic situation involving a teen who must decide how to help someone who may have an alcohol problem.

When your group receives the scenario description, rehearse your role-play and perform it in front of the class.

COACH'S BOX

Decision Making
1. State the situation.
2. List the options.
3. Weigh the possible outcomes.
4. Consider values.
5. Make a decision and act.
6. Evaluate your decision.

Self-✓Check
- Did our role-play correctly use the steps for decision making?
- Did we show several options?
- Did we identify the consequences of each option?
- Did we reach a healthy decision?

2. Practice

- Direct students to read the scenario and use the steps of the decision-making process to come up with a choice that Drew could make.
- Keep Transparency Master 8 displayed for reference as students work on their paragraphs.
- Ask volunteers to read their paragraphs aloud and discuss them as a class.

3. Apply/Assess

- You may wish to distribute Building Health Skills Reproducible Master 38 in the TCR to guide students in completing this activity.
- Divide students into small groups and distribute two index cards to each group.
- Ask students to come up with two scenarios about a teen who must decide how to help someone with a drinking problem. Have them write a brief description of the situation on each index card.
- Collect and redistribute the cards. Have each group role-play the scenario that they received and discuss the scenarios as a class.
- Remind students to refer to the Self-Check before and after they create their scenarios and perform their role-plays.

Assessment Scoring ✓

Using a rubric, student work should provide evidence of all criteria to achieve the highest score.

Skills
Student work shows
- correct use of decision-making steps.
- several options.
- possible consequences of each option.

- how values can influence decisions.
- a clear, health-enhancing decision.

Concepts
Student work provides
- a realistic alcohol-related scenario.
- accurate information about alcohol.

Checking Comprehension

Use the Chapter 13 Assessment to examine the most important ideas presented in the chapter.

Answers to Reviewing Vocabulary and Concepts

Lesson 1
1. alcohol
2. liver
3. fetal alcohol syndrome (FAS)
4. blood alcohol concentration (BAC)
5. cirrhosis
6. intoxicated

Lesson 2
7. addiction
8. alcoholism
9. detoxification
10. sobriety
11. recovery
12. Alateen

Lesson 3
13. false; more and more or many
14. true
15. false; disappoints
16. true
17. true
18. false; hidden

Thinking Critically

19. Responses might mention alcoholism, cirrhosis, and strained relationships.
20. A 4-ounce glass of liquor has more than twice as much alcohol as a 4-ounce glass of beer.
21. Responses will vary. Students may respond that seeing the destruction of alcoholism firsthand might reduce a person's chances of drinking.

CHAPTER ASSESSMENT
13

After You Read

Use your completed Foldable to review the information on the harmful effects of alcohol.

FOLDABLES
Study Organizer

Reviewing Vocabulary and Concepts

On a sheet of paper, write the numbers 1–12. After each number, write the term from the list that best completes each sentence.

- addiction
- alcohol
- alcoholism
- blood alcohol concentration (BAC)
- cirrhosis
- detoxification
- fetal alcohol syndrome (FAS)
- liver
- recovery
- sobriety
- intoxicated
- Alateen

Lesson 1

1. _____ is a depressant drug produced by a chemical reaction in fruits, vegetables, or grains.
2. Over time, excessive alcohol consumption damages the _____, the organ that chemically breaks down alcohol.
3. Children born with _____ have a set of mental and physical birth defects due to alcohol exposure.
4. _____ depends on several factors, such as gender, body size, and amount of alcohol consumed.
5. In the disease _____, scarring and destruction of liver tissue may result from alcohol consumption.
6. In some states, a person with a blood alcohol concentration of .08 is legally _____.

Lesson 2

7. _____ to alcohol is both physical and psychological.
8. _____ is a progressive, chronic disease that involves a need for alcohol.
9. During _____, the alcoholic's body adjusts to functioning without alcohol.
10. _____ involves living without alcohol.
11. _____, the process of becoming well after alcoholism, generally has three steps.
12. _____ is a support group for young people who have a friend or family member addicted to alcohol.

Lesson 3

On a sheet of paper, write the numbers 13–18. Write *True* or *False* for each statement below. If the statement is false, change the underlined word or phrase to make it true.

13. <u>Few</u> teens choose to abstain from alcohol.
14. Consumption of alcohol by teens is <u>illegal</u> in the United States.
15. Underage drinking <u>impresses</u> those who care for you.
16. Many people who used to drink alcohol are <u>giving it up</u> for a combination of health reasons and practical reasons.
17. Some healthful alternatives to alcohol use include <u>volunteering and learning a new sport</u>.
18. Alcohol advertisements often use <u>obvious</u> messages that are designed to influence people to buy their products.

Thinking Critically

Using complete sentences, answer the following questions on a sheet of paper.

19. **Relate** How can alcohol use cause health problems in later life and other adverse consequences?

INCLUSION STRATEGIES

Special Learning Needs, Behavior Problems, English Language Learners The following suggestions are helpful for students with special learning needs, students with behavior problems, and ELL students:

- Pair these students with more proficient learners who can help summarize the main concepts of the chapter.

- Direct these students to listen to the Teen Health Audio Summaries. This component provides an audio and written summary of the chapter in both English and Spanish.

- Use photographs, drawings, or magazine clippings whenever possible to help students visualize the important concepts of the chapter.

20. **Evaluate** What is wrong with this statement: "A 4-ounce glass of liquor will have the same effect as a 4-ounce glass of beer"?

21. **Analyze** How might having an alcoholic in your life influence your attitudes toward alcohol?

22. **Compare and Contrast** Discuss some ways in which alcoholism is similar to an addiction to illegal drugs. Discuss some ways in which it differs.

Career Corner

Alcohol Abuse Counselor Alcohol abuse counselors help alcoholics recover from their addictions. These professionals give emotional support and counsel patients on how to stay alcohol free. To pursue this career, you need at least a two-year degree in substance abuse counseling from a community college. Find out more about this and other health careers by clicking on Career Corner at health.glencoe.com.

22. Responses will vary. Students may say that both are mind altering and destructive to health. However, alcohol is legal for those over 21.

Test Practice
1. A
2. D
3. Answers may include "Why did you become a volunteer?" or "What do you say to victims of drunk driving accidents?"

Reteaching

 Assign Study Guide 13 in the Student Activities Workbook.

Evaluate

Use the reproducible Chapter 13 Test in the TCR, or construct your own test using the **Exam***View*® Pro Testmaker.

Enrichment

Hand out large sheets of paper, or cut up a roll of butcher paper. Have groups of students work together to plan and draw large comic strips that encourage teens to avoid alcohol. If possible, post these projects in school hallways.

Standardized Test Practice

Reading & Writing

Read the paragraphs below and then answer the questions.

Today we have, as a guest, a volunteer from MADD—Mothers Against Drunk Driving.

What do MADD volunteers do? They guide victims of drunk-driving accidents through the legal process. They also develop youth programs, such as alcohol-free proms.

Has MADD been successful? MADD's activism has resulted in a number of federal and state laws to control drunk driving. The most well-known of these is the 1984 federal law requiring states to increase the legal drinking age or lose highway funding. Since MADD's beginnings, alcohol-related traffic fatalities have declined 43 percent. MADD will not close its doors until drunk drivers stop taking lives.

1. Telling MADD's story in an interview helps the reader understand
   A exactly what MADD volunteers do.
   B how to become a volunteer.
   C how MADD started.
   D how MADD has failed to reduce drunk-driving fatalities.

2. Which sentence in the interview best shows the reader that the volunteers at MADD are very serious about their work?
   A They also develop youth programs, such as alcohol-free proms.
   B MADD's activism has resulted in a number of federal and state laws to control drunk driving.
   C Since MADD's beginnings, alcohol-related traffic fatalities have declined 43 percent.
   D MADD will not close its doors until drunk drivers stop taking lives.

3. Write a paragraph containing additional questions that you would like to ask a MADD volunteer.

 TH05_C3.glencoe.com/quiz

CHAPTER 13 ASSESSMENT **339**

Assessment ✓

Self-Assessment Direct students to review the activities that are provided throughout the chapter. Encourage each student to select one finished product or activity that demonstrates his or her best work for the chapter. Have students explain what they learned and how the examples they selected show their progress.

Career Corner

Alcohol Abuse Counselor After reviewing the career profile on the health Web site, students might:
- Describe the skills, training, and education needed.
- Role-play with a partner interviews for the position of alcohol abuse counselor.

Understanding Your Body

Unit Objectives

Students learn behaviors for personal care and examine nine systems of the body. They will learn how each one functions individually and in relation to the other eight. They will also learn about the process of growth and development during each of life's stages, from a single fertilized egg cell to the final stages of adulthood.

Unit Overview

Chapter 14
Personal Care

Lesson
1 Healthy Skin, Hair, and Nails
2 Healthy Mouth and Teeth
3 Healthy Eyes and Ears

Chapter 15
Your Body Systems

Lesson
1 Your Skeletal System
2 Your Muscular System
3 Your Circulatory System
4 Your Respiratory System
5 Your Nervous System
6 Your Digestive and Excretory Systems
7 Your Endocrine System
8 Your Reproductive System

340

DEALING WITH SENSITIVE ISSUES

Enhancing Self Esteem There are many ways to help students deal with sensitive issues, such as sharing accurate information and professional resources about the issues. Other skills you can teach include how to make good decisions about health and how to solve problems wisely. You can also give students opportunities to build their self-esteem so that they will be more likely to try to develop new skills. Convince them they have potential, and urge them to maximize their potential by working to increase their skills. Convey to them that achievements, such as good grades and athletic awards, can make them feel better about themselves. Everyone has value; it is what is done to increase that value that enhances self-esteem. **INCL** *At-Risk, Special Learning Needs, Behavior Problems*

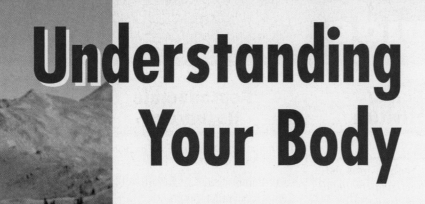

Understanding Your Body

Chapter 16
Growth and Development

Lesson
1 The Beginning of Life
2 Heredity and Environment
3 From Childhood to Adolescence
4 Adulthood and Aging

HEALTH in Action

How can taking care of your body systems be a breeze?

Staying well and looking your best don't just happen automatically—they're the rewards for practicing healthy habits. Taking care of your teeth, skin, nails, and hair not only enhances your appearance, but also contributes to your overall well-being. Eating healthy foods, staying active, and getting enough sleep will keep your body systems in tip-top shape. Once you know what to do to stay healthy, taking care of your body is a breeze!

Unit Introduction

Explain to students that the body is like a new car. In order to keep it running at an optimum level, they have to take constant care of their bodies. Just as there are preventative care measures important to a car, there are essential preventive measures important to the health of the body.

Ask students to work in pairs or small groups to make posters with the title "Keep Your Body Well Tuned." As they study the chapters in this unit, they can fill in their posters with tips on personal health and taking care of their body systems.

341

HEALTH in Action

Read the question on page 341 aloud. As a class, discuss the importance of developing and practicing healthy habits. Then lead the class in the following physical activity:

Using a soft object such as a crumpled-up sheet of paper, quiz the class on facts related to personal health care and keeping the body healthy. Ask a question, then toss the object to a student, who must answer that question. That student will then toss the ball to another student, who must answer the next question. Here are some sample questions: What's one action you can take to take care of your skin? Why is it important to get enough sleep? Accept all reasonable answers, and correct any misconceptions.

Planning Guide

Chapter 14	Skills/ Activities	Reproducible Resources	Assessment
Lesson 1 **Healthy Skin, Hair, and Nails** *pages 344–348*	**HEALTH SKILLS ACTIVITY** ▲ Protect Yourself from the Sun (*Practicing Healthful Behaviors*), page 346	*Student Activities Workbook available for use with each chapter* 📁 Parent Letter & Activities 14 📁 Concept Map 48 📁 Decision-Making Activity 27 📁 Enrichment Activity 48 📁 Lesson Plan 1 📁 Reading Tutor Activity 47 📁 Reteaching Activity 48	📁 Lesson 1 Quiz
Lesson 2 **Healthy Mouth and Teeth** *pages 349–353*	**Hands-On Health** ▲ Plaque Attack, page 352	📁 Concept Map 49 📁 Cross-Curriculum Activity 27 📁 Enrichment Activity 49 📁 Health Lab 14 📁 Lesson Plan 2 📁 Reading Tutor Activity 48 📁 Reteaching Activity 49	📁 Lesson 2 Quiz
Lesson 3 **Healthy Eyes and Ears** *pages 354–359*	**HEALTH SKILLS ACTIVITY** ▲ Reducing Noise Levels (*Advocacy*), page 359	📁 Concept Map 50 📁 Cross-Curriculum Activity 28 📁 Decision-Making Activity 28 📁 Enrichment Activity 50 📁 Lesson Plan 3 📁 Reading Tutor Activity 49 📁 Reteaching Activity 50	📁 Lesson 3 Quiz 📁 Chapter 14 Test 📁 Performance Assessment 14

TIME HEALTH | **The Truth Behind Popular Health Tips** *pages 360–361*

BUILDING HEALTH SKILLS

Seeing Beyond the Perfect Look
(*Analyzing Influences*)
pages 362–363

📁 Building Health Skills Reproducible Master 39

Standards		Technology
National	**State/Local**	
National Health Education Standard **1.1, 1.3, 1.6, 3.1, 3.4**		📷 Transparency 48 💿 TeacherWorks™
National Health Education Standard **1.1, 1.3, 1.6, 2.6, 3.1, 3.4**		📷 Transparency 49 💿 TeacherWorks™
National Health Education Standard **1.1, 1.3, 1.6, 2.6, 3.1, 3.4, 7.4, 7.5**		📷 Transparencies 50 & 51 💿 TeacherWorks™ 📼💿 MindJogger Videoquiz 💿 **Exam***View*® Pro Testmaker
National Health Education Standard **2.3, 4.2, 7.2**		📁 Building Health Skills Transparency Master 4

TeacherWorks™

Glencoe's new and exclusive TeacherWorks™ is an all-in-one planner and resource center. Access the complete Teacher Wraparound Edition electronically. Find all your classroom resources with just a few easy clicks, and print them right from your computer. Connect directly to Glencoe's customized Health Web site. Access the National Health Education Standards correlations, or insert your own state standards and match them directly to the electronic Teacher Wraparound Edition.

Language Diversity

- 🎧 English Audio Summaries
- 🎧 Spanish Audio Summaries
- 📁 English Summaries, Quizzes, and Activities
- 📁 Spanish Summaries, Quizzes, and Activities
- 📁 Spanish Parent Letters and Activities

KEY TO ABILITY LEVELS

Teaching Strategies that appear throughout the chapters have been identified by one of four codes to give you an idea of their suitability for students of varying learning styles and abilities.

L1 **Level 1** strategies should be within the ability range of all students. Often full class participation is required.

L2 **Level 2** strategies are for average to above-average students or for small groups. Some teacher direction is necessary.

L3 **Level 3** strategies are designed for students able and willing to work independently. Minimal teacher direction is necessary.

INCL Strategies are appropriate for students with particular special needs in a general classroom setting.

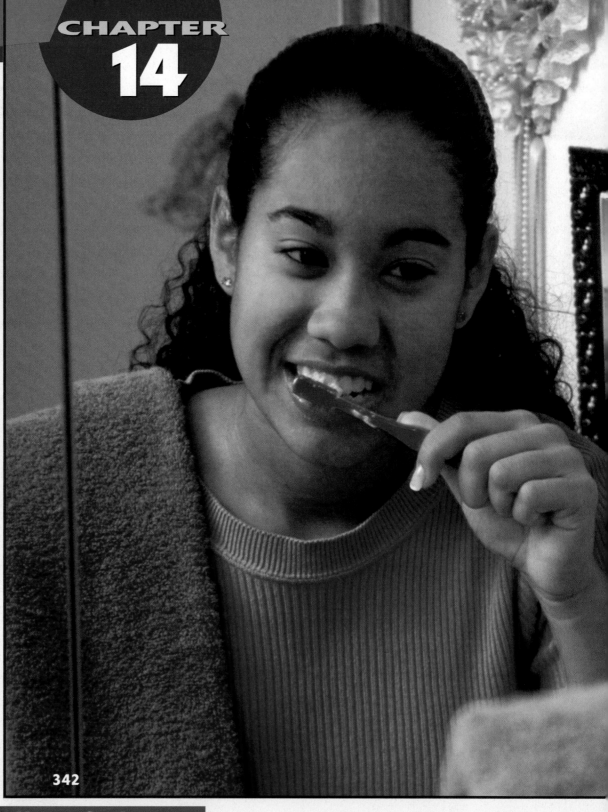

CHAPTER 14

Personal Care

Chapter at a Glance

Lesson 1 focuses on the proper care of the skin, hair, and nails and on common adolescent skin problems such as acne.

Lesson 2 discusses the roles of proper dental hygiene and diet in having healthy teeth and gums.

Lesson 3 describes the structures and functions of the eyes and ears and offers tips for maintaining healthy vision and hearing.

Health Skills

- Protect Yourself from the Sun (*Practicing Healthful Behaviors*), p. 346
- Reducing Noise Levels (*Advocacy*), p. 359
- Seeing Beyond the Perfect Look (*Analyzing Influences*), pp. 362–363

342

HANDS-ON ACTIVITY

Children's Book Encourage students to work in groups of four to write children's books for students in grades 1 to 3. The books will focus on topics from this chapter, such as the parts of the eye and basic ways to protect the eyes from injury. Remind them that, since the books are for young students, they might take a whimsical approach to the content and presentation. For example, the main character might take the reader on an undercover journey through a giant eyeball to uncover the mystery of how the eye works. Encourage students to use computer programs with graphic capabilities, or have artistic students make illustrations to accompany the text. If possible, help students arrange to share their books with the younger children.

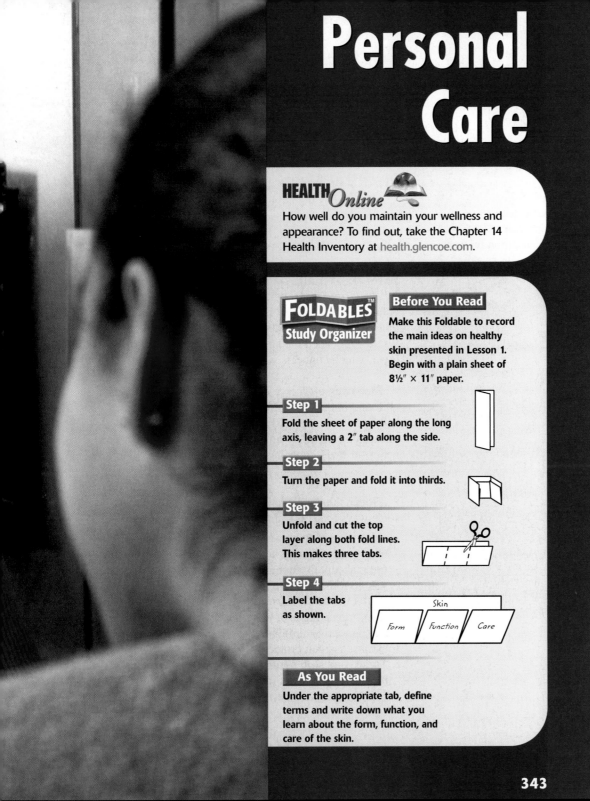

Personal Care

HEALTH *Online*

How well do you maintain your wellness and appearance? To find out, take the Chapter 14 Health Inventory at health.glencoe.com.

FOLDABLES™ Study Organizer

Before You Read

Make this Foldable to record the main ideas on healthy skin presented in Lesson 1. Begin with a plain sheet of 8½″ × 11″ paper.

Step 1

Fold the sheet of paper along the long axis, leaving a 2″ tab along the side.

Step 2

Turn the paper and fold it into thirds.

Step 3

Unfold and cut the top layer along both fold lines. This makes three tabs.

Step 4

Label the tabs as shown.

Skin
| Form | Function | Care |

As You Read

Under the appropriate tab, define terms and write down what you learn about the form, function, and care of the skin.

Chapter Introduction

Use the options below to motivate students and preview chapter content.

HEALTH *Online*

Visit **health.glencoe.com**, and have students complete Health Inventory 14 to rate their personal health care practices. For other teaching strategies, explore the Lesson Plans and select from Cross-Curriculum, Reading, or Media Literacy activities.

GLENCOE TECHNOLOGY

MindJogger Videoquiz

Use MindJogger to preview or review Chapter 14 content.

TIME HEALTH

The Truth Behind Popular Health Tips
pages 360–361

FOLDABLES™ Study Organizer

Dinah Zike Study Fold

Descriptive Writing and Sequencing Students will use their Foldable study guides to record what they learn about the skin and its care. As students read and study the material presented in Lesson 1, have them define terms and take notes on the form, function and care of the skin under the appropriate tab of their Foldable. Then ask students to describe in their own words how form affects function and how function affects care on the back of their Foldable.

Lesson 1

Healthy Skin, Hair, and Nails

① Focus

Lesson Objectives

Students will be able to

- describe the structure and functions of the skin.
- discuss ways to take care of their skin.
- recognize ways to care for hair and scalp problems.
- understand why nail care is important to their health.

Health Skills
- Practicing Healthful Behaviors, p. 346

Motivators

Quick Write
Have students refer to their questions as they read the lesson, answering them as information becomes available. Allow time to address questions left unanswered.

Bellringer Activity

Ask students to compare and contrast their skin with suits of armor. (*Similar: serves as protection; dissimilar: skin is fragile, repairs itself, needs regular maintenance*)

VOCABULARY

Ask students to think of words they associate with the word *skin*. Draw a concept map.

```
sweat    "zits"   rash
      \    |    /
        skin
      /         \
feeling         color
```

Display the terms from the vocabulary list on a chart. Ask volunteers to read those terms and relate them to the words on the map.

Healthy Skin, Hair, and Nails

Quick Write

Write down three questions you have about caring for your skin, hair, or nails.

LEARN ABOUT...

- caring for your skin and dealing with skin problems.
- caring for your hair and dealing with hair and scalp problems.
- taking care of your nails.

VOCABULARY

- epidermis
- dermis
- subcutaneous layer
- dermatologist
- dandruff
- cuticle
- hangnail
- ingrown toenail

Healthy Skin

Your skin is the largest organ of your body. Unlike other organs, such as your heart and lungs, your skin can be seen, making it an important part of your appearance. It also performs several other functions. **Figure 14.1** describes these functions.

Parts of the Skin

The visible and outermost layer of the skin is called the **epidermis** (e·puh·DER·mis). Beneath the epidermis is *a thick inner layer of skin,* called the **dermis**. Below the dermis is *a layer of fat* called the **subcutaneous** (suhb·kyoo·TAY·nee·uhs) **layer**, which connects your skin to bones and muscles.

Blood vessels, nerve endings, hair follicles, and glands are all found in the dermis. Oil glands make oils that keep the skin soft and waterproof. Sweat glands secrete perspiration, which is released through tiny holes in the skin called pores. This is the way your body cools itself.

Taking Care of Your Skin

Proper skin care can be a part of your daily routine. Here are some ways to keep your skin healthy.

- **Keep your skin clean.** Bathing or showering every day with mild soap will rid your skin of bacteria and excess oils. If you use makeup, use nongreasy products and remove them before you go to bed.
- **Protect your skin from the sun.** The sun's rays can cause premature aging and, more seriously, skin cancer. Wear sunscreen and protective clothing when in the sun. Avoid sunlight or use extra sunscreen protection between 10:00 A.M. and 4:00 P.M.
- **Treat your skin gently.** Harsh scrubbing, squeezing, or picking blemishes can result in scars. Administer appropriate first aid to cuts, scrapes, and burns.

Lesson 1 Resources

Teacher Classroom Resources

- 📁 Parent Letter & Activities 14
- 📁 Concept Map 48
- 📁 Decision-Making Activity 27
- 📁 Enrichment Activity 48
- 📁 Lesson Plan 1
- 📁 Lesson 1 Quiz

- 📁 Reading Tutor Activity 47
- 📁 Reteaching Activity 48
- Transparency 48

Student Activities Workbook

- 📁 Chapter 14 Study Guide
- 📁 Applying Health Skills 48

FIGURE 14.1

The Skin's Functions

The skin is a barrier against water. Like a formfitting raincoat, your skin keeps out water when you swim or take a bath.

The skin helps control body temperature. When you're hot, sweat glands in your skin release perspiration to cool your body down. When you're cold, blood circulation slows to conserve body heat.

The skin is a sense organ. Nerve endings in your skin let you know when something touches your body. They allow you to feel textures. They also let you know if something is hot, cold, or painful.

The skin is the first line of defense against pathogens. This is why you need to care for any cuts or burns.

Dealing with Acne

Many teens experience a skin problem called acne. During puberty, hormones can overstimulate oil glands in the face, chest, neck, and back, resulting in clogged hair follicles, or pores. Bacteria in clogged pores release chemicals that irritate the skin and cause bumps on the skin's surface, as shown in **Figure 14.2**.

Minor cases of acne can be treated with over-the-counter products and good hygiene. If the condition is serious, you might want to see a **dermatologist** (DER·muh·TAHL·uh·jist), *a physician who treats skin disorders.*

FIGURE 14.2

FORMS OF ACNE

Whiteheads, blackheads, and pimples are three common forms of acne.

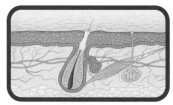
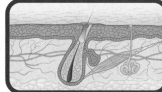
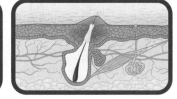

A whitehead is a pore that is clogged with an oily substance called sebum, which is produced inside the skin.

A blackhead is a pore that is clogged with sebum that has darkened after being exposed to the air.

A pimple is a clogged pore that has filled with pus. The skin may be red at the base of the pimple.

Health Literacy

Health Information Apart from its many other functions, the skin remains one of the most reliable diagnostic tools in the treatment of hay fever and other seasonal allergies. When sensitivity to an allergen is suspected, a doctor will administer a scratch test. The test consists of a series of surface injections of plant extracts and other possible immunosensitive culprits. Depending on the substance, a positive response will register in the form of a blotch or bump—either one is a sign that immunotherapy (treatment or prevention of disease by attempting to induce immunity) is needed.

Lesson 1

② Teach

VISUAL LEARNING

FIGURE 14.1 Divide the class into four groups, and assign each group one of the skin's functions listed in Figure 14.1. Have group members read and discuss the information on that function and then prepare an interesting method of sharing the information with the rest of the class. **INCL** *English Language Learners, Special Learning Needs, Behavior Problems, Different Learning Styles (Visual)*

Cross-Curriculum Activity

SCIENCE Explain that a fifth function of skin is that it helps your body make vitamin D. This vitamin is produced in the skin when it is exposed to sunlight. The amount of vitamin D produced depends on the length of exposure to sunlight and on the color of your skin. People with darker skin tend to produce less vitamin D than those with lighter skin. Have interested students determine other sources of vitamin D (*fortified milk, cereals, eggs, sardines, and salmon*). **L2**

VISUAL LEARNING

FIGURE 14.2 Ask volunteers to describe the three pictures and to read aloud the explanations of the three common forms of acne. Have students explain in their own words how all three are alike and how they are different. **INCL** *English Language Learners, Special Learning Needs, Behavior Problems, Different Learning Styles (Visual)*

HEALTH SKILLS PRACTICE

Communication Introduce the following to enhance students' communication skills: Body odor is one thing you acquire as a teen. During puberty, you sweat more. What if you're managing it okay, but your best friend isn't. In other words, he stinks. You know you need to tell him, but how do you start without hurting his feelings? Write down three possible opening sentences to talk to your friend about hygiene. Remember, you want to keep him as a friend.

HEALTH SKILLS ACTIVITY

PRACTICING HEALTHFUL BEHAVIORS

Guide students in reading and discussing the activity introduction. Ask individual students to explain the importance of each step in protecting the skin. Emphasize that melanin (the brown pigmentation produced by skin cells to protect the skin from sun damage) is not sufficient protection.

Then have students work in groups to complete the activity.

Note: This skill is introduced in Chapter 2 on pages 46–47.

Follow these tips to care for acne.

- Gently wash the infected area with mild soap and warm water every morning and evening. Do not scrub the skin.
- Choose oil-free cosmetics and haircare products.
- Use acne-fighting preparations prescribed by your doctor.
- Keep your hands and hair away from the infected area.
- Protect your skin from the sun.

Other Skin Problems

Other skin problems teens may experience include:

- **Cold sores.** These blisters or small sores near or on the lips are caused by the herpes simplex 1 virus. They usually go away in 10 to 14 days, but they can spread if you scratch them. The sores are contagious. Do not let anyone touch the sores, and always wash your hands after touching them yourself to prevent the spread of the virus.
- **Warts.** These small growths on the skin are caused by a virus and can be spread to others by touch. Over-the-counter medicine might help over time, or the wart may go away on its own. If the wart does not go away, see a doctor about treatment.

HEALTH SKILLS ACTIVITY

PRACTICING HEALTHFUL BEHAVIORS

Protect Yourself from the Sun

Protecting your skin during your teen years reduces your risk of developing skin cancer later in life. The Centers for Disease Control and Prevention (CDC) has developed a program called "Choose Your Cover." It suggests this five-step approach.

- **SEEK SHADE.** This is especially important between 10:00 A.M. and 4:00 P.M., when the sun's rays can do the most damage.
- **COVER UP.** Cover exposed skin with clothing.
- **GET A HAT.** A wide brim will shade your face, neck, and ears.
- **GRAB SHADES.** Sunglasses protect your eyes from sun damage. Try to get sunglasses rated "special purpose" or "general purpose" by the American National Standards Institute.
- **RUB ON SUNSCREEN.** Look for one that has an SPF of 15 or higher and that provides protection against UVA *and* UVB rays. Protect the tops of ears, hands, and feet.

ON YOUR OWN
Pretend you are preparing for a day at the beach. Make a list of items to include in your beach bag.

346 CHAPTER 14: PERSONAL CARE

MORE ABOUT...

Sunblocks For adequate sun protection, a sunblock with an SPF (sun protection factor) of 15 or greater is recommended, although anything above SPF 15 does not provide a significant amount of extra protection. SPF, which is rated from 2 to 15 or greater, indicates how long a person can stay in the sun without becoming burned. If you normally burn (unprotected) after 15 minutes in the sun, for example, an SPF of 8 will allow you to stay out for 8 times 15, or 120, minutes (2 hours). A SPF of 15 will increase the time you can remain outside to no more than 3 hours 45 minutes. Using a sunblock, regardless of SPF rating, does not mean that you will only tan and not burn. You will burn if you remain in the sun without protection beyond the protected length of time.

FIGURE 14.3

Taking Care of Your Hair

Keep your hair healthy by giving it daily attention. *What is your daily hair care routine?*

A Wash your hair frequently with a gentle shampoo.

B Let your hair air dry. The heat from blow dryers can rob your hair of oils and make hair ends rough and dry.

C Brush or comb your hair a few times each day to remove dirt.

D Avoid dyes, permanents, and hair spray that can damage hair. Some styling gels and conditioners can build up on your hair, making it look and feel greasy. Avoid preparations that contain alcohol, which can dry out your hair.

The Sun and Your Skin

Sunburn, caused by the ultraviolet (UV) rays in sunshine, is a sign of damaged skin. UVB rays are the primary cause of sunburn, while UVA rays contribute to skin aging and can also cause sunburn. Both types of UV rays can cause skin cancer, and both cause the skin to wrinkle and age faster than normal.

The best ways to protect your skin from cancer, and from other harmful effects of the sun, are to cover your skin with clothing and to use a sunscreen with an SPF (sun protection factor) of 15 or higher. Avoid sun lamps and tanning salons. Tanning devices can actually expose your skin to higher doses of UVA rays and can be more damaging than sunbathing. Remember that protecting your skin during the teen years will help you look and feel better for years to come.

Tattoos and Body Piercing

Any time the skin is punctured, you risk infection because pathogens can enter your body. Even if a tattoo or piercing is performed under sterile conditions, the skin is open to germs until it heals.

Healthy Hair

The same hormones that contribute to acne can also affect your hair. An oil gland is attached to each strand of hair. Normally, the oils make hair shiny and attractive. During puberty, however, the oil glands can secrete too much oil, making the hair look and feel greasy. **Figure 14.3** provides tips on taking care of your hair.

MEDIA WATCH

UV FORECASTS

The National Weather Service predicts the next day's solar-hazard ratings in the Ultraviolet (UV) Index Forecast. This daily rating ranges from 0 (minimal health risk) to 15 (serious health risk). *How can the UV Index Forecast help you protect your skin?*

LESSON 1: HEALTHY SKIN, HAIR, AND NAILS **347**

WHAT TEENS WANT TO KNOW

What's harmful about getting a tattoo? Tattooing has many serious health risks. Tattoo equipment and tattoo studios that look clean may be dangerous and unsanitary. Nonsterile needles and equipment can expose you to infections, or you may suffer an allergic reaction to the dyes or pigments used to color the skin. Worse still, you could contract hepatitis B or hepatitis C, very serious blood-borne diseases, from contaminated needles or ink. There's even the possibility that you could be exposed to HIV, the virus that causes AIDS. Also, the people who apply tattoos do not have to have licenses or any special education.

③ Assess

Evaluating

📁 Assign the Lesson 1 Review; then assign the Lesson 1 Quiz in the TCR.

Reteaching

📁 Assign Concept Map 48 or Reteaching Activity 48 in the TCR.

Enrichment

- 📁 Assign Enrichment Activity 48 in the TCR.
- Have students draw and write captions for cartoons that present tips on skin care.

④ Close

Ask students to name one positive health behavior for skin care, one for hair care, and one for nail care.

Use an emery board or nail file to smooth out the rough edges of your nails. Use a nail clipper to cut your nails. *How do you usually trim your nails?*

Hair and Scalp Problems

Dandruff, *a flaking of the outer layer of dead skin cells on the scalp,* is usually caused by a dry scalp. It can often be controlled with a special shampoo, but if the problem persists, see a doctor. You may have a skin infection or scalp condition.

An itchy scalp may be caused by head lice. These tiny insects live in hair and are spread easily from person to person. That is why you should avoid sharing combs, brushes, and hats. To get rid of head lice, use a medicated shampoo and wash all items that have touched your head, such as bedding, towels, and hats.

Healthy Nails

Fingernails and toenails grow out of the skin's dermis. Around the base of each nail is *a fold of epidermis* called the **cuticle** (KYOO·ti·kuhl). Taking care of your nails and cuticles is important for your appearance and for your health.

Some minor problems can affect nails. A **hangnail** is *a split in the cuticle along the edge of a fingernail.* If you carefully cut away the broken skin, the cuticle should heal in a few days. An **ingrown toenail** is *a condition in which the nail pushes into the skin on the side of the toe.* This can happen if you cut your toenails in a curve rather than straight across, or if you wear shoes that are too tight. If the toe becomes inflamed and sore, see a doctor because it may be infected.

Lesson 1 Review

Using complete sentences, answer the following questions on a sheet of paper.

Reviewing Terms and Facts

1. **List** Name the three layers of skin.
2. **Recall** What are two harmful effects that the sun's UV rays can have on skin?
3. **Describe** What are the two main ways you can protect your skin from the sun?
4. **Explain** How can you avoid getting an ingrown toenail?

Thinking Critically

5. **Apply** Your friend Kelly is thinking about getting his eyebrow pierced at the mall.

Based on the information in this lesson, what advice would you give him?

6. **Suggest** What advice would you give teens who spend long hours in the sun working on a tan?

Applying Health Skills

7. **Analyzing Influences** Look through teen magazines for advertisements and articles that promote tanning, tattoos, or body piercing. Bring the articles to school and discuss how these media messages might influence teen decisions.

348 CHAPTER 14: PERSONAL CARE

Lesson 1 Review

1. Epidermis, dermis, subcutaneous layer.
2. Premature aging, skin cancer.
3. Cover skin with clothing, use sunscreen.
4. Clean and cut toenails properly, do not wear tight shoes.
5. Possible responses: Consider decision carefully, make sure equipment is sterilized, educate self on procedure and healing time.
6. Responses may include telling them they are at risk for skin cancer, telling them to wear sunblock, educating them on harmful UV rays.

Healthy Mouth and Teeth

Your Mouth and Teeth

Your mouth, teeth, and tongue play important roles in your health and appearance. They allow you to taste and digest food, to speak, and to make a positive impression on others. The list below explains these roles:

- **Tasting.** When food touches sensitive regions of your tongue called taste buds, a signal goes to your brain. The brain tells you whether the food is sweet, sour, salty, or bitter.
- **Digesting.** Digestion begins in your mouth. Your teeth and tongue break the food into smaller pieces. Saliva in your mouth moistens the food and starts to change it chemically.
- **Speaking.** All the consonant and vowel sounds you make are formed by precise placements of the tongue, lips, teeth, and other parts of your mouth.
- **Appearance.** Your teeth and mouth say a lot about who you are. Healthy and clean teeth tell others that you care about yourself and your appearance.

Quick Write

Write down at least three health benefits of brushing and flossing your teeth daily.

LEARN ABOUT...

- the functions of the mouth and teeth.
- the causes of tooth decay and gum disease.
- caring for your teeth and gums.

VOCABULARY

- periodontium
- plaque
- tartar
- orthodontist
- gingivitis
- periodontal disease

Your teeth and mouth allow you to bite, chew, and taste all kinds of food. *How do your taste buds help you enjoy food?*

LESSON 2: HEALTHY MOUTH AND TEETH **349**

Lesson 2

Healthy Mouth and Teeth

① FOCUS

Lesson Objectives

Students will be able to

- list the structures and functions of the mouth and teeth.
- list the causes of tooth decay and gum disease.
- identify steps to take care of their teeth and gums.

Motivators

Quick Write
Ask students to share their responses. Discuss how hygiene habits such as these can impact each of the three areas of health.

Bellringer Activity

Have students respond to these questions in writing: When was the last time you brushed your teeth? Flossed? Went to the dentist? Bought a new toothbrush? How often do you do these things?

VOCABULARY

Conduct a contest using the vocabulary terms for this lesson. Divide the class into two teams, and have the teams line up on opposite sides of the room. Alternate asking a member of each team to spell or define one of the vocabulary terms. If the student fails to answer correctly, he or she sits down. Once all the terms have been spelled and defined correctly, the team with the most students standing wins.

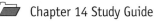

Lesson 2 Resources

Teacher Classroom Resources

- 📁 Concept Map 49
- 📁 Cross-Curriculum Activity 27
- 📁 Enrichment Activity 49
- 📁 Health Lab 14
- 📁 Lesson Plan 2
- 📁 Lesson 2 Quiz

- 📁 Reading Tutor Activity 48
- 📁 Reteaching Activity 49
- 🗳 Transparency 49

Student Activities Workbook

- 📁 Chapter 14 Study Guide
- 📁 Applying Health Skills 49

② Teach

Applying Knowledge

Have students work in groups to determine what parts of the mouth are used to produce each of the following letter sounds: *f, l, p, w, m, n* (*f—upper teeth and lower lip; l—tongue and palate; p—lips; w—lips, tongue, and palate; m—lips; n—tongue and palate*). Have each group report its conclusions, and correct any misconceptions.

• What would communication be like if a person was unable to make his or her lips meet? (*It would be extremely difficult.*)

• What does that difficulty suggest about the relationship of the mouth to the process of speaking? (*It is crucial to speech.*) **L2**

VISUAL LEARNING

FIGURE 14.4 Have students describe the picture in Figure 14.4. Ask:

Which parts of the tooth can you see in your own mouth?

Which parts cannot be seen?

Then have volunteers read aloud the descriptions of each part of a tooth. Cementum is not shown in the illustration. It is a bone-like layer that covers the dentin beneath the gumline. **INCL** *English Language Learners, Special Learning Needs, Behavior Problems, Different Learning Styles* (*Visual*)

Reading Check

Increase comprehension. Identify the causes and effects of tooth decay.

Your Teeth

Different types of teeth perform various functions. The incisors in the front of your mouth, for example, cut and tear food. The molars at the back do the major work of chewing.

As you can see in **Figure 14.4**, each tooth has three main parts: a crown, a neck, and a root. Each tooth is also made up of enamel, dentin, pulp, and cementum. The area around a tooth is called the **periodontium** (per·ee·oh·DAHN·shee·um), *a structure made up of the jawbone, the gums, and connectors called ligaments.* This structure supports the teeth.

Causes of Tooth Decay

Tooth decay is the gradual wearing away of a tooth's enamel and dentin layers. If you don't clean the food off your teeth after eating, bacteria in your mouth convert the sugars in the food into acids. Even though tooth enamel is one of the hardest substances in your body, acids can eat holes in it. **Figure 14.5** shows how tooth decay occurs.

Although tooth decay is widespread, it is one of the most preventable diseases in the United States. Some dental problems are inherited, but good habits and regular dental checkups can usually overcome them. You can make a big difference in the health and appearance of your teeth later in life by taking care of them now.

FIGURE 14.4

PARTS OF THE TOOTH

Each tooth is made up of many parts.

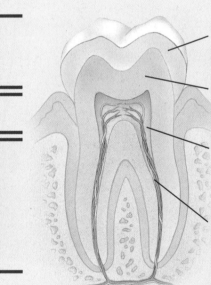

The crown is the part of the top surface of the tooth that you see.

The neck is the part of the tooth between the crown and the root.

The root is the part of the tooth inside the gum.

Enamel is the hard material that covers the crown of a tooth.

Dentin is bonelike material surrounding the pulp of a tooth.

Pulp is soft, sensitive material containing nerves and blood vessels deep within the root of a tooth.

The root canal provides a path for nerves and blood vessels. The nerves allow the tooth to feel pressure, pain, heat, and cold.

350 CHAPTER 14: PERSONAL CARE

Reading Check

Cause-and-Effect Relationships Students can be encouraged to analyze causes and effects to make sense of what they read. Have students analyze the third paragraph on page 350 by asking *What happens?* (to identify effects) and *Why does it happen?* (to identify causes). Have a volunteer read aloud the third paragraph. Ask: *Why does tooth decay happen?* (bacteria eat through tooth enamel). *What is the cause of tooth decay?* (bacteria). Mention that an effect can have several causes and vice versa. Ask: *What causes bacteria to form on teeth?* (not cleaning teeth after eating) Encourage students to look for causes and effects routinely as they read.

FIGURE 14.5

THE PROCESS OF TOOTH DECAY

When teeth are not cared for properly, tooth decay results. *What regular habits can help you prevent tooth decay?*

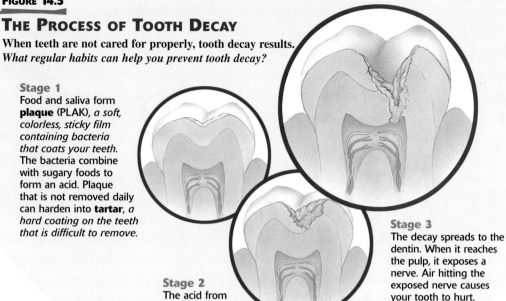

Stage 1
Food and saliva form **plaque** (PLAK), *a soft, colorless, sticky film containing bacteria that coats your teeth.* The bacteria combine with sugary foods to form an acid. Plaque that is not removed daily can harden into **tartar**, *a hard coating on the teeth that is difficult to remove.*

Stage 2
The acid from the plaque eats a hole, or cavity, in the tooth enamel.

Stage 3
The decay spreads to the dentin. When it reaches the pulp, it exposes a nerve. Air hitting the exposed nerve causes your tooth to hurt.

Taking Care of Your Teeth

You can have healthy teeth and gums for years to come if you practice sensible dental care. Here's what you need to do.

- **Brush and floss your teeth after eating and before bedtime.** Bacteria work rapidly, so it's important to remove food particles after eating. If you can't brush after a meal, rinse your mouth.
- **Choose snacks wisely.** Raw vegetables, plain yogurt, and fruits are good choices. Avoid snacks that are high in sugar or that remain in the mouth for a long time, such as soft drinks and hard or sticky candies.
- **Protect your teeth when you play contact sports.** Use a mouth guard to prevent your teeth from being chipped or knocked out during sports.
- **Get regular dental screenings.** A dentist or dental hygienist can clean your teeth and treat tooth decay and gum disease before they become serious problems.

Developing Good Character ★

Responsibility

Learning how to brush and floss properly can help you avoid pain and expense in later life. Schedule regular exams with your dentist, and ask the hygienist for tips on how to care for your teeth. Cooperate with any recommendations dental professionals give you.

LESSON 2: HEALTHY MOUTH AND TEETH **351**

Analyzing

Have students explain the role of preventive health measures, such as dental checkups, in disease prevention. Then have students talk about their attitudes about going to the dentist. Ask students what their dentists do to allay fears and lessen pain (*headphones, playing music or movies, nitrous oxide, flavored local anesthetic, and so on*). **L1**

VISUAL LEARNING

FIGURE 14.5 Ask volunteers to read aloud the title and caption; have others describe the pictures and read the accompanying explanations. Then have students answer the caption question. Ask: How does each health habit (brushing, flossing, making good food choices, and having regular dental checkups) help prevent tooth decay? **INCL** *English Language Learners, Special Learning Needs, Behavior Problems, Different Learning Styles (Visual)*

Developing Good Character ★

Responsibility

The teen years are a great time to make proper tooth care a part of one's daily routine. Have students discuss what a healthy dental care program includes. Encourage each student to make a personal plan that includes being responsible for daily maintenance care, as well as regular preventative care.

WHAT TEENS WANT TO KNOW

What causes bad breath? Halitosis is the scientific name for bad breath. The most common causes are eating strong foods such as garlic or onions, smoking, or drinking alcohol. You may also have bad breath if you have an impacted tooth or tooth decay, gum disease, or infections of the throat or sinuses. Some prescription medications, such as injectable insulin and inhaled medicines, also may cause bad breath. Less often, bad breath is a symptom of disease. For example, people with diabetes may have sweet- or fruity-smelling breath. The best treatment for the common causes of bad breath is good oral hygiene, which includes regular brushing and flossing. After a meal with onions, garlic, or other strong flavors, try chewing gum.

Lesson 2

FIGURE 14.6 Ask students:

• Take a guess. Throughout your life, how many times have you brushed and flossed your teeth?

• Are you sure you are brushing and flossing correctly?

• Then have students read and discuss the instructions for brushing and flossing correctly. **INCL** *English Language Learners, Special Learning Needs, Behavior Problems, Different Learning Styles (Visual)*

Hands-On Health

PLAQUE ATTACK

Time: 20 minutes, during two class sessions

TEACHING THE ACTIVITY

• Have volunteers read the activity introduction and instructions aloud. Discuss the steps in the activity, and encourage students to ask questions.

• Have students complete the activity at home.

• Have students meet in groups to discuss their responses to the In Conclusion questions.

• Have students write brief paragraphs in response to the second In Conclusion question.

ASSESSMENT

Use students' participation in their groups' discussions and their paragraphs to assess their learning.

FIGURE 14.6

HOW TO BRUSH AND FLOSS YOUR TEETH

Regular brushing and flossing will prevent tooth decay and gum disease

Brushing

1. Brush the outer surfaces of your teeth, using small circular or side-to-side strokes.
2. Brush the chewing surfaces.
3. Brush the inside surfaces.
4. Brush your tongue and rinse with mouthwash or water.

Flossing

1. Wrap about 18 inches of floss around the middle finger of each hand.
2. Grip the floss tightly between thumb and forefinger.
3. Slide the floss back and forth between teeth toward the gumline until it touches your gumline.
4. Forming a C with the floss around each tooth, slide the floss back and forth as you move it up and down the side of the tooth. Do the same for all of your teeth.

Brushing and Flossing

Daily brushing and flossing are essential for healthy teeth and gums. Most dentists recommend gently brushing gums and teeth with a soft-bristled toothbrush, using a fluoride toothpaste, for at least two minutes. **Figure 14.6** lists the correct methods for brushing and flossing. Replace your toothbrush every two or three months, or after an illness.

Hands-On Health

PLAQUE ATTACK

This activity will show how effective you are at fighting plaque.

WHAT YOU WILL NEED

• toothbrush
• toothpaste
• dental floss
• plaque-disclosing tablets or food coloring and water
• mirror

WHAT YOU WILL DO

1. Brush and floss your teeth the way you normally do.
2. Follow the manufacturer's instructions for using the disclosing tablets, or mix two drops of food coloring in a glass of water. Swish the colored water around your mouth and spit it out.
3. Examine your teeth in the mirror. The places where color sticks to your teeth did not get clean.
4. Brush and floss again, concentrating on the parts you missed last time. Check the results with a disclosing tablet or food coloring. Repeat if necessary.

IN CONCLUSION

What did you learn about your ability to remove plaque from your teeth? What can you do to improve your brushing and flossing?

 ## Beyond the Classroom

Community Fluoride—found naturally in water, fish, and tea—is a mineral necessary for strong bones and teeth. Its primary role in children is to protect the teeth from decay. The fluoride level in the drinking water of many communities has been increased through additional fluoridation practices. Also, people who use fluoridated toothpastes increase their intake of the mineral.

Encourage students to find out more about the level of fluoride in their community's water supply. Have them determine whether the toothpaste they use at home contains fluoride. Have students compare fluoridation in dental practices to immunization in medical practices. Ask them to discover the consequences, if any, of too high an intake of fluoride.

Orthodontics

For many adolescents, the teen years are the time when braces are applied to correct crooked or poorly aligned teeth. The main cause of these problems is heredity, but thumb sucking and tooth loss can also cause the teeth not to line up properly.

An **orthodontist** (or·thuh·DAHN·tist) is *a dentist who prevents or corrects problems with the alignment or spacing of teeth.* Orthodontists often recommend braces, which provide steady pressure on the teeth to gently move them into the desired positions.

Other Dental Problems

Some problems of the mouth and teeth result from poor dental hygiene. Bad breath, for example, is often caused by failing to clean the teeth adequately. Other causes of bad breath are tooth decay, use of tobacco, and upset stomach. Tongue brushing and mouthwash use are important for controlling bad breath.

Gingivitis (jin·juh·VY·tis) is *a common disorder in which the gums are red and sore and bleed easily.* Gingivitis is the first stage of gum disease, and it can be cured with good oral hygiene. Left untreated, gum disease can result in receding gums and tooth loss. *Advanced gum disease, in which the periodontium is infected with bacteria,* is called **periodontal** (per·ee·oh·DAHNT·uhl) **disease**. Most adult tooth loss is the result of periodontal disease.

Colored braces are a popular option for dental patients. *Why is it important for teens to feel good about the way their braces look?*

Lesson 2 Review

Using complete sentences, answer the following questions on a sheet of paper.

Reviewing Terms and Facts

1. **Vocabulary** Define *plaque*. What does plaque harden into if it is not removed?
2. **Recall** How does tooth decay occur?
3. **Explain** What kinds of snacks are most harmful to your teeth?
4. **Identify** What are four possible causes of bad breath?

Thinking Critically

5. **Evaluate** Your friend Ellis brushes his teeth "in record time." You notice that he brushes only the outer surfaces of his teeth. He says that he brushes after every meal so he doesn't have to brush more carefully. What would you recommend to him?
6. **Analyze** Explain the role of regular dental checkups in the prevention and treatment of disease.

Applying Health Skills

7. **Accessing Information** Use the Web to access information about fluoride. Find out why dentists recommend fluoride toothpaste. Prepare a brief presentation of your findings, including statistics to back up the case for fluoride use.

LESSON 2: HEALTHY MOUTH AND TEETH **353**

Health Eyes and Ears

① Focus

Lesson Objectives

Students will be able to

- name the structures and functions of the eye and ear.
- identity ways to protect and care for the eyes.
- describe the treatments for vision problems.
- identify ways to protect and care for the ears.

Health Skills
- Advocacy, p. 359

Motivators

Quick Write

List the students' responses on the board. Have students add to the list as they learn more about caring for the eyes and ears in this lesson.

Bellringer Activity

Ask students to imagine that a very good friend cannot hear. Instruct them to list three ways in which they might learn to communicate with their friend.

VOCABULARY

Randomly write each of the vocabulary terms on the board. Instruct students to divide a sheet of paper into two columns and label them *Parts of the Eye* and *Parts of the Ear*. Students should write each of the vocabulary terms where they think it belongs. Have students verify their hunches in the Glossary.

Quick Write

List the actions you take to protect your eyes and ears from damage.

LEARN ABOUT...

- how your eyes work and how to protect them.
- how your ears work and how to protect them.

VOCABULARY

- cornea
- iris
- pupil
- lens
- retina
- optometrist
- ophthalmologist
- eustachian tube
- decibel

Healthy Eyes and Ears

The Structure of the Eye

Your eyes are your windows to the world. They enable you to distinguish shapes, colors, movement, and light. It is through your eyes that you gain most of your knowledge! Although they are independent of one another, your eyes work together. **Figure 14.7** shows the main parts of the eye.

FIGURE 14.7

PARTS OF THE EYE

Each part of the eye has a specific function.

A The **cornea** is *a clear protective structure that lets in light.*

B The aqueous (AY·kwee·uhs) humor is the watery fluid in between the cornea and lens. It helps maintain pressure in the eye.

C The **iris** is *the colored part of the eye.* It controls the size of the pupil.

D The **pupil** is *a dark opening in the center of the iris.* The pupil controls the amount of light that enters the eye.

E The **lens** is *a clear flexible structure that focuses light on the retina.*

F The **retina** (RE·tin·uh) is *a thin layer of nerve cells that absorb light.* It covers the interior back of the eye.

G The optic nerve is a cord of nerve fibers that carries messages from the retina to the brain.

H The sclera (SKLEHR·uh) is *the white of the eye.* It protects the eyeball and gives it its shape.

354 CHAPTER 14: PERSONAL CARE

Lesson 3 Resources

Teacher Classroom Resources
- Concept Map 50
- Cross-Curriculum Activity 28
- Decision-Making Activity 28
- Enrichment Activity 50
- Lesson Plan 3
- Lesson 3 Quiz
- Reading Tutor Activity 49

- Reteaching Activity 50
- Transparencies 50 & 51

Student Activities Workbook
- Chapter 14 Study Guide
- Applying Health Skills 50
- Health Inventory 14

FIGURE 14.8

HOW THE EYE SEES

The eye requires light in order to see. *What happens to your vision when you enter a dark room?*

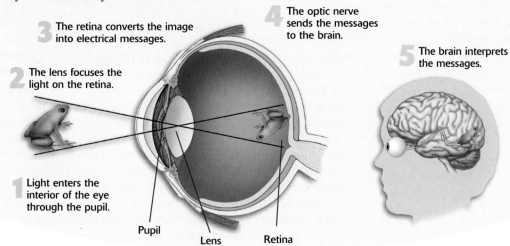

3 The retina converts the image into electrical messages.

2 The lens focuses the light on the retina.

1 Light enters the interior of the eye through the pupil.

4 The optic nerve sends the messages to the brain.

5 The brain interprets the messages.

Pupil　　Lens　　Retina

Your Eyes

The human eye is similar to a camera. It has an opening that lets in different amounts of light. As **Figure 14.8** shows, light passes through the cornea, aqueous humor, pupil, and lens to the retina. The lens can change shape to focus on objects that are close or far away.

Color Vision

Within the retina are millions of nerve endings. Some of the nerve endings distinguish objects in shades of black, white, and gray. These nerve endings are known as rods, and your eyes use them in dim light. Other nerve endings, called cones, distinguish the colors red, blue, and green. When information about these three colors is mixed, you are able to see all possible colors. Cones help you see sharp, color images in bright light. Both rods and cones send messages to the brain, which interprets the information.

A person who is missing one or more kinds of cones is unable to distinguish certain colors, an inherited condition called color blindness. In the most common form of color blindness, the person is unable to distinguish between red and green. Color blindness occurs in about 1 in 10 males and very rarely in women.

In this circle, a number is printed in another color. *A person who cannot distinguish between the colors has what condition?*

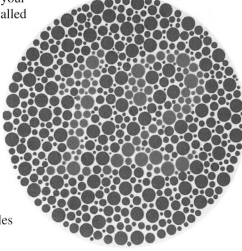

---

② Teach

VISUAL LEARNING

FIGURE 14.7 Have volunteers describe the drawing of an eye, identifying which parts are visible and which are concealed. Then have students work in groups to read about and discuss the function of each part of the eye.

• How is each part important to your ability to see?

• What do you think you can do to take good care of each part? **INCL** *English Language Learners, Special Learning Needs, Behavior Problems, Different Learning Styles (Visual)*

VISUAL LEARNING

FIGURE 14.8 Have students read the caption for Figure 14.8, and have a volunteer answer the question; he or she should explain that you can't see until your eyes adjust. Then ask: How do your eyes adjust to light? Have students read the information in Figure 14.8 to find out. **INCL** *English Language Learners, Special Learning Needs, Behavior Problems, Different Learning Styles (Visual)*

Researching

Ask a pair of interested students to learn how color blindness is inherited and to explain the process to the rest of the class. **L3**

Health Literacy

Health Information Laser in-situ keratomileusis (LASIK) is an increasingly popular surgical procedure that uses the excimer laser, a cold beam of ultraviolet light that destroys problem cells on the cornea, to improve vision. LASIK has been performed in the United States since 1995 and is considered safe and effective. Using the excimer laser, which is controlled by a computer, the ophthalmologist reshapes the cornea, enabling it to better focus images onto the retina. The procedure takes about 15 minutes per eye. Patients are awake and feel pressure, but there is no pain. LASIK is generally not considered suitable for people whose vision is still changing. Since these changes usually continue into the early 20s, LASIK is not recommended for children and teens.

Ask a group of interested volunteers to collect different kinds of protective eyewear appropriate for various sports, hobbies, and work activities. Have these volunteers show the eyewear to the rest of the class, explaining when and how each should be worn. **L2**

Cross-Curriculum Activity

SCIENCE Explain to students that as often as five times a year, the moon passes between the sun and the earth, causing a solar eclipse. If you want to observe a solar eclipse, you must protect your eyes. Regular glasses do not provide enough protection. You need a special solar light filter. Have students use the Internet to find out more about these special filters and be prepared for the next eclipse. **L3**

Investigating

Ask a group of volunteers to learn more about the training and work of optometrists, ophthalmologists, and opticians. Have these students draw a Venn diagram or other visual summary of their findings; have them share this work with the rest of the class. **L2**

Protecting Your Eyes

Protecting your eyes from injury, dust, and overexposure to sunlight is a positive health habit. Here are some guidelines.

- **Wear protective sunglasses and avoid exposing your eyes to bright light.** A day in intense sun can burn your cornea. Over time, sunlight can damage the lens, retina, and cornea, as well as give you cataracts. Never look directly into the sun.
- **Wear protective eyewear when participating in an activity that could injure your eyes.** Special eye protection is available for different sports, hobbies, and work activities.
- **Read, watch television, and use the computer in a well-lighted room.** Position the computer screen about two feet from your eyes. Prevent eyestrain by taking a ten-minute break from the computer once every hour. Take breaks while reading and watching television, as well.
- **Avoid rubbing your eyes.** Rubbing irritates your eyes. Itchy eyes may be a sign of infection or foreign objects in your eyes.
- **Avoid touching your eyeball when applying makeup.** Also, do not use old makeup or makeup that has been used by another person. After a few months, eye makeup starts to grow bacteria.

Getting Your Eyes Checked

Two kinds of professionals provide eye checkups. An **optometrist** (ahp·TAHM·uh·trist) is *a professional who checks your vision and prescribes corrective lenses.* An **ophthalmologist** (ahf·thuhl·MAHL·uh·jist) is *a medical doctor who specializes in medical and surgical treatment of the eyes, and who prescribes corrective lenses.*

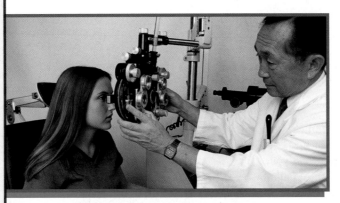

Your vision and the health of your eyes are checked during an eye examination. *When was the last time you had an eye checkup?*

If you wear glasses or contact lenses, have your eyes checked once a year. If you do not wear corrective lenses and can see properly, every two years is sufficient. Your eye doctor may also test for glaucoma and cataracts during an examination. Common vision problems include:

- **Farsightedness.** A person can see distant objects clearly, but nearby objects appear blurred.
- **Nearsightedness.** A person can see nearby objects clearly, but distant objects appear blurred.
- **Astigmatism** (uh·STIG·muh·tiz·uhm). Images are distorted or blurred because of an irregularly shaped lens or cornea.

356 CHAPTER 14: PERSONAL CARE

MORE ABOUT...

Eye Care Conjunctivitis, or "pinkeye," may result from allergic reactions, exposure to cosmetics or chlorinated water, or a bacterial infection or virus. It can be highly contagious. The following recommendations are made for anyone who suspects he or she has conjunctivitis:

- See a physician for diagnosis and treatment.

- Don't touch the eye.
- Use tissues when wiping away excretions.
- Don't wear eye makeup.
- Don't wear contact lenses until the condition has cleared up.
- Don't share washcloths and towels.

Treating Vision Problems

Most vision problems can be corrected with eyeglasses and contact lenses. Eyeglasses are a more common choice because they are often less expensive than contacts and require fewer visits to the optometrist. Moreover, eyeglasses do not require special cleaning and storage procedures.

Many Americans wear contact lenses. Soft lenses are usually more comfortable than hard lenses, but they are more difficult to clean. Extended wear contact lenses can be worn for a week at a time but increase the risk of eye infection or cornea damage.

Some vision problems can be corrected with laser surgery. This kind of surgery may eliminate the need for glasses or contact lenses. However, it is not recommended for teens because their eyes are still changing.

The Structure of the Ear

You might think of your ears as external to your head, but in fact they go deep into your skull. **Figure 14.9** shows the different parts of the ear.

FIGURE 14.9

PARTS OF THE EAR

The ear has three main parts: the outer ear, the middle ear, and the inner ear.

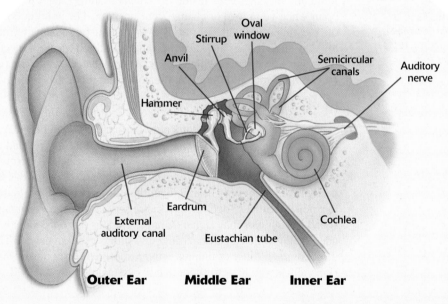

Oval window

Stirrup

Anvil

Semicircular canals

Hammer

Auditory nerve

External auditory canal

Eardrum

Eustachian tube

Cochlea

Outer Ear   **Middle Ear**   **Inner Ear**

Topic: The eye

For links to more information on the eye, go to **health.glencoe.com**.

Activity: Using the information provided at these links, write down five facts you learned about the eye and vision.

HEALTH *Online*

Encourage students to explore the Web Links for this chapter and then complete the activity.

Demonstrating

Distribute safety glasses used in science labs, and have students cover the lenses with a thin coat of petroleum jelly. Then direct students to perform various daily activities, such as pouring a glass of water or signing their names, while wearing the safety glasses. Vision will blur and resemble that of people who suffer from cataracts. Ask students to discuss how they felt about this blurring. **L1 INCL** *English Language Learners, Different Learning Styles* (*Visual*)

VISUAL LEARNING

FIGURE 14.9 Have students describe the ear pictured in Figure 14.9. Ask: Which of these parts are visible? Then have volunteers read aloud the names of the parts of the outer ear, the middle ear, and the inner ear. Have students point to each part in the picture as the name is read. **INCL** *English Language Learners, Special Learning Needs, Behavior Problems, Different Learning Styles* (*Visual*)

Cross-Curriculum Activity

LANGUAGE ARTS Have students write compositions on what their lives would be like if they could not hear. Direct them to include specific examples, and have them explain how they would need to compensate for the differences. **L2**

Health Literacy

Health Information New technology has made it possible for some people with hearing impairments to hear well again. Scientists and specialists have invented the multichannel cochlear implant. The device consists of a tiny microphone connected to a sound processor. Together, the two elements pick up sound waves and convert them to electronic signals, which are then passed to a receiver implanted in the skin behind the ear. Although the implant is not effective for individuals with congenital or profound hearing loss, it still marks an important first step in providing "ears" for the deaf.

Demonstrating

Use the following demonstration to introduce the process of hearing: Instruct students to cover their ears tightly with their hands. Read aloud a section of the textbook. Instruct students to remove their hands. Ask them to summarize what they just heard. Ask: How was your comprehension of the text affected? **L1**

Investigating

Have students work in groups to find the decibels of at least five different sounds (such as an electric toothbrush, a power lawnmower, a car horn, a jackhammer, and a gunshot). Then have group members work together to plan and draw a bar graph showing these sound measurements. **L2**

Guest Speaker

Invite a person trained in sign language to speak to the class and demonstrate signing. Have students compare and contrast oral and sign communication. **L1**

HEALTH SKILLS ACTIVITY

ADVOCACY

Guide students in reading and discussing the activity introduction and instructions. Add to their instructions that they should include in their campaigns supporting data and persuasive reasons to protect their ears.

Suggest that, as part of their planned campaigns, groups might publish articles in the school paper or publish informative brochures; have the class brainstorm a list of other possibilities. Then ask students to work in cooperative groups to complete the activity.

Note: This skill is introduced in Chapter 3 on page 61.

Keep the volume low when you listen to music. *What other ways can you protect your ears?*

✔ Reading Check

Memorize. Make a word web to organize and remember facts about the ear.

How Your Ears Work

Hearing involves a fairly complicated chain of events. First, the outer ear—the part we can see—guides sound waves deep into the ear. These sound waves travel through the external auditory canal to the middle ear, where they cause the eardrum to vibrate. This vibration moves three tiny bones—the hammer, the anvil, and the stirrup—in the middle ear.

The hammer, the anvil, and the stirrup then transmit the vibration to the oval window in the inner ear. The oval window causes fluid in the cochlea to move. The movement of this fluid sets tiny hair cells inside the cochlea into motion. The hair cells produce electrical messages that travel through the auditory nerve to the brain, which interprets the messages, enabling you to identify the sound.

In order for you to hear properly, the pressure on both sides of the eardrum must be equal. The **eustachian** (yoo·STAY·shuhn) **tube** is *the part of the ear that allows air to pass from the nose to the middle ear so the air pressure is equal on both sides of the eardrum.* The eustachian tube runs from the throat to the middle ear.

Ears and Balance

The semicircular canals in the inner ear control your balance. Fluid and tiny hair cells inside the canals send messages to your brain when you move or change your position. The brain interprets the messages and tells your body how to adjust or change to meet the new situation. Sometimes the canals send too many or too few messages to the brain, which can result in balance problems. Two common balance problems are dizziness and motion sickness.

Protecting Your Ears

Over time, loud noises can cause permanent hearing loss. A **decibel** is *a measure of the loudness of sound.* The softest sound a person with normal hearing can hear is set at 0 decibels. A normal conversation is usually about 60 decibels. Any noise level above 85 decibels can harm your hearing over time. Just one short exposure to a noise above 125 decibels can cause serious damage. A ringing sound in your ears may signal damage. Tinnitus (tin·EYE·tuhs) is a condition in which a constant ringing sound is heard in the ear. The most common cause of tinnitus is overexposure to loud noises. Generally, if you have to shout to talk over a noise, it's too loud.

358 CHAPTER 14: PERSONAL CARE

✔ Reading Check

Word Web Word webs help students organize information and provide visual support to understand and remember technical vocabulary. Write *The Ear* in a circle at the center of the chalkboard. Write the names of parts of the ear in circles connected by lines to the center (*eardrum, hammer, anvil, stirrup, cochlea, eustachian tube, and so on*). Ask students to locate these parts in the diagram on page 357 and describe what each part does. Add this information to the word web in a third set of circles, and connect each circle to the word to which it refers. Write the title *The Ear and Its Parts* on the board above the web. Ask students to draw and fill in their own word webs following your model.

Here are some ways you can protect your ears.

- Cover your ears with earmuffs, a hat, or a scarf in cold weather.
- Keep foreign objects such as sharp objects and even cotton swabs out of your ears.
- Wear hearing protection such as earplugs when you are exposed to loud noises at a concert or indoor sporting event.

HEALTH SKILLS ACTIVITY

ADVOCACY

Reducing Noise Levels

Did you know that listening to loud music for as little as 15 minutes can damage your hearing? Over time, exposure to loud sounds can cause permanent hearing loss. The list below gives you some examples of how many decibels typical sounds have.

- **60–95 DECIBELS**—hair dryer, alarm clock, ringing telephone, television.
- **110–120 DECIBELS**—rock concert, busy video arcade, football game.
- **140–150 DECIBELS**—firecracker, airplane taking off.

WITH A GROUP
Prepare a campaign to inform other students about hearing loss. Include ways to reduce noise levels and protect hearing. Be sure to include specific strategies to reduce noise levels and protect hearing.

Lesson 3 Review

Using complete sentences, answer the following questions on a sheet of paper.

Reviewing Terms and Facts

1. **Vocabulary** Define the terms *pupil* and *iris*. Use them in an original sentence.
2. **Recall** What are rods and cones? What do they enable you to do?
3. **Explain** What is the difference between farsightedness and nearsightedness?
4. **Recall** What is tinnitus? What causes it?

Thinking Critically

5. **Analyze** Your friend Magda never wears sunglasses, even when she is at the beach. She says the sun does not hurt her eyes. How might you help her better protect her health?
6. **Explain** Why is the process of hearing described as a chain of events?

Applying Health Skills

7. **Practicing Healthful Behaviors** Look for examples of loud noise levels at home. Perhaps you have a noisy vacuum cleaner. Perhaps a family member turns the volume on the television or stereo up high. List the examples you find, and then discuss with family members what can be done to reduce noise levels in your home.

LESSON 3: HEALTHY EYES AND EARS **359**

Lesson 3

③ Assess

Evaluating

📁 Assign the Lesson 3 Review; then assign the Lesson 3 Quiz in the TCR.

Reteaching

📁 Assign Concept Map 50 or Reteaching Activity 50 in the TCR.

Enrichment

- 📁 Assign Enrichment Activity 50 in the TCR.
- Provide students with books and articles on the working of the camera lens. Then have them divide a sheet of paper into two columns and list the similarities and differences between the operation of the camera lens and the eye.

④ Close

Review the major concepts of the lesson. Then ask students to name new health habits they will adopt to take better care of their eyes and ears.

Lesson 3 Review

1. See Figure 14.7 on page 354. Sentences will vary.
2. See explanations under Color Vision on page 355.
3. Farsightedness means you can see distant objects, but close objects appear blurred. Nearsightedness means you can see nearby objects clearly, but distant objects appear blurred.
4. A constant ringing sound heard in the ear caused by overexposure to loud noises.
5. Explain that the sun can damage the lens, retina, and cornea if the eyes are unprotected for long periods in the sun.
6. Responses should reflect the chain of events as described under How Your Ears Work on page 358.

The Truth Behind Popular Health Tips

① Focus

Objectives

Students will be able to

- discuss popular health tips.
- access reliable health information about these tips.
- write their own catchy health sayings.

Motivator

Bellringer Activity

Write "An apple a day keeps the doctor away" on the board. Ask students, "How many of you have heard this common health tip? What does it mean? Is it true? Why or why not?"

② Teach

Cooperative Learning

Review the six popular health tips on this spread with students. Ask, "Is there any risk in believing common health tips?" Explain that while some tips keep us from behaving in unhealthy ways (like chewing ice), others can do more harm than good (applying baby oil to the skin before sun exposure). That's why the ability to access reliable health information is so important. Divide the class into six groups. Assign each group one of the health tips on this spread. Tell each group to

- identify at least three reliable sources of information about this tip.
- briefly describe the type of information each source offers. (How are they different?)
- explain why each is a good source.
- report to the class on the validity of the popular health tip based on these sources.

The Truth Behind Popular Health Tips

Take a look at a few common health tips, and discover what's fact and what's fiction.

1. "Cutting your hair will make it grow faster."

FACT: That won't cut it. "Your hair isn't like a lawn or a rosebush, where cutting can stimulate fresh growth," says Philip Kingsley, a hair and scalp expert in New York City. The length of your hair is genetically predetermined—when it reaches a certain length, it stops growing. When you trim the ends of your hair, you're merely cutting off dead split ends. This can make hair look healthier, but it won't help it grow any faster. Gently massaging your scalp may stimulate some growth by increasing blood flow and oxygen to the area. Besides, it feels good.

 ## Beyond the Classroom

Community Explain that students are going to test how pervasive popular health tips are in the community. As a group, brainstorm as many popular health beliefs as you can, including those from this spread. (*for example, "Don't cross your eyes or they'll stay that way." "Feed a fever, starve a cold."*) Tell students that are going to conduct an informal survey with their friends and family members. Each student should pick six beliefs and ask their survey subjects, "Is this statement true? Where did you first hear this statement?" Have students record the results and report back to the class. Did the source of information play a role in whether or not subjects believed the tips were true?

2. "Baby oil is a good substitute for suntan lotion."

FACT: This slippery advice comes from the fact that the mineral oil found in baby oil decreases your skin's refractive index, says Cincinnati dermatologist Brett Coldiron, M.D. Translation: Oil makes your skin absorb more light instead of reflecting it off your skin. "Oils will tan or burn your skin faster. You're basically marinating your skin so it soaks up more sun," says Dr. Coldiron. "That is, without a doubt, the worst thing you can do for your skin." The best thing you can do for your skin is to apply a sunscreen with a sun protection factor (SPF) of *at least* 15 to all exposed areas before going outdoors.

3. "Sitting too close to the TV will make you go blind."

FACT: This isn't even close to being true. Planting yourself in front of the tube might make your eyes or your head hurt, but it won't take away your sight, says Kerry Beebe, an optometrist with the American Optometric Association. "You should sit about 8 to 10 feet from the screen, because the closer you sit to the television, the harder your eyes strain to focus," Beebe says. If you have to sit any closer, this could be a sign that you're nearsighted (which means you have trouble seeing at a distance). See an eye doctor for a vision screening to determine whether you need corrective lenses.

4. "Brushing your hair 100 strokes a day will keep it shiny and clean."

FACT: This idea is hardly a stroke of genius—and, according to Kingsley, the practice is actually bad for your hair. "If you brushed a wool sweater repeatedly, you would wear a hole in it," he says. "Likewise, your hair can get worn out." Besides: All the brushing does is spread natural oils over your hair. These can act as a dirt magnet, which will only weigh down your 'do.

5. "Chewing on ice can damage the enamel on your teeth."

FACT: This one's true. Think of it this way: If you knock two rocks together, chances are good that one of the rocks will chip. The same goes for your teeth, says Matthew Messina, D.D.S., a

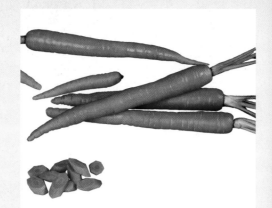

consumer adviser with the American Dental Association. "Tooth enamel is a crystal, and so is ice. When you push one against the other, one of them has to break," says Messina. This just goes to show that chewing on ice isn't all it's cracked up to be.

6. "Eating lots of carrots will make you see better in the dark."

FACT: You could see it that way. Many brightly colored fruits and veggies—including carrots, apricots, and broccoli—contain beta-carotene, a substance that the body converts to vitamin A. This vitamin *can* improve night vision, but only if your body is lacking it to begin with, says Carl Kupfer, M.D., director of the National Eye Institute at the National Institutes of Health. "Most of us get enough vitamin A in our diet, so eating lots of carrots won't change anything," says Dr. Kupfer. ◾

TIME TO THINK...

About Good Health Advice

Where do you get your health tips? Magazines? Friends? Older siblings? Create a "My Top Five List of Health Advice Sources," putting the source you rely on the most at number one. Now, evaluate your sources. How reliable is each one? Create a new list called "My Top Five List of Most Reliable Health Advice Sources." How do the two lists compare?

③ Apply

Time to Think

Ask students, "Why do you think popular health tips like theses are spread? How might these beliefs originate?" Discuss how some common health tips are based in fact but exaggerate the positive or negative effects of a food or activity. For instance, go back to the phrase, "An apple a day keeps the doctor away." While apples *are* good for you, they certainly don't guarantee that you'll never need a doctor's attention. Divide students into small groups. Ask each group to analyze four other common health tips. Questions to consider include the following:

• Is this common health tip based on fact?

• Is the fact exaggerated or distorted in the tip? If so, how?

• Do you think the average person knows that this tip is not quite true?

• If someone follows this tip, will they do more good or harm to their health?

VISUAL LEARNING

Ask students to pick one of the three images on this spread. Which common health tip is associated with this food or activity and why?

Health Literacy

Remembering Health Tips Tell students that they are going to take a true health tip and write about it in such a way that people are more likely to remember it. (For instance, "Don't chew on ice if you want your teeth to look nice.")

Give students the following guidelines:

• The health fact must be true.

• Students should identify a key audience for the health fact (teen boys, grown women, and so on).

• The fact should be presented in a catchy, memorable way *for this audience*.

• Ask for several student volunteers to share their work with the class. Do other students agree that this fact is true and is presented in a memorable way? Why or why not?

ANALYZING INFLUENCES

ANALYZING INFLUENCES

Objective

After completing the lesson, students will be able use critical thinking, such as interpreting media messages about appearance and personal health, to analyze and use health information.

Time: 40 minutes

Materials: magazines, newspapers, poster board, scissors, tape or glue, markers, pen or pencil, paper

Teacher Classroom Resources

📁 Building Health Skills Activities

• Transparency Master 4, "Analyzing Influences"

• Reproducible Master 39, "Seeing Beyond the Perfect Look"

1. Model

• Display Transparency Master 4, and review examples of internal and external influences.

• Have students read the scenario. Then lead a class discussion about Jennifer's discovery that media images are not always a reliable source of information about teens.

• Remind students that health care professionals (e.g., a pediatrician, like Jennifer's mother) are reliable sources of information about appearance and personal health issues.

• Explain that the media can be a powerful external influence because it relates to many of our internal influences such as curiosity.

SEEING BEYOND THE PERFECT LOOK

Model

As a teen, the way you feel about your personal appearance may be influenced by the images of teens you see in movies, television, or magazines. Read about a teen named Jennifer and how she learned the truth about media images.

When Jennifer looks through teen magazines, she can't help but notice how perfect the girls in the advertisements look. Their hair is never out of place, their skin never has a blemish, and their teeth are always perfect.

Jennifer used to worry that she needed to try to look just like these teens. Then her mother explained that these girls are models who are assisted by hairstylists, makeup artists, and fashion experts. The photographers even use computers to make the pictures look perfect.

Jennifer's mother, a pediatrician, said she would be happy to speak in Jennifer's health class about the importance of respecting physical differences and not believing media messages about how everyone is "supposed" to look.

362 CHAPTER 14: PERSONAL CARE

Teaching Tips

Linking Skills Explain to students how being aware of the internal and external influence in their lives can help them improve other skills such as decision making.

Learning Through Diversity Group work allows students to share their knowledge and their experiences. It also promotes social interaction among students who may not normally associate. Interaction among group members allows students to learn about different ways of living and thinking. Teachers can encourage diverse group membership by assigning members to groups. Factors that create diversity include gender, culture, and social associations at school.

Practice

Ads use "picture perfect" models to influence teens to purchase certain products or services. In small groups, look through magazines and, using scissors, cut out what the media portray as pictures of health to influence teens to use a particular personal care product. For example, cut out examples of "healthy hair," "healthy skin," and "healthy teeth." Glue or tape them to poster board.

Answer the questions below to analyze the health information in these ads. Explain your answers to the class.

1. What products are advertised with these images?
2. What messages do they contain?
3. How do they try to influence teens?
4. Do you think these messages affect the choices teens make?

Apply/Assess

Imagine that your group is responsible for writing an advice column for teens. Read the following letter and prepare a response. Base your responses on the questions in the Practice activity. Explain the role of the media in influencing individual and community health.

Dear Teen Adviser:
I'm writing because I am so frustrated. Every time I open a magazine, I see pictures of perfect teens and I want to be like them. I do all the right things to take care of my skin, my hair, and my teeth. I usually eat healthy foods, and I do some kind of physical activity almost every day. My friends tell me that I'm in great shape. However, I really want to look more like these models I see in the ads.
Some of the ads sell nutritional supplements that are supposed to make me look "picture perfect." The supplements are too expensive, and I'm afraid that they may be harmful. Please advise.

Damien

---

2. Practice

- Divide the class into small groups, and distribute materials to each group.
- Have students create posters of images that the media represent as "pictures of health" to influence teens to buy certain personal health care products. You may want to suggest to students that they focus on specific categories (e.g., healthy skin, healthy hair) as they search for images for their posters.
- Have each group answer the questions and present their poster to the class.

3. Apply/Assess

- 📁 You may wish to distribute Building Health Skills Reproducible Master 39 in the TCR to guide students in completing this activity.
- Have each group write a response to Damien's letter using the questions in the Practice section to craft their reply.
- Remind students to refer to the Self-Check before and after they write their responses.
- After each group has read their response aloud, lead a class discussion on the content of each letter. Ask: What elements in the responses that you have heard would be especially likely to influence a teen reader?

Assessment Scoring ✓

Using a rubric, student work should provide evidence of all criteria to achieve the highest score.

Skills

Student work describes

- how media present unrealistic "pictures of health."
- how media messages attempt to influence teens.

Concept

Student work provides

- accurate information about supplements.
- health-enhancing advice about the use of supplements.
- health consequences of supplements.

Checking Comprehension

Use the Chapter 14 Assessment to examine the most important ideas presented in the chapter.

Answers to Reviewing Vocabulary and Concepts

Lesson 1
1. epidermis
2. dermatologist
3. dandruff
4. hangnail
5. ingrown toenail

Lesson 2
6. periodontium
7. enamel
8. plaque
9. tartar
10. orthodontist
11. periodontal disease

Lesson 3
12. b
13. b
14. b
15. b
16. a

Thinking Critically

17. Flossing removes particles of food inaccessible to toothbrushes and helps prevent gingivitis and periodontal disease.
18. Pathogens could enter your body.
19. Responses may include telling them to avoid listening to loud music; to use earplugs when confronted with excess noise.
20. Responses will vary.

364

After You Read

Use your completed Foldable to review the information on the form, function, and care of the skin.

FOLDABLES™
Study Organizer

Reviewing Vocabulary and Concepts

On a sheet of paper, write the numbers 1–11. After each number write the term from the list that best completes each sentence.

- dandruff
- epidermis
- periodontal disease
- tartar
- dermatologist
- periodontium
- hangnail
- enamel
- orthodontist
- plaque
- ingrown toenail

Lesson 1

1. The outermost layer of skin is the _____.
2. A(n) _____ is a physician who treats skin disorders.
3. _____ is a flaking of the outer layer of dead skin cells from the scalp.
4. A(n) _____ is a split in the cuticle along the edge of a fingernail.
5. A(n) _____ can result from wearing tight shoes.

Lesson 2

6. The _____ is a structure made up of the jawbone, the gums, and connectors called ligaments.
7. A tooth cavity is the result of acid eating a hole in the tooth's _____.
8. _____ is a sticky film on your teeth that is formed by food and saliva.

9. Hardened plaque that is difficult to remove is called _____.
10. A dentist who prevents or corrects problems with the alignment or spacing of teeth is called a(n) _____.
11. Most adult tooth loss is the result of _____.

Lesson 3

On a sheet of paper, write the numbers 12–16. After each number, write the letter of the answer that best completes each statement.

12. People who can see nearby objects clearly, but for whom faraway objects appear blurred, have
    a. astigmatism.
    b. nearsightedness.
    c. farsightedness.
    d. glaucoma.
13. The thin layer of nerve cells covering the interior back of the eye is the
    a. cornea.
    b. retina.
    c. iris.
    d. pupil.
14. The amount of light that enters the eye is controlled by the
    a. retina.
    b. pupil.
    c. lens.
    d. cornea.
15. The loudness of sound is measured in
    a. degrees.
    b. decibels.
    c. watts.
    d. amps.
16. The part of the ear that allows air to pass from the nose to the middle ear is the
    a. eustachian tube.
    b. anvil.
    c. eardrum.
    d. ear canal.

INCLUSION STRATEGIES

Special Learning Needs, Behavior Problems, English Language Learners The following suggestions are helpful for students with special learning needs, students with behavior problems, and ELL students:

- Pair these students with more proficient learners who can help summarize the main concepts of the chapter.

- 🎧 Direct these students to listen to the Teen Health Audio Summaries. This component provides an audio and written summary of the chapter in both English and Spanish.

- Use photographs, drawings, or magazine clippings whenever possible to help students visualize the important concepts of the chapter.

Thinking Critically

Using complete sentences, answer the following questions on a sheet of paper.

17. Analyze Give at least two reasons for flossing your teeth every day even if you brush after every meal.

18. Explain What are the health risks associated with tattoos and body piercing?

19. Recommend What recommendations would you make to encourage your peers to protect themselves from hearing loss?

20. Synthesize Create a list of healthful habits that will help prevent vision problems as well as eye diseases and injuries.

Career Corner

Speech Therapist Students interested in how people communicate might want to consider a career as a speech therapist. These professionals work with people who have hearing and speech impairments to find possible causes and treatments. They also help patients improve their speaking skills. Speech therapists need a master's degree in audiology or speech therapy. Read more about this and other health careers by clicking on Career Corner at health.glencoe.com.

Standardized Test Practice

Reading & Writing

Read the paragraphs below and then answer the questions.

Having long nails and wearing nail polish are recent trends, right? Wrong. The idea of coloring nails began thousands of years ago. Gold manicure tools that have been found in Egyptian tombs and ancient Egyptian writings tell us that Egyptian women painted their fingernails. Long nails were a privilege reserved for those of high status because they showed that these women had servants to do the labor in their homes. In fact, Queen Nefertiti decreed that nail color could be worn only by the nobility.

Centuries later, in the United States, glamorous Hollywood stars of the 1930s made nail polish popular. Women all over the country started painting their nails. False nails, made out of plastic, also became fashionable. These were glued to nails and then polished.

Nail polish and false nails continue to be popular today.

1. What is the first paragraph mainly about?

  A how nail coloring was invented in ancient Egypt

  B the use of nail coloring in ancient Egypt

  C the rules for wearing nail coloring in ancient Egypt

  D how nail coloring has developed over the years.

2. From the information in the second paragraph, the reader can conclude that

  A people continue to use nail polish.

  B most people who use polish are rich.

  C nail polish is no longer popular.

  D nail polish should not be worn.

3. Think of a current trend. Write a paragraph explaining why you think this trend is popular.

 TH05_C3.glencoe.com/quiz

Test Practice

1. B

2. A

3. Responses should identify a specific trend and explain why it is popular.

Reteaching

📁 Assign Study Guide 14 in the Student Activities Workbook.

Evaluate

📁 💿 Use the reproducible Chapter 14 Test in the TCR, or construct your own test using the **Exam**View® Pro Testmaker.

Enrichment

Have students work in groups to make up original board games with questions about personal care. Provide time for students to play these games in class.

Assessment ✓

Self-Assessment Direct students to review the activities that are provided throughout the chapter. Encourage each student to select one finished product or activity that demonstrates his or her best work for the chapter. Have students explain what they learned and how the examples they selected show their progress.

Career Corner

Speech Therapist After reviewing the career profile on the health

Web site, students might:

• Describe the skills, training, and education needed.

• Discuss what might motivate someone to choose this career.

Planning Guide

Chapter 15	Skills/ Activities	Reproducible Resources	Assessment
Lesson 1 **Your Skeletal System** *pages 368–371*	**HEALTH SKILLS ACTIVITY** ▲ Scoliosis Screening (*Accessing Information*), page 370	*Student Activities Workbook available for use with each chapter* 📁 Parent Letter & Activities 15 📁 Concept Map 51 📁 Enrichment Activity 51 📁 Lesson Plan 1 📁 Reading Tutor Activity 50 📁 Reteaching Activity 51	📁 Lesson 1 Quiz
Lesson 2 **Your Muscular System** *pages 372–375*	**Hands-On Health** ▲ Stretch Out, page 374	📁 Concept Map 52 📁 Enrichment Activity 52 📁 Lesson Plan 2 📁 Reading Tutor Activity 51 📁 Reteaching Activity 52	📁 Lesson 2 Quiz
Lesson 3 **Your Circulatory System** *pages 376–380*		📁 Concept Map 53 📁 Cross-Curriculum Activity 29 📁 Decision-Making Activity 29 📁 Enrichment Activity 53 📁 Lesson Plan 3 📁 Reading Tutor Activity 52 📁 Reteaching Activity 53	📁 Lesson 3 Quiz
Lesson 4 **Your Respiratory System** *pages 381–384*		📁 Concept Map 54 📁 Decision-Making Activity 30 📁 Enrichment Activity 54 📁 Lesson Plan 4 📁 Reading Tutor Activity 53 📁 Reteaching Activity 54	📁 Lesson 4 Quiz
Lesson 5 **Your Nervous System** *pages 385–389*		📁 Concept Map 55 📁 Enrichment Activity 55 📁 Lesson Plan 5 📁 Reading Tutor Activity 54 📁 Reteaching Activity 55	📁 Lesson 5 Quiz

Planning Guide

Standards		Technology
National	**State/Local**	
National Health Education Standard **1.1, 1.3, 1.6, 1.8, 2.2, 3.1, 3.4**		Transparency 52 TeacherWorks™ Internet Activities
National Health Education Standard **1.1, 1.3, 1.6, 1.8, 3.1, 3.4**		Transparency 53 TeacherWorks™
National Health Education Standard **1.1, 1.3, 1.6, 1.7, 1.8, 2.6, 3.1, 3.4**		Transparency 54 TeacherWorks™
National Health Education Standard **1.1, 1.3, 1.6, 1.8, 3.1, 3.4**		Transparency 55 TeacherWorks™
National Health Education Standard **1.1, 1.3, 1.6, 1.7, 1.8, 2.6, 3.1, 3.4**		Transparency 56 TeacherWorks™

(*continued on pages 366C and 366D*)

TeacherWorks™

Glencoe's new and exclusive TeacherWorks™ is an all-in-one planner and resource center. Access the complete Teacher Wraparound Edition electronically. Find all your classroom resources with just a few easy clicks, and print them right from your computer. Connect directly to Glencoe's customized Health Web site. Access the National Health Education Standards correlations, or insert your own state standards and match them directly to the electronic Teacher Wraparound Edition.

Language Diversity

- English Audio Summaries
- Spanish Audio Summaries
- English Summaries, Quizzes, and Activities
- Spanish Summaries, Quizzes, and Activities
- Spanish Parent Letters and Activities

KEY TO ABILITY LEVELS

Teaching Strategies that appear throughout the chapters have been identified by one of four codes to give you an idea of their suitability for students of varying learning styles and abilities.

L1 **Level 1** strategies should be within the ability range of all students. Often full class participation is required.

L2 **Level 2** strategies are for average to above-average students or for small groups. Some teacher direction is necessary.

L3 **Level 3** strategies are designed for students able and willing to work independently. Minimal teacher direction is necessary.

INCL Strategies are appropriate for students with particular special needs in a general classroom setting.

Chapter 15	Skills/ Activities	Reproducible Resources	Assessment
Lesson 6 **Your Digestive and Excretory Systems** *pages 390–395*	HEALTH SKILLS ACTIVITY ▲ Encouraging Healthy Eating (*Advocacy*), page 394	*Student Activities Workbook available for use with each chapter* 📁 Concept Map 56 📁 Enrichment Activity 56 📁 Health Lab 15 📁 Lesson Plan 6 📁 Reading Tutor Activity 55 📁 Reteaching Activity 56	📁 Lesson 6 Quiz
Lesson 7 **Your Endocrine System** *pages 396–399*	HEALTH SKILLS ACTIVITY ▲ Protecting Your Body (*Stress Management*), page 398	📁 Concept Map 57 📁 Enrichment Activity 57 📁 Lesson Plan 7 📁 Reading Tutor Activity 56 📁 Reteaching Activity 57	📁 Lesson 7 Quiz
Lesson 8 **Your Reproductive System** *pages 400–405*		📁 Concept Map 58 📁 Cross-Curriculum Activity 30 📁 Enrichment Activity 58 📁 Lesson Plan 8 📁 Reading Tutor Activity 57 📁 Reteaching Activity 58	📁 Lesson 8 Quiz 📁 Chapter 15 Test 📁 Performance Assessment 15

TIME HEALTH   **How Stress Takes Its Toll** *pages 406–407*

BUILDING HEALTH SKILLS

Finding Facts About Your Body
(*Assessing Information*)
pages 408–409

📁 Building Health Skills Reproducible Master 40

Standards		Technology
National	**State/Local**	
National Health Education Standard **1.1, 1.3, 1.6, 1.8, 2.6, 3.1, 3.4, 7.4**		Transparencies 57 & 58 TeacherWorks™
National Health Education Standard **1.1, 1.3, 1.6, 1.8, 2.6, 3.1, 3.4, 3.7**		Transparency 59 TeacherWorks™
National Health Education Standard **1.1, 1.3, 1.6, 1.8, 2.6, 3.1, 3.4**		Transparencies 60 & 61 TeacherWorks™ MindJogger Videoquiz **Exam**_View_® Pro Testmaker
National Health Education Standard **2.1, 2.2**		Building Health Skills Transparency Master 1

TeacherWorks™

Glencoe's new and exclusive TeacherWorks™ is an all-in-one planner and resource center. Access the complete Teacher Wraparound Edition electronically. Find all your classroom resources with just a few easy clicks, and print them right from your computer. Connect directly to Glencoe's customized Health Web site. Access the National Health Education Standards correlations, or insert your own state standards and match them directly to the electronic Teacher Wraparound Edition.

Language Diversity

- English Audio Summaries
- Spanish Audio Summaries
- English Summaries, Quizzes, and Activities
- Spanish Summaries, Quizzes, and Activities
- Spanish Parent Letters and Activities

KEY TO ABILITY LEVELS

Teaching Strategies that appear throughout the chapters have been identified by one of four codes to give you an idea of their suitability for students of varying learning styles and abilities.

L1 **Level 1** strategies should be within the ability range of all students. Often full class participation is required.

L2 **Level 2** strategies are for average to above-average students or for small groups. Some teacher direction is necessary.

L3 **Level 3** strategies are designed for students able and willing to work independently. Minimal teacher direction is necessary.

INCL Strategies are appropriate for students with particular special needs in a general classroom setting.

Your Body Systems

Chapter at a Glance

Lesson 1 describes the functions of the skeletal system and how to keep it healthy.

Lesson 2 describes how muscles work, the different types of muscles, and how to keep the muscular system healthy.

Lesson 3 describes the parts, functions, problems, and care of the circulatory system.

Lesson 4 describes the parts, functions, problems, and care of the respiratory system.

Lesson 5 describes the parts of the nervous system and how it works. It also presents guidelines on how to protect the nervous system from injury.

Lesson 6 describes the parts, functions, problems, and care of the digestive and excretory systems.

Lesson 7 describes the parts, functions, problems, and care of the endocrine system.

Lesson 8 describes how sperm are produced, the stages of the menstrual cycle, and proper care of the male and female reproductive systems.

Health Skills

- Scoliosis Screening (*Accessing Information*), p. 370
- Encouraging Healthy Eating (*Advocacy*), p. 394
- Protecting Your Body (*Stress Management*), p. 398
- Finding Facts About Your Body (*Accessing Information*), pp. 408–409

366

HANDS-ON ACTIVITY

Name That Body Part In groups of four, students should read articles from the sports sections of newspapers and circle phrases that refer to physical motion. One recorder in each group should divide a sheet of paper into three columns and list the circled phrases in one column. The group then should decide which bones and muscles were primarily involved in each motion. The recorder should record that information in the other two columns. For example, an article may have said that one participant "pitched a fastball." That phrase would be entered in column one. In column two, the names of arm and hand bones would be listed. In column three, the names of the arm and hand muscles would be listed. (Students will need Figures 15.1 on page 369, 15.3 on page 373, or some other anatomical resource to accomplish this activity.)

Your Body Systems

HEALTH *Online*

How much do you know about behaviors that keep your body systems healthy? You can rate your habits by taking the Chapter 15 Health Inventory at health.glencoe.com.

FOLDABLES™
Study Organizer

Before You Read

Make this Foldable to organize what you learn about the skeletal system in Lesson 1. Begin with two plain sheets of 8½″ × 11″ paper.

Step 1

Collect two sheets of paper, and place them 1″ apart.

Step 2

Fold up the bottom edges of the paper, stopping them 1″ from the top edges. This makes all tabs the same size.

Step 3

Crease the paper to hold the tabs in place. Staple along the fold.

Step 4

Turn and label the tabs as shown.

Skeletal System
Parts
Problems
Care

As You Read

Under the appropriate tab, record main ideas and supporting facts about the parts, problems, and care of the skeletal system.

Chapter Introduction

Use the options below to motivate students and preview chapter content.

HEALTH *Online*

Encourage students to take the Health Inventory 15 at health.glencoe.com. Then brush up on health education by reading Professional Articles for health teachers. These articles, written by professional health educators and specialists, can help keep you informed.

GLENCOE TECHNOLOGY

MindJogger Videoquiz

Use MindJogger to preview or review Chapter 15 content.

TIME HEALTH

How Stress Takes Its Toll
pages 406–407

367

FOLDABLES™
Study Organizer

Dinah Zike Study Fold

Recording Main Ideas and Supporting Facts Students will use this Foldable study guide to record information about the parts, problems, and care of the skeletal system. As students read and discuss the material presented in Lesson 1, have them write down the supporting facts under the appropriate main idea tab of their Foldable. Encourage students to make and use this same type of study guide for the other eight body systems presented in this chapter. Foldable study guides are great test preparation tool because students can review important concepts, recall what they know, and check their responses by looking under the tabs.

Lesson 1

Your Skeletal System

❶ Focus

Lesson Objectives

Students will be able to

• describe the parts and functions of the skeletal system.

• discuss problems of the skeletal system.

• explain ways to care for the skeletal system.

Health Skills
• Accessing Information, p. 370

Motivators

Quick Write

Ask volunteers to share their responses.

Bellringer Activity

Have students list three animals with protective shells (*turtle, lobster, armadillo*). Point out that such animals have exoskeletons (*outside skeletons*). Then ask: What are some of the functions of these animals' exoskeletons? (*same as the human skeleton*)

VOCABULARY

Have students make flash cards of the vocabulary terms in the lesson. On one side of each card they should write the term and on the other side they should write these three categories: *Body System, Definition,* and *Page Reference.* Allow time for students to fill in the information on their cards. Encourage students to follow this procedure for each lesson.

Your Skeletal System

Quick Write

Make a list of words or phrases that describe the different functions of bones.

LEARN ABOUT...

● the different functions of the skeletal system.

● how joints allow different types of movement.

● how to keep your skeletal system healthy.

VOCABULARY

● skeletal system
● marrow
● joints
● cartilage
● ligaments
● tendons

Your Body's Framework

All structures need some sort of framework to give them strength and shape. Your body's framework, which is called the **skeletal system**, is *an internal system made up of bones, joints, and connective tissue.* See **Figure 15.1**.

Bones

The 206 bones that shape your skeleton are living tissue, composed of cells. Besides providing a framework for your body, bones perform many other important functions:

● **Allow movement.** Bones provide points of attachment for different muscles. Body parts, such as your arms and your legs, move when muscles pull on bones.

● **Provide support.** Your backbone is made up of 24 bones called vertebrae (VER·tuh·bray). Together, these bones support your head and upper body and also protect your spinal cord.

● **Protect other parts of your body.** Your bones provide a framework that supports your body's internal organs. Your skull protects your brain. Your ribs protect your lungs and heart from injury.

● **Form new blood cells.** Bones play a role in your circulatory system, too. Red and white blood cells are formed by **marrow**, *a tissue in the center of some bones.*

● **Store minerals.** Bones store minerals such as calcium and phosphorus for use when needed by the body.

Your bones give your body shape and provide a framework for its other systems. *Which bones protect your heart and lungs?*

Lesson 1 Resources

Teacher Classroom Resources

 Parent Letter & Activities 15

📁 Concept Map 51

📁 Enrichment Activity 51

📁 Lesson Plan 1

📁 Lesson 1 Quiz

📁 Reading Tutor Activity 50

📁 Reteaching Activity 51

 Transparency 52

Student Activities Workbook

 Chapter 15 Study Guide

📁 Applying Health Skills 5

Your body has three different types of muscle tissue: skeletal muscle, smooth muscle, and cardiac muscle. **Skeletal muscle** is *muscle attached to bones that enables you to move your body.* Because you can control skeletal muscles, they are called voluntary muscles. **Smooth muscle** is *muscle found in organs and in blood vessels and glands.* You do not consciously control the contraction of the smooth muscles. These are involuntary muscles. **Cardiac muscle**, also involuntary, is *muscle found only in the walls of your heart.* Contracting and relaxing continually, cardiac muscle enables your heart to pump blood throughout your body. **Figure 15.3** shows the major skeletal muscles of your body.

FIGURE 15.3

THE MUSCULAR SYSTEM

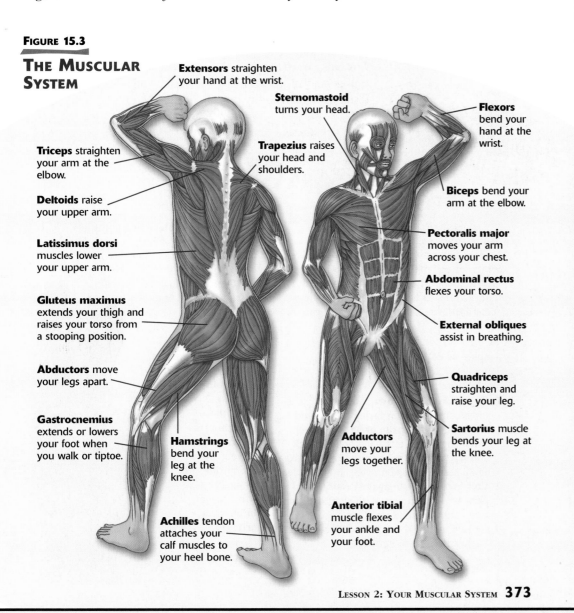

Extensors straighten your hand at the wrist.

Sternomastoid turns your head.

Flexors bend your hand at the wrist.

Triceps straighten your arm at the elbow.

Trapezius raises your head and shoulders.

Biceps bend your arm at the elbow.

Deltoids raise your upper arm.

Pectoralis major moves your arm across your chest.

Latissimus dorsi muscles lower your upper arm.

Abdominal rectus flexes your torso.

Gluteus maximus extends your thigh and raises your torso from a stooping position.

External obliques assist in breathing.

Abductors move your legs apart.

Quadriceps straighten and raise your leg.

Gastrocnemius extends or lowers your foot when you walk or tiptoe.

Hamstrings bend your leg at the knee.

Adductors move your legs together.

Sartorius muscle bends your leg at the knee.

Achilles tendon attaches your calf muscles to your heel bone.

Anterior tibial muscle flexes your ankle and your foot.

LESSON 2: YOUR MUSCULAR SYSTEM **373**

② Teach

VISUAL LEARNING

FIGURE 15.2 Have volunteers describe the two pictures and read aloud the explanations that go with them. Then have each student extend one arm, placing the other hand on the biceps. Ask students to bend and straighten their arms, noting the change in their muscles. **INCL** *English Language Learners, Special Learning Needs, Behavior Problems, Different Learning Styles* (*Visual*)

Applying Knowledge

Have half of the class identify professions requiring the use of long, strong muscles (*athletes, dancers, laborers*). Have the other half of the class identify professions requiring the use of small, delicate muscles (*eye surgeons, secretaries, pianists*). Have students compare and contrast by asking if both groups of professions use both types of muscles. **L1**

VISUAL LEARNING

FIGURE 15.3 Divide the class into several small groups, and have group members work together to name and discuss the muscles shown in Figure 15.3. If possible, give each group a small model of the human skeleton (or a small doll), and have group members point out the location of each muscle on the model. **INCL** *English Language Learners, Special Learning Needs, Behavior Problems, Different Learning Styles* (*Visual*)

INCLUSION STRATEGIES

Gifted Students Ask interested students to select and explore a specific group of voluntary muscles such as those in the back. Have them conduct research to answer these questions: What movements do these muscles make possible? Which muscles work together for each kind of movement? What exercises might be used to strengthen the muscles? What relaxation techniques might benefit muscles in that group? Once they complete their research, have them prepare detailed displays that summarize their findings. The displays should include labeled drawings; a written explanation; and if possible, a moving model.

Discussing

Tell students that the "stitches" they may feel in their sides when exercising vigorously are probably caused by inadequate delivery of oxygen to the muscles that control breathing. Have students describe their own experiences with this muscle response and tell how they deal with it. **L1**

Investigating

Have students work in pairs to select a specific muscle that might cramp and learn about the best stretches to relieve that cramp. Have each pair of students explain and demonstrate those stretches to the rest of the class. **L2 INCL** *English Language Learners, Special Learning Needs, Behavior Problems, Different Learning Styles (Kinesthetic)*

Hands-On Health

STRETCH OUT

Time: 30 minutes

TEACHING THE ACTIVITY

- Have students read the activity introduction; encourage them to discuss their own experiences with stretching.
- Have volunteers read about and demonstrate each stretch. Then have students work with partners to complete the activity.
- Ask students to share and discuss their In Conclusion responses.

ASSESSMENT

Have students keep exercise journals, recording their warm-up stretches.

Problems of the Muscular System

You may have experienced sore muscles a day or two after heavy exercise or strenuous physical activity. This soreness is caused by a buildup of acid in your muscles, and it is usually temporary. Some muscular conditions, however, are chronic, meaning that they last for long periods. Muscular problems include the following.

- **A pulled or torn muscle** has been torn away from the bone or has been damaged within itself.
- **Muscle strain** is any type of soreness that develops in a muscle because of overuse. It is caused by small tears to the muscle or tendon.
- **A cramped muscle** remains contracted rather than extending, or relaxing. It typically feels tight and sore, and is usually a sign to drink more water.
- **Muscular dystrophy** is a disorder that is usually inherited. It causes gradual weakening of the skeletal muscles, eventually resulting in an inability to walk or stand.

Hands-On Health

STRETCH OUT

Any warm-up routine should include gentle stretches. Stretching lengthens tendons, warms up ligaments, and prepares joints for activity. Stretching also improves muscle flexibility and coordination, and relieves tension and tightness. Here are some basic stretching exercises you can try.

WHAT YOU WILL NEED

- space to do the stretches

WHAT YOU WILL DO

1. **Back Scratch Stretch.** Raise right hand in the air with palm facing back. Bend elbow and place palm of hand between shoulders. Bring left hand behind back and try to touch right hand. Hold for 10 to 30 seconds. Repeat twice on each side.
2. **Calf Stretch.** Lean against wall. Put right leg behind you. With right heel on floor, slightly bend right knee. Lean forward and hold for 10 to 30 seconds. Repeat twice with each leg.
3. **Thigh Stretch.** Stand and grasp left foot behind you with right hand. Slowly pull leg back so that knee moves away from body. Hold for 10 to 30 seconds. Repeat twice with each leg.

IN CONCLUSION

1. Did you notice a difference in the way your body felt after performing the stretches?
2. Make these stretching exercises part of your warm-up routine whenever you engage in physical activity.

WHAT TEENS WANT TO KNOW

How can I prevent muscle cramps and leg pain during exercise? Use the same strategies professional athletes use to prevent muscle cramps and pain. Drink liquids before you feel thirsty. You can lose as much as two liters (one liter is a little more than a quart) of fluid during a game before you feel thirsty. Drink eight ounces of liquids before you start a game or practice, and continue drinking liquids throughout the physical activity. When you're working out or playing in extreme heat, you need to drink more liquids to make up for the additional fluid lost through perspiration. It's fluid loss that causes many painful muscle cramps. Sometimes, leg pain is caused by misuse or overuse of muscles and joints.

Care of the Muscular System

Your muscles need proper care to stay healthy and work properly. You also need to maintain muscle tone—the natural tension in the fibers of muscles. Below are some guidelines for keeping your muscles healthy.

- **Engage in regular physical activity.** The more you use your muscles, the stronger and more efficient they will become. Regular physical activity strengthens the heart muscle as well.
- **Warm up before physical activity.** A program that includes warm-up and stretching, followed by a cool-down exercise and light stretching, helps prevent muscle injury and increases muscle flexibility.
- **Eat foods containing carbohydrates and protein.** Carbohydrates are a source of energy. Protein is needed for the growth and regeneration of muscle cells.
- **Maintain a healthy weight.** Extra body weight can strain the muscles in your back. Healthful eating and regular physical activity will help you reach and maintain your appropriate weight.
- **Learn to lift properly.** The correct way to lift a heavy object is to bend your knees, keep your back straight, and use your leg muscles to do the lifting. Keep the load close to your body.

This teen knows how to protect her back by using her legs to lift a heavy box. *Name two other behaviors that protect your muscles.*

Lesson 2 Review

Using complete sentences, answer the following questions on a sheet of paper.

Reviewing Terms and Facts

1. **Vocabulary** What is the body's *muscular system,* and what three types of muscles does it include?
2. **Explain** How do skeletal muscles work together to make movement possible?
3. **List** What are four problems that occur in muscles? Which of these is typically inherited?
4. **Name** What are three practices you can follow to keep your muscles healthy?

Thinking Critically

5. **Apply** Are any activities that you engage in likely to result in muscle damage? If so, what can you do to prevent the damage?
6. **Explain** Why is it important to warm up and stretch before physical activity and to cool down and stretch afterward?

Applying Health Skills

7. **Practicing Healthful Behaviors** List your favorite activities that strengthen and tone your muscles. Share your list with classmates.

LESSON 2: YOUR MUSCULAR SYSTEM 375

Lesson 2

Analyzing

Ask volunteers to recount their personal experiences in training for team sports or athletic competitions. **L1**

❸ Assess

Evaluating

Assign the Lesson 2 Review; then assign the Lesson 2 Quiz in the TCR.

Reteaching

- Assign Concept Map 52 or Reteaching Activity 52 in the TCR.
- Have each student write three questions about the lesson content. Then have students answer one another's questions.

Enrichment

- Assign Enrichment Activity 52 in the TCR.
- Have students work with partners to plan, draw, and write comic strips that present tips on caring for the muscular system.

❹ Close

Have students drum their fingers on their desks and explain the movement they observe.

Lesson 2 Review

1. Group of structures that make your body parts move; skeletal, smooth, cardiac.
2. Muscles work in pairs; when one muscle contracts, or shortens, the other muscle extends, or lengthens.
3. Pulled or torn muscle, muscle strain, cramped muscle, and muscular dystrophy; muscular dystrophy is typically inherited.
4. Any three: engage in regular physical activity, warm up before physical activity, eat foods containing carbohydrates and protein, maintain a healthy weight, lift objects properly.
5. Responses will vary.
6. To prepare muscles for workout, help prevent muscle injury, increase flexibility.

① Focus

Lesson Objectives

Students will be able to

• describe the parts and functions of the circulatory system.

• discuss the problems of the circulatory system.

• explain ways to care for the circulatory system.

Motivators

Quick Write

Have students share their responses. Write *Physical, Mental/Emotional,* and *Social* on the board. Have students discuss how each of their responses relates to the areas of health.

Bellringer Activity

Challenge students to list three ways that the circulatory system is like the transportation system in a large city. (*They both have large and small pathways, carry things from place to place, and form a network.*)

VOCABULARY

Have students make flash cards for the vocabulary terms in the lesson, following the procedure described in Lesson 1. Remind students to fill in the three categories—*Body System, Definition,* and *Page Reference.* The completed flash cards should help students understand the parts of all the body systems.

Lesson

Your Circulatory System

Quick Write

Your heart pumps blood throughout your body 24 hours a day. What behaviors might help keep your heart healthy?

LEARN ABOUT...

• what your circulatory system does.
• the different parts of your circulatory system.
• keeping your circulatory system healthy.

VOCABULARY

• circulatory system
• cardiovascular system
• pulmonary circulation
• systemic circulation
• arteries
• veins
• capillaries

The Body's Transport System

The **circulatory** (SER·kyuh·luh·tohr·ee) **system** consists of *organs and tissues that transport essential materials to body cells and remove their waste products.* This body system is also known as the **cardiovascular** (KAR·dee·oh·VAS·kyoo·ler) **system.**

Pumped by your heart, your blood is moved through a vast circulatory network. Different organs serve as transfer stations. At some stations, blood picks up needed nutrients and other materials and delivers them to the cells. Blood also picks up waste products and carries them to other transfer stations, where they are removed from the body. See **Figure 15.4.**

FIGURE 15.4

HOW THE CIRCULATORY SYSTEM WORKS

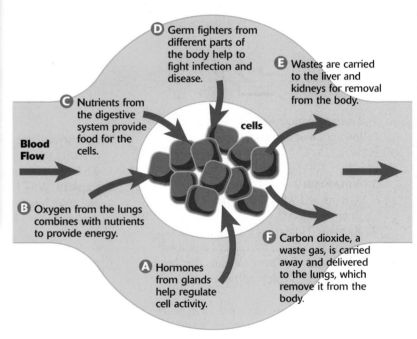

D Germ fighters from different parts of the body help to fight infection and disease.

E Wastes are carried to the liver and kidneys for removal from the body.

C Nutrients from the digestive system provide food for the cells.

cells

Blood Flow

B Oxygen from the lungs combines with nutrients to provide energy.

A Hormones from glands help regulate cell activity.

F Carbon dioxide, a waste gas, is carried away and delivered to the lungs, which remove it from the body.

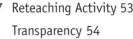

Lesson 3 Resources

Teacher Classroom Resources

 Concept Map 53

 Cross-Curriculum Activity 29

 Decision-Making Activity 29

 Enrichment Activity 53

 Lesson Plan 3

Lesson 3 Quiz

 Reading Tutor Activity 52

 Reteaching Activity 53

 Transparency 54

Student Activities Workbook

Chapter 15 Study Guide

Applying Health Skills 53

Parts of the Circulatory System

Your circulatory system includes your heart, blood vessels, and blood (see **Figure 15.5**). Your heart pumps blood through two major pathways. **Pulmonary circulation** is *the flow of blood from the heart to the lungs and back to the heart.* **Systemic circulation** is *the flow of blood to all the body tissues except the lungs.*

FIGURE 15.5

THE CIRCULATORY SYSTEM

In these drawings, red represents oxygen-rich blood, and blue represents blood containing carbon dioxide.

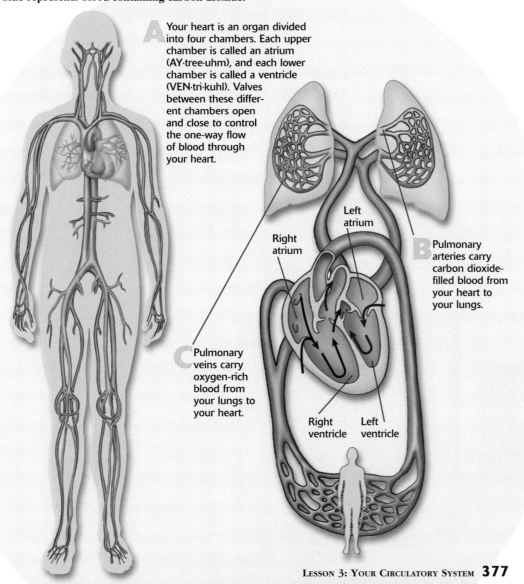

A Your heart is an organ divided into four chambers. Each upper chamber is called an atrium (AY·tree·uhm), and each lower chamber is called a ventricle (VEN·tri·kuhl). Valves between these different chambers open and close to control the one-way flow of blood through your heart.

Right atrium

Left atrium

B Pulmonary arteries carry carbon dioxide-filled blood from your heart to your lungs.

C Pulmonary veins carry oxygen-rich blood from your lungs to your heart.

Right ventricle

Left ventricle

LESSON 3: YOUR CIRCULATORY SYSTEM **377**

Lesson 3

② Teach

Demonstrating

Students can simulate the work a heart does by squeezing a tennis ball 70 times in a minute. The force needed to squeeze the tennis ball is about the same as the force needed to squeeze blood from the heart, which the heart does about 70 times a minute. **L1 INCL** *English Language Learners, Special Learning Needs, Behavior Problems, Different Learning Styles (Visual)*

VISUAL LEARNING

FIGURE 15.5 Have students work in small groups to study the drawings and read the explanations. Suggest that group members use their fingers or the eraser end of their pencils to trace the routes that blood (both oxygen-rich and that containing carbon dioxide) travel throughout the circulatory system. **INCL** *English Language Learners, Special Learning Needs, Behavior Problems, Different Learning Styles (Visual)*

Cross-Curriculum Activity

MATH The heart beats about 100,000 times in one day. Have students guess and then calculate approximately how many times their hearts have beaten since they were born (*1 yr. = 36,500,000; 1 mo. = 3,000,000*). **L2**

WHAT TEENS WANT TO KNOW

How do I take my pulse? Your pulse is the rate at which your heart beats. You can feel your pulse in places where arteries are close to the skin. Measure your pulse at your wrist. First, sit quietly. Place two fingers gently against the inside of your wrist until you feel your pulse. Don't use your thumb. Using the second hand on your watch, clock, or a stopwatch, count the number of beats for 30 seconds. Multiply the number of beats by two to obtain your pulse in beats per minute. Normal resting pulse is between 50 to 100 beats per minute. Fever, other illnesses, or anxiety increases your pulse rate. Pulse rate is also faster during and immediately after exercise. Once you have rested after exercise, your pulse should return to its normal resting rate.

Describing

Ask students whether they have ever noticed their own blood clotting. When? (*whenever their blood forms scabs*) Have them describe what happens when blood clots. (*A mass of blood congeals and hardens at the location of a cut in the skin, forming a protective shield while the skin heals.*) **L2**

Demonstrating

Invite the school nurse or a blood technician from a local hospital to demonstrate how blood is typed. (The nurse should test his or her blood or yours. Do not test students without written permission from their parents or guardians.) Ask students whether they know their blood types. **L1**

Researching

Have a small group of students use library or Internet resources to gather information about healthy blood pressure readings for adults, teens, and children. Ask these students to report their findings to the rest of the class. **L2**

Applying Life Skills

Arrange with the school nurse for students to have their blood pressure taken. After they have recorded their blood pressure, discuss the healthy range for students' blood pressure. **L1**

✓ Reading Check

The word *circulatory* comes from a Latin word meaning "to go around." Use a dictionary to find other words stemming from the same root, *circul.*

Having your blood pressure measured is a normal part of a physical exam. *What pressure measurements are taken during this procedure?*

Blood

Blood is a mixture of solids in a large amount of liquid called plasma (PLAZ·muh). The different solid components of blood are red blood cells, white blood cells, and platelets.

- **Plasma** is about 92 percent water. It transports blood solids, nutrients, hormones, and other materials.
- **Red blood cells** carry oxygen to cells and carbon dioxide away from them.
- **White blood cells** help fight disease and infection by attacking germs that enter the body.
- **Platelets** help blood form a clot at the site of a wound. A clot seals a cut and prevents excessive blood loss.

Blood Vessels

Over 80,000 miles of blood vessels transport your blood throughout your body. There are three types of blood vessels.

- **Arteries.** *Blood vessels that carry blood away from the heart to other parts of the body* are called **arteries**.
- **Veins.** *Blood vessels that carry blood from the body back to the heart* are called **veins**.
- **Capillaries.** *Tiny tubes that carry blood from the arteries to the body's cells, and then back to the veins* are called **capillaries**.

Blood Pressure

As blood is moved through your body, it exerts pressure against the walls of blood vessels. As your heart contracts to push blood into your arteries, your blood pressure is at its highest point. This is called systolic pressure. As your heart relaxes to refill, blood pressure is at its lowest point. This is called diastolic pressure.

Health professionals measure your blood pressure using an instrument called a sphygmomanometer (sfig·mo·muh·NAH·muh·ter). This instrument includes a cuff that is wrapped around your upper arm and inflated until it is tight enough to stop the flow of blood. The health professional gradually deflates the cuff until, through a stethoscope placed on your arm, she or he first hears blood pulsing through your arm. At this point, the pressure in the cuff is equal to your systolic pressure. The cuff is then deflated further, until the pulsing of blood can no longer be heard. This reading is equal to your diastolic pressure.

378 CHAPTER 15: YOUR BODY SYSTEMS

✓ Reading Check

Word Study Write *circulatory* on the board, and have students divide the word between the base *circul-* and the suffix *-atory*. Use a dictionary to model looking for words similar to *circulatory* and finding information about roots. For example, words such as *circle* and *circus* stem from the same root as *circulatory* while *cirrus* does not. List suggestions from volunteers, and ask what each word has in common with *circulatory*. Also, help students find the definition of the suffix *-atory*, which means "relating to," and have them suggest other words using the same suffix. To conclude the lesson, have students write their own definitions for *circulatory system*.

Blood Types

There are four different blood types—A, B, AB, and O. These blood types are determined by the presence or absence of certain substances. Type A blood has substance A, type B has substance B, type AB has both A and B, and type O has neither. Blood may also carry another substance—the Rh factor. Most people are Rh positive, which is written as Rh+.

Knowing a person's blood type is essential if the person needs a blood transfusion. Mixing certain blood types can cause dangerous immune responses such as fevers, difficulty in breathing, and possibly death. To avoid these responses, health professionals check the recipient's blood type and match it with a blood type that is compatible. People with type O-negative blood are called universal donors because their blood is compatible with all blood types.

Giving and Receiving Blood

People who are between the ages of 17 and 70 and in good health can give blood to the Red Cross or to other charitable organizations. The blood is frozen or refrigerated and stored in blood banks for later use by hospitals. United States regulations make it very safe to give and receive blood. A new needle is used every time blood is taken or received. All donated blood is tested for diseases such as HIV, anemia, and hepatitis. Blood that fails any test is discarded.

Problems of the Circulatory System

Some problems of the circulatory system affect the heart and blood vessels. Others affect the blood itself.

- **Hypertension** is a condition in which blood pressure is consistently higher than normal, which can lead to heart attack, stroke, or kidney failure.
- **Stroke** usually results from blood clots that block vessels in the brain, or from the rupture of a blood vessel.
- **Heart attack** is blockage of the flow of blood to the heart.
- **Arteriosclerosis** is a condition in which arteries harden, reducing the amount of blood that can flow through them.

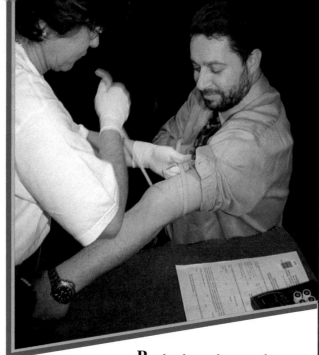

People who are between the ages of 17 and 70 and in good health can give the gift of life—their blood.

CONNECT TO
Science

ANEMIA AND YOUR FOOD
Anemia is a condition in which red blood cells cannot carry sufficient amounts of oxygen to other cells in the body. The most common type of anemia is iron-deficiency anemia. You can increase the iron levels in your diet by eating iron-fortified cereal, green leafy vegetables, dried beans, and raisins.

Lesson 3

Cross-Curriculum Activity
SCIENCE Ask students whether they have ever had a blood test. What was the situation? Why do doctors request blood tests? Note: Be aware that some students may not want to share this information. (*Blood can reveal the state of a person's health. An imbalance of constituents of the blood gives doctors an indication of what might be wrong.*) **L1**

Researching
Have volunteers contact a local blood bank. (Listings can be found in the yellow pages of the telephone directory.) Ask them to report on what measures the bank takes to screen blood and when hospitals typically need blood the most. **L3**

Cross-Curriculum Activity
SCIENCE Have students use biology books or an encyclopedia in the school library to research bruises. (*Bruises are caused by broken blood vessels under the skin; blood that has leaked from the broken vessels produces the black-and-blue color.*) **L3**

Making Charts
Have students work in small groups to make charts on large pieces of oaktag or butcher paper. Ask each group to write the heading *Foods for a Healthy Heart* on the right side and *Foods to Avoid* on the left side. Healthy foods should be listed in green; unhealthy foods, in red. Have students add pictures or drawings for visual interest. **L2**

Health Literacy

Health Information No one really knows the cause of most high blood pressure. Genetic tendency, diet, obesity, alcohol, and emotional stress are probably contributing factors. For some people, a high salt diet may contribute. High blood pressure is not common among teens; it usually develops later in life. High blood pressure usually produces no symptoms. Left untreated for years, high blood pressure may cause strokes, heart attacks, congestive heart failure, and kidney failure. A healthy diet, exercise, and maintaining a healthful weight may prevent the development of high blood pressure even if you have a family history of this condition. When changes in diet, weight loss, and exercise do not lower blood pressure to normal levels, medication may be prescribed.

❸ Assess

Evaluating

📁 Assign the Lesson 3 Review; then assign the Lesson 3 Quiz in the TCR.

Reteaching

• 📁 Assign Concept Map 53 or Reteaching Activity 53 in the TCR.

• Have students find answers to the following questions: What is the role of the circulatory system? What are three ways to avoid injuries to the circulatory system?

Enrichment

• 📁 Assign Enrichment Activity 53 in the TCR.

• Have students make flow charts showing the route that blood takes as it travels from the heart to the lungs.

❹ Close

Ask each student to name one specific action he or she can take to maintain a healthy heart and circulatory system.

Learning to manage stress by taking time to relax and get exercise will help keep your cardiovascular system healthy. *How can stress affect blood pressure?*

• **Anemia** is an abnormally low level of hemoglobin, a protein that binds to oxygen in red blood cells.
• **Leukemia** is a disease in which extra white blood cells are produced.
• **Hemophilia** is a disease in which the blood plasma does not contain substances that help the blood to clot.

Care of the Circulatory System

Keeping your heart strong and healthy will help you feel better now and may also enable you to live a longer, healthier life.

• **Limit fat in your foods.** Dietary fat can cause fatty deposits to form on the inner walls of arteries, narrowing them and increasing blood pressure. Then your heart must work harder to circulate blood.
• **Get regular physical activity.** Regular activity strengthens your heart muscle, allowing it to pump more blood with each beat.
• **Avoid tobacco.** Tobacco products contain the drug nicotine. Nicotine narrows arteries, requiring blood pressure to be higher to circulate blood through the body.
• **Manage stress.** When you are under stress, your body secretes adrenaline, a substance that increases blood pressure. High blood pressure strains the entire cardiovascular system.

Lesson 3 Review

Using complete sentences, answer the following questions on a sheet of paper.

Reviewing Terms and Facts

1. **Vocabulary** Define the term *circulatory system.* What is another name for it?
2. **Recall** Identify the three solids that make up blood. What is the liquid portion of blood called?
3. **Review** What are *arteries, veins,* and *capillaries?* Explain how they are different.
4. **List** What steps are taken in the United States to make sure that donated blood is safe?

Thinking Critically

5. **Compare and Contrast** What are *systemic circulation* and *pulmonary circulation?* Which one carries newly oxygenated blood?
6. **Analyze** Your friend Colleen has been looking tired and pale. Which circulatory disorder might she have? What can you suggest to help?

Applying Health Skills

7. **Accessing Information** Learn more about how one of the following substances affects your circulatory system: *salt, fats, cholesterol.* Prepare a brief presentation for your classmates.

380 CHAPTER 15: YOUR BODY SYSTEMS

Lesson 3 Review

1. Organs and tissues that transport essential materials to body cells and remove their waste products; cardiovascular system.
2. Solids—red blood cells, white blood cells, platelets. Liquid—plasma.
3. See Blood Vessels on page 378.
4. New needle used every time; all donated blood tested for diseases; blood that fails any test is discarded.
5. Systemic circulation is the flow of blood to all parts of body except lungs. Pulmonary circulation is the flow of blood between heart and lungs. Pulmonary circulation.
6. She may have anemia and needs to eat more iron-rich food.

Your Respiratory System

The Need for Air

Air contains oxygen, a gas the body needs to maintain life. In fact, a person can live only a few minutes without air. Breathing—inhaling and exhaling—is carried out by the **respiratory system**. This system consists of *the organs that provide the body with a continuous supply of oxygen and rid the body of carbon dioxide*. **Figure 15.6** on page 382 shows the parts of the respiratory system.

How the Respiratory System Works

The respiratory system has two important jobs. First, it supplies oxygen to the blood—oxygen that is then carried to all the cells of the body. In the cells, oxygen combines with nutrients to provide energy that the cells can use. When oxygen is used to produce energy in the cells, carbon dioxide—a waste gas—is produced. The second job of the respiratory system is to remove carbon dioxide from the blood and release it outside the body.

Quick Write

List at least three conditions or situations that can affect the health of your lungs.

LEARN ABOUT...

- the parts of your respiratory system.
- how your body uses the air that you breathe.
- keeping your respiratory system healthy.

VOCABULARY

- respiratory system
- epiglottis
- larynx
- trachea
- bronchi
- diaphragm
- alveoli

The carbon dioxide that you breathe out is absorbed by plants and converted back into oxygen. *Why do you need oxygen?*

LESSON 4: YOUR RESPIRATORY SYSTEM **381**

1 Focus

Lesson Objectives

Students will be able to

- describe the parts and functions of the respiratory system.
- explain how breathing works.
- discuss the problems of the respiratory system.
- explain ways to care for the respiratory system.

Motivators

Quick Write

Write the headings *Healthful* and *Unhealthful* on the board. As students share their responses, ask a volunteer to list them under the appropriate category.

Bellringer Activity

Ask students to write the names of three musical instruments or three activities that require them to control breathing. (*trumpet, flute, tuba; swimming, blowing up a balloon, blowing out a candle*)

VOCABULARY

Have students make flash cards for the vocabulary terms in the lesson, as in Lesson 1. Remind students to fill in the three categories—*Body System, Definition,* and *Page Reference.* The completed flash cards should help students understand the parts of all the body systems.

Lesson 4 Resources

Teacher Classroom Resources

📁 Concept Map 54

📁 Decision-Making Activity 30

📁 Enrichment Activity 54

📁 Lesson Plan 4

📁 Lesson 4 Quiz

📁 Reading Tutor Activity 53

📁 Reteaching Activity 54

🖨 Transparency 55

Student Activities Workbook

📁 Chapter 15 Study Guide

📁 Applying Health Skills 54

② Teach

VISUAL LEARNING

FIGURE 15.6 Have students point to each part of the drawing as volunteers read aloud the label and explanation. Have students pay special attention to the definitions of vocabulary words included in the labels. **INCL** *English Language Learners, Special Learning Needs, Behavior Problems, Different Learning Styles (Visual)*

Critical Thinking

Ask students why the respiratory system is dependent on the circulatory system. (*The respiratory system can only bring air into the body and eliminate carbon dioxide. The circulatory system is needed to carry the oxygen to all body cells.*) **L1**

Cross-Curriculum Activity

SCIENCE Have students research how respiration is affected by high altitudes, space travel, and being under water. What adaptations are required in each situation? Have them report their findings to the class. **L3**

Encourage students to explore the Web Links for this chapter and then complete the activity.

FIGURE 15.6

THE RESPIRATORY SYSTEM

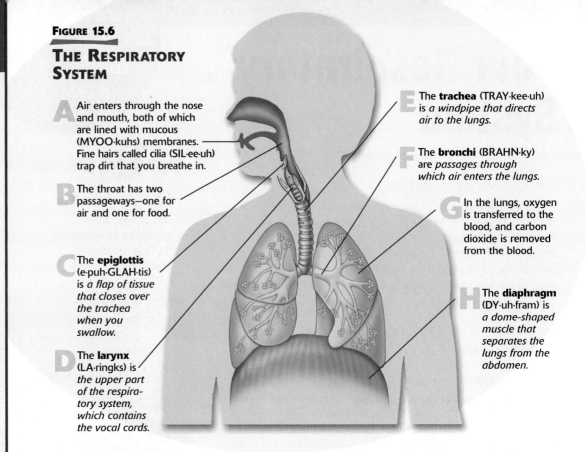

A Air enters through the nose and mouth, both of which are lined with mucous (MYOO·kuhs) membranes. Fine hairs called cilia (SIL·ee·uh) trap dirt that you breathe in.

B The throat has two passageways—one for air and one for food.

C The **epiglottis** (e·puh·GLAH·tis) is *a flap of tissue that closes over the trachea when you swallow.*

D The **larynx** (LA·ringks) is *the upper part of the respiratory system, which contains the vocal cords.*

E The **trachea** (TRAY·kee·uh) is *a windpipe that directs air to the lungs.*

F The **bronchi** (BRAHN·ky) are *passages through which air enters the lungs.*

G In the lungs, oxygen is transferred to the blood, and carbon dioxide is removed from the blood.

H The **diaphragm** (DY·uh·fram) is *a dome-shaped muscle that separates the lungs from the abdomen.*

HEALTH Online

Topic: The respiratory system

For a link to more information on the parts of the respiratory system, go to **health.glencoe.com.**

Activity: Using the information provided at this link, create your own word search puzzle that features respiratory system terms.

Inhaling and Exhaling

When you inhale, you bring air into your body from outside. When you exhale, you release air to the outside. In this process, oxygen is exchanged with carbon dioxide inside your lungs. This continual exchange of gases helps maintain a constant supply of oxygen in your cells. **Figure 15.7** describes the process of inhaling and exhaling.

Exchanging Oxygen and Carbon Dioxide

The air that you exhale contains more carbon dioxide and less oxygen than the air that you inhale. Carbon dioxide–containing blood is pumped from the heart to the lungs through the pulmonary arteries and capillaries. Carbon dioxide passes from the blood into bronchioles, which are smaller bronchial tubes, and then into **alveoli** (al·VEE·uh·ly), *microscopic air sacs in the lungs* where it is exchanged with oxygen. Oxygen passes from the alveoli to the capillaries and into the blood.

 **Health Literacy**

Health Information Hyperventilation means overbreathing. People sometimes hyperventilate when they are frightened or otherwise stressed, drawing in more oxygen than the body needs. This condition can result in a number of symptoms, ranging from numbness of the tongue and lips to tightness in the chest or fainting. When hyperventilation attacks occur, slowing down the rate of breathing and taking smaller breaths can help. Breathing into a paper bag and then breathing its contents back into the lungs can also help. Carbon dioxide is then restored to a more normal level—those levels dip during hyperventilation.

Problems of the Respiratory System

Problems of the respiratory system include the following.

- **Influenza** and colds are caused by viruses. The symptoms include coughing, runny nose, aches, and fever.
- **Bronchitis** is swelling of bronchi—the lungs' air passages—due to infection. It causes coughing, fever, and chest tightness.
- **Allergies** are immune responses to foreign substances in the environment. They can cause sneezing, itchy eyes, runny nose, and hives.
- **Asthma** is an inflammatory disease that causes the bronchi to become blocked or narrowed. Its symptoms are wheezing, shortness of breath, and coughing.
- **Pneumonia** is a lung infection caused by viruses or bacteria. It can lead to fever, chest pain, and breathing difficulties.
- **Emphysema** is a disease in which the alveoli are damaged or destroyed. Strongly linked to smoking, it causes serious breathing difficulties.
- **Tuberculosis** is a bacterial lung infection that causes a dry cough in early stages and chest pain later on.
- **Lung cancer** is a disease in which tissues of the lung are destroyed by the growth of a tumor. The cause in most cases is smoking or secondhand smoke.

CONNECT TO

Performing Arts

SELF-CARE FOR SINGERS
Professional singers must take extra care to keep their vocal cords, throat, and lungs healthy. The most important rule they follow is no smoking. Smoking irritates the vocal cords, causing the tissues to swell up with water. The increased weight of the water makes the vocal cords heavier and lowers the voice's pitch.

FIGURE 15.7

How Breathing Works

A When you inhale, your diaphragm contracts and moves down. Your ribs move out and up, increasing the size of your chest cavity. Air moves through your nose and mouth and into your lungs.

B When you exhale, your diaphragm relaxes and moves up into your chest cavity. Your ribs move in and down, reducing the size of the chest cavity and forcing air out of your lungs.

Cross-Curriculum Activity

MATH Tell students to breath normally through their noses and count the number of breaths they take in one minute. Ask them to repeat the process, this time breathing through their mouths. Then have them compare the two figures to see whether there is any difference between nasal and mouth breathing. **L2 INCL** *Different Learning Styles (Kinesthetic)*

Comparing

Have students compare their lung capacities by taking in as much air as they can and exhaling it into a balloon. After they have exhaled, have them pinch and close the balloon opening. Compare filled balloon sizes. Advise students that this is not a competition. **L1 INCL** *English Language Learners, Special Learning Needs, Behavior Problems, Different Learning Styles (Visual, Kinesthetic)*

VISUAL LEARNING

FIGURE 15.7 Have each student place one hand on his or her upper abdomen, inhale through the nose and then exhale through the mouth. Have volunteers describe what they feel. Then have students study the illustration and read and discuss the explanation of the breathing process. **INCL** *English Language Learners, Special Learning Needs, Behavior Problems, Different Learning Styles (Visual)*

MORE ABOUT...

Bronchitis Acute bronchitis comes on suddenly and is usually caused by a virus entering the respiratory system and settling in the bronchial tubes. Treatment for acute bronchitis is medication to halt the infection. Chronic bronchitis is usually caused by smoking. A person suffering from chronic bronchitis has a continuing heavy, barklike cough. The lungs secrete an excessive amount of sticky mucus as a means of dealing with the irritating smoke. The "smoker's cough" is a warning that the body may not be able to counteract the irritation of continual smoke and that the lung's passageways are narrowing. This narrowing causes pressure on the alveoli, which sometimes collapse, leading to emphysema.

Lesson 4

Guest Speaker

If possible, invite a respiratory therapist to class to discuss respiratory disorders, emphasizing the connections to smoking. **L1**

❸ Assess

Evaluating

📁 Assign the Lesson 4 Review; then assign the Lesson 4 Quiz in the TCR.

Reteaching

• 📁 Assign Concept Map 54 or Reteaching Activity 54 in the TCR.
• Have each student draw a simple sketch of the upper human body, showing and labeling the main parts of the respiratory system.

Enrichment

• 📁 Assign Enrichment Activity 54 in the TCR.
• Have students research tuberculosis to find out how the current treatment differs from the treatment 40 years ago.

❹ Close

Ask students to explain why a healthy respiratory system is essential to their health.

You can reduce your exposure to polluted air by avoiding areas with heavy traffic. *Where in your community is the air healthy for outdoor activity?*

Care of the Respiratory System

You can keep your respiratory system working at its peak by following some commonsense practices.

• **Stay active.** Regular physical activity strengthens your lungs and helps keep other parts of your respiratory system clear. It also strengthens your diaphragm, making it easier for you to breathe.
• **Avoid smoking and secondhand smoke.** Smoking cigarettes, cigars, pipes, or marijuana puts you at increased risk for lung cancer, emphysema, and other respiratory diseases.
• **Avoid polluted air.** When you breathe air that is polluted, you get less oxygen with each breath than you otherwise would. If you ride your bike, for example, choose a road with lighter traffic so you breathe cleaner air.
• **Reduce your risk of respiratory infection.** The respiratory system is highly susceptible to infection by bacteria and viruses—many of which are carried on your hands. To reduce the risk of infection, wash your hands regularly with soap and water and avoid touching your nose and mouth.

Lesson 4 Review

Using complete sentences, answer the following questions on a sheet of paper.

Reviewing Terms and Facts

1. **List** What are the two important jobs of the respiratory system?
2. **Vocabulary** Define the words *epiglottis* and *trachea*.
3. **List** Name three parts of the respiratory system. Name the parts that exchange oxygen for carbon dioxide.
4. **Recall** How does physical activity promote the health of the respiratory system?

Thinking Critically

5. **Synthesize** What happens when you inhale? What happens when you exhale?

Draw a simple diagram showing the path of air through your respiratory system and explain what is happening.

6. **Summarize** List and give a brief explanation of the diseases of the respiratory system that are caused by tobacco smoke.

Applying Health Skills

7. **Refusal Skills** While walking home from school, Nick was offered some inhalants by an older student. Write a script in which Nick applies refusal strategies for avoiding inhalants and points out the damage that these substances can cause to the respiratory system.

384 CHAPTER 15: YOUR BODY SYSTEMS

Lesson 4 Review

1. Supply oxygen to the blood; remove carbon dioxide from the blood.
2. The epiglottis is a flap of tissue that closes over the trachea when you swallow; the trachea is a windpipe that directs air to the lungs.
3. Any three: epiglottis, larynx, bronchi, trachea, diaphragm. Alveoli handle the exchange.
4. Strengthens lungs and diaphragm. Keeps respiratory system clear.
5. For an explanation of inhaling and exhaling, see Figure 15.7 on page 383. Diagrams will vary.
6. Emphysema—alveoli damaged or destroyed. Lung cancer—lung tissue destroyed by growth of tumor.

Your Nervous System

The Nerve Center

What do riding a bicycle, reading this book, and recognizing the face of a friend have in common? They all result from the activity of your body's control center—your nervous system. The *specialized cells that make up the nervous system* are called nerve cells or **neurons** (NOO·rahnz). Neurons carry information. In **Figure 15.8**, you can see that neurons send messages from the body to the brain, and from the brain to the body. These messages are in the form of electrical signals.

FIGURE 15.8

HOW THE NERVOUS SYSTEM WORKS

Neurons are specialized cells that send quick messages through the brain and body.

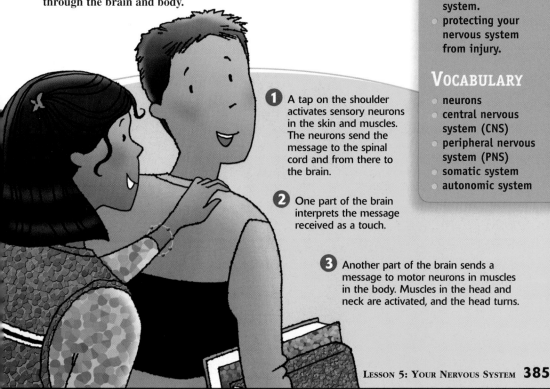

1 A tap on the shoulder activates sensory neurons in the skin and muscles. The neurons send the message to the spinal cord and from there to the brain.

2 One part of the brain interprets the message received as a touch.

3 Another part of the brain sends a message to motor neurons in muscles in the body. Muscles in the head and neck are activated, and the head turns.

LESSON 5: YOUR NERVOUS SYSTEM **385**

Quick Write

Write down at least five different kinds of information you are taking in with your senses right now.

LEARN ABOUT...

- how the nervous system works.
- the different parts of the nervous system.
- protecting your nervous system from injury.

VOCABULARY

- **neurons**
- **central nervous system (CNS)**
- **peripheral nervous system (PNS)**
- **somatic system**
- **autonomic system**

VISUAL LEARNING

FIGURE 15.8 Have students meet in groups to read and discuss the information about how the nervous system works. Then ask group members to identify other familiar sensations and responses; have them describe how the nervous system functions in each situation. **INCL** *English Language Learners, Special Learning Needs, Behavior Problems, Different Learning Styles (Visual)*

Applying Knowledge

Clarify that there are two types of neurons: 1) sensory neurons, which send messages to the spinal cord and 2) motor neurons in muscle, which receive messages from the brain and stimulate muscles to respond. Then divide the class into two sections. Each section is to take the role of one kind of neuron, sensory or motor. Describe routine tasks that involve one or more neuron types, and ask the section representing that type to stand. Say, for example, "I see my toothbrush." (The sensory neurons should rise.) "I reach for my toothbrush." (The motor neurons should rise.) **L2**

VISUAL LEARNING

FIGURE 15.9 Ask a volunteer to read aloud the title and caption for Figure 15.9. Then have students point to the correct part of the illustration as volunteers read each label aloud. Guide students in discussing the importance of each part of the nervous system. **INCL** *English Language Learners, Special Learning Needs, Behavior Problems, Different Learning Styles (Visual)*

386

Parts of the Nervous System

Your nervous system has two main parts, as shown in **Figure 15.9**. The **central nervous system (CNS)** includes *the brain and spinal cord.* It is the body's main control center. The **peripheral nervous system (PNS)** includes *the nerves that connect the CNS to all parts of the body.* A nerve is a bundle of long extensions of many neurons. A nerve acts like an electrical cord, moving electrical signals through the nervous system.

FIGURE 15.9

THE NERVOUS SYSTEM

The nervous system controls all of your body's actions. The central nervous system (yellow) and the peripheral nervous system (blue) work together. Shown here are 31 pairs of spinal nerves that branch off from the spinal cord. Each pair serves a particular part of the body.

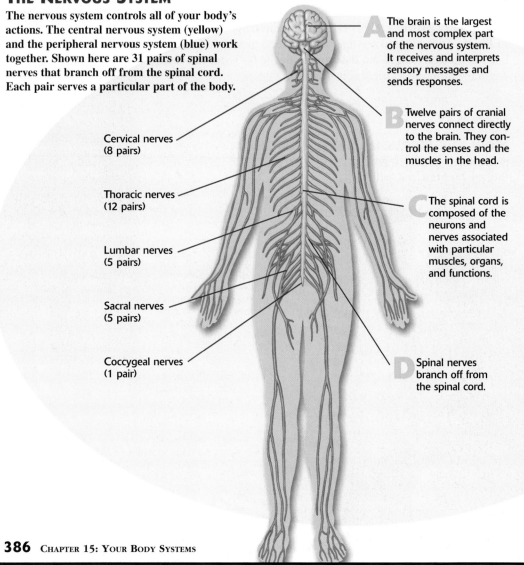

A The brain is the largest and most complex part of the nervous system. It receives and interprets sensory messages and sends responses.

B Twelve pairs of cranial nerves connect directly to the brain. They control the senses and the muscles in the head.

C The spinal cord is composed of the neurons and nerves associated with particular muscles, organs, and functions.

D Spinal nerves branch off from the spinal cord.

Cervical nerves (8 pairs)

Thoracic nerves (12 pairs)

Lumbar nerves (5 pairs)

Sacral nerves (5 pairs)

Coccygeal nerves (1 pair)

386 CHAPTER 15: YOUR BODY SYSTEMS

MORE ABOUT...

Adolescent Brain Development Recent research shows that the brains of preadolescent and adolescent students undergo a series of growth spurts that actually encourages learning. The middle school years may present a particular "key period" for learning opportunities. Different areas of the brain experience greatest growth during different periods of childhood. From ages 3 to 6, the frontal circuits are the site of particular brain growth. Between the ages of 7 and 15, the primary areas of brain development are the temporal and parietal lobes. These are the areas involved in memory and manual skills.

Central Nervous System

The central nervous system (CNS) controls two kinds of actions. Involuntary actions are those that you do not control by thinking about them, such as your heartbeat and certain digestive processes. Voluntary actions are those, such as walking and talking, that you can control.

The CNS has two main parts. The brain, shown in **Figure 15.10**, is composed of about 10 billion neurons that control all actions, thoughts, and memory. It weighs about 3 pounds and is encased in the bones of your skull.

The spinal cord is a long bundle of many nerves and associated neurons that extends from the base of the brain to the bottom of the backbone. The spinal cord relays messages from the brain to the body and from the body to the brain. Your spinal cord, which is less than 2 feet long and about the same diameter as your index finger, is protected by your backbone.

CONNECT TO
Science

BREATH CONTROL
Some automatic functions such as breathing and heartbeat occur in a regular rhythm. Breathing, unlike heartbeat, can be controlled consciously. Breathe naturally and count your breaths for a 60-second period. Then for a second 60-second period, breathe more slowly and count your breaths. *How much control does it take to override your body's natural breathing rhythm?*

FIGURE 15.10

PARTS OF THE BRAIN

Like a computer, the brain is composed of many distinct parts, each with a different function.

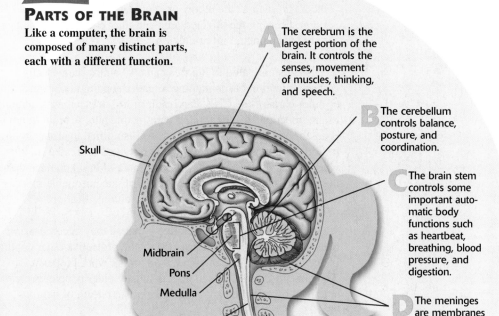

Skull

Midbrain

Pons

Medulla

Spinal cord   Vertebrae

A The cerebrum is the largest portion of the brain. It controls the senses, movement of muscles, thinking, and speech.

B The cerebellum controls balance, posture, and coordination.

C The brain stem controls some important automatic body functions such as heartbeat, breathing, blood pressure, and digestion.

D The meninges are membranes that cover the brain and the spinal cord.

LESSON 5: YOUR NERVOUS SYSTEM **387**

Lesson 5

Demonstrating

Tell students that the best way to demonstrate how the nervous system works is through actions of reflexes. Then have students work in pairs to demonstrate the patellar (knee jerk) reflex. One student sits in a chair and, in a relaxed way, crosses his or her legs. The other student uses the side of an extended hand to gently strike the soft area just under the kneecap of the first student's crossed leg. Then students switch roles. Have students discuss the reflex, describing what happened and what caused it. (*The leg jerked upward after a blow to the soft area below the kneecap; the action is a reflex arc, an automatic message between the nerves in the muscles and the brain.*) **L2 INCL** *English Language Learners, Special Learning Needs, Behavior Problems, Different Learning Styles (Kinesthetic)*

VISUAL LEARNING

FIGURE 15.10 Have volunteers describe the illustration. Ask: What portion of the area inside the skull is devoted to the brain? Then have all students point to the named parts of the brain as volunteers read aloud the labels and explanations. **INCL** *English Language Learners, Special Learning Needs, Behavior Problems, Different Learning Styles (Visual)*

Cross-Curriculum Activity

SCIENCE Bring resource books, such as life science textbooks or encyclopedias, to class that show the sizes of various animal brains. Have students compare the size of the brain of a frog, dog, or cat with the size of the human brain. **L1**

MORE ABOUT...

Epilepsy There are two major types of epileptic seizures, petit mal and grand mal. Petit mal is a milder form, usually characterized by short lapses in attention. Grand mal is characterized by a loss of consciousness and spasmodic convulsions. First aid for a grand mal seizure includes the following:

- **Do** help the person into a lying position and put something soft under the head.
- **Do** turn the person to one side to allow saliva to drain from the mouth.
- **Do** protect the head and body by clearing the area of hard or sharp objects.

Lesson 5

Guest Speaker

Have a local representative of the Multiple Sclerosis Society speak to the class on steps that are being taken to combat the disease. **L1**

Researching

Explain to students that rabies affects the central nervous system and can result in paralysis and death. It is usually caused by bites by wild animals or dogs that carry the virus in their salivary glands. Have volunteers contact the local board of health or municipal office to get information about rabies vaccinations. Then have them design posters showing their findings. **L3**

Motor vehicle accidents are the leading cause of spinal cord injuries. The second leading cause is violence, usually involving firearms.

Cross-Curriculum Activity

LANGUAGE ARTS Have volunteers use dictionaries to find the singular form of the noun meninges (*meninx*) and its derivation (*from Latin and Greek words meaning "membrane"*). Meninges is mentioned in Figure 15.10 on page 387. Have other volunteers find the meaning of the suffix *-itis* ("*inflammation of or inflammatory disease*"). Then help students discuss the component parts of the word *meningitis*. **L2**

Reading Check

Write *Central Nervous System* in a rectangle. Add *Problems* and *Care* in two ovals branching from the rectangle. List examples of each branching from these ovals.

Peripheral Nervous System

The peripheral nervous system is composed of neurons throughout the body and the nerves that connect them to the central nervous system. The PNS has two main parts. The **somatic** (soh·MA·tik) **system** is *a system dealing with actions that you control.* The nerves that lead to and from muscles in your arms and legs are part of the somatic system. The second part, the **autonomic** (aw·tuh·NAH·mik) **system**, is *a system dealing with actions you do not usually control,* such as digestion and breathing.

Problems of the Nervous System

Several diseases and disorders—most resulting from injury—can affect the nervous system.

- **Head injury** is usually caused by a blow to the head. It can also follow violent jarring of the head, causing the brain to hit the interior of the skull. This injury is called a concussion. Head injuries kill brain neurons, which cannot be replaced. A physician should immediately evaluate a person who sustains a head injury.
- **Spinal cord injury** can result from damage to the head, neck, or body. If the spinal cord is damaged or severed, paralysis of all or part of the body may result.
- **Nerve inflammation** can follow a minor injury. This condition, often called a "pinched nerve," causes pain in a single part of the body, such as the elbow or shoulder. A physician may suggest resting the affected area and may prescribe medicine to reduce pain and inflammation.

Diseases unrelated to injuries can also attack the nervous system. Infection of the meninges, called meningitis, or infection of other parts of the CNS, can result in life-threatening situations. Many infections can be treated with medication. A brain tumor is an abnormal growth of tissue that kills normal neurons around it. Some brain tumors are surgically removed or treated in other ways. In the disease epilepsy, a small area of brain damage causes the person to have seizures—episodes of uncontrollable muscle activity. Epilepsy is usually controlled with medication.

Some diseases are degenerative—that is, they become worse over time. In multiple sclerosis (MS), the protective outer coating of nerves is damaged, and nerves no longer work properly. Alzheimer's disease, which affects mostly older people, is characterized by inflamed areas in the brain and death of neurons.

Reading Check

Concept Web Making a concept web allows students to organize the information they have read. Write *Central Nervous System* in an oval at the center of the board, and draw two ovals on either side for the subtopics *Problems* and *Care*. You may wish to assign each subtopic to a small group of students to work on together. To help groups maintain their focus, point out that the topic of the lesson is in the center oval, the main ideas are the subtopic ovals, and the details are the examples branching from the ovals. Have groups complete the web on the board as well as on their own. **INCL** *Special Learning Needs*

The endocrine glands work by taking signals from the brain or from other glands. The brain receives electrical and chemical messages from the body about the presence of substances in the blood. The **pituitary** (pi·TOO·I·tehr·ee) **gland** at the base of the brain is *a gland that signals other endocrine glands to produce hormones when needed.*

FIGURE 15.14

THE ENDOCRINE SYSTEM

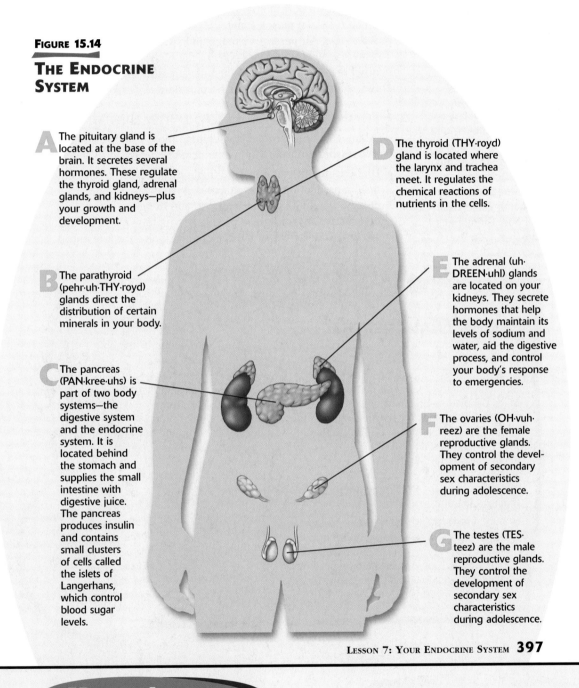

A The pituitary gland is located at the base of the brain. It secretes several hormones. These regulate the thyroid gland, adrenal glands, and kidneys—plus your growth and development.

B The parathyroid (pehr·uh·THY·royd) glands direct the distribution of certain minerals in your body.

C The pancreas (PAN·kree·uhs) is part of two body systems—the digestive system and the endocrine system. It is located behind the stomach and supplies the small intestine with digestive juice. The pancreas produces insulin and contains small clusters of cells called the islets of Langerhans, which control blood sugar levels.

D The thyroid (THY·royd) gland is located where the larynx and trachea meet. It regulates the chemical reactions of nutrients in the cells.

E The adrenal (uh·DREEN·uhl) glands are located on your kidneys. They secrete hormones that help the body maintain its levels of sodium and water, aid the digestive process, and control your body's response to emergencies.

F The ovaries (OH·vuh·reez) are the female reproductive glands. They control the development of secondary sex characteristics during adolescence.

G The testes (TES·teez) are the male reproductive glands. They control the development of secondary sex characteristics during adolescence.

LESSON 7: YOUR ENDOCRINE SYSTEM **397**

MORE ABOUT...

Glands The human body has some other glands that are not part of the endocrine system. They are called exocrine glands. While the endocrine glands release their hormones into the bloodstream, the exocrine glands deliver their chemicals directly onto the body's surface or to the site of action via tubes that are part of the glands. Examples of exocrine glands include the salivary glands, which produce saliva in the mouth; the sweat and oil glands of the skin; and the tear glands of the eye.

Lesson 7

② Teach

VISUAL LEARNING

FIGURE 15.14 Divide the class into seven groups, and assign each group one of the glands shown in Figure 15.14. Have the members of each group read and discuss the information about their assigned gland. Then have each group describe and explain that gland to the rest of the class. **INCL** *English Language Learners, Special Learning Needs, Behavior Problems, Different Learning Styles (Visual)*

Discussing

Have students describe the influence of the endocrine system on growth and development. Review some of the body changes teens go through during puberty. Point out that many of those changes are called secondary sex traits. Ask students:

• Which glands are responsible for the development of these traits? (*ovaries in females; testes in males*)

• What are some of the secondary sex traits? (*male facial hair and deeper voice, female breast development and hip broadening, and pubic hair on both sexes*) **L1**

Cross-Curriculum Activity

SCIENCE Ask volunteers to investigate which endocrine glands are found in other animals. Are these glands the same ones that humans have? Discuss the findings. **L3**

Lesson 7

Discussing

Ask volunteers to recall and describe recent experiences with their body's stress response. Ask:

• What caused the stress?

• What symptoms did you notice?

• How did you try to deal with those symptoms? **L1**

Researching

Have students research the thyroid gland. They should find out what happens to the body when there is a thyroid deficiency or an overactive thyroid. Ask: How often should this gland be checked by a doctor? Have them summarize their findings in writing. **L3**

HEALTH SKILLS ACTIVITY

STRESS MANAGEMENT

Help students read and discuss the suggestions for managing stressful events or situations. Encourage volunteers to describe their own experiences with each approach. How effective have they found each strategy?

Then have students work independently to poll others and list popular, healthful stress-management strategies.

Note: This skill is introduced in Chapter 2 on pages 39–43.

CONNECT TO

Language Arts

CHEMICAL MESSENGERS

Hormones are chemical messengers secreted by glands in your body. They act on tissue that may be a great distance from the gland. The word *hormone* comes from the Greek word *horman,* which can mean to "stir up, activate, or set in motion." Choose one of the glands shown in Figure 15.14 and use a dictionary to find what language its name came from and how the gland's name evolved.

The Body's Response to Stress

Remember the last time you were excited or anxious? You may have had sweaty palms or a pounding heart. When your brain recognizes a stressful situation, your adrenal glands respond by releasing the hormone adrenaline. This hormone prepares your body to respond to stress.

During a stress response, heart rate and the blood flow to the brain and skeletal muscles increase. Blood sugar levels and blood pressure rise. Air passages expand and sweat production increases. To conserve energy in other parts of the body, digestion and other bodily processes may slow. When the stressful stimulus withdraws, your body returns to its normal state.

Problems of the Endocrine System

Many endocrine problems, including those listed below, can be successfully treated with medicine under a physician's care.

● **Diabetes mellitus** is a disease that may be caused by inadequate insulin production by the pancreas. Symptoms include lack of energy, weight loss, extreme thirst, and frequent urination.
● **Overactive thyroid** gland produces symptoms that may include swelling in the front of the neck (called goiter), warm, moist

HEALTH SKILLS ACTIVITY

STRESS MANAGEMENT

Protecting Your Body

The stress response enables you to cope with a hazardous situation. It is sometimes called the fight-or-flight response because it prepares your body to take on danger or to get away from it quickly. The stress response becomes harmful if it goes on for too long, or if it occurs too often and in response to situations that are not hazardous. Here are some strategies for coping with a stressful event or situation.

● **TAKE A DEEP BREATH AND THINK IT THROUGH.** Is this situation serious enough to be upset over? Will it have long-term effects on your life or your relationships with others?

● **REDIRECT THE STRESS RESPONSE.** Go for a bike ride or a run. Shoot baskets in the driveway. Physical activity is a great way to defuse stressful feelings.
● **PUT THINGS INTO PERSPECTIVE.** If you find yourself repeatedly upset over small things, make a habit of stopping and putting each situation in perspective.
● **GIVE YOURSELF BREAKS.** Allow yourself some quiet time. Listen to your body and pay attention to signs of stress.

ON YOUR OWN
Poll students on the healthful strategies they use to cope with stress. Choose one and demonstrate it for the class.

MORE ABOUT...

Diabetes Diabetes is a chronic condition in which the pancreas produces too little insulin, the body is resistant to the effects of insulin, or both conditions are present in combination. Insulin is the hormone responsible for controlling blood glucose (sugar) levels. It is a major contributor to heart disease, stroke, and kidney disease. Diabetes is increasing because of the rise in obesity. Today, diabetes is diagnosed more often and at younger ages. The longer an individual has diabetes, the greater the risk of developing complications of the disease such as blindness and amputations.

skin, trembling hands, nervousness, increased sweating, disturbed sleep, and weight loss.

- **Underactive thyroid** gland can cause a dull facial expression, hoarse voice, facial puffiness, coarse, dry skin and hair, and weight gain.
- **Growth extremes** are caused by abnormal amounts of growth hormones. Too little growth hormone results in a very short person; too much growth hormone results in a very tall person.

Care of the Endocrine System

The best thing you can do for your endocrine system is to keep your body functioning at peak performance. The tips listed below remind you how to do that.

- **Eat balanced meals.** This ensures that you get the nutrients you need.
- **Get enough sleep.** Fatigue is often related to stress.
- **Engage in regular physical activity.** This keeps your body strong and helps manage stress.
- **Keep things in perspective.** Do not get overly upset about things that are not very important.
- **Have regular medical checkups.** Some hormonal disorders have subtle or unusual symptoms. Your doctor can do medical tests to establish that your hormone function is normal.

Modern technology makes it easier to identify and treat problems of the endocrine system. However, preventive care is the best way to make sure your endocrine system stays healthy.

Lesson 7 Review

Using complete sentences, answer the following questions on a sheet of paper.

Reviewing Terms and Facts

1. **Vocabulary** What is a *gland?* Explain the role of glands in the endocrine system.
2. **Review** What is the main function of the pituitary gland?
3. **Identify** Which gland is part of the endocrine system and the digestive system?
4. **Recall** What gland regulates the chemical reactions of nutrients in the cells? Where is it located?

Thinking Critically

5. **Hypothesize** Do you think the fight-or-flight response is less necessary today than in the past? Why or why not?

Applying Health Skills

6. **Accessing Information** Use reliable sources to research how the endocrine system influences growth and development during adolescence. Describe your findings in a brief report.

Lesson 7

Discussing

Guide students in discussing the importance of "keeping things in perspective." Ask:

- Why is this especially difficult for teens?
- How can you and your friends help one another avoid getting upset about minor issues?
- How can adults help teens keep things in perspective? L1

❸ Assess

Evaluating

📁 Assign the Lesson 7 Review; then assign the Lesson 7 Quiz in the TCR.

Reteaching

- 📁 Assign Concept Map 57 or Reteaching Activity 57 in the TCR.
- Have students write paragraphs explaining the role of the endocrine system and make charts with the name of each endocrine gland in the left column and its function in the right column.

Enrichment

📁 Assign Enrichment Activity 57 in the TCR.

❹ Close

Ask each student to name a gland of the endocrine system and explain its function.

Lesson 7 Review

1. A group of cells, or an organ, that secretes a chemical substance. Endocrine glands secrete hormones into the bloodstream, which carries them to the tissue they are targeted to affect.
2. It signals other endocrine glands to produce hormones when needed.
3. Pancreas.
4. Thyroid gland, located where the larynx and trachea meet.
5. Responses will vary.

1 Focus

Lesson Objectives

Students will be able to

- describe how sperm are produced.
- discuss the problems and care of the male and female reproductive systems.
- describe the stages of the menstrual cycle.
- discuss the process of fertilization.

Motivators

Quick Write

Ask volunteers to share their responses. Ask: How might knowing the correct names of their parts also be important? (*to describe a problem during a medical checkup, to better understand each system's functions*)

Bellringer Activity

Ask students to list five reasons to keep the reproductive system healthy. Have them revisit their answers at the end of the lesson.

VOCABULARY

Have students make flash cards for the vocabulary terms in the lesson, following the procedure described in Lesson 1. Remind students to fill in the three categories—*Body System, Definition,* and *Page Reference*. The completed flash cards should help students understand the parts of all the body systems.

Lesson 8

Your Reproductive System

Quick Write

Why is it important to understand the functioning of both the male and the female reproductive systems?

LEARN ABOUT...

- how sperm are produced.
- the stages of the menstrual cycle.
- ovulation and fertilization.
- keeping your reproductive system healthy.

VOCABULARY

- reproductive system
- sperm
- ovulation
- menstruation
- menstrual cycle
- menopause

The Reproductive System

Reproduction is the process by which life is continued from one generation to the next. A new human life results from the union of two specialized cells, one from a male and the other from a female. These cells, shown in **Figure 15.15**, are produced by the **reproductive** (ree·pruh·DUHK·tiv) **system,** *the organs that make possible the production of offspring.*

Unlike other body systems, the reproductive systems of males and females are not the same. As a result, the potential problems for each system are different. In addition, each system requires different care.

FIGURE 15.15

CELLS OF THE REPRODUCTIVE SYSTEM

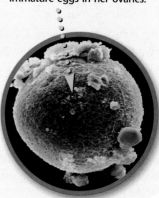

The egg cell in this photograph is magnified. At birth, a female has hundreds of thousands of immature eggs in her ovaries.

The sperm in this photograph are magnified. Approximately 400 million sperm are present in the semen released during a single ejaculation.

400 CHAPTER 15: YOUR BODY SYSTEMS

Lesson 8 Resources

Teacher Classroom Resources

 Concept Map 58

 Cross-Curriculum Activity 30

 Enrichment Activity 58

 Lesson Plan 8

 Lesson 8 Quiz

 Reading Tutor Activity 57

 Reteaching Activity 58

 Transparencies 60 & 61

Student Activities Workbook

Chapter 15 Study Guide

Applying Health Skills 58

Health Inventory 15

The Male Reproductive System

The male reproductive system produces the *male reproductive cells,* called **sperm**. Males begin to produce sperm when they reach puberty, usually between the ages of 12 and 15. The male reproductive system, shown in **Figure 15.16**, includes organs involved in the production and storage of sperm and the release of sperm outside of the body.

Sperm are produced in the testes and mature in the epididymis. From there, they travel through the vas deferens, where they are mixed with seminal (SE·mi·nuhl) fluid, which is produced by the seminal vesicles, the prostate gland, and Cowper's glands. This mixture of sperm and seminal fluid is called semen (SEE·muhn). Muscular contractions force semen through the urethra and out of the body, a process called ejaculation (I·ja·kyuh·LAY·shuhn).

FIGURE 15.16

MALE REPRODUCTIVE SYSTEM

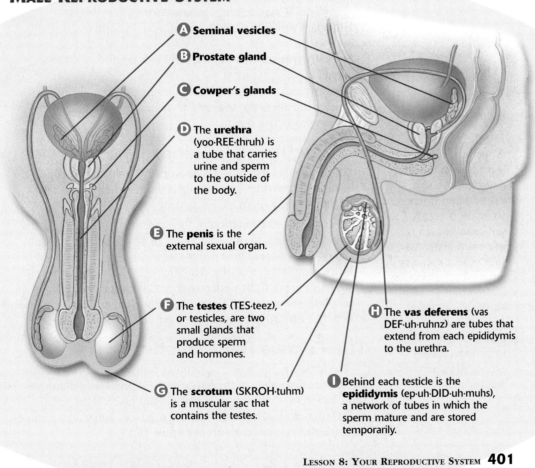

A **Seminal vesicles**

B **Prostate gland**

C **Cowper's glands**

D The **urethra** (yoo·REE·thruh) is a tube that carries urine and sperm to the outside of the body.

E The **penis** is the external sexual organ.

F The **testes** (TES·teez), or testicles, are two small glands that produce sperm and hormones.

G The **scrotum** (SKROH·tuhm) is a muscular sac that contains the testes.

H The **vas deferens** (vas DEF·uh·ruhnz) are tubes that extend from each epididymis to the urethra.

I Behind each testicle is the **epididymis** (ep·uh·DID·uh·muhs), a network of tubes in which the sperm mature and are stored temporarily.

LESSON 8: YOUR REPRODUCTIVE SYSTEM **401**

VISUAL LEARNING

FIGURE 15.15 Ask volunteers to describe the sperm and the egg cell in the pictures; emphasize that both are greatly magnified. Then guide students in reading and discussing the explanations that accompany the photographs. **INCL** *English Language Learners, Special Learning Needs, Behavior Problems, Different Learning Styles (Visual)*

Discussing

Ask volunteers to identify athletic safety equipment used to protect the organs of the male reproductive system. Help students discuss the importance of using this equipment. **L1**

VISUAL LEARNING

FIGURE 15.16 Have students meet in cooperative groups to study the illustration and read the labels and explanations. Encourage group members to discuss how the parts of the male reproductive system are connected and related. **INCL** *English Language Learners, Special Learning Needs, Behavior Problems, Different Learning Styles (Visual)*

Lesson 8

More than half of American men in their 60s have enlarged prostate glands. As many as 90 percent of men in their 80s have this condition. An enlarged prostate does not necessarily require treatment; if it does, medications and several kinds of surgery are options.

Researching

Have interested volunteers learn more about the kinds of cancer that affect male reproductive organs. Also, have them research current treatments for those kinds of cancer. Have these volunteers work together to write a summary of their findings. **L2**

Developing Good Character

Responsibility

Discuss with students the idea that one way we can all be responsible is to take steps to safeguard our health. A democratic nation that values freedom, such as ours, depends on having citizens who are well educated, both academically and ethically. Some examples of being a responsible citizen are finding out needed information to make the best decisions, performing regular self-exams to screen for cancer or other diseases, and asking health care professionals for help when needed. Ask: What are some other ways we can protect our health?

Male teens who engage in any contact sports are advised to use protective equipment to protect their external sexual organs. *For which sports would such equipment be needed?*

Developing Good Character

Responsibility

Take responsibility for your health and learn how to perform a testicular self-examination if you are male, a breast self-examination if you are female. Ask your school nurse or personal physician for information on self-examination. Mark your calendar so that you remember to perform a self-examination each month.

Problems of the Male Reproductive System

Males can experience problems with their reproductive systems ranging from merely uncomfortable to very serious.

- **Inguinal hernia** is a tissue separation that allows part of the intestine to push into the scrotum. It may follow heavy lifting.
- **Sterility** is the inability to produce enough healthy sperm to reproduce. It may follow illness or exposure to drugs.
- **Enlarged prostate gland** is a common problem associated with aging.
- **Sexually transmitted diseases (STDs)** are diseases that are spread by sexual contact.
- **Cancer** is uncontrolled cell growth that destroys healthy tissue. Cancer can affect the testicles, prostate, or less often, other male reproductive organs.

Care of the Male Reproductive System

Males should have regular checkups by a physician. The following list provides specific suggestions to help males take good care of their reproductive system.

- **Practice self-examination** of the scrotum and testicles once a month, checking for unusual lumps or swelling. Any change should be evaluated by a physician.
- **Bathe regularly** to ensure cleanliness.
- **Avoid wearing tight underwear**, and wear a protective cup or supporter during athletic activities to prevent accidental injuries.
- **Practice abstinence** from sexual activity before marriage.

The Female Reproductive System

The female reproductive system has many functions. It produces female sex hormones; it stores egg cells; it provides a place for fertilization to occur. It then nourishes and protects the fertilized egg as it grows and matures into a new human being. The female reproductive system is shown in **Figure 15.17**.

402 CHAPTER 15: YOUR BODY SYSTEMS

DEALING WITH SENSITIVE ISSUES

Self-Examinations Students may not be familiar with techniques of self-examinations; and no one should be placed in an embarrassing situation regarding familiarity with, or frequency of, self-examinations. Instead, you might ask same-gender groups to begin a project in which they create brochures for other students about the particulars of testicular and breast self-examinations. Students can use pamphlets prepared by credible health sources for their research. Make the materials available to interested students. In that way, students will teach themselves without feeling awkward or embarrassed.

FIGURE 15.17

FEMALE REPRODUCTIVE SYSTEM

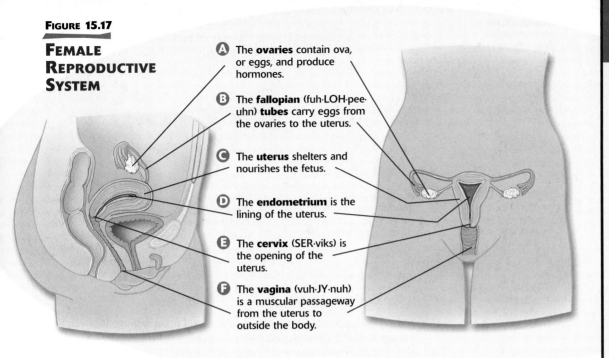

Ⓐ The **ovaries** contain ova, or eggs, and produce hormones.

Ⓑ The **fallopian** (fuh·LOH·pee·uhn) **tubes** carry eggs from the ovaries to the uterus.

Ⓒ The **uterus** shelters and nourishes the fetus.

Ⓓ The **endometrium** is the lining of the uterus.

Ⓔ The **cervix** (SER·viks) is the opening of the uterus.

Ⓕ The **vagina** (vuh·JY·nuh) is a muscular passageway from the uterus to outside the body.

The Menstrual Cycle

As a female reaches puberty, hormones cause egg cells to mature in her ovaries. **Ovulation,** *the release of one mature egg cell each month,* begins. The uterus thickens in preparation to receive and begin to nourish a fertilized egg. If fertilization does not occur, the thickened lining breaks down and is expelled. *The flow of the uterine lining out of the body* is called **menstruation**.

The **menstrual cycle** is *the sequence of events in the reproductive system that occurs from one menstruation to another.* Menstruation itself usually lasts from five to seven days. **Figure 15.18** on the next page shows the events of an average menstrual cycle. A cycle usually lasts about 28 days, but it varies from one female to another. Stress or illness may affect the length of the menstrual cycle. Female teens often have irregular cycles.

Most females begin menstruation between the ages of 9 and 16. For the first months or few years, the times of ovulation and menstruation may vary widely. This is not a cause for concern. The degree of cramps and fatigue associated with the menstrual cycle also may vary from one female to another. Menstruation occurs from puberty until menopause. **Menopause,** which usually occurs between age 40 and 60, is *a period marking the end of a female's reproductive years.*

LESSON 8: YOUR REPRODUCTIVE SYSTEM **403**

MORE ABOUT...

Toxic Shock Syndrome Toxic shock syndrome (TSS) is a rare disease that is becoming even more rare. It is caused by infection with varieties of the common bacterium *Staphylococcus aureus*. Persons with TSS have high fevers, vomiting, diarrhea, low blood pressure, and rashes resembling sunburn. In 5 percent of cases it is fatal. More than half of all cases occur in women.

Among women, TSS has been traced to use of super-absorbent tampons that absorb magnesium and provide a moist, warm home that can enable bacteria to thrive and produce toxins. Preventive measures include avoidance or intermittent use of tampons. Also, changes in tampon absorbency and composition have greatly reduced cases of TSS.

Lesson 8

Cross-Curriculum Activity

LANGUAGE ARTS Have students write paragraphs about what it means to be male or female in our culture. Ask them to underline those parts of their paragraphs that are physical descriptions.

• How much of the paragraph was devoted to the physical aspects of being male or female?

• Why is it important to recognize other aspects? **L3**

VISUAL LEARNING

FIGURE 15.17 Have volunteers identify each part of the female reproductive system shown in Figure 15.17; have other volunteers read aloud the labels and explanations. Ask students to describe the importance of each part and to explain how the parts are related. **INCL** *English Language Learners, Special Learning Needs, Behavior Problems, Different Learning Styles (Visual)*

Recalling

Direct students to work in pairs. Have each student write three questions about the parts and functions of the female reproductive system. Then have students exchange questions and write answers to their partners' questions. Have students check one another's answers. **L2**

Comprehending

Ask students to identify the organs in the female reproductive system that are also part of the endocrine system (*ovaries*). Ask volunteers to explain how those organs function in the endocrine system (*produce hormones*) and how they function in the reproductive system (*store eggs*). **L1**

Critical Thinking

Ask students to describe when changes would begin to occur in the menstrual cycle if fertilization had taken place (*after ovulation, on the day of fertilization*). **L1**

Investigating

Ask students to review, in more detail, findings about the interrelationships between PMS (premenstrual syndrome) and nutrition. Encourage them to ask their parents and health care professionals for advice on coping with PMS. **L3**

FIGURE 15.18

AN AVERAGE MENSTRUAL CYCLE

The stages of a 28-day menstrual cycle are shown here. Actual cycles vary in length from female to female, especially during the teen years.

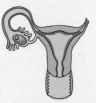 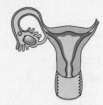 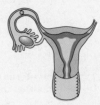 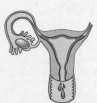

A On days 1 through 13 of the cycle, a new egg cell is maturing inside the ovary.

B On day 14 of the cycle, ovulation occurs and the mature egg is released into one of the fallopian tubes.

C From day 15 through day 20, the egg travels through the fallopian tube.

D On day 21, the egg enters the uterus. After 7 days, if the egg has not been fertilized, menstruation begins.

Fertilization

Fertilization is the joining of male and female reproductive cells to make the first cell of a new human. This cell, the fertilized egg, then moves down the fallopian tube and into the uterus. The fertilized egg attaches to the wall of the uterus and begins to grow. In the early stages, it is called an embryo. After eight weeks of development, it becomes a fetus. The uterus has layers of tissue and a rich blood supply to nourish the developing fetus. The mother's body supplies the fetus with food and oxygen.

After about 40 weeks, the fetus is mature and ready to be born. The walls of the uterus begin to contract. The contractions open the cervix and push the baby out of the uterus and through the cervix. The baby passes through the vagina and out of the female's body.

Problems of the Female Reproductive System

Females can experience problems with their reproductive systems ranging from merely uncomfortable to very serious.

- **Premenstrual syndrome (PMS)** is a collection of physical and emotional changes before and during menstruation.
- **Toxic shock syndrome** is a rare but serious bacterial infection associated with incorrect tampon use. It may produce a fever and a sunburn-like rash, and requires immediate medical care.
- **Infertility** is the inability to reproduce. It may be due to blocked fallopian tubes or failure to produce eggs.
- **Ovarian cysts** are growths on the ovary. Any pain, swelling, abdominal bloating, or feeling of heaviness in the abdomen

---

MORE ABOUT...

PMS Among female teens, painful menstrual cramps (dysmenorrhea) are the leading cause of short-term absences from school. About 75 percent of adolescent girls experience these painful cramps, but only about 25 percent of them consider it disabling. Dysmenorrhea increases among older teens because the first year or two of the menstrual cycle may not involve ovulation. The principal symptom is sharp, cramping abdominal pain that begins just before, or at the onset of, menstrual flow. Other symptoms include headache, nausea, vomiting, fatigue, irritability, dizziness, and fainting. Over-the-counter medicines, such as ibuprofen, may relieve symptoms. Regular physical activity also helps to reduce the severity of cramps.

should be evaluated by
a physician.

- **Sexually transmitted diseases (STDs)** are diseases that are spread during sexual contact.
- **Cancer** is uncontrolled cell growth that destroys healthy tissue. Cancer can affect the breasts, ovaries, uterus, or cervix.

Care of the Female Reproductive System

The following tips will help females take good care of their reproductive systems.

- **Examine your breasts.** Check once a month for unusual lumps or thickening. Any breast changes should be evaluated by a physician.
- **Bathe regularly.** During menstruation, change tampons and sanitary pads frequently.
- **Record your menstrual periods.** Your doctor will want to know when they occur and how long they last.
- **Practice abstinence.** Abstain from sexual activity before marriage.

A gynecologist is a physician who specializes in the care of the female reproductive system. Female teens are advised to have their first visit with a gynecologist once they turn 18, or sooner if they have any concerns.

Lesson 8 Review

Using complete sentences, answer the following questions on a sheet of paper.

Reviewing Terms and Facts

1. **Explain** In which part of the male reproductive system are sperm produced? In which part do they mature?
2. **List** What are four ways for males to care for their reproductive systems?
2. **Vocabulary** Define *ovulation* and *menstruation.*
4. **Review** Describe the path of an egg after it is fertilized.

Thinking Critically

5. **Compare and Contrast** What happens in the uterus if an egg is fertilized? What happens if it is not fertilized?
6. **Analyze** Identify several reasons why it is important to practice sexual abstinence.

Applying Health Skills

7. **Advocacy** With a partner, write a skit in which you present a discussion you might have with a younger sibling who is nearing puberty. Include questions and answers about the body changes to expect, along with information on behaviors that promote good health.

LESSON 8: YOUR REPRODUCTIVE SYSTEM **405**

How Stress Takes Its Toll

① Focus

Objectives

Students will be able to

- define vocabulary associated with stress and the body.
- explain the fight-or-flight response.
- discuss methods of coping with chronic low-level stress.

Motivator
Bellringer Activity

Ask students, "Have you ever experienced a fight-or-flight reaction? Did you feel the same symptoms listed on page 407 (*sharpened senses, tightening of muscles, pounding heart*)? How did you feel about the experience afterwards? Was the fight or flight reaction helpful in your situation?"

② Teach

Cross-Curriculum Activity

LANGUAGE ARTS Have students define the following words, explaining how they relate to stress. Students can refer to this spread, other sections of the textbook, and reliable online and print resources. Tell students to cite the resources they use. Discuss the results as a class, keeping in mind that definitions may vary depending upon the resource used.

- hypothalamus
- amygdala
- pituitary gland
- cardiovascular system
- hormones
- immune system
- epinephrine
- norepinephrine
- glucocorticoids

TIME HEALTH

Cerebral cortex

THREAT

Hypothalamus

Pituitary gland

Amygdala

Arteries widen

Heart beats faster

Muscles tense

Lungs ventilate faster

Adrenal glands release hormones

Stomach, digestion shuts down

How Stress Takes Its Toll

Ordinary stress can be harmful to the body as well as the mind.

1. A stress response starts in the brain...

When the brain detects a threat, a number of areas, including the hypothalamus, amygdala, and pituitary gland, go on alert and exchange information with each other. They send signaling hormones and nerve impulses through the nervous system to the rest of the body to prepare for fight or flight.

406 CHAPTER 15: YOUR BODY SYSTEMS

MORE ABOUT...

Stress Relief Advise students that along with standard methods of stress reduction, there are "alternative therapies" that may help to relax the body and mind, such as meditation and guided visualization. Have interested students research alternative therapies for stress relief. How do they work to relieve stress? Are there practitioners of these methods in the community? If so, students may want to interview them to learn more. Have students present their findings to the class.

Stress comes in two forms, each with its own chemistry:

ACUTE A response to immediate danger, acute stress turbocharges the system with powerful hormones that can damage the cardiovascular system.

CHRONIC Caused by constant emotional pressure that the victim can't control, chronic stress produces hormones that can weaken the immune system and damage bones.

2. ...and the body unleashes a flood of hormones...

Adrenal glands react to the alert by releasing the hormone adrenaline (also called epinephrine). This makes the heart pump faster and the lungs work harder to flood the body with oxygen.

The adrenal glands also release extra cortisol and other glucocorticoids, hormones that help the body convert sugars into energy.

Nerve cells release the hormone norepinephrine, which tenses the muscles and sharpens the senses to prepare for action. Digestion shuts down.

3. ...that can cause significant damage

When the threat passes, epinephrine and norepinephrine levels drop, but if danger returns frequently, increased levels of these hormones can damage the arteries. Chronic low-level stress keeps the glucocorticoids in circulation, leading to a weakened immune system, loss of bone mass, suppression of the reproductive system, and memory problems.

FIGHT OR FLIGHT

Our physical reaction to stress, known as the "fight-or-flight" response, probably evolved to help our primitive ancestors deal with a dangerous world. When faced with peril, the body had to be instantly ready to defend itself or run like the wind.

To cope, the terrified brain would signal the adrenal glands, located on top of the kidneys, to release hormones, including adrenaline (also called epinephrine) and glucocorticoids (see the diagram for more on these). The brain would also signal nerve cells to release norepinephrine. These powerful chemicals made the senses sharper, the muscles tighter, the heart pound faster, and the bloodstream fill with sugars for ready energy. Then, when the danger passed, the response would turn off.

Unfortunately, in the modern world, there are some situations that we cannot fight or flee from, such as tensions at home or at school. So our bodies' response mechanisms stay turned on for longer periods of time. Elevated levels of stress and glucocorticoids can lead to serious problems down the road.

TIME TO THINK...

About the Stress Response

The "Fight or Flight" sidebar cites tensions at home or at school as two types of situations that you cannot usually "fight" or "flee" from. Brainstorm specific situations (such as worrying about a big test that's a month away) that you can't "fight" or "flee" from, and put them in one column. In another column, list possible ways of coping with each of these situations. Share your list with the rest of the class.

3 Apply

Time to Think

Discuss the difference between low-level stress and high-level stress, brainstorming examples of each. Ask students, "What are some ways of handling these different degrees of stress? Does the fight-or-flight response apply to both? How is it the same or different?" Have students look at the third point on the spread. Ask students to write down what they think is meant by chronic low-level stress. Discuss the results of chronic low-level stress that are mentioned in the article:

- A "weakened immune system" makes one more susceptible to illness.
- "Loss of bone mass" leads to eventual osteoporosis.
- "Suppression of the reproductive system" can cause difficulty in producing children (for both males and females).
- "Memory loss" causes confusion, frustration, and, in severe cases, the inability to function independently.

Then ask, "What are some ways of reducing chronic low-level stress in your life?" (*eating healthy, utilizing time management, sleeping at least eight hours a day, and so forth*)

VISUAL LEARNING

Divide the class into pairs, and have each pair examine the photograph on pages 406–407. Ask students to discuss how the body organs pictured are responding to stress. What are some healthy ways the girl can consciously respond?

Health Literacy

Eustress vs. Distress Review with students the definition of eustress (*positive stress*) on page 39. Remind students that not all stress is necessarily bad; often it can help with motivation and personal goals. Ask students, "What are some examples of eustress? How does the body react? Are these reactions different from how the body responds to distress (*negative stress*)?" Have students make a list of the positive stresses in their lives within the last two weeks. Ask students to explain their reactions to these stresses.

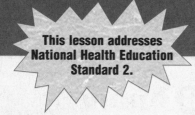

This lesson addresses National Health Education Standard 2.

ACCESSING INFORMATION

OBJECTIVE

After completing the lesson, students will be able to access valid sources of health information about body systems.

Time: two 40-minute periods (including research time)

Materials: index cards, medical reference books, library and/or Internet access

Teacher Classroom Resources

📁 Building Health Skills Activities

• Transparency Master 1, "Accessing Information"

• Reproducible Master 40, "Finding Facts About Your Body"

1. Model

• Display Transparency Master 1, and review the skill of accessing information.

• After students have read about Paul, ask them how he used the skill of accessing information to learn more about broken bones. (*He checked the family medical guide, a valid source. He then visited an Internet site that supported the information he found in the medical guide.*)

• Ask volunteers to explain how the information that Paul accessed might help him understand the importance of spending six weeks in a cast (*e.g., knowing how broken bones mend helped Paul realize that his arm might not heal properly if the cast were taken off too soon*).

FINDING FACTS ABOUT YOUR BODY

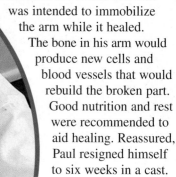

Model

Paul had always been interested in how things work. When he fell and broke his arm, he was curious to know what was going on beneath the cast that the doctor applied. He also wanted to make sure that he did all that he could to heal as quickly as possible.

To get the information he needed, he checked the family medical guide, and then followed up by visiting a medical site on the Internet. From these sources, he discovered that the X rays had enabled the doctor to find the location of the break. The cast was intended to immobilize the arm while it healed. The bone in his arm would produce new cells and blood vessels that would rebuild the broken part. Good nutrition and rest were recommended to aid healing. Reassured, Paul resigned himself to six weeks in a cast.

408 CHAPTER 15: YOUR BODY SYSTEMS

Teaching Tips

Research Techniques To make research experiences successful for students:

• Make sure information is accessible to the entire class (reserve sufficient library or computer lab time, or bring all necessary materials into the classroom).

• To get students on task quickly, allow no more than a few minutes for them to decide what part of the body to research.

• Monitor student progress closely. Students who finish early should be encouraged to research a second topic.

Practice

Read about Mandy's situation. Then answer the questions that follow.

When Mandy learned that her grandmother had suffered a stroke, she had no idea what had happened. Her parents told her that her grandmother would need special care when she came home from the hospital. Mandy thought that the best thing she could do was gain a better understanding of what a stroke was. That way she would be able to help her grandmother recover.

1. If you were in Mandy's position, where would you look for information?
2. How many sources would you use?
3. How would you make sure the information was reliable?

Apply/Assess

Choose a body system or part of a body system that you want to know more about. For example, if you know someone who has diabetes, you might want to learn more about the pancreas. If you have a friend with asthma, you might be interested in how the lungs work. Use reliable print and Internet sources to research the system or body part that you choose. Write down at least three facts that you did not know before you began your research. Prepare a "Facts about . . ." card like the one shown here, presenting the facts and the sources you used. Post your card on a classroom bulletin board.

Accessing Information

Using the skill of accessing information involves
- seeking information from reliable sources.
- checking the accuracy of the sources that you use.

Self-Check

- Did my "Facts About . . ." card contain at least three facts not included in this book?
- Did I show where I found the facts?
- Did I find reliable sources?

Facts about . . . the Appendix

1. It is about 3½ inches long and seems to have no function in humans. (AMA Family Medical Guide)
2. In appendicitis, the appendix becomes swollen, inflamed, and painful. (AMA Family Medical Guide)
3. Appendicitis affects about 1 in 500 Americans every year. (Mayo Clinic Web site)
4. The standard treatment for appendicitis is surgical removal. (Mayo Clinic Web site)

2. Practice

- Direct students to read about Mandy's situation. Then have them work in pairs to answer the questions.

- After pairs of students have finished answering the questions, solicit responses from members of the class. Write the sources that students came up with on the board.

- Review the sources listed on the board, and lead a class discussion on the reliability of each one.

3. Apply/Assess

- 📁 You may wish to distribute Building Health Skills Reproducible Master 40 in the TCR to guide students in completing this activity.

- Distribute index cards, and arrange for the class to have access to library and Internet resources to complete the assignment.

- Provide an opportunity for students to conduct research and prepare their fact cards. Remind them to review the Self-Check questions to ensure that their work is complete.

- Allow time for volunteers to read their completed index cards aloud. Use this opportunity to review key chapter concepts.

- If possible, display student work on the classroom bulletin board.

BUILDING HEALTH SKILLS: FINDING FACTS ABOUT YOUR BODY **409**

Assessment Scoring

Using a rubric, student work should provide evidence of all criteria to achieve the highest score.

Skills

Student work demonstrates

- both a print and Internet source.
- why each source is reliable and valid.
- proper citation of the source.

Concepts

Student work provides

- three facts not included in textbook.

Checking Comprehension

Use the Chapter 15 Assessment to examine the most important ideas presented in the chapter.

Answers to Reviewing Vocabulary and Concepts

Lesson 1
1. skeletal system
2. marrow
3. cartilage
4. calcium

Lesson 2
5. muscular
6. contracts
7. extend
8. smooth

Lesson 3
9. circulatory
10. pulmonary
11. systemic
12. arteries
13. veins
14. capillaries

Lesson 4
15. true
16. false; bronchi
17. false; exhale
18. false; viruses
19. true

Lesson 5
20. true
21. false; autonomic
22. true

CHAPTER ASSESSMENT 15

After You Read

Use your completed Foldable to review the information on the parts, problems, and care of the skeletal system.

FOLDABLES Study Organizer

Reviewing Vocabulary and Concepts

On a sheet of paper, write the numbers 1–14. After each number, write the term from the list that best completes each sentence.

- arteries
- capillaries
- circulatory
- contracts
- extend
- calcium
- cartilage
- muscular
- pulmonary
- marrow
- smooth
- systemic
- skeletal system
- veins

Lesson 1
1. The _____ is an internal system made up of bones, joints, and connective tissue.
2. Red and white blood cells are made by _____, a tissue in the center of some bones.
3. _____ is tissue that cushions the joints.
4. Foods high in _____ are essential for building and maintaining strong bones.

Lesson 2
5. The _____ system enables body parts to move.
6. When a muscle shortens, it _____.

7. When a muscle lengthens, it is said to _____.
8. The muscles that line the stomach and intestines are called _____ muscles.

Lesson 3
9. The body's internal transport system is called the _____ system.
10. _____ circulation is the flow of blood from the heart to the lungs and back to the heart.
11. _____ circulation is the flow of blood to all of the body tissues except the lungs.
12. Blood vessels that carry blood away from the heart to other parts of the body are called _____.
13. Blood vessels that carry blood from the body back to the heart are called _____.
14. The tiny tubes that carry blood from your arteries to your body's cells, and then back to your veins, are called _____.

On a sheet of paper, write the numbers 15–26. Write *True* or *False* for each statement below. If the statement is false, change the underlined word or phrase to make it true.

Lesson 4
15. A person can live only a <u>few minutes</u> without air.
16. Air enters lungs through the <u>trachea</u>.
17. When you <u>inhale</u>, your diaphragm relaxes and moves up into your chest cavity.
18. Influenza and colds are caused by <u>bacteria</u>.
19. Smoking cigarettes increases a person's risk of developing <u>lung cancer</u>.

INCLUSION STRATEGIES

Special Learning Needs, Behavior Problems, English Language Learners The following suggestions are helpful for students with special learning needs, students with behavior problems, and ELL students:
- Pair these students with more proficient learners who can help summarize the main concepts of the chapter.

- 🎧 Direct these students to listen to the Teen Health Audio Summaries. This component provides an audio and written summary of the chapter in both English and Spanish.
- Use photographs, drawings, or magazine clippings whenever possible to help students visualize the important concepts of the chapter.

Lesson 5

20. The <u>central nervous system</u> includes the brain and spinal cord.

21. The <u>somatic</u> system deals with actions that you do not usually control.

22. If the spinal cord is damaged or severed, <u>paralysis</u> may result.

Lesson 6

23. Most digestion takes place in the <u>stomach</u>.

24. The liver produces <u>a gastric juice</u>, which helps digest fats.

25. <u>Excretion</u> is the process of removing wastes from the body.

26. Eating spicy or acidic foods may result in <u>gallstones</u>.

On a sheet of paper, write the numbers 27–35. After each number, write the letter of the answer that best completes each sentence.

Lesson 7

27. The gland that is located at the base of the brain is the
  a. adrenal gland.
  b. parathyroid gland.
  c. pituitary gland.
  d. pancreas.

28. Development of secondary sex characteristics in females is controlled by the
  a. thyroid gland.
  b. ovaries.
  c. goiter.
  d. testes.

29. During a stress response,
  a. blood flow increases.
  b. air passages expand.
  c. digestion may slow down.
  d. all of the above.

30. Diabetes is characterized by inadequate production of
  a. amino acids.
  b. adrenaline.
  c. sugar.
  d. insulin.

Lesson 8

31. Sperm are produced in the
  a. seminal vesicle.
  b. Cowper's glands.
  c. sperm glands.
  d. testes.

32. From the epididymis, sperm travel through the
  a. prostate gland.
  b. testes.
  c. urethra.
  d. vas deferens.

33. The female reproductive system functions to
  a. store eggs.
  b. provide a site for fertilization.
  c. nourish and protect a fertilized egg.
  d. all of the above.

34. The opening of the uterus is the
  a. fetus.
  b. cervix.
  c. endometrium.
  d. ovary.

35. A blocked fallopian tube can result in
  a. infertility.
  b. PMS.
  c. STDs.
  d. toxic shock syndrome.

Lesson 6
23. false; duodenum or small intestine
24. false; bile
25. true
26. false; indigestion

Lesson 7
27. c
28. b
29. d
30. d

Lesson 8
31. d
32. d
33. d
34. b
35. a

 TH05_C3.glencoe.com/quiz

Assessment ✔

Self-Assessment Direct students to review the activities that are provided throughout the chapter. Encourage each student to select one finished product or activity that demonstrates his or her best work for the chapter. Have students explain what they learned and how the examples they selected show their progress.

Career Corner

Physical Therapist After reviewing the career profile on the health Web site, students might:
- Describe the skills, training, and education needed.
- Discuss the types of injuries that would require a physical therapist.

Thinking Critically

36. Calcium builds and maintains strong bones. Phosphorous gives bones rigidity.

37. You would not be able to bend your back.

38. Smooth muscles are found in organs such as the stomach and intestines; you do not actively control them.

39. Pulmonary: flow of blood from heart to lungs and back. Systemic: flow of blood to all body tissues except lungs.

40. To be able to receive or give a blood transfusion.

41. Washing rids hands of bacteria and viruses, which cause infection.

42. Emphysema and lung cancer.

43. The spinal cord relays messages from the brain to the body and the body to the brain to control voluntary and involuntary actions.

44. To prevent injury to the brain.

45. Fiber keeps materials moving through the digestive tract.

46. The brain receives messages from the body about substances in the blood. Pituitary gland at the base of the brain signals endocrine glands to produce hormones when needed.

Thinking Critically

Using complete sentences, answer the following questions on a sheet of paper.

36. Explain What do calcium and phosphorous do for your bones?

37. Predict How would a person's ability to move change if the backbone were a single bone instead of 24 separate bones?

38. Analyze In what ways are smooth muscles and skeletal muscles different?

39. Compare What is the difference between pulmonary and systemic circulation?

40. Apply Why do you need to know your blood type?

41. Explain Why does regular handwashing reduce your risk of catching a respiratory infection?

42. Summarize Which diseases of the respiratory system are particularly associated with smoking?

43. Analyze How are voluntary actions, such as wiggling your toes, and involuntary actions, such as breathing, related to your brain?

44. Explain Why is it important to wear a helmet when riding a bike or playing a contact sport?

45. Apply How does fiber contribute to the health of your digestive and excretory systems?

46. Synthesize What is the relationship between the brain and the endocrine system?

47. Deduce Why is the stress response sometimes harmful instead of helpful?

48. Explain Why does the menstrual cycle stop when a female is pregnant?

49. Contrast Compare and contrast changes in the male and female reproductive systems.

50. Apply Identify and list five appropriate sources of health services for the variety of illnesses and disorders covered in this chapter.

Career Corner

Physical Therapist Would you like to help people prevent or overcome physical impairments? Then you might be interested in a career as a physical therapist. These professionals help patients use physical activity and movement to recover from injuries or illnesses that affect their bodies' ability to move. They also teach patients to use crutches, wheelchairs, or artificial limbs. This profession requires a four-year degree in a related field, such as genetics or biology, and a master's degree from a physical therapy program. Learn more about this and other health careers by clicking on Career Corner at health.glencoe.com.

Standardized Test Practice

Reading & Writing

Read the paragraphs below and then answer the questions.

When you close your eyes to the world outside, you open them to the world of dreams.

Throughout history, people have felt both fear and fascination when it comes to the mystery of dreams. Some cultures developed ways to not only protect sleeping people from the evil spirits in their dreams, but also to attract pleasant dreams. The North American Aboriginal people hung "dream-catchers" above sleeping infants to keep out bad dreams and to allow in good ones. Parents in China gave their children double-headed tiger pillows to scare off any evil spirit who might approach through a dream. The Japanese created a mythological creature called a Baku who ate bad dreams. In Europe, a stone hung on a red ribbon and tied to a bedpost was said to protect the sleeper from bad dreams.

Good or bad, our dreams are a part of our lives—interesting mysteries.

1. What is the second paragraph of the passage mainly about?

A how dreams predict the future

B how to interpret dreams

C the meaning of dreams in history

D dreams in different cultures

2. Which of these statements best reflects the author's attitude toward dreams?

A Dreams can predict the future.

B Dreams are always pleasant.

C Dreams are myths.

D Dreams are an interesting part of life.

3. Write a paragraph describing a dream, and then explain if you think it means something. Explain why or why not.

---

47. It becomes harmful when it goes on for too long or if it occurs too often and in response to nonhazardous situations.

48. When an egg is fertilized, the egg and tissues do not leave the body.

49. Males and females develop different reproductive systems and different secondary sex characteristics. Responses should include information from Lesson 8.

50. Responses will vary.

Test Practice

1. D

2. D

3. Answers should include specific details about a dream.

Reteaching

📁 Assign Study Guide 15 in the Student Activities Workbook.

Evaluate

📁 💿 Use the reproducible Chapter 15 Test in the TCR, or construct your own test using the **Exam*View*®** Pro Testmaker.

Enrichment

Have a group of volunteers plan a format for a quiz show about the body systems and then write questions for the show. Have them put on the show with other students as contestants.

Planning Guide

Chapter 16	Skills/Activities	Reproducible Resources	Assessment
Lesson 1 **The Beginning of Life** *pages 416–420*		*Student Activities Workbook available for use with each chapter* 📁 Parent Letter & Activities 16 📁 Concept Map 59 📁 Cross-Curriculum Activity 31 📁 Enrichment Activity 59 📁 Lesson Plan 1 📁 Reading Tutor Activity 58 📁 Reteaching Activity 59	📁 Lesson 1 Quiz
Lesson 2 **Heredity and Environment** *pages 421–425*	**Hands-On Health** ▲ Prenatal Care Brochure, page 423	📁 Concept Map 60 📁 Enrichment Activity 60 📁 Lesson Plan 2 📁 Reading Tutor Activity 59 📁 Reteaching Activity 60	📁 Lesson 2 Quiz
Lesson 3 **From Childhood to Adolescence** *pages 426–431*	**HEALTH SKILLS ACTIVITY** ▲ Coping with Mood Swings (*Stress Management*), page 430	📁 Concept Map 61 📁 Decision-Making Activity 31 📁 Enrichment Activity 61 📁 Health Lab 16 📁 Lesson Plan 3 📁 Reading Tutor Activity 60 📁 Reteaching Activity 61	📁 Lesson 3 Quiz
Lesson 4 **Adulthood and Aging** *pages 432–435*		📁 Concept Map 62 📁 Cross-Curriculum Activity 32 📁 Decision-Making Activity 32 📁 Enrichment Activity 62 📁 Lesson Plan 4 📁 Reading Tutor Activity 61 📁 Reteaching Activity 62	📁 Lesson 4 Quiz 📁 Chapter 16 Test 📁 Performance Assessment 16

TIME HEALTH   **Can We Stay Young?** *pages 436–437*

BUILDING HEALTH SKILLS

Resolving Conflicts with Parents
(*Conflict Resolution*)
pages 438–439

📁 Building Health Skills Reproducible Master 41

Standards		Technology
National	**State/Local**	
National Health Education Standard **1.1, 1.3, 3.1**		🖨 Transparency 62 ◉ TeacherWorks™
National Health Education Standard **1.1, 1.3, 1.5, 1.7, 1.8, 2.2, 2.6, 3.1, 7.4**		🖨 Transparency 63 ◉ TeacherWorks™
National Health Education Standard **1.2, 1.3, 1.4, 1.6, 3.1, 3.4, 3.7**		🖨 Transparency 64 ◉ TeacherWorks™
National Health Education Standard **1.1, 1.8, 3.1, 3.4, 5.4**		🖨 Transparency 65 ◉ TeacherWorks™ ▣◉ MindJogger Videoquiz ◉ **Exam**_View_® Pro Testmaker
National Health Education Standard **5.4, 5.7, 5.8**		📁 Building Health Skills Transparency Master 6

TeacherWorks™

Glencoe's new and exclusive TeacherWorks™ is an all-in-one planner and resource center. Access the complete Teacher Wraparound Edition electronically. Find all your classroom resources with just a few easy clicks, and print them right from your computer. Connect directly to Glencoe's customized Health Web site. Access the National Health Education Standards correlations, or insert your own state standards and match them directly to the electronic Teacher Wraparound Edition.

Language Diversity

- 🎧 English Audio Summaries
- 🎧 Spanish Audio Summaries
- 📁 English Summaries, Quizzes, and Activities
- 📁 Spanish Summaries, Quizzes, and Activities
- 📁 Spanish Parent Letters and Activities

KEY TO ABILITY LEVELS

Teaching Strategies that appear throughout the chapters have been identified by one of four codes to give you an idea of their suitability for students of varying learning styles and abilities.

L1 **Level 1** strategies should be within the ability range of all students. Often full class participation is required.

L2 **Level 2** strategies are for average to above-average students or for small groups. Some teacher direction is necessary.

L3 **Level 3** strategies are designed for students able and willing to work independently. Minimal teacher direction is necessary.

INCL Strategies are appropriate for students with particular special needs in a general classroom setting.

CHAPTER
16

Growth and Development

Chapter at a Glance

Lesson 1 examines fertilization and describes fetal development and childbirth.

Lesson 2 examines the roles of environment and heredity in the development of the fetus and the newborn baby.

Lesson 3 introduces students to Erik Erikson's stages of physical, mental/emotional, and social growth through the teen years.

Lesson 4 examines the ways age is measured and highlights physical and mental changes that take place as a person ages.

Health Skills

- Coping with Mood Swings (*Stress Management*), p. 430
- Resolving Conflicts with Parents (*Conflict Resolution*), pp. 438–439

414

HANDS-ON ACTIVITY

Understanding Personal Traits After students have studied Lesson 2, ask them to form small groups and appoint a recorder and a spokesperson for each group. Group members should then begin to brainstorm characteristics that they think can be attributed only to inherited traits. Then they should make a separate list of characteristics that are attributed entirely to environment.

Direct them to make yet another list that identifies characteristics that could be the results of either heredity or environment, or both. When they have exhausted their possibilities, have each group's spokesperson read the longest of their lists. Encourage students to discuss why different people might have different findings.

Growth and Development

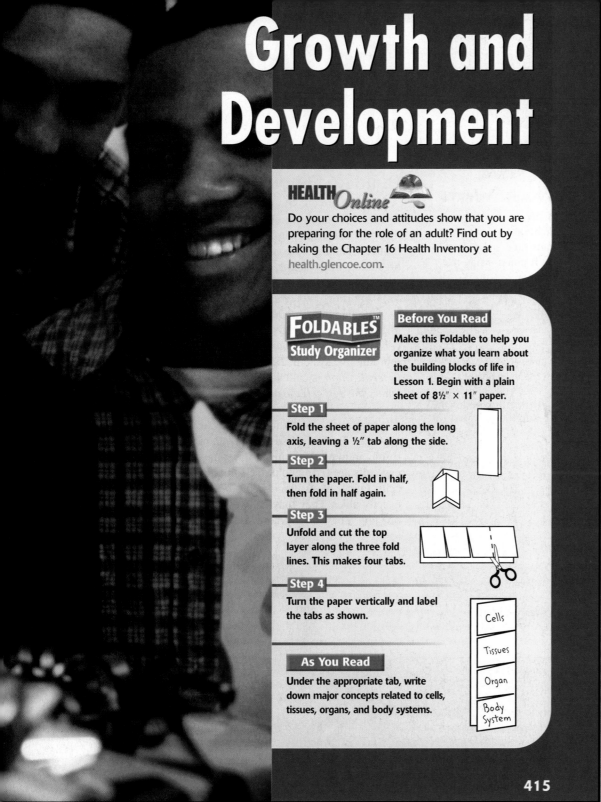

HEALTH *Online*

Do your choices and attitudes show that you are preparing for the role of an adult? Find out by taking the Chapter 16 Health Inventory at health.glencoe.com.

FOLDABLES™
Study Organizer

Before You Read

Make this Foldable to help you organize what you learn about the building blocks of life in Lesson 1. Begin with a plain sheet of 8½" × 11" paper.

Step 1

Fold the sheet of paper along the long axis, leaving a ½" tab along the side.

Step 2

Turn the paper. Fold in half, then fold in half again.

Step 3

Unfold and cut the top layer along the three fold lines. This makes four tabs.

Step 4

Turn the paper vertically and label the tabs as shown.

Cells
Tissues
Organ
Body System

As You Read

Under the appropriate tab, write down major concepts related to cells, tissues, organs, and body systems.

415

Chapter Introduction

Use the options below to motivate students and preview chapter content.

HEALTH *Online*

Have students take Health Inventory 16, or read extra credit articles at **health.glencoe.com.** By clicking on Health Updates, both students and teachers can discover the latest news on health topics.

GLENCOE TECHNOLOGY

MindJogger Videoquiz

Use MindJogger to preview or review Chapter 16 content.

TIME HEALTH

Can We Stay Young?
pages 436–437

FOLDABLES™ Study Organizer
Dinah Zike Study Fold

Expository Writing Students will use their Foldable to write about cells, tissues, organs, and body systems. As students read and study the information presented in Lesson 1, have them take notes, define terms, and list examples under the appropriate tab of their Foldable At the end of the lesson, ask students to use their notes to write an exposition on the development of life from a cell to a body system. The focus of this writing will be to present information in such a manner that someone who did not know or understand this concept before will understand it after reading what the students have written. Explain that textbooks are examples of expository writing.

Lesson Objectives

Students will be able to

- explain how life develops from a single cell into complex body systems.
- describe the growth and development of a baby before birth.
- define the three stages of childbirth.

Motivators

Quick Write

Have students share their responses. Ask students: What body systems are involved in delivering food in this manner? (*digestive, circulatory, and female reproductive systems*) Refer to Chapter 15, as necessary, to clarify misconceptions.

Bellringer Activity

Ask students: How is the developing baby inside the mother like an astronaut in a space capsule?

VOCABULARY

Copy one of the vocabulary terms on each of 11 index cards. Copy the definition of each term on each of 11 more index cards. Place the cards face down on a table, and invite pairs of students to play "Concentration." Students take turns turning over a pair of cards to match a term with its definition. If the cards match, they are left face up. If they do not match, they are returned face down.

Lesson 1

Quick Write

Write down what you know about how a baby gets food and oxygen as it grows inside its mother.

LEARN ABOUT...

- **how life begins.**
- **the development of a fetus.**
- **the birth of a healthy baby.**

VOCABULARY

- **fertilization**
- **egg cell**
- **sperm cell**
- **tissues**
- **organs**
- **uterus**
- **embryo**
- **fetus**
- **placenta**
- **umbilical cord**
- **cervix**

The Beginning of Life

Building Blocks of Life

You began your life as a single microscopic cell. That cell divided over and over again until it formed the trillions of cells that now make up your body. These cells are organized into tissues, which are organized into organs, which in turn are organized into systems, as shown in **Figure 16.1**.

Fertilization

A unique human body begins as a single cell that is the result of fertilization. **Fertilization** is *the joining together of two special cells, one from each parent.* It takes place inside the mother's reproductive system. *The cell from the mother that plays a part in fertilization* is called an **egg cell**. *The cell from the father that enters the egg cell during fertilization* is called a **sperm cell**.

Sometimes a newly fertilized egg cell separates into two fertilized egg cells. Each of these egg cells then grows into a new body. This results in identical twins of the same gender. When two different egg cells are fertilized at the same time by two different sperm cells, twins are also produced. These fraternal twins do not look exactly alike. They may be two girls, two boys, or one girl and one boy. They are no more similar than other siblings.

Identical twins come from one fertilized egg that separated in two before it began to grow. *What is the difference between identical and fraternal twins?*

416 CHAPTER 16: GROWTH AND DEVELOPMENT

 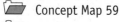 

Teacher Classroom Resources

📁 Parent Letter & Activities 16
📁 Concept Map 59
📁 Cross-Curricular Activity 31
📁 Enrichment Activity 59
📁 Lesson Plan 1
📁 Lesson 1 Quiz

📁 Reading Tutor Activity 58
📁 Reteaching Activity 59
📦 Transparency 62

Student Activities Workbook

📁 Chapter 16 Study Guide
📁 Applying Health Skills 59

FIGURE 16.1

From Cell to System

Cells form tissues, organs, and systems.

A Cell
The basic units, or building blocks, of life are called cells. There are many different kinds of cells in the human body. Each kind of cell does a specific job. This cell is a heart muscle cell. Some other kinds of cells in the body are blood, nerve, and skin cells.

B Tissue
Cells that do similar jobs make up **tissues**. Several kinds of tissues are found in the body. The heart muscle tissue, shown here, contains heart muscle cells. Brain tissue contains nerve cells.

C Organ
Different kinds of tissues are combined in larger structures called organs. **Organs** are *body parts that perform particular functions.* Heart muscle tissue is the main kind of tissue in the heart, the organ shown here. The brain, liver, and kidneys are other organs in the body.

D System
Groups of organs that work together form systems. There are a number of systems in the body, such as the circulatory system, shown here. The heart is the main organ of the circulatory system. Grouping organs into systems makes it easier to understand their functions. However, systems do not function all by themselves. All your body systems work together to keep you alive and active.

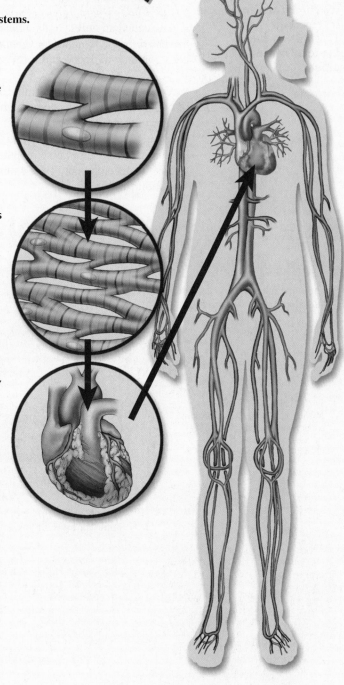

LESSON 1: THE BEGINNING OF LIFE **417**

② Teach

Discussing

Emphasize that each fertilization results in a unique individual. Ask:
- Why do two individuals with the same parents look different?
- Why are there often also similarities in their appearances? **L1**

FYI

Sperm cells are remarkably small. On average, a sperm cell is four to five microns long and only two or three microns wide. A micron is about 1/25,000 of an inch.

Discussing

Help students discuss the differences between fraternal twins and identical twins. Have volunteers identify twins they know, explaining whether they are fraternal or identical and describing how they are alike and different. **L1**

VISUAL LEARNING

FIGURE 16.1 Have volunteers read aloud the title and caption for Figure 16.1 and describe each of the pictures. Guide students in reading and discussing the information about cells, tissues, organs, and systems. Then have students sketch pictures showing how cells, tissues, organs, and systems are related. **INCL**
English Language Learners, Special Learning Needs, Behavior Problems, Different Learning Styles (Visual)

MORE ABOUT...

Prenatal Technology *Amniocentesis* is a technique in which amniotic fluid is tested for birth defects in the second trimester and for other reasons in the third trimester. These include diagnosing uterine infections and whether the fetus's lungs are mature for delivery. *Ultrasound* (or *sonography*) is a technique that converts sound waves bouncing off the fetus to an image called a sonogram. It is used throughout pregnancy to evaluate fetal growth, to diagnose certain birth defects, and for other reasons. *Fetal pulse oximetry* is a new technology used during labor and delivery that indicates how much oxygen is in the blood of the fetus. This can give doctors an indication that a Caesarian section may be necessary.

FIGURE 16.2 Have students describe the pictures showing fetal development at three, six, and nine months. Encourage volunteers to share their reactions to each. Then guide students in reading and discussing the information about development during each month of pregnancy. **INCL** *English Language Learners, Special Learning Needs, Behavior Problems, Different Learning Styles (Visual)*

Discussing

Direct students' attention to the photograph of the pregnant woman in Figure 16.2, and ask a student to read the caption aloud. Ask: Why is the condition of a pregnant woman's body so important to the health of her developing fetus? (*The developing fetus relies completely on the mother's body for its healthy growth and development.*)

Then have students describe the physiological and emotional changes that occur during pregnancy. Ask how these changes might affect the fetus. **L1**

Demonstrating

Ask students to work in pairs or small groups to develop posters showing the size of the developing fetus during each month of the pregnancy. Have them find common objects that are the same sizes as the developing fetus. Direct students to paste or staple each object to the poster next to the written size and the month of pregnancy. For example, an eraser from the top of a pencil is the size of the fetus at 1 month (1/3 inch). **L2** **INCL** *English Language Learners, Special Learning Needs, Behavior Problems, Different Learning Styles (Visual)*

✓ Reading Check

Understand sentence structure. Compare the sentences in Figure 16.2 with those in the text. How do they differ?

Growth During Pregnancy

Soon after fertilization, the cell begins to divide. It forms a cluster of cells that attaches itself to the inside wall of the uterus. The **uterus** (YOO·tuh·ruhs) is *a pear-shaped organ inside a female's body where a fetus is nourished.* The cluster of cells is now called an **embryo**, the *name for the developing organism from fertilization to about the eighth week of development.* These cells continue to divide and form cells that do specific jobs.

Over time, cells that do similar jobs combine into tissues, tissues with similar jobs combine into organs, and organs with similar jobs combine into systems. A **fetus** is *the name for the developing organism from the end of the eighth week until birth.* The baby is born about nine months after fertilization. **Figure 16.2** shows the development of the embryo and fetus during these nine months.

FIGURE 16.2
Nine Months of Development

In a remarkable process, a single cell develops into a full-grown baby.

A **End of First Month**
About ⅓ inch long. Heart, brain, and lungs are forming.

B **End of Second Month**
About 1 inch long. All other organs are developing. Arms, fingers, legs, and toes are forming. Heart is beating.

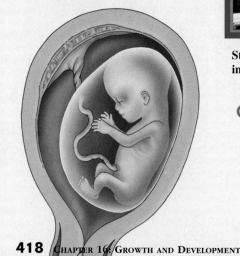

Staying active and eating healthy foods are just as important during pregnancy as they are at all other times.

C **End of Third Month**
Weighs about 1 ounce and is about 3 inches long. Fetus begins to move around.

D **End of Fourth Month**
Weighs about 6 ounces and is about 5 inches long. Facial features are well formed. Mother can feel the fetus move.

E **End of Fifth Month**
Weighs about 1 pound and is just under 10 inches long. Eyelashes and nails appear. Heartbeat can be heard.

✓ Reading Check

Sentence Structure Understanding sentence structure will aid students' reading comprehension. Have students identify conventional sentences, and describe how they are organized. Point out that conventional sentences have a subject (noun or pronoun) and a predicate (verb). Then ask students what is missing from the sentences in the diagram (*the subject*). Guide students to understand that rules for diagrams are different from rules for regular text. Diagrams are more visual, and they present information in small amounts. Have students find other ways that sentences in the diagram differ from standard sentences, such as the use of numbers or the sparse use of articles.

Growth Inside the Uterus

A fetus needs food and oxygen in order to grow and develop. The **placenta** (pluh·SEN·tuh) is *a thick, rich lining of tissue that builds up along the walls of the uterus and connects the mother to the fetus.* Food and oxygen in the mother's blood are carried to the fetus through a blood vessel in the **umbilical** (uhm·BIL·i·kuhl) **cord,** *a tube that connects the fetus and the mother's placenta.* Harmful substances, such as alcohol, nicotine, and other drugs, can cross the placenta and harm the fetus.

The umbilical cord also carries the fetus's wastes away. The waste products enter the mother's body, which then gets rid of them. After birth, the cord is cut. The place where the cord was attached to the fetus becomes the baby's navel.

CONNECT TO

Science

CHANGES DURING PREGNANCY

A pregnant female experiences many physiological and emotional changes. *Use reliable resources to find out more about these changes. In a brief paragraph, describe some physiological and emotional changes that occur during pregnancy.*

Cross-Curriculum Activity

SCIENCE Assign students to research the birth processes of various animals. Have them write brief descriptions comparing those processes with human birth. Possible topics are gestation periods, usual number of offspring born, birth itself, and early care of offspring. Have students share their research. Then, on the board, create a chart to illustrate the similarities and differences. **L3**

Speculating

Ask students to consider the role played by the umbilical cord in nurturing the embryo and the fetus. If the umbilical cord was pinched or the flow of fluid was obstructed in some way, how might the developing fetus be affected? **L1**

Recalling

Help students recall what they learned about the effects of alcohol consumption during pregnancy, especially fetal alcohol syndrome. (See Chapter 13.) **L1**

F End of Sixth Month Weighs about 1.5 pounds and is about 12.5 inches long. Can open and close mouth and swallow. Develops ability to kick. Fetus can hear sounds.

G End of Seventh Month Weighs 2 to 2.5 pounds and is about 14.5 inches long. Arms and legs can move freely. Eyes open.

H End of Eighth Month Weighs about 4 pounds and is almost 18 inches long. Hair gets longer. Skin becomes smoother.

I End of Ninth Month Weighs 7 to 9 pounds and is 18 to 20 inches long. Body organs have developed to function on their own.

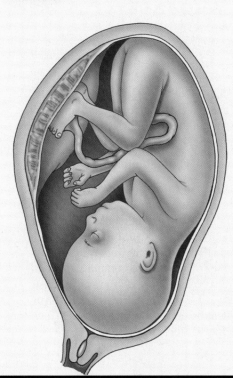

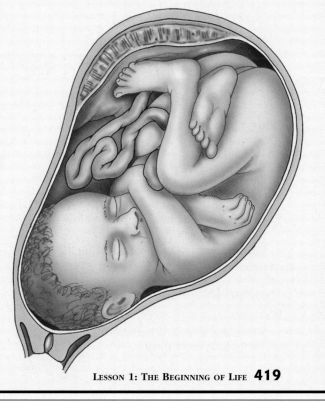

LESSON 1: THE BEGINNING OF LIFE **419**

Health Literacy

Health Information At about the fifth month, the fetus weighs only 8 ounces (227 g). At full term, however, it may weigh as much as 7 to 9 pounds (3 to 5 kg). At five months the fetus is covered with a fine, downy hair called lanugo. By the ninth month, lanugo may be present only on the shoulders and arms. During the ninth month, hundreds of pints of blood are pumped through the fetus each day. At any one time, however, the fetus has only about 1 cup (240 ml) of blood in its system. Also during the ninth month, the fetus may have scalp hairs as long as 1 inch (2.3 cm) or even longer. The eyes are usually slate colored, the final color not yet discernable.

③ Assess

Evaluating

📁 Assign the Lesson 1 Review; then assign the Lesson 1 Quiz in the TCR.

Reteaching

- 📁 Assign Concept Map 59 or Reteaching Activity 59 in the TCR.

- Have students investigate the many meanings of the word *cell*. Ask them to write each definition and use the word correctly in a sentence (one sentence for each definition). Discuss what all of these definitions have in common. (*the idea of a single unit*)

- Have students describe physiological and emotional changes that occur during pregnancy.

Enrichment

- 📁 Assign Enrichment Activity 59 in the TCR.

- Have students interview a couple who have just had a baby. Have them ask questions about the birth process and then compare the father's and mother's feelings about birth.

④ Close

Ask each student to name one reason familiarity with the birth process is important to his or her growth and development.

Stages of Birth

About nine months after fertilization, a fetus is fully developed and ready to be born. The birth process occurs in three stages:

- **Stage one.** Mild contractions, which are tightenings in the muscles of the uterus, signal the beginning of the first stage. At this point, *the entrance of the uterus,* called the **cervix,** begins to open.

- **Stage two.** By the time this stage of birth begins, the cervix is open to a width of about 4 inches. The contractions are very strong and are occurring more frequently. At the end of stage two, the contractions push the baby through the cervix and out of the mother's body.

- **Stage three.** Contractions continue after the baby is born until the placenta is pushed out of the uterus. The placenta is no longer needed. In fact, it could cause serious infection if it were not completely removed from the uterus.

After nine months of pregnancy, a female goes through three stages of birth to deliver a baby. *Which stage results in the baby's birth?*

Lesson 1 Review

Using complete sentences, answer the following questions on a sheet of paper.

Reviewing Terms and Facts

1. **Vocabulary** Define the term *fertilization*.
2. **Describe** What is a fetus like at the end of three months? At the end of six months?
3. **Recall** Describe how a growing fetus gets food and oxygen.
4. **Summarize** What happens during the three stages of birth?

Thinking Critically

5. **Explain** Cells are often referred to as the building blocks of life. Why is this an appropriate description?

6. **Relate** Why are pregnant females advised to avoid alcohol, nicotine, and other drugs and to talk to their doctor before using any medicine?

Applying Health Skills

7. **Accessing Information** Find out about classes that prepare expectant parents for childbirth and parenthood. During what month of pregnancy do classes normally begin? What topics are covered in the classes? Does your community offer different types of classes, such as exercise classes for pregnant females, childbirth education, and baby care classes? How do they differ?

420 CHAPTER 16: GROWTH AND DEVELOPMENT

Lesson 1 Review

1. The joining together of two special cells, one from each parent.
2. See Figure 16.2 on page 418.
3. A blood vessel in the umbilical cord carries nutrients and oxygen in the mother's blood to the fetus.
4. See Stages of Birth on page 420.

5. Cells combine to form tissues, tissues combine to form organs, organs combine to form body systems.
6. Responses should indicate that alcohol, nicotine, and other drugs are harmful to a developing fetus, as are certain medicines.

Heredity and Environment

The One and Only You

Every individual is unique. Each has his or her own particular looks, abilities, and personality. A number of factors influence the way a person develops. These factors can be grouped into two major categories: heredity and environment.

Heredity

Heredity is *the passing of traits from parents to their children.* Some examples of inherited traits are eye color, face shape, and even freckles. Tiny structures that are present inside human cells carry the information that enables traits to be inherited.

Quick Write

What advice would you give a pregnant female to protect the health of her developing baby?

LEARN ABOUT...

- how characteristics are inherited.
- environmental factors that can affect the developing fetus.
- different types of birth defects.
- ways a pregnant woman can protect the health of her fetus.

VOCABULARY

- heredity
- chromosomes
- genes
- genetic disorder
- environment
- prenatal care
- obstetrician
- birth defects

The members of some families share a strong physical resemblance to one another. *What are some of the characteristics that these family members share?*

Lesson 2

Heredity and Environment

① Focus

Lesson Objectives

Students will be able to

- describe the importance, and identify examples, of the roles of heredity and environment in prenatal development.
- identify problems in fetal development.
- list ways a pregnant woman can protect the health of her fetus.

Motivators

Quick Write

Have students list their ideas and add to their lists as they read the lesson.

Bellringer Activity

Ask students: What are some of the characteristics you have in common with one or both of your parents?

VOCABULARY

Instruct students to attempt to write the correct spellings for each of the vocabulary terms as you pronounce them. Next, have students correct the terms as you read aloud the proper spellings. Ask students to use each word in an original sentence.

Lesson 2 Resources

Teacher Classroom Resources

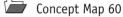 Concept Map 60

 Enrichment Activity 60

 Lesson Plan 2

 Lesson 2 Quiz

 Reading Tutor Activity 59

 Reteaching Activity 60

 Transparency 63

Student Activities Workbook

 Chapter 16 Study Guide

 Applying Health Skills 60

Lesson 2

② Teach

Cross-Curriculum Activity

LANGUAGE ARTS Tell students that the word gene comes from a Greek word meaning "to give birth to." Have them compile a list of words that are derived from that root. Have students provide meanings for all words they list. **L2**

Discussing

Initiate a discussion about the way chromosomes and genes dictate inherited traits. Be sure that students understand that genes are located on chromosomes and carry the genetic codes for individual traits. **L1**

Cross-Curriculum Activity

SCIENCE Divide the class into groups. Instruct each group to research a specific genetic disorder such as sickle-cell anemia, cystic fibrosis, Tay-Sachs disease, or hemophilia. Reports, which are to be presented to the class, should detail how common these defects are as well as what steps researchers are taking to treat and overcome them. **L3**

Demonstrating

Have students draw Venn diagrams showing the physical similarities and differences among themselves and parents or other biological relatives. **L1**

✓ **Reading Check**

The root word *natal* means "birth" and the prefix *pre-* means "before." Write your own definition of *prenatal care.*

Scientists are working hard to understand and solve genetic problems. *Why is genetic research important?*

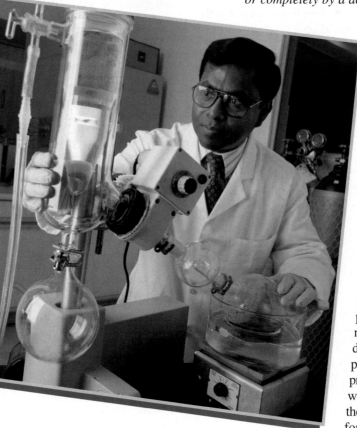

Traits are passed on through the following structures:

- **Chromosomes.** *The threadlike structures found within the nucleus of a cell that carry the codes for inherited traits* are **chromosomes** (KROH·muh·sohmz). Most cells in the human body have 46 chromosomes, which occur as 23 pairs. One chromosome of every pair comes from each parent. A sperm cell from the father has 23 chromosomes, and an egg cell from the mother has 23 chromosomes. The fertilized egg cell that results from the joining of these two cells has 46 chromosomes.
- **Genes.** *The basic units of heredity* are called **genes.** Genes are sections of chromosomes. They carry codes for specific traits, such as hair color and eye color. Children of the same parents inherit different combinations of chromosomes and genes.

Genetic Disorders

Sometimes genes carried by one or both parents can be flawed. When this happens, a baby may be born with a **genetic** (juh·NE·tik) **disorder.** This is *a disorder that is caused partly or completely by a defect in genes.*

Some genetic disorders occur when a fertilized egg cell has more than 46 chromosomes. For example, people with Down syndrome have an extra chromosome and tend to have characteristic facial features and learning disabilities. Other genetic disorders are caused by abnormal genes. Albinism is a genetic disorder that results in a person's skin, hair, and eyes having no color.

Phenylketonuria (FEE·nuhl·kee·toh·NOOR·ee·uh), or PKU, is a genetic disorder that can prevent the brain from developing normally. Scientists eventually discovered that keeping certain proteins out of the child's diet prevents the brain damage associated with PKU. Today, all children in the United States are tested at birth for PKU.

✓ **Reading Check**

Affixes and Roots Write *pre/natal* on the chalkboard. Ask students to suggest other words using the same word parts. Write each word under the appropriate column. Although *natal* may be unfamiliar to students, the root can be found in common words such as *natural, nativity,* and *native.* Have students use dictionaries to find words relating to *natal,* or write one on the board, and have students infer other related words. When you have a list for each word part, have students compare the meanings of each word. Allow students time to work on their own to write their definitions of *prenatal care* before having volunteers read their definitions aloud.

Environment

The second factor that can affect the health of a developing fetus and of a newborn child is environment. **Environment** is *the sum total of a person's surroundings*. The environment of a developing fetus is its mother's uterus. The health of the baby is affected directly by the activities and overall health of its mother.

Prenatal Care

A healthy mother improves her chances of having a healthy baby. This is why it is extremely important for a female to begin a program of prenatal care as soon as she finds out she is pregnant. **Prenatal** (pree· NAY·tuhl) **care** includes *steps taken to provide for the health of a pregnant female and her baby.*

Important to prenatal health care are regular visits to a health clinic, family doctor, or **obstetrician** (ahb· stuh·TRI·shuhn). This is *a doctor who specializes in the care of a pregnant female and her developing fetus, and who is present at the birth of the baby.* Other steps related to good prenatal health care include:

- Eating nutritious foods.
- Getting enough rest.
- Participating in moderate exercise.
- Avoiding the use of tobacco, alcohol, and other drugs, as well as all medicines except those advised by the health care provider.

Nutritious foods are particularly important during pregnancy. *How can a pregnant female make sure she is getting the nutrients she and her baby need?*

PRENATAL CARE BROCHURE

In this activity, you will create a brochure that will encourage a pregnant female to take steps to ensure that she has a healthy baby.

WHAT YOU WILL NEED
- heavy writing paper
- printed reference materials or access to the Internet
- scissors
- pens, colored markers, glue

WHAT YOU WILL DO
Gather reliable information on prenatal care topics such as nutrition, exercise, and medical checkups. Find pictures to illustrate your brochure. Plan the layout of your brochure. Then write down information, glue on pictures, and use markers to add finishing touches.

IN CONCLUSION
Make your brochure available to a pregnant female in your family or community.

Discussing

Ask students how the father of an unborn child can help ensure its health. (*by not smoking around the mother, by encouraging her to eat well and to get medical care, and so on*) **L1**

Researching

Have students learn about the Apgar test. (*a method of evaluating a newborn's physical condition, based on pulse, breathing, muscle tone, responsiveness, and skin color*) **L3**

Hands-On Health

PRENATAL CARE BROCHURE

Time: 30 to 45 minutes, two class sessions about one week apart (more if students research and make their brochures in class)

TEACHING THE ACTIVITY
- With students, read and discuss the introduction and instructions.
- Have students create their brochures.
- Read brochures before students share them with pregnant females.
- In a class discussion, have students share the feedback they received.

ASSESSMENT
Use students' brochures and their contributions to the class discussion to assess their learning.

Health Literacy

Health Information Advances in biotechnology are concerned not only with human genetic disorders but also with the intentional altering of foods. Vegetable plants, such as tomatoes and corn, are biologically altered to produce more vegetables. Vegetables can also be engineered to stay fresh longer than regular, nonmodified produce. Ask students whether they have seen any of these products in the retail markets. Ask: What are the physical characteristics? How does a consumer know whether these products are available? What health problems, if any, does this technology present to consumers? What ethical dilemmas are presented?

Analyzing

Discuss with students why the teen years are not the ideal time to bear children. Ask:

• What activities might a teen parent miss if occupied with raising a child? (*attending and graduating from school, preparing for a job, getting and keeping a job, socializing with teens who do not have children*)

• Why is a teen pregnancy risky to the baby itself? (*The baby may be of lower birth weight, which may lead to health complications or death. Also, teen may not be mentally mature enough to care for baby.*) **L1**

Cross-Curriculum Activity

MATH Encourage interested students to research the most recent statistics available regarding teen pregnancies in their county and state and, if possible, the national level. Instruct them to represent the statistics in a pie chart or graph. **L3**

Investigating

Have student volunteers write, call, or visit the local chapter of the March of Dimes to find out about the functions of the organization. **L3**

CONNECT TO Science

ULTRASOUND IMAGES
Ultrasound equipment, which uses sound waves to make pictures, allows doctors to see images of a fetus in the uterus. Such images enable them to check the size and position of the fetus and the amount of fluid surrounding the fetus. Ultrasounds taken at intervals in a pregnancy help monitor the progress of the fetus.

Birth Defects

Getting medical care, eating properly, getting enough rest and exercise, and avoiding harmful substances contribute to the health of the developing fetus and help prevent birth defects. **Birth defects** are *abnormalities present at birth that cause physical or mental disability or death.* Some birth defects are caused by a genetic disorder or by harmful substances in the fetus's environment. Certain infections during pregnancy can also lead to birth defects.

Problems in the Fetal Environment

Listed below are some of the environmental factors that can contribute to birth defects:

• **Poor nutrition.** A fetus gets all of its nourishment from its mother. If a pregnant female doesn't follow a healthy eating plan, the baby may be born too early, have a low birth weight, or both. These babies have a greater chance of having mental or physical problems.

• **Alcohol.** When a pregnant female drinks alcohol, it enters her blood, passes through the placenta, and into the blood of her baby. This can lead to fetal alcohol syndrome (FAS), a pattern of physical and mental problems in children whose mothers drank alcohol during pregnancy. Females who are pregnant or who are trying to become pregnant should avoid alcohol completely.

• **Medicines and other drugs.** A pregnant female should avoid all medicines and other drugs, unless their use has been approved by her physician. Even over-the-counter medicines can harm a developing fetus. When a pregnant female takes certain illegal drugs and prescription drugs, her baby may be born addicted to the drug.

An important part of prenatal care is regular checkups. *Why are checkups important for both a pregnant female and her unborn baby?*

PROMOTING COORDINATED SCHOOL HEALTH

Desired Results for Students As a measurement of the success of a coordinated school health program, an exiting student should demonstrate the following:

• Accepts responsibility for his or her own physical, mental/emotional, and social well-being

• Has academic skills essential to being a productive member of society

• Is self-directed as a learner and an individual

• Has high self-esteem as a learner and an individual

• Is able to solve problems, make decisions, and understand cause-and-effect relationships

For more information, consult *Planning a Coordinated School Health Program* in the TCR. 📁

- **Tobacco.** Tobacco use during pregnancy can seriously harm the fetus's growth. The baby can be born prematurely or with a low birth weight. Females who are pregnant should also avoid breathing secondhand smoke.
- **Infections.** Rubella, or German measles, can cause deafness or other serious health problems in a baby born to a female who has this disease while pregnant. A female can avoid passing rubella to her fetus by being vaccinated against the disease before she becomes pregnant.
- **STDs.** Certain sexually transmitted diseases (STDs) can also be passed from mother to fetus. STDs can cause brain damage, blindness, and even death. A pregnant female who is infected with HIV, the virus that causes AIDS, can pass the virus to her unborn child. A pregnant female should tell her doctor about any possible STDs.

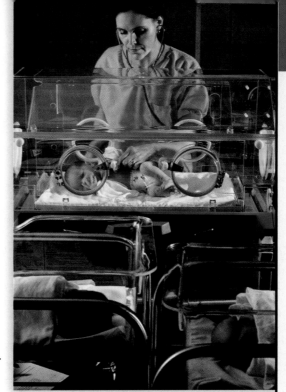

Tobacco use during pregnancy can result in premature birth and a low birth weight. *What are some other factors that can harm the health of a newborn?*

Lesson 2 Review

Using complete sentences, answer the following questions on a sheet of paper.

Reviewing Terms and Facts

1. **Vocabulary** What is a *genetic disorder?*
2. **Give Examples** List four steps a pregnant female can take to protect her own health and the health of her developing fetus.
3. **Summarize** What are five factors in the fetal environment that can contribute to birth defects?

Thinking Critically

4. **Explain** Both heredity and environment influence the way a fetus develops. Over which of these does a pregnant female have the most control? Why?

5. **Relate** Why do you think it is a good idea for a female to develop a nutritious eating plan, to eliminate all use of alcohol and other drugs, and to start an exercise program before she becomes pregnant?

Applying Health Skills

6. **Advocacy** Encourage a pregnant female to practice healthful behaviors by preparing a daily log for her to complete during her pregnancy. Include blanks to write down foods eaten at different meals and snacks. Prepare a summary section at the end where the female can place a check mark next to healthful behaviors she practiced that day.

LESSON 2: HEREDITY AND ENVIRONMENT **425**

① Focus

Lesson Objectives

Students will be able to

- describe how a child develops from infancy through childhood.
- analyze Erikson's eight stages of life.
- explore the physical, mental/emotional, and social changes that take place during adolescence.
- Compare and contrast changes in males and females.

Health Skills
- Stress Management, p. 430

Motivators

Quick Write
Draw the health triangle on the board. Ask volunteers to provide examples for each side of the triangle.

Bellringer Activity

Ask students to list at least three changes they may go through during their teen years.

VOCABULARY

Have each student create a simple crossword puzzle using the vocabulary terms. Then have students exchange puzzles. Allow several minutes for them to complete one another's puzzles.

Lesson 3

From Childhood to Adolescence

Quick Write

Describe at least three changes that occur in a person between childhood and adolescence. Use the health triangle to guide your thinking.

LEARN ABOUT...

- the characteristics of each stage of childhood.
- the physical, mental/emotional, and social changes that occur during adolescence.

VOCABULARY

- developmental tasks
- infancy
- toddlers
- preschoolers
- puberty

An important developmental task of adolescence is to develop a sense of self. Think of some of the interests and talents that define you as a unique individual.

Stages of Development

The life cycle of human beings can be divided into different stages. A number of different theories exist about how babies develop into adults. Some focus on physical growth. Others look mainly at mental or emotional growth. One widely accepted view is that of scientist Erik Erikson. Erikson divided the human life cycle into eight stages of development. These stages are described and illustrated in **Figure 16.3**.

Many aspects of social growth are defined by **developmental tasks**. These are *events that need to happen in order for you to continue growing toward becoming a healthy, mature adult.* Each stage of growth has its own specific developmental tasks.

  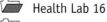  

Lesson 3 Resources

Teacher Classroom Resources
- Concept Map 61
- Decision-Making Activity 31
- Enrichment Activity 61
- Health Lab 16
- Lesson Plan 3
- Lesson 3 Quiz

- Reading Tutor Activity 60
- Reteaching Activity 61
- Transparency 64

Student Activities Workbook
- Chapter 16 Study Guide
- Applying Health Skills 61

FIGURE 16.3

ERIKSON'S STAGES OF LIFE

Each stage is associated with a developmental task that involves a person's relationship with other people.

1 Infancy
Birth to 1 year
Characteristic of stage: child is completely dependent on others to meet his or her needs
Developmental task: to develop trust
If not mastered: could result in mistrust

2 Early Childhood
1 to 3 years
Characteristics of stage: child is learning to separate from parents
Developmental task: to develop ability to do tasks oneself
If not mastered: could result in lack of confidence

3 Middle Childhood
3 to 5 years
Characteristics of stage: child begins to make decisions and to think of and carry out projects
Developmental task: to develop initiative—ability to create one's own play
If not mastered: could result in guilt—feeling guilty about the actions one takes

4 Late Childhood
6 to 11 years
Characteristics of stage: child explores surroundings and masters more and more difficult skills
Developmental task: to develop interest in performing activities
If not mastered: could result in feelings of inferiority

5 Adolescence
12 to 18 years
Characteristic of stage: adolescent searches for his or her own identity
Developmental task: to develop one's own identity—a sense of who one is
If not mastered: could result in confusion over the many roles one plays

6 Young Adulthood
19 to 30 years
Characteristic of stage: person tries to develop close personal relationships
Developmental task: to develop intimacy—forming a strong relationship with another person
If not mastered: could result in isolation—being alone

7 Middle Adulthood
31 to 60 years
Characteristics of stage: person tries to achieve something in work and is concerned with the well-being of others
Developmental task: to develop the sense of having contributed to society
If not mastered: could result in self-absorption

8 Maturity and Old Age
61 years to death
Characteristic of stage: person tries to understand meaning of own life
Developmental task: to develop integrity—feeling satisfied with one's life
If not mastered: could result in despair—feeling that one's life has not been satisfying

427

Lesson 3

2 Teach

VISUAL LEARNING

FIGURE 16.3 Divide the class into eight groups, and assign each group one of Erikson's stages of life. Have group members read about that stage and explain it to the class. After all eight groups have reported, review with students what they learned about birth in Lesson 1 and coping with loss in Chapter 4, Lesson 5. Then ask students to use Figure 16.3 and their knowledge of birth and the stages of dying to write one or two short paragraphs in which they describe the life cycle of human beings including birth, dying, and death. What photographs would students add to Figure 16.3 to illustrate their paragraphs? **INCL** *English Language Learners, Special Learning Needs, Behavior Problems, Different Learning Styles (Visual)*

Cooperative Learning

Have students work with partners, and, using the information on this page, plan items for a baby-sitting kit to match children's abilities and interests. Discuss which items fit the physical, mental/emotional, and social characteristics of a two-year old, a four-year-old, and a 10-year old. Ask whether the items would be safe and practical. Remind students to consider choking hazards with small items. **L2**

MORE ABOUT...

Developmental Theories Three other theories of growth and development were put forth by Sigmund Freud, Jean Piaget, and Abraham Maslow. Freud's theory stressed the importance of the subconscious mind. He believed that difficulty in an early stage of development set the foundation for greater difficulty in later life.

Piaget's theory was influenced by Freud but emphasized intellectual growth. Maslow shaped his theory around what he believed to be a hierarchy of needs. Needs such as self-fulfillment could not be met if basic needs, such as food and shelter, were not met.

Observing

If practical, have students observe a baby less than one year old. Have them report specific examples of how the baby moved, communicated, and gave and received affection. Have students note the exact age of the infant and record abilities regarding specific skills such as walking, talking, sitting up, and so on. Compare students' findings. As an alternative, have students review their own baby books and report on their developmental skills in the first year of life. **L3**

VISUAL LEARNING

FIGURE 16.4 Guide students in reading about and discussing the four stages of the growth years. Encourage students to describe children they know in each of these stages. Remind them to not use names. To emphasize the importance of individual differences, ask questions such as: Do all children learn to walk at the same age? Why not? **INCL** *English Language Learners, Special Learning Needs, Behavior Problems, Different Learning Styles* (*Visual*)

Cross-Curriculum Activity

SOCIAL STUDIES Have students discuss how different cultures or religions mark the passing from childhood to adolescence to adulthood. (*Confirmations, bar/bas mitzvahs, and sweet 16 parties are some examples.*) **L1**

Discussing

Ask students how understanding the development of children can help them when they babysit or take care of younger siblings. **L1**

Stages of Childhood

The theories of early physical and mental/emotional growth can be combined to describe four stages of childhood. These stages are infancy, early childhood, middle childhood, and late childhood. They are illustrated in **Figure 16.4**.

Infancy

The period of fastest physical growth in a human's life occurs during **infancy**, the *first year of life*. A child's weight typically triples and his or her height increases by about 50 percent during this year. When an infant's needs are met in a loving way, he or she learns to trust people and feel safe.

Early Childhood

Children between the ages of one and three who are learning to walk and talk are known as **toddlers**. At this stage they begin to feel proud of their achievements and are eager to do more things by themselves. Failing now and then when trying to do something new is an important part of learning and growing.

FIGURE 16.4

The Growth Years

Each person follows his or her own rate of development. Think of a child you know. Describe some of his or her developmental activities.

Infancy
A child begins to move around and to explore the world during the first year of life.

Early Childhood
In early childhood, children learn to walk, run, and climb stairs. At this time, children also begin to do things for themselves and to communicate with others.

Middle Childhood
Children between the ages of three and five can jump and hop and draw simple shapes. Pretend play helps them develop social skills and practice future roles.

Late Childhood
The physical skills of children improve steadily between the ages of 6 and 11. In late childhood, friends are important in building social skills and self-esteem.

428 CHAPTER 16: GROWTH AND DEVELOPMENT

WHAT TEENS WANT TO KNOW

Why do more kids today have learning and behavior problems? It seems as if more kids and teens have learning and behavior problems, but that is probably not the case. You hear about these conditions today because signs and symptoms of problems—such as dyslexia, a reading disorder, and attention deficit hyperactivity disorder (ADHD)—are accurately identified earlier and more often. Better recognition of the early signs of learning disabilities—such as mood, attitude, or behavioral problems—can help kids and teens receive prompt treatment. Early treatment can prevent learning and behavioral problems from interfering with school, family relationships, and friendships. Prescription medication, counseling, and special learning strategies are effective treatments.

Middle Childhood

Children between the ages of three and five are often referred to as **preschoolers**. This is a period of rapid growth during which the child becomes more coordinated in his or her movements. Playing make-believe and imitating adults are favorite activities. Children of this age often show how fast their minds are growing by asking many questions.

How adults respond to a child's behavior is important. When parents encourage new activities and questions, they promote the child's self-esteem. Parents who are impatient with a child's attempts to do things independently may make the child feel guilty about starting new activities and lower the child's self-esteem.

Late Childhood

Children between the ages of 6 and 11 grow at a more even rate than when they were younger. At this stage, school usually becomes a very important part of a child's life. Physical and mental skills steadily increase.

Children often spend a lot of time making things. If a child's creative efforts are appreciated and rewarded, pride in her or his work increases. A child's success or failure in any of the stages of childhood affects emotional development at that stage. By succeeding at later stages, a child may overcome any setbacks of earlier stages and gain self-esteem.

Adolescence

After infancy, the second fastest period of physical growth is adolescence, the time of life between childhood and adulthood. It usually begins between the ages of 8 and 14. Girls typically enter adolescence earlier than boys do. During this time many physical, mental/emotional, and social changes take place. All of these changes are interrelated, and each individual goes through them at his or her own rate. Try to recognize and accept the differences in levels of maturation.

When parents encourage a child's creativity, the child feels a sense of pride. *Why is it important to encourage a sense of pride at this stage of development?*

Cross-Curriculum Activity

LANGUAGE ARTS Explain that the books that appeal to children of different ages reflect their stages of development. Infants often enjoy picture books. Toddlers can follow an illustrated story read by an adult. Preschoolers can understand more involved stories. School-aged children read for themselves and can follow complex plots. Ask: What books did you enjoy at each stage of your childhood? **L1**

HEALTH SKILLS PRACTICE

Conflict Resolution Read aloud the following to students: Sometimes adolescence is about rebellion, and even friends end up being the targets. Negotiation is one way to reduce conflicts and get what you want. Suppose your friend says, "Let's stay home and do our homework." You want to go to a movie. Skip the fight and find the compromise. With a partner, write a strong negotiation statement that will give both of you what you want. Compare your negotiation plan with another set of students.

WHAT TEENS WANT TO KNOW

Does sleeping late on weekends make up for lack of sleep during the week? No. Unfortunately, you can't make up for lost sleep by sleeping all day on Saturday or Sunday. You can't store it up for future use either. Most teens need at least nine need more, but few teens can get by on less. In the teen years, you may notice your days filling up with more responsibilities and activities. At the same time, your body is demanding more rest. Teens need predictable sleep patterns because their bodies are growing. Besides being important for healthy growth and development, there are other reasons to try to get enough sleep. You'll yawn less and feel more energetic and alert.

Lesson 3

Making Lists

Have each student divide a sheet of paper lengthwise into thirds and label the columns, from left to right, *Physical, Mental/Emotional,* and *Social.* Then have students list several examples of growth during adolescence under each heading. Draw a corresponding chart on the board. Have volunteers give examples from their work to be listed on the board. Ask students to explain how differences in growth patterns among adolescents might affect personal health. **L1**

Finding Examples

Have students bring in newspaper or magazine features about teens. Ask whether teens are shown positively or negatively and what opinions a reader would form about teens on the basis of the features. Ask students what they think of those opinions. **L2**

HEALTH SKILLS ACTIVITY

STRESS MANAGEMENT

Have volunteers read aloud the suggestions for dealing with mood swings, and help students discuss each. Encourage them to cite specific examples and to describe the effects of each example. Then have students work independently to write their own lists as directed in On Your Own.

Note: This skill is introduced in Chapter 2 on pages 39–43.

Reading Check

Practice paraphrasing. Rewrite the lists in Figure 16.5 in your own words.

Physical Development

Adolescence begins with **puberty**, *the time when you begin to develop certain physical traits of adults of your own gender.* Many of these physical changes are shown in **Figure 16.5.** The exact age of puberty varies from person to person.

Emotional and Social Development

Emotional changes are a normal part of adolescence. Many of them are related to the activity of hormones as they prepare your body for adulthood. Mood swings, during which you feel happy one moment and unhappy the next, are common. You may find yourself wanting to spend time with members of the opposite gender. Such feelings may be confusing and even frightening.

Adolescence is a busy and challenging time. It involves important developmental tasks that you need to accomplish so that you can move successfully into adulthood. Here are some of those tasks:

- Become more independent of parents and other adults
- Learn more about who you are
- Define your values
- Learn how to think, reason, and solve problems in an adult way
- Accept your body and its characteristics
- Gain a masculine or feminine view of yourself
- Form more mature relationships with people of both genders
- Develop an interest in and a concern for your community

HEALTH SKILLS ACTIVITY

STRESS MANAGEMENT

Coping with Mood Swings

Mood swings during adolescence are common and normal. Here are some ways to help deal with mood swings.

- **TALK IT OUT.** Talk to friends and family members you trust.
- **WRITE IT DOWN.** Record your feelings in a diary or journal.
- **DO SOMETHING FUN.** Start working on a project or spend time with a friend.
- **STAY ACTIVE.** Physical activity can improve your mood and clear your thoughts.
- **GET SOME REST.** Things often look better after a quick nap or a good night's sleep.
- **TAKE TIME FOR YOURSELF.** Get away from noise and confusion for a while.
- **TALK TO A PROFESSIONAL.** See a school counselor or doctor if you feel depressed.

ON YOUR OWN
Make a list of ways to cope with mood swings. Choose one strategy and demonstrate it for the class in the form of a role-play.

Reading Check

Paraphrasing To help students examine physical development during adolescence, draw a Venn diagram on the board, and have students label each part. One circle should be labeled *Male* and the other *Female*; the intersecting part should be labeled *Both*. The diagram should be entitled "Comparing and Contrasting Physical Changes in Males and Females During Puberty." Model paraphrasing text in front of the class (e.g., making "Growth spurt occurs" into "Grows more quickly at times"). Ask students to work alone or in pairs to write the information in their own words. Have volunteers fill in the diagram on the board to complete the lesson.

FIGURE 16.5

PHYSICAL CHANGES DURING PUBERTY

Compare and contrast changes in males and females.

Male
Male hormone production increases.
Facial hair appears.
Larynx enlarges and the voice deepens.
Shoulders broaden.
Muscles develop.
Sperm production begins.
Temporary breast tenderness and enlargement can occur.

Female
Female hormone production increases.
Breasts develop.
Hips widen.
Uterus and ovaries enlarge.
Ovulation occurs.
Menstruation begins.
Body fat increases.

Both
Growth spurt occurs.
Acne may appear.
Most permanent teeth have come in.
Underarm hair appears.
Perspiration increases.
Pubic hair appears.
External genitals enlarge.

Lesson 3 Review

Using complete sentences, answer the following questions on a sheet of paper.

Reviewing Terms and Facts

1. **Vocabulary** Define *developmental tasks*.
2. **Recall** List Erikson's eight stages of the life cycle.
3. **Identify** Which are the two periods of fastest physical growth in humans?
4. **Identify** During which stage of growth do people define their values and learn to solve problems in an adult way?

Thinking Critically

5. **Hypothesize** Why is it important to recognize and accept differences in maturation levels?

6. **Analyze** How are the physical, mental/emotional, and social changes of adolescence interrelated?

Applying Health Skills

7. **Analyzing Influences** Select a teen magazine and find the ways that the articles, pictures, and advertisements try to influence teens. In what ways are teens encouraged to buy things? Why are products advertised so widely to teens?

VISUAL LEARNING

FIGURE 16.5 Describe the two teens pictured. Ask students how they know these are teens, not children. Then guide students in reading and discussing the three lists of changes during puberty. Ask students to compare and contrast changes in males and females. Emphasize that these changes take place gradually and at various ages. **INCL** *English Language Learners, Special Learning Needs, Behavior Problems, Different Learning Styles* (*Visual*)

❸ Assess

Evaluating

📁 Assign the Lesson 3 Review; then assign the Lesson 3 Quiz in the TCR.

Reteaching

📁 Assign Concept Map 61 or Reteaching Activity 61 in the TCR.

Enrichment

📁 Assign Enrichment Activity 61 in the TCR.

❹ Close

Ask students to name one new fact they learned about their personal growth and development during childhood and adolescence.

Lesson 3 Review

1. Events that need to happen in order for you to continue growing toward becoming a healthy, mature adult.
2. Infancy, early childhood, middle childhood, late childhood, adolescence, young adulthood, middle adulthood, maturity and old age.
3. Infancy, adolescence.
4. Adolescence.
5. Responses should mention the importance of respecting others.
6. Responses will vary.

Adulthood and Aging

① Focus

Lesson Objectives

Students will be able to
- define the three stages of adulthood.
- describe the three different ways to measure age.
- describe ways to make aging a positive experience.

Motivators

Quick Write
Have students identify the qualities they admire in an older person and discuss how that person influences the way they view the aging process.

Bellringer Activity

Ask students: How do the characteristics of an "older" adult differ from those of a "younger" adult?

VOCABULARY

Scramble the letters for each vocabulary term, and write the scrambled words on each of three index cards (*e.g., biological age becomes oolabicigl gea*). Display one of the cards and read the definition of that term, as it appears in the lesson, to the class. Have students try to unscramble the letters to identify the term.

Lesson 4

Adulthood and Aging

Quick Write

Describe an older person whom you admire. What qualities do you like in that person? What does that person teach you about aging?

LEARN ABOUT...

- the three stages of adulthood.
- three different ways to measure age.
- aging as a positive experience.

VOCABULARY

- chronological age
- biological age
- social age

Stages of Adulthood

The adult years are made up of three main stages: early, middle, and late adulthood. Each stage is marked by certain milestones, such as starting a career, marrying, raising children, and so on. While most people follow these stages in a predictable sequence, many do not. Some adults choose not to marry, or they marry later in life. Some choose to have no children. Many adults change careers several times. Some retire early, while others choose to continue working as long as they are able.

For many people, early adulthood is the time to marry and start a family. *What do you expect to do when you reach early adulthood?*

Lesson 4 Resources

Teacher Classroom Resources
📁 Concept Map 62
📁 Cross-Curriculum Activity 32
📁 Decision-Making Activity 32
📁 Enrichment Activity 62
📁 Lesson Plan 4
📁 Lesson 4 Quiz
📁 Reading Tutor Activity 61

📁 Reteaching Activity 62
🖥 Transparency 65

Student Activities Workbook
📁 Chapter 16 Study Guide
📁 Applying Health Skills 62
📁 Health Inventory 16

Early Adulthood

In early adulthood, most people begin working for a living. This is also the time when many people want to begin sharing their lives with another person. That desire is often met by marrying and beginning a family. However, some couples choose to have children in their thirties.

Middle Adulthood

For some people, advancing in their jobs is a major goal in their thirties, forties, and fifties. Many are also raising their children. People in middle adulthood often have a great desire to help young people, and they gain a lot of satisfaction from doing so. The middle adult years can present many demands, however. Some people find themselves stretched by building a career, caring for home and children, and caring for aging parents.

Late Adulthood

People in their mid-sixties and beyond often look forward to retirement so they can pursue interests they didn't have time for when they were busy with their careers and children. Others continue to work, and some change careers. Many choose to stay active by doing volunteer work in their community. Today, Americans are living longer than ever before. As a result, most people can look forward to many years of late adulthood. Those who take good care of their health throughout their adult life are more likely to enjoy the benefits of good health as they age.

The life cycle of humans includes aging, dying, and death. It is important to be comfortable talking about dying and death, as they are a natural part of the life cycle.

Physical activity and good nutrition are important at any age. *How are these adults contributing to their lifelong health?*

LESSON 4: ADULTHOOD AND AGING **433**

Lesson 4

② Teach

Guest Speaker

Invite grandparents of students in the class to school to discuss what life was like when they were adolescents. Be sure to talk with the guest speakers in advance to get an idea of what they will discuss. After the presentation, ask students to write a brief essay in which they compare the speaker's life as an adolescent to their own lives and to describe personal health behaviors and knowledge unique to different generations. **L1**

Identifying Goals

Have students cut pictures from magazines to create a three-part collage that depicts their goals for the three stages of life. Some areas to consider are physical, mental/emotional, and social health; career; family; and hobbies. Ask them to include a description of each stage. **L1**
INCL *English Language Learners*

Developing Good Character ★

Respect

Although some older adults are slowed by age, most enjoy active and vital lives. It is a mistake to underestimate their abilities or treat them as frail. Describe strategies to show respect for older adults.

COOPERATIVE LEARNING ACTIVITY

Examining the Needs of Older Adults As the population of older adults increases, so do residential communities and housing projects designed to meet their needs. Assign students, in groups of four, the task of planning and designing a futuristic colony for individuals and couples in late adulthood. Plans should include housing for 5,000 residents. Locations are limitless. Students should plan for the special needs of the older adults and the general needs for communication systems, energy, transportation, food, recreation, and so on. Give each group butcher paper and colored markers to draw their plans after they have brainstormed their ideas.

HEALTH
Online

Encourage students to investigate the Web Links and then complete the activity.

Discussing

Have students discuss how an individual's age might be measured differently based on chronological and social scales. Ask:

• How can expectations of how a person "should" act at a certain age be an advantage to that person?

• How can they be a disadvantage?

Ask students to give examples from their own lives to support their responses. **L1**

Finding Examples

To counter against negative stereotypes of older adults, have students find photographs, advertisements, or illustrations in magazines that show vital and active older adults. Encourage students to cut out the pictures and combine them in a poster or notebook. **L1**

FYI

Statistics indicate that by the year 2030, 80 million Americans—at least 20 percent of the population—will be aged 65 or older.

HEALTH
Online

Topic: Aging

For a link to more information on the aging process, go to **health.glencoe.com**.

Activity: Using the information provided at this link, write an essay that features five facts you learned about the aging process.

Measuring Age

Have you heard the expression "You're only as old as you feel"? It recognizes that some people feel younger than their years indicate. As **Figure 16.6** shows, age can be measured in three different ways:

• **Chronological** (krah·nuh·LAH·ji·kuhl) **age.** *Age measured in years* is **chronological age.** This is the number of your most recent birthday. We have no control over this measure of age.

• **Biological age.** *Age determined by how well various body parts are working* is **biological age.** It is affected by heredity and by health habits. People who make healthful choices throughout life show fewer signs of physical aging as they grow older.

• **Social age.** *Age measured by your lifestyle and the connections you have with others* is **social age.** Social age has to do with the activities that society expects you to perform at particular points in life. As a teen, you are expected to be in school, learning and preparing for adulthood. Later, you are expected to work, possibly have a family, and contribute to your community.

FIGURE 16.6

CHRONOLOGICAL, BIOLOGICAL, AND SOCIAL AGE

A person's chronological, biological, and social age may not all advance at the same rate. *How can your actions as a teen affect your lifelong health?*

CHRONOLOGICAL AGE

BIOLOGICAL AGE

SOCIAL AGE

434 CHAPTER 16: GROWTH AND DEVELOPMENT

MORE ABOUT...

Osteoporosis Osteoporosis is a condition where bones become weak, brittle, and easily broken. Women are affected four times as frequently as men. Bone mass peaks in early adulthood and declines with age. Building strong bones during childhood and adolescence is key to preventing osteoporosis. Calcium is vital for healthy bone growth. The average teen's diet includes about 500 mg of calcium per day, but 1300 mg is recommended for optimal bone health. Low-fat dairy products, broccoli, green leafy vegetables, and kidney beans—are good sources of dietary calcium. Weight-bearing exercises—walking, jogging, and field sports—also support bone mass and strength.

Aging: A Positive Experience

The health triangle is just as useful for older people as it is for you. Paying attention to all three sides of the triangle can help make the later years a rewarding and productive stage of life.

- **Physical health.** Older people who stay physically active, get enough rest, and follow a sensible eating plan are less likely to experience illnesses and disabilities that prevent them from enjoying themselves. Their biological age is lower than their chronological age.
- **Mental and emotional health.** Older people who keep mentally active by reading, working, and challenging themselves mentally will continue to learn. Those who have learned to be resilient are more likely to handle any changes that accompany their later years.
- **Social health.** Older people who maintain contact with family and friends have less difficulty adjusting to the later years and to the loss of loved ones. Many older people benefit from becoming involved in community programs that can use their talents and life experiences.

When you form friendships with older adults, both of you benefit. *What are some ways that your life might be made richer by having a close relationship with an older adult?*

Lesson 4 Review

Using complete sentences, answer the following questions on a sheet of paper.

Reviewing Terms and Facts

1. **Identify** What are the three stages of adulthood?
2. **Explain** What might make middle adulthood particularly demanding?
3. **Vocabulary** Define the terms *chronological age, biological age,* and *social age.*
4. **Restate** Using the information in this chapter, describe the life cycle of human beings, including birth, dying, and death.

Thinking Critically

5. **Analyze** Why might a person's chronological, biological, and social ages be different?
6. **Hypothesize** Why do you think that some older people get much more enjoyment out of their later years than others?

Applying Health Skills

7. **Practicing Healthful Behaviors** Talk to some older adults in your community. Find out what behaviors they have followed to maintain a high level of wellness. Then ask what advice they would give to teens who want to live a long and healthy life.

LESSON 4: ADULTHOOD AND AGING **435**

Lesson 4 Review

1. Early, middle, late.
2. Balancing career, home and children, caring for parents.
3. Chronological age—age in years; biological age—how well body parts function; social age—personal lifestyle and social connections.
4. Responses should include relevant information from the lesson.
5. Someone might feel healthier and younger, or older and less healthy, than they are.
6. They may feel a sense of satisfaction with their lives, serve their community, have many friends, and get along well with family members.

Finding Examples

Have students choose a familiar television show or commercial that features one or more older adults in major roles. Ask them to write down how the older adults are portrayed. Allow students to compare their findings with those of other students. Then ask: What is your opinion about the way these adults are depicted? **L2**

3 Assess

Evaluating

Assign the Lesson 4 Review; then assign the Lesson 4 Quiz in the TCR.

Reteaching

Assign Concept Map 62 or Reteaching Activity 62 in the TCR.

Enrichment

- Assign Enrichment Activity 62 in the TCR.
- Have students research and report on the goals and programs of the AARP (the American Association of Retired Persons).

4 Close

Ask students to explain why knowledge about aging enables them to be better prepared to maintain their health as they grow and develop toward adulthood.

Can We Stay Young?

❶ Focus

Objectives

Students will be able to

• discuss attitudes about aging in the United States.

• identify steps to increase individual life expectancy.

• list careers related to understanding various aspects of aging.

Motivator

Quick Write
Ask students to imagine themselves at the age of 82. Ask, "What is your life like? Where do you live and with whom? What activities fill your day? Are you happy with your life?" Give students five to ten minutes to respond in writing.

❷ Teach

Discussing

Write the title of this spread ("Can We Stay Young?") on the board. Ask students, "What are your immediate reactions to this question? What does this question imply?"(*That everyone wants to stay young.*) Have students turn to page 435 and review the section entitled "Aging: A Positive Experience." Ask students:

• Do you think aging is considered a positive experience in American culture? Why or why not?

• What are some of the factors that influence our attitudes about aging?

• What are some commonly held assumptions about the elderly in our culture?

• What are five positive aspects to aging?

Can We **Stay Young?**

Scientists are just beginning to unlock the mysteries of aging.

Today, some researchers believe that many people will live beyond age 100. How much further than 100 is it possible to go? Is 150 reasonable? What about 200? If not, why not? To answer these questions, researchers are investigating different factors in the mysterious process of aging.

Free Radicals

Like all organisms, our bodies' cells give off waste as they produce energy. One such waste product is an oxygen molecule known as a free radical—an ordinary molecule with an extra electron. The addition of the electron creates an imbalance that the molecule tries to fix by moving around, attempting to bond with other molecules or structures, including deoxyribonucleic (dee-ahk-see-REYE-boh-noo-KLAY-ik) acid (DNA), the chemical unit that makes up chromosomes. A lifetime of this movement can damage cells, which may lead to a range of disorders, including cancer and the more general signs of aging such as wrinkles and arthritis.

🏠 Beyond the Classroom

Community Write the word "gerontologist" on the board. Explain that a gerontologist is someone who studies aging and the issues of elderly people. Gerontologists, nutritionists, and other medical specialists all work to understand various aspects of aging. Identify a professional in your community who is involved in one of these fields. Ask him or her to be a guest speaker in class. Have students brainstorm a list of questions for the speaker beforehand. Questions may include the following:

• What type of education and professional background do you have?
• With whom do you work?
• Where do you work?
• What do you like most about your work?

FREE RADICALS

Inside cells' energy-generating structures, metabolism produces unstable oxygen molecules known as free radicals. These molecules bounce around the cells, damaging DNA and other structures.

Cell

Free radicals

Energy-generating structure

DNA

CARAMELIZATION

Excess sugars can bind with proteins, forming a sticky, weblike coating. Over time, the buildup of this substance can stiffen joints, block arteries, and cloud clear tissue.

Sugar

Protein

In recent years, some nutritionists have called for diets rich in fruits and vegetables that contain carotenoids (kar-AH-ten-oids), such as carrots, broccoli, and cantaloupe. These substances act as antioxidants—that is, they grab free radicals and carry them out of the body. Reducing the number of free radicals in the body may slow down the aging process.

Caramelization

When foods such as turkey, bread, and caramel are heated, proteins bind with sugars, causing the surface to darken and, in some cases, turn soft and sticky. In the 1970s, researchers wondered if the same reaction might occur in the bodies of people with diabetes, as excess glucose combined with proteins during the process of metabolism. When sugars and proteins bond, they attract other proteins. This forms a sticky, weblike network, which could stiffen joints, block arteries, and cloud clear tissues like the lens of the eye, leading to cataracts. Researchers call this process caramelization.

What does this have to do with aging? As we get older, we all experience the effects of caramelization, such as joint pain, circulatory disease, and poor vision. Researchers hope that if they can reduce caramelization, they will extend the human life span.

Telomeres

Researchers have been studying genes to find the key that will unlock the secrets of aging. Some have focused on an area at the tip of chromosomes called a telomere. Telomeres keep strands of chromosomes from unraveling, functioning much like the plastic cuff at the end of a shoelace.

As cells divide, telomeres almost always appear to grow shorter. So each time the cell splits, the daughter cells have a little less telomere to play with. When the cell reaches 100 or so replications, the telomere is reduced to a mere nub. At this point, the cell stops replicating.

Some researchers think that the genes covered by the telomere become exposed and active. This might produce proteins that trigger the tissue deterioration that is part of aging.

With a little more progress in studying telomeres, caramelization, free radicals, and other aspects of aging, researchers believe today's adults can hope to live to 120. ■

TIME TO THINK...

About Aging

Using reliable sources on the Internet or in your school's media center, research inventions, discoveries, and trends over the last century that have helped to lengthen (and shorten) the average life span. Have a class discussion about which items are important. Use the entries that the class agreed upon to create a large timeline on poster paper about life expectancy in the United States during the last 100 years.

③ Apply

Time to Think

Allow students time to complete their timelines. Then discuss them as a class. Point out that while medical discoveries, inventions, etc. have helped to increase the average life expectancy over time, heredity, environment, and individual behavior are stronger determinants of an individual's lifespan. Ask, "What steps can you take today that may increase your life expectancy?" (*Answers may include: eat right, don't smoke, get enough sleep, stay our of the sun, and so on.*) Discuss the difference between these healthful lifestyle choices and a "magic bullet" such as pill or cream designed to slow the effects of aging. Which strategy is more likely to yield a lifetime of health?

VISUAL LEARNING

Ask students to analyze the photo of a couple on bikes. Ask, "Is this an accurate portrayal of older Americans in our culture? Why or why not?"

CULTURAL PERSPECTIVES

Attitudes Toward Aging Tell students that different cultures have different attitudes about aging and older adults. For instance, in the Japanese culture, older relatives are revered as sources of experience and wisdom. In many Native American tribes, older adults have traditionally been treated with admiration and respect. Ask several interested students to do online research about these, and other, cultures and their attitudes toward aging and older adults. How are the attitudes and behaviors of these cultures the same or different from those in the United States? ■ ■ ■

RESOLVING CONFLICTS WITH PARENTS

CONFLICT RESOLUTION

Model

As you develop your personal identity during your teen years, you will begin to be more independent. You will do more things on your own, without help from your parents. Conflicts with parents can arise when teens believe they are ready to do things that their parents do not want them to do yet. Read about how a teen named Denise uses the T.A.L.K. strategies to resolve a conflict with her parents.

Denise's parents have told her that she is not allowed to go out on dates until she is 16 years old. Denise is upset because she wants to go to a movie with her friend Todd on Friday night. She takes some time out and goes to her room to think. Then she comes back and asks her parents to talk about the situation. She explains that she thinks 14 is old enough to start dating and that some of her classmates are allowed to date. Her parents point out that Denise's friends usually date in groups, not as couples. Denise asks if it would be okay for her to go to the movies with Todd if they invited some other friends along too. Her parents agree to this compromise.

438 CHAPTER 16: GROWTH AND DEVELOPMENT

Objective

After completing the lesson, students will be able to apply conflict resolution skills to conflicts with family and friends.

Time: 45 minutes

Materials:: index cards, pencil or pen

Teacher Classroom Resources

📁 Building Health Skills Activities

• Transparency Master 6, "Conflict Resolution"

• Reproducible Master 41, "Resolving Conflicts with Parents"

1. Model

• Direct students to read about Denise's conflict with her parents.

• Discuss why Denise's parents might think that she is too young to date (*they want Denise to be safe; they do not want her to get too serious about one person right now; they feel that she is not ready for the challenges of dating*).

• Display Transparency Master 6, and ask students to identify the conflict resolution skills that Denise and her parents used to reach a compromise.

2. Practice

• Check the local laws regarding teen curfews as they vary from community to community. Share this information with the class when appropriate.

Teaching Tips

Adapting Role-Plays Some students may come from families in which teens are not allowed to question what parents say. These students can develop role-plays that deal with conflicts between themselves and siblings or between themselves and other teens.

Reaching Win-Win Solutions When conflict arises, the best outcome is a win-win solution. It is important to remember that the goal of conflict resolution is not to win but to improve the relationship. Then everyone wins.

Practice

Read the following scenario and answer the questions that follow.

Fourteen-year-old Logan has a curfew—his parents expect him to be home by 9 o'clock every night. Logan thinks this is too early. He understands why a 9 p.m. curfew might be reasonable on school nights, but most of his friends like to hang out until 11 p.m. or midnight on weekends, and he hates having to leave early.

1. What does Logan want?
2. What do his parents want?
3. How could Logan use the T.A.L.K. strategies to reach a compromise with his parents?

Apply/Assess

Think of a situation that could cause conflict between teens and parents. You can use a personal situation, one that you have invented, or one of the situations described below. Write your scenario on an index card. Then team up with two other students. Choose one of your three scenarios and use it to create a role-play. One of you will play a teen, while the other two will play the teen's parents. In your role play, show how the teen and his or her parents use conflict resolution skills (T.A.L.K.) to find a solution that satisfies everyone. Present your role-play to the class.

> Parents think teen plays music too loud.

> Parents object to one of teen's friends.

> Teen objects to having to keep room tidy.

Conflict Resolution

These steps can help you resolve conflicts:

T Take a time out.
A Allow each person to talk.
L Let each person ask questions.
K Keep brainstorming to find a solution.

Self-✓Check

- Did we portray a realistic conflict?
- Did we show the steps for conflict resolution?
- Did the characters find a solution that was acceptable to all parties?

2. Practice

- Have students read the scenario and answer the questions.
- Ask why Logan's parents are being responsible by setting a curfew (*they want Logan to be safe; Logan needs time to complete his schoolwork; getting home at 9:00 helps ensure that Logan, a growing teen, gets enough sleep; Logan could get in trouble if he is out too late*).
- You may want to have volunteers role-play this situation for the class. Observers could then provide feedback on how effectively volunteers used the T.A.L.K. strategies to reach a compromise. Consider taking the role of Logan yourself to give students a chance to see things from a parent's perspective.

3. Apply/Assess

- 📁 You may wish to distribute Building Health Skills Reproducible Master 41 in the TCR to guide students in completing this activity
- Distribute an index card to each student. Ask students to come up with a situation that could cause conflict between a teen and his or her parents and write it on the card.
- Divide the class into groups of three, and have each group choose one of the scenarios to role-play for the class.
- As a class, discuss the role-plays and how realistic the compromises are.
- Remind students that different families may have different values and traditions. A compromise that is reasonable for one family may not be reasonable for another family.

Assessment Scoring ✓

Using a rubric, student work should provide evidence of all criteria to achieve the highest score.

Skills

Student work demonstrates

- a time-out from the situation.
- point of view from both sides.
- questions to clarify the conflict.
- brainstorming to find a solution.

Concept

Student work provides

- a realistic portrayal of an issue that creates conflict between teens and parents.

Checking Comprehension

Use the Chapter 16 Assessment to examine the most important ideas presented in the chapter.

Answers to Reviewing Vocabulary and Concepts

Lesson 1
1. tissues
2. organs
3. uterus
4. embryo
5. fetus
6. placenta
7. umbilical
8. cervix

Lesson 2
9. heredity
10. genes
11. genetic disorder
12. prenatal care

Lesson 3
13. c
14. c
15. a

Lesson 4
16. false; different times
17. false; age determined by how well various body parts are working
18. true

Thinking Critically

19. How her eating plan should change; how much exercise she should get; whether she should continue to work, drink alcohol, or stop smoking; what medications would be healthy; what she should do if a close friend gets sick with an infectious disease.

CHAPTER ASSESSMENT 16

CHAPTER ASSESSMENT 16

After You Read

Use your completed Foldable to review the information on cells, tissues, organs, and body systems.

FOLDABLES™
Study Organizer

Reviewing Vocabulary and Concepts

On a sheet of paper, write the numbers 1–12. After each number, write the term from the list that best completes each sentence.

```
• cervix          • placenta
• genes           • prenatal care
• embryo          • tissues
• fetus           • umbilical
• genetic disorder • uterus
• organs          • heredity
```

Lesson 1

1. Cells that do similar jobs form _____.
2. Different kinds of tissues are combined in larger structures called _____.
3. The pear-shaped organ in which a fetus is nourished is called the _____.
4. The name of the developing organism from fertilization to about the eighth week of development is the _____.
5. The name for the developing organism from the end of the eighth week until birth is the _____.
6. The thick, rich lining of tissue that builds up along the walls of the uterus and connects the mother to the fetus is called the _____.
7. A cord that connects the fetus to its mother is called the _____ cord.
8. The opening of the uterus is called the _____.

Lesson 2

9. _____ is the passing of traits from parents to their children.
10. The basic units of heredity are called _____.
11. Down syndrome is an example of a(n) _____.
12. _____ refers to steps taken to provide for the health of a pregnant female and her fetus.

Lesson 3

On a sheet of paper, write the numbers 13–15. After each number, write the letter of the answer that best completes each statement.

13. Erikson believed that people pass through _____ developmental stages of life.
    a. two
    b. four
    c. eight
    d. ten
14. The time when you begin to develop traits of adults of your own gender is called
    a. middle adulthood.
    b. early adulthood.
    c. puberty.
    d. late childhood.
15. The emotional changes of adolescence are related to the body's production of
    a. hormones.
    b. toxins.
    c. calcium.
    d. muscle.

Lesson 4

On a sheet of paper, write the numbers 16–18. Write *True* or *False* for each statement below. If the statement is false, change the underlined word or phrase to make it true.

16. The physical signs of aging occur at <u>the same time</u> in different adults.
17. A person's <u>biological age</u> is his or her age measured in years.

INCLUSION STRATEGIES

Special Learning Needs, Behavior Problems, English Language Learners The following suggestions are helpful for students with special learning needs, students with behavior problems, and ELL students:

- Pair these students with more proficient learners who can help summarize the main concepts of the chapter.

- 🎧 Direct these students to listen to the Teen Health Audio Summaries. This component provides an audio and written summary of the chapter in both English and Spanish.

- Use photographs, drawings, or magazine clippings whenever possible to help students visualize the important concepts of the chapter.

18. Social age is measured by a person's lifestyle.

Thinking Critically

Using complete sentences, answer the following questions on a sheet of paper.

19. Analyze Write a set of questions you think a pregnant female might ask her doctor about what she could do to have a healthy baby.

20. Hypothesize How do you think an older adult's biological age might be affected by not being involved in a variety of social groups?

Career Corner

Dental Hygienist Would you like to help improve people's smiles? With just one to two years of training at a college or vocational/technical school, you could become a dental hygienist. These professionals assist dentists. They help clean teeth and gums, insert fillings, and take X-rays. Hygienists work with a variety of special tools. They also have lots of contact with people. Learn more about this and other health careers by clicking on Career Corner at health.glencoe.com.

Standardized Test Practice

Reading & Writing

Read the paragraphs below and then answer the questions.

You may have heard of the terms "left brained" and "right brained." These terms refer to the fact that your brain has two sides, or hemispheres. While each hemisphere has different functions, they work together to help you think, feel, and perform the activities of daily life.

Scientists have learned that the brain's two hemispheres are specialized, with each side being better at different tasks. The left hemisphere, for example, is good with sequencing and language skills. The right hemisphere is more visual and is good at seeing relationships and patterns.

People don't use just one side of the brain, and one side does not control or dominate the other. Both sides are needed for most activities.

1. What phrase from the passage helps readers understand the meaning of the word *hemisphere*?

- **A** work together
- **B** two sides
- **C** different functions
- **D** good with sequencing

2. How does the author organize the ideas in the second paragraph?

- **A** comparing the functions of both sides of the brain
- **B** listing events in the order that they occur
- **C** explaining events in order of their importance
- **D** using cause and effect to explain the two sides of the brain

3. Write a paragraph describing your personality or the personality of a friend or family member.

 TH05_C3.glencoe.com/quiz

20. Biological age could increase because of loneliness, sadness, possible loss of interest in personal maintenance.

Test Practice

1. B

2. A

3. Answers should identify a specific person, his or her personality traits, and use facts and details to describe these traits.

Reteaching

📁 Assign Study Guide 16 in the Student Activities Workbook.

Evaluate

📁 💿 Use the reproducible Chapter 16 Test in the TCR, or construct your own test using the **Exam**_View_® Pro Testmaker.

Enrichment

Have students find out more about a specific genetic disorder. They should research current information about the disorder and prepare brief reports to present to the class.

Assessment

Self-Assessment Direct students to review the activities that are provided throughout the chapter. Encourage each student to select one finished product or activity that demonstrates his or her best work for the chapter. Have students explain what they learned and how the examples they selected show their progress.

Career Corner

Geneticist After reviewing the career profile at the Health Web site, students might:

- Write three questions a geneticist might be asked during a job interview.
- Locate recent news articles on developments in genetic research (such as in the area of biotechnology or cloning).

Diseases and Disorders

Unit Objectives

Students will learn about how communicable diseases are spread and how the body defends against them. They will examine the causes, symptoms, and treatment of common diseases like colds and flu as well as sexually transmitted diseases and AIDS. Students will also learn about causes, symptoms, and treatment of noncommunicable diseases including asthma, cancer, heart disease, and diabetes.

Unit Overview

Chapter 17
Communicable Diseases

Lesson
1 Preventing the Spread of Disease
2 The Body's Defenses Against Infection
3 Communicable Diseases
4 Sexually Transmitted Diseases
5 HIV/AIDS

Chapter 18
Noncommunicable Diseases

Lesson
1 Noncommunicable Diseases
2 Allergies and Asthma
3 Cancer
4 Heart and Circulatory Problems
5 Diabetes and Arthritis

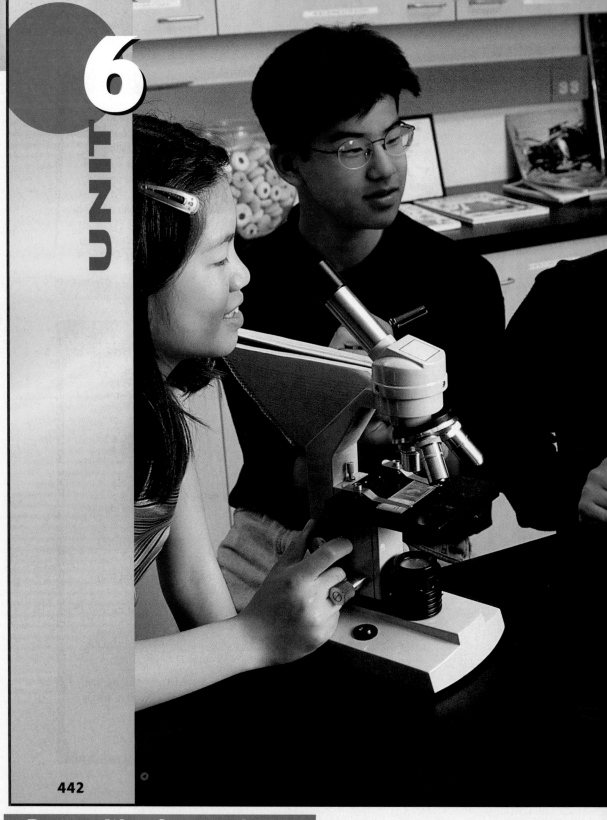

6
UNIT

442

DEALING WITH SENSITIVE ISSUES

The Importance of Listening A crucial part of communicating with students is listening to their thoughts and feelings. A teacher who is a good listener provides an environment where students feel they are being heard without being judged, corrected, or interrupted. This feeling of acceptance helps them speak more openly and confidently. A teacher who is a good listener also shows empathy for students. This ability to put yourself in another's place helps you understand not only what your students are *saying* but also what they are *feeling*. As a result, if students can't express how they feel in words, but you show you empathize with them, you will be able to share their *feelings* and show you really hear what they are saying.

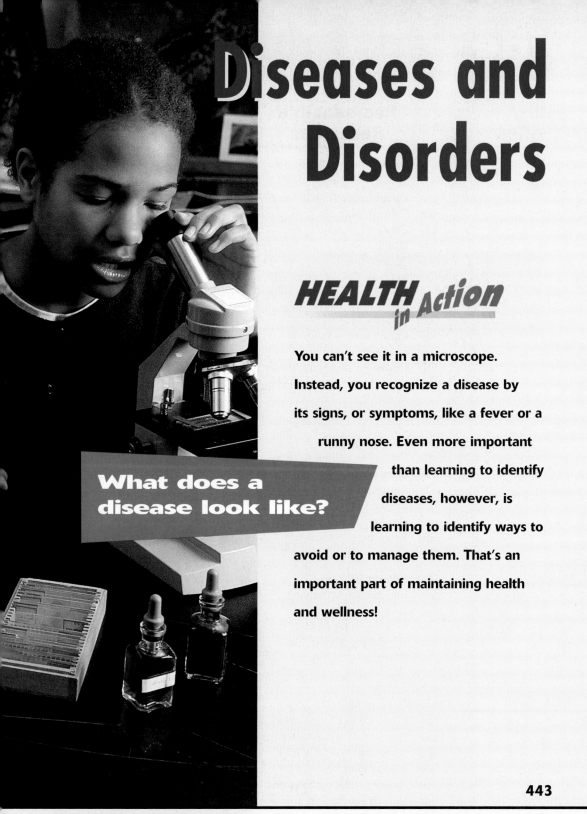

Diseases and Disorders

HEALTH in Action

You can't see it in a microscope. Instead, you recognize a disease by its signs, or symptoms, like a fever or a runny nose. Even more important than learning to identify diseases, however, is learning to identify ways to avoid or to manage them. That's an important part of maintaining health and wellness!

What does a disease look like?

Unit Introduction

On the board, write the word *disease*. Ask students to make lists of the words and/or phrases that they associate with the term.

When finished, ask a few volunteers to read their lists out loud, and write their responses on the board, separating them into two categories—communicable and noncommunicable—as you list them.

Follow with a discussion about what students know about the different diseases, and clear up any misconceptions they may have. Ask students to identify those parts, or systems, of the body that are affected by each disease. Briefly introduce them to the two specific categories you have created on the board.

Tell students that the chapters in this unit will help them understand more about how the body is affected by diseases.

443

HEALTH in Action

Read the class the question on page 443. Lead a class discussion on how to prevent or manage disease. Then lead the class in the following physical group activity:

Have the students sit or stand in a circle. Give to one student an object that can easily be passed around, such as a ball. Ask that student to name five things a person can do to prevent cancer. As the student lists five things, have him or her pass the object to the classmate on his or her right. Whoever is holding the object when the first student finishes his or her list will have to answer the next question; if the object makes it all the way around the circle before the first student finishes, he or she will have to answer the next question.

Planning Guide

Chapter 17	Skills/ Activities	Reproducible Resources	Assessment
Lesson 1 **Preventing the Spread of Disease** *pages 446–449*	**Hands-On Health** ▲ Habits for Health, page 448	*Student Activities Workbook available for use with each chapter* 📁 Parent Letter & Activities 17 📁 Concept Map 63 📁 Enrichment Activity 63 📁 Health Lab 17 📁 Lesson Plan 1 📁 Reading Tutor Activity 62	📁 Lesson 1 Quiz
Lesson 2 **The Body's Defenses Against Infection** *pages 450–453*		📁 Reteaching Activity 63 📁 Concept Map 64 📁 Enrichment Activity 64 📁 Lesson Plan 2 📁 Reading Tutor Activity 63 📁 Reteaching Activity 64	📁 Lesson 2 Quiz
Lesson 3 **Communicable Diseases** *pages 454–457*	**HEALTH SKILLS ACTIVITY** ▲ Can I Catch What's in the News? (*Accessing Information*), page 456	📁 Concept Map 65 📁 Cross-Curriculum Activity 33 📁 Decision-Making Activity 33 📁 Enrichment Activity 65 📁 Lesson Plan 3 📁 Reading Tutor Activity 64 📁 Reteaching Activity 65	📁 Lesson 3 Quiz
Lesson 4 **Sexually Transmitted Diseases** *pages 458–463*	**HEALTH SKILLS ACTIVITY** ▲ Helping a Friend Choose Abstinence (*Communication Skills*), page 460	📁 Concept Map 66 📁 Enrichment Activity 66 📁 Lesson Plan 4 📁 Reading Tutor Activity 65 📁 Reteaching Activity 66	📁 Lesson 4 Quiz
Lesson 5 **HIV/AIDS** *pages 464–467*	**HEALTH SKILLS ACTIVITY** ▲ Get the Message Out (*Advocacy*), page 466	📁 Concept Map 67 📁 Cross-Curriculum Activity 34 📁 Decision-Making Activity 34 📁 Enrichment Activity 67 📁 Lesson Plan 5 📁 Reading Tutor Activity 66 📁 Reteaching Activity 67	📁 Lesson 5 Quiz 📁 Chapter 17 Test 📁 Performance Assessment 17
TIME HEALTH	**Healthy Germs** *pages 468–469*		
BUILDING HEALTH SKILLS **Protecting Yourself and Others** (*Practicing Healthful Behaviors*) *pages 470–471*		📁 Building Health Skills Reproducible Master 42	

Standards		Technology
National	**State/Local**	
National Health Education Standard **1.1, 1.3, 1.5, 1.6, 1.8, 3.1, 3.4**		Transparency 66 TeacherWorks™
National Health Education Standard **1.3, 1.5, 1.6, 1.7, 1.8, 2.6, 3.4**		Transparency 67 TeacherWorks™
National Health Education Standard **1.1, 1.3, 1.5, 1.6, 1.7, 1.8, 2.6, 3.1, 3.4**		Transparency 68 TeacherWorks™
National Health Education Standard **1.3, 1.6, 1.7, 1.8, 2.6, 3.1, 3.4, 5.1, 5.4**		Transparency 69 TeacherWorks™
National Health Education Standard **1.3, 1.6, 1.7, 1.8, 2.6, 3.1, 3.4, 7.4**		Transparency 70 TeacherWorks™ MindJogger Videoquiz **Exam**View® Pro Testmaker
National Health Education Standard **1.1, 3.1, 3.4**		Building Health Skills Transparency Master 2d

TeacherWorks™

Glencoe's new and exclusive TeacherWorks™ is an all-in-one planner and resource center. Access the complete Teacher Wraparound Edition electronically. Find all your classroom resources with just a few easy clicks, and print them right from your computer. Connect directly to Glencoe's customized Health Web site. Access the National Health Education Standards correlations, or insert your own state standards and match them directly to the electronic Teacher Wraparound Edition.

Language Diversity

- English Audio Summaries
- Spanish Audio Summaries
- English Summaries, Quizzes, and Activities
- Spanish Summaries, Quizzes, and Activities
- Spanish Parent Letters and Activities

KEY TO ABILITY LEVELS

Teaching Strategies that appear throughout the chapters have been identified by one of four codes to give you an idea of their suitability for students of varying learning styles and abilities.

L1 Level 1 strategies should be within the ability range of all students. Often full class participation is required.

L2 Level 2 strategies are for average to above-average students or for small groups. Some teacher direction is necessary.

L3 Level 3 strategies are designed for students able and willing to work independently. Minimal teacher direction is necessary.

INCL Strategies are appropriate for students with particular special needs in a general classroom setting.

CHAPTER
17

Communicable Diseases

Chapter at a Glance

Lesson 1 defines communicable disease and details how they are spread.

Lesson 2 examines the various bodily defenses against pathogens and discusses the body's specific and nonspecific responses.

Lesson 3 discusses common communicable diseases, including colds and flu, and ways to prevent their spread.

Lesson 4 identifies and defines common sexually transmitted diseases (STDs) and explains why choosing abstinence is an important health decision.

Lesson 5 examines the effects of AIDS on the body, describes how the virus (HIV) is passed on, and outlines strategies for preventing HIV infection.

Health Skills

- Can I Catch What's in the News? (*Accessing Information*), p. 456
- Helping a Friend Choose Abstinence (*Communication Skills*), p. 460
- Get the Message Out (*Advocacy*), p 466
- Protecting Yourself and Others (*Practicing Healthful Behaviors*), pp. 470–471

HANDS-ON ACTIVITY

Microorganisms Divide the class into groups of three, and provide each group with an agar dish. Have them divide the dishes into four sections, using a colored marker. Give each student a two-inch length of cellophane tape; he or she should fold it so that one section remains untouched and clean. Tell each student to pick up a sample of the microorganisms on any surface by placing the clean section of the tape on the surface. He or she should then touch the contaminated tape to one section of the agar dish and label that section with the source of the microorganisms. Once three sections are filled (leave one clean), the dish should be covered and sealed shut. Keep the dishes in a warm environment for two to four days. For safety, do not have students open the dishes. Have students observe the experiment daily and draw conclusions.

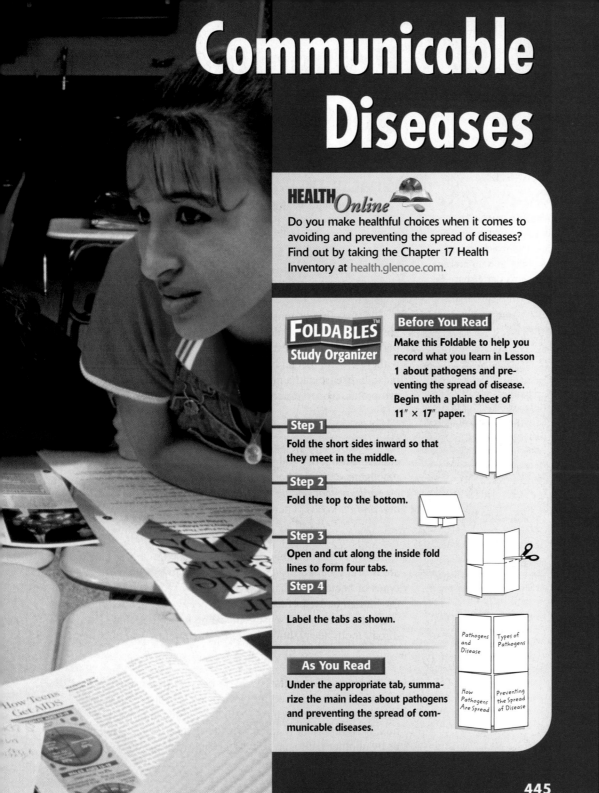

Communicable Diseases

Chapter Introduction

Use the options below to motivate students and preview chapter content.

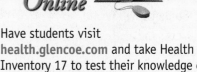

HEALTH *Online*

Do you make healthful choices when it comes to avoiding and preventing the spread of diseases? Find out by taking the Chapter 17 Health Inventory at health.glencoe.com.

FOLDABLES™ Study Organizer

Before You Read

Make this Foldable to help you record what you learn in Lesson 1 about pathogens and preventing the spread of disease. Begin with a plain sheet of 11″ × 17″ paper.

Step 1

Fold the short sides inward so that they meet in the middle.

Step 2

Fold the top to the bottom.

Step 3

Open and cut along the inside fold lines to form four tabs.

Step 4

Label the tabs as shown.

| Pathogens and Disease | Types of Pathogens |
| How Pathogens Are Spread | Preventing the Spread of Disease |

As You Read

Under the appropriate tab, summarize the main ideas about pathogens and preventing the spread of communicable diseases.

HEALTH *Online*

Have students visit **health.glencoe.com** and take Health Inventory 17 to test their knowledge of communicable diseases. For new teaching ideas, click on Teaching Today to download helpful tools such as graphic

GLENCOE TECHNOLOGY

MindJogger Videoquiz

Use MindJogger to preview or review Chapter 17 content.

TIME HEALTH

Healthy Germs
pages 468–469

445

FOLDABLES™ Study Organizer

Dinah Zike Study Fold

Descriptive Writing Students will use this Foldable study guide to record information about communicable diseases and ways in which to prevent their spread. As students read and study the information on pathogens and preventing the spread of disease in Lesson 1, have them take notes on each main topic under the appropriate tab of their Foldable. Encourage them to write down vocabulary terms and definitions under the tabs as well. After students have completed the lesson, have them summarize what they have learned about the prevention of communicable diseases.

Lesson 1

Preventing the Spread of Disease

1 Focus

Lesson Objectives

Students will be able to
- discuss the causes of communicable diseases.
- identify the types of organisms that cause diseases.
- describe how diseases are spread.
- discuss the practices that can protect them and others from disease.
- distinguish risk factors associated with communicable diseases.

Motivators

Quick Write

Have a volunteer list the students' responses on the board. Ask: Which of the actions mentioned do you think are most effective? Why?

Bellringer Activity

Have students list items that they typically share with family members or friends. Ask: How can the sharing of such items affect your health?

VOCABULARY

Copy each vocabulary term on an index card. Then write the definition of each term on a separate card. Place the cards face down on a table, and invite pairs of students to play "Concentration." The students take turns turning over a pair of cards to match each term with its definition. A pair that does not match is returned to the face down position.

Quick Write

What do you think is the single most important action you can take to help prevent the spread of disease in your home and school?

LEARN ABOUT...

- causes of communicable diseases.
- the organisms that cause diseases.
- how diseases are spread.

VOCABULARY

- communicable disease
- pathogens
- infection
- bacteria
- virus
- fungi
- protozoa
- rickettsias
- vector
- contagious period

Preventing the Spread of Disease

What Is Disease?

When you are healthy, you feel good both physically and mentally. Sometimes, however, a disease might prevent you from feeling your best. A disease is an illness that affects the proper functioning of the body or mind. *A disease that can be passed to a person from another person, animal, or object* is called a **communicable** (kuh·MYOO·ni·kuh·buhl) **disease**.

Diseases that cannot be caught from people, animals, or objects are called noncommunicable diseases. Noncommunicable diseases may be caused by lifestyle factors, conditions that people are born with, or environmental hazards. **Figure 17.1** shows how a communicable disease and a noncommunicable disease can have similar symptoms. Noncommunicable diseases are discussed in Chapter 18.

Causes of Communicable Diseases

The *tiny organisms that cause communicable diseases* are called **pathogens**. You will also hear them called germs. When pathogens enter the body, an infection may result. An **infection** is *a condition that occurs when pathogens enter the body, multiply, and damage cells.* There are many different types of pathogens.

Bacteria

Many communicable diseases are caused by bacteria. **Bacteria** are *tiny one-celled organisms that live nearly everywhere.* Most types of bacteria are harmless, and many types live on and inside the human body. In fact, your body needs certain bacteria to work properly. Common diseases caused by bacteria include strep throat, tooth decay, boils, bacterial pneumonia, and impetigo.

Viruses

A **virus** is *the smallest disease-causing organism.* Colds, flu, and hepatitis are caused by viruses. Viruses also cause diseases of childhood and adolescence, such as measles, mumps, and chicken pox. It is important to know whether a disease is caused by a virus or by another pathogen so that the right treatment can be given.

Lesson 1 Resources

Teacher Classroom Resources

📁 Parent Letter & Activities 17

📁 Concept Map 63

📁 Enrichment Activity 63

📁 Health Lab 17

📁 Lesson Plan 1

📁 Lesson 1 Quiz

📁 Reading Tutor Activity 62

📁 Reteaching Activity 63

🔦 Transparency 66

Student Activities Workbook

📁 Chapter 17 Study Guide

📁 Applying Health Skills 63

FIGURE 17.1

COMMUNICABLE OR NONCOMMUNICABLE?

Communicable diseases and noncommunicable diseases require different treatments.

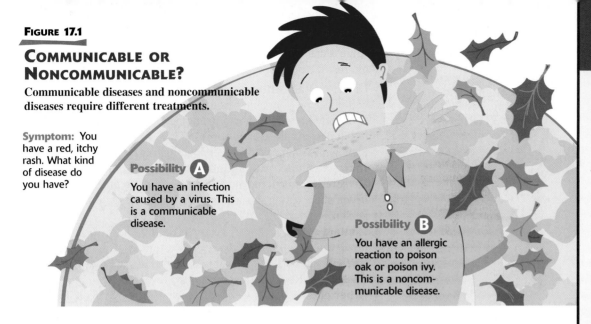

Symptom: You have a red, itchy rash. What kind of disease do you have?

Possibility (A)

You have an infection caused by a virus. This is a communicable disease.

Possibility (B)

You have an allergic reaction to poison oak or poison ivy. This is a noncommunicable disease.

In general, bacterial infections can be treated with antibiotics but viral infections cannot. Some viral infections are now treated with prescribed medications.

Other Types of Pathogens

Listed below are three other types of pathogens that cause communicable diseases.

- **Fungi** (FUHN·jy) are *primitive life-forms that feed on organic materials.* Certain fungi live in the hair, nails, and skin. Fungi cause ringworm, an infection of the scalp and skin, and athlete's foot, an infection of the skin between the toes.
- **Protozoa** (proh·tuh·ZOH·uh) are *single-celled organisms that are usually harmless but that can cause certain diseases.* Malaria is a disease caused by protozoa that live in certain kinds of mosquitoes. If an affected mosquito bites a human, the person will be infected. Water contaminated with protozoa can also cause infections.
- **Rickettsias** (rik·ET·see·uhz) are *disease-causing organisms that resemble bacteria but multiply like viruses.* They enter humans from the bites of insects such as fleas or lice. They can cause diseases such as typhus and Rocky Mountain spotted fever.

Athlete's foot is an irritating but usually harmless condition caused by fungi. *What can you do to avoid getting athlete's foot?*

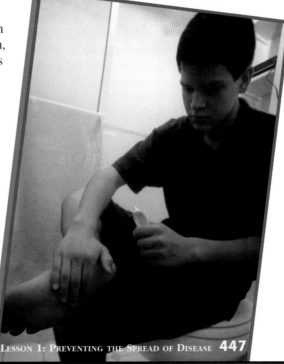

Lesson 1

② Teach

VISUAL LEARNING

FIGURE 17.1 Ask students to describe the teen in the picture and discuss what he is probably thinking. Then have volunteers read aloud the symptoms and the two possibilities. Have students explain, in their own words, why it is important to determine which disease is causing the rash. **INCL** *English Language Learners, Special Learning Needs, Behavior Problems, Different Learning Styles* (*Visual*)

Cross-Curriculum Activity

SOCIAL STUDIES Tell students that the West Nile virus causes a potentially deadly infection. An outbreak of the West Nile virus in 2000 affected parts of the northeastern United States for several months. The news reported the number of deaths and informed the public about the virus and how it is transmitted. Have students work in small groups to discuss the pros and cons of intense media coverage of a disease outbreak. **L1**

Researching

Have students work in groups to learn about the problems caused by the overuse of antibiotics. Then have group members identify and discuss factors that may contribute to these problems and steps that can be taken to limit or prevent these problems. **L2**

WHAT TEENS WANT TO KNOW

Why shouldn't I share my toothbrush or razor with my friends? Many pathogens are transmitted through body fluids such as saliva and blood. When you brush your teeth or shave with a razor, microscopic amounts of blood, invisible to the naked eye, may remain on the toothbrush bristles or razor blade. As a result, sharing toothbrushes and razors increases the potential to transmit blood-borne diseases. If people who are infected lend you a toothbrush or razor, they may spread their infections to you. Hepatitis B and hepatitis C, potentially serious viral diseases that infect the liver, are transmitted via blood. Hepatitis B and hepatitis C infections are frequently incurable and can, over the course of many years, result in liver failure and death. HIV, the virus that causes AIDS, is also transmitted via blood.

The World Health Organization estimates that between 300 million and 500 million people become ill with malaria each year; more than 1 million die of the disease.

Critical Thinking

Have students discuss the proverb "an ounce of prevention is worth a pound of cure" in terms of disease prevention. **L2**

Hands-On Health

HABITS FOR HEALTH

Time: 30 minutes

TEACHING THE ACTIVITY
- Have volunteers read aloud the activity introduction and each statement in the inventory.
- Encourage students to discuss how each behavior can affect their health.
- Have students work independently to complete and score the inventory.
- Divide students into discussion groups. Have group members share and compare their inventory scores.

ASSESSMENT
Ask students to write short paragraphs explaining what they have learned from this inventory and what changes they plan to make.

Reading Check

Separate these words into groups: *good hygiene, vaccinations, sharing glasses, ticks, insect repellent, direct contact, undercooked meat, handwashing.* **Label each group and add other words.**

How Pathogens Are Spread

Illness can occur when a pathogen enters your body. Here are some risk factors associated with communicable diseases:

- **Direct contact with an infected person.** You can pick up pathogens on your skin by coming into direct contact with an infected person. For example, you can pick up the strep throat bacteria by kissing someone who has strep throat. Some pathogens, such as HIV, are spread mainly by sexual contact.
- **Indirect contact with an infected person.** Some pathogens are spread through the air. Pathogens can also enter your body if you share eating utensils or drinking glasses with an infected person.
- **Contact with a vector.** A **vector** is *an organism, such as an insect, that transmits a pathogen.* Mosquitoes, for example, spread malaria. Ticks spread two serious diseases—Lyme disease and Rocky Mountain spotted fever.
- **Other contacts.** Pathogens can enter your body if you drink water or eat food that contains them. Improperly stored food and undercooked meat are dangerous for this reason. Another way to become infected is to receive blood that carries pathogens.

Hands-On Health

HABITS FOR HEALTH

How healthy are your habits? This activity will help you find out.

WHAT YOU WILL NEED
- pencil and paper

WHAT YOU WILL DO
Write yes or no for each statement.
1. I wash my hands after using the bathroom and before preparing or serving food.
2. I cover my nose and mouth when I cough or sneeze.
3. I avoid sharing eating utensils or drinking glasses with others.
4. I avoid drinking water from streams and lakes.
5. I make sure food is properly stored.
6. I avoid sharing combs, brushes, and towels with others.
7. When I'm sick, I avoid others during the contagious period.
8. When I'm sick, I get medical care.
9. I avoid contact with people who have diseases that I could catch.
10. I have received all the recommended vaccinations.

IN CONCLUSION
Give yourself 1 point for each yes. A score of 8–10 is very good. A score of 6–8 is good. A score of 4–6 is fair. If you score below 4, you need to work on improving your health behaviors.

Reading Check

List/Sort/Label Categorizing words will help students process and organize information. Ask students to identify similar and dissimilar characteristics of the listed words. Have students work with partners to determine different categories in which to group the words. The most obvious categories would be *Ways to Spread Pathogens* and *Ways to Prevent Pathogens from Spreading,* but accept any groupings that students can support. Next, have students choose one way to group the words, write their lists, and add more related words. End the lesson by leading a discussion about students' categories and additions.

Other Common Diseases

Some of the most common communicable diseases are described in the list below. Several other diseases are listed in **Figure 17.4**.

- **Influenza,** or **"the flu."** This disease is caused by one of three broad types of influenza viruses, each with several different strains. Flu symptoms include fever, exhaustion, chills, headache, and body ache. Yearly vaccination against the flu is recommended for older people and for people who have chronic diseases. Because the virus changes frequently, a vaccine that kills an old strain may not harm a new one.
- **Strep throat.** This infection is caused by streptococci bacteria that produce a very sore throat, fever, muscle pain, and enlarged lymph nodes in the neck. Left untreated, strep throat can lead to serious complications, including heart damage. That is why your doctor may order a strep test if your tonsils and throat are inflamed. Strep throat can be cured with antibiotics.

Reading Check

Compare and contrast. Choose two diseases from this page. List their similarities and their differences.

FIGURE 17.4

SOME COMMUNICABLE DISEASES

This figure shows the symptoms and contagious periods of several communicable diseases. *In a paragraph, determine when treatment of these illnesses at home is appropriate and when and how to seek further help when needed.*

Disease	Symptoms	Contagious Period	Vaccine
Chicken pox	Itchy rash, fever	One to five days before symptoms appear to when spots crust over	Yes
Pneumonia	High fever, chest pain, cough	Varies	For some types
Rubella	Swollen lymph nodes, rash, fever	Seven days before rash starts to five days after	Yes
Measles	Fever, runny nose, cough, rash	Three to four days before rash starts to four days after	Yes
Mumps	Fever, headache, swollen areas in neck and under jaw	Seven days before symptoms to nine days after	Yes
Whooping cough	Fever, runny nose, dry cough (with a whooping sound)	From inflammation of mucous membranes to four weeks after	Yes
Tuberculosis	Fever, fatigue, weight loss, coughing blood	Varies	Yes

---

Lesson 3

② Teach

Comprehending

Help students discuss and understand the recommendation for staying home during the first 24 hours after cold symptoms appear. Ask:

- Why is it sometimes difficult to recognize a cold during those first 24 hours?
- Why is it important to stay away from school, sports, and work during that time? **L1**

VISUAL LEARNING

FIGURE 17.4 Have volunteers read aloud the information about each listed communicable disease. Have students who might have had—or know someone who had—each disease add information about its severity and duration. Then ask: How can you protect yourself against this disease? **INCL** *English Language Learners, Special Learning Needs, Behavior Problems, Different Learning Styles (Visual)*

Synthesizing

Refer to Figure 17.4. Have groups of students find pairs of diseases that have similar symptoms. The groups should share their findings and discuss how a person can tell which of the diseases he or she has. Point out that sometimes it is very difficult to diagnose a disease in its early stages because many diseases have similar symptoms. **L2**

Reading Check

Compare/Contrast Comparing and contrasting helps students distinguish among diseases and remember their characteristics. Guide students in reading the chart in Figure 17.4. For example, you may have to help them understand that the Vaccine column is marked "Yes" only for diseases that have a vaccine. Then have students work in pairs to choose two diseases. Have them use a Venn diagram or a T-chart to list the similarities and the differences to compare and contrast the diseases. Point out the similarities among diseases, and have students discuss why knowing the differences is important.

Critical Thinking

Tell students that a person can be contagious even if she or he starts feeling better. Discuss the following situations:

• You're getting over the flu, you feel much better, and you want to go to a school dance. You were sick for three days. Should you go? (*No. Stay home because you are still contagious.*)

• Your doctor says you have the chicken pox, but you have only a few pock marks, and your clothes cover them. You really feel fine. Should you go to your after-school job? (*No, you are in the contagious period.*) **L1**

HEALTH SKILLS ACTIVITY

ACCESSING INFORMATION

Guide students in reading and discussing the questions about diseases in the news. Ask: What could you conclude about a news source that did not provide answers to these questions?

Then have students identify and read (or listen to and watch) local news stories about diseases. Have students meet in groups to discuss the stories.

Ask students to analyze risks for contracting specific diseases based on pathogenic, genetic, age, cultural, environmental, and behavioral factors. Students may wish to consult dictionaries, encyclopedias, the Internet, or other resources to find out more about risks for contracting specific diseases they read about or hear about in the news.

Note: This skill is introduced in Chapter 2 on pages 45–46.

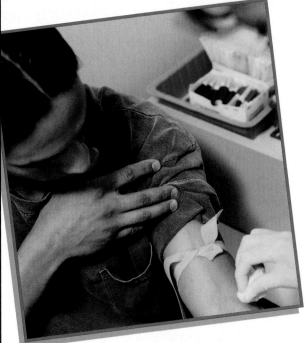

• **Hepatitis** (hep·uh·TYT·uhs). *A viral disease of the liver characterized by yellowing of the skin and the whites of the eyes* is known as **hepatitis**. There are different types of hepatitis, each caused by a different virus. They are hepatitis A, B, and C.

• **Mononucleosis** (mahn·oh·noo·klee·OH·sis). *A viral disease whose symptoms include swollen, tender areas in the neck and a sore throat* is **mononucleosis**. Mononucleosis, often called "mono," is most common in teens and young adults and is spread by direct contact. People who have mono generally feel weak and have little energy. Treatment includes complete bed rest. Recovery can take three or more weeks, and the disease can recur during the year after the first attack.

The symptoms for mononucleosis are similar to those for flu. A blood test determines if a patient has mono.

HEALTH SKILLS ACTIVITY

ACCESSING INFORMATION

Can I Catch What's in the News?

Local newspapers or news programs often report on new diseases or outbreaks of an existing disease. To find out if you are at risk, ask these questions and get the answers from reliable sources.

• **IS THE DISEASE COMMUNICABLE?** If it is, are you likely to come in direct or indirect contact with an infected person?

• **DOES THE DISEASE HAVE AN ENVIRONMENTAL CAUSE?** Some diseases arise from exposure to environmental hazards or from eating certain foods. Have you been exposed to these?

• **WHO IS AFFECTED BY THE DISEASE?** Some diseases affect certain groups of people, such as those of a specific age or gender. Are you in a vulnerable category?

• **IS THE DISEASE CONFINED TO A CERTAIN GEOGRAPHICAL AREA?** Some diseases are focused on a particular place. Do you live in that place, or have you recently traveled there?

ON YOUR OWN
Find a news report about a disease. Using these guidelines, analyze your risk for contracting the disease based on these factors: age, behavior, culture, environment, genetics, and pathogen exposure.

Health Literacy

Health Information One difference between a cold and the flu appears at the onset of the disease. Cold symptoms develop over a period of days; the flu comes on in just hours. Colds last one to two weeks, while the flu lasts three to five days. The symptoms of a cold are sneezing, a sore throat, and a runny nose. Flu symptoms include fever, a headache, a general feeling of illness, congestion in the lungs, and a cough. Colds are caused by 200 or more different viruses. There are only three types of flu viruses, with some variations. Vaccines can help prevent the flu, but no cold vaccine has yet been developed.

Good Health Habits

Good health habits reduce your chances of illness. When your body is strong and healthy, it is better able to fight off pathogens.

- Follow a sensible eating plan to maintain your overall health. A strong, healthy immune system can fight pathogens better than a weak one.
- Get plenty of rest. Fatigue reduces the effectiveness of your immune system.
- Get regular physical activity, especially when you feel stressed.
- Avoid tobacco, alcohol, and other drugs.
- Drink water only from approved water supplies. Do not drink from streams, lakes, and rivers.
- Avoid sharing personal items such as towels, toothbrushes, hairbrushes, and makeup.

Protecting your health with good nutrition and regular physical activity will help you fight diseases. *What other measures improve your overall health?*

Lesson 3 Review

Using complete sentences, answer the following questions on a sheet of paper.

Reviewing Terms and Facts

1. **Explain** Why should you stay home when cold symptoms first appear?
2. **Explain** What are the symptoms of strep throat? Why do they need to be treated?
3. **Recall** Which communicable disease is identified by a bull's-eye rash? How is it spread?
4. **List** What are the symptoms of hepatitis and mononucleosis?

Thinking Critically

5. **Summarize** Your friend Chloe has mono. What advice would you give her?
6. **Explain** How does practicing good health habits protect you from disease?

Applying Health Skills

7. **Accessing Information** Select one of the diseases mentioned in this lesson. Use reliable sources of information in the library or on the Internet to learn more about the disease. Prepare a pamphlet that gives detailed information about the causes, symptoms, and treatment of the disease.

LESSON 3: COMMUNICABLE DISEASES **457**

Lesson 3 Review

1. The most contagious period is during the first 24 hours after cold symptoms appear.
2. Very sore throat, fever, muscle pain, enlarged lymph nodes; left untreated, strep throat can lead to serious complications, including heart damage.
3. Lyme disease; by ticks.
4. Symptoms of hepatitis are yellowing of the skin and whites of the eyes; symptoms of mononucleosis are swollen, tender areas in the neck and a sore throat.
5. Responses may include avoid contact with others, see a doctor, get at least three weeks' bed rest.
6. Responses should detail how good health habits can reduce your chances of illness.

3 Assess

Evaluating

Assign the Lesson 3 Review; then assign the Lesson 3 Quiz in the TCR.

Reteaching

- Assign Concept Map 65 or Reteaching Activity 65 in the TCR.
- Have each student fold a sheet of paper into three columns. The columns should be labeled Disease, Symptoms, and Vaccine. Have students list five communicable diseases from this lesson. Then have them use the student text to complete the other two columns.

Enrichment

- Assign Enrichment Activity 65 in the TCR.
- Have students work together to develop an ad campaign that reminds teens about the best treatment for the common cold.

4 Close

Go around the room and ask students to provide one fact they learned about preventing the spread of disease from this lesson.

Lesson 4

Sexually Transmitted Diseases

① Focus

Lesson Objectives

Students will be able to
- define the term *sexually transmitted diseases*.
- explain why abstinence is the best way to avoid getting an STD.
- compare and contrast some common STDs.
- explain how some STDs can be treated.

Health Skills
- Communication Skills, p. 460

Motivators

Quick Write

As students read the lesson, have them refer to their questions. As they come across answers, they should record them with their questions in their notebooks. Address any unanswered questions during the lesson review.

Bellringer Activity

Ask students to list three health problems that can result from being sexually active.

VOCABULARY

Have students find the definition of the vocabulary term in the Glossary and write a sentence using the term.

Lesson 4

Sexually Transmitted Diseases

Quick Write

Write down three questions that you have about sexually transmitted diseases.

LEARN ABOUT...

- sexually transmitted diseases (STDs).
- why abstinence is the best way to avoid getting an STD.
- some common STDs and the problems they cause.
- how some STDs can be treated.

VOCABULARY

- sexually transmitted diseases (STDs)

What Are STDs?

Sexually transmitted diseases, or **STDs,** are *infections spread from person to person through sexual contact.* STDs are sometimes referred to as sexually transmitted infections, or STIs. In the United States, STDs are a major health problem for teens. Each year, one-quarter of all new cases of STDs occur among 15- to 19-year-olds. STDs take a toll on young people because many lack knowledge about STDs and how they are transmitted. **Figure 17.5** summarizes important facts about STDs.

FIGURE 17.5

WHAT YOU SHOULD KNOW ABOUT STDs

Learning the facts about STDs will help you avoid them.

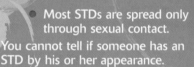

- Most STDs are spread only through sexual contact.
- You cannot tell if someone has an STD by his or her appearance.
- A person with an STD may have no symptoms.
- Many STDs can be treated, but early diagnosis is vital.
- Because treatments for STDs vary, they must be accurately identified.
- STDs can recur because the body does not build up immunity to them.
- STDs are serious diseases that can cause sterility, blindness, deafness, insanity, and death.

458 CHAPTER 17: COMMUNICABLE DISEASES

Lesson 4 Resources

Teacher Classroom Resources
- Concept Map 66
- Enrichment Activity 66
- Lesson Plan 4
- Lesson 4 Quiz
- Reading Tutor Activity 65

- Reteaching Activity 66
- Transparency 69

Student Activities Workbook
- Chapter 17 Study Guide
- Applying Health Skills 66

Practicing Abstinence

When you practice abstinence, you avoid the serious consequences of contracting an STD. This prevention is critical because STDs differ from other communicable diseases in two important ways. First, there are no vaccines for any STDs except hepatitis B. Second, your body cannot build immunity to STDs.

The only sure way to avoid getting an STD is to practice abstinence from sexual activity. Deciding to say no to sexual activity will be one of the most important health choices you ever make. Make a commitment to abstain from sexual activity. Demonstrate your commitment to abstinence through your words and behavior.

Responsible Behavior

Your actions and body language will tell others that you practice abstinence.

- Choose your friends carefully. They should share your values and support your decision about practicing sexual abstinence.
- Avoid being alone with a date. Group activities remove pressure for sexual activity.
- Know your limits and communicate them with your date before you go out.
- Say no through your words *and* your actions.
- Seek advice from a trusted adult on handling difficult situations.

Effective Communication

Below is a list of statements that someone might make to pressure you into sexual activity. Beside each statement is a sample response that shows your commitment to abstinence.

- If your date says, "If you really care for me, you would have sex with me," you can say, "If you really care for me, you would respect my decision."
- If your date says, "Sex can be safe," you can say, "Abstinence from sex is the only sure way to be safe."
- If your date says, "Everyone else is doing it," you can say, "The only thing that matters to me is what *I* choose to do. Besides, most teens *aren't* having sex."

Group activities are a good way to have fun while avoiding pressure to engage in sexual activity. *What group activities do you and your friends enjoy?*

LESSON 4: SEXUALLY TRANSMITTED DISEASES **459**

HEALTH SKILLS ACTIVITY

COMMUNICATION SKILLS

Guide students in reading about and discussing Jerome's situation. Ask:

- Why do you think Jerome wants to talk with Rick about the locker room incident?
- What response does he hope to get from Rick?

With students, analyze the importance of abstinence from sexual activity for unmarried persons of school age.

Review the listed communication skills. Then have students work with partners to role-play the conversation.

Note: This skill is introduced in Chapter 2 on pages 34–38.

Debating

Divide the class into two teams to debate whether STDs are just another group of communicable diseases or whether they are in a class by themselves. (*Support for the position that STDs are special diseases includes the following facts: No immunity to STDs can be built, there are no vaccines for them, and the symptoms can be hidden.*) **L2**

Applying Life Skills

Have students work in small groups or independently to create posters about preventing STDs. Students can display their posters throughout the school. They might also create radio and television spots that can be aired using the school's audiovisual system. **L2**

HEALTH SKILLS ACTIVITY

COMMUNICATION SKILLS

Helping a Friend Choose Abstinence

Rick and Jerome play on the school soccer team. In the locker room after practice, Rick listened to some of the other guys on the soccer team. They were boasting about their sexual experiences. Then they teased Rick about his inexperience.

On their way home from practice, Jerome wanted to talk about the incident. He thinks that most of the boys were lying about their experiences. He believes that abstinence is the best decision. What should he say to Rick?

What Would You Do?

Apply the skills for good communication to this situation. With a classmate, role-play a conversation between Jerome and Rick. The teen playing Jerome should state why he believes that abstinence is the best choice of behavior for all teens.

SPEAKING SKILLS

- Use "I" messages.
- Make clear, simple statements.
- Be honest with thoughts and feelings.
- Use appropriate body language.

LISTENING SKILLS

- Use appropriate body language.
- Use conversation encouragers.
- Mirror thoughts and feelings.
- Ask questions.

Feel Good About Your Decision

Dating should be fun, and abstinence helps teens enjoy healthy relationships. Also, teens who practice abstinence do not have to worry about STDs or pregnancy.

Common STDs

Each year, about 4 million teens contract an STD. However, many fail to get medical attention because they do not recognize the symptoms or are too embarrassed to ask for help. In all cases, diagnosis and treatment are necessary. **Figure 17.6** on page 462 lists several common STDs, along with their symptoms and treatments. HIV/AIDS, another serious STD, is discussed in Lesson 5.

Here is some general information about the most common STDs.

- **Chlamydia** (klah·MID·ee·ah) is a very common STD. It is a "silent" STD—many infected people have no symptoms. If left untreated, it can seriously damage the reproductive organs in both males and females.

460 CHAPTER 17: COMMUNICABLE DISEASES

Health Literacy

Health Behaviors Is there a parent in America who has not cautioned his or her child about the health hazards of public restrooms? Well, mother and father know best—a person *should* take precautions.

While most agents that cause STDs die outside the warm, moist environment of the human body, the herpes virus can survive outside the body on surfaces such as toilet seats and towels. Although it can survive for only a few hours, it is not known whether contact with the virus by touching such items can cause infection. Thus, it is better to take precautions, such as using seat covers and washing hands properly, when using public facilities.

- **Genital herpes** is caused by the virus herpes simplex type 2 (HSV-2). Herpes cannot be cured, and it results in periodic bouts of painful blisters on the genitals. Herpes can be passed to another person even when the blisters are not apparent.

- **Genital warts** are caused by the human papillomavirus (HPV). HPV has been linked with cervical cancer and skin cancer. It is thought that the virus may disable the skin's defenses against ultraviolet radiation from the sun.

- **Gonorrhea** is caused by bacteria. Infection can affect the entire body, causing joint pain. Some people, especially females, may not have symptoms until the disease is advanced.

- **Nongonococcal urethritis (NGU)** is an inflammation of the urethra—the tube that transports urine from the bladder. It is caused by bacteria different from those that cause gonorrhea. NGU is more common in men than in women.

- **Pelvic inflammatory disease (PID)** is a general infection of the female reproductive organs. Most women with PID became infected as a result of another STD, such as chlamydia or gonorrhea. If left untreated, PID may worsen over time and cause sterility.

- **Syphilis** is a very serious STD. If left untreated, the bacteria that cause syphilis invade the entire body, damaging the internal organs. Advanced syphilis may cause blindness, paralysis, insanity, and death.

Reading Check

Understand abbreviations. Which disease names are abbreviated with capital letters? Determine how each abbreviation is formed.

Learning the facts about STDs will help teens make the important decision to practice abstinence. Abstaining from sexual activity before marriage is the only sure way to avoid STDs. *Write an essay summarizing the facts related to STDs. In the essay, analyze why abstinence from sexual activity is the preferred choice of behavior for all unmarried persons of school age.*

LESSON 4: SEXUALLY TRANSMITTED DISEASES **461**

Lesson 4

Discussing

Have students discuss minor illnesses that they have had and have recovered from without getting medical attention (for example, a cold). Then ask:

- Why is it so important to seek medical attention if a person thinks he or she has an STD? (*Without medical treatment from a health care professional, many STDs can lead to serious complications.*)

- Why should a person in that situation not try to treat him- or herself? (*misdiagnosis, need for specific prescription medications, and follow-up probably necessary*) **L1**

Cross-Curriculum Activity

LANGUAGE ARTS Tell students that, although antibiotics can cure many STDs, some STD pathogens have become resistant to current medications. Have students define *resistant* in this context. Then have them write paragraphs about the problems such resistance poses to individuals and society. **L2**

Reading Check

Analyzing Abbreviations Determining how abbreviations are formed will help students remember the vocabulary more easily. Write STD on the board, and ask students what it stands for. Write *sexually transmitted disease* on the board, and underline the letters in the phrase used in the abbreviation. Ask students to infer the reason the words would be abbreviated, and identify characteristics of an abbreviation, such as all capital letters. Discuss other types of words, including abbreviations using periods and acronyms such as scuba. Have students identify an abbreviation that uses letters from places other than the beginning of a word (e.g., NGU). Have students determine the origin of each abbreviation on the page.

Lesson 4

VISUAL LEARNING

FIGURE 17.6 Divide the class into ten pairs or groups of students, and assign one of the listed STDs to each. Have the students in each pair or group read about their assigned STD and present a thorough explanation to the rest of the class. **INCL** *English Language Learners, Special Learning Needs, Behavior Problems, Different Learning Styles (Visual)*

Investigating

Have students learn more about the effects of herpes. In their reading, they should note how the infected individual must cope with the recurrence of the disease's symptoms. Have the students share what they have learned with the class. **L3**

Applying Life Skills

Have students work together to prepare a class list of people, resources, or organizations they can turn to for help with their personal health questions and issues. Then have students describe the qualities of a good resource. (*Listens without judging, can be trusted, and is knowledgeable.*) **L1**

A recent study by researchers at Johns Hopkins University found that 20 percent of sexually active girls ages 12 to 19 tested positive for chlamydia.

FIGURE 17.6

FACTS ABOUT COMMON STDs

Disease (Cause)	Symptoms	Treatment	What Could Happen
Chlamydia (bacteria)	Burning during urination; irritation of genitals; discharge; females may have mild or no symptoms	Antibiotics	Sterility from scarring of reproductive organs; infection of developing fetus in pregnant females
Genital herpes (HSV-2) (virus)	Painful, itchy blisters in genital area; fever; burning when urinating during outbreak	No cure; medication can relieve symptoms	Increased risk of HIV infection; brain damage or death of newborns of infected mother
Genital warts (virus)	Painless warts in genital area three weeks to six months after exposure to infected person	Topical medication; freezing or surgery to remove warts	Cancer of reproductive system; urinary blockage in males; cervical cancer in females; infection of newborn during birth
Gonorrhea (bacteria)	Discharge; swollen lymph nodes in groin; burning during urination; females may have mild or no symptoms	Antibiotics, but some strains of bacteria are drug resistant	Sterility; permanent damage to joints and body organs; infection of developing fetus in pregnant females
Hepatitis B (HBV) (virus)	Fatigue; loss of appetite; nausea; yellowing of the skin; joint pain	Prevented by vaccination; no treatment otherwise	Liver damage; liver cancer; infection of developing fetus in pregnant females
Nongonococcal urethritis (NGU) (bacteria)	Urethral discharge and discomfort in males; irritation of vagina or no symptoms in females	Antibiotics	Sterility; infection of reproductive organs; pneumonia in females; eye infection of newborn
Pelvic inflammatory disease (PID) (females only) (bacteria)	Foul-smelling discharge; tenderness in abdomen; backache; fever; vomiting; heavy menstrual periods	Antibiotics	Sterility from scarring of reproductive organs; constant pelvic pain
Pubic lice (crabs) (small insects)	Itching; presence of lice and eggs in pubic hair	Medicated soaps; washing of all bed linens and clothes	No lasting effects
Syphilis (bacteria)	Red sores in genital area; body rash; flulike symptoms; symptoms may disappear though disease is still active	Antibiotics	Increased risk of HIV infection; damage to cardiovascular system, liver, kidneys, and nervous system; blindness; insanity; death; birth defects in developing fetus of pregnant females
Trichomoniasis (protozoa)	Foul-smelling, yellowish discharge and itching in females; males may have no symptoms	Antibiotics	Infections of the bladder and urethra

462 CHAPTER 17: COMMUNICABLE DISEASES

COOPERATIVE LEARNING ACTIVITY

Issues About STDs Have students work in pairs or small groups to investigate one of the following controversial issues surrounding STDs: confidentiality of test results, legal suits against people who know they have STDs and intentionally infect others, the laws of the FDA on medicines available to treat STDs and the unavailability of certain experimental medicines, and prejudice against people with the infections. Have students report their findings to the class and, if possible, plan a panel discussion in which several or all of the issues are addressed. Encourage students to assume roles in their groups to divide up the task into manageable parts.

Other Infections to Watch For

Other types of infections may have symptoms similar to those of STDs. Urinary tract infections (UTIs) are caused by several different pathogens. In both males and females, a UTI can cause pain and burning during urination. If a urinary tract infection follows sexual activity, it might be an STD.

In females, vaginal yeast infections are fairly common. Yeasts are fungi. If they grow uncontrolled in the vagina, they produce a white discharge accompanied by itching and burning. While a vaginal yeast infection *may* result from sexual activity, not all do. Anyone who has the symptoms of a urinary or vaginal infection should see a physician for diagnosis and treatment.

If You Need Help

If you are concerned that you might have an STD, you must seek treatment right away. Most STDs respond to treatment if diagnosed early. Left untreated, they can lead to severe health problems, or even death. Talk to a responsible and caring adult about your concerns.

Early detection is the best way to treat an STD. If you suspect that you have one, you can talk confidentially with a health professional.

Lesson 4 Review

Using complete sentences, answer the following questions on a sheet of paper.

Reviewing Terms and Facts

1. **Vocabulary** Using your own words, define *sexually transmitted disease.*
2. **Recall** List four facts about STDs that teens need to know.
3. **Explain** What is the only sure way to avoid getting an STD?
4. **Summarize** Name six STDs and list a fact related to each one.

Thinking Critically

5. **Synthesize** Why should people seek medical help if they think they have been exposed to an STD, even though they have no symptoms?
6. **Discuss** Why is abstinence from sexual activity the only method that is 100 percent effective in preventing STDs?

Applying Health Skills

7. **Refusal Skills** On index cards, write as many lines as you can think of that might be used to pressure someone to be sexually active. With your teacher's approval, put all the cards from the class into a box. Take turns pulling out cards and reading them. Along with your peers, suggest appropriate refusal lines.

❸ Assess

Evaluating

📁 Assign the Lesson 4 Review; then assign the Lesson 4 Quiz in the TCR.

Reteaching

• 📁 Assign Concept Map 66 or Reteaching Activity 66 in the TCR.
• Have students work with partners to write informal outlines of the lesson. Have them use headings in the text as main heads in their outlines.

Enrichment

• 📁 Assign Enrichment Activity 66 in the TCR.
• Have each student pretend that a friend has confided a fear that he or she may have an STD. Have the student write a letter in which he or she summarizes the facts related to sexually transmitted diseases and offers suggestions to the friend about how to handle the situation.

❹ Close

Ask each student to write a statement that presents at least one reason for choosing abstinence. Ask student volunteers to read their statements. Review concepts about abstinence discussed in Chapter 6, Lesson 3, then lead students in a discussion of abstinence from sexual activity as the only method that is 100 percent effective in preventing sexually transmitted diseases.

Lesson 4 Review

1. Infections spread through sexual contact.
2. Any four: most are spread only through sexual contact; they do not show in personal appearance; most infected persons show no symptoms; early diagnosis is vital; they must be accurately identified; the body builds no immunity; they can cause serious health problems.
3. Abstinence from sexual activity.
4. See Figure 17.6 on page 462 for possible responses.
5. Some STDs have no symptoms. Early treatment is the most effective way to combat an infection.
6. Accept all reasonable responses.

Lesson 5

HIV/AIDS

① Focus

Lesson Objectives

Students will be able to

- define the terms AIDS and HIV.
- explain how HIV is spread as well as how it is not spread.
- discuss how to avoid getting HIV.
- summarize the facts related to HIV infection.

Health Skills
- Advocacy, p. 466

Motivators

Quick Write
At the conclusion of the lesson, ask students to identify any myths about HIV/AIDS that they had believed to be true.

Bellringer Activity

Instruct students to write examples of how the body's immune system helps prevent disease. After students have shared their responses, explain that AIDS impairs the effectiveness of the immune system.

VOCABULARY

Write the vocabulary terms on the board. Ask volunteers to use a dictionary to find the meanings of these words and word parts: *acquired, immuno-, deficiency, syndrome, opportunistic, infection.* Have another volunteer write the meanings on the board. Have each student write a sentence about each term that demonstrates its meaning.

464

Quick Write

Can you separate HIV/AIDS facts from myths? Write down two things that you have heard about HIV/AIDS. After reading this lesson, see whether the information was accurate.

LEARN ABOUT...

- AIDS and what causes it.
- how HIV is spread and how it is not spread.
- how to avoid getting HIV.

VOCABULARY

- acquired immunodeficiency syndrome (AIDS)
- human immunodeficiency virus (HIV)
- carrier
- opportunistic infection

What Is AIDS?

AIDS, or **acquired immunodeficiency syndrome,** is *a deadly disease that interferes with the body's natural ability to fight infection. The virus that causes AIDS* is called **HIV,** or **human immunodeficiency virus.** The only way a person can tell if he or she has been infected with HIV is through a blood test. There is currently no vaccine to prevent infection with HIV, and there is no cure for AIDS. It is usually fatal.

A person can be a carrier of HIV without having AIDS. A **carrier** is *a person who appears healthy but is infected with HIV and can pass it to others.* A person infected with HIV may be a carrier for ten or more years before starting to show symptoms of AIDS. **Figure 17.7** shows that people in various age groups might carry HIV without knowing they are infected. AIDS can affect men and women, children, and senior citizens. The primary way HIV is spread is through sexual activity with an infected person. Thus, AIDS can be prevented by practicing sexual abstinence.

FIGURE 17.7

U.S. AIDS CASES AT AGE OF DIAGNOSIS, 1999

AIDS develops months or years after infection with HIV. *How might this long time period make the spread of disease harder to control?*

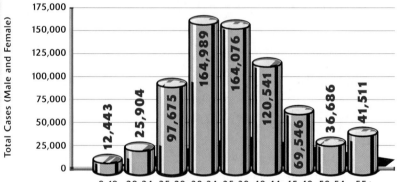

Age	Total Cases (Male and Female)
0–19	12,443
20–24	25,904
25–29	97,675
30–34	164,989
35–39	164,076
40–44	120,541
45–49	69,546
50–54	36,686
55+	41,511

Centers for Disease Control and Prevention-Divisions of HIV/AIDS Prevention: Basic Statistics—Cumulative Cases, 1999

464 CHAPTER 17: COMMUNICABLE DISEASES

Lesson 5 Resources

Teacher Classroom Resources

 Concept Map 67
Cross-Curriculum Activity 34
Decision-Making Activity 34
Enrichment Activity 67
Lesson Plan 5
Lesson 5 Quiz
Reading Tutor Activity 66

Reteaching Activity 67
Transparency 70

Student Activities Workbook

Chapter 17 Study Guide
Applying Health Skills 67
Health Inventory 17

What HIV Does to the Body

HIV attacks the immune system. As you learned earlier, T cells play an important role in the body's immunity function. They start the process of antibody production by activating B cells. HIV seeks out and destroys T cells. The damaged immune system can no longer fight the pathogens that a healthy immune system would destroy.

Shortly after being infected with HIV, some people have flulike symptoms. These symptoms may disappear for months or years, to be followed by the onset of AIDS itself. A person with AIDS may have swollen lymph nodes, fatigue, diarrhea, weight loss, and fever. To diagnose AIDS, doctors determine whether the person's T cell count is below normal.

Another signal that AIDS has developed is the presence of opportunistic infections. An **opportunistic infection** is *an infection that rarely occurs in a healthy person.* With a weakened immune system, a person with AIDS is susceptible to opportunistic infections. For example, many AIDS patients develop a type of pneumonia that can eventually cause death.

How HIV Is Spread

HIV cannot survive in the air. It is passed from one person to another only in body fluids—including blood, semen, and vaginal secretions. HIV infection can occur in the following ways:

- **Unprotected sexual contact with an infected person.** Infection with HIV can follow *one* incident of sexual activity, even if it is the first one. People who have multiple sex partners are at greatest risk.
- **Piercing the skin with a needle that was previously used by an infected person.** Many injecting drug users who share needles have contracted HIV. Drug use is not the only risky behavior, however. Any skin puncture by a contaminated needle or blade can cause HIV infection. Tattoos and body piercings performed with nonsterile materials greatly increase the risk of HIV infection.
- **Passage of HIV during pregnancy.** HIV transmission from mother to child may occur before or during birth, as well as through breast-feeding. New drug therapies have reduced the rate of HIV infection of the fetus during pregnancy.
- **Transfusions.** All donated blood is tested for HIV. The blood of a newly infected person, however, may not yet contain the antibodies that signal the presence of HIV.

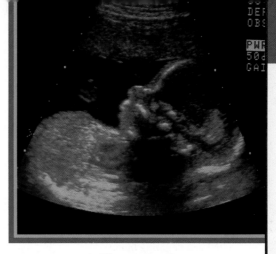

Females infected with HIV can pass the disease on to their babies. *Why should pregnant females be tested for HIV?*

Lesson 5

② Teach

VISUAL LEARNING

FIGURE 17.7 Ask a volunteer to read aloud the title and caption for Figure 17.7. Have students share their responses to the caption question; they should recognize that individuals may not know they are infected and so may infect others. Then help students read and discuss the statistics.

Note: If students are curious about the photo on this page, advise them that it is a sonogram of a fetus. **INCL** *English Language Learners, Special Learning Needs, Behavior Problems, Different Learning Styles (Visual)*

Critical Thinking

People visiting AIDS patients often wear gauze masks and protective gowns, not to protect themselves, but to protect the patient. Have students discuss why such precautions are necessary. (*Visitors could be carrying pathogens that the AIDS patient's immune system couldn't handle. The mask and gown minimize the spread of those germs.*) **L1**

Cross-Curriculum Activity

SOCIAL STUDIES Explain to students that many countries in Africa have been devastated by the spread of AIDS. By 2001, the epidemic in Africa was recognized as a global concern, and international organizations had begun to offer assistance. Ask students to choose one African country and do research to learn what is being done to treat people affected with the disease and to prevent its further spread. **L2**

Beyond the Classroom

Community To help students understand the measures communities are taking to prevent the spread of AIDS, encourage them to first learn more about one or more of the following research topics. Topics could include the search for a cure, current developments in developing a vaccine and other medicines, or prevention education. Then ask students to investigate the research being done in their state or community concerning the prevention of the disease. Students may work in small groups for this activity and, when finished, present their findings to the class.

Lesson 5

Discussing

Have students discuss and summarize the following:

- Risk factors associated with communicable diseases
- How HIV is and is not spread
- The relative safety of nonsexual contact with an AIDS patient
- How they would feel about having a student with AIDS in their class
- How they think that person would like to be treated by others **L1**

Guest Speaker

Invite a dentist or other health care professional to come to class to discuss the precautions he or she takes when treating an AIDS patient and how other patients are protected from subsequent exposure to the AIDS virus. **L1**

HEALTH SKILLS ACTIVITY

ADVOCACY

Have students read and discuss the activity introduction. Prompt the class to discuss abstinence from sexual activity as the only method that is 100 percent effective in preventing sexual transmission of HIV or acquired immune deficiency syndrome. Ask volunteers to explain what they already know about each suggestion. Ask: What is being done now and what more could you, as teens, do? Then have students demonstrate ways to use health information to help others by working in cooperative groups to complete the activity.

Note: This skill is introduced in Chapter 3 on page 61.

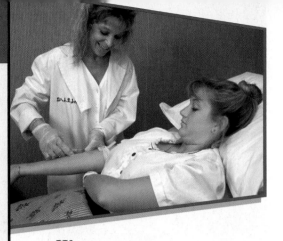

When donating blood in the United States, needles are used only once and then thrown away. *What are some other ways in which HIV is not spread?*

How HIV Is Not Spread

Unfortunately, false ideas about how HIV is spread have led to the social isolation of people with AIDS. Myths have also made some people reluctant to donate blood. Here are the facts:

- **HIV is not spread through the air.** HIV must remain in body fluids to survive. Breathing the same air as an infected person—even being coughed or sneezed on by an infected person—poses no risk of HIV infection.
- **HIV is not spread through kissing.** Kissing with the mouth closed is considered safe. In theory, open-mouthed kissing could transmit HIV if both persons have a cut or sore in the mouth.
- **HIV is not spread through casual contact with an infected person.** Shaking hands or having other casual contact with an infected person poses no risk of HIV infection.
- **HIV is not spread by mosquitoes that have bitten an infected person.** Although some blood-borne pathogens can be spread by mosquito bites, HIV is not one of them.
- **HIV is not spread by sharing eating utensils with an infected person.** You might catch another infection this way, but not HIV.
- **HIV is not spread by donating blood.** In the United States, the needles used to collect blood are sterile and used only once, then discarded. Blood donation in this country presents no risk of HIV infection.

HEALTH SKILLS ACTIVITY

ADVOCACY

Get the Message Out

Education is one of the most effective means of preventing the spread of HIV and AIDS. Here's what you can do.

- **LEARN MORE.** Invite a speaker to your school to discuss HIV/AIDS. You might ask the school nurse, a local physician, or an official of your state or local health department to share his or her knowledge.
- **SPREAD THE WORD.** Help others learn more about HIV/AIDS education and prevention. You might create a poster or write an article for the school newspaper. Create a public service announcement and submit it to a local radio station.
- **VOLUNTEER TO HELP.** Many communities have volunteer organizations that support people with AIDS. Some organizations deliver meals to patients. Others raise money for AIDS research.

AS A GROUP
Brainstorm additional ways to become an active member in the battle to conquer AIDS. Share your ideas with the class.

466 CHAPTER 17: COMMUNICABLE DISEASES

MORE ABOUT...

AIDS Tests Approximately one-third (32%) of adults in America have been tested for HIV. The most common reason for being tested is to donate blood. Current tests for HIV actually test for the presence of antibodies to HIV in a person's blood. If the test is positive, the person has been infected with HIV in the past and is, therefore, a carrier of HIV and can infect others. A negative test does not mean that she or he is not infected because it can take up to six months for antibodies to develop. The body of a person who has been recently infected may not have had time to develop antibodies yet. For this reason, people who are considered at risk for the disease are encouraged to repeat the test every six months.

Testing and Treatment

People who believe that they might be infected need to be tested for HIV. Blood tests detect the presence of antibodies to HIV. Be aware, however, that it may take up to six months after infection for a blood test to detect antibodies.

AZT is an antiviral medicine that slows the progress of HIV in the body. Newer treatment involves combining medicines called protease (PROH·tee·ayz) inhibitors and reverse transcriptase (tran·SKRIP·tayz) inhibitors. These medicines have allowed many AIDS patients to live with their disease and keep it under control. Despite antiviral medication, the HIV-infected individual can still infect others.

Preventing the Spread of HIV

Following two basic guidelines will prevent the spread of HIV.

- **Avoid sexual contact.** Many HIV infections are spread through sexual contact. Protect yourself by practicing abstinence.
- **Avoid drug use.** Drugs, including alcohol, impair your judgment and make you more likely to take risks. Drug users who share contaminated needles account for a large proportion of HIV infections.

Although great progress has been made in treating AIDS patients, HIV infection is still incurable and AIDS is fatal. This is why it is extremely important to refrain from behaviors that place you at risk for HIV infection.

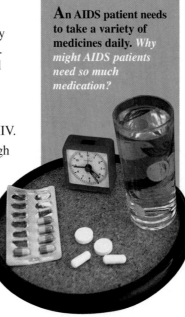

An AIDS patient needs to take a variety of medicines daily. *Why might AIDS patients need so much medication?*

Lesson 5 Review

Using complete sentences, answer the following questions on a sheet of paper.

Reviewing Terms and Facts

1. **Vocabulary** What term describes a person who has HIV but has not developed AIDS?
2. **Vocabulary** What is an *opportunistic infection?*
3. **Identify** List four ways that HIV infection *can* occur.
4. **Identify** List four ways that HIV infection *cannot* occur.

Thinking Critically

5. **Differentiate** Explain the difference between HIV and AIDS.
6. **Explain** Summarize the facts related to HIV infection and tell why HIV cannot be spread through casual contact with an infected person.

Applying Health Skills

7. **Communication Skills** Write a dialogue to discuss why abstinence from sexual activity is the only method that is 100 percent effective in preventing the sexual transmission of HIV.

LESSON 5: HIV/AIDS **467**

Lesson 5 Review

1. A carrier.
2. An infection that rarely occurs in a healthy person.
3. Unprotected sexual contact with an infected person, piercing skin with a needle previously used by an infected person, passage of HIV during pregnancy, blood transfusions.
4. Any four: air, kissing, casual contact, mosquitoes, sharing utensils, donating blood.
5. HIV is the virus that causes AIDS. AIDS is the deadly disease that interferes with the body's natural ability to fight infection.
6. Responses should include relevant information from the lesson and may mention that HIV is a fragile virus and must live in bodily fluids such as blood, semen, breast milk, or vaginal fluid.

Lesson 5

Applying Knowledge

Have students review the information in this lesson to compile and summarize the facts related to HIV infection. Have students include the fact that abstinence from sexual activity is the only method that is 100 percent effective in preventing sexual transmission of HIV. You may wish to divide the class into small groups to develop their fact sheets and then present them to the class. **L2**

❸ Assess

Evaluating

Assign the Lesson 5 Review; then assign the Lesson 5 Quiz in the TCR.

Reteaching

- Assign Concept Map 67 or Reteaching Activity 67 in the TCR.
- Guide students in discussing the photos in this lesson, explaining how each relates to HIV/AIDS.

Enrichment

- Assign Enrichment Activity 67 in the TCR.
- Have students write paragraphs describing how the rights of someone with AIDS can be protected.

❹ Close

Ask students to explain why every person should understand the facts about HIV/AIDS.

Healthy Germs

1 Focus

Objectives

Students will be able to

• recognize the seriousness of diarrhea as a medical condition.

• create recipes that include products made from fermented milk.

• identify the role of medical professionals in the research and application of probiotics.

Motivator

Bellringer Activity

Ask students, "When is the last time you ate yogurt, buttermilk, or another product made from fermented milk? Are these products a daily part of your diet? Why or why not?" Discuss student answers as a class.

2 Teach

Discussing

According to this article, one of the most promising uses of probiotics is to treat diarrhea. Ask, "Why all this fuss about such a minor complaint?" Explain that for most healthy people, a case of diarrhea is uncomfortable, but not a major health risk. However, for infants, children, and those whose system is weakened by other conditions, diarrhea can quickly lead to a life-threatening case of dehydration. Ask, "Who can tell me the definition of dehydration?" Explain that dehydration occurs when the body doesn't maintain enough fluids and salts for normal functioning. Severe dehydration causes vital organs such as the kidneys, brain, and heart to fail. In underdeveloped countries, dehydration from diseases such as dysentery and cholera kills millions of people each year.

Healthy Germs

What's new at the health-food store? Bacteria that fight diarrhea and other illnesses.

Say the word *bacteria*, and most people think of nasty germs that can make you really sick. Actually, most bacteria aren't bad for you. In fact, eating extra amounts of some bacteria can actually promote good health!

These beneficial bacteria are available without a prescription in drug and health-food stores—and in foods like yogurt. So far, the best results have been seen in the treatment of diarrhea, particularly in children. Researchers are looking into the possibility that beneficial bacteria may cure vaginal infections in women, prevent some food allergies in children, and lessen symptoms of Crohn's disease, a fairly rare but painful intestinal disorder.

Gut Reaction

Where are these good germs lurking? In your intestines! They're commonly found in the colon, which holds at least 400 species of bacteria. Which ones you have depend mostly on your environment and diet. An abundance of good bacteria in the colon usually crowds out any bad bacteria that you have ingested in food. At times, however, this balance can shift. For example, antibiotic treatment for an ear infection can kill normal intestinal germs, allowing the bad bacteria to outnumber the good. The result is often diarrhea.

MORE ABOUT...

Medical Professions Write the following professions on the board: biochemist, pediatrician, registered dietitian, medical researcher. Ask students, "What is the role of each of these professions in studying and applying new medical treatments such as probiotics? How are these professions the same or different?" Divide the class into four small work groups. Assign each group one of the professions above. Ask each group to research the role of their profession in relation to probiotics and report to the class.

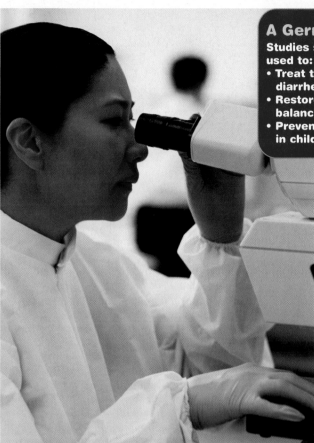

A Germ a Day...
Studies show that probiotics can be used to:
- Treat the most common forms of diarrhea.
- Restore your normal bacterial balance while taking antibiotics.
- Prevent intestinal upsets in children.

upsets caused by antibiotics. L-GG also seems to work against some viruses, including one of the most common causes of diarrhea in children.

Pediatricians at Johns Hopkins University in Baltimore, Maryland, are studying a different bacterium. It's called Bb-12, and it stimulates the immune system. Infants who are breastfed have large amounts of these bacteria in their intestines. They also have fewer intestinal upsets. Dr. José Saavedra and his fellow researchers have found that Bb-12 prevents several types of diarrhea in hospitalized infants.

Living Bacteria in Food

For generations, people have restored the balance by eating yogurt, buttermilk, or other products made from fermented milk. These foods contain living bacteria that are good for you. Nowadays, you can also swallow a few pills that contain freeze-dried germs. These preparations are called probiotics to distinguish them from antibiotics.

However, you can't always be sure that the bacteria in the products you buy are the same strains as those listed on the label—or even that they're still alive. Heat and moisture can quickly kill the bacteria in probiotics.

Among the most promising probiotics is L-GG, discovered by Dr. Sherwood Gorbach and biochemist Barry Goldin. L-GG has been used to treat traveler's diarrhea and intestinal

TIME TO THINK...

About Beneficial Bacteria
Pretend that you work for an advertising agency. Your big account is a company that produces foods made from fermented milk, which contains bacteria that are beneficial to humans. Create an ad campaign for your key products. The ads can be for magazines, billboards, radio, or TV—but they must both inform consumers about the products' health benefits and be entertaining enough to grab their attention. Present your ad campaign to the class.

❸ Apply

Time to Think

First, ask students to brainstorm foods that are made from fermented milk. These include yogurt, buttermilk, some types of sour cream, kefir, koumiss, and others. Tell students that one way to make their ad campaign more compelling is to make their "key product" appear delicious. Have students create a recipe that incorporates their product. For instance, yogurt parfaits can be made with fruit, yogurt, and granola or yogurt smoothies can be whirled in a blender. Students can include these recipes in their ad campaign of simply use the final product as a visual.

VISUAL LEARNING

Ask students to discuss the relationship between the two photos on this spread. How does the work of a scientist, seen on page 469, relate to the delicious yogurt on page 468? Is it a positive or negative relationship?

WHAT TEENS WANT TO KNOW

What is Crohn's disease? Crohn's disease is an inflammatory bowel disease that causes painful inflammation of the small intestine. Symptoms include abdominal pain, diarrhea, weight loss, rectal bleeding, and fever. No one knows exactly what causes Crohn's disease. The most popular theory is that the body's immune system over-reacts to a virus or bacteria, causing the ongoing inflammation. Surgery, nutritional supplements, and prescription drugs can help control symptoms, but there is no cure for the disease. For more information, log on to the Crohn's and Colitis Foundation of America website at www.ccfa.org.

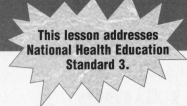

This lesson addresses National Health Education Standard 3.

PRACTICING HEALTHFUL BEHAVIORS

Objective

After completing the lesson, students will be able to demonstrate ways to prevent the spread of communicable diseases.

Time: 45 minutes

Materials: glitter or confetti (optional)

Teacher Classroom Resources

📁 Building Health Skills Activities

• Transparency Master 2d, "Practicing Healthful Behaviors"

• Reproducible Master 42, "Protecting Yourself and Others"

1. Model

• Display Transparency Master 2d, and review its content with the class.

• Have groups read about Tony and categorize the actions that he takes to protect himself from communicable diseases. Then discuss as a class. (*Categories may include: avoiding pathogens, boosting immune system, taking proper care when sick.*)

PROTECTING YOURSELF AND OTHERS

Model

Tony hates being sick because it means he can't take part in all his favorite activities. Read how Tony tries his best to protect himself from communicable diseases.

Tony avoids sharing eating utensils and drinking cups—especially with people who are sick—and he never shares combs, hats, or towels. When he takes his lunch to school, Tony uses a special lunch box that keeps cold food cold and hot food hot. He washes his hands often, especially after using the bathroom and before handling food. Tony loves to go hiking with his friends, so he knows all about how to protect himself from ticks. He always wears long pants for hiking and tucks them into his socks. After the hike, he examines himself carefully for ticks.

Tony knows that avoiding pathogens is only half the battle, however. He also needs to keep his immune system strong so that it can fight off the germs that get through. To do this, he eats healthful foods, stays active, and gets enough rest. When he does get sick, he stays home and rests until he feels better. Even though he hates missing out on the activities he enjoys, he knows that he will only feel worse if he doesn't take care of himself.

470 CHAPTER 17: COMMUNICABLE DISEASES

Teaching Tips

Reinforcing Content with a Hands-On Activity Use this activity to illustrate how easily pathogens can be spread. Place several small piles of glitter or confetti in various locations around the classroom (e.g., doorknobs, desktops, and pencil sharpeners). Do not disclose the locations of the glitter or confetti or explain why it is there. Toward the end of the class period, ask students to examine their hands, clothing, desks, and books for glitter or confetti. Explain that the glitter or confetti illustrates how easily pathogens can be spread through direct or indirect contact.

Practice

Annie has just come down with a cold. She is upset because if she stays home, she will miss the tryouts for the school play. On the other hand, she doesn't want to spread pathogens to any of her friends. Read the statements below about Annie's situation. On your own paper, write down the behaviors that can help Annie avoid spreading her pathogens to anyone else. The first one has been completed for you. Then list some other actions Annie could take to protect others from her cold.

Practicing Healthful Behaviors

To prevent common communicable diseases:
- practice good health habits.
- protect yourself.
- protect others.

1. Annie has a cold, but she hates to miss the tryouts at school. The best thing for Annie to do is to <u>stay in bed and rest</u>.

2. Annie's friend Clarice calls to say she will bring Annie's homework assignments to her house. Annie should tell Clarice to _____.

3. Each time she sneezes or coughs, Annie should _____.

4. In order to recover from her cold more quickly, Annie may need to _____.

Self-√Check

- Does our skit show ways to avoid pathogens?
- Does it show ways to avoid spreading pathogens to others?
- Does it show health habits that help the body fight pathogens?

Apply/Assess

Here's your chance to be creative. Work with a partner or a small group to create a skit about ways to prevent the spread of communicable diseases. The characters in your skit should demonstrate at least two ways to protect themselves from germs, as well as two ways to avoid spreading their own germs to others. They should also illustrate at least two health habits that can keep the immune system strong enough to fight off pathogens. Be prepared to perform your skit for the class.

2. Practice

- Have students read about Annie's situation and, working individually, complete on a separate sheet of paper the sentences that follow.
- Instruct students to compare their answers with those of their classmates. Then have them develop a list of additional actions that Annie could take to protect others from her cold.
- Ask volunteers to share the other ideas that they came up with for Annie and discuss as a class.

3. Apply/Assess

- You may wish to distribute Building Health Skills Reproducible Master 42 in the TCR to guide students in completing this activity.
- Divide the class into pairs or small groups. Direct students to create skits that feature ways to prevent the spread of communicable diseases.
- Remind students that skits should show at least two ways for the characters to protect themselves from pathogens, two ways the characters could avoid spreading their pathogens to others, and two healthful habits that can strengthen the immune system.
- Remind students to refer to the Self-Check before and after they create their skits.
- Provide an opportunity for students to perform their skits for the class. Have observers identify actions and health habits that are demonstrated in the skits.

Assessment Scoring

Using a rubric, student work should provide evidence of all criteria to achieve the highest score.

Skills
Student work demonstrates
- good health habits.
- actions that protect self and others from communicable diseases.

Concepts
Student work provides
- accurate information about the prevention of communicable diseases.
- conclusions about how communicable diseases spread.
- relationships between actions and health.

Checking Comprehension

Use the Chapter 17 Assessment to examine the most important ideas presented in the chapter.

Answers to Reviewing Vocabulary and Concepts

Lesson 1
1. communicable
2. pathogens
3. bacteria
4. viruses
5. fungi

Lesson 2
6. immunity
7. inflammation
8. B cells
9. T cells

Lesson 3
10. true
11. false; hepatitis
12. false; has an effect

Lesson 4
13. true
14. false; abstinence (from sexual activity)
15. false; genital herpes

Lesson 5
16. d
17. c
18. a

Thinking Critically

19. Examples might include becoming infected with a disease by sharing a contaminated needle or engaging in sexual activity because judgment is impaired by drugs.

After You Read

Use your completed Foldable to review the information on pathogens and communicable disease.

FOLDABLES Study Organizer

Reviewing Vocabulary and Concepts

On a sheet of paper, write the numbers 1–9. After each number, write the term from the list that best completes each sentence.

> - B cells
> - communicable
> - viruses
> - bacteria
> - T cells
> - pathogens
> - inflammation
> - immunity
> - fungi

Lesson 1

1. A(n) _____ disease can be passed to a person from another person, animal, or object.
2. _____ are tiny organisms that cause communicable diseases.
3. Tiny one-celled organisms that live nearly everywhere are called _____.
4. Colds, flu, and hepatitis are caused by _____.
5. Ringworm and athlete's foot are examples of diseases caused by _____.

Lesson 2

6. _____ is your body's ability to resist the germs that cause a particular disease.
7. The first nonspecific immune response is _____, or increased blood flow to the affected area.
8. Lymphocytes that produce antibodies are called _____.

9. Lymphocytes that attack pathogens directly and that stimulate the production of B cells are called _____.

On a sheet of paper, write the numbers 10–15. Write *True* or *False* for each statement below. If the statement is false, change the underlined word or phrase to make it true.

Lesson 3

10. Strep throat can be cured with <u>antibiotics</u>.
11. <u>Rubella</u> is a viral disease of the <u>liver</u> characterized by yellowing of the skin.
12. Fatigue <u>has no effect</u> on your immune system.

Lesson 4

13. A person with an STD may have <u>no symptoms</u>.
14. The only sure way to prevent an STD is to practice <u>good hygiene</u>.
15. An STD for which there is no known cure is <u>chlamydia</u>.

Lesson 5

On a sheet of paper, write the numbers 16–18. After each number, write the letter of the answer that best completes each statement.

16. HIV infects and destroys
    a. bacteria.
    b. B cells.
    c. protozoa.
    d. T cells.
17. HIV is passed from one person to another
    a. by mosquitoes.
    b. by shaking hands.
    c. through body fluids.
    d. through the air.
18. HIV is *not* spread by
    a. donating blood.
    b. having sex.
    c. receiving contaminated blood.
    d. sharing needles.

Thinking Critically

Using complete sentences, answer the following questions on a sheet of paper.

19. Apply Relate other drug use to communicable disease: Give three examples of how using drugs can increase the risk of contracting a communicable disease.

20. Synthesize Explain what is wrong with this statement: Once a person gets an STD and receives treatment for it, he or she can never get it again.

21. Analyze How might having a close friend who has HIV influence your attitudes toward people with AIDS?

Career Corner

Nurse Practitioner Would you like to help people stay healthy? Do you like finding answers to health problems? If so, consider a career as a nurse practitioner. These professionals gather medical histories, perform physical examinations, and prescribe medications. To become a nurse practitioner, you need at least a two-year nursing degree and specialized advanced training. Find out more about this and other health careers by clicking on Career Corner at health.glencoe.com.

Standardized Test Practice

Math

Read the paragraph below and then answer the questions.

One communicable disease that is spread by mosquitoes is West Nile virus. Outbreaks occur during times that mosquitoes are active—summer and autumn in temperate climates and all year in warmer climates. Although the symptoms are generally mild, people may become seriously ill or even die from the disease. If you go outside when mosquitoes might be present, use insect repellent to prevent them from biting you.

1. As of September 5, 2003, 174 cases of West Nile virus were reported for 2003 in Texas. Four of these people died. From this information, what is the probability that the disease will be fatal to someone in Texas who becomes ill with West Nile virus?

(A) $\frac{2}{87}$

(B) $\frac{1}{44}$

(C) $\frac{87}{2}$

(D) $\frac{44}{1}$

2. In Ohio, the probability that a person who becomes ill with the West Nile virus will die is $\frac{1}{15}$. Use a proportion to find the number of people who are likely to die if 105 people become ill with the disease.

(A) 5 people

(B) 7 people

(C) 15 people

(D) 105 people

3. As of September 5, 2003, 7 cases of West Nile virus had been reported for 2003 in Georgia, 42 cases in Louisiana, 6 cases in Missouri, 326 cases in Nebraska, and 6 cases in Indiana. What is the mode of these data? Is the mode the best way to interpret these data? What measure might be better to use?

TH05_C3.glencoe.com/quiz

20. The body does not build immunity to STDs. A person could get the same STD again.

21. Might increase awareness, compassion, understanding of disease; might decrease judgmental attitudes.

Test Practice

1. A

2. B

3. Sample answer: The mode is 6. Using the mode as a representative number indicated that the number of cases is lower than it actually is. The mean would be a better choice.

Reteaching

Assign Study Guide 17 in the Student Activities Workbook.

Evaluate

Use the reproducible Chapter 17 Test in the TCR, or construct your own test using the **Exam**View® Pro Testmaker.

Enrichment

Ask the class (or a group of class members) to develop a game show with questions about communicable diseases. Provide class time for playing the game.

Assessment

Self-Assessment Direct students to review the activities that are provided throughout the chapter. Encourage each student to select one finished product or activity that demonstrates his or her best work for the chapter. Have students explain what they learned and how the examples they selected show their progress.

Career Corner

Nurse Practitioner After reviewing the career profile on the health Web site, students might:

• Describe the skills, training, and education needed.

• Interview a nurse practitioner in the community to find out what aspects of nursing he or she enjoys the most. Have students present their findings to the class.

Planning Guide

Chapter 18	Skills/ Activities	Reproducible Resources	Assessment
Lesson 1 **Noncommunicable Diseases** *pages 476–479*	**HEALTH SKILLS ACTIVITY** ▲ Promoting a Healthful Lifestyle (*Advocacy*), page 478	*Student Activities Workbook available for use with each chapter* 📁 Parent Letter & Activities 18 📁 Concept Map 68 📁 Decision-Making Activity 35 📁 Enrichment Activity 68 📁 Lesson Plan 1 📁 Reading Tutor Activity 67 📁 Reteaching Activity 68	📁 Lesson 1 Quiz
Lesson 2 **Allergies and Asthma** *pages 480–483*	**HEALTH SKILLS ACTIVITY** ▲ Managing Chronic Conditions (*Decision Making*), page 483	📁 Concept Map 69 📁 Enrichment Activity 69 📁 Lesson Plan 2 📁 Reading Tutor Activity 68 📁 Reteaching Activity 69	📁 Lesson 2 Quiz
Lesson 3 **Cancer** *pages 484–488*		📁 Concept Map 70 📁 Decision-Making Activity 36 📁 Enrichment Activity 70 📁 Lesson Plan 3 📁 Reading Tutor Activity 69 📁 Reteaching Activity 70	📁 Lesson 3 Quiz
Lesson 4 **Heart and Circulatory Problems** *pages 489–493*	**Hands-On Health** ▲ Measuring Blood Pressure, page 490	📁 Concept Map 71 📁 Cross-Curriculum Activity 35 📁 Enrichment Activity 71 📁 Lesson Plan 4 📁 Reading Tutor Activity 70 📁 Reteaching Activity 71 📁 Concept Map 72	📁 Lesson 4 Quiz
Lesson 5 **Diabetes and Arthritis** *pages 494–497*	**HEALTH SKILLS ACTIVITY** ▲ Locating Support Groups (*Accessing Information*), page 496	📁 Cross-Curriculum Activity 36 📁 Enrichment Activity 72 📁 Health Lab 18 📁 Lesson Plan 5 📁 Reading Tutor Activity 71 📁 Reteaching Activity 72	📁 Lesson 5 Quiz 📁 Chapter 18 Test 📁 Performance Assessment 18

TIME HEALTH   **The Diabetes Explosion** *pages 498–499*

BUILDING HEALTH SKILLS

Managing Teen Stress
(*Stress Management*)
pages 500–501

📁 Building Health Skills Reproducible Master 43

Standards		Technology
National	**State/Local**	
National Health Education Standard **1.1, 1.3, 1.5, 1.6, 1.7, 1.8, 5.4, 7.4**		Transparency 71 TeacherWorks™ Internet Activities
National Health Education Standard **1.3, 1.5, 1.6, 1.7, 1.8, 3.4, 6.1, 6.2, 6.3**		Transparency 72 TeacherWorks™
National Health Education Standard **1.1, 1.3, 1.5, 1.6, 1.7, 1.8, 2.6, 3.1, 3.4**		Transparency 73 TeacherWorks™
National Health Education Standard **1.1, 1.3, 1.6, 1.7, 1.8, 2.6, 3.1, 3.4**		Transparency 74 TeacherWorks™
National Health Education Standard **1.3, 1.6, 1.7, 1.8, 2.4, 2.6, 3.1, 3.4**		Transparency 75 TeacherWorks™ MindJogger Videoquiz **Exam**View® Pro Testmaker
National Health Education Standard **3.4, 3.7**		Building Health Skills Transparency Master 3

TeacherWorks™

Glencoe's new and exclusive TeacherWorks™ is an all-in-one planner and resource center. Access the complete Teacher Wraparound Edition electronically. Find all your classroom resources with just a few easy clicks, and print them right from your computer. Connect directly to Glencoe's customized Health Web site. Access the National Health Education Standards correlations, or insert your own state standards and match them directly to the electronic Teacher Wraparound Edition.

Language Diversity

- English Audio Summaries
- Spanish Audio Summaries
- English Summaries, Quizzes, and Activities
- Spanish Summaries, Quizzes, and Activities
- Spanish Parent Letters and Activities

KEY TO ABILITY LEVELS

Teaching Strategies that appear throughout the chapters have been identified by one of four codes to give you an idea of their suitability for students of varying learning styles and abilities.

L1 **Level 1** strategies should be within the ability range of all students. Often full class participation is required.

L2 **Level 2** strategies are for average to above-average students or for small groups. Some teacher direction is necessary.

L3 **Level 3** strategies are designed for students able and willing to work independently. Minimal teacher direction is necessary.

INCL Strategies are appropriate for students with particular special needs in a general classroom setting.

CHAPTER

18

Noncommunicable Diseases

Chapter at a Glance

Lesson 1 introduces common noncommunicable diseases and their causes, and discusses how lifestyle behaviors can be a contributing factor.

Lesson 2 explains what allergies and asthma are, and examines how they affect the body.

Lesson 3 discusses how cancer develops, the warning signs and treatment, and steps to reduce the risk of developing it.

Lesson 4 describes the main types of heart disease as well as preventive measures and treatments.

Lesson 5 focuses on diabetes and arthritis, with information about the appropriate treatment of both diseases.

Health Skills

- Promoting a Healthful Lifestyle (*Advocacy*), p. 478
- Managing Chronic Conditions (*Decision Making*), p. 483
- Locating Support Groups (*Accessing Information*), p. 496
- Managing Teen Stress (*Stress Management*), pp. 500–501

474

HANDS-ON ACTIVITY

Trivia Question To introduce students to the chapter, have them scan the lessons for information to write their own quiz questions. Students may work in pairs or individually to create at least two questions per lesson. For example, in Lesson 1 they might ask: Which noncommunicable disease can result in paralysis? (*Multiple Sclerosis—MS*) Collect the questions and redistribute them for different students to answer. Then have them write their answers on the page they receive. Select a question from each lesson to write on the board and encourage the class to answer it. Which questions were more challenging to answer? Why? Discuss what students learned from this activity about noncommunicable diseases.

Noncommunicable Diseases

Chapter Introduction

Use the options below to motivate students and preview chapter content.

HEALTH *Online*

Do your habits and choices protect your lifelong health? Use the Chapter 18 Health Inventory at health.glencoe.com to rate your behaviors and choices.

Visit **health.glencoe.com**, and have students complete Health Inventory 18 to rate their knowledge of noncommunicable diseases. For other teaching strategies, explore the Lesson Plans and select from Cross-Curriculum, Reading, or Media Literacy activities.

FOLDABLES™ Study Organizer

Before You Read

Make this Foldable to record and collect information on the causes of noncommunicable diseases presented in Lesson 1. Begin with a plain sheet of 11″ × 17″ paper.

Step 1

Fold the sheet of paper into thirds along the short axis.

Step 2

Open and fold the bottom edge up to form a pocket. Glue the edges.

Step 3

Label each pocket as shown.

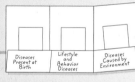

Diseases Present at Birth | Lifestyle and Behavior Diseases | Diseases Caused by Environment

As You Read

Summarize key points on the different types of noncommunicable diseases on index cards or sheets of notebook paper cut into quarter sections. Store these cards in the appropriate pocket of your Foldable.

GLENCOE TECHNOLOGY

MindJogger Videoquiz

Use MindJogger to preview or review Chapter 18 content.

TIME HEALTH

The Diabetes Explosion
pages 498–499

FOLDABLES™ Study Organizer

Dinah Zike Study Fold

Analyzing Causes and Effects
Students will use this Foldable study guide to write about three types of noncommunicable diseases. For study cards, students will need 3″ × 5″ index cards or sheets of notebook paper cut into quarter sections. As students read and discuss the material presented in Lesson 1, have them use their study cards to take notes on the following: diseases present at birth, lifestyle and behavior diseases, and diseases caused by the environment. Guide students as they sort and store these study cards in the appropriate pocket of their Foldable. Encourage them to use their study cards to prepare for quizzes and tests.

Noncommunicable Diseases

① Focus

Lesson Objectives

Students will be able to

- describe some common noncommunicable diseases and their causes.
- explain how lifestyle behaviors can contribute to diseases.
- discuss how substances in the environment can cause diseases.

Health Skills
- Advocacy, p. 478

Motivators

Quick Write

List the diseases and their possible causes on the board. Clarify any misconceptions as you introduce the lesson.

VOCABULARY

Write each vocabulary term on four separate index cards. Copy definitions of the terms as given in the lesson on each of four more cards. Mix up the cards, and give one card to each of eight students. On your signal those students should find the match for their term or definition. When they have finished, ask each student pair to read the term and its definition. Have the class verify each match.

Noncommunicable Diseases

Quick Write

List three common diseases that you think are *not* passed from person to person. What do you think causes these diseases?

LEARN ABOUT...

- the causes of noncommunicable diseases.
- how lifestyle behaviors can contribute to diseases.
- substances in the environment that can cause diseases.

VOCABULARY

- noncommunicable diseases
- chronic diseases
- degenerative diseases
- risk factors

Causes of Noncommunicable Diseases

As you learned in Chapter 17, communicable diseases are caused by the spread of pathogens. **Noncommunicable diseases**, on the other hand, are *diseases that are not transmitted by pathogens.* Diabetes is one example. You can't catch diabetes from someone who has the disease. **Figure 18.1** provides information about common noncommunicable diseases. In some cases, a noncommunicable disease may be present at birth. In other cases, the disease may develop as a result of a person's lifestyle behaviors. Sometimes the disease develops from the effects of substances in the person's environment. In many cases, the cause is unknown.

Many noncommunicable diseases are **chronic diseases**, *diseases that are present either continuously or off and on over a long time.* Asthma is a chronic disease. Some noncommunicable diseases cause body cells and tissues to break down, or degenerate. *Diseases that cause further breakdown in body cells, tissues, and organs as they progress* are known as **degenerative diseases**. An example is multiple sclerosis.

Diseases Present at Birth

Some babies are born with physical or mental disabilities resulting from birth defects or genetic disorders. The causes of many birth defects are unknown. Some may result from harmful

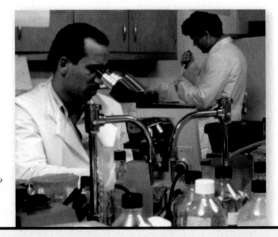

Researchers hope to find new ways of diagnosing, treating, and perhaps even preventing genetic disorders. *Who might benefit from this research?*

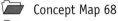

Lesson 1 Resources

Teacher Classroom Resources

- Parent Letter & Activities 18
- Concept Map 68
- Decision-Making Activity 35
- Enrichment Activity 68
- Lesson Plan 1
- Lesson 1 Quiz

- Reading Tutor Activity 67
- Reteaching Activity 68
- Transparency 71

Student Activities Workbook

- Chapter 18 Study Guide
- Applying Health Skills 68

FIGURE 18.1

COMMON NONCOMMUNICABLE DISEASES

Disease	Description
Allergies	An abnormal reaction by the body to an ordinarily harmless substance. Examples include hay fever, eczema, and food allergies.
Alzheimer's disease	A degenerative brain disorder that causes permanent loss of memory and other brain functions; mainly affects people 60 and older.
Arthritis	A group of diseases that cause body joints to swell, making movement painful and difficult; affects people of all ages.
Asthma	A disorder characterized by attacks of coughing, wheezing, and shortness of breath; results from an overreaction of respiratory airways to specific factors such as pets, foods, and pollen.
Cancer	A group of about 100 diseases that involve uncontrolled growth of abnormal cells; can affect any body tissue.
Cardiovascular disease	A group of diseases that affect the heart and blood vessels. Common forms include high blood pressure and hardening of the arteries, which can cause heart attack and stroke.
Cerebral palsy	A group of conditions that damage the brain around or before the time of birth or during the first year of life.
Cystic fibrosis	An inherited disease characterized by the production of thick, sticky mucus that clogs the respiratory system and digestive tract.
Multiple sclerosis (MS)	A disorder of the brain and spinal cord that causes serious problems with the use of limbs and with vision; can result in paralysis.
Muscular dystrophy	A group of inherited diseases characterized by a weakening of muscle tissue, especially skeletal and cardiac muscles.
Sickle-cell disease	An inherited disease of the blood that causes anemia and extreme pain; mainly affects certain ethnic groups.

substances in the environment. If a pregnant female is exposed to X rays, for example, the developing fetus may be harmed. Other birth defects are caused by lifestyle behaviors of the mother. A pregnant female who drinks alcohol, for example, may give birth to a child with fetal alcohol syndrome (FAS).

Genetic disorders are caused by a defect in genes. Genes carry hereditary information from parents to their children. Examples of genetic disorders include sickle cell disease and Down syndrome. There is no cure for most birth defects and genetic disorders. However, many people with diseases present at birth can be treated with medicine, therapy, or surgery.

Reading Check

Study charts and graphs. What types of information are provided for the diseases listed in Figure 18.1?

Reading Check

Text Organization Point out to students that Figure 18.1 contains information about a variety of common noncommunicable diseases. For each listing in the chart, there is a name on the left. Ask students to describe the types of information they find on the right next to each disease name. List on the board these types of information: def- inition statement, examples, symptoms, long- term effects, and whom the disease is likely to affect. Then challenge students to find answers in the chart to questions such as these: Eczema is an example of what type of disease? (*allergy*) Which two diseases involve the respi- ratory system? (*asthma* and *cystic fibrosis*)

❷ Teach

Critical Thinking

Have students differentiate between the terms *chronic* and *degenerative*. Ask the questions below, and have students support their answers with examples:

• Can a chronic disease also be degen- erative? (*yes; e.g., diabetes*)

• Can a degenerative disease also be chronic? (*yes; e.g., cancer*) **L2**

VISUAL LEARNING

FIGURE 18.1 Divide the class into 11 pairs or small groups, and assign each pair or group one of the non- communicable diseases listed in Figure 18.1. Have the students in each pair or group read about the assigned disease and present the information to the rest of the class, adding information or questions, as appropriate. **INCL** *English Lan- guage Learners, Special Learning Needs, Behavior Problems, Different Learning Styles* (*Visual*)

HEALTH SKILLS PRACTICE

Accessing Information Students should understand that birth defects may be caused by what a pregnant female does or does not do. Have students find out about the proper diet and health habits of a mother-to-be. Ask students to write a list of four choices a preg- nant woman can make to lessen the chances that her baby will have birth defects.

Lesson 1

Discussing

Have students brainstorm a list of ten habits common to teens at school and note any that might not be good for them. Discuss ways of changing negative habits. (*Tips include: start slow, change one habit at a time, reward positive progress, and so on.*) **L1**

HEALTH SKILLS ACTIVITY

ADVOCACY

Guide students in reading and discussing the listed healthy lifestyle behaviors. Ask them to identify information relating to abstinence. Then for each listed behavior, ask:

• What are the short- and long-term benefits?

• How can modeling this behavior help both you and your friends and family?

Then have students work in groups to plan and write their articles.

Note: This skill is introduced in Chapter 3 on page 61.

Lifestyle Behaviors and Disease

In general, it is difficult to predict who will develop a particular disease. For some diseases, however, researchers have identified certain **risk factors**. These are *characteristics that increase a person's chances of developing a disease.* Heredity, age, gender, and ethnic group are risk factors over which people have no control.

Fortunately, people do have control over a major group of risk factors—lifestyle behaviors. Examples include your eating habits, the amount of physical activity you get each day, and the amount of sleep you receive each night. Many diseases are the direct or indirect result of harmful lifestyle behaviors, such as using tobacco or eating too many fatty foods. Healthful lifestyle behaviors, on the other hand, can help prevent, control, or reduce the risk of certain diseases. Lifestyle behaviors may be influenced by cultural factors. For example, cultural traditions may include eating high-fat foods or a variety of fresh fruits and vegetables. Cultural influences can increase or decrease a person's risk for disease.

Although healthful lifestyle behaviors do not guarantee against noncommunicable diseases, they do help. By eating foods low in salt, for example, a person with a family history of high blood pressure can minimize his or her risk.

HEALTH SKILLS ACTIVITY

ADVOCACY

Promoting a Healthful Lifestyle

Be a role model by practicing healthful lifestyle behaviors. Here are some tips.

● **EAT HEALTHFUL FOODS.** Eat plenty of whole grains, fruits, and vegetables. Go easy on foods high in fat, sugar, or salt.

● **STAY PHYSICALLY ACTIVE.** Regular physical activity strengthens all body systems and helps the heart and lungs function better.

● **MAINTAIN A HEALTHY WEIGHT.** Keep your weight within the recommended range for your gender, height, age, and body frame.

● **GET ENOUGH REST.** Teens need at least nine hours of sleep a night.

● **MANAGE STRESS.** Use appropriate time management and stress reduction techniques.

● **AVOID TOBACCO AND SECONDHAND SMOKE.** Tobacco causes respiratory and heart diseases and cancer.

● **AVOID ALCOHOL AND OTHER DRUGS.** These substances harm the body and impair judgment.

WITH A GROUP
Working in small groups, select a noncommunicable disease. Prepare an article for the school newspaper emphasizing the role of healthful lifestyle behaviors in preventing that disease.

Beyond the Classroom

Community Many groups have been formed to provide psychological and physical assistance to people with noncommunicable diseases and their families. Community-supported agencies that provide educational materials and speakers often coordinate support groups too. Have students select a noncommunicable chronic or degenerative disease, locate a support agency, and write to the agency requesting information about the disease and the services for patients. These agencies may provide speakers who can. help students distinguish risk factors associated with noncommunicable diseases in general and give students greater insight into the lifelong problems that affect people with these diseases and ways in which they cope with them.

Diseases Caused by the Environment

The environmental substances listed below can cause serious health problems or make existing health problems worse for some people.

- **Chemical waste** in buried landfills creates fumes that can seep into houses constructed over them. Illness can occur years after initial exposure.
- **Certain construction materials** such as asbestos can cause lung disease after long exposure. Asbestos use is now restricted. Asbestos in existing buildings may be removed or sealed off.
- **Household chemicals,** including paints and solvents, can pollute indoor air and cause health problems.
- **Secondhand smoke** in restaurants, businesses, and homes can be harmful to nonsmokers.
- **Improper waste disposal** by manufacturers of household items such as plastics and paint creates air and water pollution. Improper disposal of household items, such as oil from the car, old paint cans, and old aerosol cans, can pose health risks as well.
- **Radon** is a colorless, odorless gas that is released from soil and rocks that contain tiny amounts of radium. Radon can seep into the air through foundations, basements, and pipes. Exposure to radon over a long span of time increases the risk of lung cancer.
- **Carbon monoxide** is a colorless, odorless gas produced when fuel is burned. It is present in fumes from car exhaust and some furnaces and fireplaces. When fuel-burning appliances do not work properly, they can produce dangerous levels of carbon monoxide. The gas can cause serious illness or even death.

Improper waste disposal can pollute water and pose serious health risks. *How can communities lower the risk of diseases caused by the environment?*

Lesson 1 Review

Using complete sentences, answer the following questions on a sheet of paper.

Reviewing Terms and Facts

1. **Vocabulary** Using your own words, define *chronic disease.*
2. **List** Name five noncommunicable diseases.
3. **Give Examples** Give an example of a lifestyle behavior of pregnant females that could cause their babies to be born with birth defects.
4. **Summarize** What kinds of substances in the environment are harmful to individual and community health?

Thinking Critically

5. **Compare** What are the differences between noncommunicable diseases and communicable diseases?
6. **Evaluate** Distinguish two risk factors associated with noncommunicable diseases. Why is it important to identify these risk factors?

Applying Health Skills

7. **Practicing Healthful Behaviors** Select a noncommunicable disease that may be a risk for you. What steps can you take to reduce your risk?

LESSON 1: NONCOMMUNICABLE DISEASES **479**

Lesson 1

Critical Thinking

Ask students to name some hazards in their own environment that might be dangerous to their health. Encourage students to discuss how they might help reduce or eliminate such hazards. **L1**

③ Assess

Evaluating

Assign the Lesson 1 Review; then assign the Lesson 1 Quiz in the TCR.

Reteaching

- Assign Concept Map 68 or Reteaching Activity 68 in the TCR.
- Have students work with partners to write their own definitions for *noncommunicable disease, degenerative disease,* and *chronic disease.*

Enrichment

- Assign Enrichment Activity 68 in the TCR.
- Have students work in groups to write and perform a rap or jingle about choosing healthful lifestyle behaviors.

④ Close

Ask students to identify and describe a common noncommunicable disease.

Lesson 1 Review

1. A disease present either continuously or off and on over a long period of time.
2. Any five from Figure 18.1 on page 477.
3. Alcohol use
4. Chemical waste, certain construction materials, household chemicals, secondhand smoke, improper waste disposal, radon, carbon monoxide.
5. Communicable diseases spread through contact and are caused by pathogens. Noncommunicable diseases do not spread through contact; they are caused by breakdown in body tissues.
6. Any two factors: lifestyle, environment, and genetics; to take measures to prevent noncommunicable diseases and help protect your health if you already have one.

479

Allergies and Asthma

Allergies and Asthma

① Focus

Lesson Objectives

Students will be able to

- describe what happens during an allergic reaction.
- summarize how allergies are diagnosed and treated.
- explain what happens during an asthma attack.

Health Skills
- Decision Making, p. 483

Motivators

 Quick Write

Ask volunteers to share their lists of substances. Discuss how the substances are similar. Then ask: Which of these substances are avoidable?

Bellringer Activity

Ask students to list as many symptoms of allergies as they can in a three-minute period.

VOCABULARY

Have each student write a paragraph using all the vocabulary terms for this lesson. Ask volunteers to read their paragraphs to the rest of the class. Correct any misconceptions.

Quick Write

List several substances to which you or people you know are allergic. How are those substances similar?

LEARN ABOUT...

- what happens during an allergic reaction.
- how allergies are diagnosed and treated.
- what happens during an asthma attack.

VOCABULARY

- allergy
- allergen
- histamines
- hives
- antihistamines
- asthma
- bronchodilator

What Are Allergies?

The immune system reacts to the presence of foreign substances by starting a process to weaken or eliminate the substance. Part of the process is the release of antibodies, which fight foreign substances in the body. Some people develop an **allergy**, or *an abnormal immune reaction to an ordinarily harmless substance. A substance that causes an allergic reaction* is called an **allergen** (AL·er·juhn). When an allergen enters a person's body, the immune system reacts as though it were harmful. Between 40 million and 50 million Americans are affected by allergies.

The most common allergens come from foods, medications, pollens or plants, mold, animals with feathers or fur, insect stings, and synthetic materials. Allergic reactions can affect small areas, such as the part of skin touched by poison oak or poison ivy. In some cases, however, the entire body can be affected. Most allergic reactions occur within seconds or minutes of the time the allergen enters the body. **Figure 18.2** shows the general stages of allergic reaction.

FIGURE 18.2

STAGES OF ALLERGIC REACTION

Some allergens such as poison ivy cause allergic reactions in many people. Almost any substance, however, can set off an allergic reaction in a person who is sensitive to it.

① Contact is made.
Allergens enter the body in three ways: through breathing (dust, smoke); through swallowing (milk, shellfish); and through touching (poison ivy, wool).

② Attack is launched.
When an allergen enters the body, special cells release chemicals (histamines) that cause the symptoms of an allergic reaction.

③ Symptoms appear.
Body responses to allergens can involve the eyes, nose, throat, skin, respiratory system, and digestive system.

480 CHAPTER 18: NONCOMMUNICABLE DISEASES

Lesson 2 Resources

Teacher Classroom Resources

 Concept Map 69

 Enrichment Activity 69

Lesson Plan 2

Lesson 2 Quiz

Reading Tutor Activity 68

 Reteaching Activity 69

 Transparency 72

Student Activities Workbook

 Chapter 18 Study Guide

Applying Health Skills 69

Reactions to Allergens

The body responds to allergens by releasing histamines. **Histamines** are *chemicals in the body that cause the symptoms of the allergic reaction.* Common symptoms include watery eyes, sneezing, and a skin rash. For some people, an allergic reaction includes **hives**, or *raised bumps on the skin that are very itchy.* **Figure 18.3** shows common body responses to allergens.

Diagnosing and Treating Allergies

How can you tell what causes an allergic reaction? The answer may be as simple as noticing that you break out in a rash whenever you eat peanuts. Perhaps you start sneezing when you are near a cat. Sometimes the cause of an allergic reaction is not easy to identify, however. In these cases, a doctor can perform various tests. In the most common test, the person's skin is scratched and tiny bits of possible allergens are applied. If the person is allergic to one of the substances, the skin in that area will turn red and swell.

Although there is no cure for allergies, there are ways to cope with them. The most basic way is to avoid the allergen. When this is not possible, a person may take **antihistamines**, *medicines that help control the effects triggered by histamines.* For example, antihistamines may relieve itching and redness around the eyes and nose. In severe cases, treatment may involve allergy shots. These provide extremely small quantities of the allergen to help the body build up immunity. This process usually takes about five years.

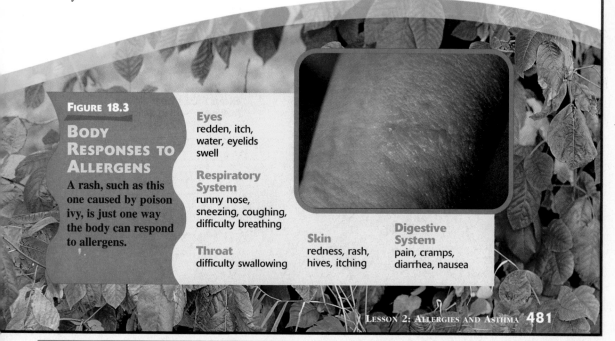

FIGURE 18.3

BODY RESPONSES TO ALLERGENS

A rash, such as this one caused by poison ivy, is just one way the body can respond to allergens.

Eyes
redden, itch, water, eyelids swell

Respiratory System
runny nose, sneezing, coughing, difficulty breathing

Throat
difficulty swallowing

Skin
redness, rash, hives, itching

Digestive System
pain, cramps, diarrhea, nausea

Health Literacy

Health Information Some people have severe allergic reactions to one or more of the 3,000 additives and preservatives in foods. A person who is allergic to a certain substance should learn its alternate names so that he or she can avoid consuming it. For example, sulfites may be listed on labels as sodium sulfite, sodium bisulfite, sulfur dioxide, potassium metabisulfite, or sodium metabisulfite. "Food intolerances" are sometimes mistaken for food allergies. A food allergy is an abnormal response to a food that is triggered by the immune system. The immune system is not responsible for the symptoms of a food intolerance even though the symptoms resemble those of a food allergy.

Examining the Issue

Remind students that emotional stress can bring on an asthma attack. Ask them to explain how the stress and the attack prove the interrelationship of the three sides of the health triangle. **L1**

Cross-Curriculum Activity

LANGUAGE ARTS Have volunteers use dictionaries to find the derivation of the word *bronchial* (from the Greek *bronkhos*, meaning "windpipe or throat"). Also, ask these volunteers to read aloud other, related words and their definitions. **L2**

Investigating

Have a group of volunteers learn about the Asthma and Allergy Foundation of American (AAFA) or a similar organization. Ask these students to share their findings with the rest of the class. **L2**

A peak flow meter measures how well a person can blow out air from the lungs. A low reading indicates that an asthma attack may be coming. *Why is it important to remain calm during an asthma attack?*

What Is Asthma?

Asthma (AZ·muh) is *a serious chronic condition that causes air passages in the respiratory system to become narrow or blocked.* More than 17 million people in the United States have asthma. About one-third of these people are under 18 years old. Some people outgrow their asthma at puberty, while others develop it as adults.

The bronchial tubes of people with asthma are unusually sensitive to certain substances. These substances are called asthma triggers. Common triggers include tobacco smoke, air pollution, and certain foods and medicines. When people with asthma come into contact with one of these triggers, they may have an asthma attack. Cold air, strenuous physical activity, strong emotions, and stress can also trigger an asthma attack. A substance that triggers an attack in one person may not affect another person who has asthma. **Figure 18.4** explains what happens during an asthma attack.

Managing Asthma

There is no cure for asthma. However, most people with asthma learn to manage the disease and lead active lives. Even those people whose asthma is triggered by physical activity can usually participate in sports.

FIGURE 18.4

ASTHMA ATTACK

Symptoms of an asthma attack include wheezing, or breathing with a whistling sound; coughing; and tightness in the chest.

A Healthy bronchial tubes are clear and open. Air passes easily through them to fill tiny air sacs in the lungs.

B During an asthma attack, muscles around the bronchial tubes tighten. The tubes narrow and their inner lining swells. Excess mucus clogs airways, making breathing difficult.

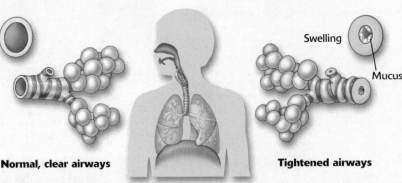

Swelling

Mucus

Normal, clear airways

Tightened airways

482 CHAPTER 18: NONCOMMUNICABLE DISEASES

MORE ABOUT...

Asthma Did you know that among children ages 5 to 17, asthma is the leading cause of school absences from a chronic illness? Students who have asthma, or whose friends or family members have asthma, may be interested in gathering more information about this breathing disorder. Suggest that they can contact one or more of the following organizations, using reference works or directories to find addresses and/or telephone numbers.

- American Lung Association
- Asthma and Allergy Foundation of America
- National Allergy and Asthma Network/Mothers of Asthmatics
- National Asthma Education Program

Coping with asthma involves avoiding asthma triggers whenever possible. Several types of medicines are also used to treat asthma. Some medicines block swelling in the bronchial tubes and decrease the amount of mucus being produced. Others, called **bronchodilators** (brahn·ko·dy·LAY·terz), are *medicines used to relax the muscles that have tightened around the airways.* When inhaled in a spray, bronchodilators can often bring relief within a few minutes.

HEALTH SKILLS ACTIVITY

DECISION MAKING

Managing Chronic Conditions

Eddie has asthma. This year, he started playing drums in the school marching band. The band has won several awards, and Eddie is proud of the band's accomplishments.

Eddie is especially excited today because his school's band is competing with other bands in the area. However, on his way to school he feels an asthma attack coming on. Eddie wants to play in the competition and does not want to let down his bandmates. He has asthma medicine with him, but is afraid that his performance will be affected anyway.

WHAT WOULD YOU DO?

Apply the skills for decision making to Eddie's situation. What are Eddie's options? What are the possible outcomes? With a classmate, role-play a scene in which Eddie tells his conductor and bandmates about his asthma.

1. **STATE THE SITUATION.**
2. **LIST THE OPTIONS.**
3. **WEIGH THE POSSIBLE OUTCOMES.**
4. **CONSIDER VALUES.**
5. **MAKE A DECISION AND ACT.**
6. **EVALUATE THE DECISION.**

Lesson 2 Review

Using complete sentences, answer the following questions on a sheet of paper.

Reviewing Terms and Facts

1. **Vocabulary** Define the term *allergy*. Use it in an original sentence.
2. **Give Examples** What are three common allergens?
3. **Summarize** List three stages of an allergic reaction.
4. **Recall** For what condition would a bronchodilator be used? What does it do?

Thinking Critically

5. **Hypothesize** Why might it be difficult for someone with allergies to avoid allergens?
6. **Synthesize** What is usually the most helpful step in preventing allergic reactions and asthma attacks?

Applying Health Skills

7. **Communication Skills** Suppose you think you have an allergy. Write a paragraph describing the effective communication skills you could use to discuss this with parents or guardians and health care professionals.

LESSON 2: ALLERGIES AND ASTHMA 483

Lesson 2

HEALTH SKILLS ACTIVITY

DECISION MAKING

Guide students in reading and discussing Eddie's situation. Review with them the decision-making steps. Then ask:

- What decisions has Eddie already made if he tells his conductor and band mates about his asthma?
- What other options does Eddie have? Emphasize that if Eddie does not tell his conductor, he will be dishonest. Also, he could hurt himself and have a poor performance.

Then have partners role-play the conversation Eddie might have.

Note: This skill is introduced in Chapter 2 on pages 28–30.

③ Assess

Evaluating

Assign the Lesson 2 Review; then assign the Lesson 2 Quiz in the TCR.

Reteaching

Assign Concept Map 69 or Reteaching Activity 69 in the TCR.

Enrichment

Assign Enrichment Activity 69 in the TCR.

④ Close

Ask each student to name one way allergies and asthma are similar and one way they are different.

Lesson 2 Review

1. An abnormal immune reaction to an ordinarily harmless substance. Sentences will vary.
2. Any three: foods, medications, pollens or plants, mold, animals with feathers or fur, insect stings, synthetic materials.
3. Contact made, attack is launched, symptoms appear.
4. Asthma. Relaxes muscles tightened around airways.
5. Allergens are widespread throughout the environment.
6. Avoid triggers when possible.

Lesson 3

Cancer

① Focus

Lesson Objectives

Students will be able to
- identify common types of cancer.
- discuss the factors that increase the risk of developing cancer.
- identify the warning signs of cancer.
- describe how cancer is diagnosed and treated.

Motivators

Quick Write

Ask volunteers to share their responses. Correct any misconceptions.

Bellringer Activity

Ask students: What is your immediate reaction when you hear the word *cancer*?

VOCABULARY

Instruct students to attempt to write the correct spelling for each of the vocabulary terms as you pronounce them. Next, have students exchange papers with another student and correct the terms as you read aloud the proper spellings. Students should get their papers back to review any corrections.

Quick Write

List at least three reasons people get cancer.

LEARN ABOUT...

- causes of cancer.
- cancer's effects on the body.
- treatments for cancer.
- ways to reduce the risk of developing cancer.

VOCABULARY

- cancer
- tumor
- benign tumor
- malignant tumor
- metastasis
- carcinogens
- biopsy
- remission
- recurrence
- mammogram

Cancer

What Is Cancer?

Cancer is *a disease characterized by the rapid and uncontrolled growth of abnormal cells.* It can affect people of any age. In the United States, one of every four deaths is from cancer. Thanks to advances in diagnosis and treatment, however, more people are successfully living with cancer than ever before. Everyone can take steps to reduce their risk of developing cancer.

Tumors

The human body has trillions of cells that continually grow and reproduce. Each year, the body forms trillions of new cells. Although the majority of new cells are normal, thousands are abnormal. Most of these abnormal cells are destroyed by the body's immune system. Sometimes, however, an abnormal cell survives. The abnormal cell then starts to reproduce itself, dividing and making more abnormal cells until they form a mass. *A mass of abnormal cells* is called a **tumor**.

There are two kinds of tumors. A **benign** (bi·NYN) **tumor** is *a tumor that is not cancerous.* A **malignant** (muh·LIG·nuhnt) **tumor** is *a tumor that is cancerous.* Cells from a malignant tumor can break away and move through the blood or lymph to other parts of the body. These cells divide and form new tumors. *The spread of cancer from one part of the body to another* is called **metastasis** (muh·TAS·tuh·suhs).

Skin cancer is the most common form of cancer in the United States. Fortunately, it can be prevented, is easily detected, and can be treated early. *What environmental factor increases the risk for skin cancer?*

484 CHAPTER 18: NONCOMMUNICABLE DISEASES

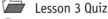

Lesson 3 Resources

Teacher Classroom Resources

- 📁 Concept Map 70
- 📁 Decision-Making Activity 36
- 📁 Enrichment Activity 70
- 📁 Lesson Plan 3
- 📁 Lesson 3 Quiz
- 📁 Reading Tutor Activity 69

- 📁 Reteaching Activity 70
- 🔊 Transparency 73

Student Activities Workbook

- 📁 Chapter 18 Study Guide
- 📁 Applying Health Skills 70

Types of Cancer

Cancer can develop in many parts of the body. Some cancers are more likely to be detected earlier than others because of routine screenings. For example, breast cancer may be detected during a yearly physical exam. Many females detect their own breast cancer while doing a monthly breast self-examination. **Figure 18.5** provides information on common types of cancer.

What Causes Cancer?

Several factors increase a person's risk of developing cancer. One of these factors is heredity. According to the American Cancer Society, between 5 and 10 percent of cancers are hereditary. This means that a person who inherits a particular faulty gene has an increased risk of developing a particular form of cancer.

FIGURE 18.5

COMMON TYPES OF CANCER

Oncology is the medical specialty that studies and treats cancer.

Skin cancer is the most common type of cancer, accounting for nearly half of all cancers. Excessive exposure to sunlight is the major cause of skin cancer. Fair-skinned and fair-haired people are at greater risk.

Breast cancer occurs most often in females over the age of 50. However, younger females can develop breast cancer, and it can also occur in males.

Cancers of the reproductive organs affect both females and males. In females, cancer can occur in the cervix, uterus, and ovaries. In males, it can occur in the prostate and testicles.

Colon and rectum (colorectal) cancer develop in the digestive tract. An eating plan low in fat and high in fiber may decrease the risk of colon and rectum cancer.

Lung cancer is the leading cause of cancer deaths. Smoking is by far the biggest risk factor for lung cancer for both males and females.

Lymphoma is a cancer that starts in the lymphatic system. It weakens the immune system, making the body more susceptible to infection.

Leukemia is a cancer of the white blood cells that starts in the bone marrow. An increase in abnormal white blood cells interferes with the production of healthy cells.

LESSON 3: CANCER **485**

MORE ABOUT...

Cancer Cancer is not just one disease—it's many diseases. The generic name *cancer* is applied to hundreds of diseases characterized by abnormal cells that multiply and spread uncontrollably. There are three main types:

• Carcinomas are cancers that occur in the skin, glands, or the lining of organs (such as the lung, liver, or brain).

• Sarcomas are cancers that occur in bone or muscle tissue.

• Leukemias are malignancies of the blood and lymphatic system.

Lesson 3

② Teach

Recalling

Have students explain the difference between a benign tumor and a malignant one. (*A benign tumor is not cancerous; a malignant one is.*) Reinforce that any tumor should be examined by a doctor. **L1**

VISUAL LEARNING

FIGURE 18.5 Divide the class into groups. Ask each group to study the list of cancers and then choose three specific diseases that interest them. Set aside time in class for student groups to use their textbooks and conduct library research to learn more about the risk factors associated with each disease they have chosen. Instruct student groups to analyze risks for contracting specific diseases based on pathogenic, genetic, age, cultural, environmental, and behavioral factors. When student research is completed, ask each group to summarize their analyses in a chart that they will present to the class. **INCL** *English Language Learners, Special Learning Needs, Behavior Problems, Different Learning Styles (Visual)*

Analyzing

Have students study the list of cancers shown in Figure 18.5 and note which are common to specific groups of people. Ask them to explain why the lung cancer in women is increasing. (*More women smoke today.*) Ask students why a person with cancer might not seek treatment. **L1**

485

Classifying

On the board, list several known carcinogens such as radiation, tobacco, toxic waste, and certain food additives. Have students work in small groups to classify the carcinogens as natural or synthetic. Ask students which carcinogens they can avoid and have them explain how. **L2**

VISUAL LEARNING

FIGURE 18.6 Have volunteers read aloud the title and caption, and have students point to the vertical word CAUTION and the vertical ABCD. Then guide students in reading and discussing each warning sign. Have volunteers give examples of each warning sign and explain the best response. **INCL** *English Language Learners, Special Learning Needs, Behavior Problems, Different Learning Styles (Visual)*

Analyzing

Divide the class into small groups. Have one student in each group fold a piece of paper in half and list the seven warning signs of cancer in the first column. In the second column, group members should list the part(s) of the body that each warning sign might be associated with. (*Answers in the second column may include the following: 1. colon, 2. skin, 3. kidney, 4. breast, 5. esophagus, 6. skin, 7. lung.*) Have groups share their responses. **L2**

Reading Check

Create your own memory aid. How would you memorize the five types of treatment on page 487?

Other types of cancer are related to lifestyle behaviors. For example, smoking and sunbathing are risk factors for cancer, as are unhealthy eating habits. Many cancers are associated with exposure to **carcinogens** (kar·SIN·un·juhns), which are *substances that cause cancer*. Common sources of carcinogens include

- tobacco, either smoked or smokeless.
- radiation, including X rays in large doses.
- chemicals used in construction and manufacturing, including asbestos and benzene.
- air and water pollution, usually the result of industrial waste.

Warning Signs of Cancer

The earlier cancer is found, the better the chance for successful treatment. Along with having regular physical exams, people can help themselves by watching for any of the warning signs of cancer. For example, females can examine their breasts for lumps. Males can examine their testicles for lumps. Both males and females can watch their skin for changes. **Figure 18.6** shows the general warning signs of cancer.

FIGURE 18.6

WARNING SIGNS OF CANCER

If you notice one of these warning signs, don't wait. Check with your doctor.

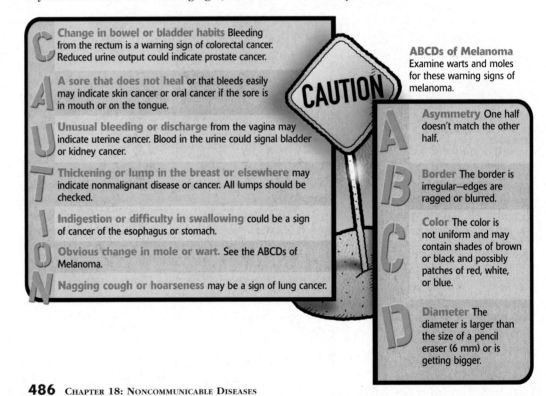

Change in bowel or bladder habits Bleeding from the rectum is a warning sign of colorectal cancer. Reduced urine output could indicate prostate cancer.

A sore that does not heal or that bleeds easily may indicate skin cancer or oral cancer if the sore is in mouth or on the tongue.

Unusual bleeding or discharge from the vagina may indicate uterine cancer. Blood in the urine could signal bladder or kidney cancer.

Thickening or lump in the breast or elsewhere may indicate nonmalignant disease or cancer. All lumps should be checked.

Indigestion or difficulty in swallowing could be a sign of cancer of the esophagus or stomach.

Obvious change in mole or wart. See the ABCDs of Melanoma.

Nagging cough or hoarseness may be a sign of lung cancer.

CAUTION

ABCDs of Melanoma Examine warts and moles for these warning signs of melanoma.

Asymmetry One half doesn't match the other half.

Border The border is irregular—edges are ragged or blurred.

Color The color is not uniform and may contain shades of brown or black and possibly patches of red, white, or blue.

Diameter The diameter is larger than the size of a pencil eraser (6 mm) or is getting bigger.

 ## Reading Check

Memory Aids Devising their own mnemonic devices, or memory aids, is an effective way for students to commit lists of facts to memory. Figure 18.6 presents two helpful mnemonics. The first, CAUTION, and the second, ABCDs of melanoma, both spell out cancer warning signs. Then have students look at the bulleted lists under the headings Types of Treatment on page 487 and Preventing Cancer on pages 487–488. Challenge students to develop personal memory aids for these two lists. If students have a difficult time with this activity, suggest rearranging the elements of each list and looking at initial letters. Possible answers include RICHS for types of treatment and ABLE for ways to prevent cancer.

Diagnosis and Treatment

A person who has one of the warning signs of cancer should see a physician right away for an examination. To diagnose cancer, the doctor will almost always examine samples of tissue under a microscope. *The removal of a tissue sample to see whether cancer cells are present* is called a **biopsy**. The doctor may also order imaging tests, such as ultrasounds, MRIs, or CAT scans. If cancer is diagnosed, the physician will stage the disease. Staging is a process of describing the extent of the cancer and how far it has spread. Staging is used to determine the best treatment.

Types of Treatment

The best way to treat cancer depends on a number of factors. These include the type of cancer, the stage of the disease, and the age and general health of the patient. Doctors follow a detailed plan called a protocol when treating cancer patients. The protocol might involve one or more of the following treatments:

- **Surgery.** During surgery, doctors remove cancer cells from the body.
- **Radiation therapy.** This treatment method involves aiming high-energy rays from radioactive substances at cancerous tissue. These rays destroy or shrink cancer cells. Radiation therapy is often used in combination with surgery.
- **Chemotherapy** (kee·moh·THEHR·uh·pee). With chemotherapy, chemicals are used to destroy cancer cells. Chemotherapy can be used to fight cancers that have spread throughout the body.
- **Immunotherapy.** This treatment method stimulates the body's immune system to fight the cancer. Immunotherapy is most often used in combination with another type of treatment.
- **Hormone therapy.** With this method, cancer is treated with hormones or with medicines that interfere with the production of hormones. Hormone therapy can destroy cancer cells or slow their growth.

When cancer treatment is successful and *when cancer signs and symptoms disappear,* the cancer is in **remission**. Cancer that is in remission is not necessarily cured, however. *The return of cancer after a remission* is called a **recurrence**.

Preventing Cancer

By making healthy lifestyle choices, you can lower your risk of developing certain cancers. Follow these recommendations:

- **Eat nutritious foods.** Choose most of the foods you eat from plant sources. Limit your intake of high-fat foods.

Lesson 3

Comprehending

Ask students to explain why cancers diagnosed in early stages are more easily treated than those diagnosed in later stages. Then ask: From this information, what can you conclude about the importance of regular checkups and routine cancer testing? Direct students to write a short paragraph in which they explain the role of treatment, such as wellness exams, in disease prevention. **L1**

Investigating

Explain to students that some doctors and researchers are exploring the usefulness of diet and other lifestyle choices in the treatment of cancer. Ask a group of volunteers to learn more about this treatment and to share their findings with the rest of the class. **L3**

Cooperative Learning

Have students work in groups to learn more about the listed types of cancer treatments:

- What are the particular advantages of each kind of treatment?
- What side effects are associated with each treatment? **L2**

Researching

Have students find out how CAT scans, PET scans, and MRI scans are used to detect tumors. Ask students to write paragraphs about each scanning technique, predicting how such devices may be used in the future. **L3**

WHAT TEENS WANT TO KNOW

Do teens get cancer? Yes. However, teens do not get cancer nearly as often as adults do. Cancer is a disease in which unhealthy cells multiply too quickly. Cancer replaces healthy cells, forms tumors, and destroys body parts. The most common cancer among teens is leukemia, a condition involving the multiplication of abnormal white blood cells. Hodgkin's disease is the most common lymphoma among teens. Lymphomas begin in the lymph nodes, where lymphocytes, white blood cells that help to fight infection, are produced. Cancer that is identified early is easier to treat. It's important to have regular checkups. Research in cancer medicine is advancing rapidly. In the future, we can look forward to safer and more effective cancer treatments.

Cross-Curriculum Activity

LANGUAGE ARTS Have students use dictionaries to find the verbs from which the nouns *remission* (*remit:* to restore to an original condition) and *recurrence* (*recur:* to show up again) are formed. **L2**

③ Assess

Evaluating

 Assign the Lesson 3 Review; then assign the Lesson 3 Quiz in the TCR.

Reteaching

- Assign Concept Map 70 or Reteaching Activity 70 in the TCR.
- Have students make lists of the following information: three health steps that help prevent cancer, the seven warning signs of cancer, three treatments for cancer, and risk factors associated with noncommunicable diseases.

Enrichment

Assign Enrichment Activity 70 in the TCR.

④ Close

Use the lesson objectives on page 484 of the Teacher Wraparound Edition to review students' understanding of the lesson content.

- **Be physically active.** Be at least moderately active for 30 minutes or more on most days. Maintain a healthy weight.
- **Limit sun exposure.** When outside, wear a hat, protective clothing, and sunscreen with an SPF of at least 15.
- **Avoid tobacco and alcohol.** Cigarette smoking is the major single cause of cancer deaths in the United States. Excessive alcohol use increases the risk of several types of cancer.

In addition to taking steps to prevent cancer, it is important to detect cancer in its earliest stages. Several types of screenings can aid in early detection. For example, a **mammogram** is *an X ray of the breast used to screen for breast cancer.* Performing regular self-exams of the breasts, testicles, and skin may also aid in early cancer detection.

Lance Armstrong overcame cancer and went on to win the world's toughest bicycle race— the Tour de France.

Lesson 3 Review

Using complete sentences, answer the following questions on a sheet of paper.

Reviewing Terms and Facts

1. **Vocabulary** What is a *tumor*? Which type of tumor is a more serious health problem: a *benign* or a *malignant* tumor? Explain.
2. **Recall** What is the major cause of skin cancer? Of lung cancer?
3. **Identify** Name three common sources of carcinogens.
4. **Explain** How are the terms *remission* and *recurrence* related?

Thinking Critically

5. **Analyze** Why is it important to discover cancer in its early stages?
6. **Synthesize** What type of foods help lower the risk of colon and rectum cancer?

Applying Health Skills

7. **Goal Setting** Research a health-related profession. Then develop a list of long-term goals and strategies that could help a person have a career in that profession.

488 CHAPTER 18: NONCOMMUNICABLE DISEASES

Lesson 3 Review

1. A mass of abnormal cells; malignant; cells from a malignant tumor can break away and travel through blood or lymph to other body parts.
2. Skin cancer: excessive exposure to sunlight; lung cancer: smoking.
3. Any three: tobacco, radiation, chemicals used in construction and manufacturing, air and water pollution.
4. Remission is when cancer signs and symptoms disappear although cancer is not necessarily cured; recurrence is the return of cancer after remission.
5. The earlier cancer is found, the better the chance for successful treatment.
6. Foods high in fiber and low in fat.

Heart and Circulatory Problems

What Is Heart Disease?

Heart disease is any condition that weakens the heart or blood vessels or interferes with the functions they perform. More adults in the United States die from heart disease than from any other cause. Most diseases of the cardiovascular system take many years to develop. Chances of developing heart disease depend partly on age and heredity and partly on lifestyle behaviors. Making wise lifestyle choices during the teen years can help reduce your risk of developing heart disease as an adult.

Arteriosclerosis and Atherosclerosis

Body cells must have a constant supply of fresh oxygen to survive. All tissues and organs depend on the flow of blood through arteries to bring this oxygen. When arteries are healthy, blood flows through them freely. **Figure 18.7** shows how blood flow through arteries can diminish.

FIGURE 18.7

HOW ARTERIES BECOME BLOCKED

As fatty substances build up in the arteries, blood flow is reduced.

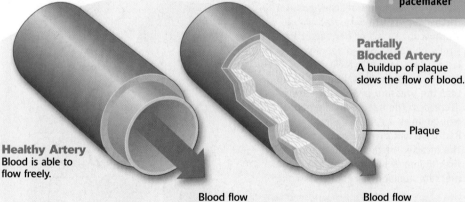

Partially Blocked Artery
A buildup of plaque slows the flow of blood.

— Plaque

Healthy Artery
Blood is able to flow freely.

Blood flow   Blood flow

Quick Write

List some behaviors that people can practice to help keep their hearts healthy.

LEARN ABOUT...

- different types of heart disease.
- ways to treat heart and circulatory problems.
- ways to prevent heart disease.

VOCABULARY

- arteriosclerosis
- atherosclerosis
- high blood pressure
- heart attack
- stroke
- pacemaker

Lesson 4

Heart and Circulatory Problems

① Focus

Lesson Objectives

Students will be able to

- identify and describe the different types of heart disease.
- describe ways to treat heart and circulatory problems.
- discuss ways to prevent heart disease.

Motivators

Quick Write
List the behaviors identified by students on the board. Ask: Why don't many people practice these behaviors?

Bellringer Activity

Ask students to compare the heart to a machine. Then have each student write one sentence telling how the two are alike and another sentence telling how they are different.

VOCABULARY

Write each of the vocabulary terms on the board. Have students look up each term in the Glossary at the back of the student text. Then ask students to write sentences incorporating each term.

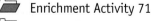
Lesson 4 Resources

Teacher Classroom Resources

- Concept Map 71
- Cross-Curriculum Activity 35
- Enrichment Activity 71
- Lesson Plan 4
- Lesson 4 Quiz
- Reading Tutor Activity 70

- Reteaching Activity 71
- Transparency 74

Student Activities Workbook

- Chapter 18 Study Guide
- Applying Health Skills 71

② **Teach**

VISUAL LEARNING

FIGURE 18.7 Ask volunteers to describe the two pictures in Figure 18.7 on page 489, explaining how they are different. Then have other volunteers read the title, the caption, and the labels. Help students discuss the dangers of arterial blockages and the steps individuals can take to prevent or reduce blockages. **INCL** *English Language Learners, Special Learning Needs, Behavior Problems, Different Learning Styles (Visual)*

Hands-On Health

MEASURING BLOOD PRESSURE

Time: 30 minutes or more (depending on the number of sphygmomanometers and stethoscopes)

TEACHING THE ACTIVITY

- With students, read and discuss the activity instructions.
- Have one pair of students demonstrate for the rest of the class.
- Then have partners work together to measure each other's blood pressure.

ASSESSMENT

Have students write their responses to the In Conclusion questions.

Arteriosclerosis (ar·tir·ee·oh·skluh·ROH·sis) is *a group of disorders in which arteries harden and become more rigid.* Arteriosclerosis reduces the amount of blood that can flow through the arteries. **Atherosclerosis** (a·thuh·roh·skluh·ROH·sis) is *a form of arteriosclerosis in which fatty substances in the blood build up on the walls of the arteries.* The buildup, called plaque, may partially or totally block the flow of blood through the arteries. Buildup in the coronary arteries that lead to the heart carries the risk of heart attack. Buildup in blood vessels leading to the brain increases the risk of stroke.

Hands-On Health

MEASURING BLOOD PRESSURE

This activity will let you hear what a doctor or nurse hears when measuring your blood pressure.

WHAT YOU WILL NEED

- a manual blood pressure measuring device (sphygmomanometer) with a dial
- a stethoscope

WHAT YOU WILL DO

1. Partner A wraps the blood pressure cuff around Partner B's upper arm and tightens the valve. Partner A squeezes the pump to inflate the cuff until the needle on the gauge reaches about 140.
2. Partner B puts the earpieces of the stethoscope in his or her ears. Partner B firmly holds the bell/diaphragm over the large artery in the arm.
3. Partner A opens the valve slightly so that the pressure in the cuff slowly decreases. The needle on the gauge will go down steadily.
4. Partner B watches the gauge and listens. The location of the needle when the first thump is heard is the top blood pressure number. The location of the needle when the last thump is heard is the bottom blood pressure number. Partner B records the reading and removes the cuff.
5. Change roles. Complete the steps again to measure Partner A's blood pressure.

IN CONCLUSION

1. Why might a doctor recommend that a patient monitor his or her own blood pressure at home?
2. Why is it important to learn how to take accurate blood pressure readings?

MORE ABOUT...

Heart Disease Several years ago, two doctors in San Francisco classified people into two groups, Type A and Type B. They identified Type A people as competitive, impatient, and driven. Type B people tended to be patient and unruffled. The doctors discovered that Type A people were more than twice as likely to develop heart disease as Type B people. To reduce their risk, Type A people need to change their behavior by following these guidelines: stop overreacting; set realistic goals; find the humor in situations that cause anger; cut down on (or cut out) tea, coffee, and cigarettes; practice relaxation techniques. More recent studies continue to indicate a correlation between stress and anger and increased risk of heart disease.

High Blood Pressure

The force of the blood on the inside walls of the arteries is your blood pressure. Blood pressure is expressed as two numbers written like a fraction. The top number is the pressure when the heart beats. The bottom number is the pressure when the heart rests between beats. A blood pressure of less than 120 over 80 is considered normal for adults. Normal blood pressure in teens is lower than in adults, and it varies with age and height.

When a person's blood pressure is usually higher than normal for his or her age, the person is said to have **high blood pressure**. High blood pressure, also called hypertension, can lead to heart attack, stroke, and kidney disease.

Heart Attack

A **heart attack** is *a condition in which blood flow to a part of the heart is greatly reduced or blocked.* If the blood is cut off for more than a few minutes, heart muscle cells are damaged and die. The following are possible warning signs of a heart attack:

- Pressure, fullness, squeezing, or pain in the chest
- Pain spreading to the shoulders, neck, or arms
- Chest discomfort with lightheadedness, fainting, sweating, nausea, or shortness of breath

Having a heart attack is an emergency situation—every second counts. If someone experiences any of these signs, seek medical assistance immediately.

Sometimes a person experiences chest pain well before a heart attack occurs. Angina pectoris is a painful condition in which blood flow to the heart is adequate to meet normal needs but not increased needs, such as climbing stairs. Angina pectoris is a sign of increased risk of heart attack.

Stroke

A **stroke** is *a condition in which a blood vessel bringing oxygen to the brain bursts or is blocked.* The bursting or blockage prevents blood from reaching part of the brain. Since brain cells cannot live without oxygen, cells in the blocked area can't function and they die. Without these brain cells, the part of the body usually controlled by those cells no longer functions.

Regular physical activity can help reduce your chance of developing high blood pressure.

Lesson 4

Cross-Curriculum Activity

LANGUAGE ARTS Explain that abnormally low blood pressure, known as hypotension, can also be a health hazard. Ask a student to look up the prefixes *hypo-* and *hyper-* and explain the meaning of each to the class. **L1**

Demonstrating

Have a school nurse take several blood pressure readings of two volunteers (preferably, a boy and a girl). Readings should be taken lying down, sitting up, standing, and after jogging in place for 30 seconds. Record the results in a chart, and have students analyze them. What conclusions can be drawn from this activity? **L1** **INCL** *English Language Learners, Special Learning Needs, Behavior Problems, Different Learning Styles (Visual, Kinesthetic)*

Cross-Curriculum Activity

SCIENCE Have pairs of students make clay models of the heart (or draw diagrams) showing the four ventricles and the aorta. Ask students to use their models or diagrams to explain what occurs during a heart attack. **L2** **INCL** *English Language Learners, Special Learning Needs, Behavior Problems, Different Learning Styles (Visual, Kinesthetic)*

Comparing

Ask students to compare a heart attack and a stroke:

- What is the most important similarity between the two events?
- What is the most important difference?
- How are the warning signs different?
- What is the best response to any of those warning signs? **L1**

PROMOTING COORDINATED SCHOOL HEALTH

Creating a Team Sometimes, school health policies respond to state mandates and programs and services of the past regardless of their appropriateness, adequacy, or effectiveness. To develop or clarify the vision for school health, the entire system of public school education must be considered. School health committees should consist of representatives of the following: parents; community members; business representatives; teachers, counselors, nurses, and other school staff; religious groups; state, county, or local health agency representatives; human services representatives; volunteer health organizations. For more information about the school health team, consult *Planning a Coordinated School Health Program* in the TCR.

Interviewing

Have volunteers talk with family members or adult friends who take medicine to lower their blood pressure. Have students ask about the ease with which the medicine can be taken, its effectiveness, and any side effects. Then ask these volunteers to discuss their findings with the rest of the class. **L2**

VISUAL LEARNING

FIGURE 18.8 Have volunteers read aloud the title, the caption, and the explanation that accompanies each picture in Figure 18.8. Guide students in discussing the size of the wire, tube, and stent used in angioplasty and in considering the delicacy of the procedure. **INCL** *English Language Learners, Special Learning Needs, Behavior Problems, Different Learning Styles (Visual)*

Practicing Life Skills

Review with students the role that cholesterol and saturated fats play in causing heart disease. The American Heart Association and other organizations provide information and recipes to enable people to follow a low-cholesterol, low-fat diet. Have students study such information and research heart-healthy meals with their families. The class may wish to issue a cookbook. **L2**

Stroke is a medical emergency. If someone experiences any of the following warning signs, seek medical assistance immediately:

- Sudden numbness or weakness, especially on one side of the body
- Sudden confusion or difficulty with speech or understanding
- Sudden difficulty seeing
- Sudden dizziness, or loss of balance or coordination

Treating Heart and Circulatory Problems

Health care professionals can offer a variety of treatment options for heart and circulatory problems. Some of these include:

- **Medication.** Many problems can be controlled with medicine. For example, people with high blood pressure can take medicine to lower their pressure.
- **Angioplasty.** When there is blockage in a coronary artery, doctors may perform angioplasty (AN·gee·uh·plas·tee). **Figure 18.8** shows the angioplasty procedure.
- **Bypass surgery.** When blockage is life threatening or other treatments do not help, bypass surgery may be necessary. Typically, a healthy vein is taken from the patient's leg or chest and is used to detour around the blockage.
- **Heart valve surgery.** A faulty valve can be replaced with an artificial one made of metal or plastic.
- **Pacemaker.** If a person's heartbeat is irregular, too fast, or too slow, doctors may recommend a **pacemaker**. This is *a small device that sends steady electrical impulses to the heart to make it beat regularly.*

FIGURE 18.8

CLEARING BLOCKED ARTERIES

More than 50 percent of cases of blocked coronary arteries are treated by angioplasty.

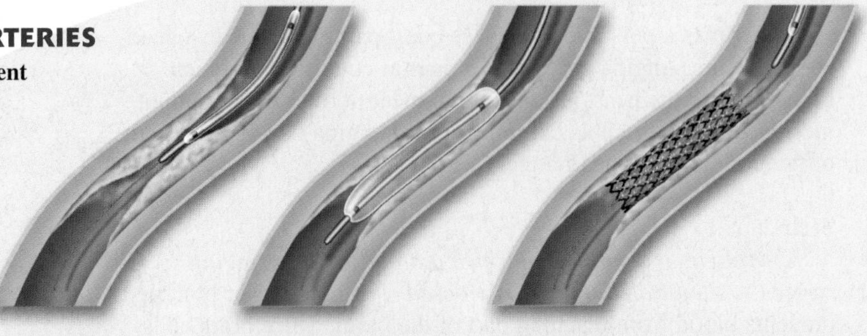

1 A puncture is made in the artery, and a thin wire is threaded through the artery to the location of the blockage. A special tube with a balloon section is sent along the wire into the blockage.

2 The balloon is inflated, flattening the plaque against the walls of the artery. Then the balloon is deflated and removed.

3 In most angioplasty procedures, doctors mount a tiny, metal structure called a stent on the balloon. After the balloon is deflated, the stent remains in place to keep the artery open.

492 CHAPTER 18: NONCOMMUNICABLE DISEASES

Health Literacy

Health Behaviors As students learn about various lifestyle diseases, encourage them to compile their own medical histories. Students should seek out and record information about their own diseases, including the common childhood diseases, and their vaccinations. Remind students that this kind of record is especially useful in dealing with health issues and making decisions about healthy habits. Encourage them to keep their medical records in a safe place and to add to their records in coming years. Note: Be sensitive to students who are adopted or for other reasons may not be able to obtain this information. Also, emphasize that students should obtain their parents' permission before sharing this information.

Preventing Heart Disease

Although symptoms usually don't appear until adulthood, heart disease can begin developing in childhood. The earlier people reduce their risk factors for heart disease, the better their chances for preventing it. Many significant risk factors can be controlled. **Figure 18.9** lists these factors, along with appropriate lifestyle behaviors.

FIGURE 18.9

CONTROLLING RISK FACTORS

Risk Factor	Healthy Lifestyle Behavior
Excess weight	Maintain a healthy weight. Being overweight forces your heart to work harder.
Physical inactivity	Add physical activity to your daily routine. Regular physical activity strengthens your heart and helps you maintain your healthy weight.
Poor eating habits	Follow an eating plan that is high in fiber and low in salt and fat. Too much salt may lead to high blood pressure. Too many fatty foods may contribute to the buildup of deposits in arteries.
Stress	Learn to manage stress in your life. Constant stress can raise your blood pressure.
Tobacco use	Avoid tobacco use and secondhand smoke. Smoking is the most important risk factor for teens.
Alcohol use	Avoid alcohol. Alcohol contributes to arteriosclerosis.

Lesson 4 Review

Using complete sentences, answer the following questions on a sheet of paper.

Reviewing Terms and Facts

1. **Vocabulary** Define *arteriosclerosis* and *atherosclerosis*. How are they related?
2. **Describe** What is the difference between a *heart attack* and a *stroke?*
3. **Identify** List four methods that doctors use to treat heart and circulatory problems.
4. **List** Name six risk factors for heart disease that can be controlled.

Thinking Critically

5. **Analyze** Why is it a good idea to have your blood pressure checked periodically?

6. **Synthesize** How will practicing healthy lifestyle behaviors as a teen help to reduce the risk of heart disease in adulthood?

Applying Health Skills

7. **Practicing Healthful Behaviors** With a family member or friend, try some low-salt, low-fat versions of the foods you normally eat. For example, try low-salt soup, low-fat cookies, or low-fat yogurt. Note which foods you liked and which ones you disliked. Report your findings to your classmates.

VISUAL LEARNING

FIGURE 18.9 Divide the class into six groups, and assign each group one of the risk factors presented in Figure 18.9. Have members of each group read about the healthy behavior that can reduce each risk factor and explain the importance of that healthy behavior. **INCL** *English Language Learners, Special Learning Needs, Behavior Problems, Different Learning Styles (Visual)*

③ Assess

Evaluating

📁 Assign the Lesson 4 Review; then assign the Lesson 4 Quiz in the TCR.

Reteaching

- 📁 Assign Concept Map 71 or Reteaching Activity 71 in the TCR.
- Have each student write three sentences about the causes, treatment for, and prevention of arteriosclerosis and high blood pressure.

Enrichment

📁 Assign Enrichment Activity 71 in the TCR.

④ Close

Have students finish this statement: Three ways to prevent heart disease are...

Lesson 4 Review

1. Arteriosclerosis is a group of disorders where arteries harden and become more rigid; atherosclerosis is a form of arteriosclerosis in which fatty substances in the blood build up on artery walls.
2. Heart attack is when blood flow to a part of the heart is reduced or blocked; stroke is when a blood vessel bringing oxygen to the brain bursts or is blocked.
3. Any four: medication, angioplasty, bypass surgery, heart valve surgery, pacemaker.
4. See Figure 18.9 on this page.
5. You can detect changes in blood pressure that may indicate that a problem is developing.
6. If you start taking care of your health now, you will have fewer problems with heart disease as you age.

Diabetes and Arthritis

① Focus

Lesson Objectives

Students will be able to
- define the two types of diabetes.
- explain ways to prevent and treat diabetes.
- name the two types of arthritis.
- discuss how arthritis is treated.

Health Skills
- Accessing Information, p. 496

Motivators

Quick Write
Discuss the students' responses. Ask: Why is knowing such information important for people of all ages?

Bellringer Activity

Ask students: Why is arthritis considered by some to be an old-age disease?

VOCABULARY

Ask students to look up the vocabulary in the Glossary and write a short paragraph using each of the terms. Then have them work in pairs to proofread one another's paragraphs, providing peer evaluations and checking for correct usage and meaning.

Quick Write

What do you think teens need to know about diabetes and arthritis? Why?

LEARN ABOUT...
- the different types of diabetes.
- ways to prevent and treat diabetes.
- the different types of arthritis.
- treatment for arthritis.

VOCABULARY
- diabetes
- insulin
- type 1 diabetes
- type 2 diabetes
- arthritis
- rheumatoid arthritis
- osteoarthritis

What Is Diabetes?

Diabetes is *a disease that prevents the body from converting food into energy.* In order to get energy from food, the body must break food down into glucose. Glucose—a simple sugar—is the main energy source that cells use to do their jobs. To transport glucose into cells, the body needs **insulin**, *a hormone produced by the pancreas.* Diabetes prevents the body from producing or using insulin. The body's cells cannot get the glucose they need, and glucose builds up in the bloodstream. Diabetes is increasing at an alarming rate. During the 1990s, diabetes rose 70 percent among people in their 30s.

Types of Diabetes

There are two main types of diabetes: type 1 and type 2. **Type 1 diabetes** is *a condition in which the immune system attacks insulin-producing cells in the pancreas.* About 5 to 10 percent of diabetes cases are type 1. **Type 2 diabetes** is *a condition in which the body cannot effectively use the insulin it produces.* The majority of people with diabetes have type 2. Type 2 diabetes is more likely to occur in people who are over the age of 40, obese, and physically inactive. However, type 2 is becoming increasingly common among children and teens.

Diagnosing Diabetes

The only way to diagnose diabetes is with a blood test taken by a health professional. According to the CDC, the following may be symptoms of diabetes:

- Frequent urination
- Excessive thirst
- Unexplained weight loss
- Extreme hunger
- Sudden vision changes
- Tingling or numbness in hands or feet
- Feeling tired much of the time
- Very dry skin
- Sores that are slow to heal
- More infections than usual

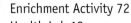
Lesson 5 Resources

Teacher Classroom Resources
- Concept Map 72
- Cross-Curriculum Activity 36
- Enrichment Activity 72
- Health Lab 18
- Lesson Plan 5
- Lesson 5 Quiz
- Reading Tutor Activity 71

- Reteaching Activity 72
- Transparency 75

Student Activities Workbook
- Chapter 18 Study Guide
- Applying Health Skills 72
- Health Inventory 18

Although some people with diabetes may have some or all of these symptoms, others may have no symptoms for years. Untreated diabetes is dangerous because it can lead to serious health problems, including blindness, kidney disease, heart disease, and stroke. If you experience any of the symptoms listed on the previous page, see your doctor as soon as possible.

Preventing and Treating Diabetes

Researchers are making progress in identifying the causes of type 1 diabetes, but there is currently no known prevention. Studies have shown that maintaining a healthy weight and participating in regular physical activity can significantly reduce the risk of developing type 2 diabetes.

There is no cure for diabetes. Treatment for type 1 diabetes involves daily insulin injections. For type 2 diabetes, a daily oral medication may be prescribed or dietary changes may be successful. People with either type of diabetes must monitor their condition carefully and follow their doctor's advice. With medication, a healthful eating plan, and physical activity, most people with diabetes can manage their condition successfully.

What Is Arthritis?

Arthritis is not one disease but many. A person diagnosed with **arthritis** (ar·THRY·tuhs) may have one of *more than 100 conditions marked by pain and swelling in body joints.* Although often thought of as a disease that affects only older people, arthritis can affect people of any age. Two types of arthritis are the most common— rheumatoid arthritis and osteoarthritis.

This teen is performing a blood glucose test to check the level of sugar in his blood. *Why do people with diabetes need to monitor their condition carefully?*

LESSON 5: DIABETES AND ARTHRITIS **495**

CONNECT TO Science

MONITORING GLUCOSE LEVELS
Today's technology provides portable blood glucose monitors that can be used anywhere. Several models give voice instructions— in a choice of languages—to guide the user through the test procedure. The machine then announces the test results. *Who might benefit most from one of these "talking" blood glucose monitors?*

Lesson 5

② Teach

Discussing

As students begin reading about diabetes, encourage willing students to share what they already know about this disease. If students are comfortable discussing their own diabetes or have permission to discuss the diabetes of family members, have them describe the effects on daily life. **L1**

Comparing

After students have read about type 1 and type 2 diabetes, have them work in groups to compare the two forms of the disease. Ask the members of each group to collaborate on a Venn diagram, listing the similarities and differences. **L2**

As recently as ten years ago, type 2 diabetes was often called adult-onset diabetes because it was diagnosed almost exclusively in adults. Now, experts at the Centers for Disease Control and Prevention estimate that as many as 1 in 50 American children has type 2 diabetes.

Discussing

Ask two students to outline on the board treatments for type 1 and type 2 diabetes. Have the class discuss the differences. **L1**

Health Literacy

Health Information Does the fact that a person lives in the United States make him or her more susceptible to diabetes? Since the 1930s, the incidence of diabetes in the United States has increased every year. In Africa and Japan, on the other hand, there has not been a similar trend.

Many scientists believe that diet may be the explanation. Diet in the United States has changed to include greater amounts of refined foods and less fiber. In Africa and Japan, however, people still eat lots of complex carbohydrates and high-fiber foods. Research also shows that, for Africans and Japanese who move to the United States, the incidence of diabetes rises.

Demonstrating

Divide the class into small groups. Ask each group to simulate the difficulty in moving that an arthritis sufferer might experience. For example, each person in one group might tape his or her fingers into fists and try to write. Students should keep track of their frustration levels when doing the activities and share their reactions with other groups. **L1** **INCL** *English Language Learners, Special Learning Needs, Behavior Problems, Different Learning Styles (Visual)*

HEALTH SKILLS ACTIVITY

ACCESSING INFORMATION

Help students discuss the usefulness of support groups. Ask: Why do you think that belonging to a support group can improve the effectiveness of some patients' treatment? Then guide students in reading and discussing the tips for finding support groups.

Have students work in small groups to gather information about local support groups. Have all the groups combine their information and present it in a class brochure to be shared with others in the school and community.

Note: This skill is introduced in Chapter 2 on pages 45–46.

Although arthritis can make some activities difficult, medical treatment can help patients live full lives.

Rheumatoid Arthritis

Rheumatoid (ROO·muh·toyd) **arthritis** is *a chronic disease characterized by pain, inflammation, swelling, and stiffness of the joints.* It is the more serious of the two most common forms of arthritis. The joints affected by rheumatoid arthritis often become deformed and no longer function normally. Joints typically affected are those of the hands, feet, elbows, shoulders, neck, knees, hips, and ankles. The effects of rheumatoid arthritis are usually symmetrical—both feet develop the symptoms at the same time and in the same pattern. The cause of rheumatoid arthritis is not known.

Treating Rheumatoid Arthritis

There is no cure for rheumatoid arthritis. Doctors generally treat the disease with medicines to relieve pain, reduce inflammation and swelling, and keep joints functioning as normally as possible. In addition, a combination of exercise, rest, joint protection, and physical therapy is usually recommended.

HEALTH SKILLS ACTIVITY

ACCESSING INFORMATION

Locating Support Groups

Research shows that belonging to a support group can help people with chronic diseases. Many members of support groups not only feel better emotionally but also find that their treatment is more successful. Here are some tips for finding support groups.

- Check with physicians or nurses to see if they know of a local support group.
- Look in the telephone book.
- Call the local hospital and ask for community resources.

- If your town has a Web site, check out any resources listed there.
- Scan the local newspaper for meeting announcements.
- Ask the national organization for the disease, such as the Arthritis Foundation, for help in finding a local support group.

WITH A GROUP

Make a list of local support groups for chronic conditions. Gather information on the activities of the groups, and make it available to other students at your school.

Beyond the Classroom

Osteoarthritis Ask students to interview older adult relatives or nursing home residents who have osteoarthritis. First, have students ask the people interviewed to describe their symptoms and the ways in which their activities are restricted by the disease. Then have students find out what, if anything, they do or use to help compensate for the restrictions on their activities (*e.g., using a cane, avoiding stairs, or using special tools for opening jars or turning on faucets*). Finally, have students use the information they collect to design a room or house that meets the special needs of people with arthritis.

Osteoarthritis

Osteoarthritis (ahs·tee·oh·ahr·THRY·tuhs) is one of the most common types of arthritis. It is a *disease that is characterized by the breakdown of the cartilage in joints.* Cartilage cushions the place where bones meet in a joint. When cartilage breaks down, the bones rub against one another. The result is pain and loss of movement.

The areas most affected by osteoarthritis are the hands and weight-bearing joints such as the knees and hips. Most people affected are over the age of 45.

Treatment of osteoarthritis focuses on relieving pain and improving joint movement. Specific treatment may include medication, heat or cold therapy, and joint protection. Weight reduction may also be recommended to reduce stress on weight-bearing joints.

People with rheumatoid arthritis are advised to exercise daily to prevent further stiffness.

FYI

Rheumatoid arthritis affects an estimated 2.1 million Americans, which is about 1 percent of the population. Although the disease usually starts in early adulthood, about 50,000 American children have rheumatoid arthritis.

③ Assess

Evaluating

📁 Assign the Lesson 5 Review; then assign the Lesson 5 Quiz in the TCR.

Reteaching

📁 Assign Concept Map 72 or Reteaching Activity 72 in the TCR.

Enrichment

• 📁 Assign Enrichment Activity 72 in the TCR.

• Have students use online or library resources to learn about the causes and effects of the increased incidence of type 2 diabetes among children and teens.

④ Close

Ask students to summarize the symptoms and treatment of diabetes and arthritis.

Lesson 5 Review

Using complete sentences, answer the following questions on a sheet of paper.

Reviewing Terms and Facts

1. **Recall** Summarize the role of insulin in the body.
2. **Vocabulary** Explain how *type 1 diabetes* differs from *type 2 diabetes.*
3. **Identify** What are five possible symptoms of diabetes?
4. **Vocabulary** Define *arthritis.*

Thinking Critically

5. **Synthesize** What do you think would be most challenging about having diabetes as a teen? Explain your responses in a paragraph.

6. **Compare and Contrast** What are the similarities between rheumatoid arthritis and osteoarthritis? What are the differences?

Applying Health Skills

7. **Analyzing Influences** In small groups, discuss magazine and newspaper ads for products for people with arthritis. What is the major point of each ad? To which age group is the manufacturer appealing? What advertising techniques are used? Do you think people who buy the product will get what they hope for? Why or why not?

LESSON 5: DIABETES AND ARTHRITIS **497**

Lesson 5 Review

1. Insulin allows cells to take in glucose, the source of the body's energy.
2. See definitions on page 494.
3. Any five: frequent urination, excessive thirst, unexplained weight loss, extreme hunger, sudden vision changes, tingling or numbness in hands or feet, feeling tired much of the time, very dry skin, slow-healing sores, more infections than usual.
4. See definition on page 497.
5. Teens might find it difficult to medicate themselves every day, monitor glucose levels, and have a healthy social life.
6. Both affect joints—rheumatoid with swelling and stiffness, osteoarthritis with breakdown of cartilage.

The Diabetes Explosion

① Focus

Objectives

Students will be able to

• explain the history of diabetes.

• describe risk factors for type 2 diabetes and ways to reduce them.

• list signs and symptoms of type 2 diabetes.

Motivator

Quick Write
According to this article, the "stakes are becoming higher" for people to exercise and eat right. Ask students, "What does this mean? How can the average teenager respond to this statement in a healthful way?"

② Teach

Cross-Curriculum Activity

SOCIAL STUDIES Read students this brief history of diabetes: The symptoms of diabetes were first recorded in ancient Egypt in 1500 B.C. By 100 A.D. the condition was termed "diabetes" which is Greek for "siphon" (meaning to drain or tap) since people with diabetes urinate so often. Until the 20th century, the only treatment for diabetes was dietary and people rarely lived for long after diagnosis. Then, in 1921, two Canadian doctors discovered insulin, a turning point in the treatment of the disease. Today, insulin injections are commonly used to regulate blood glucose levels. This, along with lifestyle changes, allow most diabetics to live a long and normal life while research continues on ways to prevent and cure the disease.

Divide the class into small research groups. Direct each group to study the history of a well-known disease or disorder and present their findings to the class, using the paragraph above as a model.

The Diabetes EXPLOSION

As the people in the United States get heavier and heavier, an old disease is showing up in younger and younger victims.

According to a report published in the medical journal *Diabetes Care*, as the population of the United States grows more obese, the number of cases of diabetes is rising, too. The disease is striking more people in younger age groups. Untreated diabetes can result in serious health problems, including blindness, amputations, and heart attacks.

Type 2 diabetes is the most common kind of diabetes. In recent years, the number of Americans with type 2 diabetes has jumped a whopping 33 percent, climbing from 4.9 percent of the population to 6.5 percent.

Health Literacy

The Diabetes Reporting Factor While diabetes rates are obviously increasing, some epidemiologists (researchers who study the incidence and prevalence of disease) question the exact numbers. Why? When a medical condition is suddenly and frequently in the news, awareness of it increases in the general public and among physicians. As a result, individuals who may have been experiencing symptoms for some time are more likely to visit a doctor's office, and once there, are more likely to ask about the publicized condition. Heightened awareness may also make physicians diagnose patients more readily. The result? Not all of the newly reported cases of type 2 diabetes may actually be new.

Younger Victims Than Ever

Though type 2 diabetes has traditionally been seen in people age 45 and older, the greatest increase appears to be among 30- to 39-year-olds. This younger group has seen a stunning 70 percent jump. Among racial and ethnic groups, Hispanics were hit hardest of all, with a 38 percent increase. Caucasians came in next at 29 percent, and African Americans were last at 26 percent.

Dr. Frank Vinicor of the Centers for Disease Control and Prevention finds this rise in the number of diabetes cases ominous: "If that were to happen in a disease like tuberculosis or AIDS, I think there would be a public outcry, and understandably. These trends are very disturbing."

While most public-health threats require a bit of detective work to figure out the cause, this one's a no-brainer. At the same time the diabetes numbers have been climbing, so have the numbers on many people's scales. In 1991 just 12 percent of the U.S. population was considered obese. By 1998 the number had risen to 20 percent. Meanwhile, the number of people considered to be at least "overweight" climbed from 44 percent to 54 percent.

All the added fat appears to make the body less responsive to sugar-processing insulin. As a result, the body produces more and more of that vital hormone. Ultimately, however, the body becomes so unresponsive to certain levels of insulin that injections of more insulin or other medication may become necessary.

Get Off the Couch!

Doctors blame part of the growing problem on America's great pastimes: sitting in front of the TV and surfing the Internet. An increasingly wired country is also becoming an increasingly lazy one, with Web-surfing young people leading the way.

What's the answer? The same as always: Shut down the computer, turn off the TV, and try participating in regular physical activity and eating moderate amounts of nutritious foods. The lecture may be the same as it's always been, but the stakes are becoming higher than ever. ◼

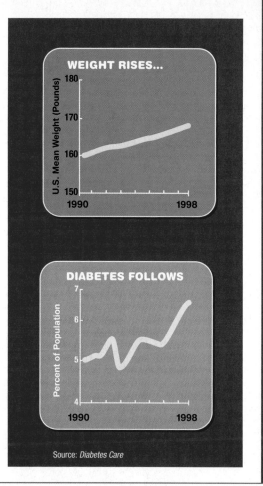

WEIGHT RISES...

U.S. Mean Weight (Pounds)

1990 — 1998

DIABETES FOLLOWS

Percent of Population

1990 — 1998

Source: *Diabetes Care*

TIME TO THINK...

About Preventing Type 2 Diabetes

It's important to get the message out to teens about how to reduce their risk of developing type 2 diabetes. In small groups, brainstorm ideas for public service announcements (PSAs) that bring attention to this serious medical condition. The PSAs should encourage teens to get regular physical activity and eat a balanced and nutritious diet. Then transform your ideas into posters that, with your teacher's permission, can be displayed around your school.

TIME HEALTH

❸ Apply

Time to Think

Before students begin their advocacy campaign, review how people can reduce their risk of developing type 2 diabetes. Explain that risk factors such as poor eating habits and lack of exercise can be addressed through lifestyle changes. However, risk factors such as family history, age, and ethnic origin cannot be changed. How might students address these factors in their campaign? Students may want to log on to the American Diabetes Association Website at www.diabetes.org and take the Diabetes Risk Test to learn more.

VISUAL LEARNING

Ask students to analyze the two graphs on page 499. How are the two graphs the same or different? (*Weight gain has shown a steady increase while diabetes rates fluctuate but show a general upward trend.*) What might account for these differences?

WHAT TEENS WANT TO KNOW

Could I have type 2 diabetes and not know it?
People can have diabetes without experiencing any noticeable signs or symptoms. In fact, according to the National Diabetes Information Clearinghouse, nearly six million people in the U.S. have undiagnosed type 2 diabetes. While only a doctor can diagnose the disorder, here are some signs and symptoms to look for:

- increased thirst
- increased hunger
- fatigue
- increased urination, especially at night
- weight loss
- blurred vision
- sores that do not heal

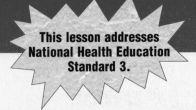
STRESS MANAGEMENT

Objective

After completing the lesson, students will be able to demonstrate strategies for coping with stress.

Time: 45 minutes

Materials: none

Teacher Classroom Resources

📁 Building Health Skills Activities

• Transparency Master 3, "Stress Management"

• Reproducible Master 43, "Managing Teen Stress"

---

1. Model

• Display Transparency Master 3, and review its content with the class.

• Direct students to read about Bradley's stressful morning. Have them work in pairs to answer the questions. (Sources of stress: *He overslept, didn't have time to eat breakfast before the bus, left his math homework at home, didn't see his friends, and later, his friends teased him. How he dealt with them: He ate a granola bar and a banana on the bus, redid his assignment in the library, and he laughed with his friends. Sources of support: He got support from efficient time management and friends after his morning calmed down.*)

• Instruct pairs to work with another pair to compare answers.

• Ask volunteers to read their responses aloud and discuss as a class.

Model

High stress levels may increase your risk of developing certain noncommunicable diseases. Learning to manage stress reduces your risk of disease and improves your mental and social health, too. Read about Bradley, a teen who had a stressful morning. What sources of stress did he experience? How did he deal with them? Where does Bradley get the support he needs to manage his stress?

Bradley overslept on Monday morning. He didn't have time for breakfast before catching the school bus, so he grabbed a granola bar and a banana to eat on the bus. When he got to school, Bradley discovered that he had left his math homework at home. Instead of hanging out with his friends before school, Bradley went to the library to redo his assignment. He missed seeing his friends, but he figured that having to tell his math teacher he did not have his homework would be even more stressful. He made a point of spending some time with his friends later on between classes. When they teased him about being a "library nerd" that morning, Bradley just joked, "You've discovered my secret." Laughing with his friends helped Bradley relax. His rough morning came to a fairly smooth end.

Teaching Tips

Sharing Responses with Peers Stress-management skills are particularly important to teens as they experience the changes associated with adolescence. Have students share their responses to these questions: Do you and your friends have similar sources of stress? Do you have similar ways of handling stress? Who provides support for you when you are experiencing stress?

Utilizing Additional Resources Physical activity is especially good for stress management. Coordinate with physical education teachers and other community resources to demonstrate the benefits and techniques for different physical activities.

Practice

Write your name on a sheet of paper. Below that, briefly describe a specific situation you have experienced that caused stress. Exchange papers with another student. Read your classmate's situation and write down a healthy way of dealing with the stress from that situation. Then exchange papers with a different student and repeat the process. Continue trading papers until each paper has suggestions from four different students. Then give each paper back to the person who wrote it.

Read your classmates' suggestions. Circle the ideas you think would work best for you. Share your situation and the responses to it with the class. Do you and your classmates have similar sources of stress? Do you have similar ways of handling stress? Who provides support for you when you are experiencing stress?

Stress Management

Stress management strategies include
- **identifying sources of stress.**
- **responding in healthy ways.**
- **building support systems.**

My sister borrows my clothes without asking.

talk to your sister

shoot some hoops or take a long walk to relieve stress

talk to your mom about it

put a sign on your closet door

 **Self-Check**

- Did my story identify one or more sources of stress in a teen's life?
- Did my story show healthy ways to manage stress?
- Did my story give examples of people who provide support?

Apply/Assess

Write a short story about a teen who experiences stress. Your story should describe a common source of teen stress, and should show how the character responds to it in healthy ways. Include a description of one or more people who provide emotional support for the teen. Be prepared to present your story to the class.

BUILDING HEALTH SKILLS: MANAGING TEEN STRESS **501**

2. Practice

- Have students write their name at the top of a sheet of paper. Then ask them to write a sentence describing a particular situation that caused them to feel stress.

- Have students switch papers with a classmate and write down a healthful way for that student to cope with the stress of his or her situation.

- Direct the class to continue switching papers until each paper contains four suggestions of how to deal with the situation.

- After each paper has been returned to its owner, ask volunteers to share their situations and the responses their classmates suggested.

- Conduct a class discussion using this question as a foundation for the discussion: "Why is it important to learn how to manage stress?"

3. Apply/Assess

- You may wish to distribute Building Health Skills Reproducible Master 43 in the TCR to guide students in completing this activity.

- Ask each student to write a short story about a teen who is experiencing stress.

- As students begin working on their stories, remind them to review the information in the Self-Check to ensure that their work is complete.

- Provide an opportunity for volunteers to read their stories aloud or to create role-plays to demonstrate strategies for coping with stress. As a class, identify the source of stress for the teen in the story, the stress-management techniques that the character used, and the people that he or she went to for support.

Assessment Scoring

Using a rubric, student work should provide evidence of all criteria to achieve the highest score.

Skills

Student work demonstrates
- common sources of stress.
- healthful responses to a stressful situation.
- support systems.

Concepts

Student work provides
- accurate information about stress management.
- a link between stress management and disease prevention.

Checking Comprehension

Use the Chapter 18 Assessment to examine the most important ideas presented in the chapter.

Answers to Reviewing Vocabulary and Concepts

Lesson 1
1. degenerative diseases
2. noncommunicable diseases
3. risk factor

Lesson 2
4. allergens
5. antihistamines
6. hives
7. histamines
8. asthma

Lesson 3
9. true
10. true
11. false; mammogram
12. true

Lesson 4
13. false; arteriosclerosis
14. false; atherosclerosis
15. true
16. false; high blood pressure

Lesson 5
17. true
18. true
19. false; osteoarthritis
20. false; rheumatoid arthritis

Thinking Critically

21. Responses might include helping the person learn more about the disease.
22. A doctor can perform a test by scratching the skin and applying the allergen. If Cole is allergic, the skin will turn red and swell.

After You Read

Use your completed Foldable to review the information on causes of noncommunicable disease.

 FOLDABLES™ Study Organizer

Reviewing Vocabulary and Concepts

On a sheet of paper, write the numbers 1–8. After each number, write the term from the list that best completes each sentence.

- allergens
- antihistamines
- asthma
- degenerative diseases
- histamines
- hives
- noncommunicable diseases
- risk factor

Lesson 1

1. _____ cause breakdown in body cells, tissues, and organs as they progress.
2. _____, such as diabetes, are not spread through contact with others who have the disease.
3. Heredity is an example of a(n) _____ that may increase a person's chances of developing a certain disease.

Lesson 2

4. Pollen and mold are examples of common _____.
5. _____ are medicines that help control the effects of allergens.
6. _____ are raised bumps on the skin that itch.
7. Chemicals in the body that cause the symptoms of an allergic reaction are called _____.
8. _____ is a chronic condition that causes tiny air passages in the respiratory system to become narrow or blocked.

On a sheet of paper, write the numbers 9–20. Write *True* or *False* for each statement below. If the statement is false, change the underlined word or phrase to make it true.

Lesson 3

9. <u>Metastasis</u> is the term used to describe the spread of cancer in the body.
10. A substance that causes cancer is called a <u>carcinogen</u>.
11. Doctors recommend a <u>biopsy</u>, which is an X ray of the breast, to screen for breast cancer.
12. <u>Cancer</u> is characterized by the rapid and uncontrolled growth of abnormal cells.

Lesson 4

13. <u>Atherosclerosis</u> is a group of diseases in which arteries harden and become more rigid.
14. <u>Arteriosclerosis</u> is a disease characterized by a buildup of plaque in the arteries.
15. An artificial <u>pacemaker</u> can be used to produce the electrical impulses that cause the heart to beat regularly.
16. Hypertension is another term for <u>stroke</u>.

Lesson 5

17. <u>Insulin</u> is a hormone produced by the pancreas.
18. <u>Diabetes</u> affects the body's ability to produce or use insulin.
19. <u>Rheumatoid arthritis</u> is characterized by a breakdown of cartilage in the joints.
20. Pain, inflammation, swelling, and stiffness of the joints are characteristic of <u>osteoarthritis</u>.

Thinking Critically

Using complete sentences, answer the following questions on a sheet of paper.

21. **Apply** How could a teen safely demonstrate care and concern for someone at school or in the community who has a noncommunicable disease?

INCLUSION STRATEGIES

Special Learning Needs, Behavior Problems, English Language Learners The following suggestions are helpful for students with special learning needs, students with behavior problems, and ELL students:

- Pair these students with more proficient learners who can help summarize the main concepts of the chapter.

- Direct these students to listen to the Teen Health Audio Summaries. This component provides an audio and written summary of the chapter in both English and Spanish.

- Use photographs, drawings, or magazine clippings whenever possible to help students visualize the important concepts of the chapter.

22. Suggest Cole thinks he might be allergic to cats. How can he find out whether his fear is correct?

23. Recommend What are some ways to reduce the risk of developing skin cancer?

24. Analyze If you had a family history of high blood pressure, what healthy lifestyle choices could help you lower your risk?

25. Hypothesize Why might it be difficult for a person who had rheumatoid arthritis to play the guitar?

Career Corner

Occupational Therapist Occupational therapists help people with disabilities regain the skills they need to live independent lives. These professionals may help someone who is physically impaired learn daily living skills such as dressing or cooking. They may also assist patients in using special equipment to perform everyday activities. Occupational therapists need a four-year degree in occupational therapy. Learn more about this and other health careers by clicking on Career Corner at health.glencoe.com.

23. Avoid exposure to sun, wear sunblock, wear a hat and protective clothing.

24. Eat healthy foods, maintain a healthy weight, avoid tobacco and alcohol, exercise, learn to manage stress.

25. Joints would be stiff. It would be painful to use hands for any skill.

Test Practice
1. D
2. B
3. Answers should identify a stressful situation and give detailed steps for dealing with it.

Reteaching
Assign Study Guide 18 in the Student Activities Workbook.

Evaluate
Use the reproducible Chapter 18 Test in the TCR, or construct your own test using the **Exam**_View_® Pro Testmaker.

Enrichment
Have each student choose a particular congenital heart disease—there are 35 in all—and write a brief report about it.

Standardized Test Practice

Reading & Writing

Read the paragraphs below and then answer the questions.

While we cannot control many of the situations that cause stress, there are actions we can take to prepare for and cope with stress.

Plan: Planning ahead can help you manage your time wisely so that you don't feel overwhelmed. For example, if you know that you have a test on Monday, you might need to study over the weekend and postpone doing something else.

Talk: Talking about your problems with trusted adults and friends can help you discover ways to cope with stress. For example, a teacher might be able to give you tips on how to study.

Relax: Find a healthful activity that you enjoy and take some time to participate in it.

For example, exercising or listening to music are not only fun, they can help reduce stress.

1. Which of the following best describes the organization of the passage?

 A ranking reasons to relieve stress

 B explaining the pros and cons of stress

 C presenting events in the order in which they occur

 D presenting steps and giving examples

2. The reader can tell from the passage that managing stress is

 A easy and fun.

 B challenging but not impossible.

 C not worth doing.

 D complicated and impossible.

3. Write a paragraph describing a stressful situation and explaining how you dealt with it.

 TH05_C3.glencoe.com/quiz

CHAPTER 18 ASSESSMENT 503

Assessment

Self-Assessment Direct students to review the activities that are provided throughout the chapter. Encourage each student to select one finished product or activity that demonstrates his or her best work for the chapter. Have students explain what they learned and how the examples they selected show their progress.

Career Corner

Occupational Therapist After reviewing the career profile on the Web site, students might:

• Discuss the wide variety of skills that an occupational therapist must possess.

• Research further the types of specialized equipment that an occupational therapist might use to help patients.

Safety and Environmental Health

Unit Objectives

Students closely examine issues of safety with an emphasis on learning safe habits as the best way to prevent injuries. Students also learn the basic principles of first aid and the reasons everyone should be concerned about the health of the environment.

Unit Overview

Chapter 19
Safety and Emergencies

Lesson
1 Safety at Home and at School
2 Safety on the Road and Outdoors
3 Safety in Weather Emergencies
4 Basic First Aid
5 First Aid for Common Emergencies
6 Life-Threatening Emergencies

Chapter 20
Environmental Health

Lesson
1 Pollution and Health
2 Preventing and Reducing Pollution

504

DEALING WITH SENSITIVE ISSUES

Reassuring Students It is important to be aware that not all students feel the same way about each sensitive issue. Just as some people are shy by nature, some people are naturally more readily embarrassed and more easily hurt than others. They may have had negative life experiences that lowered their self-esteem, thereby making them more likely to respond with feelings of guilt and shame. The goal of this unit is to inform students of the hazards in the home and in the environment. If students are not utilizing these practices, be sure to encourage them to develop these good habits. They should be aware of how to protect themselves but not made to feel they are bad people or bad citizens.

Safety and Environmental Health

HEALTH in Action

Our actions don't affect only us; they affect the world around us, too. Staying safe at home and in emergencies are good ways to protect yourself. Other habits you develop, like riding your bike instead of having someone drive you, protect the planet we all share. By behaving carefully and thoughtfully, whether at home, outside, or in traffic, you can prevent many accidents and emergencies—and help keep the skies bright for everyone.

How does riding your bike help keep the sky blue?

Unit Introduction

Ask for volunteers to describe an accident or emergency situation that they experienced. Encourage them to give specific details about their role, if any, in the handling of the emergency or how they felt during it.

Discuss how knowledge about first aid and preventive measures can help eliminate the amount of injuries that may occur in an accident or an emergency. Help students understand that, although all accidents cannot be prevented, the damage can be lessened.

Tell students that the chapters in Unit 7 will increase their awareness of safety issues in their lives and in their environment.

HEALTH in Action

Read the class the question on page 505. Ask students to name measures they can take to make their environments safer and cleaner. Then lead the class in the following physical group activity:

As a class, have students list their daily activities. Write the list on the board. Ask for volunteers to act out one of the activities silently, and have the rest of the class try to identify the activity. When a student identifies the activity, have that student name one way to perform that activity in a safer or more environmentally friendly manner. For instance, for the activity *washing the dishes*, students might mention using turning the water off when not actually in use. Repeat with each activity.

Planning Guide

Chapter 19	Skills/ Activities	Reproducible Resources	Assessment
Lesson 1 **Safety at Home and at School** *pages 508–513*	HEALTH SKILLS ACTIVITY ▲ Preparing a Fire Safety Plan (*Practicing Healthful Behaviors*), page 512	*Student Activities Workbook available for use with each chapter* 📁 Parent Letter & Activities 19 📁 Concept Map 73 📁 Cross-Curriculum Activity 37 📁 Enrichment Activity 73 📁 Lesson Plan 1 📁 Reading Tutor Activity 72 📁 Reteaching Activity 73	📁 Lesson 1 Quiz
Lesson 2 **Safety on the Road and Outdoors** *pages 514–519*		📁 Concept Map 74 📁 Decision-Making Activity 37 📁 Enrichment Activity 74 📁 Lesson Plan 2 📁 Reading Tutor Activity 73 📁 Reteaching Activity 74	📁 Lesson 2 Quiz
Lesson 3 **Safety in Weather Emergencies** *pages 520–523*	HEALTH SKILLS ACTIVITY ▲ Local Weather Emergencies (*Accessing Information*), page 522	📁 Concept Map 75 📁 Enrichment Activity 75 📁 Lesson Plan 3 📁 Reading Tutor Activity 74 📁 Reteaching Activity 75	📁 Lesson 3 Quiz
Lesson 4 **Basic First Aid** *pages 524–527*		📁 Concept Map 76 📁 Enrichment Activity 76 📁 Lesson Plan 4 📁 Reading Tutor Activity 75 📁 Reteaching Activity 76	📁 Lesson 4 Quiz

Standards		Technology
National	**State/Local**	
National Health Education Standard **1.1, 1.6, 1.8, 3.1, 3.5, 3.6**		📽 Transparency 76 📼 💿 Tape/DVD 2, Segment 5, "Avoiding Potentially Dangerous Situations" 💿 TeacherWorks™ 🖱 Internet Activities
National Health Education Standard **1.1, 1.6, 1.8, 3.1, 3.5, 3.6**		📽 Transparency 77 💿 TeacherWorks™
National Health Education Standard **1.1, 1.5, 2.1, 2.2, 3.1, 3.5, 3.6**		📽 Transparency 78 💿 TeacherWorks™
National Health Education Standard **1.7, 2.6, 3.1, 3.3, 3.5, 3.6**		📽 Transparency 79 💿 TeacherWorks™

(continued on pages 506C and 506D)

TeacherWorks™

Glencoe's new and exclusive TeacherWorks™ is an all-in-one planner and resource center. Access the complete Teacher Wraparound Edition electronically. Find all your classroom resources with just a few easy clicks, and print them right from your computer. Connect directly to Glencoe's customized Health Web site. Access the National Health Education Standards correlations, or insert your own state standards and match them directly to the electronic Teacher Wraparound Edition.

Language Diversity

- 🎧 English Audio Summaries
- 🎧 Spanish Audio Summaries
- 📁 English Summaries, Quizzes, and Activities
- 📁 Spanish Summaries, Quizzes, and Activities
- 📁 Spanish Parent Letters and Activities

KEY TO ABILITY LEVELS

Teaching Strategies that appear throughout the chapters have been identified by one of four codes to give you an idea of their suitability for students of varying learning styles and abilities.

L1 **Level 1** strategies should be within the ability range of all students. Often full class participation is required.

L2 **Level 2** strategies are for average to above-average students or for small groups. Some teacher direction is necessary.

L3 **Level 3** strategies are designed for students able and willing to work independently. Minimal teacher direction is necessary.

INCL Strategies are appropriate for students with particular special needs in a general classroom setting.

Planning Guide

Chapter 19	Skills/ Activities	Reproducible Resources	Assessment
Lesson 5 **First Aid for Common Emergencies** *pages 528–532*		📁 Concept Map 77 📁 Enrichment Activity 77 📁 Health Lab 19 📁 Lesson Plan 5 📁 Reading Tutor Activity 76 📁 Reteaching Activity 77	📁 Lesson 5 Quiz
Lesson 6 **Life-Threatening Emergencies** *pages 533–537*	**Hands-On Health** ▲ Locating Pressure Points, page 535	📁 Concept Map 78 📁 Cross-Curriculum Activity 38 📁 Decision-Making Activity 38 📁 Enrichment Activity 78 📁 Lesson Plan 6 📁 Reading Tutor Activity 77 📁 Reteaching Activity 78	📁 Lesson 6 Quiz 📁 Chapter 19 Test 📁 Performance Assessment 19
TIME HEALTH	**Preventing Wildfires** *pages 538–539*		
BUILDING HEALTH SKILLS **Avoiding Unsafe Behaviors** (*Refusal Skills*) *pages 540–541*		📁 Building Health Skills Reproducible Master 44	

Standards		Technology
National	**State/Local**	
National Health Education Standard **1.7, 2.6, 3.1, 3.5, 3.6**		Transparency 80 TeacherWorks™
National Health Education Standard **1.7, 2.6, 3.1, 3.5, 3.6**		Transparency 81 TeacherWorks™ MindJogger Videoquiz **Exam**_View_® Pro Testmaker
National Health Education Standard **5.6**		Building Health Skills Transparency Master 7

TeacherWorks™

Glencoe's new and exclusive TeacherWorks™ is an all-in-one planner and resource center. Access the complete Teacher Wraparound Edition electronically. Find all your classroom resources with just a few easy clicks, and print them right from your computer. Connect directly to Glencoe's customized Health Web site. Access the National Health Education Standards correlations, or insert your own state standards and match them directly to the electronic Teacher Wraparound Edition.

Language Diversity

- English Audio Summaries
- Spanish Audio Summaries
- English Summaries, Quizzes, and Activities
- Spanish Summaries, Quizzes, and Activities
- Spanish Parent Letters and Activities

KEY TO ABILITY LEVELS

Teaching Strategies that appear throughout the chapters have been identified by one of four codes to give you an idea of their suitability for students of varying learning styles and abilities.

L1 **Level 1** strategies should be within the ability range of all students. Often full class participation is required.

L2 **Level 2** strategies are for average to above-average students or for small groups. Some teacher direction is necessary.

L3 **Level 3** strategies are designed for students able and willing to work independently. Minimal teacher direction is necessary.

INCL Strategies are appropriate for students with particular special needs in a general classroom setting.

Safety and Emergencies

Chapter at a Glance

Lesson 1 tells how having a proper attitude toward safety helps break the accident chain and provides tips on how to prevent accidents at home and at school.

Lesson 2 presents rules for traffic and pedestrian safety and outlines safety strategies for recreational and outdoor activities.

Lesson 3 discusses the dangers associated with hazardous weather conditions and natural disasters and offers information on how to prepare for them.

Lesson 4 advises students on how to be prepared for emergencies and identifies the basic rules of first aid.

Lesson 5 advises students on how to deal with common emergencies.

Lesson 6 highlights steps for aiding a choking victim and explains when rescue breathing and CPR are needed.

Health Skills
- Preparing a Fire Safety Plan (*Practicing Healthful Behaviors*), p. 512
- Local Weather Emergencies (*Accessing Information*), p. 522
- Avoiding Unsafe Behaviors (*Refusal Skills*), pp. 540–541

506

HANDS-ON ACTIVITY

Safety Rules! Play this game to motivate students and access their prior knowledge of safety. Divide the class into two teams. State a topic from this chapter; then allow a few minutes for each student to write all the rules related to that topic he or she can think of. Students should not talk to one another and should stop writing when you call time. Each team gets one point for each different rule. Note: Both teams can have the same rule and get points. However, to get the point, someone on the team must explain how the safety rule prevents accidents or injuries. The team with the most points wins. For reinforcement and review, you can play this game again at the end of the chapter.

Safety and Emergencies

Chapter Introduction

Use the options below to motivate students and preview chapter content.

HEALTH *Online*

Find out how prepared you are to stay safe and handle emergencies. Take the Chapter 19 Health Inventory at health.glencoe.com.

HEALTH *Online*

Encourage students to take Health Inventory 19 at health.glencoe.com. Then brush up on health education by reading Professional Articles for health teachers. These articles can help keep you informed of national and state trends.

FOLDABLES™ Study Organizer

Before You Read

Make this Foldable to organize what you learn in Lesson 1 about safety at home and at school. Begin with two sheets of notebook paper.

Step 1

Fold one sheet in half from top to bottom. Cut about 1" along the fold at both ends, stopping at the margin lines.

Step 2

Fold the second sheet in half from top to bottom. Cut or shave off the fold *between* the margin lines.

Step 3

Insert the first sheet through the second sheet and align folds.

Step 4

Fold the bound pages in half to make a booklet, and label the cover as shown. Then label each page as instructed by your teacher.

Safety at Home and at School

As You Read

Take notes, define terms, and give examples of home and school safety on the appropriate page of your Foldable.

GLENCOE TECHNOLOGY

(Each format available in both English and Spanish)

Teen Health Video and DVD Series

 You may wish to use:

- Tape/DVD 2, Segment 5, "Avoiding Potentially Dangerous Situations"

MindJogger Videoquiz

Use MindJogger to preview or review Chapter 19 content.

TIME HEALTH

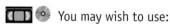

Preventing Wildfires
pages 538–539

FOLDABLES™ Study Organizer

Dinah Zike Study Fold

Organizing Data Students will use their Foldable journal to write about safety at home and at school. Have students write the title of Lesson 1 on the front of their Foldable journal. Then ask students to label the six inside pages with the following titles: "Developing Safe Habits," "The Accident Chain," "Safety in the Home," "Fire Safety," "Safety at School," and "Practicing Healthful Behaviors." Students will use their Foldable journal to take notes, define terms, and record personal experiences. On the last page of their journal—Practicing Healthful Behaviors—encourage students to list several examples of ways in which they might use what they have learned in their daily lives.

Lesson 1

Safety at Home and at School

① Focus

Lesson Objectives

Students will be able to

- describe the accident chain and how to break it.
- describe safety hazards in the home and ways to correct them.
- explain safety precautions necessary at school.

Health Skills
- Practicing Healthful Behaviors, p. 512

Motivators

 Quick Write
Allow students to share their responses, then ask: How can a person become prepared for such responsibilities?

Bellringer Activity

Ask students to write three sayings or phrases that contain the word *safe* or *safety*. (*safety first, play it safe, safety in numbers, better safe than sorry*)

VOCABULARY

Have students look up the vocabulary terms in the Glossary. Then have them guess which term you are thinking of by asking you questions that require a yes or no answer but not asking the word's definition. If students ask whether the term is a compound word and you say yes and then ask whether the second word of the term starts with a consonant, they could guess *accident chain*.

508

Lesson

① Safety at Home and at School

Quick Write

What responsibilities do you take for keeping your home and school safe? Explain your answers.

LEARN ABOUT...

- why accidents happen.
- how to break the accident chain.
- how to avoid being injured at home.
- how to stay safe at school.

VOCABULARY

- accidental injuries
- accident
- accident chain

Safety at Home and at School

Developing Safe Habits

Every hour of every day in the United States, at least one person between the ages of 10 and 19 dies as a result of an injury. About 60 percent of those deaths result from unintentional or accidental injuries, which are *injuries resulting from an accident*. An accident is *any event that was not intended to happen*. Falling on a slippery floor is an example of an accident. Most accidental injuries could have been prevented.

Injuries often result from a pattern known as an accident chain, *a series of events that include a situation, an unsafe habit, and an unsafe action*. Understanding accident chains, such as the one illustrated in **Figure 19.1**, can help you break them. Knowing how accidents happen isn't enough to stay safe, however. You also have to be safety conscious and act safely. Follow these guidelines:

- **Concentrate on what you are doing.** Be extra careful when you are tired, excited, upset, depressed, or in a hurry. Accidents and injuries are most likely to occur during these times.
- **Know your limits.** For example, don't try in-line skating down a steep hill if you are just learning to skate.
- **Think ahead.** Consider possible risks and possible consequences *before* it's too late. Plan ahead so that you won't have to walk home alone after dark.
- **Resist negative peer pressure.** Take responsibility for your own safety. Do what you feel is right, even if it goes against what your friends want you to do.

Staying within your limits is not being cowardly—it's being smart.

508 CHAPTER 19: SAFETY AND EMERGENCIES

Lesson 1 Resources

Teacher Classroom Resources

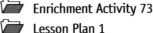 Parent Letter & Activities 19

Concept Map 73

Cross-Curriculum Activity 37

Enrichment Activity 73

Lesson Plan 1

Lesson 1 Quiz

 Reading Tutor Activity 72

Reteaching Activity 73

 Transparency 76

Student Activities Workbook

 Chapter 19 Study Guide

 Applying Health Skills 73

FIGURE 19.1

THE ACCIDENT CHAIN

Many injuries can be prevented by breaking the accident chain. *Analyze the strategies Luis could have used to prevent the accidental injury shown here.*

A The Situation Luis is in a hurry to put down his backpack and get an after-school snack.

B The Unsafe Habit Luis's habit of leaving his things on the stairs creates an unnecessary risk of someone tripping.

C The Unsafe Action Luis's father comes down the stairs without looking over the laundry basket and trips over the backpack.

D The Accident and the Injury Luis's father falls. He hurts his back and scrapes his knees.

• Change the situation   • Change the unsafe habit   • Change the unsafe action

Safety in the Home

The most common type of home injury involves falls. Other types of injuries in the home result from poisonings, electrical shocks, and guns. Fires and burns are the third leading cause of unintentional injury and death in the home. The majority of deaths and injuries in the home could have been prevented.

Preventing Falls

Most home falls happen in the kitchen, in the bathroom, and on stairs. To prevent falls in the home, avoid slippery floors by cleaning up spills promptly. Use nonskid rugs, or put a rubber pad under loose rugs to make them safer. Keep stairways well lighted and free from clutter. Many falls result from standing on chairs or furniture to reach high places. Act safely by using a step stool or ladder instead.

 Reading Check

Evaluate your own habits. Think about what you have done this week. Can you change any actions to be more safety conscious?

LESSON 1: SAFETY AT HOME AND AT SCHOOL **509**

Lesson 1

② Teach

Analyzing

Ask students to describe situations when they, or someone they know, did something that was not safe. Then divide a portion of the board into three columns with the following headings: *Peer Pressure, Emotions, Going Beyond Limits.* Review some of the situations students mentioned, and have the class decide which of the three leading reasons for not practicing safety was involved. Put check marks in the appropriate columns. Ask students whether any one reason stands out as a primary cause of risk taking. **L1**

VISUAL LEARNING

FIGURE 19.1 Have volunteers describe the pictures and read the explanations of the situation, the unsafe habit and action, and the accident and injury. Ask the question; students should recognize that Luis could have put his backpack away. **INCL** *English Language Learners, Special Learning Needs, Behavior Problems, Different Learning Styles (Visual)*

Falls are a major cause of injury to Americans under the age of 15. Every year, about 2.5 million American children are taken to emergency rooms for treatment of injuries sustained in falls.

 Reading Check

Evaluation and Analysis Analyzing their own safety behaviors may help students apply information from the chapter. Ask students to write down their schedule for the week. Then remind the class about Luis's unsafe habits in Figure 19.1, and have them find times and situations in their own schedules that may invite unsafe behavior. Ask students to write down what the situation was, the possible consequences, and the ways to prevent an accident. Have each student identify one unsafe behavior and pledge to change it. If students need prompting, provide examples such as waiting in the street for the bus, lifting weights without stretching first, or not buckling safety belts.

509

FIGURE 19.2 Ask volunteers to read aloud the title and caption for Figure 19.2; volunteers may want to share their responses to the caption question. Then have students read and discuss the information. Have volunteers name some specific products and medicines that need to be stored out of the reach of young children. **INCL** *English Language Learners, Special Learning Needs, Behavior Problems, Different Learning Styles (Visual)*

Discussing

Ask students:

• Why are young children particularly susceptible to poisoning by ingestion? (*They are likely to "investigate" materials by putting them in their mouths.*)

• What habits should be encouraged in children to reduce the danger of poisoning? (*Children should learn not to eat or taste anything that is not given to them by a trusted adult.*) **L1**

VISUAL LEARNING

FIGURE 19.3 Have students read and discuss the information about unplugging electrical devices and handling outlets. Then read the figure caption aloud and have students respond to the question; they should explain that an overloaded electrical outlet could shock someone. **INCL** *English Language Learners, Special Learning Needs, Behavior Problems, Different Learning Styles (Visual)*

FIGURE 19.2

PROTECTION FROM POISONOUS PRODUCTS

If there are young children in the home, poisonous substances should be stored out of their reach. *Where are these substances stored in your home?*

A **Keep Chemicals Out of Reach**
Store cleaning products, insecticides, and other potential poisons in high, locked cabinets that are out of the reach of young children. Use childproof catches on all doors and drawers.

B **Store Medicines Properly**
Keep medicines in their original containers with child-resistant caps. Store them in a locked cabinet out of the reach of young children. Dispose of old medicines that have passed their expiration date by flushing them down the toilet.

Preventing Poisonings

Poisoning can happen by ingestion (swallowing), absorption (through the skin), injection, or inhalation. Young children are particularly susceptible to poisoning by ingestion. Cleaning products and medicines are the most common poisons swallowed by children. **Figure 19.2** shows ways of protecting children from poisoning.

Preventing Electrical Shocks

Electrical items can cause serious injury or death if misused. In the home, replace broken or frayed electrical cords, and never run cords under rugs. Unplug appliances that are not in use or that are not working properly. Keep all electrical appliances and cords away from water. Protect children from electrical shocks by putting safety covers over unused outlets. Follow the procedures shown in **Figure 19.3** for the safe use of electrical outlets.

FIGURE 19.3

PROTECTION FROM ELECTRICAL SHOCK

Prevent electrical shock by connecting appliances safely and using the proper number of cords per outlet. *Why might an overloaded electrical outlet cause a problem?*

A **Unplug Electrical Devices Safely**
Unplug an electrical device by its plug. Never pull a plug out by its cord. Doing so can damage the protective covering on the wire.

B **Handle Outlets Safely**
Do not overload an outlet with too many plugs. Instead, use a multi-outlet power strip that has a reset button to prevent power overload.

510 CHAPTER 19: SAFETY AND EMERGENCIES

MORE ABOUT...

Internet Safety Caution students to follow these safety tips when using the Internet:

• Never give your name, address, phone number, or school name in a chat room.

• Tell your parent or guardian if you come across information that is obscene, threatening, or otherwise makes you feel uncomfortable.

• Be wary. What people tell you online may or may not be true.

• Be suspicious if someone you've never met offers or mails you gifts or money.

• Never agree to meet someone unless a parent or guardian approves. Have a trusted adult with you, and meet in a public place.

Gun Safety

The best protection against gun accidents in the home is to possess no guns. However, if they are kept in the home, strict safety precautions and strategies should be followed.

- Guns should have trigger locks and should always be stored unloaded in a locked cabinet.
- Ammunition should be stored in a separate locked cabinet.
- Anyone who will handle a gun should be trained in safe gun use.
- Guns should always be handled as if they are loaded.
- Guns should *never* be pointed at anyone.

Fire Safety

The elements needed for a fire—fuel, heat, and air—can be found in any home. For example, rags, wood, gasoline, or newspaper might be fuel. A cigarette, match, or electrical wire can provide heat. Prevent fires in the home by following these safety rules.

- Keep stoves clean to avoid burns and fires. Food particles or grease on a stove or in an oven can catch fire.
- Keep flammable objects at least 3 feet from portable heaters.
- Remind adults who smoke never to smoke in bed or on overstuffed furniture.
- Inspect electrical wires, outlets, and appliances for safety.
- Throw out old newspapers, oily rags, and other materials that burn easily.
- Use and store matches properly. Keep matches and cigarette lighters out of the reach of young children, preferably in high cabinets.
- Install smoke alarms on each level of the home, including the basement. They should be located in hallways outside bedrooms.

Every home should have working smoke alarms. *Why is it so important to check smoke alarms regularly?*

LESSON 1: SAFETY AT HOME AND AT SCHOOL **511**

CONNECT TO
Science

GREASE FIRES

If a grease fire starts in a pan on the stove, do not use water to put it out. Oil and grease float on water, causing the flames to spread. The best way to put out a grease fire is to carefully slide a lid over the pan and to turn off the burner. Let the pan cool down completely before you move it or take off the lid. You can also use baking soda to smother the flames.

Discussing

- Help students discuss the importance of refusing to handle or "play with" guns or other weapons. Ask:
- What would you do or say if you saw a gun left out in a friend's home?
- What would you do and say if a peer handed you a gun?
- What are the dangers associated with weapons?
- Why is it important to comply with rules prohibiting possession of weapons? **L1**

Analyzing

Ask students to bring to class recent newspaper articles about fires or other accidents in the home. After class members have read the articles, instruct each student to choose one of the articles and write one or two paragraphs about it. In their paragraphs, students should first summarize what happened, then analyze strategies for preventing accidental injuries. To prompt students, ask:

- What happened?
- Who was hurt?
- What were the injuries, and how severe were they?
- How might those injuries have been prevented? **L1**

Applying Life Skills

Have students prepare a home fire prevention checklist. Then have students use their checklists to inspect their homes for fire safety. **L3**

COOPERATIVE LEARNING ACTIVITY

Fire Extinguishers Divide the class into four groups. Have each group research, write, and present a report on a particular type of fire extinguisher:

- Type A for ordinary combustibles
- Type B for flammable liquids
- Type C for electrical fires
- Type D for combustible metals

Groups should select one member to present the findings to the class. Students should explain how to check the gauges to determine if they are full. To conclude this activity, have students tell where and how each type of extinguisher should be used. (*kitchen, garage, metal shop, and so on*)

HEALTH SKILLS ACTIVITY

PRACTICING HEALTHFUL BEHAVIORS

Guide students in reading and discussing the facts about plans for fire safety. Have several volunteers give examples from their own homes. Remind students that if they live in apartments, they may need to include plans for leaving the buildings as well as their own homes. Then have students work with their own families to develop fire safety plans.

Note: This skill is introduced in Chapter 2 on pages 46–47.

VISUAL LEARNING

FIGURE 19.4 Read the caption aloud and have students answer the question; they should explain that running would fan the flames and cause the fire to grow. Then ask a volunteer to read aloud the instructions for stop, drop, and roll. You may also want to have students practice this technique. You may want to take them outside to increase the safety of this activity. **INCL** *English Language Learners, Special Learning Needs, Behavior Problems, Different Learning Styles (Visual, Kinesthetic)*

Guest Speaker

Ask the school principal or other administrator to present the school's plan for evacuation in the event of fire or other school wide emergency. Have students pose questions about the role each student could take to ensure safety during evacuation. **L1**

HEALTH SKILLS ACTIVITY

PRACTICING HEALTHFUL BEHAVIORS

Preparing a Fire Safety Plan

The best protection against injury during a fire is to plan what you will do if one occurs. A good fire safety plan includes the following:

- A floor plan of each level of your home, including doors and windows. Use arrows to indicate escape routes from each room.
- A ladder or coil of rope for escaping through upstairs windows.
- An agreed-on safe location outside the home, where everyone will meet.
- A rule for everyone to leave the house immediately and call the fire department.
- A rule that no one ever goes back into the house for any reason.
- Safety measures to follow, such as testing doors for heat before opening them.

ON YOUR OWN

Develop a fire safety plan with your family, or improve an existing plan. After completing your plan, demonstrate escaping from various rooms and adjust the plan as needed. Encourage your family to practice the plan regularly.

Reducing Risk of Injury in a Fire

Knowing what to do if there is a fire in your home can reduce your risk of injury. Follow these guidelines.

- Leave the house immediately if possible. Call the fire department from a neighbor's house or a cellular phone.
- While you are in the house, stay close to the floor below the smoke, and try to keep your nose and mouth covered.
- Before opening a closed door, feel it. If it is hot, leave the room by another route.
- If your clothing catches fire, stop, drop, and roll, as shown in **Figure 19.4**.
- Never go back into a burning building—for *any* reason.
- Leave firefighting to the experts. Do not try it yourself.

FIGURE 19.4

STOP, DROP, ROLL

If your clothes catch fire, don't run. Stop, drop, and roll. *What might happen if you run?*

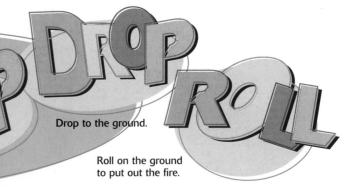

Stop. Don't run.

Drop to the ground.

Roll on the ground to put out the fire.

512 CHAPTER 19: SAFETY AND EMERGENCIES

WHAT TEENS WANT TO KNOW

How safe is soccer? According to the CDC, soccer is associated with a fairly high rate of injury—more than 200,000 individuals under age 15 are treated each year for injuries. The injury rate increases with age; for high school players, it's 8 percent per season. It is important to note that most injuries are mild and the most common site of injury is the ankle. Kicking is the most common cause of soccer injuries, followed by dribbling. Head injuries are the most serious, but they account for a very small percentage of all soccer injuries. Most injuries can be prevented if players follow the rules of the game, and wear proper safety gear, including shin guards, every time they practice and compete.

Safety at School

Because large numbers of people gather at schools, rules are established to protect the health and safety of students and teachers. For example, running isn't permitted in the halls because they are often crowded with people. Here are some strategies for preventing accidental injuries at school:

- **Play by the rules.** Many rules are designed to protect you and others. Follow the rules of the cafeteria, gym, auditorium, halls, and classrooms. It's important to understand and follow rules prohibiting the possession of weapons at school.
- **Report any weapons or unsafe activities.** If you suspect that someone has brought or plans to bring a gun or other weapon to school, report it immediately to a teacher or principal. Do the same if you witness any unsafe behaviors.
- **Wear appropriate safety gear.** Whether in science class or in sports, wear the recommended gear and follow your teacher's directions carefully.

When working with chemicals, be sure to protect your eyes and to follow your teacher's instructions. *Why are these rules important?*

Lesson 1 Review

Using complete sentences, answer the following questions on a sheet of paper.

Reviewing Terms and Facts

1. **Vocabulary** What is an *accidental injury?*
2. **List** Name the sequence of links in an accident chain.
3. **Recall** What strategies can families use to reduce their risk of injuries from guns?
4. **Give Examples** List three strategies for preventing accidental injuries at school. Analyze how each strategy can help people stay safe.

Thinking Critically

5. **Analyze** Review the guidelines for acting safely, on page 508. Briefly describe how each of these factors can reduce the risk of accidents.
6. **Explain** Why is it important to understand and follow the rules prohibiting possession of weapons at school?

Applying Health Skills

7. **Practicing Healthful Behaviors** Work with your family to identify potential hazards that could lead to accidents in your home. Demonstrate corrective action strategies to remove or reduce these hazards and prevent accidental injuries.

LESSON 1: SAFETY AT HOME AND AT SCHOOL **513**

Lesson 1

③ Assess

Evaluating

Assign the Lesson 1 Review; then assign the Lesson 1 Quiz in the TCR.

Reteaching

- Assign Concept Map 73 or Reteaching Activity 73 in the TCR.
- Have students list the parts of the accident chain and three ways to break the chain.
- Have each student write a sentence on how to avoid the following kinds of accidents: falls, poisoning, electrical shock, fire, and gun accidents.

Enrichment

- Assign Enrichment Activity 73 in the TCR.
- Have students survey their own homes to find and suggest ways to correct hazards outlined in the lesson.

④ Close

Ask students to write brief summaries of the importance of practicing safety and then list ways to prevent common accidents at home or at school.

Lesson 1 Review

1. An injury resulting from an accident.
2. Situation, unsafe habit, unsafe action, accident, and injury.
3. Guns should always be handled as if they were loaded, never pointed at anyone, kept unloaded in a locked cabinet, handled only by a trained person, and ammunition should be stored in a separate locked cabinet.
4. See Safety at School on this page.
5. Responses will vary.
6. Responses should include the idea that this will help maintain the health and safety of everyone at school.

Lesson 2

Safety on the Road and Outdoors

① Focus

Lesson Objectives

Students will be able to

- identify safety rules for use of bicycles, skates, skateboards, and scooters.
- list the do's and don'ts of pedestrian safety.
- discuss ways to stay safe while participating in outdoor recreational activities including swimming, hiking, and camping.

Motivators

Quick Write

List students' responses on the board as they are shared. Ask: What are things bike riders do that make it difficult to pay attention to all these? (*wearing headphones, doing tricks while riding, and so on*)

Bellringer Activity

Ask students to make lists of ten activities that can be done outdoors and ten that require the use of the road or sidewalk.

VOCABULARY

Have students look up *defensive driving* in the Glossary. Ask volunteers to define the term in their own words and provide examples of defensive driving. Then have a student use the term in a sentence.

Lesson 2 Safety on the Road and Outdoors

Quick Write

List at least five things a bike rider must pay attention to.

LEARN ABOUT...

- safety and traffic rules for bicycles, skates, skateboards, and scooters.
- pedestrian safety.
- avoiding injuries in the water and outdoors.

VOCABULARY

- defensive driving

Traffic Safety

Your behavior as a car passenger can be just as important as a driver's behavior. Motor vehicle collisions cause the largest proportion of all teen injuries. To reduce your risk of injury, use your thinking and decision-making skills as you follow these traffic safety rules.

- **Obey the rules of the road.** When you obey the rules of the road, other people can predict your actions. This helps prevent collisions and injuries.
- **Always buckle up.** Buckling up every time you ride in a car is a simple action that could save your life.
- **Never ride with a driver who has been drinking alcohol or using drugs.** Alcohol is involved in about 35 percent of teen driver deaths. Driving while under the influence of alcohol or drugs is not only high-risk behavior, but also against the law.
- **Never distract a driver.** Driving requires a driver's full attention. If you need to have a discussion or show the driver something, ask the driver to pull over and stop the car.

It takes only a moment to fasten a safety belt. It's a moment that could save a life. *How could a driver encourage passengers to buckle up?*

514 CHAPTER 19: SAFETY AND EMERGENCIES

Lesson 2 Resources

Teacher Classroom Resources

 Concept Map 74

 Decision-Making Activity 37

 Enrichment Activity 74

 Lesson Plan 2

 Lesson 2 Quiz

Reading Tutor Activity 73

 Reteaching Activity 74

 Transparency 77

Student Activities Workbook

 Chapter 19 Study Guide

Applying Health Skills 74

Like bikes and skates, recreational vehicles require a sense of responsibility and a knowledge of safety rules. *How can using thinking and decision-making skills help you avoid high-risk situations when riding motorized recreational vehicles and engaging in other potentially hazardous activities?*

FYI

According to the National Highway Traffic Safety Administration, safety belts saved more than 11,000 lives in 1998 alone.

Safety on Wheels and Motorized Vehicles

Many teens enjoy riding bicycles and using skates, skateboards, and scooters. Some even ride all-terrain vehicles, motorized watercrafts, and snowmobiles. These activities are fun, but they come with an increased level of risk. Learning about the risks and taking actions to avoid them can prevent injury.

Bicycle Safety

The first rule of bicycle safety is always to wear a bike helmet. Head injuries are the cause of 70 to 80 percent of the deaths from bicycle accidents. You will reduce your risk of head injury by 85 percent if you wear a helmet every time you ride a bike.

Bicycle riders should follow the rules of the road. These rules include riding with traffic—not against it—and obeying traffic signals and signs. Bicyclists should also practice **defensive driving**, which means not only obeying traffic laws but also *watching out for other people on the road and anticipating unsafe acts.* For good bicycle safety, don't ride at night or in bad weather. If you must do so, be sure to use lights and reflective clothing. You can also reduce your risk of injury by making sure that your bike has the proper safety equipment and keeping your bike in good condition. The tires, for example, should have enough tread to grip the road and should be properly inflated.

LESSON 2: SAFETY ON THE ROAD AND OUTDOORS 515

Discussing

Ask students:
- Other than car drivers, who else must obey traffic controls? (*pedestrians, cyclists, and any other road users*)
- Why is it important to obey traffic laws? (*Each road user acts on the assumption that others will be obeying the law. Someone who does not do so may act in such a way as to cause an accident.*) **L1**

Observing

Hold a traffic control identification contest. Have students note on the way to or from school all the types of traffic signals, traffic signs, and pavement markings they see. They should note the control device, its location, and the meaning of the device. **L2**

Applying Life Skills

Have students map out several bicycle routes between the school and their homes. Then have them mark danger spots and compare the routes for safety. **L3**

Health Literacy

Personal/Interpersonal Skills Point out that many communities now have paved or gravel paths restricted to use by bicyclists. The paths often pass through scenic areas. Ask students to identify bike paths in their local area, find out more about them, and make posters or brochures promoting them. Have students brainstorm ways they could advocate for the construction of a bike path (e.g., circulate a petition, write letters to newspapers, talk with local merchants and chamber of commerce members, or make a presentation before the city council). Ask students where they think a local bike path should be located. Have them explain their choices. Note: You may want to discuss in-line skating paths as well.

Applying Knowledge

Have pairs of students role-play scenes about bicycle, skate, skateboard, or pedestrian safety. One teen will make excuses such as these:

- "I've been skating for years and never had an accident. I don't need a helmet."
- "I don't want anyone to see me wearing those silly wrist guards."
- "I'm in a hurry. Let's just skip the safety equipment this time."

Have the other teen in each scene demonstrate strategies for preventing accidental injuries. Be sure this student uses good communication skills to convince his or her friend of the importance of being safe. **L1** **INCL** *English Language Learners, Special Learning Needs, Behavior Problems, Different Learning Styles (Visual)*

Investigating

Have students find, read, and bring to class news stories about local accidents involving pedestrians. **L2**

Demonstrating

Have students plan a pedestrian safety program for a group of elementary school students. They should make a list of rules they want to teach and diagram a course they could set up that would allow the children to practice the rules. The course should include intersections, stop signs, and so on. If possible, allow students to present the program to some younger students. **L2**

Wearing the right protective gear and maintaining a safe speed are two ways to prevent skating injuries.
What are other ways to prevent skating injuries?

Skates, Skateboards, and Scooters

Skates, skateboards, and scooters can be a lot of fun—if you use them safely. Many skaters and skateboarders who are injured weren't wearing protective gear when they crashed. Follow these guidelines.

- Always wear protective gear: a hard-shell helmet, wrist guards, gloves, elbow pads, and knee pads.
- Keep your speed under control.
- Watch for pedestrians and stay off busy sidewalks.
- Avoid parking lots, streets, and other areas with traffic.
- On a soft surface, practice a safe way to fall—before you head downhill.

Pedestrian Safety

Thousands of pedestrians are injured or killed in traffic accidents every year. Following the do's and don'ts below will help reduce your risk of injury while traveling on foot.

Do's

- Cross streets at crosswalks and obey traffic signals.
- Look left, right, and left again before crossing the street.
- In daylight, wear bright clothing. At night, wear reflective gear and carry a flashlight.
- If there is no sidewalk, stay to the left side of the road and walk facing oncoming traffic.

Don'ts

- Don't jaywalk, or cross the street in the middle of the block.
- Don't walk into the street from between parked cars.
- Don't enter the street without first looking left, right, and left again.
- Don't assume that a driver will see you just because you see her or him.
- Don't walk in a large group that spills off the sidewalk and onto the street.

516 CHAPTER 19: SAFETY AND EMERGENCIES

 Reading Check

Word Study Researching a word root will help students build their vocabulary as well as comprehend shades of meaning. Guide students in locating the root word in the entry for *pedestrian*. Focus their attention on the word part *ped*, which stems from the Latin word for "foot." Write the words *pedal* and *centipede* on the board. Ask students to define each word and determine how they relate to *pedestrian*. Ask students to locate other related words like *pedicure*. Write their suggestions, and have volunteers guess their meanings. As a class, write an original definition for *pedestrian* to conclude the lesson.

Recreational Safety

It's always best to play it safe when you take part in outdoor activities. If you know the risks associated with an activity you enjoy, you can take the necessary preventive actions to stay safe. When outdoors, use your common sense and follow these two general safety rules.

- **Be aware of the weather.** Try to avoid electrical storms and extreme temperatures. If you're caught outdoors in an electrical storm, seek shelter in a building or car, or under a clump of bushes. Avoid isolated trees, and get out of and away from water. If you are outside on a very hot day, drink plenty of water, stay in the shade, and avoid strenuous activity. On a very cold day, dress in layers and protect your fingers, toes, nose, and ears. Also be sure to stay dry and keep active.
- **Use the buddy system.** The buddy system is an agreement between two people to stay together. With a buddy, you can help each other avoid or cope with potentially dangerous situations in healthy ways.

Water Safety

Each year, thousands of people in the United States, including many children, die from drowning. To protect yourself and others, follow these water safety rules.

- Learn how to swim. Take a class to improve your skill.
- Don't swim alone. Always swim with a buddy and only where a trained lifeguard is on duty.
- Always wear a life jacket when boating or waterskiing. If you fall in the water, use the survival techniques shown in **Figure 19.5**.

FIGURE 19.5

SURVIVAL IN COLD WATER

Hypothermia, which is a dangerous drop in body temperature, can be life-threatening to people in cold water. If you fall into the water while boating, assume one of the positions shown here. They will help you stay warm until help arrives. *Why should even strong swimmers always wear a life jacket?*

A Lessen heat loss by drawing your knees up to your chest and keeping your upper arms close to the sides of your body. About 50 percent of heat loss is from your head, so try to keep it out of the water.

B If you are with one or more other people, huddle close together in a circle to preserve body heat. A child or smaller person who loses heat faster should be placed in the center of the circle.

LESSON 2: SAFETY ON THE ROAD AND OUTDOORS **517**

✔
Reading Check

Learn about word parts. Use a dictionary to find the root of the word *pedestrian*.

Lesson 2

HEALTH SKILLS PRACTICE

Practicing Healthful Behaviors Inspire students to put safety first. Read the following aloud: Every teen needs to think about safety, have some safety rules, and carry some safety gear. Safety rules and gear are important for many activities. For example, you should always wear a helmet when you ride your bike. List the safety rules that you follow when you are playing a sport or engaged in other activities. What safety gear is always in your backpack? Make a list, and share it with your parents. Ask them whether they have anything to add.

Analyzing

Have students determine different outdoor situations in which a buddy system would be effective in promoting safety. Have them explain their responses. (*skiing, swimming, hiking, rock climbing, canoeing, and so on*) **L1**

VISUAL LEARNING

FIGURE 19.5 Have a volunteer read the caption for Figure 19.5, and have students discuss their answers to the caption question. They should recognize that even strong swimmers may have difficulties in cold water or in strong currents. Advise students that rivers, oceans, and flood channels all have strong currents. **INCL** *English Language Learners, Special Learning Needs, Behavior Problems, Different Learning Styles (Visual)*

Health Literacy

Health Information The parts of the body most commonly affected by frostbite are the face, nose, ears, fingers, and toes. The signs of frostbite are a reddening of the skin followed by a whitening of the skin—both accompanied by a stinging sensation. The final state is numbness. If you feel a stinging sensation in any part of your body, you should go indoors and apply lukewarm water (103°–107°F) to the affected area to raise the body temperature. Do not rub the affected skin as this could cause permanent damage.

Lesson 2

Guest Speaker

Invite a Red Cross-certified swimming instructor to the class for a presentation and question-and-answer session. Have students prepare their questions in advance. The questions could cover any topic related to water safety. **L1**

Cross-Curriculum Activity

SCIENCE Have students discuss or research poisonous plants or dangerous animals, including insects, most common in the area. Have students discuss the physical characteristics of each and, if possible, bring in pictures or illustrations. **L3**

Discussing

Guide students in discussing local areas for hiking and camping. Ask:

• Where are these areas located?
• How can you identify established trails and campsites in those areas?
• Which areas have rangers? What services do they provide?
• What special safety guidelines should you follow while hiking or camping there? **L1**

Applying Knowledge

Ask students to think of outdoor sport scenes they have seen on television programs or in movies. Have them evaluate two scenes based on the attention paid to safety. Ask:

• Were people wearing helmets, knee pads, life jackets, or other safety gear?
• Did they follow the rules of the sport and act safely? **L2**

Reading Check

Paraphrase. Rewrite the hiking and camping safety guidelines in your own words.

• If you get caught in a strong current, swim parallel to the shore until the current lessens. Then swim to shore.
• Don't swim when you are tired.
• Dive only into water that you know is deeper than 9 feet and is free of obstacles, such as other swimmers or rocks. Diving into shallow water can result in spinal cord injuries. Never dive into an above-ground pool.
• Avoid drugs and alcohol. About 40 percent of teen drownings involve alcohol.
• Be aware of the weather. If you see lightning or hear thunder, get out of the water right away.

Hiking and Camping Safety

A safe and successful hike or camping trip begins with preparation. Check the weather forecast and take the proper clothing and equipment. Always tell an adult where you will be and when you expect to return. Follow these guidelines:

• **Wear protective clothing.** Wear shoes and socks that protect your feet from the terrain as well as from blisters. Dress in layers and have wet-weather gear on hand. If you will be in grassy areas, wear socks and long pants to help protect against ticks.
• **Bring equipment and supplies.** Make sure that you have a map, compass, first aid kit, flashlight with extra batteries, and an adequate supply of drinking water.
• **Follow fire safety rules.** Light campfires only where permitted, and never leave the area before the campfire is completely out. Drown it with water or bury it with dirt that is free of debris.
• **Know poisonous plants and animals.** Find out which plants and animals in the area are poisonous. Learn first aid for treating reactions to poisonous plants, insect stings, and snakebites.
• **Have a cell phone.** This will enable you to call someone in an emergency.

Outdoor Sports

Whether you enjoy summer or winter sports, always wear appropriate gear and stay within your ability level. Follow posted signs, and stay in approved locations. In the summer, the sun and heat can cause problems such as sunburn and heatstroke. Protect your skin from sunburn by wearing sunscreen, sunglasses, a hat, and appropriate clothing. During the hottest times of the day (10 A.M. to 4 P.M.), avoid direct sunlight and drink plenty of water. Pay attention to your body's signals. If you feel overheated or tired, take a break and cool down.

518 CHAPTER 19: SAFETY AND EMERGENCIES

Reading Check

Paraphrasing Learning to paraphrase will help students process and retain information. Guide students in identifying each guideline. Point out that the words in bold are the guidelines and the text that follows provides supporting details. Advise students that the language used for each point may not be language they would use themselves. Ask volunteers to restate the first guideline and its details in their own words. Write the students' suggestions on the board using the same format as the book. Have small groups work together to paraphrase each guideline and details. Check each group's work to ensure that they rewrote each point without losing the original meaning.

Earthquakes

An **earthquake** is *a violent shaking movement of the earth's surface.* In the United States, earthquakes can occur in any of the 50 states. However, they occur most often west of the Rocky Mountains. Although weak earthquakes may cause little or no damage, a severe earthquake can topple buildings and bridges. Most injuries result from collapsing walls and falling debris. If an earthquake strikes, take the following steps to help protect yourself from injury.

Teens and parents can work together to prepare for natural disasters. For example, securing the water heater to a wall with metal strappings will help keep it from falling over in an earthquake.

- **Stay inside.** If the earthquake begins while you are indoors, stay there. Crouch under a sturdy table or desk, against an interior wall, or in a strongly supported doorway. Stay away from objects that might fall, shatter, or cave in. Cover your head with your arms or a pillow.
- **If you are outdoors, stay in the open.** Keep away from buildings, trees, telephone and electrical lines, streetlights, and overpasses. If you are in a car, the driver should stop and everyone should remain inside the car.
- **Be careful afterward.** After the earthquake is over, stay out of damaged buildings. Be aware that utilities such as electrical or gas lines may have been damaged and could be hazardous. Be prepared for aftershocks—smaller quakes that occur after the main earthquake.

Lesson 3 Review

Using complete sentences, answer the following questions on a sheet of paper.

Reviewing Terms and Facts

1. **Compare** Which condition is more serious—a weather *watch* or a weather *warning*? Why?
2. **Vocabulary** Differentiate between a *tornado* and a *hurricane.*
3. **List** Name three steps to take to prepare for a hurricane.
4. **Recall** Why should you stay out of the water during a flood?

Thinking Critically

5. **Analyze** Why is it important to stay indoors during a blizzard?
6. **Synthesize** Why should you stay out of damaged buildings after an earthquake?

Applying Health Skills

7. **Practicing Healthful Behaviors** Choose a weather emergency or natural disaster from this lesson. With a partner, write and perform a skit to demonstrate strategies for staying safe and preventing accidental injuries during your chosen event.

LESSON 3: SAFETY IN WEATHER EMERGENCIES **523**

Lesson 3

Explaining

Explain the Richter scale, which is used to measure the force of an earthquake. Tell the class that an earthquake measuring 2 on the Richter scale is the smallest earthquake that can be felt, a 4.5 earthquake causes slight damage, and an 8.5 earthquake is very devastating. **L1**

③ Assess

Evaluating

Assign the Lesson 3 Review; then assign the Lesson 3 Quiz in the TCR.

Reteaching

- Assign Concept Map 75 or Reteaching Activity 75 in the TCR.
- Have each student divide a sheet of paper into five columns and label the columns *Tornado, Hurricane, Blizzard, Flood, Earthquake.* Have students write two to three safety rules in each column.

Enrichment

- Assign Enrichment Activity 75 in the TCR.
- Have students write and record public service announcements explaining appropriate preparations for weather emergencies.

④ Close

Have students identify one weather condition or emergency common to their community and at least two safety precautions discussed in this lesson.

Lesson 3 Review

1. Warning; severe weather has been sighted or is about to occur. More serious than watch, which only indicates possibility of severe conditions.
2. A tornado is a whirling, funnel-shaped windstorm that may drop from the sky to the ground; a hurricane is a strong windstorm with driving rain that originates at sea.
3. Secure your home, take loose objects inside, leave area.
4. Drowning or electrocution by fallen power lines is possible.
5. Responses will vary but may include the dangers of being outdoors and getting lost.
6. Gas and electrical lines may become hazardous; aftershocks could cause further collapse.

Lesson 4

Basic First Aid

Lesson Objectives

Students will be able to

- identify ways to prepare for an emergency situation.
- discuss universal precautions for first aid providers.
- outline the basic steps to take in an emergency.

Motivators

Quick Write
Ask several volunteers to list on the board the actions they would take. Compare and discuss the students' responses.

Bellringer Activity

Instruct students to list three words or situations they think of when they hear the term *first aid*.

VOCABULARY

Use students' responses to the Bellringer Activity to create a concept map on the board. For example:

emergency
|
first aid
/ \
check   stop
breathing bleeding

Write the vocabulary terms on the board. Ask the class to find relationships between the words and phrases on the map and the vocabulary terms. Finally, ask students to use each term in a sentence.

Basic First Aid

Quick Write

Suppose that you witnessed a car accident. List the actions you would take to provide help and the order in which you would take them.

LEARN ABOUT...

- **how to be prepared for emergencies.**
- **how to take universal precautions when giving first aid.**
- **the basic steps to follow in emergencies.**

VOCABULARY

- **first aid**
- **universal precautions**

What Is First Aid?

First aid is *the immediate temporary care given to an injured or ill person until he or she can get professional help.* Knowing what to do during certain common emergencies can prevent further damage and may even speed recovery. Equally important, though, is knowing what *not* to do. In serious cases, providing the correct first aid can make the difference between life and death. Any time first aid is needed, it's important to stay calm. Doing so will allow you to better help the victim.

Be Prepared

First aid might be needed anywhere, at any time, and without warning. Learning basic first aid skills will help you handle most common emergencies. Another way to be prepared is to keep a list of emergency numbers near all phones. All family members should know where family health records are kept. If a family member has certain allergies, for example, that information may be needed during an emergency.

It is also important to keep first-aid supplies at home and in the car and to know how to use them. You can assemble your own first-aid kit or buy a packaged kit. **Figure 19.7** provides suggestions for basic first-aid supplies. If a family member has a medical condition, specific medicines may need to be added to the kit.

It's a good idea to take along a first-aid kit when hiking or biking. *For what other types of activities might you bring a first-aid kit?*

Lesson 4 Resources

Teacher Classroom Resources

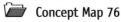 Concept Map 76

 Enrichment Activity 76

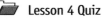 Lesson Plan 4

 Lesson 4 Quiz

Reading Tutor Activity 75

 Reteaching Activity 76

 Transparency 79

Student Activities Workbook

 Chapter 19 Study Guide

Applying Health Skills 76

FIGURE 19.7

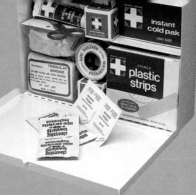

FIRST-AID SUPPLIES

Keeping a first-aid kit in your home will help your family be prepared for emergencies. *What other supplies might you add to this kit?*

Instruments: tweezers, scissors

Equipment: thermometer, cotton swabs, blanket, cold pack

Medications: antiseptic ointment, sterile eyewash, activated charcoal, syrup of ipecac

Dressings: gauze pads, adhesive tape, adhesive bandages, triangular bandage

Miscellaneous: small flashlight, tissues, hand cleaner, disposable gloves, face mask, plastic bags

Universal Precautions

People infected with HIV or hepatitis B carry the virus in their blood. Because these diseases are communicable, touching contaminated blood carries a risk. For this reason, it is important to protect yourself when giving first aid. Follow universal precautions, which are *actions taken to prevent the spread of disease by treating all blood as if it were contaminated.*

Universal precautions include wearing protective gloves when treating a victim. Use a face mask or shield when giving first aid for breathing emergencies. Cover any open wounds on your body with sterile dressings. Avoid touching any object that had contact with the victim's blood. Always wash your hands thoroughly after giving first aid.

The First Steps

Every emergency situation is unique. However, there are four steps to take for most emergencies. The sequence of steps is as follows: recognize the signs of an emergency, decide to act, call for help, and provide care until help arrives.

Recognize the Signs of an Emergency

Your senses of hearing, sight, and smell will alert you to most emergencies. Listen if you hear people calling out. Are they in trouble? Be alert to sudden loud or unusual noises such as shattering glass.

Sometimes the first sign of an emergency is an odor such as the smell of smoke. Also be alert for any strong smell that makes your eyes sting, causes you to cough, or makes breathing difficult. These sensations can signal a chemical spill or toxic gas release.

LESSON 4: BASIC FIRST AID **525**

② Teach

VISUAL LEARNING

FIGURE FIGURE 19.7 Have students name each item in the pictured first-aid kit and describe when and how it can be used. Ask volunteers to name other supplies they might want to add to a family's first-aid kit. Then have students suggest appropriate locations in the home for first-aid kits. **INCL** *English Language Learners, Special Learning Needs, Behavior Problems, Different Learning Styles (Visual)*

Applying Knowledge

Have students work with partners to collect ads from magazines or newspapers for first-aid kits. If ads are hard to find, have students research kits on the Internet or in pharmacies. Have them identify the contents of each kit, evaluate the completeness of each kit, compare the prices of the kits, and decide which kit they would buy. **L2**

Listing

Have students choose a specific activity, such as hiking or biking, for which they would take along a small first-aid kit. Then have them list the items they would include in that first-aid kit. **L1**

Applying Life Skills

Ask students whether they have ever had to act in an emergency. If yes, ask: How did you know the situation was an emergency? If no, have students describe various emergency situations that they have observed. **L1**

MORE ABOUT...

Good Samaritan Laws Most Good Samaritan laws are designed to protect health care professionals and others who provide assistance to victims of accidents or crimes. Before such laws were passed, anyone who volunteered to help risked being sued for wrongdoing by victims or their families. Good Samaritan laws prevent such suits. In general, anyone who acts reasonably and with obvious good intentions is protected by Good Samaritan laws.

Another aspect of Good Samaritan laws is included in only a few states. This provision requires witnesses or passersby to take reasonable steps to help emergency victims, at least by calling 911 or the local emergency number.

Investigating

Ask a pair of volunteers to confirm your community's emergency phone number—911 or 0 for operator. Have these volunteers share the information with the rest of the class. **L2**

Cooperative Learning

Have students meet in groups to role-play calls for help. Have group members work together to imagine and describe a specific emergency situation. Then have a pair of group members role-play the phone call a teen might make to the local emergency number. **L1**

Developing Good Character ★

Citizenship

As a good citizen, you'll want to be prepared to report accidents, fires, serious illnesses, injuries, and crimes. Check your telephone book to find the number or numbers to call for emergencies in your community. Make a list to keep by the telephone.

Decide to Act

In an emergency, evaluate the situation and decide what action is needed. Then consider your strengths and limitations before you act. For example, unless you are trained in lifesaving, don't dive into a lake to rescue someone who is drowning. Instead, you might throw the person a life preserver or some other object that floats. Your first responsibility in any situation is to protect your own safety. Never put your own life in danger to help someone else.

Some people hesitate to help others because they are afraid of doing something wrong. Almost all states have Good Samaritan laws, which protect rescuers who act responsibly from legal action. In an emergency, one action that is always beneficial is to call for help. Getting help is often the best and only action for you to take, and this alone can save a life.

Call for Help

In most of the United States, the number to call for all emergencies is 911. Dialing 0 for the operator is also an option and may be necessary in some small towns. When you call, stay

calm. Be ready to tell the emergency operator the nature of the emergency and the street address or location. The operator will notify the police, fire department, or emergency medical services. If you don't know the address, you can describe the location by using landmarks. Stay on the phone until the operator has the necessary information and tells you that you can hang up.

Provide Care Until Help Arrives

Once you have called for help, provide care by staying with the injured person and protecting him or her from further injury. Help the person maintain normal body temperature by providing a coat or blanket for warmth. Carefully loosen any tight clothing, and provide shade from the sun if necessary. Reassure the victim that help is on the way.

526 CHAPTER 19: SAFETY AND EMERGENCIES

Health Literacy

Health Information Personal emergency response systems are modular electronic units, the size of shoe boxes or smaller, that connect to the telephone system. Some have buttons with pictures representing the type of aid needed—paramedics, police, fire department. The systems also include handheld transmitters that may be worn as pendants or on the wrist, placed on a nightstand, or tucked in clothing pockets. The transmitting device places a call for help to an emergency response center. Many response centers maintain computerized data about clients, enabling the emergency personnel to know the caller's name, address, and medical history.

In general, you should not try to move a victim. Moving the person could cause pain or further injury. Wait for professional help to arrive. The only situation in which a victim should be moved is if he or she is in danger, such as in the path of oncoming traffic.

If the victim is unconscious and unresponsive, cardiopulmonary resuscitation (CPR) is needed. This technique for dealing with life-threatening emergencies is described in Lesson 6 of this chapter.

While you wait for medical help to arrive, help the victim stay calm by providing comfort and reassurance. *Why should you avoid moving an injured person?*

Lesson 4 Review

Using complete sentences, answer the following questions on a sheet of paper.

Reviewing Terms and Facts

1. **Vocabulary** Define the term *first aid.*
2. **Recall** What are four universal precautions to take when giving first aid?
3. **Summarize** List the first four steps to take when an emergency occurs.
4. **Identify** Give three examples of ways you can provide help to an injured person until professional help arrives.

Thinking Critically

5. **Analyze** Why is it so important to know basic first-aid strategies for responding to accidental injuries?

6. **Apply** If you come upon an injured person on a jogging path, should you try to drag the person to the side of the path? Why or why not?

Applying Health Skills

7. **Practicing Healthful Behaviors** With family members, discuss your family's preparedness for emergencies. Begin by listing possible emergencies. Then decide what should be done for each situation and how prepared every member is to act. Make a plan of the steps you could take to become more prepared. Demonstrate strategies for responding to accidental injuries by practicing the steps.

LESSON 4: BASIC FIRST AID **527**

Lesson 4

Discussing

Ask students to describe specific situations in which a victim must be moved (*e.g., the victim might be in traffic or on an unstable surface*). Then have them describe possible situations in which a victim clearly should not be moved. (*In most cases, victims should not be moved. This is especially true if spinal injuries are likely.*) **L1**

❸ Assess

Evaluating

Assign the Lesson 4 Review; then assign the Lesson 4 Quiz in the TCR.

Reteaching

- Assign Concept Map 76 or Reteaching Activity 76 in the TCR.
- Have students define the term *first aid* in their own words. Then have each student describe a situation in which first aid would be required.

Enrichment

- Assign Enrichment Activity 76 in the TCR.
- Have students talk with pharmacists about how time, light, moisture, or air can affect common first-aid supplies.

❹ Close

Have students explain how to recognize the signs of an emergency.

Lesson 4 Review

1. Immediate temporary care given to an injured or ill person until he or she can get professional help.
2. Any four: Wear protective gloves while treating victim, use face mask when giving aid for breathing, cover open wounds on your body with sterile dressings, avoid touching objects in contact with victim's blood, always wash hands afterward.
3. Recognize signs of emergency, decide to act, call for help, provide care until help arrives.
4. See Provide Care Until Help Arrives on page 526.
5. Sample answer: To prevent injuries from becoming more serious.
6. No, moving a victim can make injuries worse. Accident victims should be moved only when in immediate danger.

First Aid for Common Emergencies

① Focus

Lesson Objectives

Students will be able to

- explain how to recognize and evaluate common emergencies.
- describe first-aid treatments for common emergencies.
- determine when it is necessary to call for medical assistance.

Motivators

Quick Write
Allow students to share their experiences. Ask: How did the first aid provided in each situation help the injury from becoming more serious?

Bellringer Activity

Ask students to list the first five words that come to mind when they hear the word *emergency*.

Lesson 5

First Aid for Common Emergencies

Quick Write

Describe an emergency you experienced or witnessed in which first aid was needed. What help did you or others provide?

LEARN ABOUT...

- how to recognize and evaluate common emergencies.
- first-aid treatments for common emergencies.
- when to call for medical assistance.

VOCABULARY

- sprain
- fracture
- heat cramps
- heat exhaustion
- heatstroke

Common Emergencies

Sprains, bruises, and broken bones are a few of the common emergencies you may experience. Others include insect bites, burns, poisoning, foreign objects in the eye, nosebleed, fainting, heat cramps, and heatstroke. Learn how to properly treat these conditions. Also recognize the difference between a minor condition that you can treat and a more serious condition that needs professional medical assistance.

Sprains

A **sprain** is *a condition in which the ligaments that hold the joints in position are stretched or torn.* Sprains usually result from a sudden force, often a twisting movement. Ankles and knees are the most commonly sprained joints. Swelling and bruising often accompany a sprain. Serious sprains should be treated by a physician. To treat minor sprains, use the R.I.C.E. method:

- **Rest.** Rest the affected joint for 24 to 48 hours.
- **Ice.** Apply ice to reduce swelling and pain. Place a cloth between the skin and the bag of ice in order to reduce discomfort.
- **Compression.** Compress the injured part by wrapping it in an elastic bandage.
- **Elevation.** Elevate, or raise, the injured part above the level of the heart to reduce swelling.

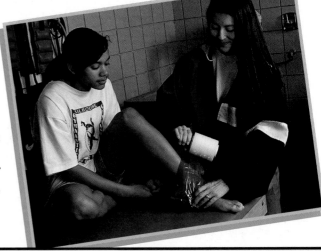

Apply a cold pack to a sprain as soon as possible after the injury to reduce inflammation. *What could you use if you did not have a cold pack available?*

528 CHAPTER 19: SAFETY AND EMERGENCIES

Lesson 5 Resources

Teacher Classroom Resources

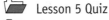 Concept Map 77

Enrichment Activity 77

Health Lab 19

Lesson Plan 5

Lesson 5 Quiz

Reading Tutor Activity 76

 Reteaching Activity 77

 Transparency 80

Student Activities Workbook

 Chapter 19 Study Guide

Applying Health Skills 77

Broken Bones

A fracture is *a break in a bone*. An open fracture is a complete break with one or both sides of the bone piercing the skin. A closed fracture does not break the skin and may be difficult to identify. Typical signs of a closed fracture include pain, swelling, and misshapen appearance. Sometimes, however, a broken bone causes no immediate pain. The only way to be sure a bone is broken is to have it X-rayed.

Insect Bites and Stings

Insect bites and stings often cause pain and swelling at the site of the bite or sting. For people who are allergic to bites and stings, however, the situation is much more serious, and possibly life-threatening. If a person develops a rash, has difficulty breathing, shows signs of shock, or is known to be allergic to stings, he or she needs professional medical help immediately.

First aid for insect bites involves washing the affected area and applying a special lotion for bites. For insect stings, you first need to remove the stinger by scraping against it with your fingernail. Once the stinger is out, apply ice or a cold pack to relieve pain and prevent swelling. If a person is bitten by a tick, the tick will burrow into the skin and needs to be removed very carefully. **Figure 19.8** shows the correct procedure for removing ticks.

Developing Good Character

Responsibility

If you are going to be in an area where contact with ticks is a possibility, wear enclosed shoes, socks, and long pants. Check your clothes and any exposed skin often. Stay on cleared paths and avoid sitting on the ground. Do a final, full-body tick-check at the end of the day. *What first-aid supplies should you have in case of a tick bite?*

② Teach

Developing Good Character

Responsibility

Emphasize to students that being responsible means planning ahead to be safe and to stay healthy. Have the class read the tips for avoiding tick bites. Then have them answer the question posed. They should note that tweezers and disinfectant wipes should be included in their first-aid supplies.

Applying Life Skills

Ask the students what items in the classroom could be used to apply first aid to a broken or injured wrist. (*Hand and wrist could be immobilized by being placed on top of a large soft-covered book. Rulers could be used as part of a splint. They could then be secured with a scarf, a belt, or an undershirt.*) **L1**

VISUAL LEARNING

FIGURE 19.8 Have a volunteer read aloud the title and the caption for Figure 19.8. Ask:

• Why do you think you should have an adult remove a tick?

• What do you think you should do if no adult is available? Why?

Then guide students in reading and discussing the method. **INCL** *English Language Learners, Special Learning Needs, Behavior Problems, Different Learning Styles (Visual)*

FIGURE 19.8

HOW TO REMOVE A TICK

If you find a tick on your body, have an adult follow the method shown to remove it.

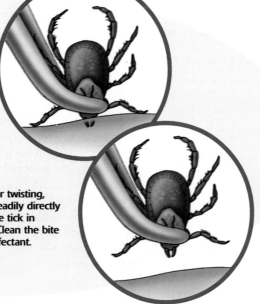
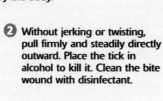

❶ Using a pair of pointed, smooth-tipped tweezers, grasp the tick by the head or mouth parts right where they enter the skin. Do not grasp the tick by the body.

❷ Without jerking or twisting, pull firmly and steadily directly outward. Place the tick in alcohol to kill it. Clean the bite wound with disinfectant.

LESSON 5: FIRST AID FOR COMMON EMERGENCIES **529**

MORE ABOUT...

Injurious Bites Bites from animals or humans can cause problems other than excess bleeding. Animal bites and snakebites cause more alarm than human bites, which are more common. Infection is the guaranteed result of any bite unless it is cleaned thoroughly. Most bites are puncture wounds and should be treated accordingly. A wild animal, such as a raccoon, that appears unusually friendly may be rabid. Those animals should be avoided. Do not assume that a dog or cat that is young or especially friendly cannot be rabid. An animal should be tested for rabies if it has bitten anyone—even if it is your pet.

FIGURE 19.9 Ask three small groups of volunteers to consider Figure 19.9; have each group read about either first-degree, second-degree, or third-degree burns. Then have the members of each group explain to the rest of the class the indications and treatment for their assigned type of burn. **INCL** *English Language Learners, Special Learning Needs, Behavior Problems, Different Learning Styles (Visual)*

Demonstrating

Have students work in pairs to role-play calls to a poison control center, giving all the necessary information about a poisoning incident. Encourage students to find the phone number for the local poison control and post it in a visible place in their homes. **L1 INCL** *English Language Learners, Special Learning Needs, Behavior Problems, Different Learning Styles (Visual)*

Discussing

Ask students to discuss burns they have received.

• How did the burn happen?

• How was it treated?

Point out that many over-the-counter ointments actually hinder the healing of burns by holding in the skin's heat. For more information on first aid procedures for electrical and chemical burns, contact the Mayo Foundation for Medical Education and Research (Mayo Clinic). **L1**

Investigating

Have students investigate types of sunscreen. They should consider brands, ingredients, and sun protection factor (SPF). Have them make recommendations to the class and explain their selection(s). **L3**

FIGURE 19.9

THREE DEGREES OF BURNS
Treatment for burns depends on the severity of the burn.

Type of Burn	Description	Treatment
First-Degree	Affects only the outer layer of the skin. The skin is usually red, but the outer layer has not been burned through. There may be swelling and pain.	Cool the burn with running water, immerse the burn in cold water, or apply cold compresses for at least 15 minutes. Cover the burn with a sterile bandage.
Second-Degree	Burns through the first layer of skin and burns the second layer of skin. Blisters develop, and the skin looks red and splotchy. Usually there is severe pain and swelling.	A burn no larger than 2 to 3 inches in diameter can be treated as a first-degree burn. If the burn is larger, or is on the hands, feet, face, groin, buttocks, or a major joint, get medical help immediately.
Third-Degree	Involves all layers of skin and may affect fat, muscle, and bone. The burned area may be charred black or appear dry and white. There may be little or no pain felt at this stage.	Call for medical help. While you are waiting, treat the victim for shock as described in Lesson 6. Do not remove burned clothing. Apply cold water to the burn, then cover with a sterile bandage or clean cloth. Keep the victim still and help him or her to sip fluids.

Burns

First aid for burns depends on the amount of skin burned, the location of the burn, and the depth of the burn. Burns to the eye or airway and burns caused by chemicals or electricity require special first-aid procedures, which are not covered here. **Figure 19.9** explains how to recognize and treat three classifications of burns.

Poisoning

A poison is a substance that causes harm when swallowed, breathed in, absorbed by the skin, or injected into the body. About half of all poisonings involve medicines or household products. Anyone who has been poisoned needs immediate treatment. Call the nearest poison control center, a 24-hour hot line that provides emergency medical advice on treating poisoning victims. Be prepared to give information about the victim and about the suspected poison. The person at the poison control center will tell you what action to take. You may be instructed to give the victim large amounts of water or milk to dilute the poison. For some types of poison, you may be told to give the victim something to induce vomiting, such as syrup of ipecac. Read the label on the container before doing so.

530 CHAPTER 19: SAFETY AND EMERGENCIES

Health Literacy

Health Information Lyme disease is caused by a type of bacteria known as a spirochete. This is a small, coiled bacteria carried by ticks, some of which are smaller than the common dog tick. The ticks usually live on animals that live in the woods, but they can spread to domestic animals and humans. The tick bite is not painful; so it may go unnoticed. The first stage of Lyme disease is a red rash that usually fades without treatment, followed by headache, stiff neck, fatigue, and joint aches. Ticks can be found outdoors in all grasses and wooded areas. Preventive measures include wearing light-colored long pants tucked into socks, long-sleeved shirts, enclosed shoes or boots, and insect repellents. Also, use tick and flea repellent collars on pets.

If the skin comes into direct contact with a poisonous chemical such as a pesticide or household cleaning agent, remove any clothing that has come into contact with the chemical. Remove as much of the chemical from the surface of the skin as you can by flooding with water for 15 minutes. While the skin is being flooded, call the nearest poison control center.

Foreign Object in the Eye

If you get a foreign object in your eye, don't rub the eye. Rubbing can cause injury. Try to flush the object out of your eye with clean water. Hold the rim of a small, clean glass filled with water against the base of your eye socket. Keeping your eye open, gently pour the water into the eye. If the object isn't washed out, repeat the process. If you cannot clear your eye, get assistance.

To help somebody else who has a foreign object in the eye, first locate the object. Gently pull the lower lid downward while the person looks up. If you do not see the object, hold the upper lid open and examine the eye while the person looks down. If the object is floating on the surface of the eye, lightly touch the object with a moistened cotton swab or the corner of a clean cloth. If you cannot remove the object, seek medical assistance immediately.

Nosebleed

Nosebleeds can be caused by an injury, by being in a very dry place, and even by a cold. If you experience a nosebleed, pinch your nose shut with your thumb and index finger and breathe through your mouth. Keep the nose pinched for 5 to 10 minutes. If bleeding lasts more than 15 minutes or if there is a lot of blood, get medical assistance immediately.

Fainting

Fainting occurs when the blood supply to the brain is cut off for a short amount of time. A person who faints loses consciousness briefly. If you feel faint, lie down or sit down and place your head between your knees. If someone else faints, follow these steps.

- Leave the person lying down. Check the airway. If the person is breathing, raise the legs above the level of the head.

- Loosen any tight clothing.

- If the person does not regain consciousness in one to two minutes, call for help. If the person is not breathing, call for help and start CPR if you are trained (see Lesson 6).

- Losing consciousness after a head injury is not fainting— call for help if this occurs. Immediate CPR is needed if there are no signs of life.

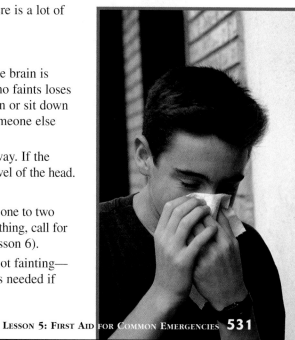

Pinching your nose can help stop your nose from bleeding. *What might cause a nosebleed?*

LESSON 5: FIRST AID FOR COMMON EMERGENCIES **531**

Lesson 5

Discussing

Ask students:

- When are people most vulnerable to eye injuries? (*when mowing lawns, sawing and doing other carpentry work, playing certain sports*)

- How could the injuries be avoided? (*In most cases, wearing goggles or safety glasses protects the eyes from injury.*) **L1**

Demonstrating

Have students demonstrate the appropriate treatment for a nosebleed. Then ask: What would you do if a toddler or young child had a nosebleed? **L1** **INCL** *English Language Learners, Special Learning Needs, Behavior Problems, Different Learning Styles* (*Visual*)

Discussing

Ask volunteers to describe the feelings that precede fainting. Ask:

- What does it mean to feel lightheaded?

- Does feeling lightheaded always lead to fainting?

- What should you do if you feel lightheaded? **L1**

Fainting can be caused by the use of medicines, alcohol, or other drugs. In these cases, the individual should receive professional medical attention.

COOPERATIVE LEARNING ACTIVITY

First-Aid Preparedness Before class, print on each of several index cards an injury that requires first aid. Some examples are sprain, broken bone, bee sting, burn, and nosebleed. Divide the class into pairs. Assign one student to be the victim and the other to be the first-aid giver. The victim draws a card to determine his or her injury. The first-aid giver must explain orally the appropriate first-aid technique while demonstrating the technique on the victim. You may wish to provide a few materials—such as bandages, ice packs, empty over-the-counter products, or cotton balls—to be used in each demonstration. Proceed with this activity until all students have had a chance to display their knowledge of first-aid techniques.

Evaluating

📁 Assign the Lesson 5 Review; then assign the Lesson 5 Quiz in the TCR.

Reteaching

• 📁 Assign Concept Map 77 or Reteaching Activity 77 in the TCR.

• Have students copy the vocabulary terms from the beginning of the lesson and, for each case, describe the emergency and the suggested treatment.

Enrichment

• 📁 Assign Enrichment Activity 77 in the TCR.

• Have students work in groups to plan, practice, and present skits that demonstrate strategies for responding to accidental injuries.

④ Close

Divide the class into small groups. Have each group prepare and present a demonstration that shows what to do in case of the following problems: sprain; fracture; insect bite or sting; poisoning; first-degree, second-degree, and third-degree burns; and a nosebleed.

Heat-Related Illnesses

Heat-related illnesses include heat cramps, heat exhaustion, and heatstroke. **Heat cramps** are *painful, involuntary muscle spasms that usually occur during heavy exercise in hot weather.* People who experience heat cramps should rest, cool down, and drink water or a sports drink that contains electrolytes. Gentle stretching exercise and gentle massage may help relieve the cramps.

It is important to rest, cool down, and drink water when suffering from heat cramps. *What are some common causes of heat cramps?*

Heat exhaustion is *a condition characterized by faintness, nausea, rapid heartbeat, and hot, red, dry, or sweaty skin.* Take someone who shows signs of heat exhaustion to a shady or air-conditioned place. Have the person lie down and slightly elevate the feet. Loosen clothing. Have the person drink cold, but not iced, water. Spray the person with cool water and fan him or her. Keep careful watch. Heat exhaustion can quickly become **heatstroke**, which is *the most serious form of heat illness.*

Heatstroke is life-threatening because the body's normal processes for dealing with heat, including sweating, close down. The main sign of heatstroke is a marked increase in body temperature—generally higher than 104°F. Rapid heartbeat and rapid and shallow breathing are other signs. If heatstroke is a possibility, treat the person as for heat exhaustion and call immediately for emergency medical assistance.

Lesson 5 Review

Using complete sentences, answer the following questions on a sheet of paper.

Reviewing Terms and Facts

1. **Vocabulary** Define the terms *sprain* and *fracture*. Use both terms in a sentence that demonstrates their meanings.
2. **Summarize** Explain the process for removing a tick from a person's body.
3. **Recall** What should you do to help someone who has swallowed a poisonous substance?
4. **Describe** What action should you take if you feel faint?

Thinking Critically

5. **Analyze** How would you respond to this accidental injury: a burn about 1½ inches in diameter that had burned through the first layer of skin and burned the second layer of skin? Explain.
6. **Compare and Contrast** How does the treatment for heatstroke differ from that for heat cramps?

Applying Health Skills

7. **Practicing Healthful Behaviors** With a classmate, write a scenario for dealing with a common emergency. Demonstrate strategies for responding to your chosen accidental injury by acting out your scenario for the class.

532 CHAPTER 19: SAFETY AND EMERGENCIES

Lesson 5 Review

1. A sprain is a condition in which ligaments holding joints in position are stretched or torn. A fracture is a break in a bone. Sentences will vary.
2. Using a pair of tweezers, grasp the tick by the head or mouth parts, where they have entered the skin. Pull outward. Place the tick in alcohol. Clean the wound with disinfectant.
3. Call poison control center; follow the directions they give.
4. Lie down or sit with your head between your knees.
5. Can be treated as first-degree burn. Cool with water or cold compresses for 15 minutes. Cover burn with sterile bandage.
6. See Heat-Related Illnesses on this page.

Life-Threatening Emergencies

When Minutes Count

In a life-threatening emergency, a person may have only minutes to live unless the right treatment is provided. If you can provide appropriate first aid in such a situation, you may save a life. For all life-threatening emergencies, try to stay calm, and call for help.

Choking

More than 3,000 people die from choking every year in the United States. Choking occurs when a person's airway becomes blocked by a piece of food or some other object. If the object is not removed, air will not reach the lungs and the person could die. A choking person usually has an expression of fear and may clutch his or her throat—the universal sign for choking. He or she may wheeze or gasp, turn reddish purple, have bulging eyes, and will be unable to speak. If the person can speak or cough, it is not a choking emergency.

Quick Write

In a life-threatening emergency, every second counts. Why is it important to stay calm at such a time?

LEARN ABOUT...

- how to deal with life-threatening emergencies.
- shock, and why it must be considered in any emergency.
- how to provide rescue breathing.
- the ABCs of CPR.

VOCABULARY

- abdominal thrusts
- shock
- CPR

A choking person needs immediate help. You may be able to clear the object from an adult's or child's throat by using the maneuver shown in **Figure 19.10** on the next page. This is the **abdominal thrusts** maneuver, which uses *quick, upward pulls into the diaphragm to force out an obstruction blocking the airway.* The first-aid procedure for a choking infant is different from the adult technique. Check with a first-aid manual to learn how to help infants.

This person is demonstrating the universal sign for choking—grabbing the throat with thumb and fingers extended. *How would you respond to someone showing signs of choking?*

---

① Focus

Lesson Objectives

Students will be able to

- explain first aid for life-threatening emergencies.
- discuss why shock must be considered an emergency.
- describe how to provide rescue breathing.
- describe how to provide CPR.

Motivators

 Quick Write
Ask students to share their responses. Ask: Why do you think some people, like medics, are able to respond to serious emergencies calmly?

Bellringer Activity

Have each student make a list of foods that may cause a person to choke and a list of eating habits that may result in choking.

VOCABULARY

Write each of the vocabulary terms on three separate index cards. Write the definitions of the terms on three additional cards. Place the cards facedown on a table, and invite pairs of students to play "Concentration." In this game, students take turns flipping over a pair of cards to match the term with its definition. If the match is not correct, both cards are returned to the face down position. Matched cards can be removed from the table or left face up.

Lesson 6 Resources

Teacher Classroom Resources
- Concept Map 78
- Cross-Curriculum Activity 38
- Decision-Making Activity 38
- Enrichment Activity 78
- Lesson Plan 6
- Lesson 6 Quiz
- Reading Tutor Activity 77

- Reteaching Activity 78
- Transparency 81

Student Activities Workbook
- Chapter 19 Study Guide
- Applying Health Skills 78
- Health Inventory 19

② Teach

Discussing

See Figure 15.11 on page 390 to review the function of the epiglottis. Discuss how a person can choke when the epiglottis is kept from functioning normally. **L1**

VISUAL LEARNING

FIGURE 19.10 Have a volunteer read aloud the title and caption for Figure 19.10, and have students answer the caption question. They should explain that a person who can speak is not choking and should not be given abdominal thrusts. Then have students read and discuss the steps for administering abdominal thrusts. **INCL** *English Language Learners, Special Learning Needs, Behavior Problems, Different Learning Styles (Visual)*

Investigating

Ask a group of volunteers to compile a list of foods or objects that pose a choking risk to infants and toddlers. **L3**

In some cases, severe emotional upset (from a personal tragedy or a disaster) can cause shock.

FIGURE 19.10

FIRST AID FOR A CHOKING ADULT OR OLDER CHILD

Before you perform abdominal thrusts, determine if the person is choking. *Why is asking if a person can speak a good way to find out if he or she is choking?*

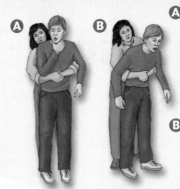

A Stand behind the person who is choking. Wrap your arms around the person's waist and tip the person slightly forward. Make a fist. Place the fist just above the person's navel but below the breastbone. Position the fist so the thumb side is against the victim's abdomen. Grasp your fist with your other hand.

B Quickly, thrust inward and upward. The motion is similar to one you would use if you were trying to lift the person off the ground. Repeat thrusts until the food or object is dislodged. If the person becomes unresponsive, call for medical help and begin CPR.

If you are choking and are alone, give yourself an abdominal thrust. There are two ways to do this. First, make a fist and position it slightly above your navel. Grasp your fist with your other hand and thrust inward and upward into your abdomen until the object pops out. The second technique is to lean over a firm object, such as the back of a chair, and press your abdomen into it.

Shock

Shock is *a life-threatening condition in which the circulatory system fails to deliver enough blood to vital tissues and organs.* The many causes of shock include injury, burns, severe infection, heat, poisoning, blood loss, and heart attack. Because shock can result from a medical emergency, you should look for signs of it when providing first aid.

Signs of shock to watch for include cool, clammy, pale or gray skin; weak and rapid pulse; and slow, shallow breathing. The pupils may be dilated, and the eyes may have a dull look. If conscious, the victim of shock may feel faint, weak, confused, and anxious.

If you think the victim is in shock or in danger of shock, call for medical help and take these precautions.

- Have the person lie down on his or her back. Raise the feet higher than the head. Try to keep the person from moving.
- Loosen tight clothing.
- Keep the person warm. Use a blanket, coat, or whatever is available as a cover.
- Do not give the person anything to drink.
- If the person vomits or bleeds from the mouth, roll the person to his or her side to help prevent choking.

✓ Reading Check

Make connections. The word *artery* comes from a Greek word meaning "way from the chest." One important set of arteries carries blood to the head. Find the name of those arteries on the next page.

✓ Reading Check

Word Origins Learning about word origins will help build students' vocabulary. The arteries that carry blood to the head are called the carotid arteries. Both the words *carotid* [cah RAH tid] and *artery* stem from Greek words. Carotid means "head or horn"; a related word is carrot (named as such because of its horn shape). Artery originally meant "windpipe" because early doctors thought all passages from the chest carried only air. The term artery was already established by the time ancient people learned more about blood vessels and airways in the body. You may wish to have students use resource material to discover the word history, or you may wish to tell the class the word histories before they identify the words *carotid arteries*.

FIGURE 19.11

PRESSURE POINT BLEEDING CONTROL

This illustration shows the areas on arms and legs that can be pressed against a bone to stop circulation to the arm or leg.

Arm
Use four fingers to press on the inside of the upper arm at the area circled in the diagram. You will press the artery at this point against the arm bone. To find the artery, feel for a pulse below the round muscle of the biceps.

Leg
Keeping your arm straight, use the heel of your hand to press the groin at the area shown in the diagram. You will press the artery at this point against the pelvic bone. You may need to use both hands to apply enough pressure.

Severe Bleeding

To stop severe bleeding, have the person lie down. If possible, raise the site of the bleeding above the level of the heart. When treating bleeding, use protective gloves whenever possible. Bleeding can usually be stopped by applying direct pressure to the wound, using a clean cloth. If that is unsuccessful, apply pressure to the artery that supplies blood to the area of the wound. See **Figure 19.11**.

Hands-On Health

LOCATING PRESSURE POINTS

In addition to the arteries leading to the arms and legs, there are two pressure points on either side of the neck. The carotid arteries, which supply blood to the head and brain, run just below the skin here. Knowing where pressure points are can help you be prepared to quickly check pulse or stop severe blood flow.

WHAT YOU WILL DO
1. Referring to **Figure 19.11**, locate the pressure points for your left and right arm and left and right leg arteries. Feel for the pulse.
2. Referring to the photograph, feel for the pulse at your right carotid. Then find the pulse at your left carotid. The carotid arteries have the strongest pulse.

IN CONCLUSION
1. Name the pressure point you would press to stop severe blood flow from the following: left calf, right forearm, right wrist, right ankle.
2. If you needed to check someone's pulse, which pressure point would you use? Why?

Lesson 6

VISUAL LEARNING

FIGURE 19.11 Ask volunteers to read the title and caption aloud and to describe the illustrations. Then guide students in reading, discussing, and demonstrating the explanation for using pressure point bleeding control on the arm and on the leg. Ask: Why is it important to become familiar with these procedures? **INCL** *English Language Learners, Special Learning Needs, Behavior Problems, Different Learning Styles (Visual)*

Hands-On Health

LOCATING PRESSURE POINTS

Time: 30 minutes

TEACHING THE ACTIVITY
- Guide students in reading and discussing the activity introduction.
- Go over activity instructions with students. Remind them to use their fingers (index and middle) to check their pulses; avoid using the thumb, where the pulse can also be felt.
- Have students complete the activity independently.

ASSESSMENT
Have students write their responses to the In Conclusion questions. Use these answers, along with their participation in the activity, to assess their work.

MORE ABOUT...

Choking First Aid If a choking victim loses consciousness, it is impossible to use the first-aid method suggested for conscious victims. Instead, roll the victim on his or her back, and perform abdominal thrusts while straddling the victim's thighs. Place the heel of one hand against the victim's abdomen, slightly above the navel and below the tip of the breastbone. Place the other hand directly on top of the first and press into the abdomen with quick upward thrusts.

VISUAL LEARNING

FIGURE 19.12 Review with students the situations in which rescue breathing is needed. Read aloud the caption, and ask students about the purpose of a breathing mask. Then guide students in reading and discussing each step in administering rescue breathing as recommended by the American Heart Association. **INCL** *English Language Learners, Special Learning Needs, Behavior Problems, Different Learning Styles* (*Visual*)

Guest Speaker

Ask someone certified in CPR, such as a trainer from the American Heart Association, to demonstrate CPR on a mannequin for the class. Allow students to practice on the mannequin, supervised by the trained professional. Emphasize that they should not practice this procedure on someone who has a heartbeat because it will put the heart into fibrillation and the person could die. **L1**

Brainstorming

Lead students in a brainstorming session of alternative barriers that could be used to avoid contact with body fluids if plastic gloves and a rescue breathing mask are not available. Ask students to suggest ways they could be more prepared to protect themselves in such situations. **L1**

Demonstrating

After students have received instruction in how to perform the techniques described in this lesson, ask student volunteers to demonstrate basic first-aid procedures including cardiopulmonary resuscitation (CPR) and the choking rescue on a mannequin.

FIGURE 19.12

THE ABCs OF CPR

The first steps of CPR involve assessment and rescue breathing. If you have an available breathing mask, follow the directions that came with the mask.

❶ **Airway.** Look inside the victim's mouth. If you see anything blocking the airway, remove it. Lay the person flat on a firm surface. Gently tilt the head back with one hand and lift the chin with the other. If you suspect head or neck injuries, do not move the victim's head. Open the airway by lifting the jaw instead.

❷ **Breathing.** Look, listen, and feel to find out if the victim is breathing. *Look* for chest movement. *Listen* at the victim's mouth for breathing sounds. *Feel* for exhaled air on your cheek. If the victim is not breathing, begin rescue breathing. Pinch the person's nostrils shut, take a normal breath and place your mouth over the victim's, forming a seal. Give two slow breaths, each about two seconds long. The victim's chest should rise with each breath.

❸ **Circulation.** Check for circulation by watching for some response to your rescue breaths, such as breathing, coughing, or movement. If there are no signs of circulation, a person trained in CPR should begin chest compressions immediately (see **Figure 19.13**). If the victim responds but is not breathing normally, give a rescue breath every five seconds.

CPR

Imagine that you are in an emergency situation in which somebody loses consciousness. You gently shake the victim and shout "Are you OK?" but the victim does not respond. If a victim is unresponsive, he or she needs cardiopulmonary resuscitation (CPR) immediately. **CPR** is *a first-aid procedure that combines rescue breaths with chest compressions to restore breathing and circulation.* Only people who have received the proper training should perform CPR.

The first steps of CPR, as recommended by the American Heart Association, are known as the ABCs—airway, breathing, and circulation. The ABC technique to use for adults and older children is shown in **Figure 19.12**. Check a first-aid manual to learn how to help younger children and infants. **Figure 19.13** illustrates the process for combining rescue breaths with chest compressions.

PROMOTING COORDINATED SCHOOL HEALTH

Community Support Tapping into local resources is a key to effectively managing a coordinated school health plan. For example, both the American Heart Association and the American Red Cross offer CPR training in communities across the country. Community involvement provides the resources and grassroots support needed to reduce fragmentation of efforts or duplication of programs. Ongoing collaboration and cooperation between the team and other community members prevents unwarranted controversy. For information about community support, consult *Planning a Coordinated School Health Program* in the TCR.

FIGURE 19.13

CPR FOR ADULTS

CPR involves both chest compressions and rescue breaths. It should be administered only by people who are properly trained and certified.

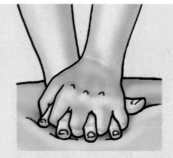

1 Position your hands. Prepare to start chest compressions by finding a spot on the lower half of the victim's breastbone. Place the heel of one hand on that point, and interlock the fingers with the fingers of the other hand. Do not allow your fingers to rest on the victim's ribs.

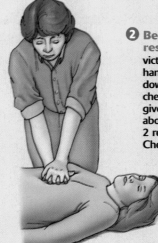

2 Begin chest compressions and rescue breathing. Lean over the victim until your shoulders are over your hands. Lock your elbows, then press down firmly and release, allowing the chest to spring back. Without pausing, give 15 chest compressions at a rate of about 100 per minute. Pause to give 2 rescue breaths (see **Figure 19.12**). Check for signs of circulation after 4 cycles, then every few minutes as you continue. Give CPR until the victim revives or help arrives.

Lesson 6 Review

Using complete sentences, answer the following questions on a sheet of paper.

Reviewing Terms and Facts

1. **Vocabulary** Define *abdominal thrust*.
2. **List** What are the signs of shock?
3. **Summarize** What strategies should you use to respond to an accidental injury that causes severe bleeding?
4. **Explain** What is *CPR?* In what circumstances should it be used?

Thinking Critically

5. **Analyze** A driver walks out after a car crash and says that he is all right. However, his skin is gray, his pupils are dilated, and his breathing is shallow. From what condition might the driver be suffering? What strategies should you use to respond to this condition?

Applying Health Skills

6. **Accessing Information** Research where first-aid procedures, including the choking rescue and CPR, are taught in your community. Find out the location, cost, requirements, and what type of certificates are issued upon completion of the class. Demonstrate basic first-aid procedures by taking the class.

VISUAL LEARNING

FIGURE 19.13 Read aloud the title and the caption for Figure 19.13; explain that a modified CPR technique is used on children. Then have students meet in groups to read and discuss the steps in performing CPR. **INCL** *English Language Learners, Special Learning Needs, Behavior Problems, Different Learning Styles (Visual)*

3 Assess

Evaluating

Assign the Lesson 6 Review; then assign the Lesson 6 Quiz in the TCR.

Reteaching

- Assign Concept Map 78 or Reteaching Activity 78 in the TCR.
- Have students describe, in their own words, how to administer first aid to an adult and to a child who is choking.

Enrichment

- Assign Enrichment Activity 78 in the TCR.
- Ask students to list the safety hazards associated with various holidays and to make bookmarks that alert the public to such holiday or seasonal hazards, including safety measures that should be taken for each.

4 Close

Ask each student to complete the following sentence: One new fact I learned from this lesson about first aid is…

Lesson 6 Review

1. Quick, upward pulls into the diaphragm to force out an obstruction blocking the airway.
2. Cool, clammy, pale, or gray skin; weak and rapid pulse; slow, shallow breathing; pupils dilated and dull look in eyes; faintness; iweakness; confusion; anxiety.
3. See Severe Bleeding on page 535.
4. A first-aid procedure that combines rescue breaths with chest compressions to restore breathing and circulation. Use if the victim is unresponsive.
5. He is in shock. Have him lie down, raise his feet higher than his head, loosen tight clothing, cover him with blanket or coat, keep him from moving, do not give him anything to drink. If he vomits or bleeds from the mouth, roll him onto his side.

Preventing Wildfires

① Focus

Objectives

Students will be able to
- create a family disaster plan.
- describe ways to protect a home from wildfire.
- identify major fire threats in their community.

Motivator

Quick Write
Ask students to imagine that their home is located in a forested area. One day they hear on the radio that a wildfire is headed their way. What would they do?

② Teach

Applying Knowledge

Tell students that while not everyone lives in an area where wildfires are a threat, a family emergency plan is useful for any emergency. Explain that the plan should include how family members will prepare and respond to an emergency. Steps may include

- contacting local authorities to find out about specific hazards in your community.
- developing an emergency supplies kit (water, clothing, first-aid kit, radio, and so forth).
- determining a meeting place where family members should meet.
- deciding how family members will keep in touch if separated.
- learning how to shut off water, gas, and electricity.

Ask students to speak with their parents and other family members about developing such a plan.

Preventing Wildfires

Wildfires can be extremely dangerous and destructive. Here are the forces that can drive wildfires and ways to prevent them.

① Column of rising hot air creates a void below.

② Fresh air rushes in, bringing more oxygen to fuel the flames.

③ Blowing embers allow the fire to jump natural barriers such as rivers and valleys.

UPHILL BATTLE
Wildfires charge rapidly up mountainsides because the heat from the fire rises and is directed at the fuel uphill, drying it out before the flames arrive.

FUEL
Decades of fighting every forest fire have left many areas dangerously full of fuel—sticks, fallen timber, pine needles, and brush.

TORNADO WINDS
In rare cases, winds within a wildfire create powerful mini-tornados that can shoot spirals of flames into the air and twist apart tree trunks.

SOIL INSULATION
Soil is an excellent insulator that can protect tree roots from a fire's heat, permitting regrowth to begin quickly.

How They Start
Wildfires result when fuel, dryness, and some kind of trigger are all present. Each factor contributes to the severity of the blaze.
- **Fuel** means flammable solids—grass, pine needles, undergrowth, smaller trees—that, with oxygen, feed the fire.
- **Dryness** can be caused by short-term weather patterns with low humidity or by a long drought.
- **Triggers** can be anything from a lightning strike to a campfire to an arsonist.

How They Spread
Weather is the primary force that drives or contains wildfires. However, once they start burning, wildfires create their own weather.
① **Smoke and heat** from fires can rise thousands of feet into the air.
② Then **cooler air** rushes in to fill the void.
③ This movement of air creates **gale-force hot winds** that dry out and preheat fuel ahead of the fire and can propel burning embers as much as half a mile.

538 CHAPTER 19: SAFETY AND EMERGENCIES

MORE ABOUT...

Fire Management Tell students that fire management in America's forests is a controversial issue. For years, forest fires were extinguished as quickly as possible. Many argue that this led to an overabundance of the small trees and undergrowth that feed a fire. Today, controlled fires are regularly set to clear out this undergrowth and encourage healthy regeneration of the forest. However, controlled burns occasionally turn into devastating wildfires that can't be contained. Have students access reliable sources of information about forest management and fires. Then, divide the class into two groups to debate the topic "Controlled burns are an effective strategy for fire prevention."

RETARDANT
Nitrogen-heavy fertilizer mixed with water coats fuel to prevent burning.

BACKFIRE

PREVAILING WIND

FIRE LINE

How to Fight Them

A fire dies when it is deprived of fuel, heat, or oxygen. The main strategy for fighting wildfires is containment: surround the fire and starve it.

- **Helicopters and tanker airplanes** can drop water or chemical retardants to slow the spread of flames.
- **Firefighters can set up fire lines,** areas cleared of any fuel that allow the fire to spread.
- **Controlled fires** are sometimes set to deny fuel to an approaching blaze. ▪

Preventing Wildfires When Camping

- **Build campfires away from overhanging branches, steep slopes, rotten stumps, logs, dry grass, and leaves. Pile any extra wood away from the fires.**
- **Keep plenty of water handy and have a shovel on hand for throwing dirt on the fire if it gets out of control.**
- **Keep the campfire small. Scrape away litter and any flammable material within a 10-foot circle. This will keep a small campfire from spreading.**
- **Be sure your match is out after the fire is lit.**
- **Never leave a campfire unattended. Even a small breeze could quickly cause the fire to spread.**
- **Drown the fire with water. Make sure all embers, coals, and sticks are wet. Move rocks—there may be burning embers underneath. Stir the remains, add more water, and stir again. Be sure all burned material has been extinguished and cooled.**
- **If you do not have water, use dirt. Mix soil or sand with the embers and continue adding and stirring until all material is cooled.**

Source: United States Department of Agriculture-Forest Service and the National Association of State Foresters

TIME TO THINK...

About Wildfires

With the class, create an ad campaign to warn others about the dangers of wildfires. Include information on how people can prevent wildfires when they're camping. To help campers remember your tips, investigate the word mnemonic (nem-ON-ik) and then create such a device for your campaign.

❸ Apply

Time to Think

Give students the option of creating an ad campaign that focuses on ways to protect a home from wildfire. Using reliable online and print resources, have students research ways to design and landscape homes with wildfire safety in mind. Ad campaigns should include information on fire-resistant building materials, fire-resistant shrubs and trees, how to create a fire "safety zone" around a home, safe storage of gasoline or other flammable materials, and so on. Have students share their work with the class.

VISUAL LEARNING

Ask students to discuss the image on this spread. Does this diagram represent the "average" wildfire appropriately? Why or why not? How might the situation change if homes or businesses were located nearby?

Beyond the Classroom

Community Ask students, "Who fights fires in our community? How are the fires they battle the same or different than wildfires?" Depending on where you live, respondents to a fire may be professional firefighters, citizen volunteers, forest service employees, or others. Contact one of these individuals and ask him or her to make a presentation to the class about fire prevention and/or preparedness. Have students brainstorm interview questions. These may include:

- What are the major fire threats in our community?
- What can people do to prevent these fire threats?
- How can people protect their homes from fire?

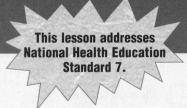

This lesson addresses National Health Education Standard 7.

REFUSAL SKILLS

Objective

After completing the lesson, students will be able to use refusal skills to avoid unsafe situations.

Time: 40 minutes

Materials: pen or pencil, paper

Teacher Classroom Resources

Building Health Skills Activities

• Transparency Master 7, "Refusal Skills"

• Reproducible Master 44, "Avoiding Unsafe Behaviors"

1. Model

• Display Transparency Master 7, and review refusal skills with the class.

• Have students read the scenario, and ask them to identify the statements that Jerry used to pressure Travis to engage in unsafe behaviors (*It's a short cut. We're not in a car; so it's safe. I've done it lots of times. Don't be such a baby.*)

• Have volunteers identify the statements that Travis used to resist his friend's pressure, and write these on the board. As a class, review each statement and determine which part of the S.T.O.P. formula it is.

AVOIDING UNSAFE BEHAVIORS

Model

At times, other teens may urge you to do things that are unsafe. Using refusal skills in these situations can help protect you from injury. Read about a teen named Travis who is out riding his bike with a classmate, Jerry. Note how Travis uses refusal skills to avoid unsafe behavior.

JERRY: Let's go this way. It's a short cut.

TRAVIS: No, we can't go that way. It's private property.

JERRY: So what? No one will see us.

TRAVIS: But it's steep and could be dangerous.

JERRY: I've ridden that way before, and I've never been hurt.

TRAVIS: Better safe than sorry. Why don't we just ride around the long way?

JERRY: Don't be such a baby. I'm going this way.

TRAVIS: I guess I'll meet up with you later, then. I'm going the long way.

JERRY: Oh, all right, have it your way. I'll go with you.

Teaching Tips

Reviewing Student Work Before students perform their role-plays for the class, briefly check each pair's script to ensure that it is appropriate, especially those who created their own scenarios.

Facilitating Student Comprehension It is helpful for students to be aware of *why* they are refusing to engage in risk behaviors. Before starting this lesson, ask students to answer the following questions on a sheet of paper: How does avoiding risk behaviors show that I have good character? How does avoiding risk behaviors support my academic goals? How will avoiding risk behaviors help me achieve my dreams? Solicit responses from several students.

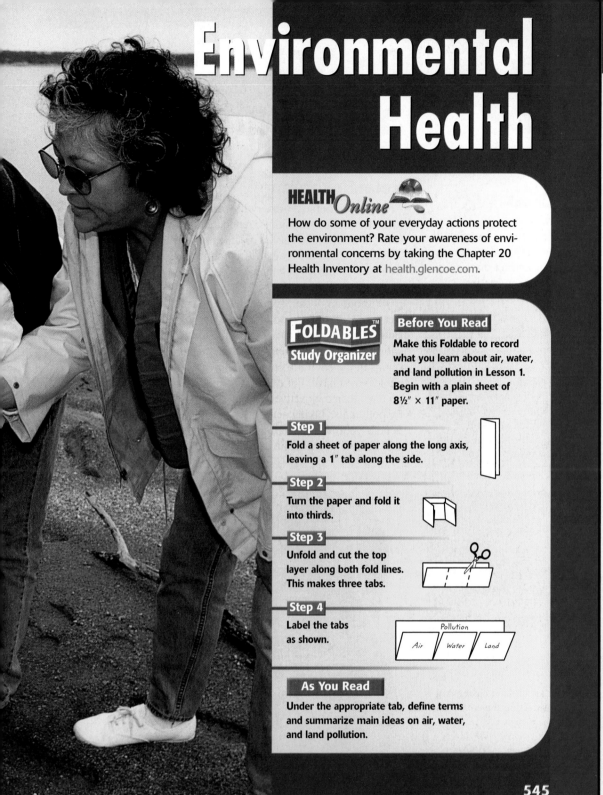

Environmental Health

HEALTH *Online*

How do some of your everyday actions protect the environment? Rate your awareness of environmental concerns by taking the Chapter 20 Health Inventory at health.glencoe.com.

FOLDABLES™
Study Organizer

Before You Read

Make this Foldable to record what you learn about air, water, and land pollution in Lesson 1. Begin with a plain sheet of 8½" × 11" paper.

Step 1

Fold a sheet of paper along the long axis, leaving a 1" tab along the side.

Step 2

Turn the paper and fold it into thirds.

Step 3

Unfold and cut the top layer along both fold lines. This makes three tabs.

Step 4

Label the tabs as shown.

Pollution
Air | Water | Land

As You Read

Under the appropriate tab, define terms and summarize main ideas on air, water, and land pollution.

Chapter Introduction

Use the options below to motivate students and preview chapter content.

HEALTH *Online*

Have students take Health Inventory 20 or read extra credit articles at **health.glencoe.com**. By clicking on Health Updates, both students and teachers can discover the latest news on health topics.

GLENCOE TECHNOLOGY

MindJogger Videoquiz

Use MindJogger to preview or review Chapter 20 content.

TIME HEALTH

Mean Clean Machines
pages 558–559

545

FOLDABLES™
Study Organizer

Dinah Zike Study Fold

Organizing Data and Narrative Writing Students will use their Foldable study guide to take notes on the different types of pollution. As students read and discuss the material presented in Lesson 1, have them define key terms and summarize the main ideas on air, water, and land pollution under the appropriate tab of their Foldable. Foldable study guides are great test-preparation tools because students can review main ideas, recall what they know, and check their responses by looking under the tabs. After students have completed the lesson, ask them to write a brief narrative on the back of their Foldable describing how pollution affects the environment.

Lesson 1

Pollution and Health

① Focus

Lesson Objectives

Students will be able to
- define pollution.
- identify what contributes to the pollution of air, water, and land.
- discuss how pollution affects the environment.

Motivators

Quick Write

Ask volunteers to share their definitions and examples. Ask: How can these forms of pollution affect your health?

Bellringer Activity

Remind students that the earth is a system. Ask students to provide examples of how pollution can affect more than one part of the earth's environment.

VOCABULARY

Prepare a worksheet that lists each of the vocabulary terms in a scrambled-letter form. For example, *pollution*, could be *ulotnloip*. (As an alternative, the scrambled words could be written on the board.) One at a time, read the definitions for each term, and challenge students to identify the correct term and write the correct spelling.

Pollution and Health

Quick Write

Write down your definition of pollution and give three examples of pollution that you have seen in your community.

LEARN ABOUT...

- **what pollution is.**
- **what contributes to pollution of the air, water, and soil.**
- **how pollution affects the environment.**

VOCABULARY

- pollution
- pesticides
- acid rain
- smog
- ozone layer
- greenhouse effect
- global warming
- landfills
- hazardous wastes

Your Environment

Your environment is everything that surrounds you. On a local level, it includes your home, school, and community. On a broader level, it includes the air you breathe, the water you drink, the trees that grow along the roadside, the climate you live in, and all the living and nonliving elements of the earth.

Without air, water, and land, life on earth would not be possible. Yet people have been polluting the very things that keep us alive. **Pollution** is a broad term that covers *any dirty or harmful substance in the environment.* It affects all living and nonliving things in the environment, and it affects some of the everyday choices you have. For example, when the air is clean, you can go outside and be active knowing your lungs won't be damaged by pollutants. Taking action to protect the environment now will benefit your health and the health of others. Future generations will be able to enjoy the results of your efforts.

Part of good citizenship is protecting the environment. *What steps can you take to preserve the natural beauty of your surroundings?*

546 CHAPTER 20: ENVIRONMENTAL HEALTH

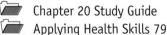

Lesson 1 Resources

Teacher Classroom Resources

- 📁 Parent Letter & Activities 20
- 📁 Concept Map 79
- 📁 Cross-Curriculum Activity 39
- 📁 Decision-Making Activity 39
- 📁 Enrichment Activity 79
- 📁 Health Lab 20
- 📁 Lesson Plan 1

- 📁 Lesson 1 Quiz
- 📁 Reading Tutor Activity 79
- 📁 Reteaching Activity 79
- 📁 Transparency 82

Student Activities Workbook

- 📁 Chapter 20 Study Guide
- 📁 Applying Health Skills 79

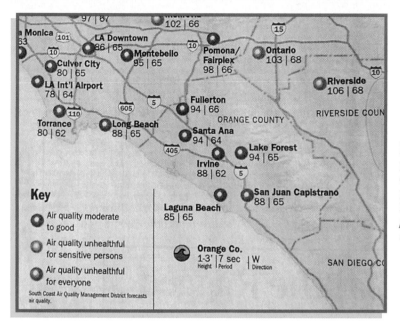

Key

 Air quality moderate to good

Air quality unhealthful for sensitive persons

Air quality unhealthful for everyone

South Coast Air Quality Management District forecasts air quality.

Most newspapers publish a daily air quality rating to warn people of air pollution levels. *How would a person with asthma use this information?*

Air Pollution

Natural events, such as an erupting volcano or a dust storm, cause some air pollution. Most air pollution, however, results from human activities that allow gases, dust, soot, and other substances to be released into the air. The major sources of air pollution are described below:

- **Burning fossil fuels.** People depend on energy to run motor vehicles, heat or cool buildings, and carry out countless daily tasks at home and at work. This energy is produced by burning oil, coal, and natural gas. Burning these fossil fuels, however, releases harmful gases such as carbon monoxide, sulfur dioxide, and nitrogen oxides into the atmosphere. Burning oil or coal also produces particulates, tiny particles of soot, ash, and other substances that can remain in the air for a long time.

- **Chemicals.** Many chemicals pollute the air. Pesticides, which are *products used on crops to control insects and other pests,* contain harmful chemicals that can get into the air. Chlorofluorocarbons (CFCs), chemicals that have traditionally been used in air conditioners and refrigerators, damage a layer of the atmosphere that protects the earth from dangerous solar radiation. Since 1987, more than 150 countries have signed an international agreement that will eventually phase out the use of CFCs.

- **Other sources.** Natural sources of air pollution include forest and grass fires, dust storms, and volcanic eruptions. Forest fires release carbon monoxide and other gases into the atmosphere that add to air pollution resulting from human activities.

Reading Check

Identify cause and effect. Write your own *If . . ., then . . .* statements about pollution.

② Teach

Discussing

Help students consider their own reasons for being concerned about pollution:

- What forms of pollution affect your enjoyment of sights and sounds in the environment?

- What dangers do you think pollution poses to your health now? In the future? **L1**

Cooperative Learning

Divide the class into three groups, and assign each group one of the major sources of air pollution. Have the members of each group read and discuss the information in their assigned section. Then have them plan and use an engaging method of sharing that information with the rest of the class. **L2**

Cross-Curriculum Activity

LANGUAGE ARTS Encourage a volunteer to look up *fossil* in a dictionary and share the meaning with the class. Ask students to surmise how fossil fuels might have gotten that name. Have them explore the origin of the term in a science resource. (*Fossil fuels are fuels produced by pressurized masses of plant and animal remains deep in the earth.*) **L2**

Reading Check

If..., Then... Statements Creating their own *If ..., then ...* statements will help students make connections between the causes and effects of pollution. Write parts of *If..., then...* statements on the board, such as "If fossil fuels are burned, then..." and "If..., then protective layers of the atmosphere are damaged." Ask students to skim this page to find ways to complete or start the sentences. Have volunteers write the rest of each sentence. Point out that the *if* part of the statement is the cause and the *then* part, the effect. Also tell the class that there may be more than one possibility for both causes and effects. Have students create their own statements based on the lesson, and discuss their statements in small groups.

Lesson 1

HEALTH Online

Encourage students to explore the Web Links for this chapter and then complete the activity.

Observing

Plan a field trip to a local park. Tell students to be on the lookout for signs of acid rain or other air pollution damage. (*wearing and discoloration of statues and plaques, discoloration of bark or leaves, large number of dead trees*) **L1**

Discussing

Guide students in discussing their experiences with smog:

• Do you think our community has smog? How do you explain your answer?

• In what other communities have you seen smog?

• How does smog make you feel physically?

VISUAL LEARNING

FIGURE 20.1 Have students study Figure 20.1. Ask:

• What form of energy is able to pass through the layer of carbon dioxide? (*light*)

• What form of energy is blocked from escaping this layer? (*heat*)

• How is this phenomenon like a covered pot of boiling water? (*as heat is applied to the pot, it causes the water to steam and the steam builds up beneath the lid*) **INCL** *English Language Learners, Special Learning Needs, Behavior Problems, Different Learning Styles* (*Visual*)

HEALTH Online

Topic: Global warming

For a link to more information on how global warming affects the environment, go to **health.glencoe.com**.

Activity: Using the information provided at this link, make a flyer that lists what teens can do to reduce global warming and protect the environment.

Effects of Air Pollution

Air pollution can have many damaging consequences for the environment. Some of the effects are described below:

• **Acid rain.** *Rain that is far more acidic than normal* is known as **acid rain**. When fossil fuels are burned, they produce sulfur dioxide and nitrogen oxides. These gases mix with water vapor and form weak acids, which then fall to the earth. Over time, the acid in the rain can destroy living things—especially trees, plants, and fish.

• **Smog.** Some gases formed by burning fossil fuels combine to produce ozone, a special form of oxygen. Ozone at ground level is a major component of **smog**, *a yellow-brown haze that forms when sunlight reacts with air pollution.* People with respiratory problems are advised to stay indoors on days when smog levels are high.

• **Destruction of the ozone layer.** Miles above the earth's surface, the **ozone layer** acts as *a shield that protects living things from ultraviolet (UV) radiation.* Certain types of air pollution cause the ozone layer to deteriorate, allowing excessive UV radiation to reach the earth's surface. In humans, this can lead to skin cancer and a weakened immune system.

• **Global warming.** *The trapping of heat by carbon dioxide and other gases in the air* is known as the **greenhouse effect** (see **Figure 20.1**). Without the greenhouse effect, the earth would be too cold to support life. However, air pollution intensifies the greenhouse effect and may be causing an unnatural degree of **global warming**, which is *a rise in the earth's temperatures.* This in turn could affect the water level of oceans and change weather patterns.

FIGURE 20.1

THE GREENHOUSE EFFECT

The heating of earth by gases in our atmosphere trapping heat is similar to how a greenhouse warms.

1 Light energy from the sun reaches the earth's lower atmosphere and is converted to heat.

2 A layer of carbon dioxide and other gases surrounding the earth traps the heat.

3 The surface of the earth and the lower atmosphere become warmer because of the trapped heat.

548 CHAPTER 20: ENVIRONMENTAL HEALTH

Health Literacy

Health Information More than 40 million Americans have allergies. Allergens are the substances that trigger allergies—many allergens are airborne. The allergens may be animal dander, plant pollen, dust, molds, chemicals, or other substances found in polluted air. Allergic reactions include sneezing; red, irritated eyes; a runny or stuffy nose; breathing complications; skin rashes, and other health problems. A doctor can treat allergies. Medications can be prescribed to reduce the symptoms of allergies. Also, shots can be given to help the body develop antibodies and undergo other changes that help block the allergic reaction. Allergies are hereditary. A child doesn't inherit a particular allergy, however, just the likelihood of having allergies.

Water Pollution

All forms of life on earth depend on water. The earth's water is polluted by various kinds of wastes, chemicals, and other substances. One form of pollution is sewage—garbage, detergents, and other household wastes washed down drains. Although sewage is treated in the United States, many countries lack the education, money, and facilities needed to treat water properly. Harmful industrial chemicals are another cause of water pollution. Some enter the water from factories. In agricultural regions, pesticides and fertilizers can wash off the land and pollute water.

Oil spills from large tanker ships are a very damaging form of water pollution. Once in the water, oil can destroy plants and animals along with their habitats. Oil can also be spilled on land, resulting in the pollution of nearby lakes, rivers, and wetlands.

CONNECT TO

Science

PESTICIDE PERILS

Prolonged exposure to pesticides has been linked to many serious health problems. *Research the health hazards of exposure to pesticides and ways to avoid this potentially harmful environmental condition.*

Lesson 1

Cross-Curriculum Activity

VISUAL ARTS Have students work in pairs to create posters showing how a chemical pollutant from a pesticide or detergent can end up in our food and water supply. Posters should show the pollutant flowing into a river or pond to begin its journey up the food chain until it is ingested by humans. Students may clip drawings or photos from magazines and newspapers, or they may create original illustrations. Have volunteers show and display their work. **L2 INCL** *English Language Learners, Special Learning Needs, Behavior Problems, Different Learning Styles (Visual)*

Hands-On Health

EFFECTS OF WATER POLLUTANTS

When detergents and garbage get into rivers and lakes, they may cause the amount of algae to change. Algae (AL·jee) are simple organisms that float on the surface of the water and use sunlight to make their food. Some forms of pollution cause algae to multiply rapidly, forming a thick layer that blocks the sunlight. Deprived of light, the algae below the surface die and decay, a process that consumes oxygen. This loss of oxygen can kill fish and other forms of aquatic life. In this activity you will observe the effects of detergents and garbage on the growth of algae.

WHAT YOU WILL NEED

- tap water that has stood uncovered for three days
- water from a pond or aquarium that contains algae
- liquid detergent
- some potato or carrot scraps
- Three clean glass jars (same size, with lids)
- pen or pencil and labels

WHAT YOU WILL DO

1. Label the jars D (detergent), G (garbage), and C (control).
2. Fill each jar halfway with tap water. Add enough pond water to bring the level to three-fourths full.
3. Add a tablespoon of detergent to Jar D and vegetable scraps to Jar G. Do not add anything to Jar C.
4. Place the jars on a windowsill for two weeks.

IN CONCLUSION

1. Observe the jars every other day. Compare and note any changes in the color of the water in each. Which jar had the largest increase of algae? Which jar had the smallest increase?
2. What do your results indicate about the effects of detergent and garbage on algae? How do these results relate to water pollution?

LESSON 1: POLLUTION AND HEALTH 549

Hands-On Health

EFFECTS OF WATER POLLUTANTS

Time: one hour over the course of two weeks

TEACHING THE ACTIVITY
- With students, read and discuss the activity introduction.
- Have students work as a class or in several groups to carry out the activity.
- In a class discussion, have students share their responses to the second set of In Conclusion questions.

ASSESSMENT
Ask students to write short paragraphs explaining what they learned from this activity.

MORE ABOUT...

Effects of Air Pollution Asthma is one of the most common chronic conditions among teens. During an asthmatic episode, the airways narrow and become obstructed, inflamed, or filled with mucus secretions. Asthma sufferers gasp for air, wheeze, gag, and feel choking sensations as they struggle to breathe. Asthma may be triggered by environmental irritants—air pollution, cold air, smoke, pollen, dust, mildew, mold, and animal hair—or by allergies, respiratory infections, and emotional stress. Like other chronic diseases, asthma has no cure. Knowing how to manage symptoms and prevent attacks help teens feel less vulnerable and more confident. By following a prescribed program of oral and/or inhaled medications, most teens with asthma lead full, active lives.

Water polluted with sewage can spread diseases such as typhoid fever and cholera. Although they are rare in the United States, these diseases pose a severe threat in other parts of the world. Eating shellfish from polluted water can cause hepatitis, a disease of the liver. Drinking water that contains lead or mercury can result in serious damage to the brain, liver, and kidneys.

Land Pollution

Land pollution results from littering and the careless disposal of household and industrial garbage. Land pollution impacts the soil, water, and air. This type of pollution includes solid waste and hazardous wastes.

Solid Waste

In the United States, the average person produces about 4.4 pounds of trash, or solid waste, every day! For the nation as a whole, this adds up to millions of tons—enough to fill a professional baseball stadium from top to bottom twice a day. Where does it all go?

Landfills cannot keep up with increasing demand. *What can you do to reduce the amount of waste you personally produce?*

Most solid waste produced by households and businesses goes to **landfills**—*huge pits where wastes are dumped and buried.* At one time, anything and everything could be dumped in a landfill, including harmful substances that could seep into the surrounding land. Today, landfills are carefully regulated to protect the environment.

One alternative to burying trash is to burn it in special furnaces called incinerators. The energy that incinerators produce can be used to make electricity. This cuts down on the burning of fossil fuels. However, incinerators are expensive to operate and can burn only certain materials. Moreover, smoke and ashes from the incinerators contribute to air pollution. For these reasons, many people believe that recycling and reusing materials is a better way to deal with solid wastes.

INCLUSION STRATEGIES

Gifted Students Ask gifted students to work in small groups to investigate risks to the health of agricultural workers that are due to the use of agricultural herbicides and pesticides. Students should collect information on the most commonly used chemicals, their agricultural uses, and their toxic effects on humans. Students can use the collected information to make a table with columns for *Substance*, *Uses*, and *Effects*. Then they should give brief oral reports of their findings to the rest of the class, using the tables as visual aids. Group members should summarize the extent of the health problems posed by agricultural chemicals and make recommendations for dealing with the problems.

Hazardous Wastes

In recent decades, advances in science and technology have led to the development of new industries and products. These advances have caused a new problem, however: hazardous wastes. **Hazardous wastes** are *human-made liquid or solid wastes that may endanger human health or the environment.* When hazardous wastes enter and pollute the soil, water, or air, they can cause injury, illness, or even death. All hazardous wastes need special handling.

Two materials that were once widely used but that are now recognized as hazardous are asbestos and lead. Asbestos is no longer used to insulate buildings because of the discovery that breathing in asbestos particles increases the risk of lung cancer. Exposure to lead affects mental development and performance and kidney function, particularly in young children. Since 1978, lead-based paint has been banned from home use. In addition, most vehicles in the United States now run on unleaded gasoline.

Familiar products that contain hazardous materials include batteries, bleach, insecticides, motor oil, antifreeze, and certain cleaning fluids. If you need to dispose of any hazardous materials, do not throw them out with the regular trash. Instead, contact your local health department or environmental agency to find out how to get these materials safely into hazardous waste storage.

You can play a part in disposing of hazardous materials safely. Find out how your community collects hazardous household items.

Lesson 1 Review

Using complete sentences, answer the following questions on a sheet of paper.

Reviewing Terms and Facts

1. **Vocabulary** What is *pollution?* Use the word in an original sentence.
2. **List** Name two sources of air pollution and two sources of water pollution.
3. **Explain** How does air pollution affect the ozone layer?
4. **Identify** Name five common products that contain hazardous materials.

Thinking Critically

5. **Synthesize** Explain how fossil fuels are related to the destruction of forests by acid rain.
6. **Explain** Why are hazardous wastes a greater problem now than they were a century ago?

Applying Health Skills

7. **Accessing Information** Use reliable resources to research the dangers of exposure to lead paint and how to avoid this potentially harmful environmental condition. Report your findings to the class.

Lesson 1

Finding Examples

Ask students to find labels on commercial products that claim the products are environmentally safe. Have them evaluate the contents and the claim for accuracy. **L3**

③ Assess

Evaluating

📁 Assign the Lesson 1 Review; then assign the Lesson 1 Quiz in the TCR.

Reteaching

- 📁 Assign Concept Map 79 or Reteaching Activity 79 in the TCR.
- Have students make outlines of the lesson's major concepts. Beside each concept, they should write a summary statement.

Enrichment

📁 Assign Enrichment Activity 79 in the TCR.

④ Close

Ask students to discuss how environmental pollution affects all three sides of the health triangle.

Lesson 1 Review

1. Any dirty or harmful substance in the environment. Sentences will vary.
2. Two of each: Air—burning fossil fuels, chemicals, forest and grass fires, dust storms, volcanic eruptions. Water—sewage, detergents, other household wastes, industrial chemicals, pesticides, fertilizers, oil spills.
3. See explanation under Effects of Air Pollution on page 548.
4. Any five: batteries, bleach, insecticides, motor oil, antifreeze, certain cleaning fluids.
5. When fossil fuels are burned, they produce gasses, which mix with water vapor and form acid rain, destroying forests over time.
6. Advances in science and technology have led to creation of new products that require hazardous materials for manufacturing.

Lesson 2

Preventing and Reducing Pollution

1 Focus

Lesson Objectives

Students will be able to

- discuss the importance of reducing, reusing, and recycling.
- describe ways to reduce air and water pollution and conserve energy.
- examine and identify actions they can take to protect the environment.

Health Skills

- Practicing Healthful Behaviors, p. 556

Motivators

 Quick Write
Have students meet in small groups to compare and add to their lists of actions. Remind them to list additional actions they could take as they study the lesson.

Bellringer Activity

Have students write descriptions of their idea of an environmentally conscious community.

VOCABULARY

Challenge students to use all the vocabulary terms in a sketch, drawing, or other visual design that emphasizes the concern everyone should have for environmental pollution.

LESSON 2

Preventing and Reducing Pollution

Quick Write

Describe what you already do to prevent and reduce pollution. As you read this lesson, list any additional actions you could take.

LEARN ABOUT...

- the three R's: reduce, reuse, and recycle.
- reducing air and water pollution.
- actions you can take to protect the environment.

VOCABULARY

- Environmental Protection Agency (EPA)
- biodegradable
- nonrenewable resources
- conservation
- precycling

Reduce, Reuse, Recycle

In countries around the world, governments are working to reduce and prevent pollution. The **Environmental Protection Agency (EPA)** is *the agency of the United States government that is committed to protecting the environment.* In addition, many states and countries work to maintain air and water quality by controlling emissions (the gases, including exhaust, that vehicles release into the air) and applying waste management strategies. Waste management involves efforts to dispose of wastes in a way that protects the health of people and the environment.

The best way for individuals to make a difference is to practice the three Rs: reduce, reuse, and recycle. *Reduce* your consumption of energy and other resources. *Reuse* items by repairing them, selling them, or donating them to a charity. *Recycle* materials so that they can be used again in another form.

Today, many people make a conscious effort to reduce the amount of trash that winds up in landfills. Many communities have introduced programs for collecting recyclable materials. The effectiveness of these programs depends on the willingness of individual citizens to cooperate.

Some communities provide color-coded bins for collecting different kinds of recyclable materials. *What does your community do to encourage recycling?*

552 CHAPTER 20: ENVIRONMENTAL HEALTH

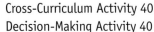

Lesson 2 Resources

Teacher Classroom Resources

 Concept Map 80
Cross-Curriculum Activity 40
Decision-Making Activity 40
Enrichment Activity 80
Lesson Plan 2
Lesson 2 Quiz
Reading Tutor Activity 80

 Reteaching Activity 80
 Transparencies 83 & 84

Student Activities Workbook

Chapter 20 Study Guide
Applying Health Skills 80
Health Inventory 20

Cleaner Air and Water

Anything people do that uses energy produced by burning fossil fuels contributes to air pollution. This includes using electrical appliances, driving a car, and running a power lawn mower. You can help keep the air cleaner by applying these strategies.

- **Walk or bike to nearby places.** When you walk or ride a bike instead of having someone drive you in a car, you help cut down on air pollution, and you get some physical activity too.
- **Use public transportation or carpool.** Buses, trains, and subways transport many people at one time. Carpooling cuts down on the number of cars on the road.
- **Avoid burning trash, leaves, and brush.** Trash should be disposed of by your local waste management facility. Leaves, grass, yard clippings, shredded newspaper, some types of food, and other items can be placed in compost piles, where they will break down naturally.

To keep water clean, use detergents that are **biodegradable**—*broken down easily in the environment.* Discard all waste materials properly. Do not pour hazardous wastes down the drain, on the ground, or into storm sewers, or put them out with the regular trash. Such actions could harm the soil and water supply.

During cold weather, you can save energy by wearing an extra layer of clothing and keeping the thermostat at about 68°F. *How else could you save energy used for heat in your home?*

Conservation

Many natural materials are **nonrenewable resources**—*substances that cannot be replaced once they are used.* Fossil fuels are one example. Once a barrel of oil is burned, it is gone forever. Because nonrenewable resources cannot be replaced, people must use them wisely.

Conservation is *the saving of resources.* The best way to conserve a resource is to use less of it. There are many ways to save energy—and therefore fossil fuels—in the home. In most homes, heating and cooling consume about 70 percent of the energy used; heating water takes another 20 percent; and lighting, cooking, and running small appliances use about 10 percent. **Figure 20.2** on the next page shows some ways to reduce your energy and water use at home.

② Teach

Cross-Curriculum Activity

MATH Have students work together to solve this problem: If you leave water running while you brush your teeth, you use about 5 gallons of water. If you use water only to wet your brush and rinse your mouth after brushing, you use ½ a gallon of water. Ask: How much water could you save each time you brush your teeth? (*4½ gallons*) Then ask: How many times a week do you brush your teeth? (*7 days × 3 times per day = 21 times per week*) Have students multiply 4½ gallons times 21 times per week to find 94½ gallons of water each week. **L2**

Researching

Ask student to learn more about the history, responsibilities, and departments of the EPA. Have them summarize their findings and describe application strategies such as emission control, water quality, and waste management, for controlling the environment. **L3**

PRACTICING LIFE SKILLS

Have students find out whether their state or community has a day reserved to honor the environment. Students should plan activities or establish their own day. Activities could include student-led minicourses on aspects of the environment, field trips, or the cleanup of a local park. **L3**

Health Literacy

Health Behaviors Specially formulated to be biodegradable, many nonpolluting cleaning products are coconut based and nonchlorinated. Equally important, these earth-friendly cleansers are packaged in boxes made of recycled paper or recyclable plastic bottles. Some cost-conscious and environmentally-conscious consumers choose to make their own nontoxic cleaners. Using natural products commonly found in the home—such as baking soda, salt, distilled white vinegar, lemon juice, liquid soap, and borax—it is possible to create all-purpose cleansers. White vinegar, for example, can be used to clean glass, countertops, and floors. Note: Advise students to consult their parents before making their own products.

FIGURE 20.2 Have volunteers read aloud the listed suggestions for conserving energy at home. Encourage students to share their reactions to each suggestion:

• Is this something you already do or can do at home?

• How important do you think this would be? Why? **INCL** *English Language Learners, Special Learning Needs, Behavior Problems, Different Learning Styles (Visual)*

Critical Thinking

Using Figure 20.2 as a starting point, have students make charts of ways to save energy. They might post them at home, where family members can use them as checklists. Ask volunteers to share their charts with classmates. Have students invent titles for their charts. **L2**

The EPA reports that every American generated 2.7 pounds of waste per day in 1960. That number has continued to rise; it is expected that, in 2005, every American will generate 4.7 pounds of waste each day.

Discussing

Ask students:

• Why is it sometimes difficult to reduce the amount of trash we create?

• What are some specific changes you can make at home and at school to reduce trash? **L1**

FIGURE 20.2

CONSERVATION IN THE HOME

The best way to conserve a resource is to use less of it. There are many ways to save energy and water at home.

Heating and Cooling
● Seal air leaks around doors, windows, and electric sockets to prevent heat from escaping.
● Keep doors and windows closed during the air-conditioning season, and keep air-conditioning at about 78°F.
● Buy an energy-efficient heating/cooling system that features a thermostat with a timer.

Lighting and Appliances
● Turn off lights when you are not using them.
● Replace traditional lightbulbs with compact fluorescent bulbs. They use less energy and last longer.
● Turn off televisions, computers, fans, and other electric appliances when you are not using them.

Water
● Never let water run unnecessarily.
● Wash clothes in warm or cold water, which uses less energy than hot water.
● Run the washing machine or dishwasher only when you have a full load, and use the short cycle when appropriate.
● If you have an older toilet, place a one-liter bottle filled with water inside your toilet tank. This will reduce the amount of water used for flushing. Another option is to replace an older toilet with a newer model that requires less water per flush.

Cooking
● Don't preheat a conventional oven for longer than necessary.
● Avoid opening the oven while cooking. Instead, use a timer and the oven door window to check if food is done.
● Heat small quantities of food in a microwave, toaster oven, or slow cooker.

Recycling and Precycling

As you learned earlier, recycling involves changing an item in some way so that it can be used again. Recycling conserves energy and natural resources and helps reduce solid waste. The most commonly collected materials for recycling are paper, aluminum, glass, plastics, and yard waste.

How does recycling help conserve energy and natural resources? Think about aluminum soda cans. Energy is needed to mine the ore that is used to make aluminum, to process the ore, and to manufacture the cans. When aluminum cans are recycled, they are changed back into sheets of aluminum. These sheets can then be used to make new cans or other aluminum products. The amount of ore taken from the ground is reduced, and much less energy is needed.

The symbol pictured here showing three curved arrows is a familiar sight on many kinds of products. It shows that an item can be recycled or that it is made of recycled materials. On plastic materials the symbol includes a number in the center. It is a code identifying the type of material. At recycling facilities, plastic objects can be sorted according to their number.

554 CHAPTER 20: ENVIRONMENTAL HEALTH

Beyond the Classroom

Community Have students form small groups and work together to describe the application of strategies such as emission control, water quality, and waste management, for controlling the environment. Then direct students to brainstorm to identify areas within their own community that need cleaning up. Encourage group members to work together to list several ideas of interest to all in the group. Then have them select one particular need, devise a plan, and then carry out a cleanup project. You may want to encourage students to include family members, friends, and other community members in their project. Have the students also come up with ideas for maintaining the areas cleaned.

FIGURE 20.3

RESULTS OF RECYCLING EFFORTS

Aluminum **3.1** 0.9 **28%**

Steel **12.4** **4.3** **35%**

Glass **12.5** **3.2** **25%**

Plastics **22.4** 1.2 **5%**

Yard Trimmings **27.7** **12.6** **45%**

Paper/Paperboard **84.1** 35.0 **45%**

Amount Discarded (in metric tons)

Amount Recycled

% Percentage Recycled

Source: U.S. Environmental Protection Agency, 2000

HEALTH SKILLS PRACTICE

Advocacy Have students observe and record in an "environmental log" environmentally harmful actions that they witness during a one-week period. Then have them list alternative actions to protect the environment. Encourage students to present their lists to the rest of the school.

VISUAL LEARNING

FIGURE 20.3 Guide students in reading and discussing the information in the bar graph. Ask questions such as these:

- How many tons of glass were discarded in the year 2000?
- How many tons of glass were recycled that year?
- Of the materials shown, which had the lowest percent recycled? Which had the highest percent recycled? **INCL** *English Language Learners, Special Learning Needs, Behavior Problems, Different Learning Styles (Visual)*

Applying Knowledge

Have each student bring at least three empty product containers to class. If this is not possible, bring in a variety of containers to pass out to groups. Then let students meet in groups to examine and discuss each container:

- Can the container be reused? If so, how?
- Can it be recycled? If so, in what group of recycling materials? **L1**

In general, recycling has been an enormous success story in terms of getting people involved. Today, thanks to recycling centers and curbside recycling programs, more than 28 percent of the solid waste produced in the United States is recycled. **Figure 20.3** illustrates the recycling efforts in the year 2000.

As Figure 20.3 also demonstrates, however, plastics recycling has not kept pace with other recycling efforts. Most recycling programs accept plastics, but not necessarily all types of plastics. Some people may be put off recycling plastics by the need to check the code number on the recycling symbol. Others may not bother to recycle because they think that plastic items break down easily in the environment. This is not so. Plastic recycling needs a boost, and almost every household could improve its recycling effort.

In addition to recycling, you can reduce your consumption of resources by **precycling**—*reducing waste before it occurs.* Below are some basic guidelines for precycling.

- Buy products in packages made of materials that can be reused or recycled, such as glass, metal, and paper.
- Look for products in refillable containers.
- Bring a cloth or reusable plastic bag to the store to carry your purchases.

LESSON 2: PREVENTING AND REDUCING POLLUTION **555**

Health Literacy

Health Behaviors Experts say that every year in the United States, over 55 million tons of garbage could be processed and reused. Much of the remaining garbage could be used as fuel in some types of power plants. In response to overcrowded landfills and increases in the cost of garbage disposal, many states have developed statewide garbage recycling programs. Recommend that students learn more about those programs offered in their communities and states. Later, they could make posters or flyers to help publicize what they have learned so that others might participate in the program.

HEALTH SKILLS ACTIVITY

PRACTICING HEALTHFUL BEHAVIORS

Have students work as a class to read and discuss the listed suggestions for environmentally conscious consumers. Then let students form small groups in which to complete the activity. Suggest that each student make a copy of the final combined list and take it home to share with family members.

Note: This skill is introduced in Chapter 2 on pages 46–47.

Cross-Curriculum Activity

LANGUAGE ARTS Most radio and TV stations are required to air public service announcements (PSAs). PSAs are 30 seconds to 1 minute in length and inform the public about something that is beneficial to society. A PSA that calls for action or offers a service has greater appeal to broadcasters than do other types of PSAs. Have students demonstrate ways to use health information to help others by writing and then videotaping or recording a PSA about preventing or reducing pollution. Set aside class time for students to share their PSAs with the entire class. **L2**

HEALTH SKILLS ACTIVITY

PRACTICING HEALTHFUL BEHAVIORS

Environment-Friendly Shopping

Every time you shop, you have the chance to help the environment. Below are some tips to help you become an environmentally conscious consumer.

- **PLAN.** Make a shopping list. It will help you buy only what you need.
- **BUY IN BULK.** Look for larger packages of foods such as cereal and snacks. Buying in larger quantities cuts down on the amount of packaging you throw away.
- **BE AWARE OF PACKAGING.** Choose products that are packaged in materials that break down easily or can be recycled.

For example, when possible, buy beverages and other food items that come in glass or aluminum containers.

- **READ LABELS CAREFULLY.** Some common household products, such as oven cleaners and paint thinners, contain substances that are harmful to humans. Look for safer commercial products or research alternative substances.

IN A GROUP

Brainstorm other ideas for environment-friendly shopping. List all the ways you can think of that will save energy, packaging, and waste. Combine all the ideas into one list that can be printed and posted on a bulletin board.

Protecting the Environment

Everyone can play a part in protecting the environment. By your everyday actions you can make a difference. Start locally by taking steps to combat pollution in your school and neighborhood, and then branch out from there. You can help others understand the importance of becoming involved. Here are some suggestions.

- **Take charge of your family's recycling effort.** Find out what recyclables are collected in your community and set up a system that the family can follow.

Some grocery stores offer a cash discount to customers who use their own shopping bags. *Why would stores encourage this practice?*

COOPERATIVE LEARNING ACTIVITY

Environmental Control Group Have the class become the "Environmental Control Group" for a section of the school grounds. The first step is to clean up the area. Assign groups of four students to clean again each day, if necessary. Following that, have students determine what they could do to improve or beautify the area. They may need to work with the staff that is responsible for the grounds to determine the possibilities. The class may decide to plant a garden or a tree, or to make an area for sitting in the shade. If it is not feasible to improve the school's exterior, select an interior project. Students take great pride in their environment when they have input and responsibility for its appearance.

- **Advocate for greater environmental awareness.** Evaluate advertising, labels, contents, and packaging as it relates to the environment. Give feedback to companies on positive ways they can affect the environment. Write letters to newspapers, and seek opportunities to express your opinions about the environment.
- **Join a conservation organization.** Ask several organizations to provide you with resources about current environmental issues. By becoming part of such a group, you can discover ways to make a difference in your community.

An important step toward a healthier environment is to get involved locally. Find out what environmental programs exist in your community.

LESSON 2: PREVENTING AND REDUCING POLLUTION **557**

557

Mean Clean Machines

➊ Focus

Objectives

Students will be able to

- brainstorm alternative modes of transportation.
- analyze transportation accessibility and barriers within their community.
- set personal goals for alternative transportation use.

Motivator

Bellringer Activity

Ask students, "How did you get to school today? What are the environmentally positive and negative impacts of your mode of transportation?" Teachers may choose to conduct a poll based on how many biked, walked, took the bus, and so forth.

➋ Teach

Brainstorming

Ask students to brainstorm alternative methods of transportation (*bike, walk, carpool, take the bus, and so on*). Discuss the benefits and barriers to these modes of transportation in the community. For instance, are there bike paths, safe places to lock bikes, buses equipped with bike racks? Does the community offer accessible public transportation? What makes it accessible (cost, location, convenience, and so on)? Be sure to consider accessibility for people with special needs. Is the subway wheelchair accessible? Are train schedules available in Braille? Are bus stops covered and/or heated in the winter?

TIME HEALTH

Mean Clean Machines

Getting around doesn't have to pollute the atmosphere. Here are some better ways to go.

This personal scooter is powered by electricity.

Because people won't give up their four-wheelers, the challenge is to reduce the auto emissions that contribute to everything from respiratory distress to global warming. The key is to find a better power source.

The first solution, which was introduced a few years ago, was battery-powered electric cars. However, electric cars have less range than gas-powered cars, and recharging the batteries isn't convenient. The newer gasoline-electric hybrid cars recharge themselves and go much farther on a gallon of gas than do conventional cars—but they aren't pollution free.

Thanks to new types of fuel and construction materials, driving a car promises to become more environmentally friendly, stylish, and fun. In the near future, we may not be whizzing around in flying cars like the Jetsons, but we will be traveling in ways never before imagined.

The best way to conserve energy and reduce pollution would be to phase out cars in favor of mass transportation. That probably isn't going to happen. Most people want a private, comfortable way to get around, and so our love of the automobile is as strong as ever. Manufacturers sell more than 17 million cars each year in the United States.

The Hydrogen Solution

Many experts believe that hydrogen will one day power electric cars. Special fuel cells can combine hydrogen with oxygen to produce electricity. The electricity, in turn, would drive a motor that can spin the wheels of the car much more quietly than a gas engine can. The only thing spewing from

558 CHAPTER 20: ENVIRONMENTAL HEALTH

COOPERATIVE LEARNING ACTIVITY

Bike-to-School Day Have students plan and host a Bike-to-School Day at their school. With the permission of the administration, students should take the following steps:

- Pick a date at least one month away.
- Promote the event through posters, the school newspaper, local media, and so on. Create persuasive slogans that detail the benefits of biking to school.

- Invite experts on biking or alternative transportation to speak at the event.
- Manage the logistics of the event. What routes will students take to school? Where will students park their bikes once they arrive at school? Will food and/or entertainment be provided?

the tail pipe would be water that is pure enough to drink. Because fuel cells and electric motors are more compact than bulky internal-combustion engines, the new technology will allow cars to have revolutionary shapes and designs.

One of the most innovative approaches to fuel-cell cars is the Hy-wire prototype. It eliminates the engine, transmission, and gas tank found in today's internal-combustion cars. In their place is a skateboard-like platform—just 6 inches thick—that houses the fuel cells, the hydrogen tank, and all the electronics needed to power the car. Electric motors placed inside each wheel get the car rolling.

A Serious Scooter

Eliminating cars altogether might be another solution to the pollution problem. After all, "it is still very energy intensive to move a 2,000- or 3,000-pound machine," says Dean Kamen, founder of DEKA Research in Manchester, New Hampshire. His solution: the $8,000 scooter that goes up to 13 miles per hour. The scooter is powered by an electric motor and runs on just a nickel's worth of electricity a day. One of the machine's coolest features is its steering and braking system: Lean forward and it accelerates; lean backward and it stops.

The Wheel Deal

For those on a tighter budget or who want to get some healthful exercise, there is always the

Gas-electric hybrids release less carbon dioxide than conventional cars.

bicycle, which appears to be mounting a comeback. After a slump in the mid-1990s, bicycle production leaped to more than 100 million units in 2000, compared with just 62 million in 1980. What about couch potatoes who refuse to pedal? At least two manufacturers think they have the answer: Have the classic two-wheeler propel itself with the help of a fuel cell! ◼

The self-propelling bicycle runs on a fuel cell.

TIME TO THINK...

About Alternative Power Sources

As a class, brainstorm different ways we might generate power to move vehicles. Choose your favorite "alternative" source and design a vehicle with an engine that runs on that source. Draw a blueprint of it and write a description of how it runs. Share your vehicle of tomorrow with the class.

③ Apply

Time to Think

Allow time for volunteers to present their designs to the class. Then have students consider the following case studies:

- Mike is a high-school student who rides his bike to school every morning. It takes him 20 minutes if he uses city streets and 30 if he take the more scenic (and safe) bike path. Once there, he locks his bike to the bike rack. Mike only carries a backpack to school.
- Tanisha is a 76-year-old woman with a walker who takes the bus to meet her friend for lunch every Thursday. The bus stop is a 2-minute walk from her house. When it rains, Tanisha chooses not to ride the bus because the bus stop is uncovered.

Ask students, "Is alternative transportation equally feasible for Mike and Tanisha? How are their experiences the same or different? What are some factors that restrict people from taking alternative transportation (*accessibility, convenience, location, weather, and so on*)? What modifications are necessary to make public transportation more accessible to those with special needs?

VISUAL LEARNING

Ask students to analyze the photographs on pages 558–559. Ask students to think of other modern modes of transportation that run on alternative fuel. Then ask, "Are you aware that there are alternative fuel sources? What are some of those sources?

 Beyond the Classroom

Community Have students consider the various forms of transportation in the community and, if feasible, set a goal to take alternative transportation to school once a week for a month. Have them write a clear goal statement, such as, "I will ride my bike to school every Friday." After one month, have students reflect on their experiences. What are the benefits of taking this particular mode of transportation to school? Is it a realistic option for getting to school on a regular basis? Why or why not? (For instance, riding a bike may be feasible in the fall, but less so in colder weather.) How might students adjust their plans to be more realistic?

PRACTICING HEALTHFUL BEHAVIORS

OBJECTIVE

After completing the lesson, students will be able to identify ways to reuse or recycle everyday products.

Time: 40 minutes

Materials: poster board or newsprint, markers, tape

Teacher Classroom Resources

📁 Building Health Skills Activities

• Transparency Master 2e, "Practicing Healthful Behaviors"

• Reproducible Master 45, "Make the Most of It"

1. Model

• Have students read the scenario. As a class, review all the actions that Jonas and his family take to conserve natural resources and reduce pollution.

• Display Transparency Master 2e, and ask students to give examples of how Jonas and his family practiced these behaviors.

• Have volunteers describe specific ways that they and their families reuse and recycle materials. Record these on the board.

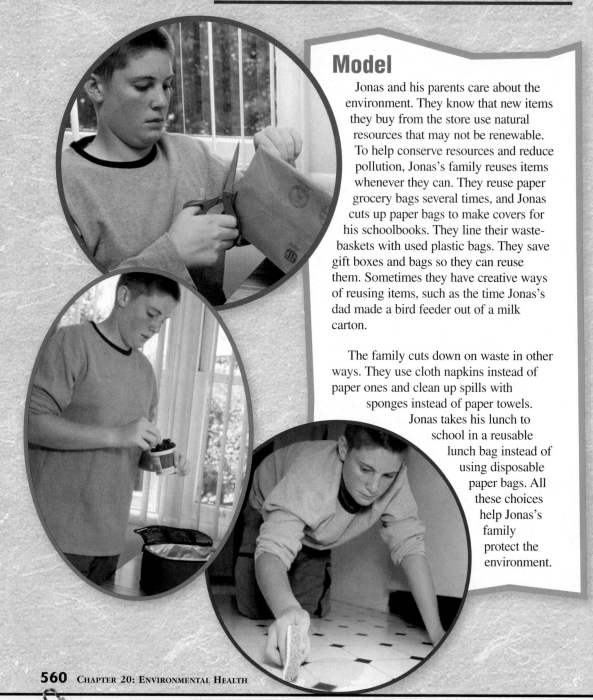

BUILDING HEALTH SKILLS

PRACTICING HEALTHFUL BEHAVIORS

MAKE THE MOST OF IT

Model

Jonas and his parents care about the environment. They know that new items they buy from the store use natural resources that may not be renewable. To help conserve resources and reduce pollution, Jonas's family reuses items whenever they can. They reuse paper grocery bags several times, and Jonas cuts up paper bags to make covers for his schoolbooks. They line their wastebaskets with used plastic bags. They save gift boxes and bags so they can reuse them. Sometimes they have creative ways of reusing items, such as the time Jonas's dad made a bird feeder out of a milk carton.

The family cuts down on waste in other ways. They use cloth napkins instead of paper ones and clean up spills with sponges instead of paper towels. Jonas takes his lunch to school in a reusable lunch bag instead of using disposable paper bags. All these choices help Jonas's family protect the environment.

Teaching Tips

Utilizing Reliable Online Resources Have students visit the EPA Student Center Web site to find activities they can do on their own or in groups. You may want to schedule one or two class periods in the library or computer lab so that students can access the site. For additional ideas, go to the EPA Environmental Center Web site.

Learning Through Diversity Group work allows students to share their knowledge and their experiences. Interaction among group members allows students to learn about different ways of living and thinking. Teachers can encourage diverse group membership by assigning members to groups.

Practice

Form small groups. Each group will discuss ways to reuse an item from the following list:

- Paper and plastic bags
- Cardboard boxes
- Bottles and jars
- Metal cans
- Old clothes
- Paper goods
- Old tires
- Plastic milk cartons

Brainstorm all the different ways you can think of to reuse this type of item. Make a list of your group's ideas and share it with the class. Then, as a class, brainstorm ways that you could reuse or repair damaged items and replace disposable items with reusable ones.

Apply/Assess

Put your ideas to work by creating a chart about reducing waste. Divide a large sheet of paper or poster board into three columns. Label the first column "Items we throw away." Keep track of all the items you throw away throughout the day. Use the first column of your chart to list the items you threw away that could be reduced, reused, or repaired. Also list all the disposable items that could have been replaced with reusable items.

Label the second column "Ways to reduce and reuse." Use it to list the changes that you could make so that you would not have to throw away as many items. For example, you could replace the paper napkin you threw away at lunch with a reusable cloth napkin. You might also limit the number of napkins used. Finally, use the third column to list the advantages of reducing, reusing, and recycling items. You could describe savings of money as well as benefits to the environment. Label this column "Why it matters." Share your chart with the class.

Practicing Healthful Behaviors

You can reduce waste by
- reusing items.
- reducing the number of items used.
- repairing broken items.
- replacing disposable items with reusable ones.

- Did I identify items that I threw away unnecessarily?
- Did I describe ways to reduce and reuse these items?
- Did I explain the benefits of reducing, reusing, and recycling?

2. Practice

- Divide students into small groups. Ask the groups to choose an item from the list, or assign one to each group. (More than one group can choose or be assigned the same item, if necessary.)

- Ask groups to come up with a list of several different ways to reuse their item, and allow time for each group to read their lists aloud. Then lead a class brainstorming session on ways to reuse or fix damaged items and substitute reusable items for disposable ones.

- To underscore the importance of reducing, reusing, and recycling, explain to the class that the manufacture and transport of each item on the list requires energy. Also, stress that energy resources such as gas and oil, will not be renewed in our lifetime.

3. Apply/Assess

- You may wish to distribute Building Health Skills Reproducible Master 45 in the TCR to guide students in completing this activity.

- Allow time for students to complete their charts. Remind them to review their work by answering the questions in the Self-Check.

- Provide an opportunity for volunteers to share their charts with the class. Lead a discussion on the ideas presented in each chart.

- Display charts in the classroom or hallway, if possible.

- Encourage students to explore the EPA Student Center site (see Teaching Tips) to learn more about conserving natural resources.

Assessment Scoring

Using a rubric, student work should provide evidence of all criteria to achieve the highest score.

Skills
Student work identifies
- items that can be reused or reduced.
- ways to reduce or reuse these items.

Concepts
Student work provides
- accurate information about reducing, reusing, and recycling.
- an explanation of reducing, reusing, and recycling choices.

Checking Comprehension

Use the Chapter 20 Assessment to examine the most important ideas presented in the chapter.

Answers to Reviewing Vocabulary and Concepts

Lesson 1
1. fossil fuels
2. pesticides
3. acid rain
4. smog
5. ozone layer
6. greenhouse effect
7. water pollution
8. landfills
9. hazardous wastes
10. asbestos

Lesson 2
11. b
12. a
13. b
14. a
15. b

Thinking Critically

16. Responses will vary.
17. Hazardous wastes could poison humans and other life forms; they need special handling.
18. Responses will vary but may indicate that precycling cuts down on materials used while recycling involves use of new materials and requires energy.
19. Responses will vary but should indicate that protecting the planet is in the best interest of personal and global health.

After You Read

Use your completed Foldable to review the information on air, water, and land pollution.

FOLDABLES Study Organizer

Reviewing Vocabulary and Concepts

On a sheet of paper, write the numbers 1–10. After each number, write the term from the list that best completes each sentence.

> - landfills
> - acid rain
> - fossil fuels
> - water pollution
> - greenhouse effect
> - asbestos
> - smog
> - hazardous wastes
> - ozone layer
> - pesticides

Lesson 1

1. The burning of _____ is a major source of air pollution.
2. Chemicals that are intended to kill or control insects are known as _____.
3. Rain that is far more acidic than normal and that destroys plants and trees is called _____.
4. When sunlight reacts with air pollution, _____, a yellow-brown haze, forms.
5. The _____ is a shield that protects living things from ultraviolet radiation.
6. The _____ is the trapping of heat near the earth's surface.
7. Sewage, industrial chemicals, and oil spills are some of the causes of _____.
8. Most solid waste produced by households and businesses is buried in _____.
9. Advances in science and technology have led to the problem of _____, or waste products that can cause illness, injury, or death.
10. _____ is a hazardous product that was once used as insulation in buildings.

Lesson 3

On a sheet of paper, write the numbers 11–15. After each number, write the letter of the answer that best completes each statement.

11. The United States government works to prevent and reduce pollution through which of the following agencies?
    a. The National Safety Council
    b. The Environmental Protection Agency
    c. Centers for Disease Control and Prevention
    d. Agency for Healthcare Research and Quality
12. You can help to keep the water clean by using detergents that are
    a. biodegradable.
    b. available in tablet form.
    c. available only in liquid form.
    d. nonrenewable.
13. Substances that cannot be replaced once they are used are
    a. precycled.
    b. nonrenewable.
    c. sustainable.
    d. radioactive.
14. Which of the following strategies will help promote clean air?
    a. using public transportation
    b. burning trash in bonfires
    c. leaving lights on when not in use
    d. burning oil instead of coal
15. The practice of reducing waste before it occurs is called
    a. presorting.
    b. precycling.
    c. recycling.
    d. reconstructing.

INCLUSION STRATEGIES

Special Learning Needs, Behavior Problems, English Language Learners The following suggestions are helpful for students with special learning needs, students with behavior problems, and ELL students:

- Pair these students with more proficient learners who can help summarize the main concepts of the chapter.

- 🎧 Direct these students to listen to the Teen Health Audio Summaries. This component provides an audio and written summary of the chapter in both English and Spanish.

- Use photographs, drawings, or magazine clippings whenever possible to help students visualize the important concepts of the chapter.

Thinking Critically

Using complete sentences, answer the following questions on a sheet of paper.

16. Apply What lifestyle changes could you make or develop in the future to conserve energy and reduce air pollution?

17. Explain Why is the disposal of hazardous wastes more of a problem than the disposal of other solid wastes?

18. Hypothesize Does precycling conserve more energy than recycling? Explain.

19. Explain Why is it necessary for people to become actively involved in protecting the environment? What might happen if people ignore environmental problems?

Career Corner

Ecologist If you're interested in the environment, you might want to consider becoming an ecologist. These health scientists study the environment. They explore the relationships among human, animal, and plant life. They also study the effects of environmental change. To enter this profession, you'll need a degree in biology or environmental science. Find out more about this and other health careers by clicking on Career Corner at health.glencoe.com.

Standardized Test Practice

Reading & Writing

Read the paragraphs below and then answer the questions.

Air, water, and land pollution can harm the health of both people and the environment. Air pollution can worsen symptoms in people with respiratory problems. Water pollution can contaminate drinking water, making people ill and killing plants and aquatic life. Hazardous substances in common products such as batteries can leak into the surrounding soil when these products are discarded improperly.

These facts make it clear—working to reduce pollution is worthwhile. Some ways to reduce pollution include using mass transit if it's available and disposing of household products properly. For example, don't pour household products such as bleach or motor oil down drains.

1. Which sentence from the passage represents the author's opinion?

A Air, water, and land pollution can harm the health of both people and the environment.

B Air pollution can worsen symptoms in people with respiratory problems.

C These facts make it clear—working to reduce pollution is worthwhile.

D Water pollution can contaminate drinking water, making people ill and killing plants and aquatic life.

2. The author probably wrote the editorial

A to explain why pollution occurs.

B to criticize people who litter.

C to describe the steps he or she takes to reduce pollution.

D to persuade readers to take steps to reduce pollution.

3. Write a paragraph describing additional ways to reduce pollution.

 TH05_C3.glencoe.com/quiz

Assessment

Self-Assessment Direct students to review the activities that are provided throughout the chapter. Encourage each student to select one finished product or activity that demonstrates his or her best work for the chapter. Have students explain what they learned and how the examples they selected show their progress.

Career Corner

Ecologist Ecologists are primarily researchers who may teach or work for private companies and governmental agencies. After reviewing the career profile on the health Web site, students might survey the community for environmental habitats that might interest an ecologist to do research. (e.g., *a new housing development that has been built near a wooded area*)

Test Practice
1. C
2. D
3. Responses should name ways not cited in the passage.

Reteaching
Assign Study Guide 20 in the Student Activities Workbook.

Evaluate
Use the reproducible Chapter 20 Test in the TCR, or construct your own test using the **Exam**View® Pro Testmaker.

Enrichment
Have students work in groups to plan and prepare ad campaigns that "sell" a specific aspect of environmental health.

563

Glossary

The Glossary contains all the important terms used throughout the text. It includes the **boldfaced** terms listed in the "Vocabulary" lists at the beginning of each lesson and that appear in text and art.

The Glossary lists the term, the pronunciation (in the case of difficult terms), the definition, and the page on which the term is defined. The pronunciations here and in the text follow the system outlined below. The column headed "Symbol" shows the spelling used in this book to represent the appropriate method.

PRONUNCIATION KEY

Sound	As In	Symbol	Example
ă	hat, map	a	abscess (AB·ses)
ā	age, face	ay	atrium (AY·tree·uhm)
a	care, their	eh	capillaries (KAP·uh·lehr·eez)
ä, ŏ	father, hot	ah	biopsy (BY·ahp·see)
ar	far	ar	cardiac (KAR·dee·ak)
ch	child, much	ch	barbiturate (bar·BI·chuh·ruht)
ĕ	let, best	e	vessel (VE·suhl)
ē	beat, see, city	ee	acne (AK·nee)
er	term, stir, purr	er	nuclear (NOO·klee·er)
g	grow	g	malignant (muh·LIG·nuhnt)
ĭ	it, hymn	i	bacteria (bak·TIR·ee·uh)
ī	ice, five	y	benign (bi·NYN)
		eye	iris (EYE·ris)
j	page, fungi	j	cartilage (KAR·tuhl·ij)
k	coat, look, chorus	k	defect (DEE·fekt)
ō	open, coat, grow	oh	aerobic (e·ROH·bik)
ô	order	or	organ (OR·guhn)
ȯ	flaw, all	aw	palsy (PAWL·zee)
oi	voice	oy	goiter (GOY·ter)
ou	out	ow	fountain (FOWN·tuhn)
s	say, rice	s	dermis (DER·mis)
sh	she, attention	sh	conservation (kahn·ser·VAY·shuhn)
ŭ	cup, flood	uh	bunion (BUHN·yuhn)
u	put, wood, could	u	pulmonary (PUL·muh·nehr·ee)
ü	rule, move, you	oo	attitudes (AT·i·toodz)
w	win	w	warranty (WAWR·uhn·tee)
y	your	yu	urethra (yu·REE·thruh)
z	says	z	hormones (HOR·mohnz)
zh	pleasure	zh	transfusion (trans·FYOO·zhuhn)
ə	about, collide	uh	addiction (uh·DIK·shuhn)

Glossary

Abdominal thrusts Quick, upward pulls into the diaphragm to force out an obstruction blocking the airway. (page 533)

Abstinence Not participating in high-risk behaviors. (page 17)

Abuse The physical, emotional, or mental mistreatment of one person by another. (page 177)

Accident Any event that was not intended to happen. (page 508)

Accident chain A series of events that include a situation, an unsafe habit, and an unsafe action. (page 508)

Accidental injuries Injuries resulting from an accident. (page 508)

Acid rain Rain that is far more acidic than normal. (page 548)

Acquired Immunodeficiency Syndrome (AIDS) A deadly disease that interferes with the body's natural ability to fight infection. (page 464)

Active listening Hearing, thinking about, and responding to another person's message. (page 37)

Addiction A physical or psychological need for a drug. (pages 277, 304)

Addictive Capable of causing a user to develop intense cravings. (page 300)

Adjustment An adaptation or change in behavior. (page 130)

Adolescence The time of life between childhood and adulthood. (page 9)

Adrenaline A hormone that gives the body extra energy. (page 40)

Advertising Sending out messages designed to interest consumers in buying a product or service. (page 59)

Aerobic exercise Rhythmic, nonstop, moderate to vigorous activity that requires large amounts of oxygen and works the heart. (page 222)

Alcohol A drug that is produced by a chemical reaction in fruits, vegetables, and grains. (page 320)

Alcoholism A progressive, chronic disease involving a mental and physical need for alcohol. (page 326)

Allergen (AL·er·juhn) A substance that causes an allergic reaction. (page 480)

Allergy An abnormal immune reaction to an ordinarily harmless substance. (page 480)

Alternatives Other ways of thinking or acting. (page 333)

Alveoli (al·VEE·uh·ly) Microscopic air sacs in the lungs. (page 382)

Amino acids Small units that make up protein. (page 197)

Amphetamine (am·FE·tuh·meen) A drug that stimulates the central nervous system. (page 278)

Anabolic steroids Drugs that cause muscle tissue to develop at an abnormally fast rate. (page 241)

Anaerobic exercise Intense physical activity that requires little oxygen but uses short bursts of energy. (page 222)

Anorexia nervosa An eating disorder characterized by self-starvation leading to extreme weight loss. (page 256)

Antibiotics (an·ti·by·AH·tiks) Medicines that reduce or kill harmful bacteria in the body. (page 272)

Antibodies Proteins that attach to antigens, keeping them from harming the body. (page 452)

Antigens Substances released by invading pathogens. (page 452)

Glossary

Antihistamines Medicines that help control the effects triggered by histamines. (page 481)

Anxiety An overwhelming feeling of dread, much like fear. (page 92)

Anxiety disorder A disorder in which intense anxiety or fear keeps a person from functioning normally. (page 96)

Appetite The psychological desire for food. (page 193)

Appropriate weight The weight that is best for your body. (page 250)

Arteries Blood vessels that carry blood away from the heart to other parts of the body. (page 378)

Arteriosclerosis (ar·tir·ee·oh·skluh·ROH·sis) A group of disorders in which arteries harden and become more rigid. (page 490)

Arthritis (ar·THRY·tuhs) More than 100 conditions marked by pain and swelling in body joints. (page 495)

Assertive Behaving with confidence and clearly stating your intentions. (page 149)

Asthma (AZ·muh) A serious chronic condition that causes tiny air passages in the respiratory system to become narrow or blocked. (page 482)

Atherosclerosis (a·thuh·roh·skluh·ROH·sis) A form of arteriosclerosis in which fatty substances in the blood build up on the walls of the arteries. (page 490)

Attitude Feelings and beliefs. (page 18)

Autonomic (aw·tuh·NAH·mik) **system** The part of the nervous system that deals with actions you do not usually control. (page 388)

B

Bacteria Tiny one-celled organisms that live nearly everywhere. (page 446)

Balance A feeling of stability and control. (page 221)

Battery The beating, hitting, or kicking of another person. (page 177)

Benign (bi·NYN) **tumor** A tumor that is not cancerous. (page 484)

Binge drinking The consumption of several alcoholic drinks in a very short period of time. (page 322)

Binge eating disorder Compulsive overeating. (page 258)

Biodegradable Broken down easily in the environment. (page 553)

Biological age Age determined by how well various body parts are working. (page 434)

Biopsy The removal of a tissue sample to see whether cancer cells are present. (page 487)

Birth defect Abnormality present at birth that causes physical or mental disability or death. (page 424)

Blended family A family that consists of a parent, a stepparent, and the children of one or both parents. (page 126)

Blizzard A very heavy snowstorm with winds up to 45 miles per hour. (page 522)

Blood alcohol concentration (BAC) The amount of alcohol in a person's bloodstream. (page 322)

Body composition The ratio of body fat to lean body tissue, such as bone, muscle, and fluid. (page 228)

Body image The way you see yourself. (page 250)

Body language The use of body movements and gestures to communicate a message. (page 35)

Body Mass Index (BMI) A measurement that allows you to assess your body size, taking your height and weight into account. (page 251)

Bronchi (BRAHN·ky) Passages through which air enters the lungs. (page 382)

Bronchodilators (brahn·ko·DY·lay·terz) Medicines used to relax the muscles that have tightened around the airways. (page 483)

Bulimia A condition in which a person eats large amounts of food and then tries to purge. (page 257)

Calories Units of heat that measure the energy used by the body and the energy that foods supply to the body. (page 192)

Cancer A disease characterized by the rapid and uncontrolled growth of abnormal cells. (page 484)

Capillaries Tiny tubes that carry blood from the arteries to the body's cells, and then back to the veins. (page 378)

Carbohydrates The sugars and starches that provide your body with most of its energy. (page 196)

Carbon monoxide A colorless, odorless, poisonous gas that is produced when tobacco burns. (page 300)

Carcinogens (kar·SIN·un·juhns) Substances that cause cancer. (page 486)

Cardiac muscle Muscle found in the walls of your heart. (page 373)

Cardiovascular (KAR·dee·oh·VAS·kyoo·ler) **system** Organs and tissues that transport essential materials to body cells and remove their waste products. (page 376)

Carrier A person who is infected with a virus and who can pass it on to others. (page 464)

Cartilage (KAHR·tuhl·ij) Strong, flexible tissue that provides cushioning at the joints. (page 370)

Central nervous system (CNS) The brain and spinal cord. (page 386)

Cervix The entrance of the uterus. (page 420)

Character The way in which a person thinks, feels, and acts. (page 119)

Character trait A quality that demonstrates how a person thinks, feels, and acts. (page 119)

Chromosomes (KROH·muh·sohmz) The threadlike structures found within the nucleus of a cell that carry the codes for inherited traits. (page 422)

Chronic diseases Diseases that are present either continuously or off and on over a long time. (page 476)

Chronological (krah·nuh·LAH·ji·kuhl) **age** Age measured in years. (page 434)

Cilia Tiny, hairlike structures that protect the lungs. (page 300)

Circulatory (SER·kyuh·luh·tohr·ee) **system** Organs and tissues that transport essential materials to body cells and remove their waste products. (page 376)

Cirrhosis (suh·ROH·sis) Scarring and destruction of the liver. (page 321)

Citizenship The way you conduct yourself as a member of a community. (page 120)

Clinical depression A mood disorder in which people lose interest in life and can no longer find enjoyment in anything. (page 98)

Clique A group of friends who hang out together and act in similar ways. (page 144)

Cold turkey Term used to describe quitting a habit, such as smoking, all at once. (page 311)

Colon (KOH·luhn) The large intestine. (page 393)

Commitment A pledge or a promise. (page 129)

Communicable (kuh·MYOO·ni·kuh·buhl) **disease** A disease that can be passed to a person from another person, animal, or object. (page 446)

Comparison shopping A method of judging the benefits of different products and services by measuring and comparing several factors, such as quality, features, and cost. (page 60)

Compromise To give up something in order to reach a solution that satisfies everyone. (page 168)

Conflict A disagreement between people with opposing viewpoints, ideas, or goals. (page 164)

Conflict resolution Solving a disagreement in a way that satisfies both sides. (page 168)

Consequences Outcomes or effects that may occur as a result of a decision or an action. (page 154)

Conservation The saving of resources. (page 553)

Consumer Anyone who purchases products or services. (page 58)

Contagious period The length of time that a disease can spread from person to person. (page 449)

Cool-down A period of low to moderate exercise to prepare your body to end a workout session. (page 234)

Coordination The smooth and effective working together of your muscles and bones. (page 221)

Cornea A clear protective structure of the eye that lets in light. (page 354)

CPR A first aid procedure that combines rescue breathing with chest compressions to restore breathing and circulation. (page 536)

Cross-training Switching between different forms of physical exercise. (page 225)

Cumulative risks Related risks that increase in effect with each added risk. (page 17)

Cuticle (KYOO·ti·kuhl) A fold of epidermis around the fingernails and toenails. (page 348)

Cycle of abuse Pattern of repeating abuse from one generation to the next. (page 179)

 D

Dandruff A flaking of the outer layer of dead skin cells on the scalp. (page 348)

Decibel A measure of the loudness of sound. (page 358)

Decision making The process of making a choice or finding a solution. (page 29)

Defensive driving Watching out for other people on the road and anticipating unsafe acts. (page 515)

Degenerative diseases Diseases that cause further breakdown in body cells, tissues, and organs as they progress. (page 476)

Dehydration Excessive water loss from the body. (page 238)

Depressants Substances that slow down body functions and reactions. (page 279)

Dermatologist (DER·muh·TAHL·uh·jist) A physician who treats skin disorders. (page 345)

Dermis (DER·mis) The thick inner layer of skin. (page 344)

Detoxification (dee·tahk·si·fi·KAY·shuhn) The physical process of freeing the body of an addictive substance. (pages 288, 327)

Developmental tasks Events that need to happen in order for you to continue growing toward becoming a healthy, mature adult. (page 426)

Diabetes A disease that prevents the body from converting food into energy. (page 494)

Diaphragm (DY·uh·fram) A dome-shaped muscle that separates the lungs from the abdomen. (page 382)

Dietary Guidelines for Americans Advice about food choices for all healthy Americans age 2 and over. (page 202)

Digestion (dy·JES·chuhn) The changing of food you eat into substances your body can use. (page 390)

Digestive system An organ system that converts food to a form useful to the body. (page 390)

Distress Negative stress. (page 39)

Divorce A legal end to a marriage contract. (page 130)

Drugs Substances other than food that change the structure or function of the body or mind. (page 270)

Earthquake A violent, shaking movement of the earth's surface. (page 523)

Eating disorder Extreme and damaging eating behavior that can lead to sickness and even death. (page 256)

Egg cell The reproductive cell from the female that joins with a sperm cell to make a new life. (page 416)

Embryo A developing organism from the time of fertilization to about the eighth week of development. (page 418)

Emotional needs Needs that affect a person's feelings and sense of well-being. (page 94)

Emotions Feelings that arise in response to thoughts, remarks, and events. (page 91)

Empathetic (em·puh·THE·tik) Able to identify and share another person's feelings. (page 143)

Empathy The ability to understand and share another person's feelings. (page 92)

Empty calories Calories that come from foods that offer few, if any, nutrients. (page 209)

Endocrine (EN·duh·krin) **system** The body's chemical communication system that regulates many functions. (page 396)

Environment The sum total of a person's surroundings. (pages 49, 423)

Environmental Protection Agency (EPA) The agency of the United States government that is committed to protecting the environment. (page 552)

Epidermis (e·puh·DER·mis) The visible and outermost layer of the skin. (page 344)

Epiglottis (e·puh·GLAH·tis) A flap of tissue that closes over the trachea when you swallow. (page 382)

Escalate To become more serious. (page 165)

Eustachian (yoo·STAY·shuhn) **tube** The part of the ear that allows air to pass from the nose to the middle ear so the air pressure is equal on both sides of the eardrum. (page 358)

Eustress Positive stress. (page 39)

Evaluate To determine the value of something. (page 30)

Excretion (ek·SKREE·shuhn) The process of removing wastes from the body. (page 393)

Excretory system The body system that removes wastes from the body. (page 392)

Glossary

Exercise Specifically planned and organized session of physical activity that improves or maintains physical fitness. (page 220)

Extended family A person's immediate family plus other relatives such as grand-parents, aunts, uncles, and cousins. (page 124)

Eye contact Direct visual contact with another person's eyes. (page 36)

Family The basic unit of society. (page 124)

Family therapy Counseling that seeks to improve troubled family relationships. (page 103)

Fatigue Exhaustion. (page 40)

Feedback A response by the listener to what the speaker has said. (page 37)

Fertilization The joining together of a male sperm cell and a female egg cell. (page 416)

Fetal alcohol syndrome (FAS) A group of alcohol-related birth defects that include both physical and mental problems. (page 323)

Fetus A developing organism from the end of the eighth week of the mother's pregnancy until birth. (page 418)

Fiber The part of fruits, vegetables, grains, and beans that your body cannot digest. (page 199)

Fight-or-flight response The process by which the body prepares to deal with a stressor. (page 40)

First aid The immediate temporary care given to an injured or ill person until pro-fessional help is available. (page 524)

Flexibility The ability of your body's joints to move easily through a full range of motion. (page 228)

Food Guide Pyramid A guide for making healthful daily food choices. (page 204)

Foodborne illness Sickness that results from eating food that is not safe to eat. (page 203)

Fracture A break in a bone. (page 529)

Fraud Deliberate deceit or trickery. (page 68)

Fungi (FUHN·jy) Primitive life-forms that feed on organic materials. (page 447)

Gallbladder A small, saclike organ that stores bile. (page 392)

Gang A group of people who associate with one another to take part in criminal activity. (page 173)

Genes The basic units of heredity. (page 422)

Genetic (juh·NE·tik) **disorder** A disorder that is caused partly or completely by a defect in genes. (page 422)

Gingivitis (jin·juh·VY·tis) A common disorder in which the gums are red and sore and bleed easily. (page 353)

Gland A group of cells, or an organ, that secretes a chemical substance. (page 396)

Global warming A rise in the earth's temperatures. (page 548)

Goal setting The process of working toward something you want to accomplish. (page 31)

Greenhouse effect The trapping of heat by carbon dioxide and other gases in the air. (page 548)

Grief The sorrow caused by loss of a loved one. (page 106)

Grief counselor Counselor who teaches coping strategies to deal with grief. (page 109)

H

Hallucinogens (huh·LOO·suhn·uh·jenz) Drugs that distort moods, thoughts, and senses. (page 282)

Hangnail A split in the cuticle along the edge of a fingernail. (page 348)

Hazardous wastes Human-made liquid or solid wastes that may endanger human health or the environment. (page 551)

Health A combination of physical, mental/emotional, and social well-being. (page 4)

Health advocacy Taking action to influence others to address a health-related concern or to support a health-related belief. (page 61)

Health care system All the medical care available to a nation's people, the way they receive the care, and the way the care is paid for. (page 63)

Health fraud The sale of worthless products or services claimed to prevent diseases or cure other health problems. (page 68)

Health insurance A plan in which private companies or government programs pay for part of a person's medical costs. page 66)

Health Maintenance Organization (HMO) An organization that provides health care for a fixed price. (page 66)

Heart and lung endurance The ability of your heart and lungs to work effectively when you exercise and to return to normal when you stop. (page 224)

Heart attack A condition in which blood flow to a part of the heart is greatly reduced or blocked. (page 491)

Heat cramps Painful, involuntary muscle spasms that may occur during heavy exercise in hot weather. (page 532)

Heat exhaustion A condition characterized by faintness, nausea, rapid heartbeat, and hot, red, dry, or sweaty skin. (page 532)

Heatstroke A serious form of heat illness in which the body's normal processes for dealing with heat close down. (page 532)

Hepatitis (hep·uh·TYT·uhs) A viral disease of the liver characterized by yellowing of the skin and the whites of the eyes. (page 456)

Heredity The passing of traits from parents to their children. (page 421)

High blood pressure A condition in which a person's blood pressure stays at a level that is higher than normal. (page 491)

Histamines Chemicals in the body that cause the symptoms of an allergic reaction. (page 481)

Hives Raised bumps on the skin that are very itchy. (page 481)

Homicide The killing of one human being by another. (page 172)

Hormones Chemical substances, produced in glands, that help to regulate many body functions. (page 9)

Hospice care Care provided to the terminally ill that focuses on comfort, not cure. (page 107)

Human Immunodeficiency Virus (HIV) The virus that causes AIDS. (page 464)

Hunger The physical need for food. (page 194)

Hurricane A strong windstorm with driving rain that originates at sea. (page 521)

I

Immune system A combination of body defenses made up of cells, tissues, and organs that fight off pathogens and disease. (page 451)

Immunity Your body's ability to resist the pathogens that cause a particular disease. (page 451)

Glossary

Individual sports Physical activities that you can do on your own or with a friend. (page 236)

Infancy The first year of life. (page 428)

Infection A condition that occurs when pathogens get inside the body, multiply, and damage body cells. (page 446)

Ingrown toenail A condition in which the nail pushes into the skin on the side of the toe. (page 348)

Inhalant Any substance whose fumes are sniffed and inhaled to produce mind-altering sensations. (page 283)

Insulin A hormone produced by the pancreas. (page 494)

Interpersonal communication The exchange of thoughts, feelings, and beliefs between two or more people. (page 34)

Intoxicated Physically and mentally impaired by the use of alcohol. (page 322)

Iris The colored part of the eye. (page 354)

Joints The points at which bones meet. (page 369)

Kidneys Organs that filter water and dissolved wastes from the blood and help maintain proper levels of water and salts in the body. (page 393)

Landfills Huge pits where wastes are dumped and buried. (page 550)

Larynx (LA·ringks) The upper part of the respiratory system, which contains the vocal cords. (page 382)

Lens A clear flexible structure of the eye that focuses light on the retina. (page 354)

Lifestyle factors Behaviors and habits that help determine a person's level of health. (page 14)

Ligaments (LI·guh·ments) Strong cords of tissue that connect the bones in each joint. (page 370)

Limits Invisible boundaries that protect you. (page 151)

Liver A large gland that has many digestive functions. (page 392)

Lymphatic (lim·FA·tik) **system** A secondary circulatory system that helps the body fight pathogens and maintain its fluid balance. (page 452)

Mainstream smoke Smoke that a smoker inhales and then exhales. (page 306)

Malignant (muh·LIG·nuhnt) **tumor** A tumor that is cancerous. (page 484)

Malnutrition A condition in which the body doesn't get the nutrients it needs to grow and function properly. (page 257)

Mammogram An X ray of the breast used to screen for breast cancer. (page 488)

Marrow A tissue in the center of some bones. (page 368)

Media Various methods for communicating information. (page 59)

Mediation A process in which a third person, a mediator, helps those in conflict find a solution. (page 169)

Medicines Drugs that are used to treat or prevent diseases and other conditions. (page 270)

Menopause A period marking the end of a female's reproductive years. (page 403)

Menstrual cycle The sequence of events in the female's reproductive system that occurs from one menstruation to the next. (page 403)

Menstruation The flow of the uterine lining out of the body. (page 403)

Mental and emotional health The ability to accept oneself and others, adapt to and cope with emotions, and deal with the problems and challenges one meets in life. (page 86)

Metastasis (muh·TAS·tuh·suhs) The spread of cancer from one part of the body to another. (page 484)

Methamphetamine A stimulant similar to amphetamine. (page 278)

Minerals Elements needed in small quantities for forming healthy bones and teeth, and for regulating certain body processes. (page 199)

Mixed message A situation in which your words say one thing but your body language says another. (page 35)

Mononucleosis (mahn·oh·noo·klee·OH·sis) A viral disease whose symptoms include swollen, tender areas in the neck and a sore throat. (page 456)

Mood disorder A disorder in which a person undergoes changes in mood that seem inappropriate or extreme. (page 97)

Muscle endurance The ability of a muscle to repeatedly exert a force over a prolonged period of time. (page 225)

Muscle strength The most weight you can lift or the most force you can exert at one time. (page 225)

Muscular system The group of structures that make your body parts move. (page 372)

Narcotics Specific drugs that are obtainable only by prescription and are used to relieve pain. (page 277)

Neglect The failure to meet a person's basic physical and emotional needs. (page 178)

Neurons (NOO·rahnz) Specialized cells that make up the nervous system. (page 385)

Nicotine An addictive drug found in tobacco leaves and in all tobacco products. (page 300)

Nicotine gum A type of chewing gum that enables a user to give up tobacco while gradually cutting down on nicotine. (page 311)

Nicotine patch A medicated patch placed on the skin that enables a user to give up tobacco while gradually cutting down on nicotine. (page 311)

Noncommunicable diseases Diseases that are not transmitted by pathogens. (page 476)

Nonrenewable resources Substances that cannot be replaced once they are used. (page 553)

Nutrient deficiency A shortage of a nutrient. (page 195)

Nutrient density The amount of nutrients relative to the number of calories they provide. (page 210)

Nutrients Substances in food that your body needs. (page 192)

Nutrition The process of using food and its substances to help your body have energy, grow, develop, and work properly. (page 192)

Glossary

O

Obstetrician (ahb·stuh·TRI·shuhn) Doctor who specializes in the care of a pregnant female and her developing fetus, and who is present at the birth of the baby. (page 423)

Online shopping Using the Internet to buy products and services. (page 62)

Ophthalmologist (ahf·thuhl·MAHL·uh·jist) A medical doctor who specializes in medical and surgical treatment of the eyes, and who prescribes corrective lenses. (page 356)

Opportunistic infection A disease that attacks a person with a weakened immune system and rarely occurs in a healthy person. (page 465)

Optometrist (ahp·TAHM·uh·trist) A professional who checks vision and prescribes corrective lenses. (page 356)

Organs Body parts that perform particular functions. (page 417)

Orthodontist (or·thuh·DAHN·tist) A dentist who prevents or corrects problems with the alignment or spacing of teeth. (page 353)

Osteoarthritis (ahs·tee·oh·ahr·THRY·tuhs) A disease that is characterized by the breakdown of the cartilage in joints. (page 497)

Over-the-counter (OTC) medicines Medicines that are safe enough to be taken without a written order from a physician. (page 271)

Overweight More than the appropriate weight for gender, height, age, body frame, and growth pattern. (page 251)

Ovulation The release of one mature egg cell each month. (page 403)

Ozone layer A shield above the earth's surface that protects living things from ultraviolet (UV) radiation. (page 548)

P

Pacemaker A small device that sends steady electrical impulses to the heart to make it beat regularly. (page 492)

Pancreas An organ that produces enzymes that assist in digestion. (page 392)

Panic A feeling of sudden, intense fear. (page 93)

Parenting The process of meeting a child's physical, mental/emotional, and social needs. (page 131)

Pathogens Tiny organisms that cause communicable diseases. (page 446)

Peer pressure The influence to go along with the beliefs and actions of other people of your age. (page 147)

Percent Daily Value The percent of the recommended daily amount of a nutrient provided in a serving of food. (page 206)

Periodontal (per·ee·oh·DAHNT·uhl) **disease** Advanced gum disease, in which the periodontium is infected with bacteria. (page 353)

Periodontium (per·ee·oh·DAHN·shee·um) A structure made up of the jawbone, the gums, and connectors called ligaments. (page 350)

Peripheral nervous system (PNS) The nerves that connect the central nervous system to all parts of the body. (page 386)

Personality The unique combination of feelings, thoughts, and behavior that makes one person different from everyone else. (page 87)

Personality disorder A variety of psychological conditions that affect a person's ability to get along with others. (page 97)

Pesticide Product used on crops to kill insects and other pests. (page 547)

Phobia Intense and exaggerated fear of a specific situation or object. (page 97)

Physical activity Any kind of movement that uses up energy. (page 220)

Physical dependence A type of addiction in which the body feels a direct need for a drug. (pages 283, 304)

Physical fitness The ability to handle the physical demands of everyday life without becoming overly tired. (page 220)

Pituitary gland A gland that signals other endocrine glands to produce hormones when needed. (page 397)

Placenta (pluh·SEN·tuh) A thick, rich tissue that lines the walls of the uterus during pregnancy and that nourishes the fetus. (page 419)

Plaque (PLAK) A soft, colorless, sticky film containing bacteria that forms on teeth. (page 351)

Point of Service (POS) plan A health plan that allows members to choose providers inside or outside the plan. (page 66)

Pollution Any dirty or harmful substance in the environment. (page 546)

Precaution A planned action taken before an event to increase the chances of a safe outcome. (page 17)

Precycling Reducing waste before it occurs. (page 555)

Preferred Provider Organization (PPO) A type of health insurance in which medical providers agree to charge less for members of the plan. (page 66)

Prejudice A negative and unjustly formed opinion, usually against people of a different racial, religious, or cultural group. (page 167)

Prenatal (pree·NAY·tuhl) **care** Steps taken to provide for the health of a pregnant woman and her baby. (page 423)

Preschooler A child between the ages of three and five. (page 429)

Prescription medicines Medicines that can be sold only with a written order from a physician. (page 271)

Preventive care Steps taken to keep disease or injury from happening or getting worse. (page 63)

Primary care physician A medical doctor who provides physical checkups and general care. (page 64)

Proteins Nutrients your body uses to build, repair, and maintain cells and tissues. (page 197)

Protozoa (proh·tuh·ZOH·uh) Single-celled organisms that are usually harmless but that can cause certain diseases. (page 447)

Psychiatrist (sy·KY·uh·trist) A medical doctor who treats mental health problems. (page 105)

Psychological dependence An addiction in which the mind sends the body a message that it needs more of a drug. (pages 282, 304)

Psychologist (sy·KAH·luh·jist) A mental health professional who is trained and licensed by the state to counsel. (page 105)

Puberty The time when you begin to develop certain physical traits of adults of your own gender. (page 430)

Public health The protection and promotion of health at the community level. (page 72)

Pulmonary circulation The flow of blood from the heart to the lungs and back to the heart. (page 377)

Pupil The dark opening in the center of the iris. (page 354)

R

Rape Any kind of sexual intercourse against a person's will. (page 176)

Recovery The process of learning to live an alcohol-free life. (page 327)

Recurrence The return of cancer after a remission. (page 487)

Refusal skills Communication strategies that help you say no effectively. (pages 37, 148)

Relationships The connections you have with other people and groups in your life. (page 118)

Remission A period during which cancer signs and symptoms disappear. (page 487)

Reproductive (ree·pruh·DUHK·tiv) **system** The organs that make possible the production of offspring. (page 400)

Resilience The ability to adapt to and recover from disappointment, difficulty, or crisis. (page 94)

Respiratory system The organs that provide the body with a continuous supply of oxygen and rid the body of carbon dioxide. (page 381)

Retina (RE·tin·uh) A thin layer of nerve cells in the eye that absorb light. (page 354)

Rheumatoid (ROO·muh·toyd) **arthritis** A chronic disease characterized by pain, inflammation, swelling, and stiffness of the joints. (page 496)

Rickettsias (rik·ET·see·uhz) Disease-causing organisms that resemble bacteria but multiply like viruses. (page 447)

Risk behavior An action or behavior that might cause injury or harm to you or others. (page 15)

Risk factors Characteristics that increase a person's chances of developing a disease. (page 478)

S

Saliva (suh·LY·vuh) Fluid produced by the salivary glands in the mouth. (page 390)

Saturated fats Fats that are solid at room temperature. (page 197)

Schizophrenia (skit·zoh·FREE·nee·uh) A severe mental disorder in which a person loses contact with reality. (page 97)

Secondhand smoke Air that has been contaminated by tobacco smoke. (page 306)

Sedentary lifestyle A way of life that involves little physical activity. (page 16)

Self-concept The view you have of yourself. (page 87)

Self-control Restraint from your own emotions and desires. (page 18)

Self-esteem The way you feel about yourself, and how you value yourself. (page 87)

Self-respect The positive feeling you have about yourself when you live up to your beliefs and values. (page 154)

Sexual harassment Uninvited and unwelcome sexual conduct directed at another person. (page 178)

Sexually transmitted diseases (STDs) Infections spread from person to person through sexual contact. (page 458)

Shock A life-threatening condition in which the circulatory system fails to deliver enough blood to vital tissues and organs. (page 534)

Side effect Any effect of a medicine other than the one intended. (page 274)

Sidestream smoke Smoke given off by the burning end of a cigarette, cigar, or pipe. (page 306)

Skeletal muscle Muscle attached to bones that enables you to move your body. (page 373)

Skeletal system An internal body system made up of bones, joints, and connective tissue. (page 368)

Small intestine A coiled, tubelike digestive organ that is about 20 feet long. (page 391)

Smog A yellow-brown haze that forms when sunlight reacts with air pollution. (page 548)

Smooth muscle Type of muscle found in organs and in blood vessels and glands. (page 373)

Sobriety Living without alcohol. (page 327)

Social age Age measured by your lifestyle and the connections you have with others. (page 434)

Social health Your ability to get along with the people around you. (page 118)

Somatic (soh·MA·tik) **system** The part of the nervous system that deals with actions that you control. (page 388)

Specialist Doctor trained to handle particular kinds of patients or medical conditions. (page 64)

Sperm Male reproductive cells. (page 401)

Sperm cell The cell from the father that enters the egg cell during fertilization. (page 416)

Sports conditioning Regular physical activity or exercise to strengthen and condition muscles for a particular sport. (page 238)

Sprain A condition in which the ligaments that hold the joints in position are stretched or torn. (page 528)

Stepparent Someone who marries a child's mother or father. (page 126)

Stimulants (STIM·yuh·luhnts) Substances that speed up the body's functions. (page 277)

Stress Your body's response to change. (page 39)

Stress management skills Ways to deal with and overcome problems. (page 41)

Stressor Anything that causes stress. (page 40)

Stroke A condition in which a blood vessel bringing oxygen to the brain bursts or is blocked. (page 491)

Subcutaneous (suhb·kyoo·TAY·nee·uhs) **layer** A layer of fat under the skin. (page 344)

Suicide Intentionally killing oneself. (page 99)

Support system A network of people available to help when needed. (page 47)

Systemic circulation Flow of blood to all the body tissues except the lungs. (page 377)

Tar A dark, thick, sticky liquid that forms when tobacco burns. (page 300)

Tartar A hard coating on the teeth that is difficult to remove. (page 351)

Team sports Organized physical activities with specific rules in which groups of people play together against other groups. (page 237)

Tendons Tough bands of tissue that attach muscles to bones. (page 370)

Therapy Treatment. (page 102)

Time management Strategies for using time efficiently. (page 43)

Tissues Groups of similar cells that perform a specific function. (page 417)

Glossary

Toddler A child between the ages of one and three who is learning to walk and talk. (page 428)

Tolerance A condition in which a person's body becomes used to the effect of a medicine and needs greater amounts of it in order for it to be effective. (page 274)

Tornado A whirling, funnel-shaped windstorm that may drop from the sky to the ground. (page 520)

Trachea (TRAY·kee·uh) Windpipe that directs air to the lungs. (page 382)

Tumor A mass of abnormal cells. (page 484)

Type 1 diabetes A condition in which the immune system attacks insulin-producing cells in the pancreas. (page 494)

Type 2 diabetes A condition in which the body cannot effectively use the insulin it produces. (page 494)

Umbilical (uhm·BIL·i·kuhl) **cord** A tube that connects the fetus and the mother's placenta. (page 419)

Unconditional love Love without limitation or qualification. (page 132)

Underweight Less than the appropriate weight for gender, height, age, body frame, and growth pattern. (page 251)

Universal precautions Actions taken to prevent the spread of disease by treating all blood as if it were contaminated. (page 525)

Unsaturated fats Fats that remain liquid at room temperature. (page 197)

Uterus (YOO·tuh·ruhs) A pear-shaped organ inside a female's body where a fetus is nourished. (page 418)

Vaccine A preparation of dead or weakened germs that causes the immune system to produce antibodies. (page 272)

Values The beliefs and ideals that guide the way a person lives. (pages 30, 119)

Vector An organism, such as an insect, that transmits a pathogen. (page 448)

Veins Blood vessels that carry blood from the body back to the heart. (page 378)

Violence Any act that causes physical or psychological harm to a person or damage to property. (page 172)

Virus The smallest disease-causing organism. (page 446)

Vitamins Substances needed in small quantities to help regulate body functions. (page 198)

Warm-up A period of low to moderate exercise to prepare your body for more vigorous activity. (page 233)

Warranty A written promise to handle repairs if a product fails to work properly. (page 61)

Wellness An overall state of well-being, or total health. (page 6)

Win-win solution An agreement that gives each party something they want. (page 169)

Withdrawal The physical and psychological symptoms that occur when someone stops using an addictive substance. (pages 287, 305)

Zero tolerance policy A policy that makes no exceptions for anybody for any reason. (page 174)

Glosario

A

Abdominal thrusts/presiones abdominales Presiones rápidas y hacia arriba que se hacen sobre el diafragma para forzar la salida de algo que esté bloqueando la vía respiratoria.

Abstinence/abstinencia No participar en conducta de alto riesgo.

Abuse/abuso El maltrato físico, emocional o mental de una persona a otra.

Accident/accidente Un suceso que ocurre de manera no intencional.

Accident chain/accidente en cadena Una serie de sucesos que incluye una situación, un hábito peligroso y un acto peligroso.

Accidental injuries/Lesiones accidentales Lesiones que resultan de un accidente.

Acid rain/lluvia ácida Lluvia que es mucho más ácida de lo normal.

Acquired immunodeficiency syndrome (AIDS)/síndrome de inmunodeficiencia adquirida (SIDA) Una enfermedad mortal que interfiere con la habilidad natural del cuerpo de combatir infecciones.

Active listening/audición activa Oír el mensaje de otra persona, pensar en el mensaje y responder.

Addiction/adicción La necesidad física o psicológica de una droga.

Addictive/adictivo Capaz de ocasionar que el consumidor desarrolle una necesidad repentina intensa.

Adjustment/ajuste Una adaptación o cambio en la conducta.

Adolescence/adolescencia El periodo de vida entre la niñez y la adultez.

Adrenaline/adrenalina Una hormona que proporciona energía adicional al cuerpo.

Advertising/publicidad El envío de mensajes diseñados para hacer que los consumidores compren un producto o servicio.

Aerobic exercise/ejercicio aeróbico Actividad rítmica ininterrumpida de intensidad moderada a vigorosa que requiere grandes cantidades de oxígeno y hace que el corazón trabaje.

Alcohol/alcohol Una droga producida por una reacción química en frutas, verduras y granos.

Alcoholism/alcoholismo Una enfermedad progresiva y crónica caracterizada por una necesidad mental y física de consumir el alcohol.

Allergen/alergeno Una sustancia que causa una reacción alérgica.

Allergy/alergia Una reacción anormal del sistema inmunológico hacia una sustancia comúnmente inofensiva.

Alternatives/alternativas Diferentes maneras de pensar o actuar.

Alveoli/alveolos Cavidades microscópicas en los pulmones.

Amino acids/aminoácidos Unidades pequeñas que forman las proteínas.

Amphetamine/anfetamina Una droga que estimula el sistema nervioso central.

Anabolic steroids/esteroides anabólicos Drogas que causan que el tejido muscular se desarrolle con rapidez anormal.

Anaerobic exercise/ejercicio anaeróbico Actividad física intensa que requiere poco oxígeno pero exige breves brotes de energía.

Anorexia nervosa/anorexia nerviosa Un trastorno en la alimentación que se caracteriza por autoinanición conducente a una pérdida de peso extrema.

Antibiotics/antibióticos Medicinas que disminuyen o matan bacterias dañinas en el cuerpo.

Antibodies/anticuerpos Proteínas que se adhieren a los antígenos para prevenir que dañen al cuerpo.

Antigens/antígenos Sustancias que liberan los agentes patógenos.

Antihistamines/antihistamínicos Medicinas que ayudan a controlar los efectos que provocan las histaminas.

Anxiety/ansiedad Un sentimiento abrumador de terror, muy parecido al miedo.

Anxiety disorder/trastorno de ansiedad Un trastorno en el cual la ansiedad intensa o el miedo impide que una persona funcione de manera normal.

Appetite/apetito El deseo psicológico de alimentarse.

Appropriate weight/peso apropiado El peso más adecuado para tu cuerpo.

Arteries/arterias Vasos sanguíneos que llevan sangre desde el corazón a otras partes del cuerpo.

Arteriosclerosis/arteriosclerosis Un conjunto de trastornos por el cual las arterias se endurecen y se tornan rígidas.

Arthritis/artritis Más de 100 afecciones que se caracterizan por el dolor y la hinchazón de las articulaciones del cuerpo.

Assertive/firme Comportarte con seguridad y declarar claramente tus intenciones.

Asthma/asma Una grave enfermedad crónica que causa el estrechamiento u obstrucción de las diminutas vías del aparato respiratorio.

Atherosclerosis/aterosclerosis Un tipo de arteriosclerosis por el cual sustancias grasas en la sangre se acumulan en las paredes de las arterias.

Attitude/actitud Sentimientos y creencias.

Autonomic system/sistema autónomo La parte del sistema nervioso que se ocupa de las acciones que generalmente tú no controlas.

 B

Bacteria/bacterias Organismos diminutos unicelulares que viven en casi todas partes.

Balance/equilibrio Un sentimiento de estabilidad y control.

Battery/agresión Dar palizas, golpear o dar puntapiés a otra persona

Benign tumor/tumor benigno Un tumor que no es canceroso.

Binge drinking/borrachera El consumo de muchas bebidas alcohólicas en un corto plazo.

Binge eating disorder/trastorno de la alimentación compulsiva Sentirse impulsado a comer demasiado.

Biodegradable/biodegradable Que se descompone fácilmente en el medio ambiente.

Biological age/edad biológica Medida de la edad, determinada según el funcionamiento de varias partes del cuerpo.

Biopsy/biopsia La extirpación de una muestra de tejido para determinar la presencia de células cancerosas.

Birth defect/defecto de nacimiento
Anormalidad presente al momento del nacimiento que causa incapacidad física o mental o la muerte.

Blended family/familia mezclada Una familia que consiste en padre o madre, padrastro o madrastra, y los hijos de uno o ambos padres.

Blizzard/ventisca Una tormenta de nieve fuerte, con vientos que llegan a 45 millas por hora.

Blood alcohol concentration (BAC)/ concentración de alcohol en la sangre La cantidad de alcohol presente en el torrente sanguíneo de una persona.

Body composition/composición del cuerpo La proporción entre la grasa del cuerpo y los tejidos magros, tales como huesos, músculos y líquidos.

Body image/autoimagen La manera en que te ves a ti mismo.

Body language/lenguaje corporal El uso de movimientos corporales y gestos para comunicar un mensaje.

Body Mass Index (BMI)/Índice de masa corporal Una medida que te permite evaluar el tamaño de tu cuerpo, teniendo en cuenta tu estatura y peso.

Bronchi/bronquios Pasajes a través de los cuales entra el aire en los pulmones.

Bronchodilators/broncodilatadores Medicinas que se usan para relajar los músculos que se han tensado alrededor de las vías respiratorias.

Bulimia/bulimia Una afección por la cual una persona come grandes cantidades de alimentos y después intenta inducirse el vómito.

Calories/calorías Unidades de calor que miden la energía que el cuerpo usa y la energía que los alimentos aportan al cuerpo.

Cancer/cáncer Una enfermedad que se caracteriza por el desarrollo rápido e incontrolable de células anormales.

Capillaries/capilares Conductos minúsculos que llevan sangre desde las arterias a las células del cuerpo, y de regreso a las venas.

Carbohydrates/hidratos de carbono Los azúcares y almidones que le proporcionan a tu cuerpo la mayor parte de su energía.

Carbon monoxide/monóxido de carbono Un gas incoloro, inodoro y tóxico que se produce al quemarse el tabaco.

Carcinogens/carcinógenos Sustancias que causan el cáncer.

Cardiac muscle/músculo cardiaco El músculo en las paredes del corazón.

Cardiovascular system/sistema cardiovascular Órganos y tejidos que transportan materia esencial a las células del cuerpo y eliminan los sus desechos.

Carrier/portador Una persona infectada con un virus que puede contagiar a otras.

Cartilage/cartílago Tejido fuerte y flexible que amortigua las articulaciones.

Central nervous system (CNS)/ sistema nervioso central El cerebro y la médula espinal.

Cervix/cuello del útero La entrada del útero.

Character/carácter La manera en la que una persona piensa, siente y actúa.

Glosario

Character trait/rasgo del carácter
Una cualidad que demuestra la manera en que una persona piensa, siente y actúa.

Chromosomes/cromosomas Las estructuras filiformes dentro del núcleo de las células que contienen los códigos de las características hereditarias.

Chronic diseases/enfermedades crónicas Las enfermedades que están siempre presentes o reaparecen repetidamente durante un largo periodo de tiempo.

Chronological age/edad cronológica La edad medida en años.

Cilia/cilios Estructuras diminutas parecidas al cabello que protegen los pulmones.

Circulatory system/aparato circulatorio Los órganos y los tejidos que transportan materias esenciales a las células del cuerpo y se llevan sus desechos.

Cirrhosis/cirrosis La cicatrización y destrucción del hígado.

Citizenship/ciudadanía La forma en que te comportas como miembro de una comunidad.

Clinical depression/depresión diagnosticada Un trastorno del ánimo por el cual la persona pierde interés en la vida y es incapaz de disfrutar de nada.

Clique/camarilla Un grupo de amigos que salen juntos y que se comportan de manera similar.

Cold turkey/parar en seco Expresión que se usa para describir la acción de abandonar un vicio de una vez, por ejemplo el fumar.

Colon/colon El intestino grueso.

Commitment/compromiso Una promesa o voto.

Communicable disease/enfermedad contagiosa Una enfermedad que se puede propagar a una persona de otra persona, un animal o un objeto.

Comparison shopping/comparación de productos Un método de evaluar los beneficios de diferentes productos y servicios al medir y comparar varios factores, tales como la calidad, las características y el precio.

Compromise/acordar Llegar a un acuerdo en el que se cede algo con el fin de llegar a una solución satisfactoria para todos.

Conflict/conflicto Un desacuerdo entre personas con puntos de vista, ideas o metas opuestos.

Conflict resolution/resolución de un conflicto Resolver un desacuerdo de manera satisfactoria para ambas partes.

Consequences/consecuencias Los resultados o efectos que pueden ocurrir como resultado de una decisión o un acto.

Conservation/conservación El ahorro de recursos.

Consumer/consumidor La persona que compra bienes o servicios.

Contagious period/periodo de contagio El periodo de tiempo en que una enfermedad se puede propagar de una persona a otra.

Cool-down/recuperación Un periodo en el que se realizan ejercicios de intensidad baja a moderada a fin de preparar al cuerpo para terminar una serie de ejercicios vigorosos.

Coordination/coordinación El funcionamiento conjunto de los músculos y los huesos de manera eficiente y sin complicaciones.

Cornea/córnea Una estructura transparente que protege al ojo y deja pasar la luz.

CPR/resucitación cardiopulmonar
Un procedimiento de primeros auxilios que

combina la respiración de rescate y compresiones sobre el pecho para restaurar la respiración y la circulación.

Cross-training/entrenamiento variado El cambiar de un ejercicio físico a otro.

Cumulative risks/riesgos acumulativos Riesgos relacionados cuyos efectos aumentan con cada uno que se añade.

Cuticle/cutícula Un doblez de epidermis alrededor de las uñas de los pies y las manos.

Cycle of abuse/ciclo de abuso Un patrón de repetición del abuso de una generación a la siguiente.

Dandruff/caspa Las escamas de piel muerta en la superficie del cuero cabelludo.

Decibel/decibel Una medida del volumen del sonido.

Decision making/tomar decisiones El proceso de hacer una selección o de hallar una solución.

Defensive driving/conducir de manera defensiva Estar atento a las otras personas en la carretera y anticipar acciones peligrosas.

Degenerative diseases/ enfermedades degenerativas Enfermedades que causan la destrucción progresiva de las células, tejidos y órganos del cuerpo a medida que avanzan.

Dehydration/deshidratación Pérdida excesiva del agua del cuerpo.

Depressants/depresivos Sustancias que disminuyen las funciones y reacciones del cuerpo.

Dermatologist/dermatólogo Médico que trata trastornos de la piel.

Dermis/dermis La capa gruesa e interna de la piel.

Detoxification/desintoxicación El proceso físico de liberar al cuerpo de una sustancia adictiva.

Developmental tasks/tareas requeridas para el desarrollo Sucesos que deben ocurrir para que continúes desarrollándote hasta llegar a convertirte en un adulto saludable y maduro.

Diabetes/diabetes Una enfermedad que impide que el cuerpo convierta los alimentos en energía.

Diaphragm/diafragma Un músculo en forma de domo que separa los pulmones del abdomen.

Dietary Guidelines for Americans/ Pautas alimenticias para los estadounidenses Consejos sobre los alimentos para todos los estadounidenses saludables de 2 años de edad en adelante.

Digestion/digestión El proceso de convertir los alimentos que comes en sustancias que tu cuerpo pueda usar.

Digestive system/aparato digestivo Un sistema de órganos que convierten los alimentos en una forma útil para el cuerpo.

Distress/angustia El estrés negativo.

Divorce/divorcio Un fin legal a un contrato matrimonial.

Drugs/drogas Sustancias, que no sean alimentos, que cambian la estructura o el funcionamiento del cuerpo o la mente.

Earthquake/terremoto El sacudimiento violento de la superficie de la tierra.

Eating disorder/trastorno en la alimentación Costumbre en la alimentación por la cual una persona come de manera extrema y nociva y que puede causar enfermedades y aun la muerte.

Egg cell/óvulo La célula reproductora femenina que se une con el espermatozoide para crear una nueva vida.

Embryo/embrión Un organismo en desarrollo desde la fecundación hasta aproximadamente la octava semana del desarrollo.

Emotional needs/necesidades emocionales Las necesidades que afectan los sentimientos y el bienestar de una persona.

Emotions/emociones Sentimientos que surgen en respuesta a pensamientos, comentarios y sucesos.

Empathetic/tener empatía Capaz de identificar y compartir los sentimientos de otra persona.

Empathy/empatía La habilidad de entender y compartir los sentimientos de otra persona.

Empty calories/calorías vacías Calorías que provienen de alimentos con poco, o ningún, valor nutritivo.

Endocrine system/sistema endocrino El sistema químico de comunicaciones del cuerpo que regula varias funciones.

Environment/medio ambiente La suma total de lo que rodea a una persona.

Environmental Protection Agency (EPA)/Agencia de Protección Ambiental La agencia del gobierno de Estados Unidos a cargo de la protección del medio ambiente.

Epidermis/epidermis La capa visible y más externa de la piel.

Epiglottis/epiglotis Una tapa de tejido que cubre la tráquea cuando tragas.

Escalate/intensificar Llegar a ser más grave.

Eustachian tube/trompa de Eustaquio La parte del oído que deja pasar aire desde la nariz al oído medio para que la presión del aire sea igual en ambos lados del tímpano.

Eustress/estrés positivo Tensión positiva.

Evaluate/evaluar Determinar el valor de algo.

Excretion/excreción El proceso de eliminar desechos del cuerpo.

Excretory system/sistema excretor El sistema del cuerpo que elimina desechos del cuerpo.

Exercise/ejercicio Actividad física específica, planeada y organizada que mejora o mantiene la condición física.

Extended family/familia extensa La familia nuclear y otros parientes tales como abuelos, tías, tíos y primos.

Eye contact/contacto visual El mirar directamente a los ojos de otra persona.

Family/familia La unidad básica de la sociedad.

Family therapy/terapía familiar Asesoramiento cuyo propósito es mejorar relaciones problemáticas entre familiares.

Fatigue/fatiga Agotamiento.

Feedback/reacción Una respuesta del oyente a lo que el orador ha dicho.

Fertilization/fecundación La unión de un espermatozoide y un óvulo.

Fetal alcohol syndrome (FAS)/ síndrome alcohólico fetal Un conjunto de defectos de nacimiento causados por el alcohol que incluyen problemas físicos y mentales.

Fetus/feto El organismo en desarrollo desde el final de la octava semana del embarazo de la madre hasta el momento del nacimiento.

Fiber/fibra La parte de las frutas, verduras, granos y frijoles que tu cuerpo no puede dirigir.

Fight-or-flight response/respuesta de lucha o huida El proceso mediante el cual el cuerpo se prepara a enfrentarse con un estresante.

First aid/primeros auxilios El cuidado inmediato y temporal que se le proporciona a una persona herida o enferma hasta que reciba ayuda profesional.

Flexibility/flexibilidad La habilidad de mover las articulaciones del cuerpo con facilidad a través del arco completo de movimiento.

Food Guide Pyramid/Pirámide Nutricional Una guía para la selección diaria de alimentos sanos.

Foodborne illness/enfermedad producida por un alimento Enfermedad que proviene de haber comido un alimento no sano.

Fracture/fractura Una rotura de un hueso.

Fraud/fraude Engaño o decepción deliberado.

Fungi/hongos Organismos primitivos que se alimentan de materias orgánicas.

Gallbladder/vesícula biliar Pequeño órgano en forma de bolsa que almacena bilis.

Gang/pandilla Un grupo de personas que se relacionan para tomar parte en actividades criminales.

Genes/genes Las unidades básicas de la herencia.

Genetic disorder/trastorno genético Un trastorno causado parcial o totalmente por defectos en los genes.

Gingivitis/gingivitis Un trastorno común que se caracteriza por el enrojecimiento y dolor de las encías que sangran con facilidad.

Gland/glándula Un grupo de células, o un órgano, que secreta una sustancia química.

Global warming/calentamiento del planeta Un aumento en las temperaturas de la Tierra.

Goal setting/establecer metas El proceso de esforzarte para lograr algo que quieres.

Greenhouse effect/efecto invernadero La retención del calor por la presencia de dióxido de carbono y otros gases en el aire.

Grief/pena El pesar provocado por la muerte de un ser querido.

Grief counselor/consejero especializado en la pena Consejero que enseña estrategias para superar una pena.

Hallucinogens/alucinógenos Drogas que alteran el estado de ánimo, los pensamientos y los sentidos.

Hangnail/padrastro Una grieta en la cutícula al lado del borde de la uña.

Hazardous wastes/desechos peligrosos Desechos líquidos o sólidos generados por los seres humanos, que pueden perjudicar la salud de las personas o el medio ambiente.

Health/salud Una combinación de bienestar físico, mental/emocional y social.

Health advocacy/promoción de la salud Tomar medidas para influir en las personas de manera que dirijan sus esfuerzos a un asunto de la salud o que apoyen una creencia relacionada con la salud.

Health care system/sistema de asistencia sanitaria Toda la asistencia médica al alcance de los ciudadanos de una nación, la manera en que ellos reciben la asistencia, y la manera en que se paga por la asistencia.

Health fraud/fraude contra la salud La venta de productos o servicios inútiles que se afirma que protegen contra enfermedades o curan otros problemas de la salud.

Health insurance/seguro de salud Un plan en el que una compañía privada o programa del gobierno paga parte de los gastos médicos de una persona.

Health maintenance organization (HMO)/organización para el mantenimiento de la salud Una organización que proporciona asistencia médica a un precio fijo.

Heart and lung endurance/ resistencia cardiaca y respiratoria La capacidad de corazón y pulmones de funcionar con eficacia cuando haces ejercicio y de regresar al ritmo normal cuando paras.

Heart attack/ataque cardiaco Una afección en la cual el flujo de sangre a una parte del corazón está considerablemente reducido u obstruido

Heat cramps/calambre debido al calor Dolorosos espasmos involuntarios de los músculos que pueden ocurrir al realizar ejercicio vigoroso cuando hace mucho calor.

Heat exhaustion/agotamiento debido al calor Una afección caracterizada por el desmayo, la náusea, el ritmo cardiaco rápido y la piel caliente, roja, seca o sudorosa.

Heatstroke/insolación Un tipo de enfermedad debido al calor grave en que los procesos normales del cuerpo que controlan los efectos del calor dejan de funcionar.

Hepatitis/hepatitis Una enfermedad vírica del hígado que se caracteriza por el color amarillo de la piel y del blanco de los ojos.

Heredity/herencia La transferencia de características de los padres a sus hijos.

High blood pressure/presión arterial alta Una afección en la que la presión arterial de una persona se mantiene a un nivel más alto de lo normal.

Histamines/histaminas Sustancias químicas en el cuerpo que provocan los síntomas de una reacción alérgica.

Hives/urticaria Granos en la piel que pican mucho.

Homicide/homicidio El acto en que una persona mata a otra.

Hormones/hormonas Sustancias químicas, producidas por glándulas, que ayudan a regular varias funciones del cuerpo.

Hospice care/asistencia para enfermos desahuciados Asistencia para personas con enfermedades incurables que apunta a brindar comodidad, no una cura.

Human immunodeficiency virus (HIV)/virus de inmunodeficiencia humana (VIH) El virus que causa el SIDA.

Hunger/hambre La necesidad física de alimentos.

Hurricane/huracán Una tormenta de vientos y lluvia torrencial que se origina en alta mar.

Immune system/sistema inmunológico Una combinación de las defensas del cuerpo, compuesta de células, tejidos y órganos que combaten patógenos y enfermedades.

Immunity/inmunidad La habilidad del cuerpo de resistir los patógenos que causan una enfermedad en particular.

Individual sports/deportes individuales Actividades físicas que puedes realizar solo o con otra persona.

Infancy/infancia El primer año de vida.

Infection/infección Una afección que se produce cuando agentes patógenos invaden el cuerpo, se multiplican y dañan las células del cuerpo.

Ingrown toenail/uña encarnada Una afección en la cual la uña se introduce en la piel al lado del dedo del pie.

Inhalant/inhalante Toda sustancia cuyos gases se aspiran para producir sensaciones alucinantes.

Insulin/insulina Una hormona producida por el páncreas.

Interpersonal communication/ comunicación entre personas El intercambio de pensamientos, sentimientos y creencias entre dos personas o más.

Intoxicated/embriagado Física y mentalmente afectado por el consumo de alcohol.

Iris/iris La parte coloreada del ojo.

Joints/articulaciones Lugares en donde se unen los huesos.

Kidneys/riñones Los órganos que filtran el agua y los desechos disueltos de la sangre y contribuyen a mantener los niveles adecuados de agua y sales en el cuerpo.

Landfills/terraplenes sanitarios Pozos enormes donde se tiran y se entierran desechos.

Larynx/laringe La parte superior del aparato respiratorio que contiene las cuerdas vocales.

Lens/cristalino La estructura transparente y flexible del ojo que enfoca la luz en la retina.

Lifestyle factors/factores del estilo de vida Conductas y hábitos que ayudan a determinar el nivel de salud de una persona.

Ligaments/ligamentos Cuerdas fuertes de tejido que unen los huesos en las articulaciones.

Limits/límites Barreras invisibles que te protegen.

Liver/hígado Una glándula grande que tiene varias funciones digestivas.

Lymphatic system/sistema linfático Aparato circulatorio secundario que le ayuda al cuerpo a combatir patógenos y a mantener el equilibrio de líquidos.

Mainstream smoke/humo directo El humo que el fumador aspira y exhala.

Malignant tumor/tumor maligno Un tumor canceroso.

Malnutrition/desnutrición Una afección por la cual el cuerpo no recibe los nutrientes que necesita para crecer y funcionar bien.

Mammogram/mamografía Una radiografía del seno que se usa para determinar si hay evidencia del cáncer.

Marrow/médula Un tejido en el centro de algunos huesos.

Media/medios de difusión Los diversos métodos de comunicar información.

Mediation/mediación Un proceso en el cual una tercera persona, un mediador, ayuda a otros a encontrar una solución al conflicto entre ellos.

Medicines/medicinas Drogas que se usan para curar o prevenir enfermedades u otras afecciones.

Menopause/menopausia Una etapa que marca el fin de los años reproductivos de una mujer.

Menstrual cycle/ciclo menstrual La serie de sucesos en el aparato reproductor de la mujer que ocurre entre una menstruación y la siguiente.

Menstruation/menstruación La eliminación de materia celular del revestimiento del útero.

Mental and emotional health/salud mental y emocional La capacidad de aceptarse a sí mismo y a otros, de adaptarse a las emociones y sobrellevarlas, y de superar los problemas y retos de la vida.

Metastasis/metástasis La propagación de cáncer de una parte del cuerpo a otra.

Methamphetamine/metanfetamina Un estimulante parecido a la anfetamina.

Minerals/minerales Elementos que se necesitan en cantidades pequeñas para la formación de dientes y huesos saludables, y para regular determinados procesos corporales.

Mixed message/mensaje contradictorio Una situación en que tus palabras expresan algo pero tu lenguaje corporal lo contradice.

Mononucleosis/mononucleosis Una enfermedad vírica cuyos síntomas incluyen hinchazón y dolor en áreas del cuello y dolor de garganta.

Mood disorder/trastorno del estado de ánimo Un trastorno en que la persona cambia de humor de manera aparentemente inapropiada o extrema.

Muscle endurance/resistencia muscular La capacidad que tiene un músculo de ejercer una fuerza repetidamente durante un largo periodo de tiempo.

Muscle strength/fortaleza muscular El peso máximo que puedes levantar o la fuerza máxima que puedes ejercer a la vez.

Muscular system/sistema muscular El grupo de estructuras que permiten el movimiento de las partes de tu cuerpo.

N

Narcotics/narcóticos Ciertas drogas específicas que se pueden obtener únicamente con receta médica y que se usan para aliviar el dolor.

Neglect/abandono El no satisfacer las necesidades básicas físicas y emocionales de una persona.

Neurons/neuronas Células especializadas que componen el sistema nervioso.

Nicotine/nicotina Una droga adictiva que se encuentra en las hojas del tabaco y en todos los productos del tabaco.

Nicotine gum/goma de mascar con nicotina Un tipo de goma de mascar cuyo efecto es permitir que el consumidor abandone el tabaco mientras el nivel de nicotina baja gradualmente.

Nicotine patch/parche de nicotina Un parche medicado que se pone en la piel y que permite que el consumidor abandone el tabaco mientras el nivel de nicotina baja gradualmente.

Noncommunicable diseases/ enfermedades no contagiosas Las enfermedades que no son causadas por agentes patógenos.

Nonrenewable resources/recursos no renovables Sustancias que no se pueden reemplazar una vez que se han usado.

Nutrient deficiency/deficiencia nutricional Una escasez de un nutriente.

Nutrient density/densidad de los nutrientes La cantidad de nutrientes comparados con las calorías que proporcionan.

Nutrients/nutrientes Sustancias en los alimentos que tu cuerpo necesita.

Nutrition/nutrición El proceso de usar alimentos y sus sustancias para ayudar al cuerpo a tener energía, crecer, desarrollarse y funcionar bien.

Obstetrician/obstetra Médico especialista en el cuidado de la mujer embarazada y el feto en desarrollo y que está presente durante el nacimiento del bebé.

Online shopping/compras en Internet El uso de Internet para comprar productos y servicios.

Ophthalmologist/oftalmólogo Médico especialista en el tratamiento médico y quirúrgico de los ojos y también receta lentes correctivos.

Opportunistic infection/infección oportunista Una enfermedad que ataca a una persona con un sistema inmunológico debilitado que rara vez afecta a una persona saludable.

Optometrist/optómetra Un profesional que examina la vista y que receta lentes correctivos.

Organs/órganos Partes del cuerpo que cumplen funciones determinadas.

Orthodontist/ortodoncista Dentista que previene o corrige problemas en el alineamiento de o el espacio entre los dientes.

Osteoarthritis/osteoartritis Una enfermedad que se caracteriza por el deterioro del cartílago en las articulaciones.

Over-the-counter medicines/ medicinas sin receta Medicinas inofensivas que se pueden consumir sin receta médica.

Overweight/sobrepeso Más del peso apropiado de acuerdo al sexo, estatura, edad, estructura corporal y ritmo de crecimiento.

Ovulation/ovulación El desprendimiento de un óvulo maduro cada mes.

Ozone layer/capa de ozono Una capa protectora sobre la superficie de la Tierra que protege a los seres vivos de la radiación ultravioleta.

Pacemaker/marcapasos Pequeño aparato que envía pulsaciones eléctricas constantes al corazón, para que los latidos sean regulares.

Glosario

Pancreas/páncreas Un órgano que produce enzimas que ayudan en la digestión.

Panic/pánico Un sentimiento repentino de miedo intenso.

Parenting/crianza de hijos El proceso de satisfacer las necesidades físicas, mentales, emocionales y sociales de un niño.

Pathogens/patógenos Organismos diminutos que causan enfermedades contagiosas.

Peer pressure/presión de pares La influencia que personas de tu misma edad tienen sobre ti para que adoptes sus creeencias y forma de actuar.

Percent Daily Value/porcentaje del valor diario El porcentaje de la cantidad diaria recomendada de un nutriente en una porción de alimento.

Periodontal disease/enfermedad periodontal Enfermedad avanzada de las encías en la cual el periostio dental se ve infectado por bacterias.

Periodontium/periostio dental Una estructura que consiste en la mandíbula, las encías y los conectadores llamados ligamentos.

Peripheral nervous system (PNS)/ sistema nervioso periférico Los nervios que conectan al sistema nervioso central con todas partes del cuerpo.

Personality/personalidad La combinación singular de sentimientos, pensamientos y conducta que hacen a una persona diferente de todas las demás.

Personality disorder/trastorno de la personalidad Una variedad de trastornos psicológicos que afectan la habilidad de una persona para llevarse bien con otras.

Pesticide/pesticida Producto que se usa en las cosechas para matar insectos y otras plagas.

Phobia/fobia Un miedo intenso y exagerado de una situación u objeto específico.

Physical activity/actividad física Todo movimiento que usa energía.

Physical dependence/dependencia física Una adicción en que el cuerpo siente una necesidad directa de una droga.

Physical fitness/buen estado físico La capacidad de cumplir con las exigencias físicas de la vida diaria sin cansarse demasiado.

Pituitary gland/glándula pituitaria Una glándula que señala a otras glándulas endocrinas la necesidad de producir hormonas.

Placenta/placenta El tejido espeso y rico que cubre las paredes del útero durante el embarazo y que nutre al feto.

Plaque/placa bacteriana Una película blanda, incolora y pegajosa que contiene bacterias y que se acumula en los dientes.

Point of Service (POS) plan/plan de lugar del servicio Un plan de salud que permite que sus miembros escojan proveedores que participen o no en el plan.

Pollution/contaminación Toda sustancia sucia o nociva en el medio ambiente.

Precaution/precaución Una acción planeada que se toma con anticipación de un suceso, a fin de aumentar las probabilidades de un resultado no peligroso.

Precycling/prereciclaje El proceso de reducir los desechos antes de que se produzcan.

Preferred Provider Organization (PPO)/organización de proveedores preferidos Un plan de seguro de salud en el cual los médicos participantes cobran menos a los miembros del plan.

Prejudice/prejuicio Una opinión negativa e injusta, generalmente en contra de personas de otro grupo racial, religioso o cultural.

Prenatal care/cuidado prenatal Medidas que se toman para cuidar de la salud de una mujer embarazada y su feto.

Preschooler/niño preescolar Un niño de entre tres y cinco años de edad.

Prescription medicines/medicinas bajo receta Medicinas que sólo se pueden vender con receta de un médico.

Preventive care/cuidado preventivo Medidas que se toman para evitar que ocurran enfermedades o daños o que empeoren.

Primary care physician/médico principal Un médico que proporciona a sus pacientes exámenes y cuidado general.

Proteins/proteínas Nutrientes que el cuerpo usa para crear, reparar y mantener células y tejidos.

Protozoa/protozoos Organismos unicelulares que en general no son dañinos pero que pueden causar ciertas enfermedades.

Psychiatrist/psiquiatra Un médico que trata trastornos de la salud mental.

Psychological dependence/dependencia psicológica Una adicción por la cual la mente envía un mensaje al cuerpo indicando que necesita mayor cantidad de una droga

Psychologist/psicólogo Un profesional de la salud mental capacitado y autorizado por el estado para aconsejar y guiar.

Puberty/pubertad La etapa de la vida en la cual comienzas a desarrollar ciertas características físicas propias de los adultos de tu mismo sexo.

Public health/salud pública La protección y el fomento de salud al nivel comunitario.

Pulmonary circulation/circulación pulmonar La circulación que lleva la sangre desde el corazón, a través de los pulmones y de regreso al corazón.

Pupil/pupila Una abertura oscura en el centro del iris.

R

Rape/violación Todo tipo de relación sexual contra la voluntad de la persona.

Recovery/recuperación El proceso de aprender a vivir una vida libre de alcohol.

Recurrence/reaparición El regreso de cáncer después de una remisión.

Refusal skills/destrezas de negación Estrategias de la comunicación para ayudarte a decir no de manera eficaz.

Relationships/relaciones Las conexiones que tienes con otras personas o grupos en tu vida.

Remission/remisión Un periodo durante el cual se desaparecen las señales y síntomas del cáncer.

Reproductive system/aparato reproductor Los órganos que posibilitan la producción de hijos.

Resilience/capacidad de recuperación La habilidad para adaptarse y recuperarse después de una decepción, dificultad o crisis.

Respiratory system/aparato respiratorio Los órganos que proporcionan oxígeno continuamente al cuerpo y que eliminan el bióxido de carbono.

Retina/retina Una capa delgada de neuronas en el ojo que absorben luz.

Rheumatoid arthritis/artritis reumatoide Una enfermedad crónica que se caracteriza por dolor, inflamación, hinchazón y anquilosamiento de las articulaciones.

Rickettsias/rickettsia Organismos que causan enfermedades, que se parecen a bacterias pero que se multiplican como los virus.

Risk behavior/conducta arriesgada Un acto o conducta que puede causarte daño o perjudicarte a ti o a otros.

Risk factors/factores de riesgo Características que aumentan la probabilidad de una persona de contraer una enfermedad.

Saliva/saliva Líquido producido por las glándulas salivales de la boca.

Saturated fats/grasas saturadas Grasas que son sólidas a temperatura ambiente.

Schizophrenia/esquizofrenia Un trastorno mental grave por el cual una persona pierde contacto con la realidad.

Secondhand smoke/humo secundario Aire que ha sido contaminado por el humo del tabaco.

Sedentary lifestyle/estilo de vida sedentaria Un modo de vivir caracterizado por la escasez de actividad física.

Self-concept/autoconcepto La manera en que te ves a ti mismo.

Self-control/dominio de sí mismo Control de tus propias emociones y deseos.

Self-esteem/autoestima La opinión que tienes de ti mismo y cuánto te valoras.

Self-respect/dignidad propia El sentimiento positivo que tienes de ti mismo cuando cumples con tus creencias y valores.

Sexual harassment/acoso sexual Conducta sexual no solicitada y fuera de lugar dirigida a otra persona.

Sexually transmitted diseases (STDs)/enfermedades de transmisión sexual (ETS) Enfermedades que se propagan de una persona a otra a través de contacto sexual.

Shock/choque Una afección que puede causar la muerte en la cual el aparato circulatorio no lleva la suficiente cantidad de sangre a tejidos y órganos vitales.

Side effect/efecto colateral Todo efecto reacción inesperada de una medicina.

Sidestream smoke/humo indirecto El humo producido por la colilla encendida de un cigarrillo, cigarro o pipa.

Skeletal muscle/músculo del sistema osteoarticular Músculo ligado a huesos que te permiten mover el cuerpo.

Skeletal system/sistema osteoarticular Sistema corporal interno compuesto de huesos, articulaciones y tejidos conjuntivos.

Small intestine/intestino delgado Un órgano digestivo enrollado y semejante a un tubo que mide unos 20 pies de largo.

Smog/smog Una neblina de color amarillo-café que se forma cuando la luz solar reacciona con la contaminación del aire.

Smooth muscle/músculo liso Tipo de músculo que se encuentra en los órganos, los vasos sanguíneos y las glándulas.

Sobriety/sobriedad Vivir sin consumir alcohol.

Social age/edad social La edad calculada de acuerdo a tu estilo de vida y las conexiones que tienes con otras.

Social health/salud social Tu habilidad para llevarte bien con las personas que te rodean.

Somatic system/sistema somático La parte del sistema nervioso relacionada con las acciones que tú controlas.

Specialist/especialista Médico que está capacitado para tratar determinada clase de pacientes o problemas de salud.

Sperm/espermatozoide Células reproductoras masculinas.

Sperm cell/espermatozoide La célula del padre que entra en el óvulo durante la fertilización.

Sports conditioning/entrenamiento deportivo Actividad física normal o ejercicios para fortalecer y entrenar los músculos para un deporte determinado.

Sprain/torcedura Una afección en que los ligamentos que mantienen las articulaciones en su lugar están distendidos o quebrados.

Stepparent/padrastro o madrastra La persona que se casa con la madre o el padre de un niño.

Stimulants/estimulantes Sustancias que aceleran las funciones del cuerpo.

Stress/estrés La reacción de tu cuerpo a cambios.

Stress management skills/habilidad de controlar el éstres Maneras de tratar y superar los problemas.

Stressor/factor estresante Todo lo que provoca el estrés.

Stroke/apoplejía Una afección que ocurre cuando un vaso sanguíneo que lleva oxígeno al cerebro estalla o se obstruye.

Subcutaneous layer/capa subcutánea Una capa de grasa debajo de la piel.

Suicide/suicidio Matarse intencionalmente.

Support system/sistema de asistencia Una red de personas dispuestas a ayudar cuando haya necesidad.

Systemic circulation/circulación sistémica El flujo de sangre a todos los tejidos del cuerpo excepto los pulmones.

Tar/alquitrán Un líquido espeso, oscuro y pegajoso que se forma al quemarse el tabaco.

Tartar/sarro Placa endurecida que se forma en la superficie de los dientes y que es difícil de quitar.

Team sports/deportes en equipo Actividades físicas organizadas, con reglas específicas, en las cuales grupos de personas juegan contra otros grupos.

Tendons/tendones Bandas de tejidos fuertes que unen los músculos y los huesos.

Therapy/terapia Tratamiento.

Time management/organización del tiempo Estrategias para usar el tiempo eficazmente.

Tissues/tejidos Masa de células similares que desempeñan una función específica.

Toddler/niño que empieza a andar Un niño de entre uno y tres años de edad que está aprendiendo a caminar y a hablar.

Tolerance/tolerancia Una afección por la cual el cuerpo de una persona se acostumbra a los efectos de una medicina y necesita mayor cantidad para que ésta sea eficaz.

Tornado/tornado Una tormenta de viento en torbellino, con forma de embudo, que gira en grandes círculos y que puede caer del cielo a la tierra.

Trachea/tráquea Vía respiratoria que dirige el aire a los pulmones.

Tumor/tumor Una masa de células anormales.

Type 1 diabetes/diabetes tipo 1 Una afección por la cual el sistema inmunológico ataca las células productoras de insulina en el páncreas.

Type 2 diabetes/diabetes tipo 2 Una afección que se caracteriza por la inhabilidad del cuerpo para usar de manera eficaz la insulina que produce.

Umbilical cord/cordón umbilical El conducto que conecta el feto a la placenta de la madre.

Unconditional love/amor incondicional Amor sin restricciones ni reservas.

Underweight/de peso insuficiente Por debajo del peso apropiado de acuerdo al sexo, estatura, edad, estructura corporal y ritmo de crecimiento.

Universal precautions/precauciones universales Medidas para prevenir la propagación de enfermedades al tratar toda la sangre como si estuviera contaminada.

Unsaturated fats/grasas no saturadas Las grasas que permanecen líquidas a temperatura ambiente.

Uterus/útero Un órgano en forma de pera dentro del cuerpo de la mujer donde se nutre un feto.

Vaccine/vacuna Un preparado de gérmenes muertos o debilitados que causa que el sistema inmunológico produzca anticuerpos.

Values/valores Las creencias y los ideales que guían la manera en que vive una persona.

Vector/vector Un organismo, por ejemplo un insecto, que transmite un agente patógeno.

Veins/venas Vasos sanguíneos que llevan la sangre desde el cuerpo de regreso al corazón.

Violence/violencia Todo acto que causa daño físico o psicológico a una persona o bien.

Virus/virus El organismo causante de enfermedades más pequeño.

Vitamins/vitaminas Sustancias que el cuerpo necesita en pequeñas cantidades para regular sus funciones.

Warm-up/precalentamiento Un periodo de ejercicio suave que se hace para preparar al cuerpo para actividad más vigorosa.

Warranty/garantía La promesa escrita de reparar un producto si no funciona bien.

Wellness/bienestar general Un estado de bienestar, o salud total.

Win-win solution/situación en que todos ganan Un acuerdo en que todos reciben algo que desean.

Withdrawal/síndrome de abstinencia Los síntomas físicos y psicológicos que ocurren cuando una persona deja de usar una sustancia adictiva.

Zero tolerance policy/normativa de tolerancia nula Una normativa en que no hay excepciones para nadie por ninguna razón.

Index

Note: Page numbers in *italics* refer to art and marginal features.

A

AA (Alcoholics Anonymous), 327
Abdominal muscle strength/endurance, 226, *227*
Abdominal thrusts, 533, *534*
Absorption of medicine, *273*
Abstinence, 17, 151–155
  advocating for, 153
  for AIDS prevention, 464
  definitions of, 152
  from drugs, 240
  for HIV prevention, 464
  and meeting emotional needs, 95
  as only 100% effective preventive measure, 155
  to prevent emotional trauma, *152*
  to prevent STDs, 459
  reasons for, 165
  rewards of, 155
  and setting limits, 151–152
  from sexual activity, 152–155
  and sexually transmitted diseases, 459–460
Abuse, 177–181
  of alcohol, 328–329
  alcohol use and abusive behavior, 328
  avoiding, 180
  coping with, 127
  cycle of, 179, 180
  of drugs, 276, 278
  effects of, 179
  emotional, 178
  help for, 180, 181
  neglect as, 178
  physical, 177
  sexual, 178
  of stimulants, 277
Acceptance
  of individual differences, 123, 429
  as stage of facing death, 107
  for strengthening relationships, 123
  and tobacco use, 309
Accessing information, 45–46
  on body systems, 408–409
  on communicable diseases, 456
  on community health care, 66
  by reading food labels, 206
  reliable sources for, *45,* 78–79
  scoliosis screening, 370
  on support groups, 496
  through health education, 19
  in weather emergencies, 522
Accident chain, 508, *509*
Accidental injuries, 508
  and alcohol use, 325
  from athletics, 402
  preventing. *See* Safety
  in workouts, 232
Accidents, 508
Accomplishment, sense of, 94
Acid rain, 548
Acne, 241, 344–345
Acquired immunity, 452
Active immunity, 452
Active listening, 37
Activity plan (fitness), 232
Addiction, 277, 304
  to alcohol, 326–329

  to amphetamines, 278
  to cocaine and crack, 279
  to diet pills, 254
  to drugs, 287
  of family member, 127
  to inhalants, 283
  to tobacco, 304–305
  types of, 304
  and withdrawal, 305
Addictive drugs, 300
Admiration, 123
Adolescence, 8–13, *427, 429–430, 431*
  alcohol use during, 323
  common stressors during, *40*
  emotional development during, 11
  in Erikson's life stages, *427*
  growth and development during, 429–430, *431*
  health care screenings during, 64, *65*
  mental development during, 10
  and parenthood, 132–133
  physical development during, 9–10, *431*
  risk behaviors during, 16
  social development during, 12–13
  and tobacco advertising, 303
  tobacco use during, 305, 308
Adrenal glands, *397,* 398
Adrenaline, 40, 380, 398
Adulthood, *427,* 432–433
Adults
  choking first aid for, 533, *534*
  discussing problems with, 9, 98, 152
  limits set by, 151
  seeking help from, 104, 310
  in support system, 47
Advertising
  of alcohol, 332
  antidrug ads, *279*
  definition of, 59
  fact vs. opinion in, 70
  and food choices, *193*
  fraud in, *69*
  hidden advertising, 60
  incomplete information in, *200*
  of medicines, *275*
  misleading information in, *46*
  of sports drinks, *238*
  techniques used in, *60*
  of tobacco, 303, *310*
  and tobacco use, 309
  truth in, *310*
  understanding appeal of, 59
  and value of bigger sizes, *209*
  verifying claims in, *46*
Advocacy, 61
  for alcohol dangers, 333
  for consumers, 70
  definition of, 61
  against drug use, 292–293
  for health, 61
  for healthy eating, 214–215, 394
  for HIV/AIDS prevention, 466
  for lifestyle, 478
  for noise reduction, 359
  for preventing school violence, 174
  for public health, 74
  supporting abstinence, 153
Aerobic exercise, 100, 231, 233, 234

Affection, 123, 153
Age and aging, 434, 435
AIDS (acquired immunodeficiency syndrome), 464–467. *See also* HIV
Air
  human need for, 381
  pollution of, 384, 547–548, 553
Al-Anon, 328
Alateen, 328
Albinism, 422
Alcohol, 320–333
  abstinence from, 17
  and alcoholism, 326–329
  alternatives to using, 333
  and birth defects, 424
  and blood alcohol concentration, 322
  and cancer prevention, 488
  as cause of conflict, 167
  as depressant, 280
  and disease prevention, 457
  and driving, 325, 326, 514
  effects of, 320–321
  effects on fetus, 424
  and fetal alcohol syndrome, 322–323, 424
  HIV and use of, 467
  and negative peer pressure, 148
  and nervous system health, 389
  reasons for drinking, 330
  reasons for refusing, 331
  and risk of sexual activity, 152
  societal effects of, 325–329
  and teen drownings, 518
  teen use of, 323
  use of, as risk behavior, 16
  and violence, 167
Alcohol abuse counselors, 339
Alcoholics Anonymous (AA), 327
Alcoholism, 326–329
Algae, 549
Allergens, 480–481
Allergies, 383, *477,* 480–481
Alternatives
  to drinking alcohol, 333
  to drug use, 289
  to tobacco use, 310, 311
Aluminum products, 554
Alveoli, 382
Alzheimer's disease, 388, *477*
American Cancer Society, 75, 311
American Heart Association, 75, 311
American Lung Association, 311
American Red Cross, 75, 379
Amino acids, 197
Amphetamines, 277, 278
Anabolic steroids, 241, 285
Analyzing influences, 48–49
  on body image, 262–263
  external influences, *23,* 48–49
  internal influences, *23,* 48
  on mental/emotional health, 23
  on parenting skills, 131
  on physical health, 22
  on self-image, 362–363
  on social health, 23
  on tobacco use, 309
Anemia, 252, *379,* 380
Anger, 92

and conflict, 165–166
  coping skills for, *166*
  expressing, 94
  managing, *166*
  physical responses to, 165
  as stage of facing death, 107
  as stage of grief process, 108
Angina pectoris, 491
Angioplasty, 492
Anorexia nervosa, 256–257
Antibiotics, 272, 275
Antibodies, 272, 452
Antidepressants, 104
Antidrug ads, *279*
Antigens, 452
Antihistamines, 481
Anus, 393
Anvil (ear), *357, 358*
Anxiety, 41, 92–94, *102,* 241, 289
Anxiety disorders, 96, *97,* 104
Appearance. *See also* Personal health care
  and physical activity, *42*
  and teeth/mouth, 349
  and tobacco use, 302
Appendicitis, 394
Appetite, 193, 201
Aqueous humor, *354*
Armstrong, Lance, *488*
Arteries, *377, 378,* 489
Arteriosclerosis, 380, 489–490
Arthritis, *477,* 495–497
Asbestos, 479, 551
Assertive behavior, 149, 310
Assisted living facilities, 67
Asthma, 383, 476, *477,* 482–483
Asthma and Allergy Foundation of
    America, 75
Astigmatism, 356
Atherosclerosis, 489–490
Athlete's foot, 447
Athletic trainers, 247
Atrium, *377*
Attention, gaining
  acceptable methods of, 31
  by demonstrating good character, 121
  sexual activity for, 95
Attitude, 18, 90
Autonomic nervous system, 388
Availability, food, *193*
Avocados, 197
Avoidance techniques, *152*
AZT, 467

B

B cells, 452, 465
BAC (blood alcohol concentration), 322
Backbone, 368, *369*
Bacteria, 272, 275, 446
Bacterial infections, 447
Bad breath, 353
Balance, 5–6, *221,* 358
Ball-and-socket joints, 369
Bar/bat mitzvahs, *9*
Barbiturates, *279, 280*
Bargaining, as stage of facing death, 107
Battery, 177
Beans, 197, 199, *204, 205,* 206, *211,* 253
Beauty products, fraud related to, *69*
Behavior. *See also* Practicing healthful
    behaviors
  assertive, 149
  generational differences in, 48
  health-promoting, 125
  for meeting emotional needs, 95
  risk behaviors, 15–17, 151, 255
  self-destructive, 16

sports-related, 239
  therapy for changing, 104
Behavioral health assessment, *65*
Belonging, need for, 94, 144
Benign tumors, 484
Better Business Bureau, 70
Beverages, 200, 201, 203
Bicycle safety, 515
Bidis, 299
Bile, 392
Billboards, 59, *303*
Binge drinking, 322
Binge eating disorder, 258
Biodegradable materials, 553
Biological age, 434
Biological therapy, 102
Biopsy, 487
Bipolar disorder, 97
Birth
  process of, 404
  stages of, 420
Birth defects, 424, 476, 477
Birthing centers, 67
Blackheads, *345*
Bladder, 393
Bleeding
  first aid for, 535
  nosebleeds, 531
Blended families, 126
Blizzards, 522
Blood, 377–379
  circulation of, 376
  donated, 465–466
  pathogens spread by, 448
Blood alcohol concentration (BAC), 322
Blood pressure, 241, 252, 378–380, 398,
    490, 491
Blood sugar level, 209, *397,* 398
Blood vessels, *321,* 373, 377, 378
BMI (Body Mass Index), 251
Body composition, 228
Body image, 250–251
  definition of, 250
  and eating disorders, 256–259
  unrealistic, 254
  and weight, 250–255
Body language, 35–38, 149
Body Mass Index (BMI), 251
Body systems
  circulatory system, 376–380
  digestive system, 390–392, 394
  endocrine system, 396–399
  excretory system, 392–394
  formation of, *417,* 418
  muscular system, 372–375
  nervous system, 385–389
  reproductive system, 400–405
  respiratory system, 381–384
  skeletal system, 368–371
Body temperature, *345*
Body wraps, 254
Bone mass, 371
Bones, 368, *369,* 371, 529
  broken, 529
  dislocations, 370
  fractures, 370, 529
Boredom, managing, 89
Braces, 353
Brain, *282, 321, 355,* 386–388, 491
Brain cancer, 241
Brain stem, *387*
Bread, 199, 202, *204, 205, 211*
Breakfast, 208
Breast cancer, 485
Breastfeeding, antibody transfer in, 452
Breathing, 41, 382, *383, 387*
Breathing emergencies, 525

Bribes, 148
Bronchi, *382*
Bronchial tubes, 482
Bronchitis, 383
Bronchodilators, 483
Brushing teeth, 47, 352
Buddy system, 517
Bulimia (bulimia nervosa), 257
Bullying, 166
Burns, first aid for, 530
Business groups, 70
Butter, 197, 203
Buying decisions, 59. *See also* Consumer
    choices
Bypass surgery, 492

C

Caffeine, 199, 201, 277
Calcium, 194, *198,* 199, 238, 370, 371
Calories, 192, *207,* 209
  adjusting intake of, 253, 254
  from carbohydrates, 196
  empty, 209
  from fats, 197, 252
  food label information on, 206
  and nutrient density, 206, 210
  and weight, 253
Camping safety, 518
Cancer, 252, *477,* 484–488
  causes of, 485, 486
  common types of, *485*
  diagnosis/treatment of, 487
  in females, 405
  in males, 402
  preventing, 487–488
  from steroid use, 241
  and tobacco use, 299, 300
  and UV rays, 346
  warning signs of, *486*
Capillaries, 378
Carbohydrates, 196, *207,* 238, 375
Carbon dioxide, 381, 382
Carbon monoxide, 300, 307, 479
Cardiac muscle, 373
Cardiopulmonary resuscitation (CPR), 526,
    531, 536, 537
Cardiovascular disease, *477*
Cardiovascular exercise, 224, 225
Cardiovascular system. *See* Circulatory
    system
Careers in health
  alcohol abuse counselor, 339
  athletic trainer, 247
  dental hygienist, 441
  ecologist, 563
  emergency medical technician, 543
  health services administrator, 81
  home health aide, 217
  medical record technician, 295
  mental health counselor, 115
  nurse practitioner, 473
  occupational therapist, 503
  physical therapist, 412
  physician's assistant, 55
  professional mediator, 187
  psychologist, 265
  registered nurse, 25
  respiratory therapist, 317
  school counselor, 161
  social worker, 139
  speech therapist, 365
Caring, *120,* 122
  in friendships, 143
  for grieving friends, *108*
  for ill family member, 128

for people with noncommunicable diseases, *478*
and self-concept, *87*
as trait of dating partner, 146
Carriers (HIV), 464
Cartilage, 370, 497
CDC. *See* Centers for Disease Control and Prevention
Cells, 416, *417,* 484. *See also specific types*
Cementum (tooth), 350
Centers for Disease Control and Prevention (CDC), 46, *73,* 346
Central nervous system (CNS), 386–388
Cereals, 199, *204, 205,* 211
Cerebellum, *387*
Cerebral palsy, *477*
Cerebrum, *387*
Cervix, *403, 404,* 420
CFCs (chlorofluorocarbons), 547
Character, 119–123
and caring, *87, 108, 478*
and citizenship, *12, 28, 123, 306, 526, 557*
community, 122
and fairness, *119*
and health, 121
at home, 122
primary traits of, 119, *120*
and respect, *258, 433*
and responsibility, *94, 148, 155, 228, 322, 331, 351, 402, 529*
at school, 122
and self-discipline, *17, 31*
and sportsmanship, *237*
Character traits, 119, *120,* 121–122
Checkups. *See* Health screenings
Cheese, 197, 204, *205,* 211
Chemical dependency
on alcohol, 326
on amphetamines, 278
on drugs, 277
on nicotine, 300, 304
Chemicals
air pollution from, 547
noncommunicable diseases related to, 479
Chemotherapy, 487
Chest compressions, 536, *537*
Chewing tobacco, 299
Chicken pox, *455*
Child abuse, 328
Childhood, *427,* 428–429
Children
choking in, 533, *534*
as market for tobacco industry, 303
and secondhand smoke, 307
Chlamydia, 460, *462*
Chlorofluorocarbons (CFCs), 547
Choices, 4. *See also* Decision making
comparing, 60
of food, 193–194. *See also* Nutrition
and H.E.L.P. criteria, 29
lifestyle, 14, *15*
right to, 61
Choking, 533–534
Cholera, 550
Cholesterol, 197, 199, 200, 203
Chromosomes, 422
Chronic diseases, 476
Chronological age, 434
Cigarettes, 299
Cigars, 299
Cilia, 300, *382*
Circulatory system, 376–380
and blood, 378–379
and bones, 368

diseases of, 489–493
parts of, 377
problems of, 379–380
tobacco's effects on, *301*
Cirrhosis, *321,* 394
Citizenship, *12, 28, 120,* 122, 123, *306, 526, 557*
Clinical depression, 97, 98
Clinics, health care, 65
Cliques, 144
Clove cigarettes, 299
Club drugs, 278, 283–284
CNS. *See* Central nervous system
Coaches, support from, 47
Cocaine, 277–279
Cocaine Anonymous, 287
Cochlea (ear), *357,* 358
Cold sores, 346
"Cold turkey," quitting, 311
Cold water, survival in, *517*
Colds, 383, 448, 454
Colon, 393
Colon and rectum (colorectal) cancer, 394, *485*
Color blindness, 355
.com Web sites, 46, 78
Commitment, 129
Common colds. *See* Colds
Communicable diseases, 446–467
causes of, 446–447
common cold, 454
defenses against, 450–453
hepatitis, 456
HIV/AIDS, 464–467
influenza, 455
mononucleosis, 456
prevention of, 457
sexually transmitted diseases, 458–463
spread of, 448, 449
strep throat, 455
symptoms/contagious periods of, *455*
vaccines for, 272
Communication, 93, 128, 130
Communication skills, 34–38
and alcohol use, 324
body language, 35
for discussing questions with parents/adults, 9, 152
for expressing emotions, 91–95
for helping abuse victims, 180
"I" messages, 35, 36
listening skills, 11, 37
refusal skills, 37–38
sending the right message, 136–137
for sexual abstinence, 459, 460
speaking skills, 11, 36
for strengthening relationships, 123
writing sympathy notes, 107
Communities
alcohol-free events in, 333
making a difference in, 122
roles in, 13
safety efforts in, 176
tobacco-free events in, 311
Community health, 66, 72, 74
influence of billboards on, *303*
media and technology influence on, 49
negative and positive relationships influencing, 13
and violence in media, *173*
Comparison shopping, 60–61
Compensation, right to, 61
Complex carbohydrates, 196
Compromise, 168
Concussion, 388
Cones (eyes), 355

Conflict, 164–167
Conflict resolution, 168–171
mediation for, 169
with parents, 438–439
practicing, 184–185
principles of, 168
T.A.L.K. strategies for, *169*
Connective tissues, 370
Consequences
of alcohol use, 320–323, 325, 331
definition of, 165
of drug misuse/abuse, 276–280
of drunk driving, 325
foreseeing, 10
of medicine use, 274, 275
of risk behaviors, 16–17
of sexual activity, 154–155
of teen parenthood, 133
of tobacco use, 299–302
of using illegal drugs, 281–285
Conservation, 553, 554
Construction materials, diseases related to, 479
Consumer advocates, 70
Consumer choices, 58–75
and health advocacy, 61
as health habits, 58–62
of health services, 63–67
new options for, 62
and problems with health care, 68–71
and public health care system, 72–75
reliable information for, 58–61
Consumer Product Safety Commission (CPSC), 73
Consumers, 58, 61, 70–71
Consumers Union, *59,* 70
Contact lenses, 356, 357
Contagious period, 449, *455*
Continuing care facilities, 67
Cooking, for good nutrition, 204
Cool-down exercises, 234, 239
Coordination, *221*
Coping skills and strategies
for abuse, 127
for anger management, *166*
for death of loved one, 109
for family changes, 128
for feelings of inadequacy, 89
for improving mental/emotional health, 88–90
for negative peer pressure, 148
for stress, *39*
using alcohol as, 327
Core ethical values, 30, 119
Cornea, *354*
Counseling
for abuse, 127, 180
for anorexia, 257
for coping with grief, 109
for eating disorders, 258, *259*
for mental/emotional problems, 103–104
for quitting tobacco, 311
Cowper's glands, 401
CPR. *See* Cardiopulmonary resuscitation
CPSC (Consumer Product Safety Commission), 73
Crack, 277, *278,* 279
Cramped muscles, 374
Creativity, 429
Crimes, 167, 172, 173, 323
Crisis centers, 180, 181
Critical issues in problem solving, 29
Critical thinking
about food selection, *209*
about health information, 45
about medicine ads, *275*

Index

about selecting health-related services/products, 70
about sports drinks claims, *238*
about tobacco ads, *310*
to analyze weight modification practices, 254
to analyze/interpret media messages, 45, 70, *209, 238, 275, 310*
for traffic safety, 514
Cross-training, 225
Crown (tooth), 350
Cultural context, *36*
Culture, 49, *193,* 478
Cumulative risks, 17
Curiosity, influence of, 48
Curl-ups, 226
Cuticle, 348
Cycle of abuse, 179, 180
Cystic fibrosis, *477*

D

Daily Values, 206, *207*
Dairy products, 197, 200, 203, 204, 206
Dandruff, 348
Date rape
and alcohol use, 323
drugs used in, 284
Dating, 146, 151, 152, 460
Deafness, 425
Death(s)
and alcohol use, 322, 323, 325
and club drug use, 284
coping with, 106, 109
from firearm injuries, 173
from flash floods, 522
and grief process, 108
and hallucinogen use, 282
from homicide, 172
from inhalants, 283
from injuries, 508
from intoxicated driving, 514
as part of life cycle, 433
from physical abuse, 127
stages of facing, 106, 107
from street drugs, 281
and tobacco use, 298, 299, 308
by violent acts, 172
Decibels, 358, 359
Decision making, 28–30
and character, 121–122
to develop focus on future, 28
on drug use, 286
and eating disorders, 258
on help for alcohol use, 336–337
influences on, 59
for managing chronic conditions, 483
negative peer pressure for, 148
process of, 29–30
on snack choices, 210
on suggesting mediation, 170
for traffic safety, 514
when friends seem depressed, 99
Defensive driving, 515
Degenerative diseases, 476
Dehydration, 238
Deliberate injuries, preventing, *172*
Delusions, 241
Demeaning statements, 123
Denial, in facing death, 106
Dental hygienist, 441
Dental screenings, *65,* 351
Dentin (tooth), 350
Department of Health and Human Services (HHS), 72, *73*

Dependence
chemical dependency, 277. *See also* Chemical dependency
on drugs, 278, 280. *See also* Addiction
physical, 283, 304
psychological, 282, 304
Depressants, 279–280, 320
Depression, 97–100, *102,* 289
clinical, 97, 98
and cocaine use, 279
and eating disorders, 256, 258
as stage of facing death, 107
as stage of grief process, 108
stress as cause of, 41
talking about, *104*
therapy for, 103
Dermatologists, 64, 345
Dermis, 344
Designer drugs, 283
Desires, influence of, 48
Detoxification, 288
Development. *See* Growth and development
Developmental tasks, 426, 430
Diabetes, 252, 258, 398, 476, 494–495
Diaphragm, *382,* 384
Diarrhea, 394
Diastolic pressure, 378
Dietary Guidelines for Americans, 202–203, 252
Diets and dieting, 16, 251, 254. *See also* Eating disorders; Nutrition
Differences, acceptance of, 123, 429
Digestion, definition of, 390
Digestive system, *301,* 390–392, 394, *481*
Dignity, respect for, 87
Disability, coping with, 126
Disasters, 109
Disease prevention. *See also specific diseases*
for communicable diseases, 449
health habits for, 457
for noncommunicable diseases, 478
and spread of HIV, 467
for STDs, 459
Diseases. *See also specific diseases*
active management of, 454
chronic, 476
of circulatory system, 489–493
communicable, 446–467
degenerative, 476
dental, 353
of nervous system, 388
noncommunicable, 476–497
from polluted water, 550
from secondhand smoke, 307
and tobacco use, 299, 300, *301*
types of, 446, *447*
Dislocations. *See* Bones
Distress, 39
Divorce, 126, 130
Doctors, 64, 65, 71
Down syndrome, 422, *477*
Drinking. *See* Alcohol
Driving
defensive, 515
and drinking, 322, 325, 326
safety guidelines for, 514
Drowning prevention, 517–518
Drug slipping, 284
Drug treatment centers, 67, 288
Drugs, 270–289. *See also* Medicines
abstinence from, 17, 240
addiction to, 287, 304
addictive, 300
alcohol, 320–333
alternatives to using, 289

amphetamines, 278
anabolic steroids, 285
antidepressants, 104
and birth defects, 424
as cause of conflict, 167
club drugs, 283–284
cocaine, 278–278
crack, 279
depressants, 279–280
and disease prevention, 457
effects on fetus, 424
hallucinogens, 282, *283*
heroin, 277
HIV and use of, 465, 467
illegal, 281–285
inhalants, 283
kicking drug habits, 287–288
marijuana, 281–282
medicines as, 270–275
methamphetamine, 278
misuse/abuse of, 276
narcotics, 277
and negative peer pressure, 148
and nervous system health, 389
performance-enhancing, 241
reasons for avoiding, 286
and risk of sexual activity, 152
stimulants, 277–279
street drugs, 281
treatment programs for abuse of, 287–288
use of, as risk behavior, 16
and violence, 167, 173
Drunk driving, 325, 326
Dry beans, 197, 199, *205, 211*
Duodenum, 391

E

Early adulthood, 433
Early childhood, *427,* 428
Ears, 357–359, 370
Earthquakes, 523
Eating. *See* Food(s); Nutrition
Eating disorders, 256–259
Eating out, 210
Ecologists, 563
Ecstasy (E, X, XTC), 284
Egg cells (ova), *400,* 403, 404, 416, 422
Eggs (food), 197, 200, *205, 211*
Ejaculation, 401
Electrical shock, 510
Embryo, 404, 418
Emergencies. *See also* First aid
natural disasters, 109
Red Cross response to, 75
steps to take in, 525–527
weather, 520–523
Emergency medical technicians, 543
Emissions control, 552
Emotional abuse, 178
Emotional development, 10, 430
Emotional health. *See* Mental/emotional health
Emotional maturity, 130
Emotional need(s), 94–95
for attention, 31, 95, 121
conflicts involving, 165
and food, 194
increased awareness of, 11
Emotions, 91–95. *See also* Mental/emotional health
during adolescence, 11
and coping with death, 109
expressing, 91–95
identifying, 92

managing, 89, 90
physical activity and changes in, 42
problems with. *See* Mental and
  emotional problems
relationship of stress to, 41
and sexual activity, *152, 155*
sharing, 128
and sports, 239
and stress management, 112–113
and teen parenthood, 133
Empathy, 92, 143
Emphysema, 299, 383
Empty calories, 209
Enamel (tooth), 350
Endocrine system, 396–399
Endometrium, *403*
Endurance
  heart and lung, 224–225
  muscle, 225–227
Energy
  calories as measure of, 192, 209, 253
  conservation of, 553, *554*
  food choice and expenditure of, 228
  from fossil fuels, 547
  from incinerators, 550
  from proteins, 197
  from sugars, 196
Environment, 546–557
  and air pollution, 547–548
  allergens in, 383
  definition of, 546
  emissions control, 552
  as external influence, 49, 546
  and land pollution, 550–551
  noncommunicable diseases related to,
    479
  and pollution prevention/reduction,
    552–557
  and prenatal development, 423–425
  protection of, 556–557
  waste management, 550–552
  and water pollution, 549–550
Environmental Protection Agency (EPA),
  552
Enzymes, 390, 391
Epidermis, 344
Epididymis, 401
Epiglottis, *382*
Epilepsy, 388
Equipment, sports, 239
Erikson, Erik, 426, *427*
Escalation of conflict, 165, 167
Esophagus, *321,* 391
Essential amino acids, 197
Ethical values, 30, 119
Eustachian tube, 358
Eustress, 39
Evaluate, definition of, 30
Excretion, definition of, 393
Excretory system, 392–394
Exercise(s), 220. *See also* Physical activity
    and fitness
  aerobic, 222, 231
  anaerobic, 222
  and bone health, 371
  cardiovascular, 224, 225
  for flexibility, 229
  limits in, 240
  for muscle strength/endurance, 226
  and osteoporosis, 370
  rating of, *230*
  relaxation, 222
  stretching, 233, 234, 374
  three stages of, 232–234
Exhaling, 382
Exhaustion, 40

Expectations, realistic, 89
Expressing emotions, 93–94
Extended family, 124
External influences, *23,* 48–49, 59, 309
Eye contact, 36, 149
Eyeglasses, 356, 357
Eyes, 354–357
  allergic responses in, *481*
  foreign objects in, 531
  health screenings for, *65*
  protecting, 356

F

Fact, opinion vs., 70
Fad diets, 254
Fainting, 531
Fairness, 119, *120,* 122, 146
Fallopian tubes, *403,* 404
Falls, preventing, 509
Families, 124–128
  and alcohol abuse, 328–329
  changes in, 126–128
  and eating disorders, 259
  as external health influence, 48
  and food choices, *193*
  and health triangle, *125*
  health-promoting behaviors in, 125
  and mental health problems, 104, 105
  positive interactions in, 127
  relating to, 12
  roles of, 124–125
  strengthening, 128
  support from, 47
  and tobacco use, 309
Family counselors, 105
Family therapy, 103
Farsightedness, 356
FAS. *See* Fetal alcohol syndrome
Fashion models, *257*
Fasting, 254
Fatigue, 40
Fat(s), 197
  in body composition, 228, 252, 253
  calories from, 252
  and circulatory system health, 380
  as nutrient, 199, 200, 203, *205,* 206, *207,*
    209
  and sports activity, 238
  trans fats, 197
Fat-soluble vitamins, 198
FDA. *See* Food and Drug Administration
Fear, 41, 48, 92, 93, 96
Feces, 393
Federal government
  consumer assistance offices, 71
  health services provided by, 72–74
  Web sites of, 46
Federal Trade Commission (FTC), 73
Feedback, 37
Feelings. *See* Emotions
Females
  calories required by, 253
  flexibility test for, *228*
  heart/lung endurance test for, *225*
  physical development in, 9, *431*
  reproductive system in, 402–405
  self-examinations for, 486
  steroids' effects on, 241
  strength/endurance tests for, *227*
Fertilization, 403, 404, 416
Fetal alcohol syndrome (FAS), 322–323,
    424, 477
Fetuses, 307, 322, 404, 418–419
Fever, 394, 451
Fiber, 199, *207*

Fight-or-flight response, 40, 398
Financial problems, 126, 133
Fingernails, 348
Fire safety, 511–512
Firearms. *See* Guns
First aid, 524–537
  cardiopulmonary resuscitation, 536, *537*
  for choking, 533–534
  for common emergencies, 528–532
  emergency procedure steps, 525–527
  for life-threatening emergencies,
    533–537
  preparation for, 524
  for severe bleeding, 535
  for shock, 534
  supplies for, 524–525
  universal precautions when giving, 525
First-degree burns, *530*
Fish, *205, 211*
Fitness. *See* Physical fitness
Flashbacks, 282
Flexibility, 228–229, *230*
Floods, 522
Flossing teeth, 47, 352
Flu, 383, 455
Fluoride, *198*
Foldables
  for alcohol, 319
  for body weight, 249
  for building blocks of life, 415
  for conflict, 163
  for decision-making process, 27
  for friendships, 141
  for good character, 117
  for health and wellness, 3
  for health consumerism, 57
  for medicines and drugs, 269
  for mental and emotional health, 85
  for noncommunicable diseases, 475
  for nutrients, 191
  for pathogens and disease, 445
  for physical activity and fitness, 219
  for pollution, 545
  for safety, 507
  for skeletal system, 367
  for skin health, 343
  for tobacco effects, 297
Food and Drug Administration (FDA), 46,
    73, 270
Food groups, 202, 204, *205,* 206, *211,* 238,
    253
Food Guide Pyramid, 202, 204–206, 208,
    209, 254
Food labels, 206, 207
Food Safety and Inspection Service (FSIS),
    73
Foodborne illness, 203
Food(s). *See also* Nutrition
  choices of, 193–194, *204*
  and emotions, 194
  pathogens spread by, 448
  preparation of, 204
  safe handling of, 203, 449
Fossil fuels, 547, 548, 553
Fractures. *See* Bones
Fraternal twins, 416
Fraud, 68, *69*
Friends, 142–143
  as external influences, 49
  and food choices, *193*
  and help with eating disorders, 259
  relating to, 12
  and tobacco use, 310
  wise choice of, 175
Fruits, 199, 200, 203, *204, 205, 211,* 253
FSIS (Food Safety and Inspection
    Service), 73

FTC (Federal Trade Commission), 73
Fungi, 447
Future, focus on, 28

G

Gallbladder, 392
Gallstones, 394
Gangs, 173
Gastric juices, 391, *450*
General anxiety disorder, *97*
Genes, 422, 477
Genetic disorders, 422, 476, 477
Genital herpes, 461, *462*
Genital warts, 461, *462*
Georgia Home Boy, 284
German measles, 425
Germs, 446. *See also* Pathogens
Gestures, 149
GHB, 284
Gingivitis, 353
Glands, 344, 396
    of endocrine system, 396–397
    muscle in, 373
    reproductive, 401
    in stomach, 391
Gliding joints, 369
Global warming, 548
Glucose, 494, *495*
Goal setting, 28, 31–33
    benefits of, 31–32
    building skills for, 32
    to develop focus on future, 28
    and limit setting, 158–159
    for physical fitness, 230–232
    process of, *33*
    receiving positive attention for, 31
    strategies for, 32
    for tobacco abstinence, 314–315
Goals
    health-related, 28
    long- and short-term, 31–32
    monitoring progress toward, 230, 235
Gonorrhea, 461, *462*
Good Samaritan laws, 526
Gossip, 148
.gov Web sites, 46, 78
Government. *See also* Federal government
    rights of consumers in, 61
    state/local health agencies, 74
    Web sites of, 46, 78
Grains, 199, 202, 204, 253
Grease fires, *511*
Greenhouse effect, 548
Grief, 106, 108–109
Grief counselors, 109
Grievous Bodily Harm, 284
Group activities, 145, 459
Group medical practices, 65
Group pressure, 166, 167
Group therapy, 103
Growth and development, 416–435
    during adolescence, 429–430, *431*
    during adulthood, 432–433
    and aging, 434–435
    and birth stages, 420
    from cells to systems, *417*
    during childhood, 428–429
    endocrine system role in, 396
    environment's effect on, 423–425
    and fertilization, 416
    of fetus, *418–419*
    heredity's effect on, 421–422
    mental, 10
    physical, 9–10
    during pregnancy, 418–419

social, 12–13
    theories of, 426–427
Growth hormones, 399
Growth patterns
    differences in, 9
    and eating disorders, 256
Gums, 353. *See also* Teeth and gums
Guns, 173, 511
Gynecologists, 405

H

Habits, 6, 448
    consumer, 58–62
    to fight off pathogens, 457
    health, 18, 46–47
    for safety, 508
Hair, 346–347
Hair follicles, 344, 345
Hallucinogens, 282, *283*
Hammer (ear), *357, 358*
Handwashing, 449
Hangnails, 348
Happiness, 92
Harassment, sexual, 178
Hashish, 281
Hazardous wastes, 551
HDL (high-density) cholesterol, 200
Head injuries, 388, 531
Head lice, 348
Health. *See also specific topics*
    of community. *See* Community health
    definition of, 4
    of individuals. *See* Individual health
    and physical abilities, 229
    promoting. *See* Health promotion
    skills related to. *See* Health skills
    during teen years, 8–13
    and wellness, 4–7
Health advocacy. *See* Advocacy
Health care providers, 47. *See also specific occupations*
Health care services, 63–67
    and health care system, 64–65
    managing problems with, 68–71
    paying for, 66
    role of, 63
    tobacco and costs of, 307
    trends in, 67
Health care system, 63–65
Health education, 19
Health fraud, 68, *69*
Health in Action
    diseases, 443
    healthy habits, 341
    healthy relationships, 83
    nutrition and physical activity, 189
    safety, 505
    self-care skills, 1
    staying substance-free, 267
Health insurance, 66, 304, 307
Health maintenance organizations (HMOs), 66
Health Online
    aging process, *434*
    alcohol, *328*
    chapter Health Inventories, 3, 27, 57, 85, 117, 141, 163, 191, 219, 249, 269, 297, 319, 343, 367, 415, 445, 475, 507, 545
    character, *122*
    consumer education, *60*
    dangers of alcohol use, *328*
    dangers of drugs, *284*
    digestive system, *392*
    eye function, *357*

food safety, *203*
    global warming, *548*
    immune system, *452*
    laughter benefits, *42*
    measuring fitness levels, *229*
    mental and emotional problems, *100*
    nervous system, *396*
    respiratory system, *382*
    tobacco statistics, *304*
    weather emergencies, *522*
Health promotion, 14–19. *See also* Personal health care
    abstaining from risk behaviors, 17
    choosing healthy lifestyle, 14
    entertainment for, *17*
    in the family, 125
    habits for, 47
    positive peer pressure to encourage, 147
    recognizing risk behaviors, 15–17
    school efforts for, *123*
    staying informed, 19
    taking more responsibility, 18
Health Resources and Services Administration (HRSA), *73*
Health screenings, 64, *65*
    dental, 351
    for endocrine system health, 399
    for females, 405
    for males, 402
    vision, 356
    wellness exams, 64
Health services administrators, 81
Health skills, 28–49. *See also specific skills*
    accessing information, 45–46
    advocacy, 61
    analyzing influences, 22–23, 48–49
    communication skills, 11, 34–38
    decision making, 28–30
    goal setting, 28, 31–33
    practicing healthful behaviors, 18, 46–47
    refusal skills, 37–38
    stress management, 39–43
Health triangle, 5–6, 8, 17, *125, 435*
Hearing, *65, 358*
Heart, 372, 373, 377
    alcohol's effects on, *321*
    and eating disorders, 257, 258
    and physical activity, *42*
    target pulse rate, 226
    and weight, 252
Heart and lung endurance, 224–225, *230*
Heart attacks, 241, 379, 491
Heart disease, 489–493
    and eating disorders, 257, 258
    prevention of, 493
    and saturated fats, 197
    and tobacco use, 299
    and trans fats, 197
Heart valve surgery, 492
Heartbeat rate, 234, 235
Heat exhaustion, 532
Heatstroke, 532
H.E.L.P. decision-making criteria, 29
Helper cells, 452
Hemophilia, 380
Hemorrhoids, 394
Hepatitis, 456, 459, *462,* 550
Heredity, 229, 421–422, 485
Hernia, 402
Heroin, 277
Herpes, 461
HHS. *See* Department of Health and Human Services
Hidden fats, 199
High blood pressure, 241, 252, 380, 491
High-density (HDL) cholesterol, 200

Hiking safety, 518
Hinge joints, 369
Histamines, 481
HIV (human immunodeficiency virus), 155, 277, 425, 464–467. *See also* AIDS
Hives, 481
HMOs (health maintenance organizations), 66
Home
    conservation of energy in, 553, *554*
    demonstrating character at, 122
    protection from violence in, *175*
    safety in, 509–511
Home health aides, 217
Homicide, 172
Honesty, 36, 87
Hormone therapy, 487
Hormones, 396, *398. See also specific hormones*
    and acne, 345
    and alcohol use, 323
    definition of, 9
    female, 403
    and hair health, 347
    and osteoporosis, 370
    production of, 397
    and stress response, 398
Hospices, 67, 107
Hospitals, 65
Hot lines, 180, 181, 530
Household chemicals, diseases and, 479
HPV (human papillomavirus), 461
HRSA (Health Resources and Services Administration), 73
Human papillomavirus (HPV), 461
Humor, 42
Hunger, 194
Hurricanes, 521
Hype, 70
Hypertension, 241, 252, 379, 380, 491
Hypnotics, 279, *280*
Hypothermia, *517*

I

"I" messages, 35, 36, 136
Identical twins, 416
Identity, personal, 87–88
IHS (Indian Health Services), *73*
Illegal drugs, 281–285
Illness. *See also* Diseases
    of family member, 126, 128
    foodborne, 203
    heat-related, 532
Image, personal, 308
Immediate family, 124
Immune system, 272, 451, 452, 465
Immunity, 451–453
Immunizations, *65*, 453
Immunotherapy, 487
Inadequacy, feelings of, 89
Incinerators, 550
Independence, 309
Indian Health Services (IHS), *73*
Indigestion, 394
Individual differences, acceptance of, 123, 429
Individual health. *See also* Personal health care
    billboards influencing, *303*
    and biological age, 434
    and character, 121
    media and technology influencing, 49
    negative relationships influencing, 13
    positive relationships influencing, 13, 47

skills related to. *See* Health skills
    taking responsibility for, 14–19
    and violence in media, *173*
Individual sports, 236
Infancy, *427,* 428
Infants
    risks of teen parenthood to, 132
    and secondhand smoke, 307
Infections. *See also* Sexually transmitted diseases
    and birth defects, 425
    and damage to skeletal system, 370
    definition of, 446
    effects on fetus, 425
    eye, 356, 357
    from ingrown toenails, 348
    medicines fighting, 272
    of nervous system, 388
    opportunistic, 465
    of respiratory system, 384
    from tattoos/piercings, 347
    urinary tract, 463
    viral vs. bacterial, 447
    yeast, 463
Infertility, 404
Inflammation, 451
Influences, 59. *See also* Analyzing influences
Influenza, 383, 455
Information
    accessing. *See* Accessing information
    reliability of, 45
    right to, 61
    unbiased, *59*
Ingestion of medicine, *273*
Ingrown toenails, 348
Inguinal hernia, 402
Inhalants, 283
Inhalation of medicine, *273*
Inhaling, process of, 382
Injection of medicine, *273*
Injuries. *See also* Safety
    accidental, 232, 325, 402, 508
    alcohol-related, 325
    deliberate, *172*
    during earthquakes, 523
    from firearms, 173
    and hallucinogen use, 282
    to nervous system, 388
    to skeletal system, 370
    from sports, 239, 240
    unintentional, 508
Inner ear, *357,* 358
Insect bites/stings, 447, 449, 529
Insulin, *397,* 494
Insulting statements, 123
Insurance, 66, 304, 307
Integrity, 87
Interests
    increased awareness of, 11
    and making new friends, *143*
    in marriage, 130
    romantic, 11
    sharing, 123
Internal influences, *23,* 48, 59, 308–309
Internet, 45, 62. *See also* Health Online
Interpersonal communication, 34–38. *See also* Communication skills; Conflict resolution; Refusal skills
Intestines, 391, 393
Intoxication, 322
Involuntary actions, 387, 388
Involuntary muscles, 373
Iris (eye), *354*
Iron, 194, *198,* 199, 238
Islets of Langerhans, *397*

J

Jealousy, 92
Jogging, 225
Joints, 369
    arthritis in, 495–497
    flexibility of, 228–229
    and stretching exercises, 233
Jumping rope, 225

K

Ketamine, 284
Kidney stones, 394
Kidneys, 257, 393, *397*
Killer cells, 452
Kübler-Ross, Elisabeth, 106

L

Labels
    food, 206, 207
    on over-the-counter medicines, 272
    on prescription medicines, 271
Land pollution, 550–551
Landfills, 550
Language arts connections, *104, 398*
Large intestine, 393
Larynx, *382*
Laser eye surgery, 357
Late adulthood, 433
Late childhood, *427, 428,* 429
Laughter, 42
Laws. *See also* Legal issues
    as external influences, 49
    health-related, *74*
Laxative use, 257
LDL (low-density) cholesterol, 200
Lead, 550, 551
Legal issues
    abuse, 179
    alcohol use, 320, 322, 331
    illegal drugs, 281–285
    physical abuse, 177
    rape, 176
    sale of alcohol, *326*
    sexual abuse, 178
    sexual activity of minors, 154
    sexual harassment, 178
Lens (eye), *354, 355*
"Let the buyer beware," 68
Leukemia, 380, *485*
Lice, 348, *462*
Life cycle, 426
    adolescence, *427, 429–430, 431*
    adulthood, 432–435
    age and aging, 434–435
    death and dying, 106, 108, 433
    early adulthood, 433
    early childhood, *427*
    fetal development, *418–419*
    infancy, *427,* 428
    late adulthood, 433
    late childhood, *427, 428,* 429
    maturity and old age, *427*
    middle adulthood, *427,* 433
    middle childhood, *427, 428,* 429
    stages of, *427*
    young adulthood, *427*
Life skills. *See* Health skills
Lifestyle
    benefits of active, 221, 223
    for counteracting risk factors, 16
    and noncommunicable diseases, 478
    and nutrition, 194
    sedentary, 16
    and social age, 434

and stress management, 41
and technology, 223
and weight gain, 251
Lifestyle factors, 14, 15
Lifting, 375
Ligaments, 350, 370
Limitations
focusing on, 87
recognizing, 89
Limits
to avoid risky/unhealthful behavior,
151–152
in physical fitness training, 229
in sports/exercising, 240
Liquid Ecstasy, 284
Liquid X, 284
Listening, 37, 180, 324
Liver, 200, 257, *321,* 392
Liver cancer, 241
Local health agencies, 74
Loneliness, 289
Long-term disability, preventing, 96
Long-term goals, 28, 31, 32
Look-alike drugs, 283
Loss, coping with, 106–109
Love, 92, 94, 95, 132, 153
Low-density (LDL) cholesterol, 200
LSD (lysergic acid diethylamide), 282, *283*
Lung cancer, 300, 383, *485*
Lung endurance, 224–225
Lungs, 252, 300, *377,* 392
Lyme disease, 448
Lymphatic system, 452
Lymphocytes, 452
Lymphoma, *485*

M
Magnesium, 199
Magnetic resonance imaging (MRI), *65*
Mainstream smoke, 306
Malaria, 447, 448
Males
calories required by, 253
emotional abuse by, 178
flexibility test for, *228*
heart/lung endurance test for, *225*
physical development in, 9, *431*
reproductive system in, 401–402
self-examinations for, 486
steroids' effects on, 241
strength/endurance tests for, *227*
Malignant tumors, 484
Malnutrition, 257
Mammograms, 488
Manic-depressive disorder, 97
Marijuana, 281–282
Marriage, 129–131, 154
Marrow, bone, 368
Math connection
healthy foods on a budget, *204*
unit pricing, *195*
Maturity, *427. See also* Adulthood
Meal planning, 208–210
Measles, *455*
Meats, 197, 200, 203–206, *211,* 253
Media. *See also* Advertising
alcohol messages in, 332
antidrug ads, *279*
avoidance techniques in, *152*
buying decisions influenced by, 59
celebrity cancer stories in, *487*
definition of, 59
as external influence on health, 49
health product ads in, *46*
and information about STDs, *459*
inspirational stories in, *32*

interpreting messages in, 45
medicine ads in, *275*
nutrition facts vs. fallacies in, *201*
pollen counts in, *481*
sports drinks ads in, *238*
and supersize portions, *209*
and tobacco use, 309
truth of information in, *18, 310*
and TV portrayals of marriage, *131*
unbiased information in, *59*
UV forecasts in, *346*
violence in, 172, *173*
and weight of fashion models, *257*
Mediation, 169–171
Mediators
peer, 171
professional, 187
qualities of, 169
Medicaid, 72
Medical record technicians, 295
Medical specialists, 64, 65
Medicare, 72
Medicines
and alcohol use, 321
approval process for, 270
and birth defects, 424
definition of, 270
drugs vs., 270
effects on fetus, 424
mixing, 275
over-the-counter, 271–272
overuse of, 275
prescription, 271
safe use of, 274
side effects of, 274
storage of, *510*
tolerance for, 274
types of, 272–273
ways of entering body, 273
Melanoma, *486*
Meninges, *387*
Meningitis, 388
Menopause, 403
Menstruation, 323, 403, *404*
Mental and emotional problems, 86–95
anxiety disorders, 96, *97*
coping with loss, 106–109
early identification/treatment of, 96
facing death, 106, 107
grief process, 108–109
help for, 101–105
mood disorders, 97–99
personality disorders, 97
suicide, 98–100
treatment for, 101–105
Mental development, 10
Mental health counselors, 115
Mental health treatment, 101–105
Mental retardation, 323
Mental/emotional health, 5, 86–95
abstinence for protection of, 17
and aging, 435
analyzing influences on, 23
behaviors harmful to, 16
coping skills to improve, 88–90
and dealing with emotions, 91–95
family's role in, *125*
improving, 88–90
indications of good, 86
interrelationship of social/physical health
and, 5
inventory of habits for, 46
and personal identity, 87–88
and physical activity, 221
and sexual activity, 155
during teen years, 8
Mercury, 550

Messages
carried by neurons, 395
hidden, 60
"I" messages, 35, 36, 136
sending intended, 136–137
"you" messages, 35, 36
Metastasis, 484
Methamphetamines, 278
Middle adulthood, *427,* 433
Middle childhood, *427, 428,* 429
Middle ear, *357,* 358
Milk, 197, 201, 203, 204, *205,* 206, *211,*
253
Minerals, 198–199, *207,* 238, 368
Miracle cures, *69*
Mirroring thoughts/feelings, 37
Mistakes, learning from, 90
Mixed messages, 35
Mononucleosis, 456
Mood, physical activity and, *42*
Mood disorders, 97–99
Mood swings, 241, 282, 430
Morphine, 277
Motivation, *31,* 42, 89
Mouth, *321,* 349, 390
Moving, 126
Moving on, in grief process, 108
MRI (magnetic resonance imaging), *65*
MS. *See* Multiple sclerosis
Mucous membranes, *382, 450*
Multiple sclerosis (MS), 388, 476, *477*
Mumps, *455*
Muscle strain, 374
Muscle strength and endurance, 225–226,
227, 230
Muscles
and bones, 368
care of, 375
flexibility of, *228*
and muscular system, 372–375
problems with, 374
relaxation exercise for, 41
types of, 373
warm-up exercises for, 233
working of, 372
Muscular dystrophy, 374, *477*
Muscular system, 372–375

N
Nails, 348
Name-calling, 148
Nar-Anon, 287
Narcotics, 277
Narcotics Anonymous, 287
National Institutes of Health (NIH), 46, *73*
National Weather Service, 520–522
Natural disasters, 109
Natural immunity, 452
Nearsightedness, 356
Neck (tooth), 350
Negative peer pressure, 148
alcohol/drugs and susceptibility to, 167
refusal skills for, 148–150
Negative relationships, health influences of,
13
Negative stress, 39
Neglect, 178
Negotiation. *See* Mediation
Neighborhood Watch programs, 176
Nerve inflammation, 388
Nerves, 385, 387
Nervous system, *301, 321,* 385–389
Neurons, 385
Neurotransmitters, *98*
NGU. *See* Nongonococcal urethritis
Nicotine, 299, 300, 380

addiction to, 304, 305
in gum/patches, 311
in pregnant women, 307
in secondhand smoke, 306
NIH. *See* National Institutes of Health
Noise, 358, 359
Noncommunicable diseases, 476–497
allergies, 480–481
arthritis, 495–497
asthma, 482–483
cancer, 484–488
of circulatory system, 489–493
diabetes, 494–495
environment-related, 479
heart disease, 489–493
lifestyle-related, 446, 478
present at birth, 476, 477
tooth decay, 350
Nongonococcal urethritis (NGU), 461, *462*
Nongovernmental health organizations, 75
Nonrenewable resources, 553
Nonsmokers, 306, 307
Nonspecific immune response, 451
Nonverbal communication, 35
Nose, 370
Nosebleeds, 531
Nurse practitioners, 64, 473
Nurses, registered, 25
Nutrient deficiency, 194, 254
Nutrient density, 210, 253
Nutrients, 192, 196–201, *207*
and calories, 206, 210
carbohydrates, 196
fats, 197
fiber, 199
food label information on, 206
minerals, 198–199
proteins, 197
sodium, 201
sugar, 200–201
vitamins, 198
water, 199
Nutrition, 192–211. *See also* Digestive
system
and birth defects, 424, 425
for bone health, 371
and caffeine, 201
for cancer prevention, 487
and cholesterol, 200
definition of, 192
for digestive/excretory health, 395
effects on fetus, 424
for endocrine system health, 399
facts vs. fallacies in media, *201*
and food choices, 193–194
guidelines for, 202–207
and hidden fats, 199
and meal/snack planning, 208–210, *211*
and noncommunicable diseases, 478
and serving sizes, 204
for sports, 238
for wellness, 196–201
Nutrition counseling, *65*
Nutrition Facts labels, 206, 207
Nuts, 197, *205, 211*

O

Oatmeal, 202
Obesity, 258
Obsessive-compulsive disorder, *97*
Obstetricians, 423
Occupational therapists, 503
Oil glands, 344, 346
Oil spills, 549
Oils, *205,* 209

Old age, *427*
Olives, 197
Online shopping, 62
Ophthalmologists, 356
Opinion, fact vs., 70
Opportunistic infections, 465
Optic nerve, *354, 355*
Optometrists, 356
.org Web sites, 46, 78
Organs. *See also* Body systems; *specific
organs*
formation of, *417,* 418
muscle in, 372, 373
support for, 368
Orthodontists, 353
Osteoarthritis, 370, 497
Osteoporosis, 370
OTC medicines. *See* Over-the-counter
medicines
Outdoor safety, 515–519
Outer ear, *357,* 358
Ova. *See* Egg cells
Oval window (ear), *357,* 358
Ovarian cysts, 405
Ovaries, *397,* 403
Overeaters Anonymous, 258
Overeating
in binge eating disorder, 258
in bulimia, 257
regular meals to avoid, 209
Over-the-counter (OTC) medicines,
271–272
Overweight, 251–252
Ovulation, 403
Oxygen, 381, 382, 489
and physical activity, *42*
in pregnant women, 307
and tobacco use, 300, *301*
and water pollution, 549
Ozone, 548

P

Pacemakers, 492
Pain
from arthritis, 496, 497
and drugs, 277
in exercise, 240
and hallucinogens, 282
medicines relieving, 272–273
Pancreas, *321, 392, 397*
Panic, 93
Panic disorder, *97*
Parathyroid glands, *397*
Parenthood, 131–133, 433
Parenting, 131, 133
Parents, 104, 429
discussing questions with, 9, 152
limits set by, 151
seeking help from, 104
in support system, 47
Passive immunity, 452
Pasta, *204, 205, 211*
Pathogens, 446–451
defense against, 450–451
spread of, 448, 449
types of, 446, 447
PCP (phencyclidine), 282, *283*
Peas, 197, 199
Pedestrian safety, 516
Pediatricians, 64
Peer mediation, 171
Peer pressure, 147–150
in cliques, 144
negative, 148–149
positive, 147, 329

recognizing, 149
refusing, 52–53
to use alcohol/drugs, 152
to use drugs, 289
Peers
as external influences, 49
relating to, 12
relationships with, 145
and tobacco use, 309
Pelvic inflammatory disease (PID), 461,
462
Penicillin, 272, 275
Penis, *401*
Percent Daily Value, 206, *207*
Performance, breakfast and, 208
Performing arts connection, *383*
Periodontal disease, 353
Periodontium, 350
Peripheral nervous system (PNS), 386, 388
Personal growth, 155
Personal health care, 344–359. *See also*
Lifestyle
circulatory system, 380
digestive and excretory systems, 395
for disease prevention, 449, 478
ears, 357–359
endocrine system, 399
eyes, 354–357
female reproductive system, 405
hair, 346–347
male reproductive system, 402
mouth, 349
muscular system, 375
nails, 348
nervous system, 389
during pregnancy, 423
respiratory system, 384
and signs of aging, 434
skeletal system, 371
skin, 344–347
teeth, 349–353
Personal identity, 87–88
Personal preferences in food, *193*
Personality, 87
Personality disorders, 97
Pesticides, 547, *549*
Phenylketonuria (PKU), 422
Phobias, *97,* 104
Phosphorus, 199, 371
Physical abuse, 127, 177
Physical activity
for anger management, 165–166
for cancer prevention, 488
and circulatory system health, 380
and diabetes, 495
for endocrine system health, 399
for fitness. *See* Physical activity and
fitness
and muscle health, 375
recommended amount of, 202
to relieve depression, 100
and respiratory system health, 384
for stress relief, 42
and weight, 254
Physical activity and fitness, 220
benefits of, 221
and body composition, 228
and drug use, 241
exercise stages for, 232–234
and flexibility, 228–229
and heart/lung endurance, 224–225
increasing level of, 221–222
monitoring progress in, 235
muscle strength and endurance, 225–226,
227
rating of activities for, *230*

safety in, 239–240
setting goals for, 230–231
sports for, 236–241
weekly plan for, 232
Physical addiction, 326
Physical dependence, 283, 304
Physical development, 9–10, 430
Physical environmental factors, 49
Physical fitness. *See also* Physical activity
  and fitness
  activity plan for, 232
  definition of, 220
  level of, 229
  lifestyle goals for, 231
  monitoring progress in, 230, 235
  and nutrition, 202
Physical health, 5
  abstinence for protection of, 17
  and aging, 435
  analyzing influences on, 22
  behaviors harmful to, 16
  family's role in, *125*
  interrelationship of
    mental/emotional/social health and, 5
  inventory of habits for, 46
  and physical activity, 221
  during teen years, 8
Physical therapists, 412
Physician's assistants, 55, 64
PID. *See* Pelvic inflammatory disease
Piercings, 346, 465
Pimples, *345*
Pinched nerves, 388
Pipes (tobacco), 299
Pituitary gland, 397
Pivot joints, 369
PKU (phenylketonuria), 422
Placenta, 419, 420
Plaque
  arterial, 490
  on teeth, *351, 352*
Plasma, 378
Plastics recycling, 555
Platelets, 378
PMS (premenstrual syndrome), 404
Pneumonia, 383, *455,* 465
PNS. *See* Peripheral nervous system
Point of service (POS) plans, 66
Poisoning, 510, 530–531
Pollen counts, *481*
Pollution, 546–557
  of air, 547–548
  of land, 550–551
  preventing/reducing, 552–557
  of water, 549–550
Pores, 344, 345
POS (point of service) plans, 66
Positive attitude, 90
Positive outlook, 41, 42, 86
Positive peer pressure, 147, 329
Positive relationships, health influences of,
  13, 47
Positive stress, 39
Positive thinking, 42
Post-traumatic stress disorder, *97*
Posture, 370, 371
Potassium, *198*
Poultry, 200, *205, 211*
PPOs (preferred provider organizations), 66
Practicing healthful behaviors, 17, 46–47.
  See also Personal health care
  building support system for, 47
  for communicable disease protection,
    470–471
  for conservation, 560–561
  for environment-friendly shopping, 556

and fire safety plans, 512
in fitness activities, 231
in health habits, 18, 46, 47
and improving self-esteem, 89
for medicine safety, 274
in meeting emotional needs, 95
in physical activities, 242–243
and setting limits, 151
for sun protection, 346
Precautions, 17
Precycling, 554, 555
Preferred provider organizations (PPOs),
  66
Pregnancy, 418–419
  abstinence as only 100% effective pre-
    ventive measure for, 155
  alcohol use during, 322–323
  birth defects and behaviors during, 424,
    425
  high-risk, 132
  medical care during, 423
  passage of HIV during, 465
  physiological and emotional changes
    during, *419*
  and tobacco use, 307
  unplanned, 154
Prejudice, 167
Premenstrual syndrome (PMS), 404
Prenatal care, 132, 322, 423
Preschoolers, 429
Prescription medicines, 271
Pressure, group, 166, 167
Pressure points, 535
Preventive care, 63, 64, 65. *See also*
  Disease prevention
Primary care physicians, 64, 65
Private medical practices, 65
Processed foods, 200, 201
Product placement, 60
Products
  and health fraud, 68–69
  influences in choosing, *58*
  warranties for, 61
Professional mediators, 187
Prostate gland, 401, 402
Protease inhibitors, 467
Proteins, 197, 206, 238, 375
Protocol, medical, 487
Protozoa, 447
Psychiatrists, 105
Psychological addiction, 326
Psychological dependence, 282, 304
Psychologists, 105, 265
Puberty, 430, *431*
Pubic lice, *462*
Public health, 72–75, 307
Pulled muscles, 374
Pulmonary arteries, *377*
Pulmonary circulation, 377
Pulmonary veins, *377*
Pulp (tooth), 350
Pulse rate, 226
Pupil (eye), *354, 355*
Push-ups, 226

R

Radiation therapy, 487
Radon, 479
Rage, 166, 241
Rape, 176, 284, 323
Rashes, 480, 481
Raves, 283
Reading skills, *332*
  for body image, *252*
  for body systems, *378, 388, 391*

for communicable diseases, *448, 455,
  461*
for conflict resolution, *166, 173*
for consumer choices, *66, 73*
for environmental health, *547*
for general health, *6, 10, 16*
for growth and development, *418, 422,
  430*
for health skills, *30, 41, 48*
for medicines and drugs, *273, 277, 287*
for mental/emotional health, *89, 92, 105*
for noncommunicable diseases, *477, 486*
for nutrition, *194, 206, 210*
for personal health care, *350, 358*
for physical activity and fitness, 234, *239*
for relationships, *143, 154*
for safety, *509, 516, 518, 535*
for social health, *126, 130*
for tobacco, *299, 309*
Reasoning, 10
Recovery (from alcoholism), 327
Recreational safety, 517–519
Recurrence of cancer, 487
Recycling, 552, 554–555
Red blood cells, 378
Red Cross, 75, 379
Reducing wastes, 552, 555
Refusal skills, 37–38
  for alcohol, 332
  and body language, 37, *38*
  definition of, 37
  for drug use, 240, 284
  memory device for, 37
  for negative peer pressure, 148–150
  for peer pressure, 52–53
  S.T.O.P criteria for, 150
  for tobacco use, 300, 310
  for unsafe behaviors, 540–541
Registered nurses, 25
Relationships, 142–155. *See also* Social
  health
  and abstinence, 151–155
  abuse in, 177, 178
  accepting individual differences in, 123
  character as foundation for, 119
  and cliques, 144
  dating, 146
  with family, 124–128
  with friends, 142–143
  and group activities, 145
  influences on individual/community
    health, 13
  and peer pressure, 147–150
  strengthening, 123
  and tobacco use, 302
Relaxation, 41
Reliability
  in friendships, 143
  of information, 45–46, 78–79
  as trait of dating partner, 146
Religious leaders, 47, 105
Remission of cancer, 487
Reproductive glands, *397*
Reproductive systems, 400–405, *485*
  female, 402–405
  male, 401–402
Rescue breaths, 536, *537*
Resilience, 94
Resolving conflict. *See* Conflict resolution
Resources
  conflicts over, 164
  conservation of, 553, 554
Respect, *120*
  abstinence and, 17
  and body size/shape, *258*
  as core ethical value, 119

for dignity of others, 87
within families, 128
in friendships, 143
for individual differences, 123
for older adults, *433*
self-respect, 18, 154
and sexual abstinence, 152, 154, 155
for strengthening relationships, 123
as trait of dating partner, 146
Respiratory system, *301,* 381–384, *481*
Respiratory therapists, 317
Responsibility, 14–19, 87, *120*
   attitude toward, 18
   for avoiding tick bites, *529*
   as core ethical value, 119
   and driving after drinking, *322*
   within families, 128
   at home, 122
   for lifestyle choices, 14–15
   in making choices, *331*
   and negative peer pressure, *148*
   of parenthood, 131
   and resiliency, *94*
   for results of actions, *155*
   and risk behaviors, 15–17
   and self-control, 18
   and self-discipline, *228*
   for self-examinations, *402*
   and staying informed, 19
   for tooth health, *351*
   as trait of dating partner, 146
Retina, *354,* 355
Reusing items, 552
Rh factor, 379
Rheumatoid arthritis, 496
Rice, 197, 202, *204, 205, 211*
R.I.C.E. first aid formula, 240, 528
Rickettsias, 447
Ringworm, 447
Risk behaviors, 15–17
   abstinence from, 17
   avoiding situations leading to, 152
   consequences of, 16–17
   and setting limits, 151
   weight-related, 255
Risk factor(s), 478, 493
   obvious and long-term, 15
   sexual activity as, 16
Risks
   cumulative, 17
   of disease. *See specific diseases*
   of teen parenthood, 132
   as unavoidable, 15
Rites of passage, *9*
Rocky Mountain spotted fever, 447, 448
Rods (eyes), 355
Rohypnol (roofies), 284
Role models
   as external influences, 49
   for parenting, 131
   and tobacco use, 309
Romantic interests, 11
Root (tooth), 350
Rubella, 425, *455*
Rules, understanding and following, 122,
   174, 513
Running, 225

S

Sadness, 92
Safety, 508–523. *See also* First aid
   and accident chain, 508, *509*
   bicycle safety, 515
   fire safety, 511–512
   food safety, 203

gun safety, 511
habits for, 508
hiking/camping safety, 518
in the home, 509–511
of medicine development, 270
in medicine use, 274
and nervous system health, 389
in outdoor activities, 515–519
for pedestrians, 516
right to, 61
at school, 513
with skates/skateboards/scooters, 516
in sports, 239–240
traffic safety, 514
from violence, 175–176
water safety, 517–518
in weather emergencies, 520–523
in workouts, 232
Saliva, 349, 390, *450*
Salt, 199, 201, 203
SAMHSA (Substance Abuse and Mental
   Health Services Administration), *73*
Saturated fats, 197, 203, *207*
Scalp problems, 348
Schedule management, 43
Schizophrenia, 97
School counselors, 47, 105, 161
School nurses, 64, 105
Schools
   anti-tobacco programs in, 306
   demonstrating character in, 122
   safety guidelines for, 513
   violence in, 174
   zero tolerance policy in, 174
Science connections
   anemia, *379*
   breath control, *387*
   calcium, *370*
   changes during pregnancy, *419*
   chemical messages, *282*
   depression, *98*
   glucose levels, *495*
   grease fires, *511*
   high-risk babies, *132*
   inflammation, *451*
   magnetic resonance imaging, *65*
   pesticides, *549*
   storm tracking, *521*
   ultrasound, *424*
Sclera, *354*
Scoliosis, 370
Scooters, 516
Screenings. *See* Health screenings
Scrotum, *401*
Second-degree burns, *530*
Secondhand smoke, 306, 307, 384, 425,
   479
Sedatives, 279
Sedentary lifestyle, 16
Self-concept, 87
Self-confidence, 87
Self-control, 18, 166, 263
Self-destructive behaviors, 16
Self-discipline, *17, 31,* 228
Self-esteem, 87–89, 256, 429
Self-examinations, 402, 405, 485, 488
Self-help groups, 181
Self-management, *44. See also* Practicing
   healthful behaviors; Stress
   management
Self-motivation, 89
Self-protection habits, 175–176
Self-respect, 18, 152, 154, 155
Semen, 401
Semicircular canals (ear), *357,* 358
Seminal fluid, 401

Seminal vesicles, 401
Sensory neurons, *385*
Serving sizes, 204, 206, *209*
Sewage, 549, 550
Sexual abuse, 178
Sexual activity
   abstinence from, 151–155, 459, 464
   consequences of, 154–155
   and HIV, 464, 465, 467
   legal implications of, 154
   love vs., 153
   meeting emotional needs through, 95
   as negative risk factor, 16
   and STDs, 459
Sexual harassment, 178
Sexually transmitted diseases (STDs), 154,
   458–463
   abstinence as only 100% effective pre-
      ventive measure for, 155, 459
   and birth defects, 425
   common, 460–462
   effects on fetus, 425
   in females, 405
   and importance of abstinence, 459–460
   in males, 402
   treatment of, 463
Shaking (as abuse), 177
Sharing, 123, 128, 130
Shelters, 181
Shock
   electrical, 510
   first aid for, 534
   as stage of grief process, 108
Shopping
   comparison, 60–61
   environment-friendly, 556
   online, 62
   options for, 62
Short-term goals, 31–32
Sickle-cell disease, 477
Side effects (medicines), 274
Sidestream smoke, 306
SIDS (Sudden Infant Death Syndrome),
   307
Sight, *65,* 355–357
Singers, *383*
Single-parent families, 126
Skateboarding, 516
Skating, 516
Skeletal muscles, 373
Skeletal system, 368–371
Skin, 344–347
   allergic responses of, *481*
   care of, *65,* 344, 345
   excretion through, 392
   HIV and punctures of, 465
   as pathogen protection, *450*
Skin cancer, 347, *485*
Sleep
   and endocrine system health, 399
   and nervous system health, 389
   and noncommunicable diseases, 478
   as stress reducer, 41
Slipping, drug, 284
Small claims courts, 71
Small intestine, 391
Smog, 548
Smoke alarms, 511
Smokeless tobacco, 299, 302
Smoking. *See also* Tobacco
   cost of, 304
   of crack, 279
   and respiratory system health, 383, 384
   statistics related to, 305, 308
Smooth muscle, 373
Snacks, 208–210, *211,* 351

Snuff, 299
Sobriety, 327
Social age, 434
Social development, 12–13, 430
Social environmental factors, 49
Social groups, importance of, 143
Social growth and development, 426
Social health, 5, 118–133. *See also* Relationships
  abstinence for protection of, 17
  and aging, 435
  analyzing influences on, 23
  behaviors harmful to, 16
  and character, 119–123
  and family relationships, 124–128
  interrelationship of mental/emotional/ physical health and, 5
  inventory of habits for, 46
  and marriage, 129–131
  and parenthood, 131–133
  and physical activity, 221
  and relationships, 118, 123
  during teen years, 8
Social life, teen parenthood and, 133
Social studies connections, *9, 36, 74, 326*
Social workers, 105, 139
Sodium, 201, 203
Soft drinks, 200, 201, 203
Solid waste (trash), 550
Somatic nervous system, 388
Sound levels, 358, 359
Soybeans, 197
Speaking skills, 36, 180, 324
Specialists, 64, 65
Specific immune response, 451
Speech therapists, 365
Sperm, *400,* 401, 416, 422
Sphygmomanometer, 378
Spinal cord, 368, *369,* 371, 386–388
Spit (tobacco), 299
Sports, 236–241
  and anabolic steroids, 241
  conditioning for, 238
  for group activities, *145*
  individual, 236
  limits in, 240
  and nutrition, 238
  protecting teeth during, 351
  safety in, 239–240, 518–519
  team, 237
  time spent in, 231
Sports drinks, *238*
Sports exams, *65*
Sportsmanship, *237*
Spousal abuse, 328
Sprains, 370, 528
Staging (of disease), 487
Standardized Test Practice. *See each chapter*
Starches, 196
State health agencies, 74
Stepparents, 126
Step-ups, 226
Sterility, 402
Steroids, 241, 285
Stimulants, 277–279
Stirrup (ear), *357, 358*
Stomach, *321,* 391
S.T.O.P. refusal criteria, 37, 150, 240
Storm tracking, *521*
Strains, muscle, 374
Strategies. *See also* Coping skills and strategies
  for avoiding school violence, 174
  for avoiding tobacco use, 310
  for avoiding violence, 167, 175

for counteracting drug use risk factors, 289
for counteracting risk factors, 16
for early identification of mental health problems, 102
to prevent accidental workout injuries, 232
to prevent firearm accidents, 173
to prevent school violence, 174
to prevent use of drugs/alcohol, 152
to prevent violence, 176
for protection from rape, 176
for protection from violence, 175–176
for quitting tobacco use, 311
for resisting negative peer pressure, 148
for resolving conflicts. *See* Conflict resolution
for setting long-term goals, 28
for strengthening family unit, 128
Street drugs, 281
Strength(s)
  focus on, 87, 89
  muscle, 225–226, *227*
Strep throat, 455
Stress, 39
  body's response to, 398
  and circulatory system health, 380
  effect on emotions, 41
  and endocrine system health, 399
  negative, 39
  physical response to, 40
  positive, 39
  strategies for coping with, *39*
  on teen parents, 133
  and tobacco use, 308
  types of, 39
Stress management, 39–43, 500–501
  and causes of stress, 40
  and changes in family, 126–127
  and dealing with emotions, 112–113
  and mood swings, 430
  physical activity for, 42
  positive outlook for, 41, 42
  relaxation for, 43
  schedule for, 43
  skills, stress management, 43–44
  stressors for teens, *40*
  suggestions for, 398
  with time management, 43
Stressors, 40
Stretching exercises, 233, 234, 374
Strokes, 300, *301,* 379, 490, 491
Subcutaneous layer (skin), 344
Substance Abuse and Mental Health Services Administration (SAMHSA), 73
Success, self-esteem and, *88*
Sudden Infant Death Syndrome (SIDS), 307
Sugars, 196, 199–201, 203, *205,* 206, *207*
Suicide, 98–100, 323
Summer sports, 519
Sun exposure
  and cancer prevention, 488
  and eyesight, 356
  and skin health, 344, 346, 347
  and UV Index Forecast, *346*
Sunscreens, 346, 347
Supersize portions, *209*
Support groups
  for abuse, 181
  for alcohol abuse, 328
  for drug use, 287
  for eating disorders, 258, *259*
  finding information on, 496
  for grief, 109

for quitting tobacco use, 311
Support system, 47
Surgery
  cancer, 487
  eye, 357
  heart, 492
Survival techniques for cold water, *517*
Swallowing, *390*
Sweat glands, 344
Sweets, *205,* 209. *See also* Sugars
Swimming, 225
Sympathy, 92
Sympathy notes, 107
Syphilis, 461, *462*
Systemic circulation, 377
Systems. *See* Body systems
Systolic pressure, 378

T

T cells, 452, 465
T.A.L.K. conflict resolution strategies, *169*
Talk therapy, 102
Tanning devices, 346
Tar, 282, 299, 300, 306
Target pulse rate, 226
Tartar, *351*
Taste buds, 349
Tattoos, 346, 465
Teachers, 47, 105
Team sports, 237
Tears, *450*
Teasing, 148, 166
Technology, 49, 223
Teen marriages, 130–131
Teen parenthood, 132–133
Teen years. *See* Adolescence
Teeth and gums, 349–353
  caring for, 351–352
  and digestive system health, 395
  parts of teeth, 350
  problems with, 353
  and smokeless tobacco use, 299
Telemedicine, 67
Tendons, 370
Tension, 289
Testes, *397,* 401
THC (Tetrahydrocannabinol), 281
Therapy, mental health, 102–104
Thinking
  adolescence and changes in, 10
  positive, 42
Third-degree burns, *530*
Threats, 148
Three Rs of abuse prevention, 180
Throat, *382, 481*
Thymus gland, 452
Thyroid gland, *397,* 398, 399
Ticks, 448, 449, *529*
Time
  and food choices, *193*
  management of, 43
  for strengthening relationships, 123
Time management, *39,* 43
Tinnitus, 358
Tissues, *417. See also specific types, e.g.:* Muscles
  connective, 370
  formation of, 418
  and stretching exercises, 233
Tobacco, 298–311
  abstinence from, 17
  addiction to, 304–305
  and appearance, 302
  and birth defects, 425
  and cancer prevention, 488

and circulatory system health, 380
cost of, 304
and disease prevention, 457
effects on body of, 301
effects on fetus, 425
forms of, 298–299
harmful substances in, 300
and noncommunicable diseases, 478
quitting use of, 305, 311
reasons for using, 308–309
refusing to use, 310
and secondhand smoke, 306, 307
societal costs of, 306–307
use of, as risk behavior, 16
use statistics for, 303
Toddlers, 428
Toenails, 348
Tolerance, 274
Tongue, 349, 353
Tooth decay, 350, *351*
Torn muscles, 374
Tornadoes, 520, 521
Toxic shock syndrome, 404
Trachea, *382*
Traffic safety, 323, 514
Tranquilizers, 279, *280*
Trans fats, 197
Transcriptase inhibitors, 467
Transfusions, blood, 465
Trauma, emotional, *152,* 155
Trends, health care, 67
Trichomoniasis, *462*
Triggers, asthma, 482, 483
Trust, 30, 119, 143
Trustworthiness, *120,* 122, 146
Truth in advertising, *310*
Tuberculosis, 383, *455*
Tumors, 388, 484
Twins, 416
Typhoid fever, 550
Typhus, 447

U

Ulcers, *321,* 394
Ultraviolet (UV) Index Forecast, *346*
Ultraviolet (UV) radiation, 346, 347, 548
Umbilical cord, 419
Unbiased information, *59*
Unconditional love, 132
Underweight, 251, 252
Unemployment, 127
Unintentional injuries, 508. *See also*
Accidental injuries
Unit pricing, *195*
Universal precautions, 525
Unsaturated fats, 197
Upper body strength/endurance, 226
Ureters, *393*
Urethra, *393,* 401
Urinary tract infections (UTIs), 463
Urine, *393*
Uterus, 403, 404, 418–420
UTIs (urinary tract infections), 463
UV Index Forecast, *346*
UV radiation. *See* Ultraviolet radiation

V

Vaccinations, 449, 451, 453
Vaccines, 272, 452, *455*
Vagina, *403,* 404
Vaginal yeast infections, 463

Values, 30, 119
conflicts over, 164
core ethical, 30, 119
definition of, 30
influence of, 48
in marriage, 130
and self-respect, 154
Valuing family members, 128
Valves, heart, *377*
Vas deferens, 401
Vectors, 448
Vegetable oils, 197
Vegetables, 199, 203, *204, 205, 211,* 253
Vegetarians, 197
Veins, *377,* 378
Ventricles, *377*
Vertebrae, 368, *369*
Victims
of abuse, 179
of violent crimes, 173
Villi, *391*
Violence, 172–176. *See also* Abuse
and alcohol/drugs, 167, 323
definition of, 172
escalation of anger to, 166
factors involved in, 172–173
preventing, 176
protecting yourself from, 175–176
in schools, 174
strategies for avoiding, 167
Viral infections, 447
Viruses, 346, 446–448
Vision, *65,* 355–357
Vision screenings, 356
Vitamins, 197, 198, *207,* 238
Vocal cords, *382*
Vocational goals, 32
Voluntary actions, 387, 388
Voluntary muscles, 373
Volunteering, 74, 95, *143,* 333, 433, 466
Vomiting, 257

W

Walking, 225
Warm-up exercises, 233, 239
Warranties, 61
Warts, 346
Waste management, 550–552
Wastes
chemical, 479
hazardous, 551
of human body, 392
noncommunicable diseases and disposal
of, 479
solid, 550
Water
for digestive/excretory health, 395
for drinking, 457
as nutrient, 199
pathogens spread by, 448
pollution of, 549–550, 553
for sports, 238
Water safety, 517–518
Water-soluble vitamins, 198
Weapons, 173, 511
dangers of, 173
following rules related to, 513
Weather emergencies, 520–523
Web sites
government, 46, 78
health inventory, 3, 27, 57, 85, 117, 141,
163, 191, 219, 249, 269, 297, 319,
343, 367, 415, 445, 475, 507, 545

Weight, 250–255. *See also* Eating disorders
appropriate, 250
and Body Mass Index, 251
and calorie intake, 252–253
and diabetes, 495
and health/fitness, 202
management tips for, 255
and muscle health, 375
overweight, 251–252
and physical activity, 254
reaching appropriate, 253–255
and tobacco use, 308
underweight, 251, 252
Weight management products, *69*
Weight training, 226
Wellness, 6–7, 196–201
Wellness exams, 64, *65*
White blood cells, 378, 451
Whiteheads, *345*
Whooping cough, *455*
Winter sports, 518
Win-win solutions, 164, 169, *170*
Withdrawal, 287–288, 305, 311
Workouts, 233–234. *See also* Exercise(s)
Worth, feelings of, 94
Writing skills
for alcohol, *320, 325, 330*
for body image, *250, 256*
for body systems, *368, 372, 376, 381,
385, 390, 396, 400*
for communicable diseases, *446, 450,
454, 458, 464*
for conflict resolution, *164, 168, 172,
177*
for consumer choices, *58, 63, 68,* 72
for environmental health, *546, 552*
for first aid, *528, 533*
for general health, *4, 8, 14,* 28
for growth and development, *416, 421,
426, 432*
for health skills, *34, 39, 44*
for medicines and drugs, *270, 276, 281,
286*
for mental/emotional health, *86, 91, 96,
101, 106*
for noncommunicable diseases, *476, 480,
484, 489, 494*
for nutrition, *192, 196, 202, 208*
for personal health care, *344, 349, 354*
for physical activity and fitness, *220,
224, 230, 236*
for relationships, *142, 147, 151*
for safety, *508, 514, 520,* 524
for social health, *118, 124, 129*
for tobacco, *298, 303, 308*

X
X, XTC (Ecstasy), 284

Y
Yearning, in grief process, 108
Yogurt, 197, 204, *205, 211*
"You" messages, 35, 36
Young adulthood, *427*

Z
Zero tolerance policy, 174
Zinc, *198*

Credits

Photographs

All-Sport Photo: Mike Powell, page 239. Aurora: Jan Sonnenmair, page 134. Comstock: page 424. Corbis: pages 368, 504, 312–313, 361; AFP, page 379; Paul Barton, page 47; Lester Bergman, page 481; Andrew Brooks, page 270; Anna Clopet, page 348; Jim Cummins, pages vi, 31, 165; Michael Kevin Daly, page 28 (bottom right); Jon Feingersh, page 427 (7); Rick Gomez, page 423; Charles Gupton, page 335; John Henley, page 256; Michal Heron, page 234; Reed Kaestner, page 220; Catherine Karnow, pages 334–335; Ronnie Kaufman, pages 12, 279, 421, 427 (6); Chuck Keeler Jr, page 320; Michael Keller, page 427 (3); Raoul Minsart, page 125 (bottom left); Bob Mitchell, pages v (left), 237; Guy Motil, page 479; Mug Shots, page 116; Jose L. Pelaez, pages 204, 248, 331, 426, 427 (2), 429, 452; Gabe Palmer, pages 179, 282; Steve Prezant, page 129; Reuters NewMedia Inc., page 488; RNT Productions, page 255; R.B. Studio, page 125 (right); Bill Ross, page 540; Chuck Savage, pages 151, 427 (5); Norbert Schafer, page 418; M.L. Sinibaldi, page 457; Ariel Skelley, page 32; Leif Skoogfors, page 485; Joseph Sohm, page 218; Dann Tardif, page 466; Tim Wright, page 298; Ed Young, pages 399, 422. Courtesy of Kerisha Harris: page 156. Courtesy Nick Casey: page 156. Custom Medical Stock: pages 447, 482, 533. Ed McDonald Photography: pages 7, 22, 33 (bottom right), 90, 143, 149, 167, 171, 451, 460. Emily Shur: pages 20, 21 (all). Eric Camden Photography: pages v (right), 59 (middle right), 69, 527, 553. FoodPix: Eisenhut & Mayer, page 257; Brian Hagiwara, page 212; John E. Kelly, page 468. Getty Images: page 77, 469; Bruce Ayers, pages 103, 106; Benelux Press, page 96; Christopher Bissell, page 178; Keith Brofsky, page 456; Gary Buss, pages viii, 125 (top left); Ron Chapple, pages 84, 508; Ken Chernus, page 41; Jim Cummins, page 497; Mel Curtis, page 5 (middle); Dale Durfee, page 2; EyeWire, page 433; Rob Gage, pages 119, 296; L. D. Gordon, page 48; David Hanover, page 366; Chip Henderson, page 130; Ziggy Kaluzny, page 177; John E. Kelly, page 193; Howard Kingsnorth, page 262; Klaus Lahnstein, page 506; Lifestock, page 360; Steven Mark Needham, page 197; John Riley, pages 82, 450; Ron Silva Productions, page 190; Don Smetzer, pages 107, 260, 263; Ann Stratton, page 196; SW Productions, pages 5 (middle left), 140; Telegraph Colour Library, pages 35, 86; Arthur Tilley, pages 9, 62; Gandee Vasan, page 340; VCG, pages 5 (middle right), 158; Garry Wade, page 436; David Young-Wolff, pages 254, 414. Image State: page 157. The Image Works: E. Crews, page 101; Bob Daemmrich, pages 8, 122, 272, 285; Sonda Dawes, page 325; M. Eastcott, page 514; J. Greenberg, page 303; Willie L. Hill, page 330; Steve Warmowski, page 276; Mitch Wojnarowicz, page 16. Index Stock: page 76; Steve Dunwell, page 360. Index Stock Imagery: Myrleen Cate, page 1; Thomas Craig, page 467; Lonnie Duka, page 515; Rick Souders, page 208; Bob Winsett, page 519. International Stock: Kirk Anderson, page 28 (top left); Scott Barrow, page 39; James Davis, page 266; Michael Paras, page 459; Patrick Ramsey, pages 71, 112; Peter Langone, page 152. Jim West, page 334. Jim Whitmer Photography: page 395. Judd Pilosoff Photography: page 209. Lon Tweeten, page 406. Masterfile: Zoran Milich, page 94. Matt Meadows Photography: pages vii (top), 34, 52, 126, 153, 172, 181, 184, 287, 374, 375, 396. Painet, Inc.: pages 11, 91, 109, 188, 214. Photo Researchers: A. Glauberman, page 300 (both); Aaron Haupt, page 318; Richard Hutchings, page 132; Ken Lax, page 378; Judy Manna, pages xi (right), 241; Will & Deni McIntyre, page 463; Motta & Familiari/Anatomy Dept./University "La Sapienza", Rome/Science Photo Library, page 400 (right); David M. Phillips, page 400 (left). Photodisc: pages 23, 78 (middle), 554. PhotoEdit: Bill Aron, page 526; Bill Bachmann, page 307; Billy Barnes, page 476; Robert Brenner, pages 93, 108; Myrleen Ferguson Cate, pages 194, 311, 353, 474, 532, 546; David Kelly Crow, page 495; Mary Kate Denny, pages 58, 121, 199, 268, 328, 416, 461; Laura Dwight, pages 362, 432; Tony Freeman, pages 75, 224, 302, 342, 420, 491, 535, 551, 552; Robert Ginn, page 271; Spencer Grant, pages 333, 402; Jeff Greenberg, page 500; Will Hart, page 444; Richard Hutchings, pages 162, 198, 480; Bonnie Kamin, page 560 (all); Richard Lord, pages 142; Felicia Martinez, page 211 (border); Michael Newman, pages 144, 182, 223, 253, 289, 355, 356, 405, 389; Dwayne Newton, page 470; Jonathon Nourok, pages 427 (8), 442; Robin L. Sachs, page 64; Susan Van Etten, page 408; Rudi Von Briel, page 183; David Young-Wolff, pages x, xi (left), 13, 17, 26, 72, 95, 99, 118, 147, 150, 154, 164, 192, 238, 250, 288, 292, 308, 346, 381, 383, 390, 392, 427 (1 & 4), 434, 435, 449, 454, 484, 496, 516, 523, 524, 547, 556. Photographik Company: pages xii, 5 (bottom), 6, 19 (all), 33 (top left), 38 (both), 45, 59 (top), 70, 102, 113, 166 (both), 168, 203, 211 (middle), 221 (all), 235, 252, 274, 305, 329, 334 (both). Phototake, NYC: Yoav Levy, page 490. Photri: Bachmann, page 240; Karen Holsinger, page 277; Michael Yelman, pages ix, 380. PictureQuest: Henryk Kaiser/Index Stock Imagery, page 14; Nicole Katano/Brand X Pictures, pages vii (bottom), 314; Phototake, page 465; SW Production/Index Stock Imagery, page 173. Robin Bowman: 135. SABA: Asnin, pages 50 (all), 51 (all). SEGWAY, page 558. Stock Boston: Mark Burnett, pages 136, 528; Bob Daemmrich, pages 4, 63, 174, 384, 438, 511, 513, 544; Lionel Delevingne, page 176; Judy Gelles, page 371; Leonard Harris, page 323; Jim Harrison, page 236; Lawrence Migdale, page 104; David Simson, page 531. Stan Musilek, page 559. Superstock: pages 37, 67, 124, 128, 349, 358, 425, 520, 525, 550. Susan Parker, page 213. Tim Fuller Photography: page 56. Todd France: page 134. Toyota, page 558–559. U.S. Food and Drug Administration: page 78 (top, bottom). Unicorn Stock: Mike Doyle, page 557. Kyra White: page 61. Workbook Stock: Mark Harmel, page 498.

Illustrations

Art and Science: pages 273, 301, 321, 354, 355, 369, 373, 377, 382, 386, 387, 391 (left), 393, 397, 417, 418, 419, 482, 492, 529, 534, 535, 536, 537. Dan Brawer: pages 243–244. Ed Gabel: pages 538–539. Joe Lertola: page 406, 437. Hilda Muinos: pages 357, 391 (right), 401, 403. Network Graphics: page 404. Parrot Graphics: page 372. Precision Graphics: pages 345, 350, 351, 489. Tim Robinson, pages 110–111. All other illustrations: The Mazer Corporation.